The Journal of Biological Chemistry
TABLE OF CONTENTS

jbc

W9-CHQ-958

REFLECTIONS

The Journal of Biological Chemistry

AUTHOR INDEX

JBC Page Design Changes

As you read through this compendium you will see that the page design has changed—starting with articles in September of 2005. Along with the redesign of the cover of JBC we have updated the layout of the inside articles. The new design compliments the change on the cover and is intended to give a fresh look and to enhance ease of readability. The changes are mostly cosmetic and include increased distinction between different elements of text, standardization of body text, enlarged formulas, more variation of the subheads, and updating of figure presentation. Each page now also includes volume, number, and date information in the folio for easier reference. We hope you like the new look and continue to enjoy the excellent editorial content.

THE JOURNAL OF BIOLOGICAL CHEMISTRY
Vol. 276, No. 1, Issue of January 5, pp. 3–11, 2001

Reflections

A PAPER IN A SERIES COMMISSIONED TO CELEBRATE THE CENTENARY OF THE JBC IN 2005

Remembering Our Teachers

Arthur Kornberg

From the Department of Biochemistry, Stanford University School of Medicine, Stanford, California 94305-5307

The spotlight on the biochemistry stage moves rapidly, leaving a star of yesterday in the dark and virtually forgotten. A substance, a procedure, or a biochemical event named after the star is eventually renamed and what seemed an assurance of immortality is gone. This has been the fate of the Cori cycle, the Cori ester, and of Carl and Gerty Cori as well.

In journals (and even more so in textbooks) discoveries are described in a logical pattern unlike the sequence of erratic and serendipitous events which led to them but seldom with references to the authors included. In the hope that we might profit from reflecting on how our scientific lives and work have been shaped by past stars, I want to consider on how they (among them my teachers, Carl Cori, Gerty Cori, and Severo Ochoa) affected mine.

Carl F. Cori (1896–1984) and
Gerty T. Cori (1896–1957)

Carl and Gerty Cori (Fig. 1) were inseparable in their personal and scientific lives and so will remain in this account. Carl F. Cori and Gerty Radnitz entered the medical school of the German University of Prague in 1914 at age 18. Carl had received his earlier schooling in the academic tradition, whereas Gerty with less academic preparation needed to absorb 8 years of Latin and 5 years of mathematics, physics, and chemistry to qualify for medical school, all of which she completed in 1 year.

Married in 1920 after their graduation and of like minds, they looked for opportunities to do science rather than clinical practice, but there were few places available to them. The turbulence after World War I, the virulence of anti-Semitism, and the uncompromising prejudice against women scientists made them seek refuge in America. There in 1922 they were offered jobs in Buffalo, New York in the New York Institute for the Study of Malignant Diseases, since renamed the Roswell Park Memorial Institute. With little equipment and few supplies they developed quantitative and precise methods to discover connections among what seemed then to be unconnected metabolic events: glucose converted to lactic acid during muscle contraction and stored as glycogen until needed again. The cycling of lactic acid and glucose between liver glycogen and muscle operated under the influence of hormones, including epinephrine and the newly discovered insulin. The Cori cycle (Fig. 2) was never as celebrated as was the circulation of blood discovered by William Harvey three centuries earlier. Nor was the Cori cycle defined molecularly as was the citric acid cycle postulated two decades later by Hans Krebs. Yet, the Cori cycle offered deep insights into the use and storage of energy and had an indelible influence on the understanding of the hormonal control of bioenergetics.

Well known by 1931 and having published many papers together with Gerty on the Cori cycle, it was Carl who was offered the Professorship of Pharmacology at Washington University School of Medicine in St. Louis, whereas Gerty would remain a Research Associate there. Despite the discouragements to women in science and the lack of facilities and equipment, they took off in a totally new direction.

No longer satisfied with describing the transit of glucose in the intact animal, they began to examine its fate *in vitro*. In water extracts of finely minced frog muscle, they found that the glucose was converted to something novel that they identified as a new sugar phosphate ester, glucose 1-phosphate, soon called the Cori ester. (One of my ambitions for fame upon entering biochemistry in 1946 was to discover a new ester. I would then be immortalized as had Arthur Harden and William Young with fructose 1,6-diphosphate, Carl Neuberg with fructose 6-phosphate, Robert Robison and Gustav Embden with glucose 6-phosphate, and more recently, Isidor Greenwald with 2,3-diphosphoglycerate.)

How was the Cori ester produced and what was its fate? These questions led to the enzyme

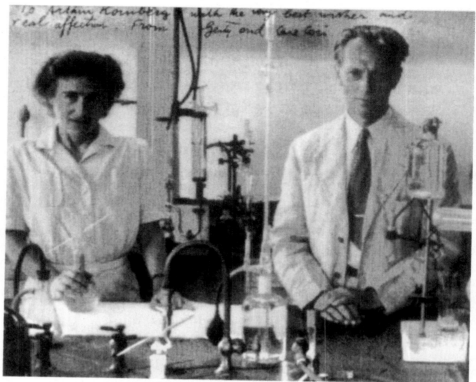

Fig. 1. **Gerty T. Cori and Carl F. Cori (c. 1947) in her laboratory.**

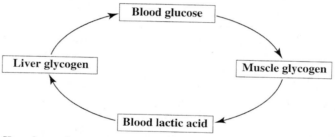

Fig. 2. **The Cori cycle.** How glucose for muscle contraction is supplied from its storage as glycogen in liver and muscle.

studies that became *the* central focus of the Cori laboratory for the next decades. The most remarkable discovery was glycogen phosphorylase, which in 1938–1939 startled the biochemical world, because the enzyme not only used phosphate to split (phosphorylyze) glucose from the ends of chains to produce glucose 1-P but in reverse could elongate a glycogen polymer by serial additions of glucose from glucose 1-phosphate. This was the first large biological molecule made outside a living cell. Also, their analysis of alternative structures of glycogen phosphorylase led them to the discovery that an enzyme function can be regulated by phosphorylation, dephosphorylation, and an allosteric effector.

After phosphorylase, many glycolytic enzymes were purified by the Coris and others who came to their laboratory. With the expert guidance of Arda Green, an outstanding protein chemist who joined them in 1942, some of these purified proteins were crystallized, including phosphorylase. By 1947, when after a year in Severo Ochoa's laboratory, I came to St. Louis (as a commissioned United States Public Health Service officer on a 6-month assignment), the Cori laboratory was the mecca of enzymology. During and immediately after World War II following destruction of European laboratories, the Coris were at the forefront of biochemistry, focused on enzymes. They welcomed refugees from everywhere to join them. Unlike the prevailing culture in American academia, they showed no discrimination toward men or women, husbands with scientist wives, Jews, or gentiles.

The Coris, who became my most devoted patrons, were generous to accept the novice in science I still was in 1947. Although I had finished college in 1937, 3 years ahead of schedule, I was now only a sophomore in biochemistry at what seemed a rather advanced age. I felt that I had squandered nearly 10 years in clinical training and studies of rat nutrition. In daring to choose to be a biochemist, I was reassured by the Coris whose career path from clinical medicine to enzymology had been even more extended and who often asserted that medical training was useful because it widened one's view of bioscience.

The Cori laboratory in 1947 was the most vibrant place in biochemistry. Scientists from everywhere flocked there to share in the excitement at the frontiers of intermediary metabolism, bioenergetics, enzymology, and protein chemistry. When I arrived, I was audacious enough to seek the answer to aerobic phosphorylation. That failed, but working with Olov Lindberg, a postdoctoral fellow from Stockholm, I did discover a seemingly dull enzyme, nucleotide pyrophosphatase, which eventually led me to coenzyme biosynthesis and beyond. It was in the Cori laboratory that I first learned from J.-M. Wiame, a postdoctoral fellow from Belgium, that the diagnostic metachromatic granules in *Corynebacterium diphtheriae* that I had observed as a student in medical school consisted of inorganic polyphosphate, the polymer of my current infatuation.

A dramatic event that spring was the imminent visit of Hugo Theorell, the celebrated Swedish biochemist who would win the Nobel Prize in 1955. The gala banquet planned by the Coris for the evening of his arrival included the social, artistic, and scientific aristocracy of St. Louis. Gerty acquired a hairdo, used make-up, and bought a new dress for the first time in anyone's memory. Olov Lindberg went to the airport to meet the flight, but Theorell was not on it. When he came back to the laboratory without the guest, Carl asked for the first time to examine the telegraphic correspondence. Sure enough, Theorell was due exactly a week later. Poor Olov was devastated and when Theorell did appear, the fever had abated.

The Coris always exuded a contagious work ethic, optimism, and a broad view of bioscience. After Carl and Gerty, six more would receive Nobel Prizes based on the training and outlook received at that time from the Coris and the ambience around them: Severo Ochoa and myself (1959), Luis Leloir (1970), Earl Sutherland (1971), Christian de Duve (1974), and Edwin Krebs (1991).

Carl and Gerty complemented each other in every way. Gerty would flit through the open door to Carl's tiny office throughout the day with results from the laboratory in which she was totally engaged. Carl was calm and analytical in contrast to Gerty, who was agitated and intuitive. They gossiped about people and events—Carl with amused concern, Gerty with intensity and compassion. I recall Gerty waving a newly arrived journal, "We've been attacked"; on careful search of the paper for the offensive slight, I could not find it.

Carl's erudition and formidable intelligence could be intimidating. He could also be dismissive. To a request from Christian de Duve in 1947 to spend 6 months in his laboratory to pursue an important idea about insulin action, Carl responded that he did not accept people for less than a year and, "With you," he added, "there is the additional difficulty that we do not see eye to eye with respect to the action of insulin."

Upon returning to the National Institutes of Health from St. Louis, I was asked to form an Enzyme Section, which I could do by inviting Leon Heppel and Bernard Horecker to join me. Together with Herbert Tabor, the four of us held daily lunch seminars in which we digested virtually every paper in this Journal even more thoroughly than our brown bag lunches. Once when Gerty Cori visited me on the occasion of a National Science Foundation board meeting, she lamented my being trapped in a government laboratory. I tried to reassure her that with full freedom and resources to do what I wished and with bright and motivated colleagues, I was enjoying an ideal academic environment.

The Coris had been largely responsible for my being offered the chairmanship of a newly created Microbiology Department at the Washington University Medical School in 1953. It had been a difficult transition for me to move from the National Institutes of Health. Among the problems were the brutally hot summers in St. Louis, from which I managed to escape to California. When I had to tell the Coris in 1957 that I decided to move to Stanford (taking the St. Louis claim to be "The Gateway to the West" literally), Carl was for the first time angry with me and sputtered: "Where will you go on vacation?" To which Gerty, close by, said: "Carlie, maybe we should have gone to California when they asked us."

In 1947, the Coris could celebrate the award of the Nobel Prize for Medicine or Physiology "for their discovery of the course of the catalytic conversion of glycogen"; an equal share went to Bernardo Houssay of Argentina for his discovery of the role of the anterior pituitary hormone in sugar metabolism. That year also brought the ghastly revelation that Gerty had a fatal anemia. For the next 10 years of her life, despite frequent transfusions, pain, and

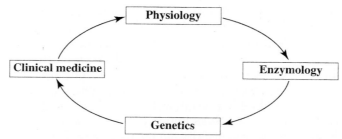

FIG. 3. **The Cori cycle II.** Sugar metabolism *physiology* in diabetes led to the *enzymology* of intermediary metabolism, then to the *genetics* of glycogen storage diseases, and finally to *clinical diagnosis* by enzyme assays of a liver biopsy.

fatigue, she maintained a full schedule of work, travel, and social activity. This fortitude and courage enabled her to do her pioneering work on molecular diseases and complete what I will later refer to as the Cori cycle II.

Among my many debts to the Coris is their discovery of glycogen phosphorylase whose actions encouraged me to seek an enzyme for DNA synthesis. It would be a mistake to assume that my discovery of DNA polymerase and the mechanism of DNA replication was inspired by the epochal Watson and Crick paper, which 2 years earlier had proposed that the spontaneous assembly of nucleotides in the synthesis of a DNA chain was directed by base pairing with each strand of the parental duplex. Glycogen phosphorylase, not base pairing, was what led me to DNA polymerase.

Having been educated by the Coris, Severo Ochoa, and other stars in the galaxy of that time, I had adopted the dogma that enzymology is the most effective way toward understanding biologic events. I had found enzymes that assemble the coenzymes (NAD, NADP, FAD) and the pyrimidine and purine nucleotides, and now I hoped to go further to find the enzyme of DNA synthesis. I had in mind an enzyme, which like the Cori glycogen phosphorylase would extend a DNA chain by successive additions of a properly activated nucleotide. I never imagined that my assays would lead to an enzyme, unlike any others, that took directions from its substrate and would assemble nucleotides by Watson-Crick base pairing to create a complementary copy of the parental DNA chain.

Gerty read widely and voraciously in history, biography, and modern novels, as well as in science. Aware of Oswald Avery's paper showing that DNA was the genetic substance, she made it a point to tell me: "You must read this. It is *very* important." She had recognized the significance of DNA at least 5 years before it was given proper attention by the celebrated genetics group at the California Institute of Technology. In relating genetics to enzymes, she had been fascinated by a number of severe diseases in children characterized by excessive glycogen storage. She showed that each disease was because of a singular genetic error responsible for either a defective or missing enzyme in glycogen metabolism. The diagnoses could be made simply with assays of a tiny liver biopsy.

Although Harvey Itano and Linus Pauling had earlier shown sickle cell anemia to be due to an inherited alteration in hemoglobin, it was Gerty's enzymology that inspired the great surge of medical investigation and diagnosis of a large number of enzyme deficiency diseases. Cori cycle II (Fig. 3) is their odyssey from clinical medicine to physiology, to enzymology and genetics, and finally full circle back to clinical medicine.

The Cori cycle and the Cori ester have been renamed, and attributions to the Coris are reasonably buried in the dustbin of history. But the lives of Carl and Gerty Cori and their monumental achievements deserve to be remembered as much as those of the political, military, arts, and sports stars of their era.

Severo Ochoa (Se-ver'-o O-cho'-a) (1905–1993)

Perhaps the most important feature that characterizes the few who emerge from the pack of trained, intelligent, motivated scientists is the capacity to withstand distractions and disappointments in life at home and at large, in institutional duties and politics, and in lack of resources and recognition, and also to resist the temptations of fame and fortune. Severo Ochoa (Fig. 4) was one of those few.

Born in the coastal village of Luarca in the Asturias province of northern Spain, Ochoa enrolled as a medical student at the University of Madrid in 1922. Although Ramón y Cajal, whom he idolized, had just retired, his fame still inspired those who might pursue a research career. There were few if any graduate studies in the biomedical sciences (either in Spain or

FIG. 4. **Severo Ochoa at a Beckman model DU spectrophotometer (c. 1955).**

elsewhere in Europe at the time), and the medical curriculum was the only recourse. Upon completing his medical courses and with no inclination toward clinical practice, he directly sought opportunities for experimental work.

Ochoa's peregrinations from one laboratory to another (nine in Europe and three in the United States) were determined in part by seeking out those at the frontier of chemical aspects of physiology and metabolism but even more so by circumstances far beyond his control. Social and political turbulence and a state of war in Spain, Germany, and the United Kingdom drove him from one refuge to another. Buffeted by all these events, he was unwavering in his devotion to science. He always remained on course in the face of all kinds of adversities, experimental and societal. His conviction that hard work would be rewarded sustained him during the most difficult hours and permeated the atmosphere around him.

Ochoa's very first paper was in English as was his second, a micromethod for creatine published in 1929 in this Journal, the first of hundreds that would appear in these pages over the next six decades. Upon completion of his medical thesis, he set out for Germany to spend the next 2 years in the laboratory of Otto Meyerhof (first in Berlin and then in Heidelberg). Meyerhof was renowned for his work on the energetics of muscle contraction for which he had been awarded, along with A. V. Hill, the Nobel Prize in Physiology or Medicine for 1922. To quote Ochoa: "Meyerhof was the teacher who most contributed toward my formation and the most influential in directing my life's work."

In 1932, with an appreciation of the importance of cell-free systems, Ochoa worked on his first enzyme, glyoxylase, with H. W. Dudley at the National Institute of Medical Research in London. Returning to Madrid, he worked on the chemistry of muscle contraction, but with the outbreak of the Spanish Civil War in 1936, he once again sought haven for a year in Meyerhof's laboratory in Heidelberg. This time he explored the action of cozymase, later known as DPN (diphosphopyridine nucleotide) and currently as NAD (nicotinamide adenine dinucleotide).

Meyerhof, with his status under attack by German racial laws, wrote A. V. Hill in the United Kingdom who found a place for Ochoa for a year in the Marine Biological Laboratory in

Plymouth. After that he was able to join Rudolph A. Peters in the biochemistry laboratory of Oxford University where, in studies of thiamin pyrophosphate in pyruvate metabolism, he was lured by oxidative (aerobic) phosphorylation. The obligate coupling of phosphorylation to the oxidation of pyruvic acid was observed by Ochoa and at the same time by Herman Kalckar in Copenhagen and by Vladimir A. Belitzer in the Soviet Union; Ochoa later estimated the number of phosphates fixed per oxygen atom consumed (P:O ratio) to be near three. Once again, the state of war in the United Kingdom enveloped all research activity and drove Ochoa, an alien, to accept in 1941 an invitation to St. Louis to join the laboratory of Carl and Gerty Cori.

In explorations of phosphorylation in disrupted liver tissue, he found a curiosity, inorganic pyrophosphate (PP_i). Because its source and fate were so vague, the finding was never published. During the year (1946) that I spent in Ochoa's laboratory, he mentioned the PP_i phenomenon a number of times to Efraim Racker, Alan Mehler, and me at lunch in the cafeteria we called "Salmonella Hall." However, its strangeness made it difficult to retain the experimental details of its origin, and we would pester him to repeat the story. Even Ochoa's patience could be tried, and finally he forbade any further mention of PP_i. When I joined the Cori laboratory the next year, I tried to find the source of PP_i. I failed then but did discover the source of PP_i several years later when it emerged as the entity released from nucleoside triphosphates in the synthesis of coenzymes, nucleic acids, and also proteins, fatty acids, and key metabolic intermediates.

After 1 year in St. Louis, Ochoa was offered a position as Research Associate in the Department of Medicine in the New York University School of Medicine, where he would remain for 32 years until retirement in 1974. With the least favorable facilities, Ochoa embarked on the discovery and characterization of the enzymes that he hoped would explain how cells derive virtually all their chemical energy. His confidence was based on the success in earlier decades in resolving and reconstituting alcoholic fermentation and glycolysis. The expectation was that discrete, isolatable enzymes would be identified as responsible for aerobic phosphorylation. The tricarboxylic acid cycle had just been proposed by Hans Krebs to explain how pyruvate was metabolized to carbon dioxide and water. Key intermediates in the cycle were the tricarboxylic acids (citrate and isocitrate), the enzymology of which Ochoa believed would help clarify aerobic phosphorylation.

The pursuit of aerobic phosphorylation, the Holy Grail of biochemistry, inspired me to seek out Ochoa's laboratory in 1946. I wanted to learn the enzymology and the new biochemistry I had not been taught in medical school 8 years earlier. My training in internal medicine had been interrupted in 1942 when (as a commissioned officer in the United States Public Health Service) I served briefly as a ship's doctor in the Navy and then was assigned to study rat nutrition at the National Institute (*sic*) of Health. With the war concluded and with nutritional science in its twilight and bored with the feeding and bleeding of rats for 3 years, I was able to persuade the Director of the National Institutes of Health to let me spend some months away learning about the new and exciting world of enzymes.

I was very fortunate that Ochoa was willing to take me, a complete novice in all aspects of biochemistry. In 1946, he occupied borrowed space in an old laboratory of Professor Isidor Greenwald in the New York University Department of Biochemistry. (Earlier, he had been summarily evicted from space in the Psychiatry Department in the Bellevue Hospital of the Medical School; upon returning from a concert one Sunday afternoon, he found his desk and equipment moved out into the hall.) When I arrived, his group consisted of a graduate student (Alan Mehler) and two technical assistants. Initially appointed as a Research Associate in Medicine and in 1945 as an assistant professor at the advanced age of 40, his stature in science was recognized the next year with the offer of a full professorship and chairmanship of the Department of Pharmacology. His reluctance to accept this promotion and associated responsibilities was characteristic of his indifference to academic titles and authority. "Why do I need a professorship?" he asked Efraim Racker, close by in the Department of Bacteriology. "I can do my work where I am now. Will the research work not suffer if I become a department chairman?" What finally persuaded him were two modern, well equipped laboratories developed by the previous chairman, James A. Shannon, later the Director of the National Institutes of Health. It was only in 1954 that Ochoa moved back across First Avenue to assume the vacated chairmanship of the Department of Biochemistry.

A prized possession of Ochoa's then was one of the new and scarce Beckman DU spectro-photometers (Fig. 4) (valued then at $1,500) and granted to him on loan, as was the policy of the American Philosophical Society. Patterned along the lines of the instrument devised by Otto Warburg in Germany, it was the highly effective successor to the laborious and insensitive respirometric assays of metabolic reactions that had been relied upon for several decades.

With the spectrophotometer in constant use, we were all in dread that "the philosophical Beckman," as it was called, would be reclaimed, but it never was. It remained and died of old age. Those early months in 1946, learning the rudiments of dynamic biochemistry, enzyme fractionation, and spectrophotometry, were the most exciting in my life. I was awed by enzymes and fell instantly in love with them. I have since had love affairs with many enzymes (none as enduring as with DNA polymerase), but I have never met a dull or disappointing one.

The day I came into the Ochoa laboratory after Christmas in 1945 several pig hearts fresh from the slaughterhouse awaited me. My project was to separate aconitase (an activity that converts citrate in two stages to isocitrate) into its two presumed component enzymes. Starting with a water extract of the ground-up heart muscle, I tried over the next months, using ammonium sulfate fractionation and other maneuvers, but failed to separate aconitase into two discrete enzymes. (Perhaps this explains why the Japanese translation of my autobiography, *For the Love of Enzymes*, is entitled *It Started with a Failure*.) Some years later when aconitase was purified to homogeneity by others, it was found to be a single polypeptide.

As events proved, the separated enzymes of the citric acid cycle could account for the oxidative reactions but not for the bulk of the energy captured by aerobic phosphorylation. Unlike the energetic couplings in alcohol fermentation and glycolysis, intact mitochondria were later discovered by others to be the means used in generating a proton motive force that results in the ultimate coupling of ATP synthesis to oxidative steps in the cycle.

A chance discovery in 1955 proved to be the cited basis of Ochoa's Nobel Prize Award 4 years later. Marianne Grunberg-Manago, a postdoctoral fellow, while exploring possible mechanisms of aerobic phosphorylation, observed an activity in a bacterial extract that exchanged $[^{32}P]P_i$ into ADP. The responsible enzyme, purified with Ochoa's urging and direction, astonishingly converted ADP and other nucleoside diphosphates into RNA-like $(NMP)_n$ polymers.

$$n\text{ADP} \rightarrow [\text{AMP}]_n + n\text{P}_i \qquad \text{(Eq. 1)}$$

$$[^{32}P]P_i + [\text{AMP}]_n \rightarrow [\text{AMP}]_{n-1} + [^{32}P]\text{ADP} \qquad \text{(Eq. 2)}$$

The initial hope that this enzyme, named polynucleotide phosphorylase, might be responsible for the biosynthesis of ribonucleic acid (RNA) was dispelled by the lack of a requirement for a DNA template to direct the assembly of a specific RNA message, the indiscriminate assembly of a polymer of any one or a mixture of nucleoside diphosphates, and finally the discovery of true RNA polymerases, which copy DNA templates with great specificity using nucleoside triphosphates rather than diphosphates. The role of polynucleotide phosphorylase in the bacteria in which it has been found is the disposal of RNA with salvage of its precious nucleotides.

Although polynucleotide phosphorylase was disappointing for its lack of a biosynthetic role, it was the first enzyme that could make RNA-like chains and proved to be of great value in deciphering the genetic code. After Marshall Nirenberg's discovery that polyuridylic acid, $(U–U–U)_n$, can encode a protein-like polymer of phenylalanine, Ochoa (with help from Leon A. Heppel) employed polynucleotide phosphorylase to synthesize a variety of RNA-like polymers, which were then used to identify many of the nucleotide triplets that encode the amino acids in the synthesis of proteins.

The 1959 award of the Nobel Prize in Physiology or Medicine to Ochoa and me "for their discovery of the mechanisms in the biological synthesis of ribonucleic acid and deoxyribonucleic acid" could have substituted "RNA-like polymers" for "ribonucleic acid" in anticipation of the role these polymers would play in the elucidation of the genetic code. Ochoa could reasonably have shared the 1968 Nobel Prize with R. W. Holley, H. G. Khorana, and M. Nirenberg, cited "for their interpretation of the genetic code and its function in protein synthesis."

After the Nobel Prize ceremonies in Stockholm in 1959, a hero's welcome would have awaited Ochoa in Spain, but his ties to the defeated Republican government and opposition to the Franco regime made return impossible for him at that time. He had become a United

States citizen, a devoted New Yorker, and a true internationalist in spirit. Nevertheless, he persuaded me, despite my own strong aversion to Franco, to go to Spain in his stead and arranged an attractive itinerary with receptions by his intimate friends and relatives. My late wife, Sylvy, and our three sons (Ken, 9; Tom, 11; and Roger, 12) were given the most affectionate welcome and expression of kinship in our opposition to their fascist government.

To illustrate the remarkable influence of Ochoa's enthusiastic and optimistic personality, I will relate a vignette engraved in my memory. It took place in December 1946. Nearing the end of the year in his laboratory, my most formative year in science, I was about to leave for the Cori laboratory in St. Louis. With Mehler, we had discovered and partially purified the malic enzyme that catalyzed the reaction: malate $\rightleftharpoons$ pyruvate + CO_2.

Now we were completing a very large scale preparation starting with several hundred pigeon livers. Four of us including Morton Schneider, Ochoa's talented and devoted assistant, had worked for several weeks to reach the last step in which successive additions of alcohol finally yielded the precipitate which we believed, from small scale trials, would have the enzyme in an adequate state of purity. We had only to fill in some details in a paper we had already prepared for publication.

Late one night, Ochoa and I were dissolving the final enzyme fraction, which had been collected in many glass centrifuge bottles. I had just poured the dissolved contents of the last bottle into a measuring cylinder that contained the entire enzyme fraction. Then I brushed against and overturned one of the empty, wobbly bottles on the crowded bench. That bottle knocked over another and the domino effect reached the cylinder with the enzyme. It fell over and all of the precious material spilled on the floor. It was gone forever. Ochoa tried to be reassuring, but I remained terribly upset. By the time I got home by subway train an hour later, Ochoa had called several times because he was so worried about my safety.

The next morning back in the laboratory I glanced at the supernatant fluid beyond the last fraction. I might have discarded it because in our trial procedures it had been inactive. However, I had saved and stored it in the freezer at −15 °C and now noticed that the previously clear fluid had become turbid. I collected the solid material, dissolved it, and assayed it for activity. "Holy Toledo," I shrieked. This fraction had the bulk of the enzyme activity and was severalfold purer than the best of our previous preparations. Severo came running over to share my relief and pleasure, greatly amused by the "Holy Toledo."

Why did I save and assay the fraction we assumed was inactive? Because Ochoa's enthusiasm and optimism was infectious. Rather than suffusing a blinding intelligence, Ochoa taught me that with an ethic of unremitting experimental work, good things eventually happen. I believed they would for me as they had for him.

Fascinated by every aspect of biochemistry and involved in all, his work ranged from muscle contraction and photosynthesis to vitamins and virus replication. He delved into the intricacies of the synthesis and breakdown of carbohydrates, lipids, nucleic acids, and proteins and played a major role in the drama of the genetic code. A courtly, charming, El Greco-like figure, intensely competitive and ambitious, he was eager to describe his latest findings, absorb those of others, and at times even appeared to intrude in all domains with little concern.

To celebrate his 70th birthday in 1975, Ochoa chose as guests the scientists he most respected worldwide. Symposia and celebratory dinners, starting in Barcelona, were followed by a visit with Salvador Dali in his museum in his hometown in Figueras and culminated in a gala of events in Madrid. It was a party, the likes of which has not been seen in scientific circles before or since.

Throughout his career, Severo had the constant and loyal support of his wife, Carmen. While in New York, they were the most gracious hosts in their modest apartment to an uninterrupted parade of students, postdoctoral fellows, visiting scientists, and colleagues. They especially enjoyed music, fine food, travel, and good company. With no children and attachments to his beloved New York weakened by the loss of most of his contemporaries in science, he and Carmen finally returned to Madrid in 1985. Her death shortly thereafter was a loss from which he never recovered despite the adoration of devoted family, friends, and students.

To the legion of postdoctoral fellows, students, and sabbatical guests who came to him from every corner of the world and left to become leaders in science and to the Spanish nation, Severo Ochoa will live on in their memory as a great teacher and an inspiration for the pursuit of science.

Envoi

In this brief essay, I have regretfully not included H. A. Barker, Herman Kalckar, Efraim Racker, Harland Wood, and so many others of my colleagues and students who have also been my teachers.

BIBLIOGRAPHY

Carl and Gerty Cori

McGrayne, S. B. (1993) *Nobel Prize Women in Science*, Birch Lane Press, Carol Publishing Co., New York

Cori, C. F. (1969) The call of science. *Annu. Rev. Biochem.* **38,** 1–20

Kalckar, H. M. (1958) Gerty T. Cori. *Science* **126,** 16

Ochoa, S. (1958) Gerty T. Cori, biochemist. *Science* **126,** 16

Randle, P. (1986) Carl Ferdinand Cori. *Biogr. Mem. Fellows R. Soc.* **32,** 67

Cohn, M. (1992) Carl Ferdinand Cori. *Biogr. Mem. Natl. Acad. Sci.* **61,** 78–109

Larner, J. (1992) Gerty Theresa Cori. *Biogr. Mem. Natl. Acad. Sci.* **61,** 110–135

Severo Ochoa

Kornberg, A., Horecker, B. L., Cornudella, L., and Oró, J. (eds) (1975) *Reflections on Biochemistry. In Honour of Severo Ochoa.* Essays by participants in the celebration of his 70th birthday. Pergamon Press, New York

Kornberg, A. (1993) Severo Ochoa. *Nature* **366,** 408 (obituary)

Kornberg, A. (1997) Severo Ochoa. *Proc. Am. Philos. Soc.* **141,** 479–491

Losada, M. (1994) Ochoa. *Hombre de Ciencia y de Bien. Secretario de Publicaciones de la Universidad de Sevilla,* pp. 1–48 (in Spanish)

New York Times (1993) Severo Ochoa, biochemist, a Nobel winner 88, dies. November 3. Obituary

Ochoa, S., and Valdecasas, J. G. (1929) A micromethod for the estimation of creatine in muscle. *J. Biol. Chem.* **81,** 351

Ochoa, S. (1980) The pursuit of a hobby. *Annu. Rev. Biochem.* **49,** 1–30

Sols, A., and Estrevez, C. (eds) (1975) *Trabajos Reunidos de Severo Ochoa 1928–1975.* Published by Servicio de Publicaciones, Ministerio de Educacion y Ciencia Cuidad Universitaria, Madrid-3, Spain. Reviewed by A. Kornberg in *Trends Biochem. Sci.* (1976) **1,** 267–268

THE JOURNAL OF BIOLOGICAL CHEMISTRY
© 2001 by The American Society for Biochemistry and Molecular Biology, Inc.

Vol. 276, No. 31, Issue of August 3, pp. 28629–28636, 2001
Printed in U.S.A.

Reflections

A PAPER IN A SERIES COMMISSIONED TO CELEBRATE THE CENTENARY OF THE JBC IN 2005

JBC Centennial
1905–2005
100 Years of Biochemistry and Molecular Biology

Reflections of a Fortunate Biochemist

Published, JBC Papers in Press, June 8, 2001, DOI 10.1074/jbc.R100040200

Irwin Fridovich

From the Department of Biochemistry, Duke University Medical Center, Durham, North Carolina 27710

While contemplating the writing of this article I reread some of my early publications and in so doing was appalled at my profound ignorance. That, of course, is the advantage of hindsight. It is also an indication of how much has been learned by me and by others during the intervening half-century. That is the beauty of science; it is a collaborative work in progress that builds knowledge and understanding of the real world. I hope it may be interesting (for readers concerned with the process as well as with the results) to recount how we progressed from abysmal naiveté to our current informed view of the biology of oxidation stress. The goal of modesty is served by allowing for the probability that our successors 5 decades hence will consider the knowledge we have achieved pitifully incomplete.

Sulfite Oxidation

Abraham Mazur introduced me to the wonders of biochemistry in an undergraduate course and then during a year spent working in his laboratory at Cornell Medical School. At the end of that year he recommended graduate work and sent me to Duke Medical School to work with Philip Handler, the chairman of the Department of Biochemistry. Handler was the most impressive person I have ever met. He was blessed with a photographic memory, an incomparable mastery of language, and excellent judgment. He assigned me to work with Murray Heimberg, who was then a senior graduate student. He was older than the usual graduate student, having devoted several years to fighting World War II. At one time during this conflict Murray had lost half of his body weight because of malnutrition while a prisoner of war, but he had entirely recovered when I knew him.

We worked long hours, measuring O_2 uptake with Warburg microrespirometers and methylene blue bleaching in evacuated Thunberg tubes with a Coleman colorimeter. We found that α-hydroxysulfonic acids dissociated to carbonyl compounds plus sulfite and that sulfite was then oxidized to sulfate in the liver extracts we were studying (1). Thus began my long infatuation with sulfite oxidation.

It had already been established that sulfite was readily oxidized by a free radical chain mechanism, but I did not know this and had to discover it for myself. Thus I found that sulfite could reduce cytochrome c and, of course, at the same time cytochrome c could oxidize sulfite. When this was done anaerobically the stoichiometry was 2 cytochrome c reduced per sulfite oxidized, as expected. However, in the presence of dissolved O_2 thousands of sulfites were oxidized per cytochrome c reduced. This could be rationalized by assuming that each time sulfite transferred an electron to cytochrome c, the resulting sulfur trioxyradical started a chain reaction between sulfite and O_2 as follows.

$$SO_3^= + Cyt\ c\ Fe(III) \longrightarrow SO_3^- + Cyt\ c\ Fe(II)\ \}\ \text{initiation} \tag{Eq. 1}$$

$$SO_3^- + O_2 \longrightarrow SO_5^- \tag{Eq. 2}$$

$$SO_5^- + SO_3^= \longrightarrow SO_5^= + SO_3^- \Big\}\ \text{propagation} \tag{Eq. 3}$$

$$SO_5^= + H_2O \longrightarrow SO_4^= + H_2O_2\ \}\ \text{formation of products} \tag{Eq. 4}$$

The truly impressive amplification provided by this chain reaction fascinated me and so I played with it to see what it could be used for. Sulfite oxidation ultimately provided: an ultrasensitive manometric assay for xanthine oxidase (2); a method for detecting long lived flavin radicals generated photochemically (3); a method for ultrasensitive manometric actinometry (4); and much more besides.

Xanthine Oxidase

It was sulfite oxidation that led to xanthine oxidase, which in turn led to superoxide and to the superoxide dismutases. Thus a soluble fraction of liver, able to catalyze the oxidation of sulfite, lost this activity upon dialysis, and adding back the concentrated dialysate restored that activity. A search for the dialyzable cofactor of sulfite oxidation yielded hypoxanthine (5). Because hypoxanthine is a substrate for xanthine oxidase we were led to that enzyme. In time we realized that xanthine oxidase, when acting on its substrates aerobically, could initiate the oxidation of sulfite (2). This should have told me that xanthine oxidase was generating a radical from O_2, and that radical (O_2^-) was initiating the oxidation of sulfite. However, I was woefully slow and that illumination was not to be achieved for several more years.

Cytochrome c Reduction

Xanthine oxidase was a fascinating enzyme in its own right with several prosthetic groups and broad specificity with regard to both electron donors and acceptors. One of its intriguing properties was the ability to cause the O_2-dependent reduction of cytochrome c (6). It had been suggested that H_2O_2, produced from O_2, was the reductant of cytochrome c, and this explained the O_2 dependence of cytochrome c reduction. That was easily shown not to be the case. While studying this cytochrome c reduction I noted that some preparations of cytochrome c were rapidly reduced whereas others were not. Moreover the samples of cytochrome c that could not be reduced by xanthine oxidase inhibited the reduction of those that could be reduced and did so without interfering with the reduction of O_2 by the xanthine oxidase. This inhibition, which was incorrectly attributed to a myoglobin impurity (7), was actually because of superoxide dismutase present in some of the preparations of cytochrome c.

The oxygen requirement for cytochrome c reduction was explored, and the K_m O_2 for cytochrome c reduction was found to be 30 times greater than was K_m O_2 for O_2 reduction (8). This apparent discrepancy would be understood years later (9) as the increase in the proportion of univalent over divalent reduction of O_2 as the pO_2 was increased.

There were other indications that the reduction of cytochrome c was different in kind than the reduction of O_2. Thus a catechol disulfonate (Tiron) was found to inhibit cytochrome c reduction by xanthine oxidase while having no effect on net O_2 reduction (8). This is now understood as being due to the scavenging of O_2^- by catechols. At the time, O_2 was conceived of as facilitating the reduction of cytochrome c by serving as an electron transporting bridge between the enzyme and the cytochrome. Free O_2^- could not easily be proposed because its redox potential was thought to be very negative making its production thermodynamically unfavorable (10).

Chemiluminescence

The xanthine oxidase reaction had been reported by John Totter (11) to elicit luminescence from lucigenin, and oxygen radicals had been proposed to play a role. When L. Greenlee (12) joined the laboratory he was asked to explore this lucigenin luminescence. Greenlee used an old Farrand fluorimeter with its light turned off as a photometer, and he worked in a darkened room so that he could observe light emission while making additions to the reaction mixtures. O_2 was found to be essential for luminescence, but the intensity of the light produced was greatest when the reaction mixtures were equilibrated with ~2% O_2. Either more or less O_2 diminished light production. This, with additional data, was taken to mean that light resulted when O_2^- reacted with reduced lucigenin (12).

A Diversion to Acetoacetic Decarboxylase

Work with xanthine oxidase was interrupted by a year long sabbatical spent with F. H. Westheimer in the Department of Chemistry at Harvard University. At our first meeting he invited me to work on anything I chose to do, but I wanted to explore some of his interests, which included decarboxylation. Consequently I started to work on acetoacetic decarboxylase. Frank Westheimer is a superb chemist and a wonderful teacher and I learned a lot during that year.

The department was well equipped for organic synthesis but did not contain a single spectrophotometer. Roberta Colman, who was also working on the acetoacetate decarboxylase, was using Warburg microrespirometers to assay the enzyme. I was determined to avoid that laborious method and envisioned a spectrophotometric assay. When I brought this thought to Frank he doubted the feasibility of a spectrophotometric assay but nevertheless purchased a very good spectrophotometer for me that very day. Before the week was out I had a workable and convenient assay (13). One of the things I noticed at the outset was the inhibition of acetoacetic decarboxylase by monovalent anions, such as the halides. By happenstance Roberta Colman had been working in a buffer that contained enough chloride to very substantially inhibit the enzyme. When I was introduced to her husband some weeks later he said "you're the monster who made Roberta redo all of her kinetic studies on the decarboxylase."

More Diversions

When I returned to Duke Medical School, Philip Handler indicated that I should quit working on xanthine oxidase and branch out into other areas. Hence during the early 1960s I followed up on several chance observations I had made previously. One of these that intrigues me to this day is the ability of amines to markedly extend the range of pH over which horseradish peroxidase is optimally active (14). I am still hoping that someone will reinvestigate this and provide a mechanism.

Steady state kinetic studies of enzyme action were then fashionable, and I had noticed that urea and guanidinium could competitively inhibit xanthine oxidase and could do so at concentrations far below those needed for unfolding proteins (15). The inhibitory power of guanidinium salts was found to vary markedly from lot to lot. I then isolated the symmetrical triazine that was responsible for this variability (16). While working with triazines I found some that were powerful inhibitors of uricase (17) and was pleased to see this information applied to raising the urate level of mice by feeding them my uricase inhibitor (18).

Acetoacetic decarboxylase was not entirely abandoned, and we found that the activity of the isolated enzyme could be irreversibly doubled by mild heating (19). We could offer no explanation for this thermal activation, but it now seems possible that self-splicing was involved. This process, in which a sequence of amino acids is removed from a protein, has been reported several times. The piece removed in this self-splicing is termed an intein. An incident that reveals the stature of Frank Westheimer deals with this autoactivation of acetoacetic decarboxylase. After exploring the phenomenon I submitted a descriptive manuscript to the *Journal of Biological Chemistry*. The editor (John Edsall) sent it to Westheimer for review, who called me to say that he had the manuscript; that he had noticed the same autoactivation; that I was somewhat ahead on this project; and that he was recommending publication without revision. Would that everyone was as honest and generous as Frank Westheimer.

On to Superoxide Dismutase

All the foregoing pales to insignificance beside the discovery of SOD.[1] That xanthine oxidase might univalently reduce O_2 had been enunciated, and the differences between the reduction of O_2 to H_2O_2 and the roles of O_2 in mediating cytochrome *c* reduction, initiating sulfite oxidation, and eliciting lucigenin luminescence had been noted. However, such were the misconceptions among radiation chemists and physical chemists concerning the properties of O_2^- that it seemed foolhardy to propose free O_2^- as a product of the xanthine oxidase reaction. A fallback position that could still explain our many observations was to propose bound O_2^-. In that case cytochrome *c* would have to bind to xanthine oxidase, as would the protein competitive inhibitors of cytochrome *c* reduction.

At this point Joe M. McCord joined my laboratory as a graduate student and was asked to measure that presumed binding. After several heroic efforts provided no evidence for binding he decided to prove that there was no binding. He asked me whether K_m was independent of enzyme concentration. I responded that it was, so long as substrate concentration exceeded enzyme concentration. With that assurance he produced kinetic data showing that K_m xanthine was, as expected, independent of the concentration of xanthine oxidase. In contrast K_m cytochrome *c* or K_i for the inhibitors of cytochrome *c* reductions was very much a function of the concentration of xanthine oxidase.

To this day I recall the stunning impact of that data. Previous misconceptions were swept away, and it was immediately clear that xanthine oxidase was releasing O_2^- into free solution, where it could reduce cytochrome *c*, initiate sulfite oxidation, or be intercepted by the protein

---

[1] The abbreviation used is: SOD, superoxide dismutase.

inhibitors of cytochrome c reduction. It was also clear that those inhibitors of cytochrome c reduction must be acting catalytically, and the only feasible way they could do so was by dismutating O_2^- into $H_2O_2 + O_2$ (20). Bravo Joe McCord!

$$O_2^- + O_2^- + 2H^+ \longrightarrow H_2O_2 + O_2 \qquad\qquad (Eq.\ 5)$$

Now we knew exactly what to do, and the SOD activity in bovine erythrocytes proved to be abundant and stable and it was soon purified (21). Moreover its activity was demonstrated using electrochemically generated O_2^- in place of the flux of O_2^- made by xanthine oxidase and using tetranitromethane in place of cytochrome c. Joe and I felt like kids in a toy shop. We could and did use the newfound SOD to explore the role of O_2^- in diverse reactions (22, 23) and to measure the effect of reaction conditions on the proportion of univalent over divalent O_2 reduction by xanthine oxidase (9). We recognized that our Cu,Zn-SOD had long been studied by others as an abundant cuproprotein of unknown function and given the names hepatocuprein, cerebrocuprein, hemocuprein, etc. We had found the biological activity of the "cupreins," and I could sympathize with those protein chemists who must have felt cheated. A similar situation arose when J. M. McCord and B. B. Keele, Jr. isolated the SOD from *Escherichia coli* (25) and Richard Weisiger isolated a very similar SOD from mitochondria (26). These SODs contained Mn(III) and were undoubtedly the same as the avimanganin that had been isolated and studied by Michael Scrutton, again as a metalloprotein of unknown function.

Knowledge of the sequence and of the structure of proteins has long been seen as useful for deducing evolutionary relationships and mechanisms of action. The sequences of the Cu,Zn-SOD and of the Mn-SOD (to be discussed below) were determined by the laborious methods then available (27), and the homologies in sequence that bespoke a common evolutionary origin for the mitochondrial and bacterial SODs were determined (28). A sample of the Cu,Zn-SOD was given to our in-house crystallographers, David and Jane Richardson. They and their students determined its structure by methods that are still "black box" to me (29, 30). I revealed my complete ignorance of the methods to the Richardsons by asking for the structure only 3 weeks after I had given them the protein sample. They informed me that crystallization was proceeding at its own stately pace and it would take a bit longer. It took a few years longer.

Physiological Function of SODs

If O_2^- could be made in quantity by xanthine oxidase, it seemed obvious that it would be made by other enzymes as well, and if it could readily cause the oxidation of sulfite and of epinephrine, it could surely cause unwanted oxidations within cells. If SODs were so active and abundant, it seemed to us that they must serve as a defense against O_2^-, much as catalases defend against H_2O_2. Those views demanded support, which was soon forthcoming. Thus a survey of microorganisms revealed that aerobes contained abundant SOD, whereas obligate anaerobes contained little or none (31). In addition SOD was seen to be induced by aerobic growth (32), and the induced level of SOD protected against the lethality of hyperbaric O_2 (33). More definitive evidence was provided by the phenotypic deficits of the SOD-null mutants produced by Danielle Touati (34, 35). In the fullness of time SOD-null mutants were prepared in a variety of prokaryotes, in yeast, and then in mice.

Pulse Radiolysis

Pulse radiolysis seemed to be the ideal method for directly assaying the activity of SOD and for measuring the rate constant for the SOD/O_2^- reaction. Perusal of the literature of pulse radiolysis suggested that Joseph Rabani might be a willing collaborator. He was working at the Hebrew University in Jerusalem but made periodic trips to the United States to collaborate with someone at Johns Hopkins University. We arranged a meeting and he was willing to study SOD by pulse radiolysis. However this was the time when terrorists were sending letter bombs, and Israelis were particular targets. Rabani advised me that my shipment of SOD would be held up unless I could make it look innocuous, even unimportant. I achieved these criteria by injecting a concentrated solution of Cu,Zn-SOD into a 10-foot length of 1-mm polyethylene tubing. The ends were then sealed with 5-min epoxy, and the tubing, formed into a flat coil, was taped into a reprint. This reprint, in an unsealed envelope, was delivered to Rabani's laboratory without incident. Given that the enzyme had not been refrigerated for over a week while enroute, I have always regarded the rate constant of $2.3 \times 10^9\ \text{M}^{-1}\ \text{s}^{-1}$ (36) as a lower limit because the Cu,Zn-SOD, albeit a stable protein, must have suffered some loss of activity enroute to Jerusalem. Moreover, the specific activity of the sample sent to Rabani was 3,200 units/mg, and we have since prepared samples with an activity of 5,000 units/mg.

An Iron-containing SOD

We had seen the blue-green Cu,Zn-SOD from erythrocytes and the reddish Mn-SOD from *E. coli* and from liver mitochondria. Yet it was clear that there was another SOD in *E. coli*. This was revealed by the activity stain devised by Charles Beauchamp (37). Fred Yost launched into the isolation of this new *E. coli* SOD. As he approached the successful isolation of this SOD I noticed that the normally outgoing and friendly Fred Yost was going out of his way to avoid me. When I asked his good friend Mick Gregory about this I was told that Fred's SOD had the wrong color and he was afraid I would not like this result. I was delighted with this new SOD, which proved to contain iron (38). In *E. coli* the Fe-SOD proved to be constitutive and was present in aerobic or anaerobic cultures. The Mn-SOD, in contrast, was expressed only in aerobic cultures and was subsequently shown to be regulated as part of the soxRS regulon (39, 40).

Paraquat

During 1975 I had the good fortune of encountering Hosni M. Hassan. He proved to be unusually insightful and productive, and we published many excellent papers together. The one that stands out in my memory dealt with the effect of paraquat on *E. coli* (41). Hosni showed that this widely used herbicide caused a marked induction of Mn-SOD, which rendered the cells resistant toward the toxicities of O_2 and of the quinone streptonigrin. Because paraquat also increased cyanide-resistant respiration it seemed obvious that paraquat engaged in a cycle of alternate reduction and autoxidation within *E. coli*. This would increase the production O_2^- while providing a cyanide-insensitive route for electron flow to O_2.

A wide variety of quinones and dyes were subsequently shown to behave similarly. Enhanced sensitivity to paraquat has become a routinely observed phenotypic marker for SOD-null mutants. If the toxicity of paraquat is largely a reflection of the O_2^-, whose production it mediates, then paraquat toxicity should be dependent upon O_2, and that is the case. Moreover, preventing the up-regulation of Mn-SOD with puromycin should greatly increase that toxicity, and that too is the case (42).

Two Catalases in E. coli

Having described the SODs in *E. coli* that eliminate O_2^-, it seemed incumbent upon us to examine the catalase that disposes of the H_2O_2. This was undertaken by Al Claiborne who soon found that *E. coli* makes two catalases. One of these was only a catalase whereas the other was a dual catalase/peroxidase (43, 44). We referred to them as hydroperoxidases I and II, and they were subsequently studied in detail by Peter Loewen and his associates.

A Non-enzymic SOD

Fred Archibald came to my lab in 1980. He was a very fine microbiologist and could repair anything from automobiles to spectrophotometers. We had previously seen that *Lactobacillus plantarum* lacked SOD yet was aerotolerant (45). Fred was asked to examine this organism. Fortunately he was new to the laboratory and was not familiar with our usual practices. Thus, after only a few days of work he asked me why I had asserted that *L. plantarum* lacked SOD. He had found abundant SOD activity in the extracts of this organism. Ever mindful of possible interference by metal contaminants, I asked him whether he had dialyzed those extracts and included EDTA in the assay buffer. Fred's response was negative on both counts.

It quickly developed that *L. plantarum* contained a dialyzable, heat-stable, and EDTA-sensitive SOD activity. Given that this organism grows best on manganese-rich medium, it did not take long to show that manganese was accumulated to an intracellular concentration of ~25 mM and that non-enzymic Mn(II) was, in fact, serving as the functional replacement for SOD (46, 47). The stability of the activity to boiling had ruled out a Mn-SOD with a dissociable manganese.

An Ultrasensitive Assay for SOD

We were asked to examine both mycoplasmas and methanogens for their content of SOD. It was apparent that we would need an assay more sensitive than any we had previously devised. The usual assays depended upon competition between SOD and some indicating scavenger of O_2^-. If the indicating scavenger had a low rate of reaction with O_2^- the assay was more sensitive. Suppose that the indicating scavenger could be omitted? The assay finally devised used the xanthine oxidase reaction to establish a steady state level of O_2^- and only then to add cytochrome c as the indicating scavenger. There was a sudden increase in $A_{550\,nm}$ that reflected the steady state level of O_2^-, followed by a linear increase in $A_{550\,nm}$ reflecting the ongoing flux of O_2^-. SOD revealed its activity by decreasing the sudden increase in $A_{550\,nm}$. This strategy provided an ~100-fold increase in sensitivity (48).

Lactobacillus plantarum Again

In the 1960s E. A. Delwiche working at Cornell University reported that *L. plantarum* contained a CN^--sensitive catalase when grown on heme-enriched medium but produced a CN^--insensitive catalase when grown in the absence of heme. Delwiche named the latter enzyme pseudocatalase. We isolated it and found a manganese-containing catalase (49) that was essential for the survival of this organism in aerobic stationary phase (50). This enzyme was subsequently studied by x-ray crystallography and shown to contain a binuclear cluster of manganese atoms at its active site.

An Old Bottle of Glycerol

During the summer of 1980 my daughter Sharon was working in my laboratory. Her project was to isolate an SOD from plant mitochondria. Each morning on the way to the laboratory we stopped at a market and purchased a head of cauliflower. Because Sharon's goal was the mitochondrial Mn-SOD, she included CN^- in the assay mixtures to suppress activity due to the Cu,Zn-SOD. After a while she found that the plant Mn-SOD was unstable and I suggested that 10% glycerol might stabilize it. Sharon soon reported that CN^- plus glycerol could reduce cytochrome c. The only possible explanation seemed to be an impurity in the glycerol, which had been on the shelf for over 10 years. Glycerol from a fresh bottle did not support the reduction of cytochrome c so we tried an oxidation product of glycerol, namely glyceraldehyde. CN^- plus glyceraldehyde or a variety of other α-hydroxycarbonyls could reduce cytochrome c or O_2 (51). This seemed bizarre because CN^- had been used with such compounds to synthesize sugars for over a century. Had no one noticed the oxidation? Perusal of old literature on the Fischer-Kiliani synthesis, in which aldose sugars were incubated with CN^- yielding a cyanohydrin that could then be hydrolyzed and then reduced to the isomeric pair of longer chain sugars, finally led to a paper in which the author specified filling the flask to the top and sealing it tightly with a rubber stopper before incubating it overnight. He must have noticed a decrease in yield when these simple means of excluding oxygen were not used. Subsequent study of the mechanism of this cyanide-catalyzed oxidation of sugars revealed a role for enediolate tautomers and radical intermediates (52, 53). This chemistry is now pertinent to the process of non-enzymic glycation thought to be important in diabetes mellitus and in aging.

How Super Is Superoxide?

Increasing intracellular production of O_2^- by raising pO_2 or by addition of redox cycling compounds or by mutational deletion of SOD imposes nutritional auxotrophies, such as the need for branched chain amino acids. O. R. Brown suggested (54) that this was because of inactivation of the dihydroxyacid dehydratase that catalyzes the penultimate step in the relevant biosynthetic pathway. The possibility that O_2^- could directly inactivate this dehydratase was exciting to us because there were still those who were asserting that O_2^- was a biologically benign species. We found that O_2^- did inactivate this enzyme (55) and other [4Fe-4S] cluster-containing dehydratases, such as the 6-phosphogluconate dehydratase (56) and aconitase (57).

Because oxidation of the [4Fe-4S] clusters of dehydratases causes loss of iron and because "free" iron can react with H_2O_2 to produce $HO^•$, that could lead to widespread damage to DNA, proteins, and membranes. This would moreover provide an explanation for the oft reported damaging synergism between O_2^- and H_2O_2. Soon after we proposed this (58) it was supported by experimental data (24). There is an interesting difference between the *in vitro* and *in vivo* ways by which O_2^- and H_2O_2 interact to produce $HO^•$. Thus, in the test tube, O_2^- served as a reductant for adventitious Fe(III) or Cu(II), and the resultant Fe(II) or Cu(I) then reduced H_2O_2 to $HO^- + HO^•$ Such a mechanism was simply not plausible in the reducing environment of the cell, which would keep any free iron or copper in their reduced states. This problem was solved by the finding that *in vivo* O_2^- serves to provide free Fe(II) through its oxidative attack on the [4Fe-4S]-containing dehydratases.

Motivation and Funding

I would like to stress that the work that led to the discovery of the superoxide dismutases did not seem, at the time it was being pursued, to have any relevance to human health or disease. It was merely interesting, and we were motivated purely by curiosity. At the time, that was enough justification and one could get funding from the National Institutes of Health to support such work. Alas that is no longer enough and one has to envision health relevance or not get funded.

Curiosity about the chemistry of life continues as do the experiments to satisfy that curiosity. In recent years we have been: exploring the role of oxidative stress in heat shock and stationary phase death; finding a Cu,Zn-SOD in the periplasm of *E. coli*; clarifying the subcellular distribution of SODs in liver cells; making low molecular weight catalysts of the dismutation reaction that may be useful as pharmaceuticals for treating reperfusion injuries and inflammations; exploring the role of oxygen-derived radicals in adaptive mutagenesis; explaining the nutritional auxotrophies imposed by lack of SOD activity; studying the basis of the oxygen-dependent toxicity of short chain sugars; adding to the list of enzymes that are known to be controlled by the soxRS regulon; and wondering whether the univalent oxidation of bicarbonate to the carbonate monoanion radical is a factor in oxidative stress, Curiosity remains undiminished at age 72 years and so there will by more—if health and strength allow.

Summary

Each of my published papers ignites a flood of memories of the students and postdoctoral fellows I worked with, of the competitors we contended with, and of the pleasures of achieving an understanding of something formerly hidden from view. I have here recorded only a small fraction of those memories, but that is enough to give the reader a feeling for what we did and how we did it. Hence I close now with gratitude to those co-workers whose efforts have been mentioned herein and with apology to those whose equally meritorious accomplishments were not. I should add that many talented scientists have been drawn to the study of the biology of superoxide, because it has proven to have relevance to diverse physiological and pathological processes. At the time of this writing there are several journals devoted to this field and a PubMed search of the term superoxide dismutase pulled up 20,067 references.

REFERENCES

1. Heimberg, M., Fridovich, I., and Handler, P. (1953) The enzymatic oxidation of sulfite. *J. Biol. Chem.* **204**, 913–926
2. Fridovich, I., and Handler, P. (1958) Xanthine oxidase. III. Sulfite oxidation as an ultrasensitive assay. *J. Biol. Chem.* **233**, 1578–1580
3. Fridovich, I., and Handler, P. (1960) Detection of free radicals in illuminated dye solutions by the initiation of sulfite oxidation. *J. Biol. Chem.* **235**, 1835–1838
4. Fridovich, I., and Handler, P. (1959) Utilization of the photosensitized oxidation of sulfite for manometric actinometry. *Biochim. Biophys. Acta* **35**, 546–547
5. Fridovich, I., and Handler, P. (1956) Hypoxanthine as a cofactor for the enzymatic oxidation of sulfite. *J. Biol. Chem.* **221**, 323–331
6. Horecker, B. L., and Heppel, L. A. (1949) The reduction of cytochrome *c* by xanthine oxidase. *J. Biol. Chem.* **178**, 683–690
7. Fridovich, I. (1962) Competitive inhibition by myoglobin of the reduction of cytochrome *c* by xanthine oxidase. *J. Biol. Chem.* **237**, 584–586
8. Fridovich, I., and Handler, P. (1962) Xanthine oxidase. V. Differential inhibition of the reduction of various electron acceptors. *J. Biol. Chem.* **237**, 916–921
9. Fridovich, I. (1970) Quantitative aspects of the production of superoxide anion radical by milk xanthine oxidase. *J. Biol. Chem.* **245**, 4053–4057
10. George, P., and Griffith, J. S. (1959) Electron transfer and enzyme catalysis. in *The Enzymes* (Boyer, P. D., Lardy, H., and Myrback, K., eds) 2nd Ed., Vol. 1, pp. 347–389, Academic Press, New York
11. Totter, J. R., DeDugros, E. C., and Riveiro, L. (1960) The use of chemiluminescent compounds as possible indicators of radical production during xanthine oxidase action. *J. Biol. Chem.* **235**, 1839–1842
12. Greenlee, L., Fridovich, I., and Handler, P. (1962) Chemiluminescence induced by operation of iron-flavoproteins. *Biochemistry* **1**, 779–783
13. Fridovich, I. (1963) Inhibition of acetoacetic decarboxylase by anions. The Hofmeister lyotropic series. *J. Biol. Chem.* **238**, 592–598
14. Fridovich, I. (1963) The stimulation of horseradish peroxidase by nitrogenous ligands. *J. Biol. Chem.* **238**, 3921–3927
15. Fridovich, I. (1964) Competitive inhibition of xanthine oxidase by urea and guanidinium ion. *J. Biol. Chem.* **239**, 3519–3521
16. Fridovich, I. (1965) A new class of xanthine oxidase inhibitors isolated from guanidinium salts. *Biochemistry* **4**, 1098–1101
17. Fridovich, I. (1965) The competitive inhibition of uricase by oxonate and related derivatives of s-triazines. *J. Biol. Chem.* **240**, 2491–2494
18. Norrlind, B., and Kihlberg, R. (1973) A short assay for the estimation of dietary purine compounds. Using a rat model system with inhibition of uricase. *J. Nutr.* **103**, 1262–1269
19. Neece, M. S., and Fridovich, I. (1967) Acetoacetic decarboxylase. Activation by heat. *J. Biol. Chem.* **242**, 2939–2944

20. McCord, J. M., and Fridovich, I. (1968) The reduction of cytochrome *c* by milk xanthine oxidase. *J. Biol. Chem.* **243,** 5753–5760

21. McCord, J. M., and Fridovich, I. (1969) Superoxide dismutase. An enzymic function for erythrocuprein (hemocuprein). *J. Biol. Chem.* **244,** 6049–6055

22. McCord, J. M., and Fridovich, I. (1969) The utility of superoxide dismutase in studying free radical reactions. I. Radicals generated by the interaction of sulfite, dimethyl sulfoxide, and oxygen. *J. Biol. Chem.* **244,** 6056–6063

23. McCord, J. M., and Fridovich, I. (1970) The utility of superoxide dismutase in studying free radical reactions. II. The mechanism of the mediation of cytochrome *c* reduction by a variety of electron carriers. *J. Biol. Chem.* **245,** 1374–1377

24. Keyer, K., Strohmeier-Gort, A., and Inlay, J. A. (1995) Superoxide and the production of oxidative DNA damage. *J. Bacteriol.* **177,** 6782–6790

25. Keele, B. B., Jr., McCord, J. M., and Fridovich, I. (1970) Superoxide dismutase from *Escherichia coli* B. A new manganese-containing enzyme. *J. Biol. Chem.* **245,** 6176–6181

26. Weisiger, R. A., and Fridovich, I. (1973) Superoxide dismutase. Organelle specificity. *J. Biol. Chem.* **248,** 3582–3592

27. Steinman, H. M., Naik, V. R., Abernathy, J. L., and Hill, R. L. (1974) Bovine erythrocyte superoxide dismutase. Complete amino acid sequence. *J. Biol. Chem.* **249,** 7326–7338

28. Steinman, H. M., and Hill, R. L. (1973) Sequence homology among bacterial and mitochondrial superoxide dismutases. *Proc. Natl. Acad. Sci. U. S. A.* **70,** 3725–3729

29. Richardson, J. S., Thomas, K. A., Rubin, B. H., and Richardson, D. C. (1975) Crystal structure of bovine Cu,Zn superoxide dismutase at 3 Å resolution: chain tracing and metal ligands. *Proc. Natl. Acad. Sci. U. S. A.* **72,** 1349–1353

30. Tainer, J. A., Getzoff, E. D., Beem, K. M., Richardson, J. S., and Richardson, D. C. (1982) Determination and analysis of the two angstrom structure of copper,zinc superoxide dismutase. *J. Mol. Biol.* **160,** 181–217

31. McCord, J. M., Keele, B. B., Jr., and Fridovich, I. (1971) The enzyme based theory of obligate anaerobiosis. The physiological function of superoxide dismutase. *Proc. Natl. Acad. Sci. U. S. A.* **68,** 1024–1027

32. Gregory, E. M., and Fridovich, I. (1973) Induction of superoxide dismutase by molecular oxygen. *J. Bacteriol.* **114,** 543–548

33. Gregory, E. M., and Fridovich, I. (1973) Oxygen toxicity and the superoxide dismutase. *J. Bacteriol.* **114,** 1193–1197

34. Carlioz, A., and Touati, D. (1986) Isolation of superoxide dismutase mutants in *Escherichia coli.* Is superoxide dismutase strictly necessary for aerobic life? *EMBO J.* **5,** 623–630

35. Farr, S. B., D'Ari, R., and Touati, D. (1986) Oxygen-dependent mutagenesis in *Escherichia coli* lacking superoxide dismutase. *Proc. Natl. Acad. Sci. U. S. A.* **83,** 8268–8272

36. Klug, D., Rabani, J., and Fridovich, I. (1972) A direct demonstration of the catalytic action of superoxide dismutase through the use of pulse radiolysis. *J. Biol. Chem.* **247,** 4839–4842

37. Beauchamp, C., and Fridovich, I. (1971) Superoxide dismutase. Improved assays and an assay applicable to acrylamide gels. *Anal. Biochem.* **44,** 276–287

38. Yost, F. J., Jr., and Fridovich, I. (1973) An iron-containing superoxide dismutase from *Escherichia coli.* *J. Biol. Chem.* **248,** 4905–4908

39. Wu, J., and Weiss, B. (1991) Two divergently transcribed genes, *soxR* and *soxS,* control a superoxide response regulon in *Escherichia coli.* *J. Bacteriol.* **173,** 2864–2871

40. Amabile-Cuevas, C. F., and Demple, B. (1991) Molecular characterization of the *soxRS* genes of *Escherichia coli.* Two genes control a superoxide stress regulon. *Nucleic Acids Res.* **19,** 4479–4484

41. Hassan, H. M., and Fridovich, I. (1977) Regulation of the synthesis of superoxide dismutase in *Escherichia coli.* Induction by methyl viologen. *J. Biol. Chem.* **252,** 7667–7672

42. Hassan, H. M., and Fridovich, I. (1978) Superoxide radical and the oxygen enhancement of the toxicity of paraquat in *Escherichia coli.* *J. Biol. Chem.* **253,** 8143–8148

43. Claiborne, A., and Fridovich, I. (1979) Purification of the *o*-dianisidine peroxidase from *Escherichia coli* B. Physicochemical characterization and analysis of its dual catalatic and peroxidatic activities. *J. Biol. Chem.* **254,** 4245–4252

44. Claiborne, A., Malinowski, D. P., and Fridovich, I. (1979) Purification and characterization of hydroperoxidase II of *Escherichia coli* B. *J. Biol. Chem.* **254,** 11664–11668

45. Gregory, E. M., and Fridovich, I. (1974) Oxygen metabolism in *Lactobacillus plantarum.* *J. Bacteriol.* **117,** 166–169

46. Archibald, F. S., and Fridovich, I. (1981) Manganese and defenses against oxygen toxicity in *Lactobacillus plantarum.* *J. Bacteriol.* **145,** 442–451

47. Archibald, F. S., and Fridovich, I. (1981) Manganese superoxide dismutase and oxygen tolerance in some lactic acid bacteria. *J. Bacteriol.* **146,** 928–936

48. Kirby, T. W., and Fridovich, I. (1982) A picomolar spectrophotometric assay for superoxide dismutase. *Anal. Biochem.* **127,** 435–440

49. Kono, Y., and Fridovich, I. (1983) Isolation and characterization of the pseudocatalase of *Lactobacillus plantarum.* A new manganese-containing enzyme. *J. Biol. Chem.* **258,** 6015–6019

50. Kono, Y., and Fridovich, I. (1983) Functional significance of manganese catalase in *Lactobacillus plantarum.* *J. Bacteriol.* **155,** 742–746

51. Robertson, P., Jr., Fridovich, S. F., Misra, H. P., and Fridovich, I. (1981) Cyanide catalyzes the oxidation of alpha-hydroxyaldehydes and related compounds: monitored as the reduction of dioxygen, cytochrome *c* and nitroblue tetrazolium. *Arch. Biochem. Biophys.* **207,** 282–289

52. Mashino, T., and Fridovich, I. (1987) Mechanism of the cyanide-catalyzed oxidation of alpha-ketoaldehydes and alpha-ketoalcohols. *Arch. Biochem. Biophys.* **252,** 163–170

53. Mashino, T., and Fridovich, I. (1987) Superoxide radical initiates the autoxidation of dihydroxyacetone. *Arch. Biochem. Biophys.* **254,** 547–551

54. Brown, O. R., and Seither, R. L. (1983) Oxygen and redox-active drugs: shared toxicity sites. *Fundam. Appl. Toxicol.* **3,** 209–214

55. Kuo, C. F., Mashino, T., and Fridovich, I. (1987) Alpha,Beta-dihydroxyisovalerate dehydratase. A superoxide-sensitive enzyme. *J. Biol. Chem.* **262,** 4724–4727

56. Gardner, P. R., and Fridovich, I. (1991) Superoxide sensitivity of the *Escherichia coli* 6-phosphogluconate dehydratase. *J. Biol. Chem.* **266,** 1478–1483

57. Gardner, P. R., and Fridovich, I. (1992) Inactivation-reactivation of aconitase in *Escherichia coli*: a sensitive measure of superoxide radical. *J. Biol. Chem.* **267,** 8757–8763

58. Liochev, S. I., and Fridovich, I. (1994) The role of superoxide in the production of hydroxyl radical *in vitro* and *in vivo.* *Free Radic. Biol. Med.* **16,** 29–33

THE JOURNAL OF BIOLOGICAL CHEMISTRY
© 2001 by The American Society for Biochemistry and Molecular Biology, Inc.

Vol. 276, No. 42, Issue of October 19, pp. 38329–38336, 2001
Printed in U.S.A.

Reflections

A PAPER IN A SERIES COMMISSIONED TO CELEBRATE THE CENTENARY OF THE JBC IN 2005

JBC Centennial
1905–2005
100 Years of Biochemistry and Molecular Biology

A Trail of Research from Lipoic Acid to α-Keto Acid Dehydrogenase Complexes

Published, JBC Papers in Press, July 26, 2001, DOI 10.1074/jbc.R100026200

Lester J. Reed

From the Biochemical Institute and Department of Chemistry and Biochemistry, University of Texas, Austin, Texas 78712

In this article I shall retrace a trail of research that began with the isolation and characterization of a microbial growth factor and led to elucidation of the structure, function, and regulation of α-keto acid dehydrogenase complexes. The high points of this trail are presented below.

Isolation and Characterization of Lipoic Acid

This trail of discovery started in the spring of 1949, about 6 months after I joined the faculty of the Department of Chemistry at the University of Texas. At that time I started working on the isolation of a factor that replaced acetate in the growth medium for certain lactic acid bacteria. Research on the "acetate-replacing factor" was initiated by Esmond Snell and associates at the University of Wisconsin and then at the University of Texas. I inherited this project in the spring of 1949. We established that this factor is widely distributed in animal, plant, and microbial cells and that liver is a rich source. The factor is tightly bound to liver protein and is released by proteolysis or by acid hydrolysis. At that time pharmaceutical companies were processing large amounts of pork and beef liver to obtain extracts suitable for treatment of pernicious anemia. The active principle was shown later to be vitamin B_{12}. Fresh liver was extracted with warm water, and the residual liver proteins and fatty material were dried and sold as an animal feed supplement. Arrangements were made with Eli Lilly and Co. to obtain liver residue, and we developed procedures for extracting and purifying the acetate-replacing factor. We progressed to the point of being able to process about 6 pounds of liver residue at a time. A 16,000–50,000-fold purification was achieved.

In the late 1940s and early 1950s several other groups were trying to isolate factors that were similar to, if not identical with, the acetate-replacing factor. These factors included the "pyruvate oxidation factor" of I. C. Gunsalus and associates that was necessary for oxidation of pyruvate to acetate and carbon dioxide by *Streptococcus faecalis* cells grown in a synthetic medium. Gunsalus was also collaborating with Eli Lilly and Co. In the fall of 1950, the Lilly Research Laboratories merged the two separate collaborations to facilitate isolation of the acetate-replacing/pyruvate oxidation factor. The Lilly group adapted and scaled up isolation procedures developed by us. Instead of processing 6-pound batches of liver residue at a time, they were able (using commercial equipment) to process 250-pound batches. Concentrates of the factor that were 0.1–1% pure were sent to my laboratory for further processing. I obtained the first pale yellow crystals of the factor, about 3 mg, on or about March 15, 1951, a truly memorable occasion. It was partially characterized and given the trivial name α-lipoic acid (1). The isolation involved a 300,000-fold purification. A total of ~30 mg of crystalline lipoic acid was eventually isolated. We estimated that ~10 tons of liver residue were processed to obtain this small amount of the pure substance. And to think that I was processing about 6 pounds of liver residue at a time, convinced that I would eventually isolate the pure material. We established that lipoic acid is a cyclic disulfide, either 6,8-, 5,8-, or 4,8-dithiooctanoic acid. That the correct structure is 6,8-dithiooctanoic acid (1,2-dithiolane-3-valeric acid) was established by synthesis of DL-lipoic acid, first achieved by E. L. R. Stokstad and associates at Lederle

Laboratories. I was intrigued by this simple yet unique substance and wanted to know more about its biological function, *i.e.* with what and how does it function in living cells. Little did I know then that this trail would take me through five decades of research that has turned out to be a fascinating and rewarding chapter of modern biochemistry, elucidation of the mechanism of oxidative decarboxylation of α-keto acids.

Elucidation of the Nature of Functional Form of Lipoic Acid

Prior to the isolation of lipoic acid and its characterization as a cyclic disulfide, contributions from several laboratories had established the cofactor requirements for the oxidative decarboxylation of α-keto acids represented by the equation shown below.

$$RCOCO_2^- + CoASH + NAD^+ \rightarrow RCOSCoA + CO_2 + NADH$$

In addition to CoA and NAD^+, thiamin diphosphate, a divalent metal ion, and protein-bound lipoic acid are required. A requirement for FAD was demonstrated later. The presence of a disulfide linkage in lipoic acid led Gunsalus to propose that lipoic acid underwent a cycle of reactions in α-keto acid oxidation comprising reductive acylation, acyl transfer, and electron transfer. Lipoic acid was visualized as functioning after thiamin diphosphate and before CoA and NAD^+. Gunsalus, Lowell Hager, and associates obtained evidence for this proposal using lipoic acid and derivatives thereof in substrate amounts. However, the physiological reactions presumably involve catalytic amounts of protein-bound lipoic acid. Elucidation of the nature of the functional form of lipoic acid was essential for verification of the postulated reactions and for further clarification of mechanism. We decided to focus our attention initially on *S. faecalis* (strain 10C1), which had been grown on a lipoic acid-deficient medium. As shown by Gunsalus and associates these cells did not oxidize pyruvate or α-ketobutyrate unless lipoic acid was added to the preparations. However, attempts to activate cell-free extracts of the lipoic acid-deficient cells with lipoic acid or natural extracts containing complex forms of lipoic acid were unsuccessful. We discovered that cell-free extracts of the deficient cells could be activated by incubation with lipoic acid prior to addition of substrate and supplements. Approximately 30 min of preincubation were required for maximal activation. Activity was reduced only slightly by dialysis, suggesting that lipoic acid was converted to the enzymatically active, "bound" form during the incubation. That such is the case was shown by experiments with lipoic acid-$^{35}S_2$. By fractionation of the lipoic acid-deficient extracts, we determined the components required and the nature of the reactions involved in activation of the extract by lipoic acid. One fraction contained the apopyruvate oxidation system, and a second fraction contained a lipoic acid-activating system. A requirement for ATP was established, suggesting that lipoic acid was activated through its carboxyl group before incorporation into the apopyruvate oxidation system. Based on the results of Paul Berg and others at that time, demonstrating that acyl adenylates are produced by enzyme-catalyzed interaction of organic acids and ATP, we demonstrated that lipoic acid and ATP could be replaced by synthetic lipoyl adenylate. The lipoic acid-activating system, *i.e.* lipoate-protein ligase, was also detected in *Escherichia coli* and partially purified.

During the course of these studies with cell-free extracts of lipoic acid-deficient *S. faecalis*, several amides of lipoic acid were synthesized for testing as possible antagonists of the lipoic acid-activating system. These amides did not inhibit activation of the cell-free extract by lipoic acid. On the contrary, these amides could replace lipoic acid, provided ATP was present. These observations suggested that hydrolysis of the amides occurred during incubation with the cell-free extract or the partially purified enzyme preparations. The hydrolytic enzyme, designated lipoyl X-hydrolase and later shown to be a lipoamidase, was purified about 100-fold. The availability of lipoamidase facilitated our preliminary studies in the late 1950s on the biosynthesis of lipoic acid in *E. coli*. Possible radioactive precursors were included in the growth medium. The PDH[1] and KGDH complexes were purified and treated with lipoamidase. The released lipoic acid was extracted into benzene and its radioactivity was determined. We found that octanoate-1-^{14}C was incorporated into lipoic acid as a unit, C-1 of lipoic acid corresponding to C-1 of octanoic acid. Recently, Michael Marletta, John Cronan, and associates have shown that lipoyl synthase, which contains an iron-sulfur cluster, catalyzes the insertion of sulfur at C-6 and C-8 of octanoyl-acyl carrier protein to produce lipoyl-acyl carrier protein.

Lipoamidase and lipoate-protein ligase proved to be invaluable in providing direct, unequiv-

---

[1] The abbreviations used are: PDH, pyruvate dehydrogenase; KGDH, α-ketoglutarate dehydrogenase; BP, binding protein; tE_2, truncated E_2.

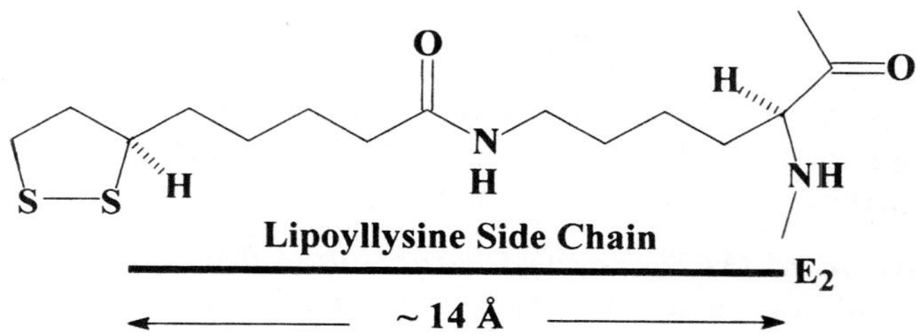

Lipoyllysine Side Chain

~ 14 Å

FIG. 1. **Functional form of lipoic acid.** The carboxyl group of lipoic acid is bound in amide linkage to the ϵ-amino group of a lysine residue in the acyltransferase component (E_2) of the α-keto acid dehydrogenase complexes. This linkage provides a "swinging arm" that facilitates communication between active sites.

ocal evidence of the involvement of protein-bound lipoic acid in the CoA- and NAD$^+$-linked oxidative decarboxylation of pyruvate and α-ketoglutarate and in providing clarification of the mechanism of model reactions catalyzed by the pyruvate and α-ketoglutarate dehydrogenase complexes and components thereof. This evidence comprised a demonstration of inactivation and reactivation of the enzyme or enzyme complex accompanying, respectively, release and reincorporation of the lipoyl moiety.

When *E. coli* (Crookes strain) was grown aerobically in the presence of lipoic acid-^{35}S$_2$, the radioactive substance was incorporated into the pyruvate and α-ketoglutarate dehydrogenation systems, due to the presence of lipoate-protein ligase. The availability of the highly purified complexes permitted rapid progress in the late 1950s in identification of the moiety to which lipoic acid is bound. The protein-bound radioactive lipoyl moiety was oxidized with performic acid, and the protein was partially hydrolyzed with 12 N hydrochloric acid (3 h at 105 °C). From the hydrolysates Hayao Nawa (2) isolated in good yield a ninhydrin-positive, radioactive conjugate, which was identified as ϵ-*N*-(6,8-disulfooctanoyl)-L-lysine by degradation and synthesis. The lipoyl moiety in the two complexes therefore is bound in amide linkage to the ϵ-amino group of a lysyl residue (Fig. 1).

Purification, Resolution, and Reconstitution of the E. coli PDH and KGDH Complexes

Prior to 1950 pyruvate and α-ketoglutarate oxidation had been studied mainly with particulate preparations that were unsuitable for detailed analysis. Solubilization of bacterial and animal α-keto acid oxidation systems in the early 1950s in the laboratories of Severo Ochoa and David Green was a significant advance. Seymour Korkes, Gunsalus, and Ochoa succeeded in separating the pyruvate oxidation system of anaerobically grown *E. coli* (strain ATCC 4157) into two components, designated Fraction A and Fraction B. Subsequently, Hager and Gunsalus found that extracts of aerobically grown *E. coli* (Crookes strain) contained 30–50 times the pyruvate oxidation activity of the anaerobically grown 4157 cells. Using lipoic acid and dihydrolipoic acid in substrate amounts they showed that Fraction A contained a lipoyl transacetylase and that Fraction B contained a lipoyl dehydrogenase. Richard Schweet and associates isolated a CoA- and NAD$^+$-linked pyruvate oxidation system from pigeon breast muscle in a highly purified state, with an apparent molecular weight of about 4 million. D. R. Sanadi and associates isolated a CoA- and NAD$^+$-linked α-ketoglutarate oxidation system from pig heart with an apparent molecular weight of 2 million.

In my laboratory we developed mild procedures for purification of the pyruvate and α-ketoglutarate oxidation systems from *E. coli* (Crookes strain). By the late 1950s Masahiko Koike (3) succeeded in isolating these enzyme systems as highly purified functional units with molecular weights in the millions. It was very exciting to see in the analytical ultracentrifuge of my friend and collaborator at NIH, William Carroll, a major symmetrical peak for each of the two highly purified preparations and that the boundary of the yellow color of the flavoprotein was associated with the main peak. The molecular weights of these multienzyme units were determined to be 4.8 and 2.4 million, respectively. By careful and persistent work over a period of several years, we dissected the pyruvate and α-ketoglutarate dehydrogenase complexes into their component enzymes, characterized them, and reassembled the large functional units from the isolated enzymes (4). We demonstrated that the individual enzymes are linked in the two complexes by non-covalent bonds and that by proper selection of experimental conditions the enzymes could be separated from one another without loss of enzymatic activity. We showed that each of these functional units is composed of multiple copies of three enzymes, a pyruvate and an α-ketoglutarate decarboxylase-dehydrogenase (E_1), a dihydro-

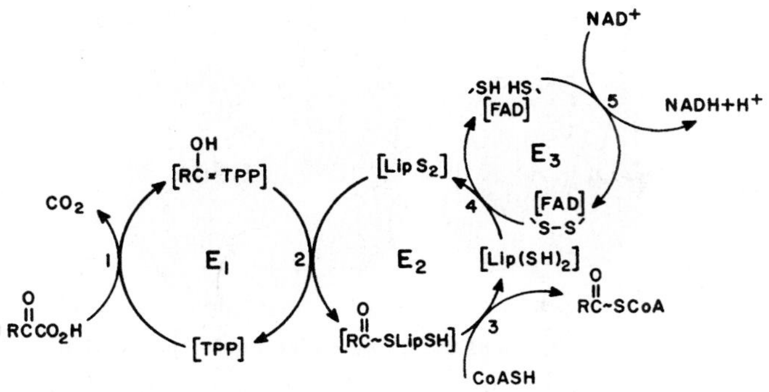

FIG. 2. **Reaction sequence in α-keto acid oxidation.** *TPP*, thiamin diphosphate; *LipS₂* and *Lip(SH)₂*, lipoyl moiety and its reduced form.

lipoamide acetyltransferase and a succinyltransferase (E_2), and a flavoprotein, dihydrolipo-amide dehydrogenase (E_3). These three enzymes, acting in sequence, catalyze the reactions shown in Fig. 2. E_1 catalyzes both the decarboxylation of the α-keto acid (Reaction 1) and the subsequent reductive acylation of the lipoyl moiety, which is covalently bound to E_2 (Reaction 2). E_2 catalyzes the acyl transfer to CoA (Reaction 3), and E_3 catalyzes the reoxidation of the dihydrolipoyl moiety with NAD^+ as the ultimate electron acceptor (Reactions 4 and 5).

Binding experiments showed that the pyruvate dehydrogenase (E_1) and the flavoprotein (E_3) do not combine with each other, but each of these components does combine with the acetyl-transferase (E_2). The acetyltransferase serves a dual function, a catalytic function and a structural function, *i.e.* a scaffold for binding and localizing E_1 and E_3. In dilute acetic acid (0.83 M, pH 2.6) the acetyltransferase dissociated into inactive subunits with a molecular weight of about 70,000. Dilution of the acidic solution into suitable buffers resulted in restoration of enzymatic activity and the characteristic structure of the native acetyltrans-ferase unit. The acetyltransferase appeared to be a self-assembling system. The two flavopro-teins (from the PDH and KGDH complexes) were shown to be interchangeable with respect to both complex formation and function, and enzymatic, physical, and immunochemical data indicated that the two flavoproteins were very similar if not identical.

It was evident that the lipoyl moiety undergoes a cycle of transformations, *i.e.* reductive acylation, acyl transfer, and electron transfer, involving three separate enzymes within a complex in which movement of the individual enzymes is restricted and from which interme-diates do not dissociate. A possible molecular basis of these interactions emerged from our discovery that the lipoyl moiety is bound in amide linkage to the ε-amino group of a lysyl residue in the E_2 component of the PDH and KGDH complexes. This linkage provides a flexible arm, about 14 Å in length (Fig. 1), conceivably permitting the lipoyl moiety to rotate among the active sites of E_1, E_2, and E_3, *i.e.* a "swinging arm" active site coupling mechanism. Some 15 years later, spin label experiments by Richard Perham and Cees Veeger and their associates provided evidence that the lipoyllysyl residues are essentially free to rotate in the PDH complex. Our subsequent finding (see below) that the lipoyllysyl moiety is part of a "super arm," *i.e.* a lipoyl domain, led to the proposal that movement of lipoyl domains as well as rotation of lipoyl moieties may provide the means to span the physical gaps between catalytic sites on E_1, E_2, and E_3, as well as facilitate communication between lipoyl moieties.

Macromolecular Organization of α-Keto Acid Dehydrogenase Complexes

These were exciting times for us in the late 1950s and early 1960s. Our concept of the macromolecular organization of the PDH complex that emerged from these biochemical studies is that of an organized mosaic of enzymes in which each of the component enzymes is uniquely located to permit efficient coupling of the individual reactions catalyzed by these enzymes. This concept was confirmed and extended by electron microscopy studies conducted by my associate Robert Oliver. Electron micrographs of the *E. coli* PDH complex and its component enzymes negatively stained with phosphotungstate revealed that the complex had a polyhedral structure with a diameter of about 300 Å, that the acetyltransferase (E_2) occupied the center of the polyhedron, and that the molecules of E_1 and E_3 were distributed on its surface. The shape of the acetyltransferase indicated that it had a cubelike structure. The shape of the succinyltransferase component of the *E. coli* KGDH complex was very similar. These results, together with biochemical data, demonstrated that both E_2s consist of 24 apparently identical polypeptide chains arranged as eight trimers (morphological subunits) at

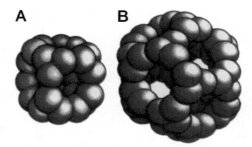

Fig. 3. **Schematic representations of the 24-mer and 60-mer polyhedra of E_2 cores.**

the vertices of a cube (Fig. 3A). This proposed structure was confirmed later by x-ray diffraction analyses carried out by collaborators David DeRosier and Marvin Hackert demonstrating that both acyltransferases possess 432 molecular symmetry. Our interpretative model of the macromolecular organization of the *E. coli* PDH complex in the mid-1960s depicted 12 E_1 dimers and 6 E_3 dimers arranged, respectively, on the 12 edges and in the 6 faces of the cubelike E_2.

Multidomain Structure of Dihydrolipoamide Acyltransferases

All dihydrolipoamide acyltransferases possess a unique multidomain structure. This architectural feature was revealed initially in my laboratory in the late 1970s by limited proteolysis studies of the *E. coli* dihydrolipoamide acetyltransferase containing [2-³H]lipoyl moieties. Dennis Bleile (5) found that limited tryptic digestion at pH 7.0 and 4 °C cleaved the E_2 subunits (M_r ~64,500) into two large fragments, an outer lipoyl-bearing domain and an inner catalytic and subunit binding domain. The latter fragment (M_r ~29,600) had a compact structure, and it possessed the intersubunit binding sites of the acetyltransferase, the binding sites for E_1 and E_3, and the catalytic site for acetyl transfer. The assemblage of compact catalytic and subunit binding domains constitutes the inner core of the acetyltransferase, conferring the cubelike appearance of this E_2 seen with the electron microscope. The other tryptic fragment (M_r ~31,600), designated the lipoyl domain, contained the covalently bound lipoyl moieties and had an extended structure. We suggested that the two domains are connected by a trypsin-sensitive hinge region and that movement of lipoyl domains and not simply rotation of lipoyllysyl moieties may provide the means to span the physical gaps between catalytic sites on the complex. These early findings on the domain structure of dihydrolipoamide acyltransferases were confirmed and extended by studies involving molecular genetics, limited proteolysis, and proton NMR spectroscopy in the laboratories of John Guest and Richard Perham. Briefly, the amino-terminal part of the acyltransferases contains one, two, or three highly similar lipoyl domains, each of about 80 amino acid residues. The lipoyl domain (or domains) is followed by another structurally distinct segment that is involved in binding E_3 and/or E_1. These domains are linked to each other and to the carboxyl-terminal part of the polypeptide chain (catalytic domain) by flexible segments (hinge regions) that are rich in alanine, proline, and charged amino acid residues. These segments are thought to provide flexibility to the lipoyl domains, facilitating active site coupling within the multienzyme complexes.

Regulation of Mammalian PDH Complex by Phosphorylation-Dephosphorylation

In the late 1960s part of our research effort was directed toward isolation and characterization of the mammalian PDH and KGDH complexes, which are localized to mitochondria within the inner membrane-matrix compartment. Procedures were developed for preparation of mitochondria on a large scale from bovine kidney and heart (with the advice and assistance of my friend and colleague, Daniel Ziegler), and relatively mild procedures were developed to isolate the PDH and KGDH complexes from the mitochondrial extracts. In the course of attempts to stabilize these complexes in crude extracts of bovine kidney mitochondria, Tracy Linn observed that the PDH complex, but not the KGDH complex, underwent a time-dependent inactivation in the presence of ATP. A systematic investigation revealed that the bovine kidney and heart PDH complexes are regulated by a phosphorylation-dephosphorylation cycle (6). Phosphorylation and concomitant inactivation of the complex is catalyzed by an ATP-dependent kinase, which is tightly bound to the complex, and dephosphorylation and concomitant reactivation are catalyzed by a Mg^{2+}-dependent phosphatase, which is loosely attached to the complex. It seemed curious at the time (1968) that inactivation of the PDH complex by phosphorylation had not been detected earlier. The explanation may lie in a remark by Henry Lardy after receiving a preprint of our paper on the phosphorylation and inactivation of the PDH complex. (This finding) "explains why we have never been able to get pyruvate to be oxidized in submitochondrial particles, because we invariably add ATP to keep things in the 'optimum' state." This control mechanism was subsequently confirmed in the laboratories of Otto Wieland, Philip Randle, S. E. Severin, and other investigators with preparations of the PDH complex from other mammalian tissues and from pigeon breast muscle, plant tissue, and *Neurospora crassa*.

In the early 1960s the three known examples of enzyme regulation by phosphorylation-dephosphorylation were phosphorylase, phosphorylase kinase, and glycogen synthase. Our results with the mammalian PDH complex indicated that this regulatory mechanism is more general than had been recognized previously. Edwin Krebs mentioned in the fourteenth Hopkins Memorial Lecture (1984) that in the early 1960s some investigators wondered whether "this was an esoteric type of control system restricted to one limited area of carbo-hydrate metabolism . . . with the finding from Lester Reed's laboratory that pyruvate dehy-drogenase is regulated by phosphorylation-dephosphorylation the field broke out of the more restricted area."

Over a period of several years our group separated the bovine kidney and heart PDH complexes into their component enzymes (E_1 ($\alpha_2\beta_2$), E_2, E_3, PDH kinase, and PDH phosphatase) and characterized the individual enzymes (7). We showed that the $E_1\alpha$ subunit undergoes phospho-rylation on three seryl residues. We were surprised by the appearance in the electron microscope of negatively stained preparations of the mammalian dihydrolipoamide acetyltransferase (E_2). Its morphological subunits appeared to be located at the vertices of a pentagonal dodecahedron instead of at the vertices of a cube. Thus, our electron microscope studies revealed that there are two distinct polyhedral forms of E_2, the cube and the pentagonal dodecahedron (Fig. 3). The former design, a cube, consists of 24 E_2 subunits (8 trimers) arranged with octahedral (432) symmetry. This design is exhibited by the E_2 components of the *E. coli* PDH and KGDH complexes and by the E_2 components of the mammalian KGDH and branched chain α-keto acid dehydrogenase complexes. The latter design, a pentagonal dodecahedron, consists of 60 E_2 subunits (20 trimers) arranged with icosahedral (532) symmetry. E_2 components of this morphol-ogy are found in the PDH complexes from mammalian and avian tissues, fungi, and the Gram-positive bacterium *Bacillus stearothermophilus*. A morphological unit consisting of three E_2 subunits appeared to be important in the assembly of both types of polyhedral forms. These conclusions were confirmed and extended by results from x-ray diffraction analysis by collabo-rators David DeRosier and Marvin Hackert and by Wim Hol and associates.

The bovine heart PDH complex has a molecular weight of about 9.5 million. Its subunit composition is 60 E_2 subunits, ~30 E_1 tetramers ($\alpha_2\beta_2$), and 12 E_3 dimers, which are posi-tioned on the E_2 core by 12 E_3-binding protein (protein X) monomers (see below). We proposed that the E_1 tetramers are located on the 30 edges and the E_3 dimers in the 12 faces of the E_2 pentagonal dodecahedron.

Hormonal regulation of the mammalian PDH complex is particularly fascinating because it involves signal transduction not only across the cell membrane but also across the inner mitochondrial membrane to target the PDH phosphatase and, consequently, the PDH com-plex, located in the mitochondrial matrix. It is now known that the major regulators of the phosphatase activity are Ca^{2+} and Mg^{2+}, which involve the hormones epinephrine and insulin, respectively. In the early 1970s our group partially purified PDH phosphatase from bovine heart and kidney mitochondria and showed that it requires Mg^{2+} or Mn^{2+} for activity. Richard Denton, Philip Randle, and associates subsequently reported that Ca^{2+} stimulates the activity of the phosphatase in the presence of Mg^{2+}. Flora Pettit and Thomas Roche in my group showed that Ca^{2+} mediates translocation of the phosphatase to the E_2 component of the PDH complex, presumably in proximity to its substrate, phosphorylated E_1, thereby increasing the rate of dephosphorylation. This Ca^{2+}-mediated translocation apparently is the molecular basis of the epinephrine-induced activation of PDH phosphatase observed by other investigators.

In my laboratory in the early 1980s Martin Teague, Flora Pettit, and co-workers purified PDH phosphatase to near homogeneity and showed that it consists of a Mg^{2+}-dependent and Ca^{2+}-stimulated catalytic subunit (50 kDa; PDPc) and a flavoprotein of unknown function (100 kDa; later designated PDPr). Zahi Damuni showed that polyamines, particularly spermine, increase the sensitivity of PDH phosphatase to Mg^{2+}. Richard Denton and associates subse-quently showed that insulin stimulates the activity of PDH phosphatase in adipose tissue by

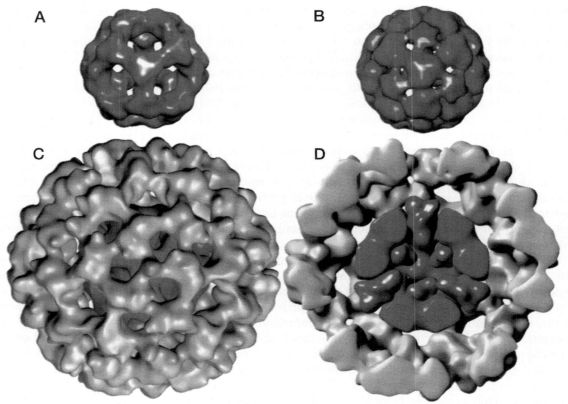

FIG. 4. **Surface shaded representations of three-dimensional reconstructions of *S. cerevisiae* PDH complex and its subcomplexes viewed along a 3-fold axis of symmetry.** A, tE_2; B, the $tE_2 \cdot BP\text{-}E_3$ subcomplex has 12 copies of $BP\text{-}E_3$ (*red*) buried deep inside the 12 pentagonal openings of the tE_2 scaffold (*green*); C, structure of the wild-type PDH complex consisting of the tE_2 inner core (*green*) with the $BP\text{-}E_3$ components (*red*) bound on the inside (9) and the tetrameric E_1 molecules (*yellow*) bound on the outside (Z. H. Zhou, L. J. Reed, and J. K. Stoops, manuscript in preparation). Binding of E_1 to the tE_2 core increases the diameter of the structure from 250 to 500 Å; D, cutaway reconstruction of the PDH complex from C showing the disposition of $BP\text{-}E_3$ and E_1 relative to tE_2.

increasing the sensitivity of the phosphatase to Mg^{2+}. Spermine apparently mimics the insulin effect. The function of PDPr remained a mystery until Janet Lawson in the early 1990s cloned and expressed cDNA encoding PDPc. By comparing the properties of recombinant PDPc and the native PDH phosphatase heterodimer (PDPc bound to PDPr), we obtained insight into the function of PDPr. Jiangong Yan (8) found that PDPr decreases the sensitivity of PDPc to Mg^{2+} and that spermine increases the sensitivity of PDH phosphatase but not PDPc to Mg^{2+}, apparently by interacting with PDPr. We interpreted these observations to indicate that PDPr blocks or distorts the Mg^{2+}-binding site of PDPc and that spermine produces a conformational change in PDPr (allosteric effect) that reverses its inhibitory effect. These observations raise the intriguing prospect that an insulin-induced allosteric effect on PDPr may underlie its stimulation of PDH phosphatase activity.

Structure-Function Relationships in the PDH Complex from S. cerevisiae

To gain further understanding of structure-function relationships in eukaryotic PDH complexes, we initiated in the late 1980s molecular genetics studies of the PDH complex in the yeast *Saccharomyces cerevisiae*. The genes encoding the five proteins comprising the complex ($E_1\alpha$, $E_1\beta$, E_2, BP, and E_3) were cloned, sequenced, expressed, and disrupted. Studies on E_3-binding protein (BP) confirmed and extended previous studies of Thomas Roche and of Gordon Lindsay and their associates with the protein X component of the bovine PDH complex. BP and E_2 apparently evolved from a common ancestor. BP possesses an amino-terminal lipoyl domain, followed by an E_3-binding domain, and then by a carboxyl-terminal domain that is involved in anchoring BP to the inner core of E_2. The availability of recombinant BP, E_3, and the inner core of E_2 (truncated E_2 (tE_2)) provided an opportunity to elucidate the binding stoichiometry and localization of BP and $BP\text{-}E_3$ complex on tE_2. In the 1990s cryoelectron microscopy and three-dimensional image reconstruction (three-dimensional electron microscopy) in collaboration with James Stoops and Timothy Baker and their associates revealed a unique structural organization of the $tE_2 \cdot BP\text{-}E_3$ complex (9). As revealed previously by x-ray crystallography (Wim Hol and associates) and by three-dimensional electron microscopy, the 60-mer tE_2 consists of 20 cone-shaped trimers arranged at the vertices of a pentagonal dodecahedron (Fig. 4). The 20 trimers are connected by 30 bridges to form an empty cagelike structure, with the tip of the trimer directed toward the center of the cage. Our results showed that BP binds near the tips of the E_2 trimers within the central cavity and anchors an E_3 dimer inside each of the 12 pentagonal faces. The unusual finding that the geometric constraints of the tE_2 scaffold determine the extent and disposition of BP-E_3 binding provides a satisfactory explanation of the observation that tE_2 binds a maximum of 12 copies of BP-E_3 complex. Three-dimensional electron microscopy of wild-type PDH complex from *S. cerevisiae* and $E_2 \cdot E_1$ subcomplex thereof shows that the disposition of E_1 tetramers around the E_2 core is also restricted. Research on the structural organization of *S. cerevisiae* PDH complex is continuing. Recent three-dimensional electron microscopy studies reveal that individual molecules of tE_2 exhibit an unusual size variability of 20% (10). We have proposed that expansion and contraction of the 60-mer core is thermally driven and that protein dynamics is an integral component of the function of the PDH multienzyme complex.

I hope these reflections have given some appreciation of the thrill and excitement I have experienced in establishing this trail of research from lipoic acid to the structure, function, and regulation of the α-keto acid dehydrogenase complexes. I have been accompanied in the various stages of this journey by excellent associates, including undergraduate, graduate, and postdoctoral students, technicians, and members of the senior staff of the Biochemical Institute, and by collaborators at other universities and institutes. I am pleased to acknowledge the Clayton Foundation for Research and the National Institutes of Health for generous financial support.

REFERENCES

1. Reed, L. J., DeBusk, B. G., Gunsalus, I. C., and Hornberger, C. S., Jr. (1951) Crystalline α-lipoic acid: a catalytic agent associated with pyruvate dehydrogenase. *Science* **114,** 93–94
2. Nawa, H., Brady, W. T., Koike, M., and Reed, L. J. (1960) Studies on the nature of protein-bound lipoic acid. *J. Am. Chem. Soc.* **82,** 896–903
3. Koike, M., Reed, L. J., and Carroll, W. R. (1960) α-Keto acid dehydrogenation complexes. I. Purification and properties of pyruvate and α-ketoglutarate dehydrogenation complexes of *Escherichia coli*. *J. Biol. Chem.* **235,** 1924–1930
4. Koike, M., Reed, L. J., and Carroll, W. R. (1963) α-Keto acid dehydrogenation complexes. IV. Resolution and reconstitution of the *Escherichia coli* pyruvate dehydrogenation complex. *J. Biol. Chem.* **238,** 30–39
5. Bleile, D. M., Munk, P., Oliver, R. M., and Reed, L. J. (1979) Subunit structure of dihydrolipoyl transacetylase component of pyruvate dehydrogenase complex from *Escherichia coli*. *Proc. Natl. Acad. Sci. U. S. A.* **76,** 4385–4389
6. Linn, T. C., Pettit, F. H., and Reed, L. J. (1969) α-Keto acid dehydrogenase complexes. X. Regulation of the activity of the pyruvate dehydrogenase complex from beef kidney mitochondria by phosphorylation and dephosphorylation. *Proc. Natl. Acad. Sci. U. S. A.* **62,** 234–241
7. Linn, T. C., Pelley, J. W., Pettit, F. H., Hucho, F., Randall, D. D., and Reed, L. J. (1972) α-Keto acid dehydrogenase complexes. XV. Purification and properties of the component enzymes of the pyruvate dehydrogenase complexes from bovine kidney and heart. *Arch. Biochem. Biophys.* **148,** 327–342
8. Yan, J., Lawson, J. E., and Reed, L. J. (1996) Role of the regulatory subunit of bovine pyruvate dehydrogenase phosphatase. *Proc. Natl. Acad. Sci. U. S. A.* **93,** 4953–4956
9. Stoops, J. K., Cheng, R. H., Yazdi, M. A., Maeng, C-Y., Schroeter, J. P., Klueppelberg, U., Kolodziej, S. J., Baker, T. S., and Reed, L. J. (1997) On the unique structural organization of the *Saccharomyces cerevisiae* pyruvate dehydrogenase complex. *J. Biol. Chem.* **272,** 5757–5764
10. Zhou, Z. H., Liao, W., Cheng, R. H., Lawson, J. E., McCarthy, D. B., Reed, L. J., and Stoops, J. K. (2001) Direct evidence for the size and conformational variability of the pyruvate dehydrogenase complex revealed by three-dimensional electron microscopy. *J. Biol. Chem.* **276,** 21704–21713

REVIEWS

Denton, R. M., McCormack, J. G., Midgley, P. J. W., and Rutter, G. A. (1987) Hormonal regulation of fluxes through pyruvate dehydrogenase and the citric acid cycle in mammalian tissues. *Biochem. Soc. Symp.* **54,** 127–143
Guest, J. R., Angier, S. J., and Russell, G. C. (1989) Structure, expression, and protein engineering of the pyruvate dehydrogenase complex of *Escherichia coli*. *Ann. N. Y. Acad. Sci.* **573,** 76–99
Gunsalus, I. C. (1954) Group transfer and acyl-generating functions of lipoic acid derivatives. in *The Mechanism of Enzyme Action* (McElroy, W. D., and Glass, B., eds) pp. 545–580, Johns Hopkins University Press, Baltimore
Perham, R. N. (2000) Swinging arms and swinging domains in multifunctional enzymes: catalytic machines for multiple reactions. *Annu. Rev. Biochem.* **69,** 961–1004
Randle, P. J. (1986) Fuel selection in animals. *Biochem. Soc. Symp.* **14,** 799–806
Reed, L. J. (1957) The chemistry and function of lipoic acid. *Adv. Enzymol.* **18,** 319–347
Reed, L. J. (1974) Multienzyme complexes. *Acc. Chem. Res.* **7,** 40–46
Roche, T. E., and Patel, M. S. (eds) Alpha-keto acid dehydrogenase complexes: organization, regulation, and biomedical ramifications. *Ann. N. Y. Acad. Sci.* **573,** 1–462
Roche, T. E., Liu, S., Ravindran, S., Baker, J. C., and Wang, L. (1996) Role of the E2 core in the dominant mechanisms of regulatory control of mammalian pyruvate dehydrogenase complex. in *Alpha-Keto Acid Dehydrogenase Complexes* (Patel, M. S., Roche, T. E., and Harris, R. A., eds) pp. 33–52, Birkhaüser Verlag, Basel, Switzerland
Wieland, O. H. (1983) The mammalian pyruvate dehydrogenase complex: structure and regulation. *Rev. Physiol. Biochem. Pharmacol.* **96,** 123–170

THE JOURNAL OF BIOLOGICAL CHEMISTRY
© 2001 by The American Society for Biochemistry and Molecular Biology, Inc.

Vol. 276, No. 45, Issue of November 9, pp. 41527–41542, 2001
Printed in U.S.A.

Reflections

A PAPER IN A SERIES COMMISSIONED TO CELEBRATE THE CENTENARY OF THE JBC IN 2005

JBC Centennial
1905–2005
100 Years of Biochemistry and Molecular Biology

Reflections on Glycobiology*[1]

Published, JBC Papers in Press, September 11, 2001, DOI 10.1074/jbc.R100053200

Saul Roseman

From the Department of Biology and the McCollum-Pratt Institute, The Johns Hopkins University, Baltimore, Maryland 21218

Glycobiology has become a "hot" subject,[2] a timely one for "Reflections." The primary reason, I think, is illustrated in Fig. 1, which shows the surface of an erythrocyte in cross-section. Just outside the plasma membrane of this and nearly all cells is a coat of fuzzy material called the glycocalyx, consisting of a myriad of carbohydrate-rich molecules, polysaccharides, proteoglycans, glycoproteins, and glycolipids. If the cell shown here was a fibroblast or an intestinal epithelial cell that secretes polysaccharides or mucins, it would be difficult to determine the location of the cell boundary; the polymers begin on the cytoplasmic face of the lipid bilayer, within it, or on its periphery, but it is not clear where they end. These extensive, complex structures must serve essential roles in cell surface phenomena, but we are only beginning to understand what some of these functions are. I believe that the glycoconjugates or glycans can serve as important informational macromolecules.

In this remarkable age of genomics, proteomics, and functional proteomics, I am often asked by my colleagues why glycobiology has apparently lagged so far behind the other fields. The simple answer is that glycoconjugates are much more complex, variegated, and difficult to study than proteins or nucleic acids. To understand where we are and to appreciate what it has taken to get here requires some background, so this article will briefly survey the history of glycobiology from early studies on fermentation to the beginning of the contemporary era.

The Past

Although glycobiology antedates biochemistry by many millenniums, their histories are inextricably linked. The principal foundations of both fields lie in the development of organic chemistry during the 19th century and in studies on the process of fermentation of glucose and sucrose.

---

* This work was supported by Grant GM51215 from the National Institutes of Health.

[1] The original title of this article was: "Glycobiology: Past, Present, and a Very Bright Future." It was intended to show something of the development of major concepts and to recognize the excellent contributions of pioneers in the field. I had no problem until the modern era, when I realized that it would take volumes to adequately describe the diversity of glycans and to cover, however briefly, current work and investigators. So, with regret, I am limited to the past, where I tried to capture some of the flavor of the field, the origins of some contemporary ideas, and how they may tie to the future. Insofar as the chemistry is concerned, I have chosen to emphasize the cell surface and extracellular matrix because these are where most of the glycoconjugates are found. The focus is on two examples, the cartilage aggrecan aggregate because it illustrates the enormous complexity that is possible with glycans and the erythrocyte surface and the ABO blood groups, which in some respects, at least, may be a model for other cell surfaces.

[2] A recent issue of *Science* features glycobiology (1), and the April, 2001 meeting of the Carbohydrate Division of the American Chemical Society emphasizes glycobiology as a major subject; their prestigious C. S. Hudson Award was presented to a well known glycobiologist, Y. C. Lee. How times have changed! In the 1950s, glycobiology was not a popular subject. There were a few interested biochemists at the meetings, and we had an annual lunch (Karl Meyer, Al Dorfman, Dick Winzler, Roger Jeanloz, Ward Pigman and a few others). After lunch, one might as well go home. My papers (glucosamine metabolism) were invariably scheduled as either last or next to last on Friday afternoon at the Federation Meetings in Atlantic City. The most hilarious incident was when my paper (next to last) was announced at one of these sessions. When I reached the platform, the chairman of the session apologized because he had to leave to make a train. My audience consisted of the next speaker and the slide projectionist. I stayed for the last paper, but unfortunately I never asked the projectionist how he liked the presentations. I had the same experience

Fig. 1. **The erythrocyte glycocalyx.** This is revealed in electron microscopy by special staining methods. It is up to 1400 Å thick, and the oligosaccharide filaments are 12–25 Å in diameter. (Taken from Voet and Voet, *Biochemistry*, with permission of the publisher. Original was by courtesy of Harrison Latta, UCLA).

Fermentation—Fermentation was known to the cave man and has been the subject of intense study ever since. The Old Testament has many references to wine and libations, the first being to Noah (Genesis, 9:20–21): "Noah, the husbandman, began and planted a vineyard. And he drank of the wine and was drunk."[3] Treatises and philosophical discourses were published on the process during and after the Middle Ages.[4] Fermentation was not confined to making alcohol but has been used for thousands of years to make cheese, soy sauce, etc.

The first chapter of the biochemical classic *Alcoholic Fermentation* by Arthur Harden (1st edition, 1911) reviews the history. (*a*) The most important early study was that of Lavoisier (1789) who quantitatively established the stoichiometry of the process and concluded that the sugar was split into two parts, one of which was oxidized (carbonic acid) at the expense of the other (alcohol). Furthermore, "if it were possible to recombine these two substances, sugar would result." The methodology was insufficient to permit him to see an increase in the weight of the yeast or of other products that were formed. (*b*) Yeast at the time was regarded as a catalyst, much like alumina or diatomaceous earth, and during the first *60 years* of the 19th century, this was the prevailing view of the leading chemists and journal editors of the time (Liebig, Berzelius, Wohler). This was despite the fact that in 1837 three independent investigators, Cagniard-Latour, Schwann, and Kutzing, presented evidence that yeast was a living organism, an idea that was ridiculed by the establishment. (*c*) In 1860, the pivotal experiments of Louis Pasteur finally laid this ghost to rest (5), and he showed unequivocally that yeast was a living organism. He also did careful stoichiometry. The balance sheet showed that about 95% of the C,H,O of the sugar was converted to CO_2 and ethanol. The remainder, from 1.6 to 5%,

---

at the American Chemical Society meetings. Starch chemistry was a big thing for members of the Carbohydrate Division, and they walked out on papers devoted to the glycoconjugates or hexosamines. At one such meeting, my audience consisted of other members of the laboratory waiting to drive back to Ann Arbor with me. It was, however, a great time to do this kind of research. There was virtually no pressure. The handful of us in this country who worked in the field were supported by the National Institutes of Health. I can capture a little of the intellectual flavor of the times by my experience when I submitted my first independent application. It stated that I would work on the enzymatic synthesis of one of the monosaccharides in the glycoconjugates, but I did not know which to choose. I then listed about four monosaccharides (glucosamine, fucose, glucuronic acid, and galactosamine) and possible preliminary experiments for each; I would work on whichever problem appeared most fruitful. I was funded, and a short time later I met one of the members of the Study Section (Ef Racker) who told me that it was the best application he had read. What would happen today with an application that was so "unfocused" and with such nonspecific aims? Equally important to the National Institutes of Health support, we received unsparing help from a number of farsighted physicians such as Walter Bauer at Massachusetts General Hospital, who not only created a high caliber research unit (Roger Jeanloz, Jerome Gross, Karl Schmid, Morris Soodak, and others) but was also instrumental in the Helen Hay Whitney Foundation. In my case, it was William Robinson and Ivan Duff at the Rackham Arthritis Unit at the University of Michigan. Only once (when I was first interviewed) did I have to explain to Bill Robinson how work on *Escherichia coli* might relate to arthritis. Thus, we had the luxury of following our noses and serendipity wherever the work took us. We started with studies on the intermediary metabolism of glucosamine, which led in turn to the structure of the sialic acids and the discovery of *N*-acetylmannosamine, to the intermediary metabolism of these compounds, to CMP-sialic acid and its enzymatic synthesis, to the glycosyltransferases, and finally to the phospho-transferase system for sugar uptake by bacteria (reviewed in Refs. 2 and 3). In recent years, the complex process of chitin catabolism by marine bacteria has become a major project (4).

[3] This reference was kindly called to my attention by Dr. Michael Edidin.

[4] One that struck a chord was a 74-page treatise by John Richardson (1790) entitled "Theoretic Hints on an Improved Practice of Brewing Malt-liquors . . . ". He defines fermentation as: "A spontaneous internal motion of constituent parts, which occasions a spontaneous separation and removal from their former order of combination, and a remarkable alteration in the subject, by a new arrangement and re-union." Not a bad definition of intermediary metabolism and the thermodynamics of glycolysis.

consisted of substances that the "yeast had taken from the sugar." The result of this and subsequent work by Pasteur led to his famous dictum, "no fermentation without life." In an extension of this work, he came to the conclusion (1875) that fermentation was the result of life without oxygen, the cells being able under anaerobic conditions to avail themselves of the energy liberated by the decomposition of substances containing combined oxygen (*i.e.* anaerobic glycolysis). (*d*) Enzymes (called ferments), generally hydrolases, were known during the 19th century; indeed, invertase (*i.e.* sucrase) had been extracted from yeast. In 1858, Traube proposed that fermentation resulted from the action of ferments secreted by cells on sugar. Many attempts were made to extract yeast cells and obtain cell-free fermentation of sugar but without success. Finally, while attempting to preserve yeast extracts for therapeutic purposes, Eduard Buchner succeeded in 1897. The preservative was sugar, and he noted that carbon dioxide was formed. This fortunate and serendipitous result marks the beginning of biochemistry as we know it today. It is interesting to note that the *Journal of Biological Chemistry* was founded only a few years later by Christian Herter.

The story would not be complete without summarizing what was learned between Buchner's landmark result in 1897 and the publication of Harden's monograph in 1911. Kinetic experiments were conducted using yeast extracts and glucose, and the rate of fermentation was followed by measuring the rate of CO_2 evolution. The following results, especially by Harden and Young, were obtained. (i) Fructose and mannose were fermented as well as glucose, but the yeast had to be "trained" (*i.e.* adapted) for the extract to ferment galactose. They speculated that different ferments were required for galactose utilization. (ii) Inorganic phosphate was required. (iii) A hexose diphosphate was isolated, characterized as fructose-di-P, and was shown to be an intermediate in the process. (iv) The extract was *pressure filtered* through a gelatin film, giving a dialysate and a "residue." *Neither alone supported fermentation, but it was restored by mixing the two*. The residue contained the heat-labile zymase, and the dialysate contained the heat-stable coenzyme(s) or cozymase. Soon after, it was shown that yeast anaerobic glycolysis was closely connected to anaerobic glycolysis by muscle and muscle extracts. The cozymase, of course, was the source of ATP, NAD^+, etc.

Development of Organic and Carbohydrate Chemistry—The close connection between the development of organic chemistry and biochemistry in the 19th century is summarized in an exemplary, early textbook (6). However, carbohydrate history goes back many centuries earlier. Cellulose in the form of cotton, for instance, was known from ancient times, and sucrose was one of the first organic substances to be crystallized (300 A.D., from the juice of sugar cane in India). Because the climate in Europe was not favorable for growing sugar cane, alternative sweetening agents were sought early in the 19th century, leading to the discovery of new sugars (glucose, fructose, mannose, galactose, etc.), all with the same elementary composition $(CH_2O)_n$. Clarifying the structural relationships between these compounds occupied carbohydrate chemists for most of the century. Finally, the structure of D-glucose was established by Emil Fischer in 1891, which marks the beginning of modern carbohydrate chemistry. Fischer's multitudinous and brilliant contributions were likewise in the fields of amino acid and purine/pyrimidine chemistry. It is worth reminding the reader that chromatography and electrophoresis were unknown at the time, and substances were purified by fractional crystallization and characterized by elemental analyses and their physical properties (melting point, optical rotation, solubility, etc.).[5] In this age of

---

[5] My interest in carbohydrate chemistry began as a graduate student working in the laboratory of Karl Paul Link at the University of Wisconsin. He was both a carbohydrate and natural products chemist, with very high standards and an ability to inspire the best in us. The laboratory had isolated and characterized dicumarol as the hemorrhagic factor in spoiled sweet clover hay prior to my arrival (warfarin is a synthetic analogue). My project was to study the metabolism of its parent compound, 4-OH-coumarin, which was not toxic. Four large dogs used as subjects were fed the drug and maintained in very large metabolic cages so that their urine could be collected. (In those days, graduate students took complete and very good care of their animals, including feeding, exercising them, and cleaning their cages.) The metabolic product turned out to be 4-OH-coumarin β-D-glucuronide. However, this had to be established by synthesis and also by elemental analysis. I spent a very muggy, frustrating summer in Madison recording the swings on a microbalance and learning how to do microanalyses before the standards finally came out right. Somewhat later, I developed considerable experience with fractional crystallization, particularly of anomeric glycosides. They were being synthesized for Joshua Lederberg, a young faculty member in a neighboring department (genetics), who was using them for assaying the expression of glycosidases, such as β-galactosidase in *E. coli.* Fractional crystallization, like elemental analysis, is tedious work, but above all it is a real art and when it works, it is most gratifying. In doing this kind of work, we even invoked the help of the Lord. To this day my children remember that my wife Martha (who is not a scientist) concluded the evening prayers over the Sabbath candles with the following phrase: "and may Daddy have crystals." It worked!

electronics and the internet, one always thinks that science moves forward too slowly, but it is mind boggling to realize how far we have come since the 1890s (Fischer, Buchner).

Glycobiology in the 20th Century: Chemistry

Structural Studies on Glycosaminoglycans (Mucopolysaccharides)—Although mucins from various sources were studied by organic chemists as early as 1846 (see reviews by Blix, Gottschalk, and Morgan (7)) and were thought to contain sugars, there was always an unresolved question of purity. In 1925, the distinguished chemist, P. A. Levene, who had made fundamental contributions to the structures of the nucleic acids, published a monograph entitled "Hexosamines and Mucoproteins." Chondroitin sulfate had been isolated in 1884 from cartilage, but the nature of its monosaccharides and structure were controversial until Levene showed conclusively that the constituents were D-glucuronic acid, chondrosamine (D-galactosamine), acetic acid, and sulfuric acid in equimolar ratios. He depicted the structure as GalNAc linked to GlcUA and sulfated at C-6 on the GalNAc. As might be expected from the available methodology and misinformation on sugar ring structures, there were major errors in the structural assignment, including the fact that it was a tetrasaccharide. Similarly, mucoitin sulfate (*i.e.* hyaluronic acid) was depicted as a tetrasaccharide containing GlcNAc but also sulfate. He also questioned whether substances such as ovalbumin were "glucosidoproteins" or whether such substances even existed.

In 1934 (8), hyaluronic acid was isolated in pure form from vitreous humor, and its correct composition was determined. This groundbreaking paper was the first of many from Karl Meyer's laboratory, creating a science from chaos. His laboratory subsequently isolated and characterized the chondroitin sulfates, keratan sulfate, and various hyaluronidases.[6]

Establishing the structures of heteropolysaccharides can be exceptionally difficult, and the problems can be summarized as follows: (i) identification and quantitation of the monosaccharides; (ii) D- or L-configurations; (iii) branched or unbranched; (iv) sequence; (v) α or β anomers; (vi) pyranose or furanose rings; (vii) positions of the linkages; (viii) many of these polymers are derivatized (*e.g.* phosphate, sulfate, acetate, etc.), and polymers with different biological and chemical properties are formed, depending on the position of the linkage in the derivative; and (ix) to complicate matters even further, some of the polymers and oligosaccharides are covalently linked to proteins or lipids.

One of the major problems confronting workers in this field was protein and how to get rid of it because it was regarded as a contaminant of the "mucopolysaccharides," now called glycosaminoglycans or GAGs.[7] Protein was not easily removed.[8] Meyer, for instance, thought that the protein formed ionic bonds with the polysaccharides. In the 1950s, Maxwell Schubert's laboratory showed that cartilage chondroitin sulfate was linked to protein, thus opening a new chapter in the chemistry of these polymers, now called *proteoglycans*. The next essential step was to characterize the linkage region between the GAG and the protein. Work on different polymers around the same time (late 1950s) by Pigman (mucins), Kabat (blood group substances), and Muir (chondroitin sulfate) suggested that the sugars were linked to

---

[6] Karl Meyer was a delightful person with a keen sense of humor. His exchanges with Albert Dorfman at the meetings were the highlight for many of us. For instance, at one meeting Al gave a talk, and in the questioning period Karl asked Al, "How did you quantitate the keratosulfate?" Al responded that he had not. In a stage whisper, Karl said: "I thought as much." Al, with whom I did my postdoctoral work, was a principal figure in the field. He held both M.D. and Ph.D. degrees but what made him really unusual was his expertise in both fundamental biochemical research and in clinical practice (pediatrics). He was a leader in the University of Chicago Medical School and later became Chair of Pediatrics. Al came around to see me every day, and we would get into the most vigorous discussions on how to interpret results, the next experiments, etc. He had to be the most tolerant person, considering that I was fresh out of graduate school and was convinced that I knew everything there was to know (it has been downhill ever since). My paying job was to direct the pediatric blood chemistry laboratory, which was actually very interesting because one had to develop ultramicroanalytical methods, especially for samples from the newborn, which were often obtained by heel puncture. Most of my research was conducted late in the afternoon and evening. Al lived across the Midway and could see the laboratory window (top floor of Bobs Roberts Hospital) from his bedroom. I always left the lights on when I went home.

[7] The abbreviations used are: GAG, glycosaminoglycan; PAPS, 3'-phosphoadenosine-5'-phosphosulfate; MGT, multiglycosyltransferase; GT, glycosyltransferase; ST, sialyltransferase.

[8] At the University of Chicago we were fortunate to have the large meat packing houses close by, which were sources of necessary tissues, such as bovine eyes (for vitreous humor), testis (for hyaluronidase), etc. The isolation of chondroitin sulfate started with bovine nasal septa, which were obtained by working on the line and cutting them out of the skulls as they came by on a belt (very hard on the hands). The cartilage was ground and extracted with about 0.1 N NaOH for several days in the cold with constant stirring. The alkaline extract was then deproteinized and the polysaccharide isolated. By hindsight we know now that the alkaline extraction procedure split the polysaccharide from its O-serine (or threonine) linkage in the protein by β-elimination.

serine.[9] In 1964, Lindahl and Roden found that the "linkage fragment" in heparin was *O*-β-D-xylopyranosyl-L-serine (reviewed in Ref. 10). They later showed that the sequence at the linkage region in these polymers (chondroitin sulfates, dermatan sulfate, and heparan sulfate) to which the polysaccharide is attached is GlcUA-Gal-Gal-Xyl-Ser. In skeletal keratan sulfate, the *O*-linkage is to α-GalNAc in place of the Xyl.

At the same time, a different class of complex carbohydrates, now call *glycoproteins*, was the subject of intensive study. Neuberger's laboratory in England showed by isolation and synthesis that the linkage region in ovalbumin is β-GlcNAc→Asn, *i.e.* to the amide N of asparagine. There are, of course, a wide variety of *N*-linked glycoproteins, particularly the glycoproteins in serum. Since the overriding question in these early studies was purity, the isolation and characterization of the major serum glycoprotein, α_1-acid glycoprotein (orosomucoid), by Karl Schmid was a key breakthrough. The protein (44 kDa) contained 17% hexose and 12% hexosamine.

A characteristic of carbohydrate polymers is that they are polydisperse or microheterogeneous. The template mechanisms of protein and nucleic acid synthesis do not apply to the carbohydrate polymers, thereby resulting in polydispersity. Human orosomucoid, for instance, contains 6 oligosaccharide chains per molecule, but the chains are different from each other. In the collection of molecules called orosomucoid, at least 8 oligosaccharides have been identified (11). Each oligosaccharide can contain up to 5 different kinds of sugars, a given sugar can occur several times in the chain, and the number of possible combinations is overwhelming (see below).

Aggrecan Aggregate—The major components of cartilage are collagen and a huge macromolecular complex called the aggrecan aggregate. An electron micrograph of one such aggregate is shown in Fig. 2*A*, and Fig. 2*B* presents a schematic view of 6 aggrecan monomers bound to hyaluronan. Determining the details of these structures is an extraordinary achievement in this field, equivalent (at least) to delineating the structure of collagen. The structure was developed through work in the laboratories of Hascall, Muir, and Heinegard and has recently been reviewed (12, 13). This unusually complex "molecule" can have an apparent mass of $>6 \times 10^9$ Da and is a composite of all of the structural units described above. The relationship between the structure of the aggregate and its function is briefly discussed below.

The Erythrocyte Surface, Human Blood Group Activity, and Erythroglycan (Poly-N-acetyllactosamine)—The frequent incompatibility of the blood of a donor and recipient was recognized in the 17th century. Starting with the work of Landsteiner (1900), who defined the ABO group, we now know that there are at least 27 such families of human blood group substances expressed on the surfaces of erythroid cells and often other cells as well. The general characteristic of these antigens is that they comprise integral membrane glycoproteins, both *O*- and *N*-linked, and in some cases, glycolipid. Thus far, it has been shown that the glycan units are the epitopes in four of the systems, ABO, Lewis, P, and H/h.[10] Some aspects of the ABO system will be discussed here.

Work on the ABO family was greatly aided by finding these activities in water-soluble form in various secretions and mucins, such as ovarian cysts. The major antigenic determinants were established by Morgan and his co-workers (particularly Watkins and Aminoff) and by Kabat and his co-workers (reviewed in Ref. 14). These determinants were sugars at the non-reducing termini of oligosaccharide chains linked via Ser and Thr to polypeptides, similar to the mucins. Blood group O chains were terminated by a trisaccharide Gal(β,1–4)[Fuc-(α,1–2)]GlcNAc–X. Blood group A activity was expressed by linking an α-GalNAc to C-3 of the Gal, whereas in B activity a Gal is substituted for the GalNAc.

The erythrocyte membrane was quite another problem. Although Yamakawa showed that red blood cell glycolipids exhibited such activity (1953), this conclusion was disputed as late as 1956 (14). It is now clear that the antigens are carried on the erythroid surface by both lipids and polypeptides (see review by Hakomori (15)).

These structures are closely related to the glycosaminoglycan keratan (desulfated keratan sulfate). The repeating unit in this GAG is *N*-acetyllactosamine: Gal-(β,1–4)-GlcNAc-(β,1–3)

---

[9] In the alkaline β-elimination step, the oligo- or polysaccharides glycosidically linked to serine or threonine are first released from the protein and then degraded by the alkali at the reducing end of the chain, a reaction called "peeling." An important advance in the field was Carlson's alkaline borohydride procedure, which reduced the aldehyde group as the glycosidic bond was cleaved and protected the oligomer from alkaline degradation (9).

[10] I am very grateful to Dr. Olga Blumenfeld (Department of Biochemistry, Albert Einstein Medical School) for helpful discussions on the blood group substances.

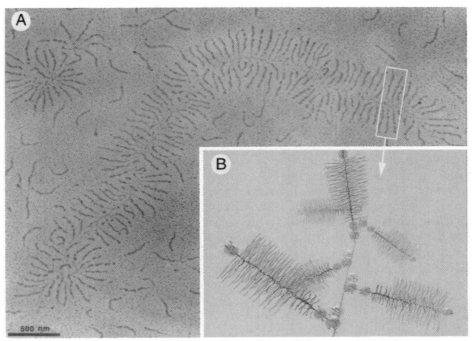

FIG. 2. **Electron micrograph of a proteoglycan aggregate purified from calf epiphyseal cartilage.** *A*, the aggregate was spread as a monolayer in a cytochrome *c* film. Under these conditions the chondroitin sulfate chains of the proteoglycan collapse onto the core protein so that each monomer (aggrecan) of the aggregate is distinct. The nearly uniform length of the monomers is characteristic of proteoglycans from young cartilages, with each ~3.5 million Da in molecular mass. This aggregate contains ~180 aggrecan monomers, and the overall molecular mass of the aggregate is ~6.5 billion Da. The central strand of hyaluronan is ~5500 nm in length. The *boxed area* encloses 6 monomers, the number depicted in the model in *B*. (Micrograph kindly provided by Joseph Buckwalter, University of Iowa.) *B*, model of a portion of the proteoglycan aggregate showing 6 aggrecan monomers (see *box* in *A*). Each of the six monomers is depicted with a central core protein strand to which the glycosaminoglycans are covalently linked, giving the appearance of bristles. The core protein (~250,000 Da) contains a midregion with ~100 chondroitin sulfate chains (*blue*) of ~30,000 average molecular weight and a nearly equal number of keratan sulfate chains (*red*) of ~10,000 average molecular weight. The monomers are anchored (non-covalently) to the central hyaluronan strand (*orange*) by: (*a*) a hyaluronan-binding site in the N-terminal globular-1 (Gl) domain (*pink sphere*) of the core protein, and (*b*) a link protein (*crystal sphere*) that binds to both hyaluronan and to the G1 domain of aggrecan. The core protein of aggrecan contains two other globular domains, G2 and the C-terminal G3, shown as *green* and *lavender spheres*, respectively. The functions of G2 and G3 are not known. The globular domains of aggrecan also contain *N*-linked oligosaccharides (*red Y symbols*). The model is fully extended as it would appear in dilute solution. In the tissue the structure would be compressed to approximately one-tenth its extended size. See Ref. 13 for additional details. (Model and supplemental three-dimensional, rotational view kindly provided by Mark Sabo (Art Department) and Vincent Hascall, Cleveland Clinic Foundation.)

linked to the next Gal in the chain. The same structural unit but in shorter chains than the polysaccharide, called poly-*N*-acetyllactosamine or polylactosamine, is found both *O*- and *N*-linked to integral membrane proteins on many cell surfaces and is also found linked to ceramide. Polylactosamine can be straight chain or branched and can be "decorated" with Fuc or sialic acid residues. Apparently the first references to Gal-, GlcNAc-, and Fuc-rich glyco-peptides in cell membranes came from work by the eminent geneticist/molecular biologist Francois Jacob and his group on the cell surface antigens found in early embryonic differen-tiation (reviewed in Ref. 16). At about the same time (17, 18), Laine and co-workers isolated "erythroglycan" by extensive Pronase digestion of lipid-free red blood cell stroma and charac-terized the large branched oligosaccharides (7,000–10,000 Da) by methylation, etc. "Band 3," the major red blood cell integral membrane protein and the anion transporter, is the source of the polylactosamine, and it accounts for more than 30% of the total Gal and GlcNAc in the red blood cell membrane. Further, at its non-reducing termini the polymer can carry Fuc and αGal or αGalNAc, thereby becoming an antigenic determinant for A, B, or O activity. The large quantity of polylactosamine peptide derived from the red blood cell membrane corresponds to most of the antigenic sites in the intact erythrocyte (about 2×10^6). There is now an extensive literature on polylactosamine, its enzymatic synthesis (19), and how branching occurs during development, tumorigenesis, etc.

Blood group activity is also carried by glycolipids, which are present in small quantities in the red blood cell membrane (reviewed by Hakomori (15). They consist of a large number of compounds derived from *N*-acetyllactosamine oligomers. This family comprises oligosaccharides, both straight and branched chain, linked to glucosylceramide and terminated by one of the antigenic determinant sugars. The glycolipids change, especially with respect to branching, during the development of erythroid cells.

Glycobiology in the 20th Century: Biosynthesis

Isotope Experiments—The complex carbohydrates contain up to 8 different monosaccharides, including D-xylose, hexoses, hexosamines, and hexuronic acids, in addition to various sialic acids, such N-acetylneuraminic acid (NAN or NeuAc). Until 1950, we did not know how most of these monosaccharides were biosynthesized. For the 6-carbon sugars, the theories ranged from (*a*) direct conversion of the 6-carbon skeleton of D-glucose to the sugar to (*b*) fragmentation of glucose through glycolysis and other catabolic cycles and recombination of suitable fragments. It was suggested, for example, that the $GlcNH_2$-6-P carbon skeleton was formed by condensing glyceraldehyde-3-P (G3P) and serine, with subsequent reduction of the carboxyl to the aldehyde. And how could L-fucose possibly arise directly from D-glucose without inversion of the carbon skeleton by 180°, which would give the L- from a D-sugar?

These problems were addressed by treating an appropriate biological system with specifically labeled glucose, such as 1-[^{14}C]- and 6-[^{14}C]glucose in companion experiments. The pure polymer was isolated and hydrolyzed, and the monosaccharides were isolated and dissected carbon by carbon to determine the specific activity at each C-atom in the skeleton.[11] If the origin of the 6-carbon hexoses was via fragmentation of the Glc 6-carbon chain, followed by recombination, isotope scrambling would result.[12] The results were conclusive, showing that the 6-carbon skeleton of Glc was converted intact to $GlcNH_2$, glucuronic acid, galactose, and mannose. Surprisingly, D-Glc was converted to L-Fuc without inversion (20).

Enzyme Experiments—The next step, of course, was to determine the pathways of synthesis and degradation using appropriate "ferments." A review (21) published in 1959 shows how rapidly the field grew in 10 years. Many of the anabolic/catabolic pathways were established, and although they have since been added to and somewhat modified, the essential elements remain the same today.

Sialic acid was a separate problem in that enzymatic studies could not proceed until after its correct structure was established (22), and N-acetyl-D-mannosamine was found to occur naturally and to be a precursor of NeuAc. Glucosamine-6-P is the precursor of all nitrogen-containing sugars and is formed from Fru-6-P and glutamine (23), although the catabolic enzyme, GlcN-6-P deaminase (24), which gives Fru-6-P and NH_3 as products, is reversible and can be utilized anabolically when the synthase is mutated in bacteria.

Sugar Nucleotides, Dolichol, and PAPS—Aside from establishing the intermediary metabolism of the monosaccharides, there were five major developments in the field over the course of the next 20 years (listed in order of the discussion): (*a*) isolation of "active sulfate" or PAPS (1958); (*b*) recognition of lectins (sugar-binding proteins) in animal tissues; (*c*) identification of dolichol-linked oligosaccharides as intermediates in the synthesis of the Man-rich core oligosaccharides of N-linked glycoproteins (1976); (*d*) isolation of the sugar nucleotides (1950); (*e*) elucidation of the pathways of synthesis and degradation of the complex carbohydrates and of the number and specificities of the glycosyltransferases.

The precursor of the sulfated glycoconjugates, such as chondroitin sulfate, is 3′-phosphoadenosine-5′-phosphosulfate (or PAPS) characterized and enzymatically synthesized by Robbins and Lipmann (25). PAPS is, of course, "high energy" or "active" sulfate.

Ricin was apparently the first lectin (proteins that bind carbohydrates) recognized more than a century ago. Early in their history, lectins were found to agglutinate erythrocytes depending on blood type. Lectins by now have become a field unto themselves, and the work of I. J. Goldstein, who developed quantitative methods for accurately defining specificity, as

---

[11] My major postdoctoral project was to determine the modes of synthesis of the glucosamine and glucuronic acid moieties in hyaluronic acid. The biological system was a strain of Group A streptococcus that secreted the polysaccharide, and the organism was grown (in a rich medium) on 1-[^{14}C]- and 6-[^{14}C]glucose. One of the many problems was the cost of the labeled sugars (far too expensive for these experiments). [^{14}C]NaCN was more reasonable, and the labeled sugars were synthesized from this starting material. In the experiments, because of the rich medium, the labeled glucose, acetate, and lactate were isolated from the medium, as well as the polysaccharide, and were dissected as well. Konrad Bloch, who was a Professor in the Department of Biochemistry, was of enormous help to me during this phase of the work.

[12] For instance, at the triose-P level, because of triose-P isomerase 1-[^{14}C]glucose would become 1,6-[^{14}C]hexose, and the specific activity at C-1 would be half that of the 1-[^{14}C]glucose used for the experiment.

well as in isolating new lectins, is especially significant. The plant lectins are not only powerful tools for analyzing macromolecules and cell surfaces, but the field became particularly interesting to cell biologists when it was realized that animal cells express lectins.

In 1968, Ashwell and co-workers (26) discovered that liver hepatocytes bind and take up asialoglycoproteins (the asialoglycoprotein endocytosis receptor). This receptor is a Gal-specific lectin in mammals and GlcNAc-specific in birds. It is called the "Ashwell protein" in what follows. Animal lectins, such as the Siglecs (bind to sialic acids), Ig superfamily lectins, selectins, the integrins, CAMs (cell adhesion molecules), collectins, CD44, and others, have now become major areas of research.[13]

Lipid-linked intermediates were discovered around 1964–1965 by three groups (reviewed by Osborn (27)). These studies were conducted in the laboratories of Horecker, Robbins, and Strominger, who were working on the enzymatic synthesis of bacterial lipopolysaccharides and the peptidoglycan cell wall. This work led to similar studies in a number of laboratories on lipid-linked intermediates in the biosynthesis of complex carbohydrates in eukaryotic organisms, including yeast, plants, and higher animals (for review, see Ref. 28). A polyisoprenoid, dolichol, was known to occur in animal tissues and was identified as the lipid carrier of the carbohydrate groups. This early work led to the well established dolichol pathway for the synthesis of the *N*-linked glycoproteins (29). The dolichol pathway does not apply to the *O*-linked glycoproteins or to the glycolipids.

The isolation and characterization of sugar nucleotides is one of the most important achievements in the field of carbohydrate metabolism in the 20th century. They were discovered in two laboratories at about the same time, those of Luis Leloir in Argentina and of James Park in this country. Leloir's group (Caputto, Cardini, Paladini, and Cabib) was working on the enzymatic synthesis of Glc-6-P from Gal-1-P using yeast extracts and found that a heat-stable cofactor ("cozymase") was required. One of the factors was isolated and fully characterized as UDP-Glc (30). This was followed by isolation of UDP-Gal and recognition that the "galactowaldenase" reaction (epimerization at C-4) occurred at the level of the sugar nucleotides. In an independent discovery, Park found that *Staphylococcus aureus* treated with penicillin (which inhibits cell wall synthesis) accumulated considerable quantities of UDP derivatives and showed that they contained the cell wall sugar muramic acid and amino acids (31). The Park compounds are intermediates in cell wall biosynthesis.

The list of sugar nucleotides is huge (32). It includes virtually every naturally occurring monosaccharide, purines, pyrimidines, and in some cases, 2-deoxyribose in place of ribose. They are most frequently formed by the action of pyrophosphorylases, which catalyze the reaction (N indicates nucleoside): NTP + glycose-1-P → PP$_i$ + N-P-P-glycose. As usual, the sialic acids are exceptions in that the nucleotide is CMP (not the diphosphate). CMP-sialic acid, originally isolated from *E. coli* (33), is formed by condensation of NeuAc or *N*-glycolylneuraminic acid and CTP (34, 35). A similar nucleotide (36) was obtained with 2-keto-3-deoxyoctanoic acid (KDO), a component of bacterial lipopolysaccharides.

Functions of the Sugar Nucleotides—Some sugars in glycoconjugates (Man, GlcNAc, NeuAc) are synthesized from Fru-6-P, whereas others (Gal, GlcUA, Xyl) are synthesized as nucleotide sugars from UDP-Glc or, in the case of L-Fuc, from GDP-Man. Aside from their participation in the biosynthesis of monosaccharides, the sugar nucleotides serve as glycose donors in the biosynthesis of oligo- and polysaccharides. Enzymes that utilize sugar nucleotides as donors are designated *glycosyltransferases* and are the major catalysts for generating the glycosidic bond (also formed by transglycosidases and phosphorylases).

Glycosyltransferases were first reported by the Leloir group (37, 38). The enzymes catalyzed the synthesis of disaccharides (trehalose, sucrose) and of the $\alpha,1\rightarrow4$ linkage in glycogen. At the time, it was generally believed that the $\alpha,1\rightarrow4$ linkage in glycogen was synthesized from Glc-1-P by reversing the glycogen phosphorylase-catalyzed reaction.

The following general glycosyltransferase catalyzed reaction occurs in animal tissues.

---

[13] In the 2-year period 1999–2000, SciFinder lists 1400 papers on selectins and 5900 on the integrins. Early in my service on National Institutes of Health Study Sections, our section, which comprised a distinguished group of biochemists, reviewed what I think may have been the first National Institutes of Health application for funds to study a plant lectin (concanavalin A). A vigorous debate ensued with those opposed asking why a plant protein that binds carbohydrates should be of any interest to the National Institutes of Health. It should be funded by the National Science Foundation! Fortunately, the application was funded. In this connection it was this same group that reviewed applications by Fritz Lipmann and by Luis Leloir, which were of course funded; these applications basically consisted of describing what the applicants planned to do with very little detail or particular focus. How would they fare today?

Glycose—PP(U or G) + HO-acceptor → (U or G)DP + **Glycoside**—O-acceptor

REACTION 1

In the case of the sialic acids, such as NeuAc, the donor is CMP-NeuAc.

Specificity of the Glycosyltransferases, Biosynthetic Pathways, and Multiglycosyltransferase Systems—At the time we began to study macromolecular glycans (around 1960), nothing was known about the biosynthetic pathways leading to glycoproteins, mucins, and glycolipids. To undertake this work, we required substrate quantities of the sugar nucleotides. Fortunately Moffatt and Khorana (39) had just published a method for the synthesis of UDP-Glc. A very fruitful and enjoyable summer in Vancouver led to a modified, general method for the synthesis of sugar nucleotides (40),[14] giving us the tools for studying glycosyltransferases.

Some 15–20 glycosyltransferases were characterized, and it soon became obvious that they formed families such as sialyl-, Gal-, GlcNAc-, GalNAc-, Glc-, and Fuc-transferases. The enzymes we studied are involved in the synthesis of the mucins, glycolipids, and terminal trisaccharides of *N*-linked glycoproteins, and the results can be summarized as follows (see Ref. 2 for review). 1) Each glycosyltransferase is specific for both the donor sugar nucleotide *and the acceptor.* 2) A *different* transferase usually catalyzes each step in a pathway. When a sugar occurs twice in a molecule, such as NeuAc in disialoganglioside, two different transferases are required.[15] 3) Chain elongation can be at the non-reducing end or can form branch points. 4) The product of one reaction is the substrate for the next, which leads to the concept of *multiglycosyltransferase (MGT) systems,* namely that the transferases required for synthesis of one glycoconjugate are associated. A different MGT system is required for mucins, glycoprotein trisaccharide termini, and glycolipids (*e.g.* gangliosides). 5) Polydispersity in glycoconjugates is explained by the MGT hypothesis. For instance, Svennerholm (41) showed that there is a particular array of human brain gangliosides of different chain length and complexity. This array exactly fits the pathway that is predicted by the specificities of the enzymes in the corresponding MGT. One would expect to find only the final products of the pathway (*e.g.* tetrasialoganglioside) if all conditions were optimum for each enzyme and they are expressed at high enough levels. It should be noted that many of the transferases require Mn^{2+} for activity and not necessarily at the same concentrations,[16] and this may be an important means of regulating these activities. 6) There is some evidence to support the idea that glycosyltransferases in an MGT complex bind to one another. In the original work, we found that all of the transferases in a given MGT were found in the same particulate fraction, ultimately identified as the Golgi apparatus (42). The Gal-transferase involved in synthesizing the Gal-*O*-Xyl-*O*-Ser (protein) linkage region in chondroitin sulfate was purified by binding to the immobilized xylosyltransferase, and it coprecipitates with antibody directed at the xylosyltransferase (43). Recent papers present evidence for binding of a glycolipid GalNAc-transferase to a Gal-transferase (44, 45).

The Structure of the Acceptor Can Determine Glycosyltransferase Activity—The activity of a GT is not only determined by whether the acceptor is a glycolipid, mucin, or an *N*-linked glycoprotein but can also depend on the fine structure of the termini in these potential acceptors. One example will be given. Enzymatically synthesized, labeled CMP-NeuAc and CMP-*N*-glycolylneuraminic acid (34) were used to detect and characterize sialyltransferases (STs), first from rat mammary gland and then in colostrum (goat, bovine, human), bacterial extracts (for synthesizing colominic or polysialic acid), submaxillary gland, and embryonic chicken brain (summarized in Ref. 2). Bovine colostrum and human milk contain mixtures of

---

[14] I arrived with the sugar 1-phosphates and was given space on John Moffatt's bench. He measured my waist and marked off the corresponding width on the bench top. Fortunately, my waist was substantially greater than his.

[15] The glycosyltransferases that synthesize the GAGs have exceptional characteristics. (*a*) Elongation of the polysaccharide chains in chondroitin sulfate, heparan sulfate, and in one hyaluronan (produced by *Pasteurella*) takes place in a stepwise manner at the non-reducing ends of the polymers. In these cases, a *single* glycosyltransferase transfers first one and then the other glycose unit from their respective sugar nucleotides to the ends of the chain. (*b*) Single glycosyltransferases also catalyze hyaluronan synthesis by eukaryotic and Streptococcal cells, but in these cases elongation occurs at the *reducing* ends of the chain by mechanisms that are not entirely clear. One phenomenon that has always intrigued this reviewer is how the enzymes or cells "know" when to stop the process of polysaccharide elongation (see Ref. 12 for review).

[16] One mechanism for regulating glycosyltransferase activity could well be via local Mn^{2+} concentrations. A brief literature search found references to analyses of tissues, mostly autopsy material, for trace metals including Mn^{2+} but little on its transport. The relevant analyses will require that they be conducted on actively metabolizing cells and organelles (such as the Golgi) to preserve the *in vivo* ion gradients.

3′-sialyllactose (NeuAc-α2,3-Galβ1,4Glc) and 6′-sialyllactose (NeuAc-α2,6-Galβ1,4Glc). The rat mammary gland ST synthesizes 3′-sialyllactose when incubated with CMP-NeuAc and lactose, whereas the colostrum enzyme yields the 6′-isomer. The colostrum enzyme shows great specificity for its acceptors (46). In quantitative terms, when the efficiency of the enzyme is expressed as V_{max}/K_m the following values were obtained (% relative to N-acetyllactosamine): Gal(β,1–4)GlcNAc or N-acetyllactosamine, 100; Gal(β,1–4)Glc or lactose, 2; Gal(β,1–3)GlcNAc, 13; Gal(β,1–6)GlcNAc, 0.4; and asialoorosomucoid, 1000.

Thus, the nature of the penultimate sugar in an acceptor, the precise linkage of the terminal to the penultimate sugar, and the size of the acceptor can all play major roles in determining the activity of a given GT.

The total number of GTs thus far identified exceeds many hundreds (reviewed in Ref. 47). Many of the structural genes have been cloned, and the enzymes were overexpressed, purified to homogeneity, and characterized kinetically. At least two have been crystallized and their three-dimensional structures determined. Insofar as the topics covered here are concerned, the GlcNAc transferases that act on polylactosamine ((Gal-(β1,4)-GlcNAc-(β1,3))$_n$), a constituent of many cell membranes, are of considerable interest (see review by Renkonen (19)). One GlcNAc transferase is required for increasing the chain length at the non-reducing terminal Gal. Two others add GlcNAc to internal Gal residues, thereby starting the branching process. One of the branching enzymes works at the distal end of the chain, and the other acts "centrally." Both are greatly influenced by the presence of Fuc residues on the chains. Thus, the combination and interplay of the GalT, the three GlcNAc transferases, the FucT, and possibly the sialyltransferases determine the final structure on the cell surface, but how these are regulated with respect to each other remains to be determined.

Speculations on Cell-Cell Adhesion

The human brain contains approximately a trillion neurons, and each averages around 10^3 connections with other cells or about 10^{15} specific connections. How can this happen given a total of about 40,000 genes in the human genome? The data banks list 72,000 publications on "cell adhesion," and they report CAMs (cell adhesion molecules), cadherins, catenins, ephrins, Eph receptor tyrosine kinases, laminins, selectins, integrins, their relationships to the extracellular matrix and the cytoskeleton, to cytokines, and much, much more.

In some instances, the role of carbohydrates is well documented. (*a*) Leukocyte extravasation (recruiting leukocytes from the blood to the site of infection, injury, or lymphatic circulation) involves a sequence of complicated interactions between the leukocytes and the blood capillary endothelium comprising selectins, other proteins, and carbohydrates (reviewed in Ref. 48). (*b*) CD44, a cell surface receptor, binds to hyaluronan (12). (*c*) Myelin-associated glycoprotein is a Siglec (sialic acid-specific lectin) that binds to complex gangliosides, an interaction essential for maintaining normal myelin structure (49, 50).

As indicated below, there is now a rapidly developing interest in the role of glycans in development and in cell recognition. However, in surveying the literature, it appears that some old ideas bear repeating. The discussion will be limited to cell-cell recognition.

Specific Intercellular Adhesion—The crucial importance of cell recognition in development was well established in the late 1800s. In normal embryos, cells exhibit exquisite *adhesive specificity*. They "know" where they are, and they "know" where they are going. Under *in vitro* conditions, cells adhere nonspecifically to many substances, including tissue culture plastic, glass, serum proteins, etc. Nevertheless, adhesive specificity can be demonstrated *in vitro* and was shown in 1907 in a classic case of serendipity. Wilson (51) found that when single-cell suspensions from two species of marine sponges were mixed they first aggregated to form a heterologous chimera, but with time they *sorted out* to yield aggregates of homotypic cells. Holtfreter (1930s) obtained the same results with cell suspensions from different embryonic tissues. Although cadherins are thought to be involved in cell sorting, the underlying biochemical basis is very complex, and yet to be fully explained.[17] It was subsequently demonstrated that adult cells, such as hepatocytes and mycocytes (55, 56), exhibit adhesive specificity and

---

[17] Humphreys (52) showed that dissociation of the sponges to single cells released species-specific, heat-labile, large molecular weight "aggregation factors." These observations were followed by a series of studies from many laboratories, particularly by Burger's group. Polysaccharides, sulfated polysaccharides, proteoglycans, and lectins have been invoked as participants in a multistep process, some of which require Ca^{2+}. In a recent paper (53), a unique supramolecular circular proteoglycan complex is described as one of the components involved in the process. One of the N-linked glycans contains glucuronic acid, fucose, mannose, galactose, N-acetylglucosamine, and sulfate (54).

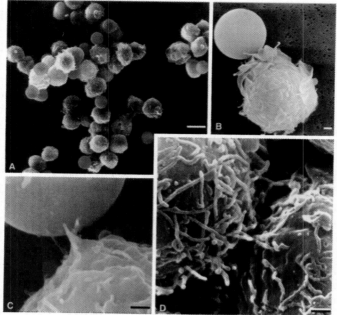

FIG. 3. **Scanning electron micrographs of chicken hepatocytes and immobilized chicken plasma membrane glycolipid.** A quantitative procedure was devised for assaying the effects of immobilized glycolipids and similar substances on the rate of adhesion of chicken hepatocytes (81). A glycolipid, present in trace quantities in chicken liver, was the only substance of many pure and mixed lipids and glycolipids tested that stimulated the adhesion of these (but not rat) hepatocytes. The scanning electron micrographs are as follows. *A,* mixture of chicken hepatocytes and polystyrene beads (*red balls*) previously immersed in a dilute solution of the specific glycolipid. No such structures were seen with beads treated with the inactive lipids. *B* and *C,* cell and bead. The filopodia-like structures were observed in all cases of cell-bead adhesion. *D,* cell-cell adhesion. Filopodia-like structures are evident in the regions of contact. These experiments were conducted with purified but not homogenous preparations of the glycolipid. The specific glycolipid has recently been purified to apparent homogeneity by Dr. Ming Chuan Shao and Barbara Rauch. (The photographs were kindly prepared by Michael McCaffery of the Integrated Imaging Center, Department of Biology, Johns Hopkins University.)

that in liver homogenates, the specific factor was localized to the plasma membranes (56). The active factor(s) in the chick membranes is a trace glycolipid (Fig. 3).

A quantitative assay (57) was used to study the kinetics of homologous adhesion (58) and showed that the process is multistep. The first step does not require metabolic energy; the cells form a loose association that dissociates even by simple dilution of the suspension. In the second energy-requiring step, the aggregate is stabilized and can only be dissociated by vigorous treatment, *e.g.* proteases. In the third step, the stable aggregates synthesize collagen and sulfated GAGs. All of this *takes minutes* at 37 °C.

Insofar as the underlying biochemical mechanisms are concerned, there are two obvious questions. (*a*) What cell surface molecules participate in the process? (*b*) How is the information transmitted to the interior of the cell? Two hypotheses were suggested to answer these questions, as indicated in Figs. 4 and 5.

Hypothesis I: Carbohydrates Are Involved in Specific Intercellular Adhesion—Two mechanisms were proposed (2) for carbohydrate participation as indicated in Fig. 4. 1) Cell adhesion is mediated by hydrogen bonds between carbohydrates on neighboring cells. That hydrogen bonds can be important in maintaining carbohydrate structures is exemplified by polysaccharides such as cellulose and chitin. 2) Cell adhesion is mediated by the binding of carbohydrates to cell surface proteins and enzymes. There were two reasons for extrapolating from proteins to enzymes and in particular to the glycosyltransferases. (*a*) The glycosyltransferases as a class appeared to be much more specific than the lectins, a critical requirement for specific intercellular adhesion. (*b*) If glycosyltransferases are involved, then one cell could also modify the surface of its neighbor. However, extracellular modification requires an extracellular cell surface or soluble enzyme and a source of sugar nucleotides and/or PAPS, either from the cytoplasm or extracellularly. Is any of this possible? 1) *Enzymatically active, soluble extracellular glycosyltransferases do occur* in the fluid surrounding intact embryonic chicken brain and in embryonic and adult chicken serum, vitreous humor, and human spinal fluid (59). 2) *Cell surface glycosyltransferases may occur.* Chick embryonic neural retina cells transferred Gal from UDP-Gal to soluble high molecular weight acceptors (60), suggesting that the reaction

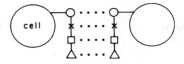

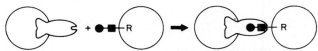

FIG. 4. **Hypothesis I: carbohydrates are involved in specific intercellular adhesion.** The suggested mechanisms are as follows. (*a*) Hydrogen bonding between oligosaccharide chains on adjacent cell surfaces. The scheme is not meant to imply that hydrogen bonds can only form between identical monosaccharides. (*b*) Enzyme-substrate complex. The model is meant to suggest that cells can bind to and/or modify adjacent cells or extracellular matrix through the action of cell surface glycosyltransferases. See text for discussion.

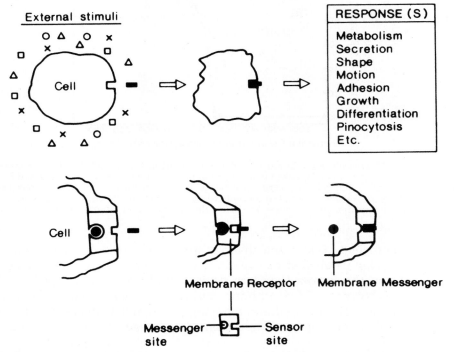

FIG. 5. **Hypothesis II: membrane messengers.** An extrapolation of the Sutherland second messenger idea. A variety of extracellular signals are received by cell membrane receptors, which in turn send specific messages to the cytoplasm or nucleus. The membrane is a transducer, and the membrane messengers were suggested (82, 83) to comprise both low and high molecular weight substances, such as proteins. Additionally, it was suggested that in some cases the messenger molecules would act stoichiometrically (*e.g.* repressors of operons), whereas in others, they could be enzymes.

was catalyzed by a cell surface Gal-transferase. Evidence for and against this conclusion has been presented by other laboratories, and at this time, it remains controversial. However, Fig. 3 suggests that only a vanishingly small percent of the cell surface appears to be involved early in specific cell-cell interactions. If cell surface glycosyltransferases participate in these interactions, they may be present in traces and difficult to detect by any method, including immunological procedures. 3) *Sugar nucleotides may be secreted.* In a recent paper (61), a G protein-coupled plasma membrane receptor for UDP-Glc was identified in a wide variety of human tissues, including many regions of the brain. Thus, extracellular sugar nucleotides may indeed occur.

Hypothesis II: Membrane Messengers—In 1958–1962, a series of studies by Sutherland and co-workers (62, 63) led to the characterization of cAMP, adenylate cyclase, and the effects of certain hormones on this enzyme. Sutherland designated cAMP as the "second messenger" (hormones were the first messenger). This seminal work surely ranks as one of the most important biochemical findings of the past century. Somewhat later, Rasmussen invoked Ca^{2+} as another "second messenger." These hypotheses were obviously correct, but it seemed to us

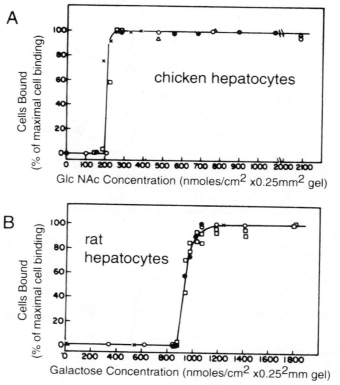

Fig. 6. **Effect of quantitative changes in carbohydrate concentration on cell binding in a model system.** A variety of carbohydrates were covalently linked to polyacrylamide gels and tested with chicken and rat hepatocytes. As expected, the cells bound to the gels in accord with the known specificities of the Ashwell receptor, chicken to GlcNAc, and rat to Gal. In this model system, the concentrations of the sugars in the gels were varied, as indicated. A threshold or critical concentration effect is observed. Below this concentration, there is no binding, and above it, all the cells bind to the gels.

that they were insufficient. Could the diverse stimuli received by a cell and the many responses that these signals elicited be explained by only two second messengers? A "membrane messenger" hypothesis was therefore devised in 1974 as illustrated in Fig. 5. The membrane acts as a "transducer" containing multiple receptors that respond to external signals by releasing specific intracellular messengers. Signal transduction by the plasma membrane is now well established, and a section of each issue of this Journal is devoted to papers in this field.

Quantitative Changes in Carbohydrate Ligands Can Have Global Effects on Cellular Phenotypic Behavior—Qualitative changes in carbohydrate composition of the cell surface or the substrata to which the cell adheres can have far reaching effects on cell behavior, but what of quantitative changes? Although the Ashwell protein catalyzes receptor-mediated endocytosis of glycoproteins in hepatocytes, it does not participate in intercellular adhesion. Nevertheless, it served as a useful model to answer this question.

We have often tried to mimic cell surfaces by adsorbing or covalently linking potential carbohydrate ligands to solid matrices (*e.g.* Fig. 3). This approach was used to test hepatocytes (64, 65) with sugar derivatives covalently linked to polyacrylamide gels. Chicken hepatocytes specifically adhered to GlcNAc-derivatized gels and rat hepatocytes to Gal-derivatized gels, in accord with the known specificities of the Ashwell receptors in the two cell types. However, there was a remarkable *threshold* or *critical concentration* effect of the sugars as shown in Fig. 6. Below this concentration of sugar in the gel, the cells did not bind to the gels. At the threshold, ~15% increases in GlcNAc and Gal concentrations, respectively, in the gels resulted in 100% cell binding to the gels.[18]

---

[18] An interaction between a protein and its monovalent ligand may be weak, but if the ligand is polyvalent such that many protein molecules can interact, the binding affinity for the polyvalent ligand greatly increases. An excellent example of this is CD44, a cell surface receptor that binds to hyaluronan (12). Hyaluronan oligosaccharides with 6–10 sugars are sufficient to interact with CD44 monovalently, and relatively high concentrations of these oligosaccharides can prevent binding of macromolecular hyaluronan, which otherwise binds with high affinity. However, the interaction of the monovalent oligosaccharides with CD44 is sufficiently weak that they do not remain bound through a

The physiological implications are plain if this model represents what can happen in cell adhesion. A non-adherent cell can become adherent by a slight change in the cell surface concentration of the appropriate ligand and/or its receptor or in the extracellular matrix. Even more likely, the "grouping" of receptors or ligands into microdomains in the plasma membrane results in binding, and the size of these domains is apparently affected (regulated?) by other factors, such as cholesterol.

The Future: Glycans as Informational Macromolecules

The particular advantage of carbohydrates is that they have enormous potential for serving as informational macromolecules, starting with their *de novo* biosynthesis. Laine (67), for instance, has calculated that a hexasaccharide has 10^{12} isomeric permutations. Second, the glycans are readily modified after synthesis of the core structure. A few such modifications are sulfation (thought to be essential for leukocyte extravasation), *O*-acetylation of individual sugars such as sialic acid, addition of a few sugar residues that can convert blood group O to A or B, or initiating a branch point by the action of the branching GlcNAc transferases on polylactosamine. For instance, in the neural retinotectal system where neuronal pathfinding is essential, immunological methods have shown a dorsoventral gradient in a cell surface antigen of the rat embryonic neural retina (68). The antigen was identified as 9-*O*-acetyl-GD3. At the same time, there was no apparent gradient of the parent ganglioside GD3. Thus, relatively few enzymes can create a large number of molecular variants.

There is no doubt that the molecular events underlying embryogenesis, especially of the nervous system, will be the major goal of biology well into the foreseeable future. Experiments in a number of laboratories are now in progress to elucidate the roles of glycans in these processes, and some of these are cited above. However, other examples can be given. (*a*) By constructing specific glycosyltransferase mutants in mice and other organisms, the synthesis of specific glycans or classes of glycans can be eliminated. This approach has shown that gangliosides and glycoproteins of the *N*-glycan type are essential for the survival of the embryo and/or its normal development in the mouse (69) and in the nematode *Caenorhabditis elegans* (70).[19] (*b*) A number of papers have reported that proteoglycans and glycosaminoglycans, especially heparan, are essential for normal development of *Drosophila* and *C. elegans*. The affected genes include *Wingless*, *tout-velu*, *sugarless*, *sulfateless*, *dally*, and *sqv 3,7,8* (71–77). (*c*) Notch receptors are highly conserved intercellular signaling pathways that direct embryonic cell-fate decisions. The activities of these receptors are regulated by Fringe proteins, and recent evidence (78, 79) shows that Fringe is a fucose-specific GlcNAc-transferase.

To summarize, the huge gap between the 10^{15} specific connections in the brain and the number of genes in the human genome can readily be filled by the glycans.

It is presumptuous to try to predict the future. Who, in the 1960s, could have predicted what happened to the field we called genetics? At the moment, primary interest seems to be shifting from genomics to proteomics and functional proteomics. But as others have said, glycobiology is the field of the future. However, the problems are formidable, as I have tried to indicate in this brief overview.

One "problem" is nothing more than a false perception. On several occasions I have heard structural biologist colleagues state that the glycan units in a glycoprotein, for instance, cannot be important because they are too flexible to be seen in an x-ray crystal structure or by NMR. In other words, if they don't have structure, how can they have function? That this conclusion is gratuitous requires no more than a moment's reflection.

For instance, one important physiological property of cartilage is that it is reversibly compressible, acting like a spring to the application of a force. This feature emanates from the flexibility of the aggrecan aggregate, which can be compressed to one-tenth its volume. Hyaluronan provides another example. It is essential as a lubricant in joint fluids where it has high viscosity and an extended helical or possibly random coil structure. It is more restricted in the aggrecan aggregate but must still be flexible, and it forms a gel in cumulus cell-oocyte complexes (12).

---

routine washing step (66). The cytoplasmic tail of CD44 interacts with anchorin in the cytoskeleton. Therefore, interaction of CD44 with its polyvalent, linear ligand can contribute to alignment and stabilization of the cytoskeleton and consequently influence cell behavior.

[19] Unpublished data: on the *N*-type glycoproteins by Schachter *et al*; on the gangliosides by Sandhoff, Proia *et al*.

These should be sufficient to make the point. Glycans *are* different because frequently they are flexible and adjust to physiological need. In other words, in these substances, *function defines structure*, not vice versa. Certain glycans clearly have highly favored conformations, and lectins may have evolved to reflect those particular three-dimensional structures. Furthermore, whereas energy minimization methods can yield the thermodynamically favored conformers, the less favored conformers may be the biologically active structures that bind to their ligands.

It would not be a big surprise if different conformers of a single oligosaccharide interacted with different ligands or receptors or enzymes or possibly even other carbohydrates under different physiological conditions. It is this interplay between proteins and different conformers that likely allows a single carbohydrate structure, such as hyaluronan, to be used in many different ways. In the excellent book by Cantor and Schimmel on the conformation of macromolecules (80), they raise a number of questions about carbohydrate polymers similar to those discussed above and then say: "These are all interesting questions, but it will probably take much hard work to answer most of them." Amen to that! What is lacking is adequate biophysical methodology.

The problem is much more complicated when we deal with membranes. Trying to assign structure or even distribution (if it is not random) of a particular glycolipid on the surface seems impossible at this point because of fluidity of the external monolayer of the lipid bilayer. If glycolipids do exist primarily in "rafts" or domains, these domains are in a constant state of flux and motion within the monolayer, and their sizes, frequency of formation, etc., depend on the lipid composition of the remainder of the monolayer and whether they are or are not associated with membrane-bound signaling proteins, such as the Src family of kinases. The same problem exists with cell surface glycoproteins, except possibly for those tethered to cytoplasmic components, such as the cytoskeleton. Even in the latter case, publications suggest that perturbation of the cell can rapidly result in drastic reorganization of the cytoskeleton.

Thus, it appears that present methods will permit us only to obtain "snapshots" of limited areas of the cell surface. There is no doubt that the task ahead of us is difficult, but if cells "talk" to other cells via cell surface substances such as the glycans, the problem cannot be avoided. I am optimistic. Breakthrough technological advances are produced at an astonishing rate these days.

Who could have predicted the development of polymerase chain reaction and its consequences?

Acknowledgments—I am especially grateful to Drs. Ronald Schnaar and Mark Roseman for critical reading of this manuscript and for many helpful suggestions. The sections on aggrecan and the aggrecan aggregate and Fig. 2 could not have been written without the help of Dr. Vincent Hascall, who also provided numerous other insightful comments.

REFERENCES

1. (2001) *Science* **291,** 2263–2502
2. Roseman, S. (1970) *Chem. Phys. Lipids* **5,** 270–297
3. Roseman, S. (1989) *FEMS Microbiol. Rev.* **63,** 3–12
4. Keyhani, N. O., and Roseman, S. (1999) *Biochim. Biophys. Acta* **1473,** 108–122
5. Conant, J. B. (1952) *Pasteur's Study of Fermentation*, Harvard University Press, Cambridge, MA
6. Fruton, J. S., and Simmonds, S. (1953) *General Biochemistry*, John Wiley & Sons, Inc., New York
7. Gottschalk, A. (1972) *Glycoproteins: Their Composition, Structure and Function*, Elsevier Science Publishers B.V., Amsterdam
8. Meyer, K., and Palmer, J. W. (1934) *J. Biol. Chem.* **107,** 629–634
9. Carlson, D. M. (1966) *J. Biol. Chem.* **241,** 2984–2986
10. Roden, L. (1980) in *The Biochemistry of Glycoproteins and Proteoglycans* (Lennarz, W. J., ed) pp. 267–371, Plenum Press, New York
11. Yoshima, H., Matsumoto, A., Mizuochi, T., Kawasaki, T., and Kobata, A. (1981) *J. Biol. Chem.* **256,** 8476–8484
12. Hascall, V. C. (2000) *Glycoconj. J.* **17,** 599–608
13. Wight, T. N., Heinegard, D. K., and Hascall, V. C. (1991) in *Cell Biology of Extracellular Matrix* (Hay, E. D., and Olson, B., eds) pp. 45–78, Plenum Press, New York
14. Kabat, E. A. (1956) *Blood Group Substances*, Academic Press, New York
15. Hakomori, S.-I. (1999) *Biochim. Biophys. Acta* **1473,** 247–266
16. Jacob, F. (1979) *Curr. Top. Dev. Biol.* **13,** 117–137
17. Järnefelt, J., Rush, J., Li, Y.-T., and Laine, R. A. (1978) *J. Biol. Chem.* **253,** 8006–8009
18. Laine, R. A., and Rush, J. S. (1988) *Adv. Exp. Med. Biol.* **228,** 331–347
19. Renkonen, O. (2000) *Cell. Mol. Life Sci.* **57,** 1423–1439
20. Heath, E. C., and Roseman, S. (1958) *J. Biol. Chem.* **230,** 511–519
21. Roseman, S. (1959) *Annu. Rev. Biochem.* **28,** 545–578
22. Comb, D. G., and Roseman, S. (1960) *J. Biol. Chem.* **235,** 2529–2537
23. Ghosh, S., Blumenthal, H. J., Davidson, E., and Roseman, S. (1960) *J. Biol. Chem.* **235,** 1265–1273

24. Comb, D. G., and Roseman, S. (1958) *J. Biol. Chem.* **232,** 807–827
25. Robbins, P. W., and Lipmann, F. (1957) *J. Biol. Chem.* **229,** 837–851
26. Morell, A. G., Irvine, R. A., Sternlieb, I., Scheinberg, I. H., and Ashwell, G. (1968) *J. Biol. Chem.* **243,** 155–159
27. Osborn, M. J. (1969) *Annu. Rev. Biochem.* 501–538
28. Waechter, C. J., and Lennarz, W. J. (1976) *Annu. Rev. Biochem.* **45,** 95–112
29. Kornfeld, R., and Kornfeld, S. (1985) *Annu. Rev. Biochem.* **54,** 631–664
30. Caputto, R., Leloir, L. F., Cardini, C. E., and Paladini, A. C. (1950) *J. Biol. Chem.* **184,** 333–350
31. Park, J. T. (1952) *J. Biol. Chem.* **194,** 877–904
32. Gabriel, O. (1982) *Methods Enzymol.* **83,** 332–353
33. Comb, D., Watson, D., and Roseman, S. (1966) *J. Biol. Chem.* **241,** 5637–5642
34. Roseman, S. (1962) *Proc. Natl. Acad. Sci. U. S. A.* **48,** 437–441
35. Kean, E. L., and Roseman, S. (1966) *J. Biol. Chem.* **241,** 5643–5650
36. Ghalambor, M. A., and Heath, E. C. (1963) *Biochem. Biophys. Res. Commun.* **10,** 346–351
37. Cabib, E., and Leloir, L. F. (1958) *J. Biol. Chem.* **231,** 259–275
38. Leloir, L. F., Olavarria, J. M., Goldemberg, S. H., and Carminatti, H. (1959) *Arch. Biochem. Biophys.* **81,** 508–520
39. Moffatt, J. G., and Khorana, H. G. (1958) *J. Am. Chem. Soc.* **80,** 3756–3761
40. Roseman, S., Distler, J. J., Moffatt, J. G., and Khorana, H. G. (1961) *J. Am. Chem. Soc.* **83,** 659–663
41. Svennerholm, L. (1963) *J. Neurochem.* **10,** 613–623
42. Schachter, H., Jabbal, I., Hudgin, R., Pinteric, L., McGuire, E. J., and Roseman, S. (1970) *J. Biol. Chem.* **245,** 1090–1100
43. Schwartz, N. B., and Roden, L. (1975) *J. Biol. Chem.* **250,** 5200–5207
44. van Meer, G. (2001) *Proc. Natl. Acad. Sci. U. S. A.* **98,** 1321–1323
45. Giraudo, C. G., Daniotti, J. L., and Maccioni, H. J. F. (2001) *Proc. Natl. Acad. Sci. U. S. A.* **98,** 1625–1630
46. Bartholomew, B. A., Jourdian, G. W., and Roseman, S. (1973) *J. Biol. Chem.* **248,** 5751-5762
47. Varki, A., and Marth, J. (1995) *Semin. Dev. Biol.* **6,** 127–138
48. Ebnet, K., and Vestweber, D. (1999) *Histochem. Cell Biol.* **112,** 1–23
49. Collins, B. E., Kiso, M., Hasegawa, A., Tropak, M. B., Roder, J. C., Crocker, P. R., and Schnaar, R. L. (1997) *J. Biol. Chem.* **272,** 16889–16895
50. Collins, B. E., Yang, L. J. S., Mukhopadhyay, G., Filbin, M. T., Kiso, M., Hasegawa, A., and Schnaar, R. L. (1997) *J. Biol. Chem.* **272,** 1248–1255
51. Wilson, H. V. (1907) *J. Exp. Zool.* **5,** 245–258
52. Humphreys, T. (1967) in *The Cell Surface and Specific Cell Aggregation* (Davis, B. B., and Warren, L., eds) pp. 195–210, Prentice-Hall, Englewood Cliffs, NJ
53. Jarchow, J., Jurgen, F., Anselmetti, D., Calabro, A., Hascall, V. C., Gerosa, D., and Burger, M. M. (2000) *J. Struct. Biol.* **132,** 95–105
54. Misevic, G. N., and Burger, M. M. (1990) *J. Biol. Chem.* **265,** 20577–20584
55. Albanese, J., Kuhlenschmidt, M. S., Schmell, E., Slife, C. W., and Roseman, S. (1982) *J. Biol. Chem.* **257,** 3165–3170
56. Obrink, B., Kuhlenschmidt, M. S., and Roseman, S. (1977) *Proc. Natl. Acad. Sci. U. S. A.* **74,** 1077–1081
57. Orr, C. W., and Roseman, S. (1969) *J. Membr. Biol.* **1,** 109–124
58. Umbreit, J., and Roseman, S. (1975) *J. Biol. Chem.* **250,** 9360–9368
59. Den, H., Kaufman, B., McGuire, E. J., and Roseman, S. (1975) *J. Biol. Chem.* **250,** 739–746
60. Roth, S., McGuire, E. J., and Roseman, S. (1971) *J. Cell Biol.* **51,** 536–547
61. Chambers, J. K., Macdonald, L. E., Sarau, H. M., Ames, R. S., Freeman, K., Foley, J. J., Zhu, Y., McLaughlin, M. M., Murdock, P., McMillan, L., Trill, J., Swift, A., Aiyar, N., Taylor, P., Vawter, L., Naheed, S., Szekeres, P., Hervieu, G., Scott, C., Watson, J. M., Murphy, A. J., Duzic, E., Klein, C., Bergsma, D. J., Wilson, S., and Livi, G. P. (2000) *J. Biol. Chem.* **275,** 10767–10771
62. Rall, T. W., and Sutherland, E. W. (1962) *J. Biol. Chem.* **237,** 1228–1232
63. Hardman, J. G., Robison, G. A., and Sutherland, E. W. (1971) *Annu. Rev. Physiol.* **33,** 311–336
64. Schnaar, R. L., Weigel, P. H., Kuhlenschmidt, M. S., Lee, Y. C., and Roseman, S. (1978) *J. Biol. Chem.* **253,** 7940–7951
65. Weigel, P. H., Schnaar, R. L., Kuhlenschmidt, M. S., Schmell, E., Lee, R. T., Lee, Y. C., and Roseman, S. (1979) *J. Biol. Chem.* **254,** 10830–10838
66. Lesley, J., Hascall, V. C., Tammi, M., and Hyman, R. (2000) *J. Biol. Chem.* **275,** 26967–26975
67. Laine, R. A. (1994) *Glycobiology* **4,** 759–767
68. Sparrow, J. R., and Barnstable, C. J. (1998) *J. Neurosci. Res.* **21,** 398–409
69. Kawai, H., Allende, M. L., Wada, R., Kono, M., Sango, K., Deng, C., Miyakawa, T., Crawley, J. N., Werth, N., Bierfreund, U., Sandhoff, K., and Proia, R. L. (2001) *J. Biol. Chem.* **276,** 6885–6888
70. Chen, S., Zhou, S., Sarkar, M., Spence, A. M., and Schachter, H. (1999) *J. Biol. Chem.* **274,** 288–297
71. Bulk, D. A., Wei, G., Toyoda, H., Kinoshita-Toyoda, A., Waldrip, W. R., Esko, J. D., Robbins, P. W., and Selleck, S. B. (2000) *Proc. Natl. Acad. Sci. U. S. A.* **97,** 10838–10843
72. Toyoda, H., Kinoshita-Toyoda, A., Fox, B., and Selleck, S. B. (2000) *J. Biol. Chem.* **275,** 21856–21861
73. Toyoda, H., Kinoshita-Toyoda, A., and Selleck, S. B. (2000) *J. Biol. Chem.* **275,** 2269–2275
74. Nakato, H., Futch, T. A., and Selleck, S. B. (1995) *Development* **121,** 3687–3702
75. Perrimon, N., and Bernfield, M. (2000) *Nature* **404,** 725–728
76. Baeg, G. H., Lin, X., Khare, N., Baumgartner, S., and Perrimon, N. (2001) *Development* **128,** 87–94
77. Toyoda, H., Kinoshita-Toyoda, A., Fox, B., and Selleck, S. B. (2000) *J. Biol. Chem.* **275,** 21856–21861
78. Brückner, K., Perez, L., Clausen, H., and Cohen, S. (2000) *Nature* **406,** 411–415
79. Moloney, D. J., Panin, V. M., Johnston, S. H., Chen, J., Shao, L., Wilson, R., Wang, Y., Stanley, P., Irvine, K. D., Haltiwanger, R. S., and Vogt, T. F. (2000) *Nature* **406,** 369–375
80. Cantor, C. R., and Schimmel, P. R. (1980) *Biophysical Chemistry: The Conformation of Macromolecules,* First Edition, W. H. Freeman, San Francisco
81. Park, L., Kuhlenschmidt, M., and Roseman, S. (1983) *Fed. Proc.* **42,** 2129 (abstr.)
82. Roseman, S. (1974) in *Cell Surface in Development* (Moscona, A. A., ed) pp. 255–271, John Wiley & Sons, Inc., New York
83. Roseman, S. (1974) in *Neuroscience, Study Program* (Schmitt, F. O., ed) 3rd Ed., pp. 795–804, MIT Press, Cambridge, MA

THE JOURNAL OF BIOLOGICAL CHEMISTRY
© 2001 by The American Society for Biochemistry and Molecular Biology, Inc.

Vol. 276, No. 46, Issue of November 16, pp. 42619–42631, 2001
Printed in U.S.A.

Reflections

A PAPER IN A SERIES COMMISSIONED TO CELEBRATE THE CENTENARY OF THE JBC IN 2005

JBC Centennial
1905–2005
100 Years of Biochemistry and Molecular Biology

Hitler's Gift and the Era of Biosynthesis

Published, JBC Papers in Press, September 14, 2001, DOI 10.1074/jbc.R100051200

Eugene P. Kennedy‡

From the Department of Biological Chemistry and Molecular Pharmacology, Harvard Medical School, Boston, Massachusetts 02115

Before the Second World War biochemistry in the United States had a strong flavor of clinical chemistry. It was much occupied with problems of analysis of blood and tissues and the determination of the structures of body constituents. This was important and indeed essential work, but American students had to go abroad to Germany or to England for training in what came to be called dynamic aspects of biochemistry. After the war, the flow of students was largely reversed. This transformation was in considerable part the result of new insights and new approaches brought to America by immigrant scientists.

It is a remarkable fact that as late as 1945 when I began graduate studies in biochemistry at the University of Chicago almost nothing was known about the linked reactions leading to the biosynthesis of *any* of the major types of cell constituents, carbohydrates, lipids, proteins, or nucleic acids. However, this picture was about to change with dramatic rapidity. The latter half of the 20th century became the era of biosynthesis. Now, in 2001, we know in great detail the patterns of reactions leading to the formation of each of these classes of cellular materials, although to be sure much remains to be learned about the regulation and integration of biosynthetic processes in living organisms.

The achievements of three biochemists, Fritz Lipmann, Rudolf Schoenheimer, and Konrad Bloch, greatly stimulated this flowering of biosynthetic studies in the United States at the mid-20th century. Each had been driven out of Germany by the brutal anti-Semitism of the Nazi regime. Each was an important part of what has been called Hitler's gift (1) to American and British science.

In helping to bring about the transition to the era of biosynthesis, Fritz Lipmann made clear the crucial role of "energy-rich" phosphates in driving biosynthetic reactions and showed how this principle operated in the formation of the much sought and highly elusive "active acetate" involved in so many pathways. Rudolf Schoenheimer helped put into the hands of biochemists their most subtle and versatile approach, that of the isotope tracer technique, and with its aid revealed the dynamic state of body constituents. Konrad Bloch's work on the formation of cholesterol illustrated how the insights of Lipmann and Schoenheimer could be combined in a masterpiece of biochemistry to solve a problem of great medical as well as biological significance.

Fritz Lipmann: The Energetics of Biosynthesis

Fritz Lipmann (Fig. 1), who helped to shape the development of modern biochemistry, was born in Koenigsberg, East Prussia in 1899 into a Jewish family of the professional class (2). In 1917, he began the study of medicine. In 1918, while still a medical student, he was drafted into the German army and spent the rest of the war in the medical corps in France. Released from the army, Lipmann resumed his medical studies and received the M.D. degree in 1921. He soon abandoned plans for the practice of medicine in favor of biochemical research, but he always valued the broad view of biology his medical education had given him, concluding: "The

‡ To whom correspondence may be addressed. E-mail: eugene_kennedy@hms.harvard.edu.

FIG. 1. **Fritz Lipmann.** Photo by John Brook, made available through the courtesy of Ms. Freda Hall Lipmann.

biological education to which the observant student is exposed in medicine is a superior preparation for any career." Indeed, the study of medicine offered the most comprehensive view of biology then available. Many of the greatest figures in biochemistry early in the 20th century, including Warburg, Meyerhof, and Krebs, were trained as physicians. The breadth of his background helped give Lipmann the confidence that nothing in biology was beyond his range. Again and again, he proved ready to tackle new problems, no matter how far removed from previous work in his laboratory.

Turning to a career in research rather than the practice of medicine, Lipmann realized that the most fruitful approach to biological problems was through chemistry. He began a program leading to a Ph.D. in chemistry. His work for the dissertation, begun in 1927, was carried out in the laboratory of Otto Meyerhof. Meyerhof, whose work on glycolysis in muscle earned him a Nobel Prize, had a laboratory on the first floor of the Kaiser-Wilhelm Institute for Biology in Berlin, a city that was then the leading center of science in the world. Lipmann felt that his experience in Meyerhof's laboratory was in many ways the origin of all his later work. His most intense admiration, however, was reserved for Warburg. As Lipmann later recalled (3): "At the top of everything, on the uppermost floor, was Otto Warburg. Warburg already had a mystery about him. We admired him boundlessly but saw little of him . . . "

In Meyerhof's laboratory, Lipmann worked on the role of creatine phosphate in muscle contraction. It was of course known that muscle contraction, with its attendant production of lactic acid, is intimately linked to glycolysis. The energetics of this linkage, however, remained obscure. Lipmann (3) commented on " . . . the vagueness of the understanding, then prevalent, of both the intermediary path of glycolysis and the mechanism of action of energy-rich phosphate." This work did much to turn Lipmann's thinking to the role of phosphorylated intermediates in energy transduction.

In 1930, Lipmann was already aware that a career for a Jewish scientist in Germany was fraught with difficulty and peril. There began a period of *Wanderjahre* before he finally found a position that offered both independence and scope. However, he wished to remain in Berlin at least for a time to be near his fiancee Freda Hall (3). He became an assistant to Albert Fischer, working on problems of tissue culture. In 1931 during a hiatus in the work of Fischer's laboratory caused by its move from Berlin to Copenhagen, Lipmann, newly married to Freda Hall, traveled to the United States to work at the Rockefeller Institute in New York in the laboratory of Phoebus A. Levene on the biochemistry of phosphoproteins. Here he succeeded in isolating phosphoserine from partial acid hydrolysates of egg phosphoprotein.

In 1932, Lipmann rejoined Fischer's group in its new quarters in the Carlsberg Laboratories in Copenhagen, where he was to remain until 1939. He was free to work independently in pursuit of his own ideas. At about this time, Otto Warburg was making his great discoveries elucidating the central mechanisms of glycolysis. Why the splitting of glucose involved phosphorylated intermediates had long been a great puzzle, which Warburg now solved.

In 1905 Arthur Harden, working in London, had discovered that glycolysis requires a heat-stable, organic cofactor, which he termed "cozymase." This cofactor proved to be remarkably elusive. In 1929, more than two decades later, Hans von Euler received a Nobel Prize for his work on its isolation and characterization, but it is clear from his Nobel lecture that he had at that time no real idea of its true structure and function. It was Warburg and his collaborators (4) who isolated "cozymase" and showed that it contains a pyridine ring that undergoes alternate reduction and re-oxidation. It is of course the famous coenzyme NAD now known to function in many hundreds of enzyme-catalyzed redox reactions. Warburg also discovered that the oxidation of 3-phosphoglyceraldehyde by NAD is linked to the uptake of orthophosphate and the formation of 1,3-diphosphoglyceric acid. This acyl phosphate may then react with ADP to form ATP. For the first time, the *bioenergetic function* of glycolysis became clear. A portion of the free energy released during the breakdown of glucose is made available to the cell as ATP.

Lipmann followed these developments closely and they deeply influenced his thinking. In 1939, he turned to an investigation of the role of phosphate in the oxidation of pyruvate in extracts of the organism then called *Bacterium acidificans longissimum* (Delbrueckii). He discovered (5) that the oxidation of pyruvate was coupled to the uptake of orthophosphate and the phosphorylation of AMP (presumably with the formation of ATP).

By analogy with the role of 1,3-diphosphoglyceric acid in glycolysis, he formulated the following reactions.

Pyruvate + phosphate → acetyl phosphate + 2[H]

Acetyl phosphate + AMP → "adenosine polyphosphate"

REACTIONS 1 AND 2

The isolation from these enzyme preparations of highly labile acetyl phosphate present only in very small amounts was really not feasible with the methods then available. Lipmann neatly got around this difficulty by synthesizing acetyl phosphate from acetyl chloride and trisilver phosphate. He then showed that this synthetic compound, like the presumed intermediate, was effectively utilized for the formation of "adenosine polyphosphate" in these extracts. (Much later, when I worked in Lipmann's laboratory and read his early papers, I was greatly taken by this strategy. I learned from it that it is sometimes easier to synthesize a suspected intermediate in an enzyme system than to isolate it, a lesson that led me to synthesize CDP-choline first and then demonstrate its role as coenzyme.)

The work on acetyl phosphate marked the beginning of Lipmann's long and productive engagement with both the role of phosphate esters in energy transduction and the problem of "active acetate." In July of 1939, with the Nazi menace ever more threatening, Fritz and Freda Lipmann left Copenhagen for the United States. There followed a difficult period in which he sought without success a position that would offer him security and scope commensurate with his talents. In 1940, he was invited to present a talk in a symposium at the University of Wisconsin in Madison attended by many of the leading figures in American biochemistry. Lipmann, never a facile or polished speaker, vastly underestimated the time needed for the material he wished to present and finally, midway through his discourse, had to be interrupted by the chairman of the session (3). Later he felt that this painful episode was one of the factors that made it difficult for him to secure a suitable position.

In 1940, Lipmann was invited by F. F. Nord to contribute a chapter to the first volume of the series, *Advances in Enzymology*. As Lipmann later (3) wrote: " . . . I was happy when he accepted my suggestion that I write about the role of phosphate bonds as carriers in energy transformations and in biosynthesis. This had begun to impress me as an extension of my experience with acetyl phosphate. Some of the propositions made in that article must have been more novel than I realized."

Now, in 2001, it is very difficult to realize the impact of this article (6), particularly on American biochemists who had not closely followed the work in European laboratories.

Lipmann clearly distinguished between two classes of phosphate compounds in living cells. The first class, phosphate esters of alcohols such as glycerophosphate with a free energy of hydrolysis of 2–4 kcal, was termed by Lipmann as "energy-poor" phosphates, designated in the shorthand which he introduced as (−ph). These were to be sharply distinguished from another class comprising pyrophosphates, acyl phosphates, enol phosphates, and nitrogen-linked phosphates such as phosphocreatine. The free energy of hydrolysis of phosphates of this class is of the order of 8–12 kcal. In Lipmann's terminology these are energy-rich phosphate bonds, designated with a symbol that was to become famous as the "wiggle bond" (∼ph).

A great generalization was stressed in his essay. Photosynthesis and the breakdown of organic foodstuffs provide energy to living cells, some part of which is captured in useful form as "energy-rich" phosphates, leading to the formation of ATP. Lipmann pointed out: "Indications are found that the phosphate current can be utilized to carry out mechanical work . . . (and) to synthesize protoplasmic material as lecithin, nucleic acid, and so forth." Lipmann made it clear that the energy needed to drive biosynthetic processes must come from ATP either directly or, as was soon to be found, indirectly. Before this time biosynthetic processes could be studied only in intact animals or in preparations such as tissue slices (developed by Warburg) in which cellular structure remained intact. The principal conceptual barrier to the study of cell-free systems was now removed. Biochemists began to add ATP (of varying degrees of purity!) to their enzyme systems when searching for biosynthetic reactions.

The 1941 essay is revealing in many ways of Lipmann's style, which had a personal flavor even when dealing with chemical thermodynamics. These were problems about which he had thought deeply, and he conveyed his ideas in striking and forceful metaphors. Thus he spoke of a "phosphate potential" in analogy to an electrical potential and a "phosphate current" that conveys energy as "energy-rich" phosphates are hydrolyzed. Critics pointed out that his use of the term "bond energy" to denote the energy released in breaking a bond was the opposite of the conventional use to denote the energy of bond formation, but Lipmann (3) tended to wave aside such criticism. "The physical chemist remains aloof. He may be forced to accept the usage, but he usually refrains from referring to the dilettante who originated it."

Lipmann's search for a suitable position now found a happy outcome in a rather unusual way. In 1941 Dr. Oliver Cope offered him an appointment in the Department of Surgery at the Massachusetts General Hospital. Although the space made available was at first quite limited, he was given complete freedom to follow his own ideas. Lipmann's years at the Massachusetts General Hospital were highly productive and led him to a Nobel Prize in 1953.

In 1941 the identity of "active acetate," also described as the "two-carbon unit," was one of the most pressing problems in intermediary metabolism. A growing body of evidence suggested that "active acetate" was the fundamental building block for the synthesis of sterols and fatty acids. Derived from the oxidation of pyruvate or of fatty acids, it could also react with oxalacetate to form citrate and thus enter the Krebs cycle for the final common pathway of oxidative metabolism. Strongly encouraged by his success in identifying acetyl phosphate as an intermediate in the bacterial oxidation of pyruvate, Lipmann set out to examine its possible role as the elusive "active acetate" in animal tissues.

He chose to study the acetylation of sulfanilamide, known to occur in liver, because of the ease with which this aromatic amine could be diazotized and coupled with a chromogen to form an intensely colored dye. The conversion of sulfanilamide to the unreactive N-acetyl derivative could thus be easily measured. He succeeded in obtaining preparations from pigeon liver that actively acetylated sulfanilamide but to his considerable disappointment found that acetyl phosphate did not stimulate acetylation but instead was rapidly hydrolyzed (7). Significantly, however, he found that ATP as well as acetate was required for acetylation and further reported that enzyme preparations, inactivated by storage overnight at 7 °C, could be restored to activity by the addition of boiled liver extract.

Nachmansohn and Machado had previously described a cofactor needed for the acetylation of choline. With the arrival of Kaplan in his laboratory, Lipmann's cofactor was purified about 100-fold and shown to be active also in the acetylation of choline (8). It appeared to be a general coenzyme for acetylation and hence the designation coenzyme A or CoA. The next step was the discovery (9) in 1947 that CoA, by then purified about 700-fold, contains the vitamin pantothenic acid. This was a very great advance.

A little later, in 1950, recommended by H. A. Barker, I entered Lipmann's laboratory as a postdoctoral fellow following the footsteps of Earl Stadtman, who had just departed to take up a position at the National Institutes of Health. Stadtman had also come to Lipmann from Barker's laboratory. Lipmann's group at this time included David Novelli, John Gregory, Morris Soodak, Harold Klein, Charles Du Toit, and Lipmann's research assistant, Ruth Flynn. We were crammed into a single, tiny laboratory in the Massachusetts General Hospital next to the famous Ether Dome, scene of the first (or so it was claimed) use of diethyl ether as an anesthetic. In the course of the year we were to move into spacious, even rather elegant, quarters in a newly constructed research building.

With abundant hair just turning gray and usually wearing a soft bow tie and a dark blue shirt, Lipmann presented a figure closer to that expected of an artist rather than a scientist. He spoke softly, and his sentences often trailed off into the distance. Lipmann's manner toward those who worked in his laboratory was rather formal. He was friendly but a little aloof. He inspired nevertheless not only loyalty and admiration but also lasting affection in those who worked under his direction.

At this time, Lipmann's chief goal was the final purification of coenzyme A, which was proving very difficult, and the determination of the structure of "active acetate," the intermediate with so many crucial roles in metabolism. Because acetyl phosphate, shown to be an activated form of acetate in bacteria, was so labile, we surmised that acetyl-CoA, whatever its structure might be, would be even more labile, and this supposed lability was assumed to explain the failure of our efforts to isolate it.

One day in 1951, I came upon an article in *Angewandte Chemie* (10) from the laboratory of Feodor Lynen. He and his student Ernestine Reichert reported evidence for an essential sulfhydryl residue in CoA. They had isolated acetyl-CoA and proved it to be a thioester! I brought the article at once to Lipmann who had not learned previously of this development. He was generous in praise of the work although Lynen had stolen some of his thunder. He was particularly impressed by the fact that in isolating acetyl-CoA from yeast, they had begun by boiling the yeast. We should have realized, Lipmann pointed out, that an intermediate that plays such varied roles is unlikely to be so extremely labile as we had feared. Lipmann also noted that thioesters must be added to the list of biologically active "energy-rich" compounds. "Yes," he mused in a discussion at this time, "there is a world of sulfur, like the world of phosphorus, only smaller!"

In 1953 Lipmann shared the Nobel Prize with H. A. Krebs. Although the citation for the prize emphasized his work on CoA, Lipmann placed greater stress on his contributions to bioenergetics. "In my own judgment," he wrote (3), "there was greater scope in the recognition that ~P, as I had dubbed it, was acting as a biological energy quantum, carrying energy packages to metabolic function and biosynthesis."

In 1957, he moved to the Rockefeller Institute. He continued to be remarkably productive in a wide variety of biosynthetic problems, further developing his grand themes of group activation and the energetics of biosynthesis until his death in 1986 at the age of eighty-seven.

Rudolf Schoenheimer and the Dynamic State of Body Constituents

The single most important technical advance that transformed biochemistry in the 20th century was the isotope tracer technique. Without it, the rapid growth of our knowledge of biosynthesis would be simply inconceivable. Georg Hevesy was the first to explore the biological usefulness of radioactive tracers in studies of the uptake of radiolead and its movement into tissues of plants (11). It is to Rudolf Schoenheimer (Fig. 2), however, that we owe the brilliant exploitation of the concept of *isotopic tagging*, that is the introduction of isotopes into specific positions of organic molecules, whose metabolic transformations could then be traced.

Valuable accounts of Schoenheimer's career have been published by Kohler (12) and by Young and Ajami (13). He was born in Berlin in 1898 (12). Like Lipmann, he studied medicine and received the M.D. degree from the University of Berlin in 1922. Again like Lipmann, he recognized the need for deeper knowledge of chemistry and spent 3 years in the laboratory of Karl Thomas in Leipzig, working largely on problems such as the chemical synthesis of peptides.

In 1926, Schoenheimer went to the Institute of Pathological Anatomy in Freiburg as assistant to Ludwig Aschoff, a leading expert on atherosclerosis (12). Schoenheimer began an investigation on the deposition of cholesterol into the arteries of rabbits fed a high level of cholesterol in the diet. He was to pursue his interests in cholesterol metabolism for the rest of his life.

FIG. 2. **Rudolf Schoenheimer.** From Ref. 13 with permission. Photo made available through the courtesy of Mrs. Peter Klein.

It was here in Freiburg in 1930 that Schoenheimer encountered Hevesy, who wished to study the partition of labeled lead between normal and tumor tissue (12). Realizing his inadequate background in biology, Hevesy asked Aschoff to suggest a collaborator for this work. Aschoff suggested Schoenheimer. Later, Hevesy (14) wrote: "It was in the course of these investigations that Schoenheimer became familiar with the method of isotopic indicators, which he applied several years later with such great success . . . Never were more beautiful investigations carried out with isotopic indicators than those of the late Professor Schoenheimer . . . "

Although the collaboration with Hevesy was undoubtedly significant for Schoenheimer's thinking, his development of the use of isotopes was to go far beyond the scope of Hevesy's approach. In 1933 Schoenheimer, like so many others, was forced to leave Germany. The Josiah Macy Foundation in the United States had begun in 1931 to support Schoenheimer's research, and the director of the foundation, Ludwig Kast, now arranged an appointment for Schoenheimer in the Department of Biological Chemistry at Columbia, with salary and research funds supplied by the Foundation (12).

Hans T. Clarke, an organic chemist by training, had assumed the direction of the Department of Biological Chemistry in 1928, and he proceeded to make it the finest department in the United States. In an account of his career (15), Clarke stated: "Among the many benefits which accrued to Columbia University from the racial policy adopted by the Germans under the Third Reich was the arrival in our laboratory of various European-trained biochemists, notably Erwin Chargaff, Zacharias Dische, Karl Meyer, Rudolf Schoenheimer and Heinrich Waelsch. Erwin Brand, who joined our group during the same period, reached this country somewhat earlier. The scientific achievements subsequently made by these men are so well known that their enumeration is unnecessary." Clarke modestly omitted to mention that his own vision and humane instincts in welcoming these gifted refugees were by no means to be found in every American academic institution.

In 1932, also at Columbia University in the Department of Chemistry, Harold Urey discovered deuterium, the heavy isotope of hydrogen, by demonstrating the presence of new bands in the positions predicted for a form of hydrogen of mass 2, in the spectrum of a sample of hydrogen enriched in the heavier isotope by fractional distillation of liquid hydrogen. In 1934, Urey received a Nobel Prize for this work. Because separation of the isotopes of an element is a function of the ratio of their masses, isotopes of the heavier elements are very difficult to separate. Deuterium, however, has twice the mass of ordinary hydrogen, and its preparation in pure form or as D_2O (immediately dubbed "heavy water") is comparatively straightforward and was very soon undertaken in the laboratories of Urey and G. N. Lewis among many others.

The discovery of a completely new form of a substance of such universal importance as water immediately attracted great public interest all over the world. When Urey received his Nobel Prize in 1934, Palmer, in his laudatory introduction of Urey, mentioned that large amounts of heavy water were already being produced by an electrolytic process at the Norsk Hydro Concern in Norway at the rate of about a half-liter per day (16). In 1940 after a more sinister use of heavy water as the moderator for atomic piles had emerged, this Norwegian heavy water production facility was taken over by the German army of occupation. It then became the target for heroic and tragic efforts of Norwegian patriot saboteurs and the allied air forces to destroy it. The Germans finally dismantled it in 1945. The first biological experiments with D_2O were relatively crude. For example, Lewis (17) reported that tobacco seeds suspended in pure D_2O failed to germinate, and flatworms died when placed in water containing more than 90% D_2O. In these and other early experiments, the emphasis was on replacement of H_2O as a medium for growth by D_2O and not on the specific replacement of hydrogen by deuterium in molecules of biological importance.

Urey, a physical chemist, stated that he was a biologist at heart. Indeed, at a later stage of his career at the University of Chicago he turned to fundamental biological research. With his gifted collaborator Stanley Miller, he designed experiments that demonstrated the ready synthesis (under conditions that simulated the atmosphere of the early earth) of molecules that might plausibly be considered to be building blocks for the formation of cell substances. These studies greatly influenced many later investigations of the origin of life.

To promote the applications of the deuterium isotope to biological research, Urey persuaded Warren Weaver, head of the Rockefeller Foundation, to provide funds to permit David Rittenberg, a recent Ph.D. in physical chemistry in Urey's department, to come to the Department of Biological Chemistry (12). As Hans Clarke commented (15): "In 1934, Schoenheimer made a new contact which proved to exert a fundamental influence on the nature of his work . . . David Rittenberg came from Urey's group to the laboratory in which Schoenheimer had been working for a year. From their association there developed the idea of employing a stable isotope as a label in organic compounds, destined for experiments in intermediary metabolism, which should be biochemically indistinguishable from their natural analogs . . . "

This new conception of Schoenheimer and his collaborators was a far cry from the simple measurement of the movement of a radioactive ion from one part of a plant or animal to another, as had been done by Hevesy. In the new approach, the fate of the molecule into which the isotope had been incorporated was studied, not simply the isotope itself. Perhaps the nearest intellectual predecessor of this idea was the approach of Knoop, who in 1904 "labeled" fatty acids by the attachment of a phenyl residue to the ω-carbon atom. Knoop found that if the fatty acid had an even number of carbon atoms, phenylacetic acid (linked to glycine in a so-called detoxification reaction) was recovered from the urine of dogs to which it had been fed. If on the other hand, the fatty acid had an odd number of carbon atoms, benzoic acid was similarly recovered. Knoop concluded that the phenyl residue could not be cleaved from the ω carbon to which it was linked and more significantly correctly concluded that fatty acid oxidation in animal tissues must involve oxidation at the β-position. This result strongly influenced later studies of fatty acid oxidation, but the work was subject to the objections that phenyl-substituted fatty acids are very different from natural fatty acids, and a more serious limitation was that this type of labeling was not generally suitable for substances other than fatty acids.

Schoenheimer was well aware of Knoop's work. In a brief review in 1935 (18), Schoenheimer and Rittenberg pointed out: "Many attempts have been made to label physiological substances by the introduction of easily detectable groups such as halogens and benzene nuclei. However, the physical and chemical properties of the resulting compounds differ so markedly from those of their natural analogs that they are treated differently by the organism. The interpretation of metabolic experiments involving such substances is therefore strictly limited. We have found the hydrogen isotope deuterium to be a valuable indicator for this purpose . . . We have prepared several physiological compounds (fatty acids and sterol derivatives) containing one or more deuterium atoms linked to carbon, as in methyl or methylene groups . . . The number of possible applications of this method appear to be almost unlimited."

At this period, mass spectrometers were still rare and finicky instruments. It was an advantage of these early experiments that the content of deuterium in organic compounds could be determined comparatively simply by combustion of the compound and very precise measurement of the density of the water so produced.

In 1935, it was a widely held doctrine that the bodily constituents of an adult animal were quite stable, while foodstuffs in the diet were immediately metabolized to provide energy and the end products excreted. In their earliest experiments, Schoenheimer and Rittenberg found evidence to overturn this doctrine. When fatty acids labeled with deuterium were fed to mice, most of the deuterated fat was first deposited in the fat depots. The fat burned in the body was not taken directly from the diet but from adipose tissue. Schoenheimer (19) concluded: "These first experiments with isotopes showed that the fats of the depots are not inert storage materials but are constantly involved in metabolic reactions."

To study the synthesis of fatty acids, Bernhard and Schoenheimer (20) administered D_2O to mice and later measured the isotope content of their fatty acids. The saturated fatty acids were found to contain relatively high levels of deuterium, but the polyunsaturated linoleic and linolenic acids, known to be essential components of the diet, contained only traces. They concluded that the mice carried out a very active *de novo* synthesis of saturated but not of essential fatty acids. Because the total fat content of the mice did not change, the results indicated a rapid breakdown of body fats, equal to the rate of synthesis.

As might be expected, an important objective of Schoenheimer's new program was an investigation of the metabolism of cholesterol. When cholesterol was isolated from mice given D_2O, Rittenberg and Schoenheimer (21) found from the rate of incorporation of deuterium into it that cholesterol must be continually renewed with a half-time of the order of 3 weeks. To account for the extensive incorporation of stably bound deuterium into the cholesterol molecule, it was concluded that its synthesis, like that of fatty acids, must involve the condensation of many small molecules.

A major extension of the range Schoenheimer's investigations came with the concentration of the isotope ^{15}N by Urey and his collaborators in 1937. It was immediately applied to studies of the metabolism of amino acids and proteins. In 1938, Schoenheimer *et al.* (22) reported the first experiments in which an amino acid in the diet, tyrosine, was labeled with [15]N. "The original aim of this exploratory experiment was merely to find out whether in nitrogen equilibrium, the nitrogen in the urine is derived from the food proteins directly, or whether dietary nitrogen is deposited, with liberation of an equivalent amount of tissue nitrogen for excretion . . . The results indicate that in our rat the nitrogen of at least one amino acid, tyrosine, was only partly excreted in the urine, while almost half of it was retained in the body proteins."

Here was another blow at the doctrine that ingested foods were immediately metabolized and the products promptly excreted. Schoenheimer now found this view very naïve. If one puts a penny into a gumball machine, he asked, and a gumball comes out, does the machine turn copper into gum?

Schoenheimer had now become the central figure in Clarke's Department of Biological Chemistry. New and larger laboratory facilities were made available for him. His enthusiasm and vision attracted collaborators and students. As Kohler (12) has pointed out, he had become the leader of perhaps the first multidisciplinary biochemical laboratory. A physicist was needed for the preparation and measurement of isotopes. An organic chemist was employed for the synthesis of isotopically labeled compounds, because of course none were available commercially. Biochemists were required for the separation and analysis of cell constituents. Technicians for animal care were also needed. Schoenheimer's background in chemistry as well as in biology and medicine made him especially effective in the leadership of this disparate group.

Schoenheimer's investigations of protein metabolism, carried out with amino acids containing ^{15}N in the amino group and deuterium on the carbon chains provided results that had the greatest impact on biochemical thought. Briefly summarized (19), body proteins were found to be in a state of continuous turnover. "The peptide bonds have to be considered as essential parts of the proteins and one may conclude that they are rapidly and continually opened and closed in the proteins of normal animals. The experiments give no direct indication as to whether the rupture is complete or partial." The work thus raised questions that were to challenge the next generation of biochemists.

Together with the earlier work on fat metabolism, a new and remarkable picture of the overall metabolism of animals emerged. Schoenheimer summarized his conclusions (19): "The large and complex molecules and their component units, fatty acids, amino acids, and nucleic acids, are constantly involved in rapid chemical reactions. Ester, peptide, and other linkages open; the fragments thereby liberated merge with those derived from other large molecules and with those absorbed from the intestinal tract to form a metabolic pool of components indistinguishable as to origin ... This idea can scarcely be reconciled with the classical comparison of a living being to a combustion engine nor with the theory of independent exogenous and endogenous types of metabolism ... The classical picture must thus be replaced by one which takes account of the dynamic state of body structure."

In 1941, Schoenheimer was invited to give the prestigious Dunham Lectures at the Harvard Medical School. The materials and notes that he prepared for the lectures, from which some of the quotations above are taken, were later published (19) under the title "The Dynamic State of Body Constituents." This lucid summary of his innovative work made a deep impression on the biochemists of the generation to follow.

Schoenheimer had apparently been subject to attacks of depression and was undergoing a period of considerable personal stress when tragically in September of 1941 he ended his own life (12). Forty-three years of age at the time of his death, he was at the height of his powers. Fortunately many of the projects that he had begun were carried forward by very able collaborators, one whom took up the cholesterol problem.

Konrad Bloch and the Biosynthesis of Cholesterol

Konrad Bloch (Fig. 3) was born in 1902 in Neisse, a town in the eastern German province of Silesia, the second child of a prosperous Jewish family (23). In his boyhood, Bloch evinced little interest in science other than nature studies, but his attendance in a course of organic chemistry at the Munich Technische Hochschule taught by Hans Fischer marked a turning point for him. Fischer, later to receive a Nobel Prize, was one of the remarkable group of gifted German chemists who then dominated the study of natural products. Although Fischer's lectures were delivered in a monotone, Bloch found the material fascinating and he realized that he had found his field (23).

In 1934, the brutal Nazification of Germany prevented Bloch from continuing his studies there. Hans Fischer came to his rescue by recommending his appointment at the Schweizerisches Hoehensforschungs Institut in Davos, Switzerland, the scene where Thomas Mann placed the tuberculosis sanitarium in his novel *The Magic Mountain*.

In Davos, Bloch worked for a time on the lipids of the tubercle bacillus. In 1936, however, he was refused permission to continue to reside in Switzerland. Desperate, he applied to R. J. Anderson at Yale, with whom he had some correspondence concerning his research. He promptly received two letters, the first from the Dean of the Medical School of Yale University informing him that he had been appointed assistant in Biological Chemistry and the second from Anderson informing him that there was no salary attached to this position. He showed the first letter, but not the second, to the United States consul in Frankfurt and received a life-saving visa to immigrate to the United States.

Upon arrival in New York, Bloch applied to Hans Clarke's department for admission as a graduate student. The sole formality in those happy days was an interview with Clarke himself. The most important question, Bloch later jested, was: "Do you play a musical instrument?" Fortunately, Bloch could say that he played the cello, an answer agreeable to Clarke, who loved chamber music.

Shortly after completion of his work for the Ph.D. degree under Clarke's supervision, Bloch joined Schoenheimer's group. In 1940, Schoenheimer suggested that he investigate the origin of the hydroxyl oxygen in cholesterol. Was it water or O_2? The thought that it might be molecular oxygen showed the remarkable prescience of Schoenheimer because direct oxygenation was without precedent at that time. Unfortunately, Bloch found the technical problems

FIG. 3. **Konrad Bloch.** Photo made available through the courtesy of Mrs. Konrad Bloch.

of the mass spectrometry of oxygen compounds intractable in the state of technology of 1940 and was forced to give up the project. In 1956, however, he returned to the problem and with his student Tchen (24) showed that molecular oxygen is indeed the source of the hydroxyl oxygen.

As Bloch (23) recalled: "Schoenheimer's untimely death in 1941 left his associates without the leader and the inspired leadership they so admired. We feared that we might have to look for jobs elsewhere, but Hans Clarke encouraged us to continue as heirs to the wealth of projects Schoenheimer had begun and developed . . . How the division of 'spoils' came about I do not recall—it may have been by drawing lots. At any rate, David Shemin 'drew' amino acid metabolism, which led to his classic work on heme biosynthesis. David Rittenberg was to continue his interest in protein synthesis and turnover, and lipids were to be my territory."

Bloch now began his independent studies of the biosynthesis of cholesterol. It was a formidable enterprise. In the era before NMR, infrared, and mass spectroscopy, the determination even of the chemical structure of cholesterol, with its 27 carbon atoms arranged in four rings and with a branched hydrocarbon side chain, had been a challenge to the world's greatest chemists of natural products. The Nobel Prizes in chemistry for 1927 and 1928 had been awarded to Heinrich Wieland and Adolf Windaus, respectively, for their work on the structure of cholesterol and the closely related bile acids, but it was not until 1932 that the fully correct structure was established.

In his 1928 Nobel lecture (25), Windaus stated: "This formula [of cholesterol] is very complicated and has no similarity to the formulae of sugars, fatty acids, or the amino acids which occur in protein. The synthesis of such a substance appears to the chemist particularly difficult, and up to now I have not dared to attempt it, as success is extremely improbable. Furthermore, the majority of physiologists have not been inclined to believe the animal organism capable of such a synthesis, for it is known that other seemingly simpler syntheses— *e.g.* that of tyrosine and tryptophane—have not succeeded in the animal organism."

Bloch of course knew that Windaus' pessimistic view of the capabilities of the animal organism was unfounded. Schoenheimer and Rittenberg had demonstrated the extensive incorporation of deuterium from D_2O into cholesterol in the mouse and concluded that cholesterol must be synthesized by the joining of a number of small molecules.

The pathway for the biosynthesis of cholesterol from acetate, involving more than 30 separate enzyme-catalyzed reactions, can now be found in every textbook of biochemistry. A detailed review is beyond the scope of this essay. Here we will consider only the principal landmarks in its three major stages: 1) acetate to "activated isoprene"; 2) "activated isoprene" to squalene; and 3) squalene to cholesterol.

Bloch's studies began with investigations of the overall process of formation of cholesterol in the intact organism. Stimulated by a report from the German workers Sonderhoff and Thomas (26), indicating that acetate is efficiently converted into the sterols of yeast, Bloch began a series of studies demonstrating the incorporation of specifically labeled acetate into cholesterol in the intact animal. These studies were continued and expanded after his move in 1946 to the Department of Biochemistry at the University of Chicago, where his good friend Earl Evans, also a product of Hans Clarke's department, had become chairman.

I was a graduate student in the Department at this time, and so I came to know Konrad Bloch, first as a teacher and later as a colleague and friend. He was a man of personal qualities commensurate with his great abilities. His manner with students was friendly and easy. He was painstakingly generous in acknowledging the research contributions of his colleagues and of other laboratories. He was widely cultured, devoted to music, literature, and art.

In the mid-1940s, Bloch (23) was completely convinced of the truth of Lipmann's dictum that energy-requiring biosynthetic reactions are driven by ATP, directly or indirectly. Before this period the synthesis of peptide bonds had been observed only by reversal of the reactions catalyzed by proteases. In a project quite unrelated to the cholesterol problem, he and his students began to investigate the synthesis of the tripeptide glutathione as a possible model of protein synthesis. They were indeed able to show that the assembly of glutathione requires the successive activation of glutamate and glutamylcysteine by ATP, but unfortunately the mechanism proved to shed little light on the ribosomal synthesis of proteins.

Bloch was also very much aware of the potential power of microbial genetics for the analysis of metabolic pathways, and he enrolled as a student in the famous course in microbiology taught by C. B. Van Niel at the Hopkins Marine Station in Pacific Grove, CA. When a mutant of the mold *Neurospora crassa* was isolated in Tatum's laboratory that grew only when acetate was added to the medium, Bloch was eager to follow this lead. He and his collaborators found that isotopically labeled acetate was converted to ergosterol in this mutant essentially without dilution of the isotope. Clearly the sterol could be built up entirely from acetate.

In the conversion of acetate to cholesterol, which of the carbon atoms of cholesterol were derived from the carboxyl group and which from the methyl group? Studies carried out over a number of years in the laboratories of Cornforth and of Popjak, as well as of Bloch, achieved the ambitious goal of defining the origin of each of the 27 carbon atoms of cholesterol as either the methyl or the carboxyl carbon of acetate. This work placed important constraints on possible structures of intermediates in the scheme.

It had been known for some time that squalene (a branched, acyclic hydrocarbon found in abundance in the livers of sharks) when fed to animals increases the levels of cholesterol in their tissues. To test the idea that squalene might be a precursor of cholesterol, Bloch went to the Biological Research Station in Bermuda to attempt the preparation of isotopically labeled squalene in shark liver, but the shark proved to be an intractable subject for study (23). "All I was able to learn was that sharks of manageable length are very difficult to catch and their oily livers impossible to slice." Back at the University of Chicago, however, his student Robert Langdon was able to prepare labeled squalene by feeding rats labeled acetate along with unlabeled squalene as an isotopic trap. Labeled squalene so obtained was then fed to rats and found to be converted to cholesterol (27). This was an important result. In the dissection of every biosynthetic pathway, it is particularly helpful to identify an intermediate in the middle of the chain of reactions; the researcher can then trace the pathway both backwards and forwards. At this stage in his work, in 1954 Bloch moved to the Department of Chemistry at Harvard, where he was to remain for the rest of his career.

Squalene, containing 30 carbon atoms, could plausibly be considered to be built up from 6 units of isoprene, a branched, unsaturated compound containing five carbon atoms. Isoprene was already known to be a building block of other naturally occurring hydrocarbons such as rubber, although the nature of the biologically active "isoprene donor" remained unknown.

Robinson (28) had suggested that squalene might be folded to form the basic structure of cholesterol directly. Bloch, however, after illuminating discussions with his Harvard colleague Robert Woodward considered that lanosterol, with a structure closely similar to cholesterol but with three "extra" methyl groups, was likely to be an intermediate in this transformation.

Up to this point, Bloch's experimental approach to the cholesterol problem had been largely confined to isotopic tracer studies with intact animals or with tissue slices in which cellular structure was preserved intact, but now he turned increasingly to the study of cell-free enzyme systems. Rat liver homogenates, prepared by the methods developed by Nancy Bucher, were found to catalyze the transformation of labeled squalene to lanosterol and of lanosterol to cholesterol. Although much work remained to be done, Bloch had established the landmarks for the final stages of the biosynthesis of cholesterol (29).

The focus now was turned to the first stages of the pathway, the conversion of acetate to the "active isoprene donor." A mutant strain of *Lactobacillus acidophilus* had been found to grow only when acetate was added to the medium. A substance that very efficiently replaced the acetate requirement was identified by workers at Merck, Sharpe and Dohme (30) as mevalonic acid (isolated as the lactone). Mevalonic acid was then shown to be a very efficient precursor of squalene and of cholesterol in homogenates of liver (31). These findings opened the way for the elucidation of the reactions leading to the formation of the "active isoprene unit" of which mevalonate was clearly the precursor. Progress in this area now became fast and furious with important contributions from the laboratories of Rudney, Lynen, Cornforth, and Popjak among others.

Bloch and his collaborators showed that the overall conversion of labeled mevalonic acid to squalene in extracts of bakers' yeast required ATP as well as reduced pyridine nucleotide and manganese ions. His colleague Chen then discovered the phosphorylation of mevalonate to a monophosphate. The further conversion of this monophosphate to the important intermediates isopentenylpyrophosphate and dimethylallylpyrophosphate was elucidated largely by work in Lynen's laboratory.

The synthesis of squalene via geranyl pyrophosphate and farnesyl pyrophosphate was next documented. As shown by the early studies of Bloch, squalene is converted in a series of steps to lanosterol, which after several further transformations gives rise to cholesterol.

It is impossible, of course, in this highly condensed account to do justice to the vast amount of work, still ongoing in laboratories over the world, that has led to our present knowledge of the biosynthesis of cholesterol. It was Bloch, however, who was a prime mover in all three phases of the problem. For this work he was awarded a Nobel Prize, with Feodor Lynen, in 1964.

Working out the pathway for the assembly of the complex structure of cholesterol was an exemplary achievement of the era of biosynthesis, important not only because of the intrinsic interest of its enzymology but also because of its significance for medicine. High levels of blood cholesterol, characteristic of populations in developed countries, strongly increase the danger of heart disease and stroke. An understanding of the detailed route of biosynthesis made it possible to determine that the synthesis of mevalonate from HMG-CoA is a rate-making step in the production of cholesterol. This advance made possible the development of drugs, the family of statins, that reduce levels of blood cholesterol with a minimum of toxic side effects. These drugs are among the most useful in modern medicine.

Konrad Bloch made outstanding contributions to fields other than the biosynthesis of cholesterol, including the enzymic synthesis of fatty acids and the mechanism of enzyme action (23). He died on October 15, 2000 at the age of eighty-eight.

The development of any field of science is inevitably the work of many hands. Obviously, Lipmann, Schoenheimer, and Bloch cannot be regarded as single handedly transforming American biochemistry. Their work was nonetheless a great gift to their adopted country and a shining manifestation of the international character of science.

REFERENCES

1. Medawar, J., and Pyke, D. (2001) *Hitler's Gift*, Arcade Publishing, New York
2. Lipmann, F. (1953) *Annu. Rev. Biochem.* **54,** 1–32
3. Lipmann, F. (1971) *Wanderings of a Biochemist*, Wiley-Interscience, New York
4. Warburg, O. (1949) *Wasserstoffuebertragende Fermente*, Editio Cantor, Freiburg, Germany

5. Lipmann, F. (1939) *Nature* **144,** 33–34
6. Lipmann, F. (1941) *Adv. Enzymol.* **1,** 99–162
7. Lipmann, F. (1945) *J. Biol. Chem.* **160,** 173–190
8. Lipmann, F., and Kaplan, N. O. (1946) *J. Biol. Chem.* **162,** 743–744
9. Lipmann, F., Kaplan, N. O., Novelli, G., Tuttle, L. G., and Guirard, B. M. (1947) *J. Biol. Chem.* **167,** 869–870
10. Lynen, F., and Reichert, E. (1951) *Angew. Chem.* **63,** 47–48
11. Hevesy, G. (1923) *Biochem. J.* **17,** 439–445
12. Kohler, R. E., Jr. (1977) *Hist. Studies Phys. Sci.* **8,** 257–298
13. Young, V. R., and Ajami, A. (1999) *Proc. Nutr. Soc.* **58,** 15–32
14. Hevesy, G. (1948) *Cold Spring Harbor Symp. Quant. Biol.* **13,** 129–150
15. Clarke, H. T. (1958) *Annu. Rev. Biochem.* **27,** 1–14
16. Palmer, W. (1966) in *Nobel Lectures Chemistry 1922–1941,* pp.333–338, Elsevier Science Publishing Co., Inc., New York
17. Lewis, G. N. (1934) *Science* **79,** 151–153
18. Schoenheimer, R., and Rittenberg, D. (1935) *Science* **82,** 156–157
19. Schoenheimer, R. (1949) *The Dynamic State of Body Constituents,* Harvard University Press, Cambridge, MA
20. Bernhard, K., and Schoenheimer, R. (1940) *J. Biol. Chem.* **133,** 707–712
21. Rittenberg, D., and Schoenheimer, R. (1937) *J. Biol. Chem.* **121,** 235–253
22. Schoenheimer, R., Ratner, S., and Rittenberg, D. (1939) *J. Biol. Chem.* **127,** 333–344
23. Bloch, K. (1987) *Annu. Rev. Biochem.* **56,** 1–19
24. Tchen, T. T., and Bloch, K. (1956) *J. Am. Chem. Soc.* **78,** 1516–1517
25. Windaus, H. O. (1996) in *Nobel Lectures Chemistry 1922–1941,* pp. 105–121, Elsevier Science Publishing Co., Inc., New York
26. Sonderhoff, R., and Thomas, H. (1937) *Ann. Chem.* **530,** 195–213
27. Langdon, R. G., and Bloch, K. (1952) *J. Biol. Chem.* **200,** 129–144
28. Robinson, R. J. (1934) *J. Chem. Soc. Ind.* **53,** 1062–1063
29. Bloch, K. (1965) *Science* **150,** 19–28
30. Wolf, D. E., Hoffman, C. H., Aldrich, P. E., Skeggs, H. R., Wright, L. D., and Folkers, K. (1956) *J. Am. Chem. Soc.* **78,** 4499
31. Tavormina, P. A., Gibbs, M. H., and Huff, J. W. (1956) *J. Am. Chem. Soc.* **78,** 4498–4499

THE JOURNAL OF BIOLOGICAL CHEMISTRY

Vol. 276, No. 48, Issue of November 30, pp. 44357–44364, 2001
Printed in U.S.A.

Reflections

A PAPER IN A SERIES COMMISSIONED TO CELEBRATE THE CENTENARY OF THE JBC IN 2005

JBC Centennial
1905–2005
100 Years of Biochemistry and Molecular Biology

The Story of Glutamine Synthetase Regulation

Published, JBC Papers in Press, October 3, 2001, DOI 10.1074/jbc.R100055200

Earl R. Stadtman

From the Laboratory of Biochemistry, NHLBI, National Institutes of Health, Bethesda, Maryland 20892-8012

In 1960, I went on sabbatical leave from the National Institutes of Health (NIH) and spent the first 6 months in the laboratory of Feodor Lynen in Munich and the second 6 months in the laboratory of Georges Cohen at the Pasteur Institute in Paris. Both were remarkable experiences. In Lynen's laboratory, I initiated a new project that led to the demonstration that vitamin B_{12}-coenzyme is required for the conversion of methylmalonyl-CoA to succinyl-CoA (1–3). In Cohen's laboratory, I participated in an ongoing project designed to elucidate the mechanism involved in the regulation of aspartokinase activity in *Escherichia coli*. This problem was of special interest because it was well known that the ATP-dependent conversion of aspartate to aspartyl phosphate is the first step in a branched pathway that leads to the biosynthesis of three different amino acids, lysine, threonine, and methionine. Working together with Cohen and his co-worker, Gisele LeBras, we succeeded in separating two different aspartokinases from *E. coli* extracts and obtained evidence suggesting the existence of still another. One of these aspartokinases was subject to specific feedback inhibition and to repression by lysine, whereas the other was subject to feedback inhibition and to repression by threonine (4, 5). This was the first demonstration that multiple enzymes may be involved in the catalysis of initial steps in branched metabolic pathways and that the levels and activities of each one of the multiple enzymes may be differentially regulated by repression and/or feedback inhibition by a particular product of one of the branches in the pathway (6).

From Aspartokinase to Glutamine Synthetase

After returning to NIH, I resumed my studies on the metabolism of heterocyclic compounds, a project that I had been working on before going on sabbatical. This investigation was interrupted when a young postdoctoral fellow, Clifford Woolfolk, joined the laboratory. He had read the papers we had published on the regulation of aspartokinase and was interested in working on that project in my laboratory. I informed Clifford that all of that work had been carried out in Georges Cohen's laboratory and that I did not feel it was appropriate to continue the study at NIH. However, if he was interested in working on the regulation of branched metabolic pathways, I would be pleased to support the study of another enzyme that catalyzes the first common step in a branched metabolic pathway. I suggested that he examine metabolic maps and identify those enzymes that satisfied this criteria. I emphasized also that the enzyme selected for study should be one for which simple assays are available. Woolfolk came up with three suggestions: glutamic dehydrogenase, glutamine synthetase (GS),[1] and phosphoribosyl-pyrophosphate synthetase. His initial studies on glutamic dehydrogenase revealed no feedback inhibitory characteristics. He then looked at *E. coli* GS and was rewarded by the finding that the activity of this enzyme was subject to feedback inhibition by seven different end products of glutamine metabolism, namely histidine, tryptophan, AMP, CTP, carbamyl-P, glucosamine-6-P, and NAD^+, and also by glycine and alanine (7). This exciting discovery

---

[1] The abbreviations used are: GS, glutamine synthetase; ATase, adenylyltransferase; UTase, uridylyltransferase.

initiated a dramatic change in the focus of much of the research in the Laboratory of Biochemistry and for almost 35 years has occupied the time and energies of numerous highly talented postdoctoral fellows, visiting scientists, and senior associates, including Clifford Woolfolk, B. M. Shapiro, Ann Ginsburg, P. Boon Chock, S. G. Rhee, Wayne Anderson, Henry Kingdon, Amiel Segal, Michael Brown, Joseph Ciardi, E. G. Engleman, Sharon Francis, J. S. Hubbard, J. J. Villafranca, Stuart Adler, Richard Miller, K. Nakamura, Filiberto Cimino, Stanley Prusiner, Thomas F. Deuel, S. B. Hennig, Steven Tronick, D. Purich, S. Shaltiel, G. Magni, and Mark Fisher. In the meantime, all of these participants have gone on to distinguish themselves as leading investigators in diverse fields of science.

Cumulative Feedback Regulation

In continuing studies, Woolfolk developed procedures for the partial purification of GS from crude extracts of *E. coli*. In studies with these enzyme preparations, he showed that whereas saturating levels of any one of the feedback inhibitors could only partially inhibit activity of GS, mixtures of various combinations of these inhibitors were more effective than any one alone and that a combination of all of the inhibitors led to about 90% inhibition of GS activity. It was clear from this study that the various inhibitors were probably binding to different allosteric sites on the enzyme. This finding together with results of kinetic measurements led to the proposition that the activity of GS is regulated by a mechanism that we refer to as *cumulative feedback inhibition* (7, 8). According to this mechanism, overproduction of an end product of just one of the metabolic branches could lead to inhibition of only that fraction of GS that is needed to supply glutamine for the synthesis of that particular end product. Additional feedback control of the first committed step in the unique branch leading to that end product would presumably also be subject to inhibition by the same end product, thus guaranteeing that the uninhibited fraction of GS is then available only for synthesis of end products of other branches in the metabolic pathway. Moreover, because their effects are more or less independent, overproduction of the end product of another branch or branches in the pathway would have a *cumulative effect* leading to further inhibition of the GS activity as dictated by overall demand for its product, glutamine.

GS Structure and Physical Characteristics

In 1966, Bennett Shapiro joined the Laboratory of Biochemistry. He collaborated with Woolfolk in studies leading to the isolation of GS as a homogeneous crystalline protein. Later in studies with Ann Ginsburg, he established that GS is a large protein of about M_r 600,000, consisting of 12 apparently identical M_r 50,000 subunits, and is dependent on Mg(II) or Mn(II) for catalytic activity (9). Shapiro also showed that upon treatment with EDTA the enzyme undergoes conversion to a "relaxed" catalytically inactive configuration that is accompanied by exposure of cysteine sulfhydryl groups (10), and upon treatment with 1 M urea this relaxed form of the enzyme undergoes time-dependent complete subunit dissociation. Moreover, upon addition of Mn(II) or Mg(II) the subunits can undergo re-association to a "tightened" configuration with activities comparable with that of the native, so-called "taut," form (11). Subsequently, Mark Fisher demonstrated that in the presence of ATP the dissociated subunits could also be converted to the "taut" form by the *E. coli* chaperonin (12). In continuing studies, Shapiro and Ginsburg demonstrated that GS has two binding sites for divalent cations; one is involved in the interconversion of the "relaxed" and "tightened" configurations, whereas the other is involved in the binding of the ATP substrate to the enzyme (13, 14). Subsequently, Shapiro took a sample of the pure enzyme to the National Institute for Medical Research in London, where R. C. Valentine, an expert in electron microscopy, examined its structure. They confirmed that the enzyme is composed of 12 subunits and showed that the subunits were arranged in two superimposed hexagonal arrays. They showed further that the "relaxed" form of the enzyme obtained by EDTA treatment retained the dodecameric structure, but upon conversion to the "taut" form by the addition of Mn(II) the double hexagon molecules underwent face-to-face interactions forming long hexagonal tubes that subsequently undergo lateral associations to form paracrystalline "wheat-shaped" structures (15). Needless to say, GS became the subject of numerous detailed kinetic studies by Boon Chock, Ann Ginsburg, S. G. Rhee, and their co-workers, but it is beyond the scope of this presentation to summarize the results of those studies.

Adenylylation of GS Governs Its Susceptibility to Feedback Inhibition

When the original supply of pure GS obtained by Shapiro and Woolfolk was nearly exhausted, it became necessary to prepare a new batch of the enzyme. About this time, Henry Kingdon joined the laboratory as a clinical associate. His first assignment was to isolate a new sample of GS from crude extracts of *E. coli* using the procedure developed by Woolfolk and Shapiro. Much to our surprise and considerable concern, the new homogeneous enzyme preparation was insensitive to inhibition by most of the end products that had been shown to inhibit the earlier batch of enzyme. In addition, the new GS preparation was almost completely dependent on the presence of Mg(II) for catalytic activity, whereas the earlier preparation exhibited greater activity with Mn(II). The amino acid compositions of both preparations were identical, indicating that we were dealing with the same protein. Other studies established that the difference in activities was not because of the isolation procedure, differences in assay conditions, changes during storage, or interconversion between taut and relaxed forms. However, there was a difference in the *E. coli* growth conditions used for the preparation of cell-free extracts. The first GS preparation was isolated from cells grown in media containing glycerol and glutamate as the sole carbon and nitrogen sources, and the cells were harvested in the stationary phase of growth, whereas the second batch of GS was from cells grown on media containing glucose and growth-limiting levels of ammonium chloride and was harvested during the log phase of growth. In subsequent studies, it was confirmed that these differences in growth conditions were responsible for the observed differences in enzyme characteristics (16). However, it did not explain why the two apparently identical enzyme preparations differed in their sensitivities to feedback inhibition and divalent cation specificity. This was finally resolved when a comparison of the UV spectra revealed that the first preparation exhibited a higher absorbance at 260 nm, suggesting the presence of a nucleotide adduct (17). This was confirmed by showing that treatment of the older preparation with snake venom phosphodiesterase led to the release of AMP and conversion of the enzyme to a form that was insensitive to feedback inhibition (17). It soon became evident that the susceptibility of GS to cumulative feedback inhibition is under strict control by a novel mechanism involving the adenylylation of a specific amino acid residue in each subunit of the enzyme. These results led also to the consideration that if adenylylation represents an important mechanism for the regulation of GS activity, then there should be enzymes that catalyze the interconversion of GS between adenylylated and unadenylylated forms, in analogy to the kinase- and phosphatase-catalyzed interconversion of some enzymes between phosphorylated and unphosphorylated forms. Led by this consideration, Kingdon *et al.* (18) identified a highly specific adenylyltransferase (ATase) in *E. coli* extracts that catalyzes transfer of the AMP moiety of ATP to the hydroxyl group of a particular tyrosyl residue in each subunit of GS with concomitant formation of inorganic pyrophosphate. In further studies, it was established that, depending on the time of incubation and the concentration of transferase used, preparations of GS containing 1–12 adenylylated subunits could be obtained and that the fraction of a given GS preparation that could be inhibited by various feedback inhibitors was governed by the number of adenylylated subunits that it contained.

Shapiro also demonstrated that cell-free extracts contained an activity that could catalyze the removal of adenylyl groups on GS (19). Curiously, he found that two separable protein fractions (P_I and P_{II}) were required for maximal deadenylylation activity. This activity was dependent upon the presence of Mn(II), α-ketoglutarate, UTP, and inorganic phosphate and was also greatly stimulated by the presence of ATP (20). The requirement for inorganic phosphate was explained later when Wayne Anderson showed that the deadenylylation reaction involves a phosphorolytic cleavage of the adenylyl-*O*-tyrosyl bond, yielding ADP and unadenylylated GS (21). In further experiments, Anderson, together with Barbara Hennig and Ann Ginsburg, purified Shapiro's P_I protein and showed that it was, in fact, an ATase that could catalyze both the adenylylation and deadenylylation of GS (Reactions 1 and 2 in which n = 1–12) and that its activity was modulated by the P_{II} protein and by glutamine, 2-oxoglutarate, ATP, and UTP (22–24).

$$\text{GS} + n\text{ATP} \rightarrow \text{GS(AMP)}_n + n\text{PP}_i$$

$$\text{GS(AMP)}_n + n\text{P}_i \rightarrow \text{GS} + n\text{ADP}$$

REACTIONS 1 AND 2

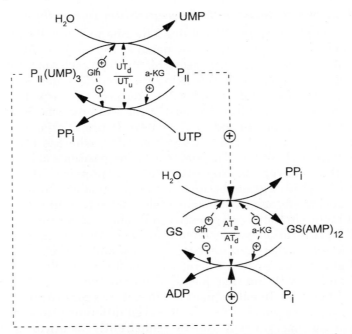

FIG. 1. **The bicyclic cascade that regulates GS activity.** Interrelationship between the cyclic interconversion of the regulatory protein between uridylylated ($P_{II}(UMP)_4$) and unuridylylated (P_{II}) forms, and the cyclic interconversion of GS between adenylylated ($GS(AMP)_{12}$) and unadenylylated forms, and the reciprocal control of these interconversions by L-glutamine (Gln) and α-ketoglutarate (α-*KG*). AT_a and AT_d denote the adenylylation and deadenylylation sites of adenylyltransferase, respectively; UT_d and UT_u denote the deuridylylation and uridylylation sites of uridylyltransferase, respectively. Reprinted with permission from Rhee *et al.* (Rhee, S. G., Chock, P. B., and Stadtman, E. R. (1985) in *The Enzymology of Post-translational Modification of Proteins* (Freedman, P. B., and Hawkins, H. C., eds) Vol. 2, pp. 273–297, Academic Press, New York).

Purification of the P_{II} Regulatory Protein and the Demonstration That Its Regulatory Activity Is Subject to Uridylylation and Deuridylylation of a Tyrosine Residue

At this stage of development of the problem, Amiel Segal and Michael Brown joined the Laboratory of Biochemistry and were charged with the responsibility of trying to elucidate further the interaction between ATase and the P_{II} protein and also to elucidate the puzzling role of UTP in this process. They found that, like GS, the P_{II} protein exists in two forms: (*a*) an unmodified form that in the presence of glutamine stimulates the adenylylation of GS by interactions at the adenylylation site (ATa) of the ATase and (*b*) a uridylylated form (P_{II}-UMP) that in the *absence* of glutamine and in the presence of 2-oxoglutarate stimulates the deadenylylation of GS by interactions at the deadenylylation site (ATd) of ATase (25). This led to further studies by Mangum *et al.* on the role of P_{II} in GS regulation (26) and studies by Garcia and Rhee (27) showing that the uridylylation and deuridylylation of P_{II} is catalyzed by the same uridylyltransferase (UTase). Subsequently, Adler *et al.* (28) obtained a homogeneous preparation of P_{II} and showed that it is a protein of about M_r 44,000, which was later shown by other workers to be a trimer (29). In continuing studies, Adler and Purich showed that uridylylation of P_{II} involves covalent attachment of a uridylyl group from UTP to a particular tyrosine residue in each subunit (Reaction 3, where $n = 1$–3) and that deuridylylation of the uridylylated P_{II} is a hydrolytic process (Reaction 4).

$$n\text{UTP} + P_{II} \rightarrow P_{II}(UMP)_n + n\text{PP}_i$$

$$P_{II}(UMP)_n + n\text{H}_2\text{O} \rightarrow P_{II} + n\text{UMP}$$

REACTIONS 3 AND 4

The Bicyclic Cascade

In view of the results summarized above, it became evident that the activity of GS in *E. coli* is finely controlled by a cascade system composed of two tightly linked interconvertible enzyme/protein cycles, each one of which is catalyzed by a bifunctional enzyme (Fig. 1). From a detailed analysis of the enzymes involved in this bicyclic cascade, it was found that the activity of GS is subject to regulation by over 40 metabolites. Some of these exert their effects by interacting directly with GS, whereas others serve as substrates or allosteric effectors of one or both of the enzymes, ATase and UTase, that catalyze the nucleotidylation and denucleotidylation reactions of GS and the P_{II} protein. Of these effectors, 2-oxoglutarate, glutamate, ATP, UTP, and P_i are of special significance. The latter three compounds serve as co-substrates in the nucleotidylation/denucleotidylation reactions, whereas glutamine and 2-oxo-glutarate serve as important allosteric effectors of the bifunctional enzymes. Glutamine inhibits and 2-oxoglutarate stimulates the ability of ATase to catalyze the P_{II}-dependent adenylylation of GS, whereas each effector has an opposite effect on the capacity of ATase to catalyze the deadenylylation of GS. In an analogous manner, glutamine inhibits the ability of UTase to catalyze the uridylylation of P_{II} and to stimulate its ability to catalyze the deuridy-lylation of P_{II}-UMP. In contrast, 2-oxoglutarate stimulates the uridylylation of P_{II}. The diverse effects of these various effectors on the activity of GS led to the proposition that the dynamic interconversion of an enzyme between covalently modified and unmodified forms provides a mechanism by which the activity of an enzyme can be shifted gradually from one level to another commensurate with cellular demand. This concept was supported by the studies of Brown *et al.* (25) showing that the fraction of GS subunits that could be adenylylated varied in response to changes in the levels of multiple metabolites that govern the activities of the cascade enzymes. Thus, when GS was incubated in a mixture containing ATP, UTP, P_i, 2-oxoglutarate, glutamine, Mg(II), and/or Mn(II) and the two bifunctional enzymes, ATase and UTase, within a few minutes the average number of adenylylated subunits in GS reached a steady-state value. Moreover, a change in the concentration of any one of the five metabolites or Mn(II) produced a shift in the level of adenylylated subunits, either to higher or lower values depending upon which metabolite concentration was varied. It was further observed that after a steady-state level of adenylylation was established, the concentration of ATP continued to decrease, indicating that under a specified set of conditions a dynamic steady state is established in which the rates of adenylylation and deadenylylation of GS are equal. It follows that the steady-state level of adenylylated subunits and, therefore, the specific catalytic activity of GS and its susceptibility to cumulative feedback inhibition are specified by the relative concentrations of the positive and negative effectors (metabolites) that govern activities of the cascade enzymes. In subsequent studies, Rhee and co-workers (30–33) took advantage of molecular biological techniques to obtain strains of *E. coli* that overproduce UTase and P_{II} and were able to obtain highly purified preparations of these proteins. Then, in a monumental effort, they determined the values of 21 interaction constants that govern the protein/protein and protein/effector interactions that are involved in various steps of the GS bicyclic cascade. With this knowledge, it was possible to carry out *in vitro* experiments that verified in every important detail the theoretical predictions of the cascade model. Furthermore, verification of these basic principles was obtained by Umberto Mura in studies on the adenylylation of GS in permeabilized *E. coli* cells, subjected to varying concentrations of ATP, UTP, 2-oxoglutarate, glutamine, and P_i (34, 35).

Immunochemical Studies

A University of Maryland graduate student, Robert Hohman, was granted permission to carry out his thesis research in the Laboratory of Biochemistry. His studies were concerned with the development of AMP-specific antibodies that could be used to separate adenylylated and unadenylylated forms of GS and that could detect variations in protein configurations elicited by partial adenylylation of the enzyme or by allosteric interactions. From a comparison of the extent of immunoprecipitation of GS preparations containing various ratios of adeny-lylated/unadenylylated subunits, it was established that the initial binding of antibodies to GS is a function of the total number of adenylylated subunits per dodecamer and that partially adenylylated enzyme preparations are composed of subpopulations of GS molecules that differ in their tendency to form precipitable aggregates due presumably to differences in the topo-graphical distribution of antigenic determinants on the surface of the enzyme. Some distributions may favor intramolecular reactions of the bivalent antibody with two different adeny-lylated subunits within the same GS molecule to form soluble immune complexes, whereas other distributions may favor intermolecular cross-linkage of the bivalent antibodies with adenylyl groups of two different molecules leading to precipitation. Significantly, results of these studies highlight the fact that immunoprecipitibility of multivalent protein antigens by bivalent antibodies is a function of the intramolecular epitope density (36–38).

Theoretical Analysis of Cyclic Cascades

Based on the results summarized above, my colleague, Boon Chock, an expert enzyme kineticist, carried out a detailed theoretical analysis of a bicyclic cascade system analogous to that described above for the regulation of GS activity (39–43). This analysis revealed that coupled cyclic cascade systems are endowed with regulatory potentials far beyond our imagination. It was shown that: (*a*) cascades are capable of signal amplification, *i.e.* the concentration of an effector needed to provoke a large change in the level of the covalently modified target enzyme can be orders of magnitude lower than the K_m for the binding of that effector to converter enzymes; (*b*) cascades can serve as rate amplifiers and, therefore, can facilitate a change from one steady-state level of covalent modification to another within the millisecond time range; (*c*) cascades are capable of generating high cooperativity (sigmoidal response) to increasing concentrations of a given effector; (*d*) cascades serve as metabolic integration systems. They are able to monitor continuously the intracellular concentrations of a large number of metabolites. This leads to continuous shifts in the steady-state ratio of covalently modified and unmodified forms of an enzyme and, therefore, to changes in its activity commensurate with metabolic demand. With these properties, it is understandable that mechanisms involving reversible covalent modifications of proteins are widely used in cellular regulation of signal transduction.

Thus ended a most enlightening and rewarding story of GS regulation. However, it was the beginning of another story in which GS has played a dominant role. As an outgrowth of our studies in the field of regulation, I became aware of the fact that the intracellular concentrations of many enzymes are determined by the nutritional state of the organism. In response to nitrogen or carbon starvation, the concentration of a given enzyme may either increase or decrease. Although considerable information was available on the mechanism of protein synthesis, almost nothing was known about the mechanism(s) involved in the regulation of protein degradation. In studies designed to learn more about the latter, it was demonstrated that when either *E. coli* or *Aerobacter aerogenes* is forced into a state of stationary growth by nitrogen limitation, there is a rapid decline in the level of GS and several other enzymes. It was then established that under these conditions, the proteolytic degradation of GS is initiated by reactive oxygen-mediated oxidative inactivation of the enzyme. This was the beginning of another chapter in the GS story that has led to the elucidation of biochemical mechanisms involved in the oxidative inactivation of proteins and the role they play in protein degradation, aging, and in a number of diseases. It is beyond the scope of this article to summarize these studies (for review, see Refs. 44 and 45).

The story of GS reviewed here summarizes results of studies carried out in the Laboratory of Biochemistry, NHLBI, National Institutes of Health. I have not referred to studies carried out in H. Holzer's laboratory in Freiburg, Germany, that were carried out in parallel to those described here and led to similar findings (46–49) (for reviews by Holzer *et al.*, see also Refs. 19, 25, 26, 50, and 51 for discussions of the relationships between our results and those in Holzer's laboratory). Also, I have not described the results of beautiful experiments by David Eisenberg on the crystal structure of GS (52–54), extending our knowledge of its structure and confirming in many respects the conclusions arrived at from our studies.

REFERENCES

1. Stadtman, E. R., Overath, P., Eggerer, H., and Lynen, F. (1959) The role of biotin and vitamin B$_{12}$ in propionate metabolism. Biochem. Biophys. Res. Commun. **2**, 1–7
2. Eggerer, H., Overath, P., Lynen, F., and Stadtman, E. R. (1960) On the mechanism of the cobamide coenzyme-dependent isomerization of methylmalonyl-CoA to succinyl-CoA. J. Am. Chem. Soc. **82**, 2643
3. Stadtman, E. R., Overath, P., Eggerer, H., and Lynen, F. (1961) The function of biotin and vitamin B$_{12}$-coenzyme in the oxidation of fatty acids with an uneven number of carbon atoms. In *Proceedings of the Symposium on Drugs Affecting Lipid Metabolism*, pp. 68–74, Elsevier Science Publishers B.V., Amsterdam
4. Stadtman, E. R., Cohen, G. N., LeBras, G., and deRobichon-Szulmajster, H. (1961) Feedback inhibition and repression of aspartokinase activity in *Escherichia coli* and *Saccharomyces cerevisiae*. J. Biol. Chem. **236**, 2033–2038
5. Stadtman, E. R., Cohen, G. N., and LeBras, G. (1961) Feedback inhibition and repression of aspartokinase activity in *Escherichia coli*. Ann. N. Y. Acad. Sci. **94**, 952–959
6. Stadtman, E. R. (1963) Symposium of multiple forms of enzymes and control mechanisms. II. Enzyme multiplicity and function in the regulation of divergent metabolic pathways. Bacteriol. Rev. **27**, 170–181
7. Woolfolk, C. A., and Stadtman, E. R. (1964) Cumulative feedback inhibition in the multiple end-product regulation of glutamine synthetase activity in *Escherichia coli*. Biochem. Biophys. Res. Commun. **17**, 313–319
8. Woolfolk, C. A., and Stadtman, E. R. (1967) Regulation of glutamine synthetase. III. Cumulative feedback inhibition of glutamine synthetase from *Escherichia coli*. Arch. Biochem. Biophys. **118**, 736–755
9. Woolfolk, C. A., Shapiro, B., and Stadtman, E. R. (1966) Regulation of glutamine synthetase. I. Purification and

properties of glutamine synthetase from *Escherichia coli*. *Arch. Biochem. Biophys.* **116**, 177–192

10. Shapiro, B. M., and Stadtman, E. R. (1967) Regulation of glutamine synthetase. IX. Reactivity of the sulfhydryl groups of the enzyme from *Escherichia coli*. *J. Biol. Chem.* **242**, 5069–5079

11. Woolfolk, C. A., and Stadtman, E. R. (1967) Regulation of glutamine synthetase. IV. Reversible dissociation and inactivation of glutamine synthetase from *Escherichia coli* by the concerted action of EDTA and urea. *Arch. Biochem. Biophys.* **122**, 174–189

12. Fisher, M. T. (1992) Promotion of the *in vitro* regeneration of dodecameric glutamine synthetase from *Escherichia coli* in the presence of GroEL (chaperonin-60) and ATP. *Biochemistry* **31**, 3955–3963

13. Shapiro, B. M., and Ginsburg, A. (1968) Effects of specific divalent cations on some physical and chemical properties of glutamine synthetase from *Escherichia coli*. Taut and relaxed enzyme forms. *Biochemistry* **7**, 2153–2167

14. Denton, M. D., and Ginsburg, A. (1969) Conformational changes in glutamine synthetase from *Escherichia coli*. I. The binding of Mn^{2+} in relation to some aspects of the enzyme structure and activity. *Biochemistry* **8**, 1714–1725

15. Valentine, R. C., Shapiro, B. M., and Stadtman, E. R. (1968) Regulation of glutamine synthetase. XII. Electron microscopy of the enzyme from *Escherichia coli*. *Biochemistry* **7**, 2143–2152

16. Kingdon, H. S., and Stadtman, E. R. (1967) Regulation of glutamine synthetase. X. Effect of growth conditions on the susceptibility of *Escherichia coli* glutamine synthetase to feedback inhibition. *J. Bacteriol.* **94**, 949–957

17. Shapiro, B. M., Kingdon, H. S., and Stadtman, E. R. (1967) Regulation of glutamine synthetase. VII. A new form of the enzyme with altered regulatory and kinetic properties. *Proc. Natl. Acad. Sci. U. S. A.* **58**, 642–649

18. Kingdon, H. S., Shapiro, B. M., and Stadtman, E. R. (1967) Regulation of glutamine synthetase. VIII. ATP: glutamine synthetase adenylyltransferase. An enzyme that catalyzes alteration in the regulatory properties of glutamine synthetase. *Proc. Natl. Acad. Sci. U. S. A.* **58**, 1703–1710

19. Shapiro, B. M., and Stadtman, E. R. (1968) Glutamine synthetase deadenylylating enzyme. *Biochem. Biophys. Res. Commun.* **30**, 32–37

20. Shapiro, B. M. (1969) The glutamine synthetase deadenylylation enzyme from *Escherichia* resolution into two components, specific nucleotide stimulation and cofactor requirements. *Biochemistry* **8**, 659–710

21. Anderson, W. B., and Stadtman, E. R. (1970) Glutamine synthetase deadenylylation reaction yielding ADP as nucleotide product. *Biochem. Biochem. Res. Commun.* **41**, 704–709

22. Anderson, W. B., Hennig, S. B., Ginsburg, A., and Stadtman, E. R. (1970) Association of ATP:glutamine synthetase adenylyltransferase activity with P_I component of the glutamine synthetase adenylylation system. *Proc. Natl. Acad. Sci. U. S. A.* **67**, 1417–1424

23. Hennig, S. B., Anderson, W. B., and Ginsburg, A. (1970) Adenosine triphosphate:glutamine synthetase adenylyl-transferase of *Escherichia coli* glutamine synthetase: two active forms. *Proc. Natl. Acad. Sci. U. S. A.* **67**, 1761–1768

24. Anderson, W. B., and Stadtman, E. R. (1971) Purification and functional roles of the P_I and P_{II} components of *Escherichia coli* glutamine synthetase deadenylylation system. *Arch. Biochem. Biophys.* **143**, 428–443

25. Brown, M. S., Segal, A., and Stadtman, E. R. (1971) Modulation of glutamine synthetase adenylylation and deadenylylation is mediated by nucleotide transformation of the P_{II} regulatory protein (*E. coli*/protein-bound uridine nucleotide/adenylyltransferase/2-oxo-glutarate-cascade regulation). *Proc. Natl. Acad. Sci. U. S. A.* **68**, 2949–2953

26. Mangum, J. H., Magni, G., and Stadtman, E. R. (1973) Regulation of glutamine synthetase deadenylylation by the enzymatic uridylylation and deuridylylation of the P_{II} regulatory protein. *Arch. Biochem. Biophys.* **158**, 514–525

27. Garcia, E., and Rhee, S. G. (1983) Cascade control of *Escherichia coli* glutamine synthetase. Purification and properties of P_{II} uridylyltransferase and uridylyl-removing enzyme. *J. Biol. Chem.* **258**, 2246–2253

28. Adler, S. P., Purich, D., and Stadtman, E. R. (1975) Cascade control of *Escherichia coli* glutamine synthetase. Properties of the P_{II} regulatory protein and the uridylyltransferase-uridylyl removing enzyme. *J. Biol. Chem.* **16**, 6264–6272

29. Carr, P. D., Cheah, E., Suffolk, P. M., Vasudevan, S. G., Dixon, N. E., and Ollis, D. L. (1996) X-ray structure of the signal transduction protein P-II from *Escherichia coli* at 1.9 angstrom. *Acta Crystallogr.* **52**, 93–104

30. Rhee, S. G., Park, S. C., and Koo, J. H. (1985) The role of adenylyltransferase and uridylyltransferase in the regulation of glutamine synthetase in *Escherichia coli*. *Curr. Top. Cell Regul.* **27**, 221–231

31. Rhee, S. G., and Chock, P. B. (1983) Purification and characterization of uridylylated and unuridylylated forms of regulatory protein P_{II} involved in the glutamine synthetase regulation in *Escherichia coli*. *Isoenzymes Curr. Top. Biol. Med. Res.* **8**, 141–153

32. Son, H. S., and Rhee, S. G. (1987) Cascade control of *Escherichia coli* glutamine synthetase. *J. Biol. Chem.* **262**, 8690–8695

33. Suh, S. W., and Rhee, S. G. (1983) Preliminary x-ray crystallographic studies and molecular symmetry of the P_{II} regulatory protein from *Escherichia coli*. *J. Biol. Chem.* **258**, 10294–10295

34. Mura, U., and Stadtman, E. R. (1981) Glutamine synthetase adenylylation in permeabilized cells of *Escherichia coli*. *J. Biol. Chem.* **256**, 13014–13021

35. Mura, U., Chock, P. B., and Stadtman, E. R. (1981) Allosteric regulation of the state of adenylylation of glutamine synthetase in permeabilized cell preparations of *Escherichia coli*. *J. Biol. Chem.* **256**, 13022–13029

36. Hohman, R. J., and Stadtman, E. R. (1978) Use of AMP-specific antibodies to differentiate between adenylylated and unadenylylated *E. coli* glutamine synthetase. *Biochem. Biophys. Res. Commun.* **82**, 865–870

37. Hohman, R. J., Rhee, S. G., and Stadtman, E. R. (1980) Anti-AMP antibody precipitation of multiply adenylylated forms of glutamine synthetase from *E. coli*. *Proc. Natl. Acad. Sci. U. S. A.* **77**, 7410–7414

38. Hohman, R. J., and Stadtman, E. R. (1982) Relationship between epitope density and immunoprecipitation of multivalent antigens by bivalent antibody: immunoprecipitation of adenylylated glutamine synthetase by anti-AMP antibodies. *Arch. Biochem. Biophys.* **218**, 548–560

39. Stadtman, E. R., Chock, P. B., and Adler, S. P. (1975) Metabolic regulation of coupled covalent modification cascade systems. In *Metabolic Interconversion of Enzymes* (Shaltiel, S., ed) pp. 142–149, Springer-Verlag New York Inc., New York

40. Stadtman, E. R., and Chock, P. B. (1977) Superiority of interconvertible enzyme cascades in metabolic regulation: analysis of monocyclic systems. *Proc. Natl. Acad. Sci. U. S. A.* **74**, 2761–2765

41. Chock, P. B., and Stadtman, E. R. (1977) Superiority of interconvertible enzyme cascades in metabolic regulation: analysis of multicyclic systems. *Proc. Natl. Acad. Sci. U. S. A.* **74**, 2766–2770

42. Shacter, E., Chock, P. B., and Stadtman, E. R. (1984) Regulation through phosphorylation/dephosphorylation cascade systems. *J. Biol. Chem.* **259**, 12252–12259

43. Shacter, E. Chock, P. B., and Stadtman, E. R. (1984) Energy consumption in a cyclic phosphorylation/dephos-phorylation cascade. *J. Biol. Chem.* **259**, 12260–12264

44. Berlett, B. S., and Stadtman, E. R. (1997) Protein oxidation in aging, disease, and oxidative stress. *J. Biol. Chem.* **272,** 20313–20316
45. Stadtman, E. R., and Berlett, B. S. (1998) Reactive oxygen-mediated protein oxidation in aging and disease. *Drug Metab. Rev.* **30,** 225–243
46. Holzer, H., Mecke, D., Liess, K., Wulff, K., Heilmeyer, E., Jr., Gancedo, C., Schutt, H., Battig, A., Heinrich, P., and Wolf, D. (1969) Enzyme-catalyzed chemical modification of glutamine synthetase from *E. coli. FEBS Symp.* **19,** 171–177
47. Holzer, H. (1969) Characterization of glutamine synthetase inactivating and activating enzyme from *Escherichia coli.* In *Alfred Benson Symposium I. The Role of Nucleoside for the Function and Conformation of Enzymes* (Kalckar, H. M., Klenow, H., Ottesen, M., Munch-Petersen, A., and Thaysen, J. H., eds) pp. 94–110, Munksgaard Press, Copenhagen, Denmark
48. Holzer, H. (1969) Regulation of enzymes by enzyme-catalyzed chemical modification. *Adv. Enzymol.* **32,** 297–326
49. Ebner, E., Wolf, D., Gancedo, C., Elsasser, S., and Holzer, H. (1970) ATP:glutamine synthetase adenylyltransferase from *Escherichia coli* B. Purification and properties. *Eur. J. Biochem.* **14,** 535–544
50. Stadtman, E. R. (1969) On the structure and allosteric regulation of glutamine synthetase from *Escherichia coli.* In *Alfred Benson Symposium I. The Role of Nucleoside for the Function and Conformation of Enzymes* (Kalckar, H. M., Klenow, H., Ottesen, M., Munch-Petersen, A., and Thaysen, J. H., eds) pp. 142–149, Munksgaard Press, Copenhagen, Denmark
51. Shapiro, B. M., and Stadtman, E. R. (1970) The regulation of glutamine synthetase in microorganisms. *Annu. Rev. Microbiol.* **24,** 501–524
52. Almassy, R. J., Janson, C. A., Hamlin, R., Xuong, N. H., and Eisenberg, D. (1986) *Novel subunit-subunit interactions in the structure of glutamine synthetase. Nature* **323,** 304–309
53. Yamashita, M. N., Almassy, R. J., Janson, C. A., Casicio, D., and Eisenberg, D. (1989) Refined atomic model of glutamine synthetase at 3.5 Å resolution. *J. Biol. Chem.* **264,** 17681–17690
54. Liaw, S.-H., Pan, C., and Eisenberg, D. (1993) Feedback inhibition of fully unadenylylated glutamine synthetase from *Salmonella typhimurium* by glycine, alanine, and serine. *Proc. Natl. Acad. Sci. U. S. A.* **90,** 4996–5000

THE JOURNAL OF BIOLOGICAL CHEMISTRY
© 2002 by The American Society for Biochemistry and Molecular Biology, Inc.

Vol. 277, No. 13, Issue of March 29, pp. 10747–10752, 2002
Printed in U.S.A.

Reflections

A PAPER IN A SERIES COMMISSIONED TO CELEBRATE THE CENTENARY OF THE JBC IN 2005

JBC Centennial
1905–2005
100 Years of Biochemistry and Molecular Biology

Postdoctoral Years

Published, JBC Papers in Press, January 22, 2002, DOI 10.1074/jbc.R100069200

Mildred Cohn

From the Department of Biochemistry and Biophysics, University of Pennsylvania School of Medicine, Philadelphia, Pennsylvania 19104-6059

Everyone tends to idealize the past, particularly in one's retirement years. I am as guilty as any one of my generation in indulging in nostalgia for the "good old days," but for the purposes of this paper, I shall avoid any judgments and only discuss the differences in the way research was done in biochemistry from my experiences in the late 30s through the 40s compared with the present. The primary difference is the phenomenal increase of pace; not only has the output per individual increased manyfold, but the number of research workers producing results has exploded.

There are a number of reasons for the rise in productivity; foremost among them are the advances in technology and the concomitant commercial availability of materials and instrumentation. In 1937 when I joined the laboratory of Vincent du Vigneaud at George Washington University Medical School as a postdoctoral fellow, he was interested in initiating metabolic tracer studies on sulfur-containing amino acids with stable isotopes; suitable radioactive isotopes, tritium and ^{14}C, had not yet been discovered. The only stable isotope commercially available was deuterium, which could be analyzed by density methods such as the falling drop technique that I had to set up. My experience with such methodology as a graduate student in the laboratory of Harold Urey at Columbia University was the reason I had been hired. I was the only member of du Vigneaud's group who had a background in chemical physics as well as being the only woman.

If du Vigneaud was typical of bioorganic chemists of his day, they certainly had a distorted view of the capabilities of physical chemists. The first week I was in his laboratory, he asked me to repair a Leeds and Northrup suspension galvanometer and was disappointed when I told him that I could not do it. By chance, soon thereafter a representative of the Aminco Instrument Company visited and du Vigneaud made the same request of him. To my delight, the response was, "I wouldn't touch it with a ten foot pole. Send it back to Leeds and Northrup." I was partially vindicated.

A few months later, du Vigneaud installed an internal phone system that connected his office to the research laboratories. Its design was such that it could be switched on and off only at the master station in his office. All of us worried about Big Brother overhearing our conversations because we never knew whether the system was on or off. Because the Chief, as he liked to be called, was sensitive to our uneasiness, he asked me to modify the system so that it could be switched on and off at the substations. I was appalled; I knew nothing about telephone circuits. In desperation, I consulted a friend, Shelley Krasnow, who headed an instrument company. When I told him my problem, he laughed and said, "Telephone circuits are among the most complicated circuits; I'll have my electronics engineer have a look at it." The report of the expert stated that the modification would require an additional wire to be laid throughout the system. When I transmitted the information to du Vigneaud, the project was dropped.

I did redeem myself occasionally, upholding the reputation of physical chemists. In setting up the falling drop method, which measured the density of water to 1 ppm, I had to construct a water bath that held constant to 0.001 °C, which required a small DC fan. The power of the city of Washington had been converted fairly recently from DC to AC by the Potomac Power Company (the medical school had retained a DC line for research needs). As a consequence there was not a DC fan to be found in the shops of Washington. As a last resort, I called on Shelley Krasnow again, and he informed me that I could undoubtedly find what I needed at the Potomac Power Company's warehouse because they had replaced all customers' DC appliances with comparable AC ones. When I contacted the company, they invited me to come and choose what I wanted, and because I was asking on behalf of a non-profit institution, they would give me the equipment on indefinite loan. When I saw five floors filled with all kinds of useful electrical appliances and their willingness to part with them, I phoned du Vignéaud and apprised him of the situation. Not only did I get the fan I needed but the laboratory received four large floor fans (these were the days before air conditioning) and three motors. My reputation was somewhat salvaged.

For du Vigneaud's studies on the metabolism of sulfur-containing amino acids, rats were fed pure amino acid diets as devised by Rose (1). Of the 20 amino acids in the diet, only 10 were commercially available; the other 10 had to be synthesized or extracted in the investigator's laboratory. During the months of June and July, all research ceased in the laboratory as the graduate students and postdoctoral fellows prepared amino acids for the following year's research.

I was excepted from this annual task because, having been trained as a physical chemist, I had no expertise in organic synthesis. Nevertheless, a couple of years later when we were at Cornell Medical College and du Vigneaud wanted to synthesize deuteriomethyl-methionine for transmethylation studies (2), he asked me to synthesize CD_3OD. Isotopically labeled compounds were not commercially available. Fortunately I remembered that Professor Zanetti of the Columbia chemistry department had synthesized deuteriomethyl alcohol a few years earlier. He helpfully agreed to allow me to synthesize it in his laboratory from CO and deuterium gas at 10,000 pounds pressure (achieved with a homemade compressor that invariably leaked) using a DuPont catalyst of unknown composition at 300 °C. After a month of continually repeating the procedure, I had prepared about 100 g of the product. In retrospect, it's surprising that I lived through that experience without mishap because I was working without a hood with toxic CO and potentially explosive deuterium and CO gases.

In pursuit of his transsulfuration studies to determine whether only the sulfur or both the carbon chain and sulfur were transferred in the conversion of methionine to cysteine, du Vigneaud needed doubly labeled (^{13}C and ^{34}S) methionine. The project of synthesizing the labeled compound was assigned to Kilmer, a postdoctoral fellow, and it took him a whole year of hard work to produce the desired product (3). The precious compound was fed to rats by stomach tube, a procedure that I had to learn how to do.

I do remember a near catastrophe during the course of this study. The rats had to be fed daily including the weekend and with rats above a certain size, I needed assistance, someone to hold the rat while I administered the diet by stomach tube. Saturdays presented no problem because everyone worked half a day on Saturdays at that time. On Sundays I usually found a graduate or postdoctoral student in the laboratory as well. One Sunday I arrived with my husband, Henry Primakoff, a theoretical physicist, and no one was to be found in the laboratory. As an emergency measure, I decided to draft Henry to assist me. I carefully demonstrated to him how to hold the animal. Once he held the rat, I inserted the bit (a piece of dowel pin with a hole in it), through which I threaded the catheter tube which was attached to a hypodermic syringe containing the liquid diet. Unfortunately I had neglected to warn him that when the stomach tube reached its destination, the rat often reacted by urinating or defecating or both. And this particular rat did react in this fashion. Henry, taken by surprise, let go of the rat who promptly took off, pulling the catheter tube off the hypodermic syringe. There he was scampering around the animal room with the bit in his mouth and the red catheter tubing hanging out of it. It took us an anxiety-filled hour to retrieve him. I never asked Henry to assist me again. Nevertheless, in the end, it was one of the most satisfying experiments I have ever been involved in, yielding an unequivocal answer; all the sulfur and none of the carbon in the newly formed cysteine originated from methionine (4).

A quite different aspect of the pace of research in the 30s and 40s is illustrated in connection with the establishment of the intermediate in the conversion of methionine to cysteine discussed above. Several investigators had suggested hypotheses for the pathway. Among them was Erwin Brand who suggested cystathionine as the intermediate in a publication in 1936 (5). du Vigneaud was intrigued by this hypothesis and asked Brand to synthesize the compound and test its competence as an intermediate. Furthermore he told Brand that he would wait 5 years for Brand to do the experiment and if Brand did not do it in that time period, he, du Vigneaud, would do it. Accordingly after 5 long years, du Vigneaud with Brown successfully undertook the synthesis of cystathionine (6) and then proceeded with the metabolic experiments to prove that it was indeed the intermediate. With the accelerated pace of research and competition today, such an incident hardly seems credible.

Shortly after we moved to Cornell Medical College in 1938, I was given the task of devising a preparative electrophoresis apparatus at 10,000 V and of designing a microelectrophoresis apparatus for determining isoelectric points of peptides, which I did. A Tiselius electrophoresis apparatus was constructed under my supervision from blueprints kindly supplied by Dr. Longsworth of Rockefeller Institute. Obviously one of my unanticipated functions was as a resource for all instrumentation.

With the happy outcome of the experiment with doubly labeled methionine, du Vigneaud decided that we needed a mass spectrometer in the laboratory so that we could do our own analyses of ^{13}C in future experiments. None was available commercially, so I was assigned the task of constructing one, no easy task at any time, but the difficulty was exacerbated by the problem of obtaining materials during World War II. It was with considerable trepidation that I accepted the assignment. I well remembered that during my graduate student days, Professor Urey had hired a physicist to build a mass spectrometer and his instrument never worked. However, I knew that Harry Thode with whom I had overlapped in Urey's laboratory and who was now a chemistry professor at McMaster University in Canada had recently designed a new mass spectrometer. Incidentally, although the mass spectrometer had been invented by an Englishman, Aston, during the war when mass spectrometers were sorely needed for the atomic bomb project, Thode was the only scientist in the British Commonwealth who knew how to build one.

I contacted Thode and he generously offered to duplicate and send me the essential part of his instrument, a glass tube containing the ion gun and bent at 90° for the detectors. Of course, I still had to incorporate the vacuum system, the magnet, and all the electronics to have a working system. In retrospect, some of my adventures seem amusing, but they were not amusing at the time. A non-magnetic metal shield was needed inside the glass tube to rid the system of ions that hit the wall of the tube, and I thought flexible Greenfield cable made of nichrome V, a non-magnetic alloy, would serve the purpose. I had acquired the nichrome and needed to find a company to fabricate the cable for me. After refusals from several companies chosen from the yellow pages of the New York telephone directory with responses like, "Lady, don't you know there is a war on?", I decided to approach the top corporation, the Anaconda Copper Company. Not only did they agree to produce the desired cable, they refused payment, their policy for non-profit institutions.

I also had to weld the nichrome plates to platinum leads. To accomplish this, I found an appropriate step-down transformer but discovered that a timer for the 16 amp current would cost about $1500, an excessive amount to pay to make five welds. When I consulted an electrical engineer friend, he queried, "Are you willing to spend five cents per weld?" The question was rhetorical. He continued, "You buy fuses of five or ten amps depending on the time you want the 16 amp current to flow. They are very reproducible, always blowing after the same time interval when overloaded." Thus another problem solved.

Another skill, now obsolete, that was essential to using the instrument was glass blowing. Each gaseous sample, enclosed in a custom-blown tube with a break seal, had to be sealed to the spectrometer inlet system. The most challenging glass blowing feat I ever undertook for the replacement of a filament was the breaking and resealing of the glass envelope, three inches in diameter, without changing the precise geometry of the metal plates within it.

The construction of the spectrometer was eventually completed although it never performed to my satisfaction. One day du Vigneaud was holding forth about it to a group of medical students. It was his custom to conduct guided tours of the research laboratories of the department once a year to groups of about 15 students to give them an appreciation of biochemical research and perhaps entice some of them to engage in research. When he had finished describing the mass spectrometer and its applications, he informed the students that it had been built by one of the research associates, namely me. Whereupon one of the students asked, "But can she cook?" du Vigneaud's response was, "I don't know but she has two children." Had I passed?

One might question why during World War II was I building a mass spectrometer for tracer studies of metabolic reactions, research unrelated to the war effort. du Vigneaud had an answer. Although most of the postdoctoral fellows in our laboratory were devoting their efforts to war-related research (the chemical synthesis of penicillin), du Vigneaud said, "Some day this war will be over and we do not want to lose continuity in basic research completely and have to rebuild from scratch after the war." So three or four of us who were not eligible for the draft, kept basic research going. At the time and in retrospect, I think it was a wise policy.

Despite spending so much effort on constructing apparatus and having my experimental work restricted to du Vigneaud's research program, it was during those 9 postdoctoral years that I conceived approaches to biochemical problems, which I implemented and developed in the subsequent years of my career as an independent investigator. From the work on transmethylation and transsulfuration in du Vigneaud's laboratory, I was convinced of the power of isotopes to elucidate biochemical reaction pathways. It occurred to me that isotopic oxygen would be most useful in determining mechanisms of biochemical reactions in isolated enzyme systems. At Washington University I was able to initiate studies, with Cori's blessing, to determine whether the C–O or O–P bond was cleaved in the C–O–P moiety of ^{18}O-labeled phosphorylated substrates enabling the reactions to be categorized as either phosphoryl transfer or organic group (glucosyl, acyl) transfer reactions (7). The method was extended to investigate more complex systems such as oxidative phosphorylation. Should ^{18}O-inorganic phosphate form a carbon-oxygen linkage as in phosphorylase reactions and be followed by a phosphoryl transfer with the rupture of the O–P bond, the organic moiety remaining would contain ^{18}O. Succinate formed from the malonate-inhibited oxidation of α-ketoglutarate is an example (8). Oxidative phosphorylation accompanying electron transfer revealed an unexpected catalysis of an inorganic phosphate-water exchange reaction (9).

My interest in magnetochemistry arose from a 1936 paper of Pauling and Coryell (10) on determining the bond type of iron in heme and related compounds by measuring their magnetic susceptibilities. In du Vigneaud's laboratory, not only was zinc insulin available as originally crystallized by Abel but also cobalt and nickel insulins as well. It occurred to me that if I followed Pauling's method to measure the magnetic properties of the paramagnetic forms of insulin, I might be able to determine the type of metal bonding in the protein. I broached the subject to du Vigneaud, and he encouraged me in the project. He had been investigating the amino acid composition of insulin at a time when the protein nature of hormones was hotly debated. In fact, the 12% cystine content of insulin led to his initial involvement with the interconvertibility of sulfur-containing amino acids. However, his interest in the structure of insulin continued even when his main focus was on metabolism of sulfur-containing amino acids. To measure magnetic susceptibility, I needed a Gouy balance. Fortunately I remembered that a fellow graduate student in physics, Iskendarian, had constructed a highly sensitive version to measure the magnetic susceptibilities of H_2O *versus* D_2O. He generously allowed me to use his instrument, which was so sensitive to vibration in the basement of Pupin Hall that I could only do experiments after midnight when truck traffic ceased. The results were disappointing. Because of the large diamagnetic contribution from the protein, the small paramagnetic contribution that I was trying to determine, the difference between Co-insulin and Zn-insulin was too inaccurate to be interpreted.

When electron paramagnetic resonance (EPR) techniques became available, I reconsidered the use of the magnetic properties of metal ions because there was no longer the limitation of a diamagnetic contribution in this method. At this time, my research was focused on the role of metal ions in enzyme catalysis, particularly reactions of ATP that invariably require a divalent metal ion. Magnesium, the most common obligatory ion for activation, could be substituted by paramagnetic manganese for activation and could be observed by EPR (11). Later when nuclear magnetic resonance (NMR) instrumentation became available, I extended my studies of ATP reactions utilizing the magnetic properties of ^{31}P (12, 13) to elucidate the mechanism of enzymatic reactions of ATP and of the protons of H_2O (14) to report changes in the structure at the active site as enzymes complexed their substrates. It was undoubtedly my initial training as a chemical physicist that led me to attempt to reduce the difficulty of interpreting the complexity of biochemical systems by using single atoms (O, Mn, P, H) as indicators of phenomena occurring in the complex systems. Advantage was taken of the physical properties of the atoms, the mass of oxygen, and the spectroscopic manifestation of the magnetic properties due to the electronic (EPR) and nuclear (NMR) structure of atoms.

Coming from a chemistry department in a Graduate School of Arts and Sciences, I found the organization of basic sciences in the medical schools in the 30s and 40s to be extremely hierarchical, modeled on the German system. There was usually only one full professor, the chairman of the department. When du Vigneaud arrived at Cornell, there were two assistant professors and one associate professor from the previous regime. The associate professor left after 1 year, and one of the assistant professors was absorbed into du Vigneaud's research group, leaving one independent faculty member, an assistant professor. It was so different from the Columbia chemistry department where there were at least seven full professors, three in the physical chemistry group. When I joined Carl Cori's department at Washington University Medical School in 1946, he was the sole full professor; Gerty Cori was a research associate professor and there were four independent assistant professors. Gerty Cori was promoted to the rank of full professor in 1947, a few months before she was awarded the Nobel prize jointly with Carl.

The source of financial support for research aided and abetted such a system. There was no general support of research by government agencies; the National Science Foundation did not exist and the National Institutes of Health were not awarding extramural grants until after World War II. Only well established scientists were likely to receive grants from foundations and industry. For example, du Vigneaud was supported initially primarily by the Rockefeller Foundation and the Eli Lilly Company and subsequently primarily by the American Cyanamid Company; Cori's research was supported by Eli Lilly and (as were all preclinical departments at Washington University) also from the income of the clinical departments. For both men, the industrial support had no strings attached. The funds available to younger members of the department depended on the largesse of the chairman.

The junior members of the faculty worked alone or occasionally collaborated with other members of the department; graduate and postdoctoral students tended to work with the Professor. And even the Professor published with only one or two collaborators for each paper. Of the 87 papers in the January and February 1940 issues of the *Journal of Biological Chemistry*, 98% have one to three authors. On the other hand, of the approximately similar number of papers that currently appear in 1 week (92 papers in the January 7, 2000 issue of the *Journal*), 32% have one to three authors, and 68% have more than three, ranging from four to fifteen authors (big science *versus* small science). Not only have the number of authors per paper increased, but the total number of papers published in the ever proliferating number of journals has reached astronomic values. The flood of information has led to the demise of the generalist; in the 40s, the average biochemist could read papers in every area in the *Journal of Biological Chemistry* and follow them. To read every one of the 49,500 pages published in the year 2001 in this *Journal* alone, a biochemist would have to read about 1000 pages per week for each of 52 weeks of the year.

Another striking difference is the collaborative character of current research. In the January and February 1940 issues of the *Journal*, 93% of the contributions came from single institutions and 7% resulted from the collaboration of two institutions, but in the year 2000 (January 7 issue), 52% originated from one institution and 48% from the collaboration of two to five institutions, some among institutions from different countries. This phenomenon results partly from the high degree of specialization today and the sophistication of methodologies, which can no longer be encompassed in one individual's laboratory or even in one department or institution. Large research institutions have Core Facilities of many technologies where an individual investigator can obtain services from nucleic acid sequencing to custom knock-out mice. Also many instruments, services, and routine materials can be readily obtained commercially but they are costly. Biomedical research is consequently much more expensive than it used to be, and researchers must spend an inordinate amount of time seeking funding.

Should one yearn for the past, for the days when the pace was slower and probably less stressful, when time was spent making routine compounds and building standard equipment rather than writing grant applications and reports? Does the satisfaction of having done it all alone compensate for the slower rate of attaining answers? Should one yearn for the days when young investigators could do independent research only if they were in the good graces of chairmen who controlled all the funds? Should one yearn for the "good old days?" Old, certainly; good, arguable.

REFERENCES

1. Womack, M., Kemmerer, K. S., and Rose, W. C. (1937) Relation of cystine and methionine to growth. *J. Biol. Chem.* **121,** 403–410
2. du Vigneaud, V., Chandler, J. P., Cohn, M., and Brown, G. B. (1940) The transfer of the methyl group from methionine to choline and creatine. *J. Biol. Chem.* **134,** 787–788
3. Kilmer, G. W., and du Vigneaud, V. (1944) A synthesis of methionine containing isotopic carbon and sulfur. *J. Biol. Chem.* **154,** 247–253
4. du Vigneaud, V., Kilmer, G. W., Rachele, J. R., and Cohn, M. (1944) On the mechanism of the conversion *in vivo* of methionine to cystine. *J. Biol. Chem.* **155,** 645–651
5. Brand, E., Block, R. J., Kassell, B., and Cahill, J. F. (1936) Carboxymethylcysteine metabolism, its implications on therapy in cystinuria and on the methionine-cysteine relationship. *Proc. Soc. Exp. Biol. Med.* **35,** 501–506
6. Brown, G. B., and du Vigneaud, V. (1941) The synthesis of S-(β-amino-β-carboxyethyl)-homocysteine. *J. Biol. Chem.* **137,** 611–615
7. Cohn, M. (1949) Mechanisms of cleavage of glucose-1-phosphate. *J. Biol. Chem.* **180,** 771–781
8. Cohn, M. (1951) A study of oxidative phosphorylation with inorganic phosphate labeled with oxygen 18 in phosphorus metabolism (McElroy, W. D., and Glass, B., eds) pp. 374–376, The Johns Hopkins Press, Baltimore, Maryland
9. Cohn, M. (1953) A study of oxidative phosphorylation with O^{18}-labeled inorganic phosphate. *J. Biol. Chem.* **201,** 735–750
10. Pauling, L., and Coryell, C. D. (1936) The magnetic properties and structure of the hemochromogens and related substances. *Proc. Natl. Acad. Sci. U. S. A.* **22,** 159–163
11. Cohn, M., and Townsend, J. (1954) A study of manganous complexes by paramagnetic resonance absorption. *Nature* **173,** 1090–1093
12. Cohn, M., and Hughes, T. R. (1962) Nuclear magnetic resonance spectra of adenosine triphosphate. II. Effect of complexing with divalent metal ions. *J. Biol. Chem.* **237,** 176–181
13. Nageswara Rao, B. D., Kayne, F., and Cohn, M. (1979) ^{31}P NMR studies of enzyme-bound substrates of rabbit muscle pyruvate kinase. Equilibrium constants, exchange rates, and NMR parameters. *J. Biol. Chem.* **254,** 2689–2696
14. Cohn, M. (1963) Magnetic resonance studies of metal activation of enzymic reactions of nucleotides and other phosphate substrates. *Biochemistry* **2,** 623–629

THE JOURNAL OF BIOLOGICAL CHEMISTRY
© 2002 by The American Society for Biochemistry and Molecular Biology, Inc.

Vol. 277, No. 16, Issue of April 19, pp. 13355–13362, 2002
Printed in U.S.A.

Reflections

A PAPER IN A SERIES COMMISSIONED TO CELEBRATE THE CENTENARY OF THE JBC IN 2005

JBC Centennial
1905–2005
100 Years of Biochemistry and Molecular Biology

Osvald T. Avery and the Nobel Prize in Medicine

Published, JBC Papers in Press, February 28, 2002, DOI 10.1074/jbc.R200002200

Peter Reichard

From the Department of Biochemistry, Medical Nobel Institute, MBB, Karolinska Institutet, 17177 Stockholm, Sweden

In 1944 the *Journal of Experimental Medicine* published a paper by Osvald T. Avery and collaborators (1) entitled "Studies on the Chemical Nature of the Substance-inducing Transformation of Pneumococcal Types. Induction of Transformation by a Desoxyribonucleic Acid Fraction Isolated from *Pneumococcus* type III." Avery reported the results of more than 15 years of systematic attempts to identify the chemical nature of the substance that changes a heritable property of a bacterium. He demonstrated that DNA is the chemical equivalent of the then purely formal concept of genes. Considering the scientific developments during the remaining 20th century this was arguably the most important discovery in physiology or medicine of the century. Avery lived until 1955 but was never even in the vicinity of a Nobel Prize in physiology or medicine. Why?

The scientific community was not very interested in nucleic acids in 1944. Only a few scientists were active in this field. One of them was Einar Hammarsten, Professor of Chemistry at the Karolinska Institute in Stockholm. In 1924 he had published a thesis (2) about the preparation and properties of DNA or thymonucleic acid as it was called at that time. In the ensuing 20 years he worked with both DNA and RNA. Only a few students joined his endeavor. Most notable among them was Torbjörn Caspersson who by 1944 already was Professor and head of a Nobel Institute at the Karolinska Institute. Caspersson was surrounded by a large group of young enthusiastic collaborators. Some of them were graduate students; others had already established themselves in medical specialties such as microbiology, virology, and pathology. Caspersson headed one of the most active research centers at the Karolinska Institute. He had developed a new ultraviolet microscope to study nucleic acid and protein metabolism (3), and he and his collaborators applied the new methodology to many different biological systems.

I have described elsewhere (4) my intent in 1945 to start my graduate studies with Caspersson and how, instead, I turned to Hammarsten and became his student. I stayed in his laboratory until his retirement in 1957 and (in particular during the early years) listened to many of his monologues both on nucleic acid research and on Nobel prizes. Later on, as Professor at the Karolinska Institute after 1964, I became rather heavily involved in the work of the Nobel committee during a 20-year period and had the opportunity to learn about deliberations of earlier committees. As described below, I became introduced to Avery's work already as a young graduate student but only later in life began to ask myself questions about why he never received a Nobel Prize. Here, I make an attempt to give my answer. I will first briefly describe the organization of the Karolinska Institute's Nobel activity in the middle of the previous century. I will then in more detail discuss the research carried out by the groups of Hammarsten and Caspersson, their concepts about the biological function of nucleic acids, and how this may have affected their attitude to Avery's work.

FIG. 1. **Oswald T. Avery (1877–1955).** Courtesy of The Rockefeller University Archives.

The Karolinska Institute and Its Nobel Activities at the Mid-20th Century

The Karolinska Institute was and is the medical school of Stockholm. In 1944 the faculty consisted of ~25 full professors, each representing a clinical or preclinical specialty. Hammarsten's chair was in chemistry, a name that dated back to the days of its first occupant, the famous Jöns Jacob Berzelius, and was a matter of no small pride. Hammarsten had a complete medical education, as had all his colleagues in the faculty, but was rather disdainful of that fact. Only a very limited number of the institute's professors carried out research. The state did not provide money for this purpose until some years after the war, and research depended largely on a few private sources. In this respect, the Rockefeller Foundation played a large role, with Hammarsten and his collaborators being major recipients of support for many years. With Warren Weaver at the helm the Foundation supported mainly biochemical and biophysical research for which Weaver coined the name molecular biology, probably the first use of this term. In Hammarsten's case, the Rockefeller Foundation provided not only the major part of the yearly research budget but also postdoctoral fellowships for young Swedish scientists to allow them to work for some time in an American laboratory. As one of the recipients I can testify to their importance for widening the horizon of a young researcher brought up in a small and closed scientific community.

Once a year the 25 professors of the Institute decided on the winners of the Nobel Prize in Physiology or Medicine and announced their names. A Nobel committee of three members, appointed for a 3-year period, had discussed the competing candidates and made a proposal for the prize. Each year the committee temporarily adjoined several additional professors to its discussion. As only a few professors were active scientists the number of knowledgeable committee members was quite limited. Hammarsten had not a very high opinion of most of his colleagues and delighted in telling the story of how Otto Warburg, Nobel laureate in 1931, had expressed his surprise that "so ein obskurer Aeropag" was given the task to select Nobel Prize winners. Because of his scientific qualifications and seniority Hammarsten participated continuously in the deliberations for the prize during the period of 1946–1955. He had considerable influence on the choice of laureates and would in all probability have been able to make Avery a winner had he set his mind to it. Other knowledgeable faculty members who could have come out for Avery were Caspersson and Berndt Malmgren. The latter was Professor of Bacteriology and originally a close collaborator of Caspersson. Finally, there was Hugo Theorell who was Chairman of Biochemistry at the medical Nobel Institute. In his case, a major complication was that he himself was a serious candidate for the prize and indeed received it in 1955. Caspersson also was a candidate during that period. One can imagine that under those circumstances neither Theorell nor Caspersson would strongly favor Avery for a Nobel Prize.

Fig. 2. **Einar Hammarsten (1889–1958).** Professor of Chemistry at the Karolinska Institute, 1928–1957. Courtesy of Professor Ulf Lagerkvist.

Each year the Nobel committee invites scientists all over the world to propose the names of candidates. Some of the nominations are then further evaluated in a written report, often but not always by a committee member, and the committee then orders the candidates into one of three groups: 1) not worthy of the prize; 2) at present not worthy of the prize; or 3) worthy of the prize. The final discussion involves only the last group, which always contains several names. To win the prize, strong candidates must as a rule be nominated and their work evaluated for several years.

Avery as a Candidate, 1932–1946

The first prerequisite to win a Nobel Prize thus is to be nominated. Starting in the early 1930s Avery (Fig. 1) was nominated almost yearly for the Nobel prize for his and Michael Heidelberger's discovery that the antigenic specificity of type III pneumococci depends on their polysaccharide coat and not (as was generally believed) on a surface protein. Their work thus demonstrated the biological specificity of polysaccharides. Many scientists were critical of this conclusion and suggested that the antigenic properties depended on protein contamination. Further work by Avery's group soon dispelled this objection. Before 1946 his work was evaluated in four written reports, one of them by Hammarsten. In all cases the work was not considered worthy of a Nobel Prize.

Starting in 1946 the nominations also began to cite Avery's work on bacterial transformation by DNA. Each year the committee received several nominations, some of them by outstanding scientists including former and future Nobel Prize winners. It is striking, however, that for a long time most nominations included Heidelberger's name and concerned the antigenic specificity of polysaccharides and not transformation by DNA. The latter work was discussed for the first time in 1946 in a brief evaluation by Hammarsten, who was critical and believed that Avery's DNA was contaminated with protein and that protein (and not DNA) was the transforming agent. History had repeated itself.

Einar Hammarsten

Let us now consider the scientific work of the Swedish groups. Einar Hammarsten (Fig. 2) was a remarkable person. His father was the predicant of the royal family and known for his brilliant sermons in the cathedral. His uncle Olof identified pentose in nucleic acids when he was Professor of Physiological Chemistry in Uppsala and later became President of the University. Einar excused the profession of his father by saying that the family of his grandfather was poor and that there was no money to support the younger son, his father, who therefore instead of studying medicine as his older brother had to accept a fellowship at the theological faculty. For his uncle, who gave up research to become President of the University, he had no excuse. Einar was completely dedicated to research and up to an advanced age worked long days at the bench in the laboratory. He spoke unkindly of his colleagues in the faculty who preferred to spend their time earning money in private practice.

In his thesis (2) Einar had applied a new, gentle method for the preparation of DNA from thymus, avoiding the then common treatment with strong alkali. His DNA differed in many ways from that prepared by the older methods. It was highly viscous, had a low osmotic pressure, and gave fibers on precipitation with alcohol. During the following years he and his collaborators studied this preparation with several of the then available methods of physical chemistry including ultracentrifugation in The Svedberg's newly developed machine and concluded that DNA had a very high molecular weight, possibly about one million (5–8). This clearly did not agree with the then prevalent hypothesis introduced by Phoebus Levene at the Rockefeller Institute that both DNA and RNA were simple tetranucleotides consisting of one of each of the common nucleotides (9). Obviously such a simple structure could not be the genetic material. In a different line of research Einar's student Erik Jorpes demonstrated that RNA from pancreas contained an excess of guanine and thus could not be a tetranucleotide (10, 11). Such results flew in the face of the tetranucleotide idea but were not appropriately recognized in comparison with the chemical work of Levene. One contributing factor was that Einar Hammarsten was not a great communicator. He published very sparsely, and his papers were not always easy to understand.

When I came to his laboratory he had for many years unsuccessfully tried to obtain "native" DNA free of protein. He, better than anybody else, could appreciate the difficulties that Avery faced in trying to remove protein from DNA. Furthermore, Einar believed that the destruction of the transforming principle by deoxyribonuclease was due to proteolytic contaminants in the impure enzyme preparation. This enzyme had been partially purified from pancreas by Avery's collaborator, Maclyn McCarty (12). It was at this point that I came into the picture. I was now a graduate student of Einar and was looking for a thesis project. He suggested that I should crystallize pancreatic deoxyribonuclease and study its properties. To this purpose he provided me with two reprints; one was McCarty's paper, and the other was a paper by Moise Kunitz (13) describing the crystallization of ribonuclease. Einar himself had no experience with enzyme purification, and I was completely left to my own non-existing resources. This was rather typical of him; obstacles were there to be overcome. Noticing my hesitation he admonished me with one of his often used wisdom words: "Rädda pojkar får inte ligga med vackra flickor" (easily frightened boys don't sleep with beautiful girls). I was unsuccessful and had to give up. Kunitz, the great master, crystallized deoxyribonuclease within a few years (14).

At that time Einar had already started a completely new and highly ambitious project. George Hevesy had come from Copenhagen to Stockholm in connection with the Jewish exodus from Denmark in 1943. In 1944 he received the Nobel Prize in chemistry for his work on "the use of isotopes as tracers in the study of chemical processes." Einar realized the enormous potential of the tracer technique for biological experiments and investigated together with Hevesy the incorporation of ^{32}P-labeled phosphate into RNA and DNA in rats (15). The isotope was rapidly incorporated into RNA but not into DNA, reflecting the metabolic stability of DNA. A major impetus for this experiment was provided from the work of Caspersson who from ultraviolet microscopy of cells had suggested that RNA synthesis was required for the synthesis of proteins in the cytoplasm (see below).

Einar wanted to use isotope experiments to investigate this question himself. Schoenheimer's group at Columbia University in New York had at that time already published much of their pioneering work with deuterium and ^{15}N on the synthesis of lipids and proteins that led them to the concept that proteins are continuously renewed in cells (16). Einar decided that this was the way to go: to study nucleic acid synthesis and its relation to protein synthesis with stable isotopes. This required a mass spectrometer, but there was no such machine in the whole of Sweden. So let's build one. Considering that the government provided no money for research and Einar completely lacked the required expertise it was indeed a daunting task. However, obstacles are there to be overcome. After several years and with the aid of two American scientists, Richard Abrams and David Rittenberg, there was a functioning mass spectrometer in the laboratory in 1946. The machine was a prerequisite for a series of theses that appeared from the laboratory during the following years including my own experiments with ^{15}N-labeled nucleosides that resulted in the discovery of ribonucleotide reduction (4).

FIG. 3. **Thorbjörn Caspersson (1910–1997).** Professor of Cell Research and Genetics at the Karolinska Institute, 1944–1977. Courtesy of Professor Nils Ringertz.

Sadly, the technique was unsuitable to solve Einar's question concerning the relation between nucleic acid and protein synthesis.

Torbjörn Caspersson

Caspersson (Fig. 3) had collaborated with Hammarsten in some of the early experiments characterizing DNA, but soon he demonstrated a great talent to construct optical machinery. In his thesis he described the development of a monochromatic ultraviolet microscope and its use to measure the content of nucleic acids and proteins in individual cells (3). Nucleic acids were quantitated from their absorption at 260 nm. A distinction between RNA and DNA could be made with the Feulgen reagent, which is specific for the deoxyribose component of DNA. Proteins were quantified from their absorption at 280 nm. Both RNA and DNA absorb strongly at 260 nm and could be determined with some confidence. Proteins have a much weaker absorption in the ultraviolet; the absorption depends on the amino acid composition, and it is affected both by the presence of nucleic acids and by unspecific light-scattering effects. Despite these difficulties Caspersson believed that it was possible to use the technique to determine changes in protein content of individual cells and even to distinguish between different classes of proteins.

During most of his ensuing scientific life Caspersson improved the instrumentation in collaboration with highly skilled engineers. Improving the machinery was his greatest joy in the laboratory. Later in life he employed the new microscope and fluorescent technology to chromosome banding (17), a technique that revolutionized medical genetics as it made possible the identification of single human chromosomes.

Already before 1940 Caspersson had discovered that cells engaged in rapid protein synthesis contain much larger amounts of RNA than resting cells (18). Also Jean Brachet in Brussels arrived independently at the same conclusion using a completely different technique (19). Both suggested that RNA had a central role in protein synthesis.

At about this time Caspersson also reported that the DNA of insect chromosomes was localized in distinct bands (20, 21), reminiscent of the bandlike structure of genes, and suggested that DNA was involved in gene replication. It would have been only a small step to the insight that DNA is the genetic material, but Caspersson never took this step. Instead, he wrote that only the structure of proteins offered enough variations to function as genes (20) and suggested that DNA during gene reproduction underwent a polymerization of smaller groups into a larger aggregate (21) that could serve as a rack on which extended protein molecules were reproduced. He supported this idea with results from Astbury's x-ray crystallographic work (22) that demonstrated that the spacing of nucleotides in DNA was identical to the spacing of the side chains of a fully extended polypeptide chain. The Caspersson group also had distinct ideas of how RNA participates in protein synthesis (23, 24). From measurements of the 280 nm absorption of cells during protein synthesis it was proposed that basic proteins of the cell nucleus migrate from the heterochromatin to the membrane of the cell nucleus and there induce the synthesis of RNA, resulting in the synthesis of globular proteins in the cytosol. Proteins were thus placed at center stage, with both DNA and RNA performing auxiliary functions.

Avery as a Candidate 1952–1955

My contact with Avery's work had been brief but alerted me to his ideas. His results were not a major theme of discussion in the laboratory, and I had no inkling that Avery could have been in the vicinity of a Nobel Prize. Even though the awarding of the Nobel Prize is and was shrouded in great secrecy, Hammarsten did not hesitate to comment on the committee's discussions, especially when in his opinion it had resulted in a flawed decision, but I never heard Avery's work mentioned in that context. Hammarsten did not believe that genes consisted of DNA. This was obviously not because he viewed DNA as a simple tetranucleotide. He himself had demonstrated the macromolecular nature of DNA, which together with variations in base sequence provided the structural requirements for biological specificity. This concept was reinforced in a memorable seminar by Erwin Chargaff, who visited Stockholm around 1947. His analyses of DNA by paper chromatography demonstrated considerable variations in the base composition of DNA from various organisms. Chargaff was enthusiastic about Avery's results and actually proposed him for the Nobel Prize. For me his seminar was memorable because it illustrated the power of chromatography and induced me to use starch chromatography for the purification of nucleosides in our tracer experiments (4).

Why then did Hammarsten not accept Avery's conclusion? First, there was his own experience that proteins also always contaminated highly purified preparations of DNA, but he was also influenced by Caspersson's model for the metabolic interrelation between proteins and nucleic acids, which gave nucleic acids a secondary role. It was to elaborate on Caspersson's ideas that he had decided to start the construction of a mass spectrometer.

In the meantime the evidence for DNA was mounting. Avery had retired but others continued his work at the Rockefeller Institute. Citrate is a strong inhibitor of deoxyribonuclease, and its inclusion during the purification of the transforming principle greatly increased its yield (25). Most importantly, there appeared reports of other DNA-dependent instances of bacterial transformation. Rollin Hotchkiss (26) transferred penicillin resistance with DNA preparations from appropriate strains of pneumococci, André Boivin in Paris (28) reported that DNA induced directed mutations in *Escherichia coli*, and Hattie Alexander and Grace Leidy (27) reported DNA mediated transformation in *Hemophilus*. A separate line of evidence in favor of DNA came from Boivin and the two Vendrelys (29). They found that all mammalian diploid cells contain the same amount of DNA, twice the amount of haploid cells. This provided a parallel to the halving of the number of genes from somatic to germ cells.

Nevertheless the old paradigm of genes being proteins and DNA only providing a structural support during gene replication did not die easily. As Maclyn McCarty relates in his lovely book (30), Avery himself did not loudly spread the new gospel. He apparently had a quiet and self-effacing personality, presented his work in a low key manner, and was adverse to speculation. His presentations were few, and when invited to speak at larger meetings he usually sent his younger collaborators. I was particularly struck by the description of his refusal in 1946 to travel to England to receive the prestigious Copley Medal from the Royal Society (30). It was, instead, brought to him to the laboratory in New York by the President of the Society, Sir Henry Dale. Avery was a modest man and hardly a prophet for his ideas. Of course he would never have dreamt to come to Stockholm to give a lecture and present his work.

How did all this affect the Nobel committee? In 1952 Malmgren, Professor of Bacteriology and former collaborator of Caspersson (24), prepared the first detailed evaluation of Avery's work on transformation for the committee. He also discussed Hotchkiss' experiments in support of Avery and now considered it unlikely that protein was involved in transformation. Nevertheless he then concluded that the final evidence for DNA as the transforming principle was missing and that Avery therefore at the present time was not worthy of a Nobel Prize. This also became the conclusion of the committee.

The turning point in the general opinion came with the paper by Alfred Hershey and Martha Chase (31) in 1952 and, in particular, the paper by Jim Watson and Francis Crick (32) in 1953. The first publication demonstrated that ^{32}P-labeled DNA but not ^{35}S-labeled protein entered *E. coli* during infection with bacteriophage T4. Because viruses were recognized as counterparts of genes the experiment strongly supported the ability of DNA alone to show genetic activity. Hershey was a member of the highly influential phage group who had viewed Avery's claims with considerable skepticism. From a recent book (33) commemorating Alfred Hershey it appears that he actually had not expected the outcome of his experiment. Indeed the amount of ^{35}S (= protein) introduced into *E. coli* indicated a much larger contamination by protein than in Avery's experiments, but now time was ripe and Hershey's experiment was generally accepted as transfer of genetic information by DNA. The famous paper by Watson and Crick demonstrating the complementarity of the two strands of the DNA double helix provided a molecular explanation for gene replication and dealt the final blow to the protein paradigm.

In 1954, after the appearance of the two publications, Hammarsten made a third evaluation of Avery's work for the committee. The report was very short. It is somewhat surprising that no mention was made of the new discoveries. Hammarsten now accepted that DNA and not protein is the transforming principle. He pointed out that the discovery was of great importance but concluded that the mechanism for the transformation was completely unknown and that for this reason the discovery at the present time was not worthy of a Nobel Prize. This became again the conclusion of the committee.

Before sitting in judgment on the Nobel committee we should consider some of the elements involved in the committee's yearly deliberations. Nobel's testament stipulates that the prize should go to a discovery that "during the preceding year shall have conferred the greatest benefit on mankind." For the medicine prize this stipulation has never been met. It takes time to verify a discovery and to understand its importance, as is evident from Avery's case. There are several examples in which a prize in medicine was given prematurely for a discovery that later on was faulted, most blatantly in 1926 to Fibiger for his discovery of the "Spiroptera carcinoma," a non-existing disease. Nobel prizes therefore go to well established discoveries, which are recognized by a large majority of the scientific community. A prize to Avery could therefore hardly be considered seriously before 1952–1953. The committee can, however, be faulted for accepting in 1952 and in 1954 the conclusion of its experts that Avery was not worthy of the Nobel Prize.

Avery died in 1955. There was a window of 2 years during which he could have become a Nobel laureate. I believe that this window would have been too narrow, even if the 1952 evaluation had been positive. Nobel committees move rather slowly, and a discovery resulting in a prize is generally in the forefront of the committee's deliberations for several years, in competition with other discoveries. In 1953 the prize went to Krebs (citric acid cycle) and Lipmann (coenzyme A) and in 1954 to Enders, Weller, and Robbins (poliomyelitis virus). Hammarsten had been fighting for the biochemical prize, and the strength of the second group whose work resulted in the development of the polio vaccine is obvious. Both groups had been strong candidates for several years. With hindsight we can blame the committee for having bypassed the greatest biological discovery of the century, but considering the circumstances of that period it is understandable.

Circumstances changed rapidly. Acceptance of DNA came overnight. A few years after Avery's death we find the names of J. Lederberg (1958), A. Kornberg (1959), and F. Crick, J. Watson, and M. Wilkins (1962) among the laureates. The composition of the Nobel committee had changed. The number of professors at the Karolinska Institute increased dramatically and made possible an increase and renewal of the committee that greatly expanded its scientific expertise.

Avery was 65 years old in 1944 when he published his first paper on the transforming ability of DNA. It is a good thought that a great discovery can be made at an advanced age. Considering the increase in longevity in our time, it may now even be possible to live and receive a Nobel Prize for the discovery.

REFERENCES

1. Avery, O. T., MacLeod, C. M., and McCarty, M. (1944) *J. Exp. Med.* **79,** 137–158
2. Hammarsten, E. (1924) *Biochem. Z.* **144,** 383–466
3. Caspersson, T. (1936) *Acta Med. Scand.* **73,** Suppl. 1, 1–151
4. Reichard, P. (1995) *Annu. Rev. Biochem.* **64,** 1–28
5. Caspersson, T. (1934) *Biochem. Z.* **270,** 161–163
6. Caspersson, T., Hammarsten, E., and Hammarsten, H. (1935) *Trans. Faraday Soc.* **31,** 367–389
7. Hammarsten, E. (1939) *J. Mt. Sin. Hosp.* **6,** 115–125
8. Signer, W., Caspersson, T., and Hammarsten, E. (1938) *Nature* **141,** 122
9. Levene, P. A., and Bass, W. (1931) *Nucleic Acids,* The Chemical Catalog Co., New York
10. Hammarsten, E., and Jorpes, E. (1922) *Z. Physiol. Chem.* **118,** 224–232
11. Jorpes, E. (1928) *Acta Med. Scand.* **68,** 503–573
12. McCarty, M. (1946) *J. Gen. Physiol.* **29,** 123–139
13. Kunitz, M. (1940) *J. Gen. Physiol.* **24,** 15–31
14. Kunitz, M. (1948) *Science* **108,** 19–20
15. Hammarsten, E., and Hevesy, G. (1946) *Acta Physiol. Scand.* **11,** 335–343
16. Schoenheimer, R. (1949) *The Dynamic State of Body Constituents,* Harvard University Press, Cambridge, MA
17. Caspersson, T., Farber, S., Foley, G. E., Kudynowski, J., Modest, E. J., Simonsson, E., Wagh, U., and Zech, L. (1968) *Exp. Cell Res.* **49,** 219–222
18. Caspersson, T., and Schultz, J. (1938) *Nature* **143,** 602–603
19. Brachet, J. (1937) *Arch. de Biol.* **48,** 529–548
20. Caspersson, T. (1937) *Protoplasma* **27,** 463–467
21. Caspersson, T., and Schultz, J. (1938) *Nature* **143,** 294–295
22. Astbury, W. T., and Bell, F. O. (1938) *Nature* **141,** 747–748
23. Caspersson, T., and Thorell, B. (1941) *Chromosoma* **2,** 132–154
24. Malmgren, B., and Hedén, C.-G. (1948) *Arch. Pathol.* **24,** 437–447
25. McCarty, M., and Avery, O. T. (1946) *J. Exp. Med.* **83,** 97–104
26. Hotchkiss, R. D. (1951) *Cold Spring Harbor Symp. Quant. Biol.* **16,** 457–461
27. Alexander, H., and Leidy G. (1953) *J. Exp. Med.* **97,** 17–31
28. Boivin, A. (1947) *Cold Spring Harbor Symp. Quant. Biol.* **12,** 7–17
29. Boivin, A., Vendrely, R., and Vendrely, C. (1948) *C.R. Hebd. Séances Acad. Sci. Paris* **226,** 1061–1063 ·
30. McCarty, M. (1985) *The Transforming Principle,* W. W. Norton & Company, Inc., New York
31. Hershey, A., and Chase, M. (1952) *J. Gen. Physiol.* **36,** 39–56
32. Watson, J., and Crick, F. (1953) *Nature* **171,** 737–738
33. Stahl, F. W. (ed) (2000) *We Can Sleep Later. Alfred D. Hershey and the Origins of Molecular Biology,* Cold Spring Harbor Laboratory Press, New York

THE JOURNAL OF BIOLOGICAL CHEMISTRY
© 2002 by The American Society for Biochemistry and Molecular Biology, Inc.

Vol. 277, No. 23, Issue of June 7, pp. 20113–20116, 2002.
Printed in U.S.A.

Reflections

A PAPER IN A SERIES COMMISSIONED TO CELEBRATE THE CENTENARY OF THE JBC IN 2005

JBC Centennial
1905–2005
100 Years of Biochemistry and Molecular Biology

The First Years of the Journal of Biological Chemistry

Published, JBC Papers in Press, April 17, 2002, DOI 10.1074/jbc.R200004200

Joseph S. Fruton

From the Historical Library, Yale School of Medicine, New Haven, Connecticut 06520

Two men were responsible for the establishment of the *Journal of Biological Chemistry* (*JBC*) in 1905: John Jacob Abel (1857–1938) (Fig. 1) and Christian Archibald Herter (1865–1910) (Fig. 2). Both had spent some time in German laboratories and come to admire the *Zeitschrift für physiologische Chemie*, founded by Felix Hoppe-Seyler in 1877. The joint effort to promote the new science of biochemistry in the United States brought together a pharmacologist and a physician of rather different social background but with a shared enthusiasm about the place of modern chemistry in medical research and education.

The son of a German immigrant farmer in Ohio, Abel overcame considerable financial difficulties before receiving a Bachelor of Philosophy degree at the University of Michigan in 1883. After graduation he married Mary Hinman and spent a year in the Department of Biology at the Johns Hopkins University. With his wife's encouragement and material support, he went to Germany alone for a medical education (1, 2). The first two years of what turned out to be a seven-year stay (1884–1890) were spent in Carl Ludwig's Institute of Physiology in Leipzig. Abel then worked in Oswald Schmiedeberg's Laboratory of Pharmacology in Strassburg near Hoppe-Seyler's Laboratory of Physiological Chemistry. After receiving his M.D. at Strassburg in 1888, he went to Vienna for clinical training and spent 1888–1889 in Berne at the Biochemical Institute of Marceli Nencki. Abel derived particular stimulation from Schmiedeberg's insistence on the academic status of pharmacology and profited greatly from Schmiedeberg's and Nencki's chemical programs of research. He published three chemical papers from the Berne Laboratory and before returning to the United States did some joint research with Edmund Drechsel in Leipzig (3).

Upon his return to the United States, Abel became lecturer (then professor) of materia medica and therapeutics at the University of Michigan, but in 1893 he moved to the new medical school at Johns Hopkins University to be professor of pharmacology, with an obligation also to teach the course in physiological chemistry. Among his numerous research achievements were studies on epinephrine, posterior pituitary hormones, and insulin (4).

Herter's father also came to the United States from Germany during the 1850s and ran a highly profitable firm of decorators and architects that provided houses for the richest people in New York City. One of these people was the grain merchant David Dows, whose daughter Susan married young Herter in 1885, the year he received his M.D. degree from the Columbia College of Physicians and Surgeons. He then worked with William Henry Welch in Baltimore and with Auguste Forel in Zurich, but his initial interest in neurology derived from the latter gave way to bacteriology and biochemistry. In 1893, he occupied a house at 819 Madison Avenue, with the fourth floor equipped as a chemical laboratory and invited young scientists to work there on problems of their own choosing (5). During 1903–1904, he worked at the Frankfurt Institute of Paul Ehrlich on 1,2-naphthoquinone-4-sulfonate as a staining material (6) and continued this investigation in New York (7). His principal clinical interest was in the bacterial infections of the intestinal tract (8). The lectures Herter gave as professor of path-

FIG. 1. **John Jacob Abel**

FIG. 2. **Christian Archibald Herter**

ological chemistry at Bellevue Hospital Medical College (1898–1903) and professor of pharmacology and therapeutics at the Columbia College of Physicians and Surgeons (1903–1910) were said to have been very popular.

In 1901, Herter met John D. Rockefeller, Jr. at the home of the pediatrician L. Emmett Holt to discuss Frederick T. Gates' proposal of a medical research institute. As the project developed Herter became a friend of Simon Flexner and of Phoebus Aaron Levene, whom Flexner had brought to the Rockefeller Institute in 1905. Herter was member of the Board of Directors (and treasurer) of the Rockefeller Institute and was involved in the planning of the addition of the hospital. By 1908, it was under construction but Herter died on December 5, 1910. According to George Corner, "the nature of Herter's illness, if it was ever diagnosed, was not recorded. It seems to have been myasthenia gravis" (9).

Although no letter has survived it appears that the stimulus for the new journal came from Abel, and the enterprise was launched in March 1905. Abel and Herter were the editors, and they selected 22 associate editors, who included Russell H. Chittenden, Phoebus A. Levene, Jacques Loeb, Lafayette B. Mendel, and Thomas B. Osborne. Herter also brought into service Alfred Newton Richards (1876–1966) (Fig. 3), a Yale College graduate who had received his Ph.D. in physiological chemistry at Columbia in 1901 and had become an instructor in Herter's department of pharmacology in 1903. In that year, Richards spent some months in Schmiedeberg's laboratory in Strassburg, where he also met Franz Hofmeister, the successor of Hoppe-Seyler (10). Richards later wrote that "it was decided that the format of the *Journal (of Biological Chemistry)* should closely resemble that of Hoppe-Seyler's *Zeitschrift der physiologische Chemie* and that the price to subscribers should be so low that young workers could afford it" (11). The first issue appeared in October 1905. There was a board of directors with Herter as president, Edward Kellogg Dunham as treasurer, and Richards as secretary.

In 1905, the Englishman Henry Drysdale Dakin (1880–1952) (Fig. 4) accepted Herter's invitation to work in his private laboratory. By that time Dakin had become a skilled chemical craftsman through experience as an analyst's apprentice, pupil of Julius Berend Cohen (professor of chemistry in Leeds), work at the Lister Institute, and research in Heidelberg with Albrecht Kossel. Some 25 of his organic and biochemical papers (of 145) had already been published, and he continued at his previous rate of productivity at the Herter laboratory (12, 13).

Herter's untimely death in 1910 confronted the *Journal* with a crisis. Abel had resigned in 1909 to devote his attention to the *Journal of Pharmacology and Experimental Therapeutics,*

FIG. 3. **Alfred Newton Richards**

FIG. 4. **Henry Drysdale Dakin**

and the editorial board appointed by the directors (Simon Flexner replaced Herter as president) was composed of Dakin, Dunham, Mendel, and Richards (now professor of pharmacology at the University of Pennsylvania) as managing editor. In 1925, Dakin wrote in a letter: "Up to Herter's death there was always a deficit to be made up out of private pockets and to avoid this annual tribulation I pushed the idea of a Journal Fund in Herter's memory" (14). In 1911, friends of Herter and relatives of Mrs. Herter set up the Christian A. Herter Memorial Fund, which has provided stability to the operation of the *JBC*.

At the request of Herter's widow, Dakin took over the laboratory. During 1913–1914 he had Harold Dudley as a guest; they enjoyed considerable success, notably the discovery of the enzyme glyoxalase. Near the beginning of his career, Dakin had discovered arginase, and this association with enzymes led Dakin's friends to call him "zyme." His book on oxidations and reductions in the animal body (15) attracted considerable attention. In 1916 Dakin and Susan Herter were married, and two years later they moved to a house in Scarborough-on-Hudson, with a laboratory in a separate building (16). Dakin continued to serve on the editorial board of the *JBC* until 1930 and as chairman of the financial committee for the rest of his life.

Dakin retained his British nationality. When war broke out in 1914 and he failed to find an opportunity to aid the war effort, he joined a French unit organized by Alexis Carrel, a member of the Rockefeller Institute, with which he had close contact in New York. Dakin gained considerable fame for his development of the buffered hypochlorite antiseptic solution.

In 1914, Richards asked to be relieved of his duties as managing editor, and the directors persuaded Donald Dexter Van Slyke (1883–1971) (Fig. 5) of the Rockefeller Institute to accept the job, and the business management was taken over by the administrative offices of the Institute. Van Slyke came to the Institute in 1907 after receiving his Ph.D. at the University of Michigan for work with the organic chemist Moses Gomberg (17). Except for a year in Emil Fischer's laboratory, until 1914 Van Slyke was a member of Levene's group and worked on the chemistry and metabolism of proteins. In 1911, he invented an apparatus for the quantitative determination of primary aliphatic amino groups for these studies. This nitrous acid method was the first of many valuable gasometric procedures devised by Van Slyke.

FIG. 5. **Donald Dexter Van Slyke**

In 1914 Van Slyke was offered the post of chief chemist at the recently opened hospital of the Rockefeller Institute. After accepting the offer with some trepidation he proceeded to lay the foundations of a quantitative clinical chemistry through studies of acidosis and kidney disease (18, 19). Equally noteworthy were his studies of gas and electrolyte equilibria in blood (20) and the discovery of 5-hydroxylysine as a constituent of collagen. In 1948, Van Slyke reached the Rockefeller retirement age and moved to the Brookhaven National Laboratory, where he continued his research. He concluded his service to the *JBC* in 1925, when the Rockefeller Institute decided to discontinue publication of the *Journal*. The directors offered the management of the *JBC* and the Herter Fund to the American Society of Biological Chemists, who accepted in December 1925.

For further details see the valuable articles by Alfred N. Richards (11) and John T. Edsall (14).

REFERENCES

1. Voegtlin, C. (1939) John Jacob Abel. *J. Pharmacol. Exp. Ther.* **67**, 373–406
2. Dale, H. H. (1939) John Jacob Abel. *Obit. Not. Fell. Roy. Soc.* **2**, 577–585
3. Abel, J. J., and Drechsel, E. (1891) Ueber ein neues Vorkommen von Carbaminsäure. *Archiv für Physiologie*, pp. 236–243, Veit & Co., Leipzig
4. Murnaghan, J. H., and Talalay, P. (1967) John Jacob Abel and the crystallization of insulin. *Perspect. Biol. Med.* **10**, 334–380
5. Hawthorne, R. M. (1974) Christian Archibald Herter. *Perspect. Biol. Med.* **18**, 24–39
6. Ehrlich, P., and Herter, C. A. (1904) Über einige Verwendungen der Naphtochinonsulfonsäure. *Hoppe-Seyler's Z. Physiol. Chem.* **41**, 379–392
7. Herter, C. A. (1905) The color reactions of naphthaquinone sodium-monosulfonate and some of their biological applications. *J. Exp. Med.* **7**, 79–110
8. Williams, O. T. (1911) In memory of Christian A. Herter. *Biochem. J.* **5**, xxi–xxxi
9. Corner, G. W. (1964) *A History of the Rockefeller Institute of Medical Research, 1901–1953. Origins and Growth*, p. 554, Rockefeller Institute Press, New York
10. Schmidt, C. F. (1971) Alfred Newton Richards. *Biogr. Mem. Natl. Acad. Sci.* **42**, 271–318
11. Richards, A. N. (1956) Journal of Biological Chemistry: recollections of its early years and of its founders. *Fed. Proc.* **15**, 803–806
12. Hartley, P. (1952) Henry Drysdale Dakin. *Obit. Not. Fell. Roy. Soc.* **8**, 129–148
13. Clarke, H. T. (1952) Henry Drysdale Dakin. *J. Chem. Soc.* 3319–3324
14. Edsall, J. T. (1980) The Journal of Biological Chemistry after seventy-five years. *J. Biol. Chem.* **255**, 8939–8951
15. Dakin, H. D. (1912) *Oxidations and Reductions in the Animal Body* (2nd edition, 1922), Longmans, Green, London
16. Hawthorne, R. M. (1983) Henry Drysdale Dakin, biochemist (1880–1952): the option of obscurity. *Perspect. Biol. Med.* **26**, 553–566
17. Hastings, A. B. (1976) Donald Dexter Van Slyke. *Biogr. Mem. Natl. Acad. Sci.* **48**, 309–360
18. Peters, J. P., and Van Slyke, D. D. (1931) *Quantitative Clinical Chemistry. Vol. I, Interpretations* (1931, Rev. 1946); *Vol. II, Methods* (1932, Rev. 1943), Williams & Wilkins, Baltimore
19. Amsterdamska, O. (1998). Chemistry in the clinic: the research career of Donald Dexter Van Slyke. in *Molecularizing Biology and Medicine. New Practices and Alliances, 1910s–1970s* (de Chadarevian, S., and Kamminga, H., eds) pp. 47–82, Harwood, Amsterdam
20. Edsall, J. T. (1985) Carbon dioxide transport in blood: equilibrium between red cells and plasma. *Hist. Philos. Life Sci.* **7**, 105–120

THE JOURNAL OF BIOLOGICAL CHEMISTRY
Vol. 277, No. 30, Issue of July 26, pp. 26709–26716, 2002

Reflections

A PAPER IN A SERIES COMMISSIONED TO CELEBRATE THE CENTENARY OF THE JBC IN 2005

JBC Centennial
1905–2005
100 Years of Biochemistry and Molecular Biology

Regulation, Restriction, and Reminiscences

Published, JBC Papers in Press, June 5, 2002, DOI 10.1074/jbc.R200013200

Arthur B. Pardee

From the Dana-Farber Cancer Institute, Boston, Massachusetts 02115

Choose a job you love, and you will never have to work a day in your life—Confucius

These reflections cover more than 60 years of my research, selected from among those that I consider to be of greatest scientific interest. It is a personal account, not a general review of all contributions, and so I have not included the numerous references into which my contributions are imbedded. I regret that I could not include other topics and colleagues. Some details, anecdotes, etc. are described in my previous reviews and overviews.

Subjects of my research may appear to be quite diverse. This is because from childhood I was fascinated by reading about explorers of new territories. They are my heroes, rather than the developers who came later. So in science my goal is always to explore new questions. There is, however, a central theme: the molecular basis of regulation. It can be observed at all levels of biological complexity. The goal and theme that bind together the disparate subjects of my investigation are to gain understanding of the general molecular mechanisms that underlie regulatory processes and their defects in diseases, principally in cancer.

Beginnings

Biological science has changed dramatically since I began research. One can liken the evolution of techniques to slide rules becoming computers. My undergraduate training was in chemistry at University of California, Berkeley (1938–1942), where I was fortunate in being taught by Nobel laureates William Giaque (freshman chemistry) and Melvin Calvin (undergraduate research). I did my Ph.D. under Linus Pauling at the California Institute of Technology (1942–1947), performing some of the first studies with purified antibodies. I was pretty cheeky; when Pauling noted that a graduate student should know how to spell "phenol*pt*halein," I noted back that "so should a professor." Graduate studies were interrupted by World War II, during which I performed research on chemical warfare agents and then on uranium, learning very directly about toxic substances and radioactivity, respectively. The death of my mother in 1942 directed me toward doing what I could against cancer, so I then took a Merck postdoctoral fellowship with Van Potter at the University of Wisconsin (1947–1949). His research was on deregulation in cancers of oxidative phosphorylation and the Krebs cycle, studied mainly with tissue homogenates. I learned a great deal under his wise guidance and was very productive. However, I decided that the time was not ripe for me to pursue cancer problems because of my inadequate knowledge of metabolic pathways, their regulation, and techniques for investigation. Therefore I shifted to more amenable bacterial systems.

I joined the faculty of the biochemistry department and the virus laboratory at University of California, Berkeley, of which Wendell Stanley was Director, in 1949. Subsequently I made several novel discoveries. We, simultaneously with others, discovered ribonucleoprotein particles in bacteria, later named ribosomes, and also found photosynthetic particles that we called chromatophores (1). I wanted to learn whether virus infection changes the metabolism of the host and discovered that nine enzyme activities changed after infection of *Escherichia coli* with bacteriophage (2). These included deoxyribonuclease, suggesting involvement of phage DNA in infection. Later when we replaced thymidine with bromodeoxyuridine in phage DNA many mutants were produced, which is consistent with DNA being the genetic material of the virus (3). This research led to my being chosen a Young Biochemist in 1953 to represent the United States at the International Biochemistry Congress in Paris and to tour Europe, both remarkable experiences.

Regulation of Enzyme Activity

I first thought about metabolic regulation while I was a postdoctoral fellow. We demonstrated that oxalacetate inhibits succinic dehydrogenase, several steps back in the Krebs cycle (4). I wondered whether this "feedback" could keep reactions of the complex cycle in balance. I initially investigated coordination between molecular syntheses in *E. coli* and found linkages: that nucleic acid precursors are required for protein synthesis (5) and furthermore nucleic acid synthesis depends on the presence of amino acids (6). However, concurrent synthesis of DNA was not necessary.

Feedback and Allosteric Inhibition—Living organisms usually produce their constituent molecules in amounts sufficient to meet their needs, no more or less. Is there a general mechanism to explain this economical metabolic regulation? In 1950 biochemists did not ask this question; they were very busy creating a map of metabolism in which all roads were of the same intensity although traffic flow along some was far greater than on others. Richard Yates and I (and independently Ed Umbarger) reported a general control mechanism: we for the pyrimidine pathway and he for the isoleucine-valine biosynthetic pathway. Its principle is similar to regulating heat production of a furnace by a thermostat. An end product biosynthetic pathway can be an inhibitor of its initial enzymatic reaction. Thereby, in a living cell end product in excess economically shuts down its own synthesis. The feedback mechanism has now been verified for numerous pathways, and it remains a subject of active investigation (7). Regulation is complex for some of these, involving branching to produce several end products as studied by Earl Stadtman or of an enzyme with several substrates like ribonucleotide reductase as elucidated by Peter Reichard.

The breakthrough came when I was using mutants defective in steps of the pathway that synthesizes the pyrimidines by seven successive enzyme-catalyzed reactions. I noticed that the metabolite synthesized prior to the absent reaction of a mutant accumulated as expected, but not when I made available the end product of the pathway. This observation was literally breathtaking, because I perceived that it suggests a novel mechanism for control of metabolism. Richard Yates and I reported at a 1954 AAAS meeting that "uracil blocks an enzyme step between aspartate and ureidosuccinate formation, and this block may be an important regulatory mechanism in the cell." In three subsequent papers (8–10) we established this regulation. These discoveries led to perhaps the first review on regulation of metabolism (11).

Regulatory Sites—The molecular mechanism of feedback inhibition immediately created a problem. The general conception of inhibitors then was that they compete with substrate quite specifically for binding to an active site of the enzyme. How can a pyrimidine inhibit the enzyme aspartate transcarbamylase since it is structurally very dissimilar to the substrates, aspartate and carbamyl phosphate? I addressed this question after I returned from a sabbatical in Jacques Monod's laboratory (see below). The uncertainties posed by results obtained with crude extracts made me decide to first obtain the pure enzyme, which Margaret Shepherdson and I isolated and crystallized (12). With this pure enzyme, John Gerhart demonstrated that the inhibitor is the ultimate end product cytidine triphosphate (CTP), which has no structural similarity to the substrates aspartate or carbamyl phosphate (13). An indication of a regulatory site distinct from the catalytic site was that ATP activates the enzyme in contrast to the inhibitory CTP (Fig. 1). ATP, which is not a substrate, evidently cannot bind to the active site because this would have to be inhibitory, and therefore it must bind to a different, regulatory site.

The key came from an unusual observation. Gerhart kept getting variable results of inhibition by CTP, although the pure enzyme always had high catalytic activity. When we examined his data closely we noticed that inhibition was strong at the beginning of each week and decreased thereafter. His procedure was that each Monday he thawed an aliquot of the deep-frozen enzyme and stored it in the refrigerator for later use. Hypothesizing that the enzyme must change its properties during this cold storage, he warmed it systematically and found that brief exposure to 65 °C abolished inhibition by CTP but not catalytic activity. Thus,

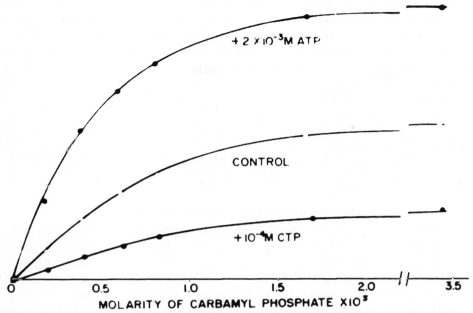

$+2 \times 10^{-3} M$ ATP

CONTROL

$+10^{-4} M$ CTP

0   0.5   1.0   1.5   2.0   3.5

MOLARITY OF CARBAMYL PHOSPHATE X10³

FIG. 1. **Aspartate transcarbamylase activity is inhibited by CTP and activated by ATP.**

we dissociated sites that we named regulatory as distinct from functional ones (14). Gerhart went on to separate the regulatory and catalytic subunits of the enzyme, later investigated in detail by physical chemistry and x-ray diffraction.

At the same time, Jean-Pierre Changeux in the laboratory of Monod investigated the mechanism of feedback inhibition of the isoleucine-valine pathway discovered by Ed Umbarger, and from kinetic studies concluded that there are inhibitory sites in addition to catalytic ones. These may be the first molecular demonstrations of regulation of protein function by a small molecule. Monod conceived the generalization of allostery, which he called "the second secret of life." The two types of binding sites on proteins, one functional and the other regulatory, permit regulation of any biological reaction by a process in which a regulatory molecule need have no structural similarity to the molecules acted upon (15). He combined three lines of research to create the allosteric concept: (i) feedback inhibition with regulatory sites; (ii) control of gene expression (see below); and (iii) cooperative binding of oxygen to the subunits of hemoglobin (16).

Another major development arising from feedback inhibition is the finding that enzymes often function in complexes with other proteins rather than as single proteins, which was then the biochemical concept. An early example is Prem Reddy's report that DNA synthesis is not catalyzed by its polymerase acting alone but by a multienzyme complex that we named "replitase" (17), a finding that initially met with considerable opposition. It should not have been surprising because proteins are synthesized by very large multiprotein complexes, ribosomes, and we now know that complexes consisting of RNA polymerase plus regulatory transcription factors synthesize RNA. Reports of feedback inhibition, regulatory subunits, allosteric sites, and multiprotein complexes now abound in the literature.

Regulation of Enzyme Expression by Repression

In addition to regulation of enzyme activity as outlined above, there evidently was another major regulation that determined amounts of enzymes. Enzyme activities were known to "adapt," to change dramatically, as a function of the nutrients provided to bacteria. This mechanism would provide a coarse control of metabolic regulation relative to fine regulation by feedback inhibition. I began to investigate such regulatory mechanisms for enzyme synthesis early in the 1950s (10, 18). When in 1957–1958 I had the opportunity to take a sabbatical leave I decided to go to the laboratory in Paris of Jacques Monod, the outstanding investigator of this problem. He studied the dramatic changes of β-galactosidase activity in *E. coli* as a function of availability of β-galactosides and other carbon sources.

Monod, Francois Jacob, and I discovered the general molecular mechanism of this process. It is by action of a protein we named the repressor that specifically blocks gene expression, which is released when a low molecular weight inducer molecule binds to it. Specifically, expression of the β-galactosidase gene, and two adjacent genes, is inhibited by a repressor molecule that binds to an upstream operator sequence of the bacterial DNA. This negative regulation is released by binding of a β-galactoside to an allosteric site of the repressor (19). This has often been reviewed (15, 20, 21). This research is the basis for current concepts of the major mechanism for regulating gene expressions in both prokaryotes and eukaryotes.

Our investigations of gene expression provided one of the origins for discovery of messenger RNA. Since the enzyme probably is not made directly on DNA, we proposed from kinetics an unstable intermediate between gene and enzyme (22). This was soon thereafter shown by others to be an RNA. In accord with an unstable intermediate, we then demonstrated that the enzyme begins to be produced about a minute after its gene is activated and quickly ceases after the inducer is removed (23). Monica Riley demonstrated that destruction of the gene by radioactive decay of incorporated ^{32}P causes cessation of enzyme synthesis (24).

Membrane Changes of Cancer Cells

I moved to Princeton in 1961 to become the first Chairman of the Biochemical Sciences Department. Techniques by this time had progressed sufficiently to make tissue culture of mammalian cells feasible for investigators in general. In 1963 an opportunity to participate in a cancer meeting in South America reinitiated my thinking about cancer. I needed a topic and so speculated that cancer and normal cells differ in surface functions that regulate growth by interacting with the extracellular environment (25). However, little was then known about growth factors, as supplied in serum, or of their receptors, so I turned to a surface-related activity that I had investigated in relation to β-galactosidase induction, transport of small molecules across the membrane into *E. coli*. These experiments had provided a valuable lesson. Monod and Jacob proposed the operon model: that adjacent genes, in particular for β-galactosidase and galactoside transport (permease), are co-induced by galactosides. I objected that the galactinol induces the transport system but not the enzyme. The solution to this dilemma is that this sugar is an α-galactoside, which induces a different permease that tests positive in the assay for β-galactoside permease, and so the operon hypothesis was not contradicted (26).

Molecular mechanisms of transport were then unknown. To learn about them, Jacques Dreyfuss and I investigated sulfate ion uptake (27) and identified a novel class of transport-related proteins. A mutant of *Salmonella typhimurium* that could not grow on sulfate did not accumulate the ion and so was defective in its transport, but we noted that a very small amount of sulfate was associated with these bacteria. We hypothesized that this sulfate is bound to a protein located outside the cell membrane, and our experiments demonstrated a small protein located between cell wall and membrane to which sulfate binds firmly. Its synthesis is repressed by sulfate, so by derepression in cells grown with an organic sulfur source and followed by a selective release technique we were able to obtain crystals after only 4-fold purification,. This sulfate binding protein is one of the first transport proteins to be purified and the first of the "binding proteins" that are involved in active transport and chemotaxis (28).

We then turned to investigating transport into normal and cancer cells. In a series of studies we showed that their transport of small molecules differs and is highly regulated, being altered by viral transformation, cell-cell contact, and serum addition, and it changes through the cell cycle (29). At this time Max Burger and Allan Goldberg joined my laboratory and investigated carbohydrate differences on cancer *versus* normal cell surfaces (30), and Dennis Cunningham investigated phospholipid turnover (31). To begin studies of growth regulation by externally supplied growth factors we compared their requirements by normal and transformed cells (32).

Disregulation of the Cell Cycle in Cancer

In 1972–1973 my late wife Ruth Sager and I took a sabbatical with Sir Michael Stoker at the Imperial Cancer Research Fund Laboratory in London. Our objectives were to learn about cancer, especially applications of tissue culture. We worked long hours, surprising our colleagues by sometimes returning to the laboratory after dinner; to make up for this, we made several exciting and informative trips around Europe.

I soon decided that the hallmark of cancer on which I should focus was deregulated cell proliferation, and Ruth chose genetic defects for her subject of investigation, an area in which she later made major contributions. The process of cell proliferation is organized as the cell cycle, which provided a good starting point for me because I previously studied cell cycle events in synchronized bacteria (33, 34). My initial question was where in the cycle growth regulation is exerted. I discovered that regulation for normal cells is exerted in late G_1 phase, at about 2 h prior to initiation of DNA synthesis. This is in contrast to prior proposals that growth control is exerted prior to cell division. Thus, a wholly different set of molecular events came into consideration, molecules involved in which were soon identified. I named the time of this process the restriction point, a term that survives today (35). Lee Hartwell at this time applied his cycle-regulating yeast mutants to demonstrate that growth of yeast is similarly regulated in G_1 at "start." The restriction point and start are the first demonstrations of what Hartwell later named "checkpoints."

Importantly, I showed that these restriction point requirements are relaxed in cancer cells, providing a basis for the greater proliferative capacity of cancer (36). This research on restriction point control and its relevance to cancer have been summarized (37). We proceeded to investigate related molecular events in G_1. Expression of the oncogenic protein Myc was changed in cancer cells (38); we showed that transit through G_1 is influenced by serum supply, growth factors, and nutrients, and actin and other proteins are synthesized sequentially after cells enter the cycle (39). Rapid protein synthesis was needed to enter S phase, especially by normal as compared with cancer cells, which suggests the requirement for growth control of a protein with a short half-life. Indeed, we discovered only one protein (p68) of many detected as a spot on two-dimensional gels that had the three required characteristics. It increased in G_1, was unstable, and more was present in cancer cells (40). Henry Yang and I demonstrated one of the first changes of protein phosphorylation during G_1, which differed between normal and transformed cells (41).

Ruth and I moved to the Dana-Farber Cancer Institute and Harvard in 1975. I investigated the then unknown post-restriction point events at the end of G_1 that initiate onset of DNA synthesis. My laboratory developed the appearance at the end of G_1 of thymidine kinase as an alternative marker for S phase initiation, one that is more subject to molecular investigation than is DNA synthesis (42). Prem Reddy and I showed that several enzymes involved in DNA synthesis are produced at the G_1/S interface and translocate into the nucleus where they form a "replitase" multiprotein complex for DNA synthesis (17). It contains E2F, retinoblastoma-like protein, and Cdc2 kinase. It binds to the mouse thymidine kinase gene promoter (43). With the discovery of cycle-dependent kinases (Cdks) and cyclins (providing another example of interacting catalytic and regulatory proteins) we asked whether one of these molecules is the restriction point protein. We concluded that cyclin E is the most promising candidate (44). Furthermore, we found that cyclin E is over expressed in cancer, and it potentially provides a molecular marker for cancer (45).

End Notes: Applications to Cancer

By 1990 research on regulation of the cell cycle was so plentiful and in such good hands that I decided to apply the basic knowledge I had gained to the study of cancer. On the one hand I tried to find methods for detecting cancer earlier and on the other searched for novel agents to treat it more effectively. This recent research will only be touched upon here.

Gene Expression and Differential Display: Cancer Detection—I wanted to discover molecular changes that underlie cancer. These could indicate mechanisms of transformation and furthermore could provide tools for cancer detection and therapy. Peng Liang and I invented the differential display technique for detecting the subset of mRNAs that are present in a cell and with it could discover changes in deregulated gene expressions in cancer (46). This method is based on synthesizing short cDNAs from 3′ ends of many mRNAs and then displaying them on sequencing gels for side-by-side comparisons of the products from normal and cancer cells. It has been applied extensively to discover changes of gene expression; there are now about 2000 citations of it (47). Examples from my laboratory include discovering a gene whose expression changes downstream of *ras* oncogene activity (48) and another that defectively regulates mitosis in cancers (49).

The concept of expression genetics (also named functional genomics) has been excellently summarized (50). Katherine Martin and Ruth Sager systematically applied differential display to discover hundreds of genes whose expressions are defectively regulated in breast cancers. Their research has continued in my laboratory, demonstrating that selected markers readily distinguished estrogen receptor positive from negative human breast cancers and other properties (51). Then we determined whether these markers permit cancer detection in small samples of patient blood. We had shown that this approach is feasible (52). Sensitivity of the assay is sufficient to detect solid tumor cells disseminated in 3 cc of blood samples from patients (53). Expression-based blood assays, as developed with the screening approach described here, have the potential to detect and classify solid tumor cells originating from virtually any primary site in the body. Earlier detection should be effective in reducing cancer mortality, especially as better therapies are developed.

Novel Chemotherapies—Based on cell cycle control studies, long ago I proposed a modification of chemotherapy based upon protecting normal cells from drug-induced death, thereby increasing the therapeutic index (54). This concept has recently been developed further (55). As another checkpoint-based approach, Ching Lau and I discovered that a caffeine derivative selectively makes DNA-damaged cancer cells pass through their G_2 checkpoint, causing chromosome fragmentation and death (56). This effect was specific for killing cancer cells put into mice (57). These findings led to clinical trials, unfortunately unsuccessful because of nausea and vomiting.

We are now developing several potential anticancer therapies. A natural product β-lapachone (58) combined with taxol is remarkably effective against tumors implanted into mice (59). We also reported anti-AIDS effects of β-lapachone and two other compounds (60). An important novel chemotherapy is based upon specifically causing programmed cell death (apoptosis) of cancer cells, as demonstrated with β-lapachone by Chiang Li (61). As another chemotherapeutic approach, Debajit Biswas demonstrated that the kinase C inhibitor Go6976 specifically causes apoptosis of estrogen receptor negative (ER−) breast cancer cells and the disappearance of tumors from their implantation in mice (62). This drug blocks activation of transcription factor NF-κB, which is elevated by epidermal growth factor in many ER− cancers. NF-κB is anti-apoptotic, and Go6976 recreates the apoptotic capacity of these cells, a novel demonstration of a chemotherapeutic principle.

In conclusion, my scientific path has meandered, not following any central direct pathway, if such a pathway exists, but rather it led along byways and across unexplored terrain toward my goal of learning about the defects of molecular regulation that underlie cancer. My wish is that these results will prove to be useful.

Dedicated to my late wife, Ruth Sager.

Address correspondence to: arthur_pardee@dfci.harvard.edu.

REFERENCES

1. Schachman, H. K., Pardee, A. B., and Stanier, R. Y. (1952) Studies on the macromolecular organization of microbial cells. *Arch. Biochem. Biophys.* **38,** 245–260
2. Pardee, A. B., and Kunkee, R. E. (1952) Enzyme activity and bacteriophage infection. II. Activities before and after virus infection. *J. Biol. Chem.* **199,** 9–24
3. Litman, R. M., and Pardee, A. B. (1960) The induction of mutants of bacteriophage T2 by 5-bromouracil. IV. Kinetics of bromouracil-induced mutagenesis. *Biochim. Biophys. Acta* **42,** 131–140
4. Pardee, A. B., and Potter, V. R. (1948) Inhibition of succinic dehydrogenase by oxalacetate. *J. Biol. Chem.* **176,** 1085–1094
5. Pardee, A. B. (1954) Nucleic acid precursors and protein synthesis. *Proc. Natl. Acad. Sci. U. S. A.* **40,** 263–270
6. Pardee, A. B., and Prestidge, L. S. (1956) The dependence of nucleic acid synthesis on the presence of amino acids in *E. coli. J. Bacteriol.* **71,** 677–683
7. Helmstaedt, K., Krapppmann, S., and Braus, G. H. (2001). Allosteric regulation of catalytic activity: *Escherichia coli* aspartate transcarbamylase *versus* yeast chorismate mutase. *Microbiol. Mol. Biol. Rev.* **65,** 404–421
8. Yates, R. A., and Pardee, A. B. (1956) Pyrimidine biosynthesis in *E. coli. J. Biol. Chem.* **221,** 757–770
9. Yates, R. A., and Pardee, A. B. (1956) Control of pyrimidine biosynthesis in *E. coli* by a feedback mechanism. *J. Biol. Chem.* **221,** 743–756
10. Yates, R. A., and Pardee, A. B. (1957) Control by uracil of formation of enzymes required for orotate synthesis. *J. Biol. Chem.* **227,** 677–692
11. Pardee, A. B. (1959) The control of enzyme activity. *The Enzymes,* 2nd Ed., pp. 681–716, Academic Press, New York
12. Shepherdson, M., and Pardee, A. B. (1960) Production and crystallization of aspartate transcarbamylase. *J. Biol. Chem.* **235,** 3233–3237
13. Gerhart, J. C., and Pardee, A. B. (1962) The enzymology of control by feedback inhibition. *J. Biol. Chem.* **237,** 891–896
14. Gerhart, J. C., and Pardee, A. B. (1963) The effect of the feedback inhibitor, CTP, on subunit interactions in aspartate transcarbamylase. *Cold Spring Harbor Symp. Quant. Biol.* **28,** 491–496
15. Monod, J. (1966) From enzymatic adaptation to allosteric transitions. *Science* **154,** 1475–1483
16. Pardee, A. B. (1985) Roots. Molecular basis of biological regulation: origins from feedback inhibition and allostery. *BioEssays* **2,** 37–40
17. Reddy, G. P. V., and Pardee, A. B. (1980) Multienzyme complex for metabolic channeling in mammalian DNA replication. *Proc. Natl. Acad. Sci. U. S. A.* **77,** 3312–3316
18. Pardee, A. B., and Prestidge, L. S. (1955) Induced formation of serine and threonine deaminases by *Escherichia*

coli. J. Bacteriol. **70,** 667–674

19. Pardee, A. B., Jacob, F., and Monod, J. (1959) The genetic control and cytoplasmic expression of "inducibility" in the synthesis of β-galactosidase by *E. coli. J. Mol. Biol.* **1,** 165–178

20. Jacob, F. (1996) Genetics of the bacterial cell. *Science* **152,** 1470–1478

21. Pardee, A. B. (1985) Roots. Molecular basis of gene expression: origins from the pajama experiment. *BioEssays* **2,** 86–89

22. Pardee, A. B. (1958) Experiments on the transfer of information from DNA to enzymes. *Exp. Cell Res.* **6,** (suppl.) 142–151

23. Pardee, A. B., and Prestidge, L. S. (1961) The initial kinetics of enzyme induction. *Biochim. Biophys. Acta* **49,** 77–88

24. Riley, M., and Pardee, A. B. (1962) β-Galactosidase formation following decay of ^{32}P in *E. coli* zygotes. *J. Mol. Biol.* **5,** 63–75

25. Pardee, A. B. (1964) Cell division and a hypothesis of cancer. Symposium on the control of cell division and the induction of cancer. *Natl. Cancer Inst. Monogr.* **14,** 7–20

26. Prestidge, L. S., and Pardee, A. B. (1965) A second permease for methyl-thio-D-galactoside in *Escherichia coli. Biochim. Biophys. Acta* **100,** 591–593

27. Dreyfuss, J., and Pardee, A. B. (1965) Evidence for a sulfate-binding site external to the cell membrane of *Salmonella typhimurium. Biochim. Biophys. Acta* **104,** 308–310

28. Pardee, A. B. (1968) Membrane transport proteins. *Science* **162,** 632–637

29. Pardee, A. B., Jimenez de Asia, L., and Rozengurt, E. (1974) Functional membrane changes in cell growth: significance and mechanism. In: *Control of Proliferation in Animal Cells* (Clarkson B., and Baserga, R., eds) pp. 547–561, Cold Spring Harbor Press, New York

30. Burger, M. M., and Goldberg, A. R. (1966) Identification of a tumor-specific determinant on neoplastic cell surfaces. *Proc. Natl. Acad. Sci. U. S. A.* **57,** 359–366

31. Cunningham, D. D. (1972) Changes in phospholipid turnover following growth of 3T3 mouse cells to confluency. *J. Biol. Chem.* **247,** 2464–2470

32. Cherington, P. V., Smith, B. L., and Pardee, A. B. (1979) Loss of epidermal growth factor requirement and malignant transformation. *Proc. Natl. Acad. Sci. U. S. A.* **76,** 3937–3941

33. Abbo, F. E., and Pardee, A. B. (1960) Synthesis of macromolecules in synchronously dividing bacteria. *Biochim. Biophys. Acta* **39,** 473–485

34. Masters, M., and Pardee, A. B. (1965) Sequence of enzyme synthesis and gene replication during the cell cycle of *Bacillus subtilis. Proc. Natl. Acad. Sci. U. S. A.* **54,** 64–70

35. Pardee, A. B. (1974) A restriction point for control of normal animal cell proliferation. *Proc. Natl. Acad. Sci. U. S. A.* **71,** 1286–1290

36. Rossow, P. W., Riddle, V. G. F., and Pardee, A. B. (1979) Synthesis of labile, serum-dependent protein in early G_1 controls animal cell growth. *Proc. Natl. Acad. Sci. U. S. A.* **76,** 4446–4450

37. Pardee, A. B. (1989) G_1 events and regulation of cell proliferation. *Science* **246,** 603–608

38. Campisi, J., Gray, H. E., Pardee, A. B., Dean, M., and Sonenshein, G. E. (1984) Cell-cycle control of *c-myc* but not *c-ras* expression is lost following chemical transformation. *Cell* **36,** 241–247

39. Riddle, V. G. H., Dubrow, R., and Pardee, A. B. (1979) Changes in the synthesis of actin and other cell proteins after stimulation of serum-arrested cells. *Proc. Natl. Acad. Sci. U. S. A.* **76,** 1298–1302

40. Croy, R. G., and Pardee, A. B. (1983) Enhanced synthesis and stabilization of a M_r 68,000 protein in transformed Balb/c-3T3 cells: candidate for restriction point control of cell growth. *Proc. Natl. Acad. Sci. U. S. A.* **80,** 4699–4703

41. Yang, H., and Pardee, A. B. (1987) Cell cycle and growth factor-dependent phosphoprotein of 78 kDa differently regulated in normal and transformed mouse fibroblasts. *J. Cell. Physiol.* **133,** 377–382

42. Dou, Q.-P., and Pardee, A. B. (1996) Transcriptional activation of thymidine kinase, a marker for cell cycle control. *Prog. Nucleic Acid Res. Mol. Biol.* **53,** 197–217

43. Pardee, A. B. (1994) Growth dysregulation in cancer cells. *Adv. Cancer Res.* **65,** 213–228

44. Dou, Q. P., Levin, A. H., Zao, S., and Pardee, A. B. (1993) Cyclin E and cyclin A as candidates for the restriction point protein. *Cancer Res.* **53,** 1493–1497

45. Keyomarsi, K., O'Leary, N., Molnar, G., Lees, E., Fingert, H. J., and Pardee, A. B. (1994) Cyclin E, a potential prognostic marker for breast cancer. *Cancer Res.* **54,** 380–385

46. Liang, P., and Pardee, A. B. (1992) Differential display of eukaryotic messenger RNA by means of the polymerase chain reaction. *Science* **257,** 967–971

47. Pardee, A. B., and McClelland, M. (eds) (1999) *Expression Genetics: Differential Display,* BioTechniques Books, Natick, MA

48. Liang, P., Averboukh, L., Zhu, W., and Pardee, A. B. (1994) Ras activation of genes: Mob-1 as a model. *Proc. Natl. Acad. Sci. U. S. A.* **91,** 12515–12519

49. Ford, H. L., Kabingu, E. N., Bump, E. A., Mutter, G. L., aand Pardee, A. B. (1998) Abrogation of the cell cycle checkpoint associated with overexpression of HSIX I: a possible mechanism of breast carcinogenesis. *Proc. Natl. Acad. Sci. U. S. A.* **95,** 12608–12613

50. Sager, R. (1997) Expression genetics; shifting the focus from DNA to RNA. *Proc. Natl. Acad. Sci. U. S. A.* **94,** 952–955

51. Martin, K. J., Kritzman, B. M., Price, L. M., Koh, B., Kwan, C. P., Zhang, X., Mackay, A., O'Hare, M. J., Kaelin, C. M., Mutter, G. L., Pardee, A. B., and Sager, R. (2000) Linking gene expression patterns to therapeutic groups in breast cancer. *Cancer Res.* **60,** 2232–2238

52. Fournier, M. V., Guimaraes, F. C., Paschoal, M. E. M., Ronco, L. V., Carvalho, M. G. C., and Pardee, A. B. (1999) Identification of a gene encoding a human oxysterol-binding protein homolog: a potential general marker for blood dissemination of solid tumors. *Cancer Res.* **59,** 3748–3753

53. Martin, K. J., Graner, E., Li, Y., Price, L. M., Kritzman, B. M., Fournier, M. V., Rhei, E., and Pardee, A. B. (2001) High-sensitivity array analysis of gene expression for the early detection of disseminated breast tumor. *Proc. Natl. Acad. Sci. U. S. A.* **98,** 2646–2651

54. Pardee, A. B., and James, L. J. (1975) Selective killing of transformed baby hamster kidney (BHK) cells. *Proc. Natl. Acad. Sci. U. S. A.* **72,** 4994–4998

55. Blagosklonny, M. V., and Pardee, A. B. (2001) Exploiting cancer cell cycling for selective protection of normal cells. *Cancer Res.* **161,** 4301–4305

56. Lau, C. C., and Pardee, A. B. (1982) Mechanism by which caffeine potentiates lethality of nitrogen mustard. *Proc. Natl. Acad. Sci. U. S. A.* **79,** 2942–2946

57. Fingert, H. J., Pu, A. T., Chen, Z., Googe, P. B., Alley, M. C., and Pardee, A. B. (1988) *In vivo* and *in vitro* enhanced antitumor effects by pentoxifylline in human cancer cells treated with thiotepa. *Cancer Res.* **48,** 4375–4381

58. Pardee, A. B., Schlegel, R., and Boothman, D. A. (1987) Pharmacological interference with DNA repair. In:

Anticarcinogenesis and Radiation Protection (Cerutti, P., Nygaard, O. F., and Simic, M. G., eds) pp. 431–436, Plenum Publishing, New York

59. Li, C. J., Li, Y.-Z., Pinto, A. V., and Pardee, A. B. (1999) Potent inhibition of tumor survival _in vivo_ by β-lapachone plus taxol: combining drugs imposes different artificial checkpoints. _Proc. Natl. Acad. Sci. U. S. A._ **96,** 13369–13374

60. Li, C. J., Zhang, L. J., Dezube, B. J., Crumpacker, C. S., and Pardee, A. B. (1993) Three inhibitors of type 1 human immunodeficiency virus long terminal repeat-directed gene expression and virus replication. _Proc. Natl. Acad. Sci. U. S. A._ **90,** 1839–1842

61. Li, C. J., Wang, C., and Pardee, A. B. (1995) Induction of apoptosis by β-lapachone in human prostate cancer cells. _Cancer Res._ **55,** 3712–3715

62. Biswas, D. K., Dai, S-C., Cruz, A., Weiser, B., Graner, E., and Pardee, A. B. (2001) The nuclear factor kappa B (NF-κB): a potential therapeutic target for estrogen receptor negative breast cancers. _Proc. Natl. Acad. Sci. U. S. A._ **98,** 10386–10391

THE JOURNAL OF BIOLOGICAL CHEMISTRY
© 2002 by The American Society for Biochemistry and Molecular Biology, Inc.

Vol. 277, No. 32, Issue of August 9, pp. 28351–28363, 2002
Printed in U.S.A.

Reflections

A PAPER IN A SERIES COMMISSIONED TO CELEBRATE THE CENTENARY OF THE JBC IN 2005

JBC Centennial
1905–2005
100 Years of Biochemistry and Molecular Biology

Enzyme Ingenuity in Biological Oxidations: a Trail Leading to Cytochrome P450

Published, JBC Papers in Press, June 5, 2002, DOI 10.1074/jbc.R200015200

Minor J. Coon

From the Department of Biological Chemistry, Medical School, University of Michigan, Ann Arbor, Michigan 48109

Those unfamiliar with basic research in biochemistry and related fields may assume that important discoveries are the result of brilliant ideas that are single mindedly pursued until, many years later, the answer is obtained, perhaps along with important biomedical applications. The progress of science is almost always more haphazard, as ambitious young scientists are influenced by their teachers, by the cooperative or competitive work of others, the availability of new techniques, and chance findings that may lead to different goals. Sixty years ago as an undergraduate at the University of Colorado, I took my first biochemistry course in the Chemistry Department taught by Professor Reuben Gustavson and had the good fortune to be invited by him to join his small research group studying steroid hormones. I had a tremendous amount to learn but was fascinated from then on with research and the possibility of making new discoveries.

In these reflections the influence of my mentors/teachers, whom I much admired for their personal qualities and achievements, is acknowledged. Although my research over the years has taken many unexpected turns, a common thread has been an interest in biological oxidations, particularly those not readily explainable according to the predictions of organic chemistry. This curiosity has led to fundamental studies on the properties and mechanism of action of cytochrome P450, now often described as the most versatile biological catalyst known. Although this was not my original goal, the mammalian isoforms of this enzyme have turned out to be of biomedical importance because of their central involvement in the metabolism of steroids, drugs, and chemical carcinogens.

William C. Rose

William Cumming Rose was a dedicated and inspiring teacher and an outstanding pioneer in biochemistry and nutritional science who spent most of his career at the University of Illinois (1). Young Will attended schools in small communities in North Carolina and South Carolina until the age of 14, when the inadequacy of the education caused his father to remove him from school and tutor him at home. He had been introduced to Latin, Greek, and Hebrew and was well prepared by the time he entered college. Will wished to attend a large University, but his father thought his son at age 16 was too young and convinced him to attend Davidson College in North Carolina, a school for which he developed a lifelong affection. While in graduate school at Yale University, Rose decided on the branch of chemistry he would pursue, which was biochemistry, under the guidance of Lafayette Mendel in the Sheffield Scientific School. In 1911, upon completion of his Ph.D. thesis, Rose left Yale for an instructorship in physiological chemistry at the University of Pennsylvania, followed by advanced study with Franz Knoop at the University of Freiburg and then a faculty position at the University of Texas in Galveston before he became professor and head of the Division of Biochemistry in the Chemistry Department at the University of Illinois. This provided a permanent and very supportive home for his scientific career for the next 35 years.

Fig. 1. **Inscription on bronze plaque given annually to recipients of the William C. Rose Award in Biochemistry.** The inscription directly below Dr. Rose's portrait is an excerpt from an article that appeared in 1935 in *The Journal of Biological Chemistry* (*J. Biol. Chem.* **112,** 283). It reads as follows: "The data demonstrate conclusively that the crystalline compound is the new essential we have been endeavoring to isolate for several years. Furthermore, the experiments recorded in Chart 1 represent the first successful efforts to induce growth in animals upon diets carrying synthetic mixtures of highly purified amino acids in place of proteins." This work marks the discovery of threonine.

In research Rose displayed a gift for meticulous experimentation and for thoroughness and clarity in his publications. As a teacher he imbued students who attended his carefully prepared lectures with enthusiasm for biochemistry. The subject came alive with his engrossing stories about the early history of the field and the personalities involved. No mention of his remarkable ability as a teacher would be complete without reference to the seminars and lectures at which he imparted scientific knowledge and also entertained his audience as an incomparable raconteur. His research interests included the intermediary metabolism of amino acids, creatine, uric acid, and related compounds, and he was renowned for the discovery, isolation, and identification of a new amino acid as α-amino-β-hydroxy-n-butyric acid, which he named threonine (2). This was the culmination of experiments in which rats failed to grow on diets containing the 19 previously known amino acids. Thus, painstaking efforts over many years led to the missing growth factor found in proteins and in hydrolysate fractions therefrom.

When I arrived in Urbana to undertake graduate study in 1943, the identity of the 10 amino acids essential for growth in rats and the 8 essential for the maintenance of nitrogen equilibrium in the human (that is, male graduate students) was already known (3, 4). It fell my lot to isolate, purify, and analyze amino acids and then feed them to fellow students enlisted as human guinea pigs in experiments involving daily nitrogen balance determinations. The diets consisted of the mixture of amino acids under study, the known vitamins, cornstarch, corn oil, sucrose, butter fat, inorganic salts, and Celluflour (a product providing roughage but no nutritive value, nitrogen, or flavor). The only taste thrill in this otherwise bland fare was a

FIG. 2. **Photograph of Severo Ochoa taken from the *New York Times* (7).**

large brown "candy" containing a bitter liver extract as a possible source of unknown vitamins flavored with peppermint oil and sweetened with sugar. In those days the recruits were grateful for the free rations, the dollar a day they were paid, and the prospect of seeing their initials in print in Rose's widely read publications. The resulting papers established the quantitative requirements for the essential amino acids, the availability of some of the D-isomers or N-acetyl derivatives, and the role of cysteine and tyrosine in sparing methionine and phenylalanine, respectively. The morale of the subjects was maintained over many weeks by the prospect of collecting data for doctoral theses, the obvious importance of our findings for human welfare, and the infectious enthusiasm of Dr. Rose. An added benefit in my case was that, while consuming these daily rations, I had ample time to think about experiments on the metabolism of the essential amino acids I might pursue later in my career, as described below.

Rose's students were somewhat in awe of the professor, perhaps wondering whether they could meet his exacting standards or hope to emulate the seeming ease with which he succeeded in all of his professional endeavors. They learned in time that behind his somewhat reserved and formal manner was a genuine warmth and an understanding that young scientists develop their full potential only by profiting from their mistakes. His research achievements earned him wide recognition and many honors. On the occasion of his 90th birthday his former students, colleagues, and friends assembled in Urbana to join him in the celebration. He was much surprised when presented with a handsome bronze plaque announcing the establishment of the William C. Rose Award and Lectureship. As indicated in Fig. 1, the plaque to be given to all awardees shows his likeness and a sketch of the Noyes Laboratory with the structures of the essential amino acids and the stereochemistry and crystal structure

FIG. 3. **Vladimir Prelog at Bürgenstock in 1989 (11).**

of threonine, with a quotation and chart from his classical 1935 paper published in the *Journal of Biological Chemistry* (2). This award, now administered by the American Society for Biochemistry and Molecular Biology, has been given annually, and the lectures are presented at the Society's national meetings. Until his death at age 98, Will Rose took a keen interest in those selected for the award named for him. He and his wife Zula exerted a wonderfully positive influence on all who knew them and took a personal interest in the 90 graduate students who studied under him, of whom 56 received the Ph.D. degree. In later years he often commented on his happy family life until his wife's death in 1965, his exciting professional life, and the thrill of watching his students grow into professional stature.

Severo Ochoa

In the first paper of this series on Reflections, Arthur Kornberg (5) has written perceptively of his deep admiration for Severo Ochoa, whom he knew particularly well from his stay in that laboratory in 1946 and their close friendship until Severo's death in 1993. Accordingly, I will comment only briefly on my exposure to that exciting New York University laboratory during the year 1952. After a few years as a junior faculty member at the University of Pennsylvania I had not yet earned an official sabbatical but came to realize that a knowledge of enzymology was crucial to further progress in my studies on amino acid metabolism. My colleague Jack Buchanan at Pennsylvania State University advised me that the Ochoa laboratory was possibly the world's finest in enzymology at that time, and I acted on that sound advice and was most fortunate to have an acceptance. My research there involved studying the details of acetoacetate synthesis and breakdown and led to the purification and characterization of coenzyme A transferase, now called acetoacetyl-succinic thiophorase, from heart muscle (6).

The Ochoa laboratory was crowded and still in the Pharmacology Department in an old building on First Avenue, with limited equipment, including the single Beckman DU spectrophotometer mentioned by Kornberg. Nevertheless it was an exciting place to pursue research,

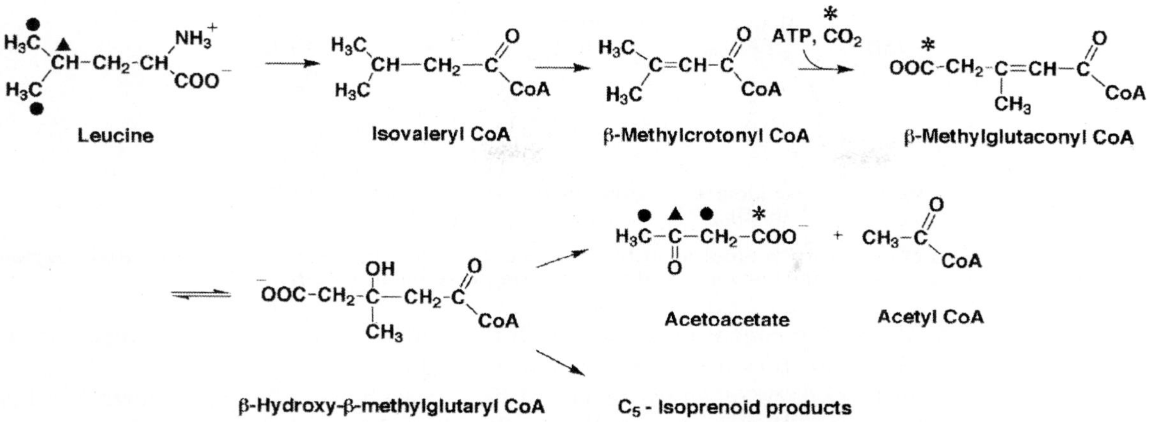

FIG. 4. **Metabolic steps in the conversion of leucine to acetoacetate, with the radioactive labeling pattern obtained from the methyl carbons (●) and γ carbon (▲) of the amino acid and from CO_2 (*).**

with Severo's ever optimistic support, intense lunchtime and afternoon discussions that included such luminaries as Otto Loewi, Ephraim Racker, and occasionally Sarah Ratner, and a legion of visiting postdoctoral fellows, present and former students, and sabbatical guests from every corner of the world. Combined with an ethic of unremitting experimental work, the environment was ideal for a visitor to master enzymology as an essential tool in understanding carbohydrate and lipid metabolism.

Unlike other scientific departments I had been exposed to at American universities, Ochoa's department was more in the European or Japanese tradition of a group revolving around "the professor." Ochoa (shown in Fig. 2) was ambitious and inspiring, exceptionally well informed, and completely dedicated to science. In describing his career in Europe and the United States (8), he stated that biochemistry had been his "only and real hobby," but he greatly appreciated art and music and fully enjoyed their availability in New York City. In the laboratory he talked only of science, but under more relaxed circumstances his very broad cultural interests came to the fore.

Vladimir Prelog

Because of my increasing interest in mechanistic aspects of enzyme action, I subsequently took advantage of a sabbatical leave to improve my knowledge of organic chemistry and spent 1961–1962 with Professor Vladimir Prelog, Director of the Organic Chemistry Laboratory of the Eidgenössische Technische Hochschule (Swiss Federal Institute of Technology) in Zürich. Widely known for his studies on natural products and his outstanding contributions to stereochemistry (9), Prelog had developed an interest in enzyme stereoselectivity, and I began working on oxidoreductases in *Curvularia falcata*. The goal was to establish the absolute stereochemical course of hydride transfer to carbonyl groups of substrates such as decalin-1-one, decalin-2-one, and decalin-1,4-diones. Of interest, all the stereogenic carbon atoms formed by microbial reduction possess the same S-configuration, independent of the configuration of the other stereogenic centers in the molecule or whether the hydroxyls are in the axial or the equatorial positions. Two *Curvularia* enzymes, one believed to favor transfer of hydrogen into the axial position and another to favor the equatorial position, proved to be very difficult to purify. We found, however, an enzyme with oxidoreductase activity toward alicyclic ketones in pig liver that could be purified and was shown to be the 3-oxoacyl-acyl carrier protein reductase component of a fatty acid synthetase (10).

Vlado Prelog (see Fig. 3) was a frequent visitor to the United States and was elected as a Foreign Associate of the National Academy of Sciences. He said that he preferred the academic system in which scientific departments had a number of independent full professors. After he succeeded the famous Leopold Ruzicka in 1957 at the Eidgenössische Technische Hochschule, he established a "collegiate leadership" in which all appointed professors participated, surely an unusual arrangement at that time in Continental Europe. This gave him more time for research, for which he received innumerable honors, culminating in the 1975 Nobel Prize in Chemistry, which he shared with John Cornforth. After his mandatory retirement the following year, Prelog was required to have the title of postdoc-

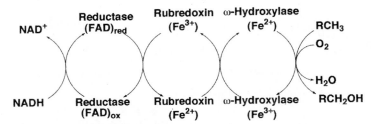

FIG. 5. **Conversion of octane to octanol or of laurate to ω-hydroxylaurate in the reconstituted enzyme system from** *P. oleovorans* **under aerobic conditions in the presence of NADH.**

toral student (Fachhörer) to continue his work, thus eventually leading to his autobiography entitled "My 137 Semesters of Chemistry Studies" (11).

In addition to his legendary pleasure in scientific study, he was widely known for his charming and witty personality. I can hardly recall a meeting with him, even a research conference, where he didn't regale us with his never ending supply of anecdotes about almost every famous chemist or biochemist (including those from the past), jokes, and humorous comments about the shortcomings of totalitarian political regimes, which he deplored.

Branched Chain Amino Acid Oxidation

In the fall of 1947 I had joined the faculty of the Department of Physiological Chemistry at the University of Pennsylvania, where I undertook studies on amino acid metabolism. The department was one of the first in this country to work with radioactive carbon-14 as a tracer in intermediary metabolism, and several of the senior faculty were widely known for their studies on this subject: Jack Buchanan on purine biosynthesis, D. Wright Wilson on pyrimidine biosynthesis, and Samuel Gurin on fatty acid oxidation. So little was known about amino acid metabolism in general at that time that it was difficult to make a specific choice, but I was intrigued by the branched chain compounds leucine, isoleucine, and valine. The main reason was that their metabolic fates might throw some light on the origin of the branched carbon structures of numerous biologically occurring compounds, including steroids, vitamins A, E, and K, and a variety of products in plants, thought to be derived from five-carbon units according to the biogenetic isoprene rule (12). Another reason to study leucine in particular was its known ketogenic property (acetoacetate production) in animals, because the intermediate thought to be formed by deamination and oxidative decarboxylation, isovaleric acid, was obviously blocked in the β-position from the entry of a carbonyl group and, therefore, could not undergo the classical β-oxidation that occurs with straight chain fatty acids.

I undertook the chemical synthesis of the substrates labeled with radioactivity in specific positions, no easy task because ^{14}C-labeled barium carbonate was the only commercially available starting material, incubated the purified compounds with liver slices, and analyzed the acetoacetate formed. To my surprise, the isopropyl group of leucine (and isovaleric acid) provided the terminal three carbons of this product, but the carboxyl carbon was unaccounted for. Radioactive CO_2 was then employed in other experiments and found to provide the missing carbon atom. These results (13, 14) and subsequent experiments with heart extracts (15) thus led to the discovery of a new ATP-dependent carbon dioxide fixation in mammalian metabolism.

The scheme in Fig. 4 shows our knowledge of leucine metabolism as we became aware of the role of coenzyme A and identified the involvement of the β-hydroxy-β-methylglutaryl-CoA cleavage enzyme in generating acetoacetate (16). We had originally thought from experiments with crude enzyme preparations that the substrate in the carboxylation reaction was β-hydroxyisovaleryl-CoA, but it was later correctly identified as the unsaturated compound β-methylcrotonyl-CoA (17, 18). In summary, we found that nature had solved the problem of a difficult oxidative reaction by introduction of an energy-dependent carboxylation as a crucial step. Of additional interest, our results showed how leucine metabolism is integrated into the main pathways of lipid metabolism and steroid biosynthesis. As is well known, the details of cholesterol biosynthesis were elegantly elucidated by Konrad Bloch and Feodor Lynen.

Hydrocarbon Oxidation by Gasoline Bugs

After moving to a faculty position at the University of Michigan and then returning from sabbatical leave in the Prelog laboratory some years later, I decided to work on the oxidation

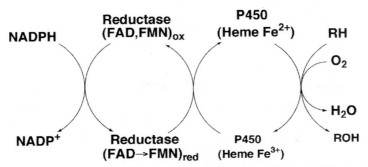

FIG. 6. **Conversion of any of a variety of substrates (RH) to products (ROH) in the P450-containing reconstituted enzyme system from liver microsomes under aerobic conditions in the presence of NADPH.**

of hydrocarbons, which (because of their poor chemical reactivity) might be an even greater challenge than leucine for enzymatic degradation. James Baptist, a postdoctoral associate from Illinois, agreed to undertake this problem and set about isolating a suitable bacterium from soil samples by an enrichment culture technique with hexane as the carbon source (19). The organism eventually obtained, a strain of *Pseudomonas oleovorans* that was dubbed the "gasoline bug" by our colleagues, grew well on several straight chain alkanes (or on leucine) but not on cyclohexane or methylbutane. Cell-free extracts were obtained that required the addition of NADH for the aerobic conversion of radioactive octane to octanol (20). Thus, it was evident that alkane oxidation at a terminal methyl group involved oxygenation as the initial step rather than an ATP-dependent carboxylation reaction, as in leucine metabolism. We subsequently found that, when presented with fatty acids as substrates, the bacterial system preferred to attack the terminal methyl carbon atom to give the ω-hydroxy acids (21) rather than to utilize a more chemically feasible α- or β-oxidation pathway. More will be said about ω-oxidation below in connection with related mammalian enzyme systems.

By preferential extraction of the bacterial cells and column chromatography, three enzyme components were separated and found to be required for the conversion of octane to octanol or of laurate to ω-hydroxylaurate in the reconstituted enzyme system (22) (Fig. 5). These were purified to homogeneity and characterized as follows: a red, nonheme iron protein containing two iron atoms but no labile sulfide and identified spectrally as rubredoxin (23), previously found only in anaerobes; a flavoprotein containing one molecule of FAD and found to be the NADH-rubredoxin reductase (24); and the ω-hydroxylase, which was relatively insoluble in that it formed aggregates of very high molecular weight, had an indistinct spectrum, and lost activity upon dialysis that was restored by the addition of ferrous ions (25, 26). The instability and other properties of the hydroxylase made it a difficult candidate for detailed mechanistic studies, but this enzyme system in *P. oleovorans* has continued to be investigated by others.

Cytochrome P450: Solubilization, Resolution, and Reconstitution of the Enzyme System from Liver Microsomal Membranes Active in Fatty Acid ω-Oxidation

Verkade *et al.* (27) in the Netherlands discovered ω-oxidation when they fed fatty acids of intermediate chain length (or their esters or glycerides) to dogs and human subjects and isolated the resulting urinary dicarboxylic acids, and Carter (28) and Bergström *et al.* (29) later reported that some α- and β-substituted fatty acids undergo a similar attack in animals. We undertook a study to determine the enzymatic mechanism of this intriguing oxidative process in the late 1950s, but the instability and insolubility of the liver microsomal enzyme system prevented further progress, and we turned our attention to the more tractable bacterial system, as described above.

Then, almost 10 years later, Anthony Lu joined our research group as a postdoctoral associate after completion of his graduate studies at the University of North Carolina. He impressed me as a highly talented and enthusiastic young scientist who would welcome a challenging problem, and I suggested that we again attempt to characterize the fatty acid ω-hydroxylating enzyme system of liver microsomes, making use of what we had learned about the bacterial system. The rest of this story is now well known. The hepatic system was resistant to the isolation and purification methods employed with the pseudomonad, but fortunately, we were not discouraged by the lack of knowledge at that time about membrane-bound enzymes in general and microsomal enzymes in particular. Thanks to Anthony's painstaking efforts for more than 2 years, the hydroxylating system eventually yielded to

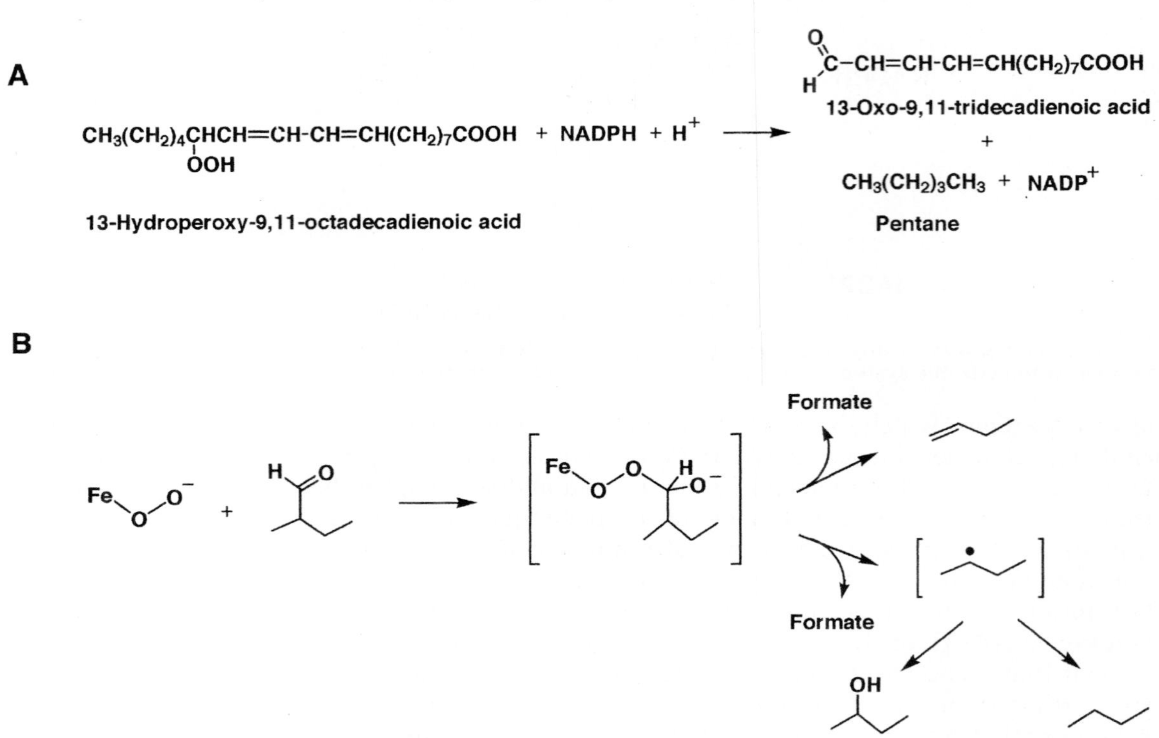

A

$$CH_3(CH_2)_4\underset{\underset{OOH}{|}}{C}HCH{=}CH{-}CH{=}CH(CH_2)_7COOH \ + \ NADPH \ + \ H^+ \ \longrightarrow$$

13-Hydroperoxy-9,11-octadecadienoic acid

$$\underset{H}{\overset{O}{\|}}C{-}CH{=}CH{-}CH{=}CH(CH_2)_7COOH$$

13-Oxo-9,11-tridecadienoic acid

+

$$CH_3(CH_2)_3CH_3 \ + \ NADP^+$$

Pentane

B

FIG. 7. **Reactions catalyzed by P450.** *A*, reductive cleavage of a lipid hydroperoxide to give an aldehyde acid and an alkane. *B*, oxidative cleavage of a model aldehyde to yield formate and, as the other product, an olefin, alcohol, or alkane; aldehydic drugs and naturally occurring compounds such as steroids are known substrates.

solubilization with various detergents in the presence of agents to protect against enzyme denaturation by the detergents. Column chromatography of the resulting preparations (again with detergents and protective agents) yielded a red fraction containing cytochrome P450 (identified by the spectral change upon addition of carbon monoxide to the reduced protein), a yellow fraction containing the flavoprotein NADPH-cytochrome P450 reductase (assayed by reduction of cytochrome *c* as an artificial electron acceptor), and a colorless, heat-stable fraction (30, 31). The last of these was shown by Henry Strobel, another postdoctoral associate from North Carolina, to contain phospholipids, of which phosphatidylcholine was especially active (32). When mixed and incubated together under precise conditions, the three components yielded a reconstituted enzyme system that converted lauric acid to ω-hydroxylauric acid in the presence of NADPH and oxygen, as shown in Fig. 6 (31).

In the progress of science we all build on previous findings, and we had the benefit of knowing that microsomes contain a carbon monoxide-binding pigment of unknown function (33–35), which was identified as a hemeprotein and designated "P-450" by Omura and Sato (36). Furthermore, the groundbreaking work of Omura, Sato, Cooper, Rosenthal, and Estabrook (37) had shown by photochemical action spectroscopy that this pigment in hepatic microsomes is responsible for the hydroxylation of several steroids and drugs. Thus, we had in our hands the solubilized hemeprotein P450 from rabbit liver microsomes capable of oxidizing not only fatty acids at the terminal position but a huge variety of other substrates of much greater biochemical and pharmacological interest. The same methods led to the successful solubilization and resolution of the P450-containing enzyme system of human liver microsomes (38). In addition, a visitor from France, Jean-Michel Lebeault, brought a strain of *Candida tropicalis* to my laboratory, and we found that, when grown on the long chain hydrocarbon tetradecane, it produced cytochrome P450 as the lauric acid ω-oxygenating catalyst that could be solubilized and reconstituted into a functional enzyme system (39). His company was investigating the use of petroleum as a source of yeast protein for human consumption, and on a visit to Marseilles I was offered a "yeast protein burger" that was devoid of the color and odor of the crude petroleum on which the organism had been grown. Although undoubtedly nutritious, the product was relatively bland in flavor as compared with the taste thrill of peppermint-flavored liver I recalled from my previous experience with nutrition experiments in graduate school. In the discussion that follows, subsequent work in our laboratory on catalytic and mechanistic studies with the microsomal system is briefly sum-

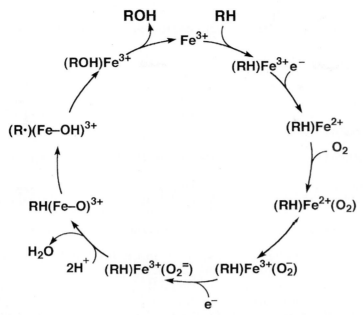

FIG. 8. **Mechanism of action of P450 in substrate oxygenation, where Fe represents the heme iron atom.**

marized. This has become an enormous field of endeavor, and no attempt will be made in these reflections to provide a comprehensive review. Mention should be made, however, of the seminal contributions of Gunsalus and colleagues with P450cam, a soluble (non-membrane-bound) cytochrome from a bacterial source, which is highly specific for camphor hydroxylation (40).

Cytochrome P450: Purification and Characterization of Multiple Isoforms

Studies with the purified components of the liver microsomal enzyme system have provided insights into structure, function, regulation, and mechanism that would not have been possible with microsomal membranes (41). Predictions from studies with intact microsomes varied from a single P450 enzyme with very broad specificity to an almost unlimited number, each specific for a different low molecular weight foreign compound, just as an antibody is specific for an individual foreign macromolecule. The induced synthesis of drug-metabolizing enzymes supported the existence of several discrete P450s (42), and purification and characterization clearly established the occurrence of a large family of distinct enzymes, including many that individually have numerous substrates (41). These are called isozymes even though that term was coined to describe multiple forms of an enzyme differing in properties such as substrate affinity, maximum activity, or regulation but identical in function. What is now called the P450 superfamily includes members with many different functions.

It took over 5 years for methods to be developed, including column chromatography in the presence of detergents, for the first mammalian P450, the phenobarbital-inducible form, to be purified and thoroughly characterized (43). It was called P450LM$_2$ (liver microsomal form 2), and shortly thereafter several other distinct forms, including β-naphthoflavone-inducible P450LM$_4$, were purified and shown to differ in physical and catalytic properties (44), leaving no doubt that multiple P450 isoforms occur in microsomes. Further convincing evidence for multiplicity was provided by the differences in amino acid composition and COOH-terminal amino acid residues (45).

Subsequently still more P450s were identified, including the ethanol-inducible form from liver (46) and unique forms from nasal microsomes (47), as well as numerous other forms from a variety of species, tissues, and organelles by many investigators. The nomenclature became increasingly difficult to follow, sometimes including names of inducers or of any of a variety of substrates, and under the leadership of Daniel Nebert (48) a system was devised based on divergent evolution as judged by sequence similarity. For example, P450LM$_2$ became P450 2B4 and the corresponding gene became *CYP2B4* to indicate family 2, subfamily B, and individual enzyme (or gene) number 4. Fortunately, NADPH-cytochrome P450 reductase, the enzyme that transfers electrons to the heme iron atom of P450 and was first purified by Janice

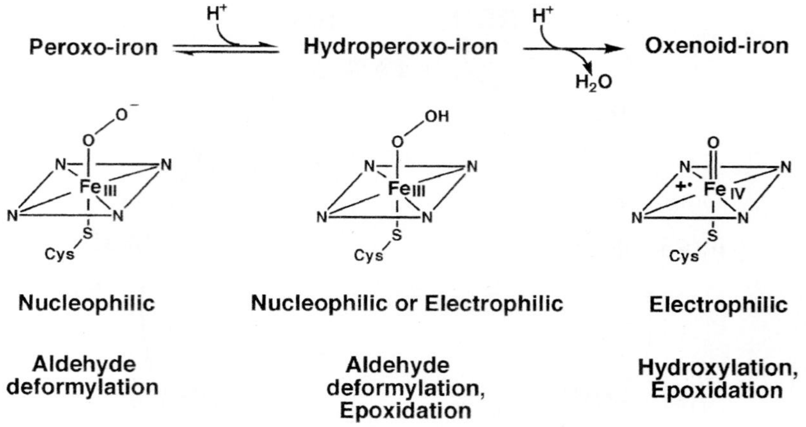

FIG. 9. **Proposed versatility in P450 oxygenating species.**

Vermilion and then shown to have separate roles in the FAD and FMN cofactors (49), exists as a single form.

Knowledge of the P450 superfamily is expanding rapidly, and it is evident that this cytochrome occurs throughout nature, including bacteria, fungi, plants, and animals (50). Of particular interest to the biomedical field, the human species has about 60 functional P450 genes. Detailed analysis of the human genes will be needed to identify and characterize the complete set of polymorphisms (51) and disease-causing mutations.

Cytochrome P450: Catalysis of Multiple Reactions with Innumerable Substrates

Considering the rapid progress made in recent years on the characterization of many isoforms, it may seem surprising that P450, a name first used for a red pigment having a reduced CO-difference spectrum with a major band at an unusually long wavelength (about 450 nm), has not been changed to a terminology based on function. Even the term cytochrome is unsuitable, because P450 usually acts as an oxygenase rather than simply as an electron carrier. Since many of the individual P450s catalyze multiple reactions, the usual method of naming enzymes is inadequate for these hemeproteins. The name "diversozymes" has been suggested for P450s, because they are unmatched in the broad scope of their functions (52).

The diverse reactions catalyzed include aliphatic and aromatic hydroxylation, *N*-oxidation, sulfoxidation, epoxidation, oxidative ester and amide cleavage, *N*-, *S*-, and *O*-dealkylation, peroxidation, *ipso*-substitution, deamination, desulfuration, and dehalogenation, as well as reactions such as reduction of azo groups, nitro groups, *N*-oxides, and epoxides that involve only electron transfer and partially justify the term cytochrome for this enzyme. Additional reactions attributable to P450 continue to be discovered (53). Two of these, one reductive and one oxidative, and both believed to involve radical chemistry will be mentioned. Cumene hydroperoxide was found to undergo reductive cleavage in the reconstituted enzyme system containing P450 and the reductase in the presence of NADPH; acetophenone was formed, and the missing one-carbon product was identified as methane by gas chromatographic/mass spectrometric analysis. As shown in Fig. 7A, the study was extended to the 13-hydroperoxide of linoleic acid, which yields pentane and an aldehyde acid (54). Lipid peroxidation is generally looked on as a destructive process in membranes of living cells, but molecular oxygen plays no role in the reductive reaction shown. It may be noted that the exhalation of pentane and other hydrocarbons by various species, including the human, is believed to be a measure of this pathophysiological process, now known to involve P450. Another P450-catalyzed reaction of much interest is the oxidative demethylation that accompanies steroid aromatization, for which a role for an oxygen-derived peroxide has been suggested (55). We have examined the deformylation of a variety of aldehydes and have proposed a peroxyhemiacetal-like adduct as a transient enzyme-bound intermediate (56) as shown in Fig. 7B. Presumably the intermediate rearranges by a concerted or sequential β-scission to yield the products, formic acid from the aldehyde group and an olefin, an alcohol, or an alkane from the remaining structure. This reaction is particularly relevant to the mechanism of oxygen activation by this versatile catalyst, as described below.

The number of organic compounds that serve as P450 substrates was cautiously estimated in the 1980s to be in the hundreds or even the thousands, but currently no one familiar with the field is surprised at the prediction of a million or more. These include physiologically occurring compounds such as fatty acids, steroids, eicosanoids, lipid hydroperoxides, retinoids, and amino acids. Equally unexpected is the very large list of xenobiotic substrates, including almost all drugs (with many more being produced each year by the pharmaceutical industry), procarcinogens (57), antioxidants, solvents, anesthetics, dyes, pesticides, petroleum products, alcohols, and products derived from plants such as flavorants and odorants. With respect to the metabolism of drugs, most are inactivated by P450, but some are activated and others yield products that inactivate the cytochrome itself (58). Such information is therefore useful for the design and development of potential new drugs. The ability of this catalyst to metabolize a multitude of organic compounds that can now be produced readily by combinatorial techniques but do not occur naturally on this planet indicates that the number and variety of P450 substrates are almost unlimited. However, the oxygenation of substrates by the mammalian cytochromes is not necessarily indiscriminate. Particularly with compounds of physiological importance, the attack on the substrate can be both positionally and stereochemically specific.

Cytochrome P450: Mechanism of Action and Evidence for Multiple Forms of Activated Oxygen

The mechanistic details of enzyme-catalyzed hydroxylation reactions have long been of interest, and biochemists and chemists have been particularly intrigued by the possibility that P450 generates an unusually powerful species capable of oxidizing relatively inert substrates. The availability of the purified microsomal cytochromes and versatility of these catalysts in the metabolism of almost any organic compound of mechanistic interest helped facilitate rapid progress. For example, John Groves, a former member of our chemistry faculty, suggested a collaboration with Ronald White and me on norbornane oxidation. Sure enough, the *exo*-tetradeuterated compound was hydroxylated by P450 2B4; the results suggested an initial hydrogen abstraction to give a carbon radical intermediate (59). Furthermore, P450 has also been found to be versatile with respect to the oxidant, for NADPH, the reductase, and molecular oxygen could be replaced by hydrogen peroxide (60) and, surprisingly, also by almost any substituted cumene hydroperoxide, benzyl hydroperoxide, or perbenzoic acid (61). The accompanying scheme (Fig. 8) indicates the main contributions from this and other laboratories (62). The identification of oxene, $(Fe-O)^{3+}$, as the ultimate oxidant remains elusive, but mounting evidence is now available that multiple oxidants are involved in P450 function.

In the last few years we have carried out site-directed mutagenesis of mammalian P450s 2B4 and 2E1 in which the active site threonine was substituted by alanine to learn more about the details of oxygen activation. In so doing we have taken advantage of evidence from other investigators that the corresponding mutation in bacterial P450cam interferes with the conversion of dioxygen to the oxenoid species by disrupting proton delivery to the active site (63, 64). Our results with the truncated, heterologously expressed enzymes (65) support the involvement of three functional species produced during the reduction of oxygen (66–68) as shown in Fig. 9. The occurrence of multiple oxidizing species may contribute to the remarkable versatility of the P450 family of isozymes in the modification of drugs and other substrates (69). Furthermore, highly reactive "radical clocks" employed as mechanistic probes have confirmed that two distinct electrophilic oxidants effect hydroxylation in cytochrome P450-catalyzed reactions (70, 71). A related long standing question is whether the thiolate supplied by a cysteine residue as the proximal heme ligand contributes to the chemical reactivity of these catalysts. Replacement of the active site cysteine-436 by serine has recently been shown to convert P450 2B4 into an NADPH oxidase with negligible monooxygenase activity (72).

Many colleagues, including students, postdoctoral associates, and other collaborators have contributed to the progress of our research. Regretfully, not all could be adequately recognized in this brief presentation. In addition, I have benefited from friendships and interactions with many others in what has become the vast P450 field—so vast, in fact, that the present number of investigators, like that of the isoforms and their substrates, may be unmatched.

Address correspondence to: mjcoon@umich.edu.

REFERENCES

1. Carter, H. E., and Coon, M. J. (1995) William Cumming Rose, a biographical memoir. *Biogr. Mem. Natl. Acad. Sci.* **68**, 3–21
2. McCoy, R. H., Meyer, C. E., and Rose, W. C. (1935) Feeding experiments with mixtures of highly purified amino

acids. VIII. Isolation and identification of a new essential amino acid. *J. Biol. Chem.* **112**, 283–302

3. Rose, W. C., Haines, W. J., and Johnson, J. E. (1942) The role of the amino acids in human nutrition. *J. Biol. Chem.* **146**, 683–684

4. Rose, W. C. (1947) The role of the amino acids in human nutrition. *Proc. Am. Philos. Soc.* **91**, 112–116

5. Kornberg, A. (2001) Remembering our teachers. *J. Biol. Chem.* **276**, 3–11

6. Stern, J. R., Coon, M. J., del Campillo, A., and Schneider, M. C. (1956) Enzymes of fatty acid metabolism. IV. Preparation and properties of coenzyme A transferase. *J. Biol. Chem.* **221**, 15–31

7. *New York Times* (1993) Severo Ochoa, biochemist, a Nobel winner 88, dies. November 3. Obituary

8. Ochoa, S. (1980) The pursuit of a hobby. *Annu. Rev. Biochem.* **49**, 1–30

9. Arigoni, D., Dunitz, J. D., and Eschenmoser, A. (2000) Vladimir Prelog, 23 July 1906–7 January 1998. *Biogr. Mem. Fellows R. Soc.* **46**, 445–464

10. Dutler, H., Coon, M. J., Kull, A., Vogel, H., Waldvogel, G., and Prelog, V. (1971) Fatty acid synthetase from pig liver. 1. Isolation of the enzyme complex and characterization of the component with oxidoreductase activity for alicyclic ketones. *Eur. J. Biochem.* **22**, 203–212

11. Prelog, V. (1991) My 132 semesters of chemistry studies. In *Autobiographies of Eminent Chemists* (Seeman, J. I., series ed) American Chemical Society, Washington, D. C.

12. Ruzicka, L. (1953) The isoprene rule and the biogenesis of terpenic compounds. *Experientia* **9**, 357–396

13. Coon, M. J., and Gurin, S. (1949) Studies on the conversion of radioactive leucine to acetoacetate. *J. Biol. Chem.* **180**, 1159–1167

14. Coon, M. J. (1950) The metabolic fate of the isopropyl group of leucine. *J. Biol. Chem.* **187**, 71–82

15. Bachhawat, B. K., Robinson, W. G., and Coon, M. J. (1954) Carbon dioxide fixation in heart extracts by β-hydroxyisovaleryl coenzyme A. *J. Am. Chem. Soc.* **76**, 3098

16. Bachhawat, B. K., Robinson, W. G., and Coon, M. J. (1955) The enzymatic cleavage of β-hydroxy-β-methylglutaryl coenzyme A to acetoacetate and acetyl coenzyme A. *J. Biol. Chem.* **216**, 727–736

17. Hilz, H., Knappe, J., Ringelmann, E., and Lynen, F. (1958) Methylglutaconase, a new hydratase involved in the metabolism of branched chain carboxylic acids. *Biochem. Z.* **329**, 476–489

18. del Campillo-Campbell, A., Dekker, E. E., and Coon, M. J. (1959) Carboxylation of β-methylcrotonyl coenzyme A by a purified enzyme from chicken liver. *Biochim. Biophys. Acta* **31**, 290–292

19. Baptist, J. N., Gholson, R. K., and Coon, M. J. (1963) Hydrocarbon oxidation by a bacterial enzyme system. I. Products of octane oxidation. *Biochim. Biophys. Acta* **69**, 40–47

20. Gholson, R. K., Baptist, J. N., and Coon, M. J. (1963) Hydrocarbon oxidation by a bacterial enzyme system. II. Cofactor requirements for octanol formation from octane. *Biochemistry* **2**, 1155–1159

21. Kusunose, M., Kusunose, E., and Coon, M. J. (1964) Enzymatic ω-oxidation of fatty acids. II. Substrate specificity and other properties of the enzyme system. *J. Biol. Chem.* **239**, 2135–2139

22. Peterson, J. A., Basu, D., and Coon, M. J. (1966) Enzymatic ω-oxidation. I. Electron carriers in fatty acid and hydrocarbon hydroxylation. *J. Biol. Chem.* **241**, 5162–5163

23. Peterson, J. A., and Coon, M. J. (1968) Enzymatic ω-oxidation. III. Purification and properties of rubredoxin, a component of the ω-hydroxylation system of *Pseudomonas oleovorans*. *J. Biol. Chem.* **243**, 329–334

24. Ueda, T., and Coon, M. J. (1972) Enzymatic ω-oxidation. VII. Reduced diphosphopyridine nucleotide-rubredoxin reductase: properties and function as an electron carrier in ω-hydroxylation. *J. Biol. Chem.* **247**, 5010–5016

25. McKenna, E. J., and Coon, M. J. (1970) Enzymatic ω-oxidation. IV. Purification and properties of the ω-hydroxylase of *Pseudomonas oleovorans*. *J. Biol. Chem.* **245**, 3882–3889

26. Ruettinger, R. T., Olson, S. T., Boyer, R. F., and Coon, M. J. (1974) Identification of the ω-hydroxylase of *Pseudomonas oleovorans* as a nonheme iron protein requiring phospholipid for catalytic activity. *Biochem. Biophys. Res. Commun.* **57**, 1011–1017

27. Verkade, P. E., Elzas, M., van der Lee, J., de Wolff, H. H., Verkade-Sandbergen, A., and van der Sande, D. (1932) Studies on the metabolism of fats. *Proc. K. Ned. Akad. Wet.* **35**, 251–266

28. Carter, H. E. (1941) The oxidation of branched-chain fatty acids. In *Biological Symposia* (Lewis, H. B., ed) Vol. 5, pp. 47–63, Jacques Cattell Press, Lancaster, PA

29. Bergström, S., Borgström, B., Tryding, N., and Westöö, G. (1954) Intestinal absorption and metabolism of 2:2-dimethylstearic acid in the rat. *Biochem. J.* **58**, 604–608

30. Lu, A. Y. H., and Coon, M. J. (1968) Role of hemoprotein P-450 in fatty acid ω-hydroxylation in a soluble enzyme system from liver microsomes. *J. Biol. Chem.* **243**, 1331–1332

31. Lu, A. Y. H., Junk, K. W., and Coon, M. J. (1969) Resolution of the cytochrome P-450-containing ω-hydroxylation system of liver microsomes into three components. *J. Biol. Chem.* **244**, 3714–3721

32. Strobel, H. W., Lu, A. Y. H., Heidema, J., and Coon, M. J. (1970) Phosphatidylcholine requirement in the enzymatic reduction of hemoprotein P-450 and in fatty acid, hydrocarbon, and drug hydroxylation. *J. Biol. Chem.* **245**, 4851–4854

33. Ryan, K. J., and Engel, L. L. (1957) Hydroxylation of steroids at carbon 21. *J. Biol. Chem.* **225**, 103–114

34. Klingenberg, M. (1958) Pigments of rat liver microsomes. *Arch. Biochem. Biophys.* **75**, 376–386

35. Garfinkel, D. (1958) Studies on pig liver microsomes. I. Enzymic and pigment composition of different microsomal fractions. *Arch. Biochem. Biophys.* **77**, 493–509

36. Omura, T., and Sato, R. (1962) A new cytochrome in liver microsomes. *J. Biol. Chem.* **237**, 1375–1376

37. Omura, T., Sato, R., Cooper, D. Y., Rosenthal, O., and Estabrook, R. W. (1965) Function of cytochrome P-450 of microsomes. *Fed. Proc.* **24**, 1181–1189

38. Kaschnitz, R. M., and Coon, M. J. (1975) Drug and fatty acid hydroxylation by solubilized human liver microsomal cytochrome P-450-phospholipid requirement. *Biochem. Pharmacol.* **24**, 295–297

39. Lebeault, J. M., Lode, E. T., and Coon, M. J. (1971) Fatty acid and hydrocarbon hydroxylation in yeast: role of cytochrome P-450 in *Candida tropicalis*. *Biochem. Biophys. Res. Commun.* **42**, 413–419

40. Gunsalus, I. C., and Sligar, S. G. (1978) Oxygen reduction by the P450 monooxygenase systems. *Adv. Enzyme Regul.* **47**, 1–44

41. Porter, T. D., and Coon, M. J. (1991) Cytochrome P-450. Multiplicity of isoforms, substrates, and catalytic and regulatory mechanisms. *J. Biol. Chem.* **266**, 13469–13472

42. Conney, A. H. (2003) Induction of drug-metabolizing enzymes: a path to the discovery of multiple cytochromes P450. *Annu. Rev. Pharmacol. Toxicol.*, in press

43. van der Hoeven, T. A., and Coon, M. J. (1974) Preparation and properties of partially purified cytochrome P-450 and reduced nicotinamide adenine dinucleotide phosphate-cytochrome P-450 reductase from rabbit liver microsomes. *J. Biol. Chem.* **249**, 6302–6310

44. Haugen, D. A., van der Hoeven, T. A., and Coon, M. J. (1975) Purified liver microsomal cytochrome P-450. Separation and characterization of multiple forms. *J. Biol. Chem.* **250**, 3567–3570

45. Haugen, D. A., and Coon, M. J. (1976) Properties of electrophoretically homogeneous phenobarbital-inducible and β-naphthoflavone-inducible forms of liver microsomal cytochrome P-450. *J. Biol. Chem.* **251**, 7929–7939

46. Koop, D. R., Morgan, E. T., Tarr, G. E., and Coon, M. J. (1982) Purification and characterization of a unique isozyme of cytochrome P-450 from liver microsomes of ethanol-treated rabbits. *J. Biol. Chem.* **257,** 8472–8480

47. Ding, X., and Coon, M. J. (1988) Purification and characterization of two unique forms of cytochrome P-450 from rabbit nasal microsomes. *Biochemistry* **27,** 8330–8337

48. Nebert, D. W., Adesnik, M., Coon, M. J., Estabrook, R. W., Gonzalez, F. J., Guengerich, F. P., Gunsalus, I. C., Johnson, E. F., Kemper, B., Levin, W., Phillips, I. R., Sato, R., and Waterman, M. R. (1987) The P450 gene superfamily: recommended nomenclature. *DNA* **6,** 1–11

49. Vermilion, J. L., Ballou, D. P., Massey, V., and Coon, M. J. (1981) Separate roles for FMN and FAD in catalysis by liver microsomal NADPH-cytochrome P450 reductase. *J. Biol. Chem.* **256,** 266–277

50. Nelson, D. R. (1999) Cytochrome P450 and the individuality of species. *Arch. Biochem. Biophys.* **369,** 1–10

51. Ingelman-Sundberg, M., Oscarson, M., and McLellan, R. A. (1999) Polymorphic human cytochrome P450 enzymes: an opportunity for individualized drug treatment. *Trends Pharmacol. Sci.* **20,** 342–349

52. Coon, M. J., Vaz, A. D. N., and Bestervelt, L. L. (1996) Peroxidative reactions of diversozymes. *FASEB J.* **10,** 428–434

53. Guengerich, F. P. (2001) Common and uncommon cytochrome P450 reactions related to metabolism and chemical toxicity. *Chem. Res. Toxicol.* **14,** 611–650

54. Vaz, A. D. N., Roberts, E. S., and Coon, M. J. (1990) Reductive β-scission of the hydroperoxides of fatty acids and xenobiotics: role of alcohol-inducible cytochrome P-450. *Proc. Natl. Acad. Sci. U. S. A.* **87,** 5499–5503

55. Akhtar, M., Calder, M. R., Corina, D. L., and Wright, J. N. (1982) Mechanistic studies on C-19 demethylation in oestrogen biosynthesis. *Biochem. J.* **201,** 569–580

56. Roberts, E. S., Vaz, A. D. N., and Coon, M. J. (1991) Catalysis by cytochrome P-450 of an oxidative reaction in xenobiotic aldehyde metabolism: deformylation with olefin formation. *Proc. Natl. Acad. Sci. U. S. A.* **88,** 8963–8966

57. Putt, D. A., Ding, X., Coon, M. J., and Hollenberg, P. F. (1995) Metabolism of aflatoxin B1 by rabbit and rat nasal mucosa microsomes and purified cytochrome P450, including isoforms 2A10 and 2A11. *Carcinogenesis* **16,** 1411–1417

58. Osawa, Y., and Coon, M. J. (1989) Selective mechanism-based inactivation of the major phenobarbital-inducible cytochrome P-450 from rabbit liver by phencyclidine and its oxidation product, the iminium compound. *Drug Metab. Dispos.* **17,** 7–13

59. Groves, J. T., McClusky, G. A., White, R. E., and Coon, M. J. (1978) Aliphatic hydroxylation by highly purified liver microsomal cytochrome P-450. Evidence for a carbon radical intermediate. *Biochem. Biophys. Res. Commun.* **81,** 154–160

60. Nordblom, G. D., White, R. E., and Coon, M. J. (1976) Studies on hydroperoxide-dependent substrate hydroxylation by purified liver microsomal cytochrome P-450. *Arch. Biochem. Biophys.* **175,** 524–533

61. Blake, R. C., II, and Coon, M. J. (1980) On the mechanism of action of cytochrome P-450. Spectral intermediates in the reaction of P450 LM$_2$ with peroxy compounds. *J. Biol. Chem.* **255,** 4100–4111

62. White, R. E., and Coon, M. J. (1980) Oxygen activation by cytochrome P-450. *Annu. Rev. Biochem.* **49,** 315–356

63. Martinis, S. A., Atkins, W. M., Stayton, P. S., and Sligar, S. G. (1989) A conserved residue of cytochrome-P-450 is involved in heme-oxygen stability and activation. *J. Am. Chem. Soc.* **111,** 9252–9253

64. Imai, M., Shimada, H., Watanabe, Y., Matsushima-Hibiya, Y., Makino, R., Koga, H., Horiuchi, T., and Ishimura, Y. (1989) Uncoupling of the cytochrome P-450cam monooxygenase reaction by a single mutation, threonine-252 to alanine or valine: possible role of the hydroxy amino acid in oxygen activation. *Proc. Natl. Acad. Sci. U. S. A.* **86,** 7823–7827

65. Larson, J. R., Coon, M. J., and Porter, T. D. (1991) Purification and properties of a shortened form of cytochrome P-450 2E1: deletion of the NH$_2$-terminal membrane insertion signal peptide does not alter the catalytic activities. *Proc. Natl. Acad. Sci. U. S. A.* **88,** 9141–9145

66. Vaz, A. D. N., Pernecky, S. J., Raner, G. M., and Coon, M. J. (1996) Peroxo-iron and oxenoid-iron species as alternative oxygenating agents in cytochrome P450-catalyzed reactions: switching by T302A mutagenesis of cytochrome P450 2B4. *Proc. Natl. Acad. Sci. U. S. A.* **93,** 4644–4648

67. Guengerich, F. P., Vaz, A. D. N., Raner, G. M., Pernecky, S. J., and Coon, M. J. (1997) Evidence for a role of a perferryl-oxygen complex, FeO^{3+}, in the N-oxygenation of amines by cytochrome P450 enzymes. *Mol. Pharmacol.* **51,** 147–151

68. Vaz, A. D. N., McGinnity, D. F., and Coon, M. J. (1998) Epoxidation of olefins by cytochrome P450: evidence from site-specific mutagenesis for hydroperoxo-iron as an electrophilic oxidant. *Proc. Natl. Acad. Sci. U. S. A.* **95,** 3555–3560

69. Coon, M. J., Vaz, A. D. N., McGinnity, D. F., and Peng, H.-M. (1998) Multiple activated oxygen species in P450 catalysis: contributions to specificity in drug metabolism. *Drug Metab. Dispos.* **26,** 1190–1193

70. Toy, P. H., Newcomb, M., Coon, M. J., and Vaz, A. D. N. (1998) Two distinct electrophilic oxidants effect hydroxylation in cytochrome P450-catalyzed reactions. *J. Am. Chem. Soc.* **120,** 9718–9719

71. Newcomb, M., Shen, R., Choi, S.-Y., Toy, P. H., Hollenberg, P. F., Vaz, A. D. N., and Coon, M. J. (2000) Cytochrome P450-catalyzed hydroxylation of mechanistic probes that distinguish between radicals and cations. Evidence for cationic but not for radical intermediates. *J. Am. Chem. Soc.* **122,** 2677–2686

72. Vatsis, K. P., Peng, H.-M., and Coon, M. J. (2002) Replacement of active-site cysteine-436 by serine converts cytochrome P450 2B4 into an NADPH oxidase with negligible monooxygenase activity. *J. Inorg. Biochem.,* in press

THE JOURNAL OF BIOLOGICAL CHEMISTRY
Vol. 277, No. 37, Issue of September 13, pp. 33531–33536, 2002
Printed in U.S.A.

Reflections

A PAPER IN A SERIES COMMISSIONED TO CELEBRATE THE CENTENARY OF THE JBC IN 2005

JBC Centennial
1905–2005
100 Years of Biochemistry and Molecular Biology

Biochemistry during the Life and Times
of Hans Krebs and Fritz Lipmann

Published, JBC Papers in Press, June 17, 2002, DOI 10.1074/jbc.R200019200

John M. Buchanan

From the Department of Biology, Massachusetts Institute of Technology, Cambridge, Massachusetts 02139-4307

This essay reviews some of the types of problems under investigation during the period of 1940–1950 and the influence two exceptional scientists would have on my early development as a biochemist. To put my life into some kind of perspective in regard to this particular period, I should provide some data about my early academic situation. I started my graduate studies with a Master's degree from the Department of Biological Chemistry at the University of Michigan, whose Chairman was Howard B. Lewis. He was a dynamic lecturer and one of the pioneers of research in intermediary metabolism. For my Doctorate degree I moved to Harvard Medical School to work with A. Baird Hastings (see Fig. 3). Both Lewis and Hastings were principal mentors during my career. I then spent 10 years on the faculty of the Department of Physiological Chemistry, School of Medicine, University of Pennsylvania in Philadelphia with a 2-year sabbatical period at the Medical Nobel Institute with Hugo Theorell. Eventually I returned to the Boston area as Head of the Biochemistry Program in the Department of Biology, Massachusetts Institute of Technology.

These features of my academic life establish the setting from which I would view the imprint that my seniors, for example, Krebs (Fig. 1) and Lipmann (Fig. 2), would make on my chosen field of intermediary metabolism. The whole approach to biochemical research had a monumental advance with the availability of radioactive or stable isotopes of carbon. In 1939 Hastings (Fig. 3) had been able to arrange for the production of ^{11}C by our cyclotron in Cambridge. Its very short half-life, however, limited the types of problems that could be finished within a 4–5-h time limit. Despite this, a team of organic chemists and biochemists was able to synthesize two forms of lactic acid, one labeled on the carboxyl carbon (1) and the other on the α or β carbons (2), feed either one to fasted rats, and then isolate and measure the radioactivity of the liver and muscle glycogen. The initial goal was to determine whether these experiments confirmed the validity of Schoenheimer's proposal (3) of the *Dynamic State of Body Constituents*. Indeed, lactic acid did contribute to the pool of glycogen precursors. However, a new finding did emerge, namely, in its conversion to liver glycogen the carboxyl carbon of lactic acid is replaced in part with carbon originating from carbon dioxide (4, 5). Research on the utilization of carbon dioxide as a substrate of reactions had been pioneered by Harland Wood and Chester Werkman (7, 8) in microbial systems, but the existence of this reaction in higher systems had yet to be verified. The Wood-Werkman reaction involves the carboxylation of pyruvate to yield oxalacetate.

$$CH_3COCOOH + CO_2 \leftrightarrow HOOCCH_2COCOOH$$

REACTION 1

Pyruvate is formed by the oxidation of lactic acid ($CH_3CHOHCOOH$).

Earl Evans (9) of the University of Chicago had spent a sabbatical year in Krebs' laboratory in England working on reactions of a cycle of reactions that had been proposed by Krebs (10,

Fig. 1. **Hans Krebs.**

11) for the oxidation of pyruvate by its condensation with oxalacetate to yield citric acid. Then, through a series of reactions involving cisaconitic acid, isocitric acid, α-ketoglutaric acid, and succinic, fumaric, and malic acids, oxalacetic acid is regenerated. Thus, any of the aforementioned acids could behave catalytically in the cycle because the end product of the reaction, oxalacetate, would be available to react with pyruvate for another round of the cycle. Krebs initially proposed the involvement of a seven-carbon compound, oxalcitraconic acid, which by oxidative decarboxylation would yield the six-carbon citric acid. As will be seen, a better proposal would emerge when it was realized that pyruvate was not the actual reactant in the initial condensation with oxalacetate but rather a two-carbon compound produced by the oxidative decarboxylation of pyruvate. However, the path to this conclusion did not emerge easily.

Liver tissue differs from muscle in a major way in that oxalacetate can be formed directly from pyruvate and carbon dioxide by the Wood-Werkman reaction, and hence the addition of an organic acid of the cycle would not be required in this tissue. Aware of this finding, Krebs had written to Hastings about coming to Harvard to test this proposed role of carbon dioxide with radioactive ^{11}C. However, this visit proved impossible in 1940 because of England's serious involvement in World War II. However, Evans and Slotin (12), using pigeon liver minces, were able to conduct the experiment in Chicago and reported that α-ketoglutarate was labeled only in the carboxyl group proximal to the keto group. This finding appeared to require a restatement of the cycle with cisaconitate being the product of the reaction of pyruvate and oxalacetate because citric acid is a symmetrical compound, and the isotope should therefore be expected to appear in either carboxyl group of α-ketoglutarate to an equal extent.

FIG. 2. **Fritz Lipmann.**

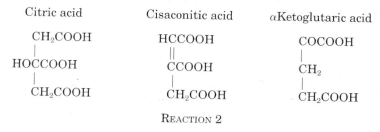

REACTION 2

This paradox was temporarily resolved by a theory proposed by Ogston (13) that even though citric acid appeared to be symmetrical, in fact it reacts asymmetrically with an enzyme if the latter binds to its substrate with a three-point attachment. Thus, under these circumstances citric acid could remain in the cycle. However, from recent work in Koshland's laboratory on isocitrate dehydrogenase they recognized fallacies in hidden assumptions of Ogston's hypothesis. They reported that the three-point attachment model could not be the reason for the distinction. In fact, they found that "the major difference was the orientation of the fourth group or the hydroxyl group of citric acid" (14).

However, this hypothesis did not arrive in time to keep us from making a similar erroneous conclusion in some research we had commenced at the University of Pennsylvania. At Pennsylvania we had the opportunity of working with the stable isotope of ^{13}C, where time was not a factor in our experiments. A team composed of Samuel Gurin, Warwick Sakami, D. W.

Fig. 3. **Baird Hastings.**

Wilson, and myself decided to tackle the problem of how fatty acids and ketone bodies are oxidized, possibly through the Krebs cycle (15), a proposal that had been advocated previously by others (16, 17). A pressing problem at that time was the question of whether fatty acids could be converted to carbohydrates. I think that this problem arose because diabetic patients oxidized fats when the metabolism of carbohydrates was prevented by a lack of insulin.

Our experimental tissues were homogenates of guinea pig or rabbit kidneys. To these preparations we added carboxyl labeled acetate or carboxyl and carbonyl doubly labeled acetoacetate together with banks of unlabeled members of the citric acid cycle, principally α-ketoglutarate. At the end of the incubation we isolated the residual α-ketoglutarate and its oxidation products, succinic and fumaric acids. In the case of α-ketoglutarate we found that the isotopic carbon was present entirely in the carboxyl carbon distal to the keto group. Thinking that our experiments supported those of Evans, we also published our belief that citric acid was not a member of the tricarboxylic acid cycle. Of course, the Ogston hypothesis, which was reported soon after our publication, invalidated our conclusion.

However, our results did provide an explanation of our principal objective of whether fatty acids and ketone bodies are or are not converted to carbohydrates or carbohydrate precursors. As an acetate molecule is oxidized by the reactions of the citric acid cycle, two molecules of carbon dioxide are produced by one turn of the cycle. However, the two molecules of carbon dioxide did not have their origin in the original acetate. The acetate carbons remained in the oxalacetate produced in the first cycle. Then, by equilibrium reactions in the carbohydrate metabolic pool, some labeled carbon may be found in glucose intermediates and in glycogenic amino acids such as alanine. However, this evidence does not justify a conclusion that fatty acids are converted to carbohydrates in the conventional sense, because there is no net gain in the amount of carbohydrate precursor in the form of oxalacetate. Only a normal molecule is replaced by a labeled one.

Perhaps the greatest advance in concepts of intermediary metabolism during these years was the eventual realization that a carbohydrate precursor, pyruvate, and a fatty acid representative, acetate or a ketone body, utilize a common oxidative pathway, through the participation of an active derivative of the two-carbon compound, acetate. The identity of this derivative took a long time to emerge. The classic experiments of Medes, Weinhouse, and Floyd (18) had proven decisively that β-oxidation of a fatty acid occurred with some of the product undergoing oxidation via the tricarboxylic acid (TCA) cycle and the residue condensing into ketone bodies, acetoacetic acid and β-hydroxybutyric acid. Furthermore, although acetoacetate breaks down into two-carbon units in liver slices in preparation for oxidation, they do not reform acetoacetate with carbon atoms in any different distribution than was originally present (19).

It took a long time for researchers to concur that ketone bodies are not simply dead-end products of fat metabolism, there being evidence both pro and con with the several tissue systems used in experiments. For instance, Krebs and Eggleston (20) reported in one study with heart tissue that all of the acetoacetate disappearing in their experiment could be accounted for by the formation of β-hydroxybutyric acid. In our kidney homogenates the optimal metabolism of acetoacetic acid was achieved when an acid of the citric acid cycle was present in the incubation, particularly α-ketoglutaric acid. As was later discovered, there is a coenzymic function relating the oxidation of α-ketoglutaric acid and the activation of acetoacetate for its oxidation (21) (see below).

The conclusion of this essay examines the history of the search for the identity of the active derivative of acetate and how the final form of the citric acid cycle was achieved.

Lipmann had gained his early reputation by his proposal of how chemical energy, stored in polyphosphate compounds such as ATP, provides the energy required for biosynthetic reactions (22). Although his concept of "high energy phosphate" required reinterpretation, it was useful in explaining how compounds could become activated and participate in certain reactions. One such example was the production of acetylphosphate in pyruvate oxidation (23). As attractive as this compound seemed as a participant in certain microbial systems, it was not co-reactive with oxalacetate in the citric acid cycle.

Lipmann then turned to a study of the acetylation of sulfonamides (24), which led him to the discovery of coenzyme A. At first this research seemed to have limited significance. However, this attitude changed rapidly when the composition of purified coenzyme A (25) was established in research with Dr. Beverly Guiard as a derivative of pantothenic acid, a vitamin under investigation at the University of Texas, in the laboratories of Esmond Snell and Roger Williams. Coenzyme A was a cofactor relating the transacetylation reactions (21, 26) of pyruvate and α-ketoglutarate oxidation to the activation and oxidation of acetoacetate. Also importantly it was a participant with oxalacetate in the synthesis of citric acid. As a result of the famous paper by Novelli and Lipmann (27) the full significance of this coenzyme was finally realized and the two worlds of Hans Krebs and Fritz Lipmann converged. In 1953 their combined works were recognized by a joint award of the Nobel Prize in Medicine or Physiology. In Boston there was a substantial celebration for Fritz as a prominent and much beloved member of the biochemical and medical faculty of Harvard Medical School.

Both Lipmann and Krebs had been born and educated in Germany. Before World War II both had met and worked together in the laboratory of Otto Meyerhof and Otto Warburg, two of Germany's most outstanding biologists. Because of the Nazi persecution of Jews, Krebs emigrated to England, and Lipmann as well as Meyerhof emigrated to the United States. Both Krebs and Lipmann established distinguished schools of students in their adopted countries. Lipmann contributed to many other areas of biochemistry, including the reactions of protein synthesis. Krebs in turn had published two important papers that were to influence my life on the biosynthesis of hypoxanthine in pigeon liver slices (28, 29). In these papers methods were reported on the chemical degradation of uric acid to its individual carbon and nitrogen atoms. With the availability of the ^{13}C and eventually ^{14}C isotopes, the study of the biosynthesis of uric acid became possible in 1946 (30–33). This goal was expanded in 1948 by G. Robert Greenberg (then at Western Reserve University) by his evidence that purines are synthesized in pigeon liver homogenates and extracts (34) in the form of their ribonucleotides (35). It has been a source of pleasure to me that our two laboratories have enjoyed mutually cordial relationships over the years. The dual but independent approach to the clarification of the individual steps in this biosynthetic system was essential. Even more satisfying has been my close friendship with my own group of gifted and productive students and postdoctoral fellows.

The story of purine biosynthesis, however, is for another time. This essay has tried to place two great scientists, Hans Krebs and Fritz Lipmann, in the context of the time when their studies on carbohydrate and fat metabolism were of primary interest to the biochemical community. I met Krebs only twice, once when I was in England in 1947 to attend an International Congress of Physiology. The second time was at a reception following the Dunham Lectures at Harvard Medical School. Invited to make some comments on that occasion, I was able to convey to him how much my own scientific endeavors had depended on the background he had provided in the biochemical literature.

Address correspondence to: E-mail: enbuchanan@mymailstation.com.

REFERENCES

1. Conant, J. B., Cramer, R. D., Hastings, A. B., Klemperer, F. W., Solomon, A. K., and Vennesland, B. (1941) *J. Biol. Chem.* **137,** 557–566
2. Vennesland, B., Solomon, A. K., Buchanan, J. M., Cramer, R. D., and Hastings, A. B. (1942) *J. Biol. Chem.* **142,** 371–377
3. Schoenheimer, R. (1942) *Dynamic State of the Body Constituents*, Harvard Dunham Lecture, Harvard University Press, Cambridge, MA
4. Solomon, A. K., Vennesland, B., Klemperer, F. W., Buchanan, J. M., and Hastings, A. B. (1941) *J. Biol. Chem.* **140,** 171–182
5. Vennesland, B., Solomon, A. K., Buchanan, J. M., and Hastings, A. B. (1942) *J. Biol. Chem.* **142,** 379–386
6. Buchanan, J. M., Hastings, A. B., and Nesbett, F. B. (1942) *J. Biol. Chem.* **145,** 715–716
7. Wood, H. G., and Werkman, C. H. (1936) *Biochem. J.* **30,** 48–53; (1938) **32,** 1262–1271
8. Wood, H. G, Werkman, C. H., Hemingway, A., and Nier, A. O. (1940) *J. Biol. Chem.* **135,** 789–790
9. Evans E. A., Jr. (1940) *Biochem. J.* **34,** 829–837
10. Krebs, H. A., and Johnson, W. A. (1937) *Enzymologia* **4,** 148–156
11. Krebs, H. A., and Eggleston, L. V. (1940) *Biochem. J.* **34,** 1383–1395
12. Evans, E. A., Jr., and Slotin, L. (1940) *J. Biol. Chem.* **136,** 301–302; (1941) **141,** 439–450
13. Ogston, A. G. (1948) *Nature* **162,** 963
14. Koshland, D. E., Jr. (2001) *Biochem. Mol. Biol. Ed.* **30,** 27–29
15. Buchanan, J. M., Sakami, W., Gurin, S., and Wilson, D. W. (1945) *J. Biol. Chem.* **157,** 747–748; (1945) **159,** 695–709
16. Breusch, F. L. (1943) *Science* **97,** 490–492
17. Wieland, H., and Rosenthal, C. (1945) *Ann. Chem.* **554,** 241–260
18. Medes, G. S., Weinhouse, S., and Floyd, N. F. (1945) *J. Biol. Chem.* **157,** 35–41; (1945) **157,** 751–752
19. Buchanan, J. M., Sakami, W., and Gurin, S. (1947) *J. Biol. Chem.* **169,** 411–418
20. Krebs, H. A., and Eggleston, L. V. (1944) *Nature* **154,** 209–210
21. Stryer, L. (1988) *Biochemistry,* 3rd Ed., p. 479, W. H. Freeman & Co., San Francisco
22. Lipmann, F. (1941) *Adv. Enzymol.* **1,** 99–162
23. Lipmann, F., and Tuttle, L. C. (1944) *J. Biol. Chem.* **153,** 571–582
24. Lipmann, F. (1945) *J. Biol. Chem.* **160,** 173–190
25. Lipmann, F., Kaplan N. O., Novelli, G. D., Tuttle, L. G., and Guiard, B. M. (1947) *J. Biol. Chem.* **167,** 869–870
26. Lipmann, F. (1943) *Bacteriol. Rev.* **17,** 1–16
27. Novelli, G. D., and Lipmann, F. (1950) *J. Biol. Chem.* **182,** 213–228
28. Edson, N. L., Krebs, H. A., and Model, A. (1936) *Biochem. J.* **30,** 1380–1385
29. Örström, A., Örström, M., and Krebs, H. A. (1939) *Biochem. J.* **33,** 990–994
30. Sonne, J. C., Buchanan, J. M., and Delluva, A. M. (1946) *J. Biol. Chem.* **166,** 395–396
31. Buchanan, J. M., and Sonne, J. C. (1946) *J. Biol. Chem.* **166,** 781
32. Sonne, J. C., Buchanan, J. M., and Delluva, A. M. (1948) *J. Biol. Chem.* **173,** 69–79
33. Buchanan, J. M., Sonne, J. C., and Delluva, A. M. (1948) *J. Biol. Chem.* **173,** 81–98
34. Greenberg, G. R. (1948) *Arch. Biochem.* **19,** 337–339
35. Greenberg, G. R. (1951) *J. Biol. Chem.* **190,** 611–631

THE JOURNAL OF BIOLOGICAL CHEMISTRY
© 2002 by The American Society for Biochemistry and Molecular Biology, Inc.

Vol. 277, No. 41, Issue of October 11, pp. 37967–37972, 2002
Printed in U.S.A.

Reflections

A PAPER IN A SERIES COMMISSIONED TO CELEBRATE THE CENTENARY OF THE JBC IN 2005

JBC Centennial
1905–2005
100 Years of Biochemistry and Molecular Biology

Bioinorganic Chemistry: A New Field or Discipline? Words, Meanings, and Reality

Published, JBC Papers in Press, August 6, 2002, DOI 10.1074/jbc.X200002200

Helmut Beinert

From the Institute for Enzyme Research and Department of Biochemistry, College of Agricultural and Life Sciences, University of Wisconsin, Madison, Wisconsin 53726-4087

To the uninitiated it may seem that bioinorganic chemistry is a new field although, on the other hand, reports on metals bound to proteins or enzymes date way back into the 19th century and may probably be found in earlier centuries if we replace the terms "proteins" and "enzymes" with "animal or plant tissues." Potassium ferricyanide was prepared from blood, McMunn described what he called histohematins (now cytochromes) in tissues, Hoppe-Seyler made spectroscopic investigations on hemoglobin, G. Bertrand worked on what he called an oxidase from plant tissues, which he named laccase; he recognized that it was a metal protein and even proposed that the metal was a "coenzyme," with which he may have been the first to propose the idea of a catalytic metal protein. Spitzer drew attention to the involvement of iron bound to protein or nucleic acid nitrogen in tissue respiration, Warburg and Keilin and their collaborators described polyphenol oxidase, a copper protein, and ferritin was described as an iron storage protein. In the 1930s Keilin and Hartree found copper in cytochrome c oxidase. By the middle of that century, zinc and molybdenum were discovered in enzymes, and non-heme iron was recognized as a necessary component in mitochondrial preparations that are active in substrate oxidation. Thus there is a long trail of discovery of metals in proteins or in other components of living creatures, metals that were required for their structure or function, although details of what the functions implied were initially missing and hard to come by.

At this point it seems worthwhile to define what is actually meant by the terms "inorganic" and "organic" in connection with our present theme or in the context of chemistry as a scientific discipline. Although the term "organic" will for many evoke the connotation that it has to do with life (the counterpart "inorganic" then referring to lifeless matter) in chemistry "organic" has come to mean merely pertaining to the chemistry of carbon compounds. Inorganic, on the other hand, is generally perceived as referring to the chemistry of metal compounds, whereas other non-carbon non-metal elements are not specifically excluded. Because metals of many kinds are found in living matter, *e.g.* sodium, potassium, and calcium in considerable quantities, and because all metals are subjects of inorganic chemistry, there must then, by definition, always have been an inorganic component of biochemistry. Thus, according to this reasoning, "inorganic biochemistry" and "bioinorganic chemistry" certainly are no new subjects; rather they may only be new words.

The Hassle About an Acceptable Name for the Field of Our Endeavors

Nevertheless, the terms obviously had to be justified. The editor of the first volume of *Inorganic Biochemistry*, Gunter L. Eichhorn, says in 1974 in the preface to the book: "Until recently, the title *Inorganic Biochemistry* would have appeared paradoxical to most, and it may even now appear so to many, because biochemistry sounds organic"; and this was about 30 years ago! As I have witnessed this period and also some decades before that, I will briefly describe my experiences. When I was a student in the 1930s, what Eichhorn calls paradoxical would doubtless have been considered outright ridiculous, certainly in Germany. When I studied chemistry there it was the great period of the development of organic chemistry, synthetic and analytical, of natural products chemistry, the time of the discovery of "factors" (some of them later called vitamins), and I heard it said often in chemical circles that biochemistry was in essence nothing but organic chemistry. Actually even the word biochemistry was frowned upon, as it had acquired some taste of quackery through the use of the word by some eager promoters of what may today be called "alternative medicine." The term "biochemistry," as far as I know, was in some sense generally established when Sir Frederic Gowland Hopkins named his department in Cambridge by that title in 1914, although the actual building that had this name was only occupied in 1924. In Germany this subject, "biochemistry," was not taught within a faculty of the Naturwissenschaften but had the designation "physiological chemistry" and was only accessible to medical students, and not to chemistry students, as I was. When I inquired whether I might get an exceptional permission, I was advised by friends in the faculty that physiological chemistry was actually largely a "Gemurkse," which means a messy business, going under the slogan, "Tierchemie ist Schmierchemie," and I would do better to concentrate on chemistry. It was only Felix Hoppe-Seyler who was influential enough to be allowed to establish an Institute of Applied Chemistry within the Faculty of Medicine at Tübingen, which then was soon renamed physiological chemistry and was assigned to a separate Faculty of Science. As such it has survived Hoppe-Seyler for many years as well as his journal, which now goes under the title "Biological Chemistry." Feodor Lynen was the first to have a Max-Planck Institute for Biochemistry in Munich in 1954, after which biochemistry departments then started sprouting up elsewhere. However, even in the United States the departments of physiological chemistry only slowly disappeared.

Development of the Field

It is true that the major polymers in living matter are carbon compounds, whereas the transition metals are only present in traces (except *e.g.* for iron in the globins or in ferritin); however, there is no life without transition metals, which are required as catalysts. From what was said above, there was a gap of about 30 years between the 1940s and the 1970s when there must have been a great step forward in appreciating the significance of transition metals in biology. I experienced the transition during that period most vividly in two typical examples. I had the fortune to meet Edward Hartree during a visit to Oxford and I asked him, of course, about his work with Keilin in the 1930s on copper in cytochrome *c* oxidase, which had also been the object of my studies (1). He said that they were absolutely sure copper was there and was bound tightly to the protein; they determined how much was there in comparison to heme, but after that what else could they do? As spectroscopy was not applicable to copper,[1] they had no method to tell them about its function. Thus Keilin decided not to pursue this aspect further. I may call this the "Keilin-Hartree dilemma"; almost all of metal biochemistry suffered from this shortcoming. The second example came with my good fortune to be invited to all seven sessions in the series on copper proteins, usually referred to as the "Manziana Conferences," initiated and perpetuated by Bruno Mondovì of Rome, Jack Peisach of New York, and Bo Malmström of Göteborg and their colleagues until 1995 (3). The 1972 to 1976 meetings still were under the spell of the Keilin-Hartree dilemma. The aspect of function largely eluded us. In the copper field the advent of EPR clearly broke the ice. With this technique (and thereafter with other spectroscopies) much more sense could be made of the metal-to-protein stoichiometry and the electronic absorption spectra that had been available so far. Now, all of a sudden, those designations, such as CuA and CuB in cytochrome oxidase or Type I, II, or III copper in ceruloplasmin assumed distinct character. Things were not as simple with iron, because there a new type of iron protein had to be discovered, the iron-sulfur (Fe-S) proteins. The discovery predates somewhat the developments just presented, but the more detailed exploration of this new field approximately also falls into the same period. The coordination chemistry of copper is relatively simple as compared with that of iron, and it eventually took several different types of spectroscopies such as Mössbauer (MB), electron nuclear double resonance (ENDOR), x-ray absorption spectroscopy (XAS), extended x-ray absorption fine structure (EXAFS), magnetic circular dichroism (MCD), and NMR, which were just developed in those years to a state such

---

[1] The broad 830 nm absorption of cytochrome *c* oxidase was only discovered in 1961 (2) and was probably not observable with Keilin's microspectroscope.

that it became feasible to apply them to biological material with relatively low concentrations of the target structures and with limited stability.

Approach between Disciplines

In those copper protein meetings it was a most stimulating get together of groups that had barely talked to each other before: the chemical physicists that were trained in ligand field theory and were on speaking terms with pioneers such as Carl Ballhaüsen (4) and on the other side us, the enzyme chemists, used to getting our hands dirty with awkward messes of animal, plant, or bacterial origin, from which our objects had to be purified. We could not understand our data without the wisdom of the spectroscopists, and they were anxious to get their minds on the challenging and fascinating problems in metal coordination that nature had to offer. This fortunate mutual approach between these disciplines (the coordination chemists, the spectroscopists or chemical physicists, and the biochemists) took place in that 10–20-year span starting around the 1970s. There followed a period of intensive research on the functions of these proteins, and, no wonder, enzymes played a dominant role in this as compared with other metal proteins that serve other roles with the result that biological inorganic chemistry was often identified with the biochemistry of metal enzymes. This, of course, led to some resentment (5) in the ranks of those interested in metal proteins with other functions such as transport, as *e.g.* hemocyanins, or metals involved in geological processes or stabilization of biological structure (6). In this period as more structural and spectroscopic data became known, chemists started taking considerable interest in complex biological structures such as hemocyanin for instance or polyphenol oxidases, exploring their copper-oxygen chemistry. This then led to similar investigations on iron-oxo-systems, which eventually opened up the whole new field of Fe-oxo-proteins (7). A strong relationship of the chemistry of the metal-oxygen reactions to those involving free radical mechanisms soon became apparent (8). A similar relationship was found in the Fe-S protein field (9).

During that period, starting with the 1970s, the flood of volumes on inorganic biochemistry, bioinorganic chemistry, metals in biological systems or whatever they were called started pouring out and there soon was also a *Journal of Inorganic Biochemistry*, starting in 1972, joined more recently, in 1996, by the *Journal of Biological Inorganic Chemistry*.

A particularly good example of the rapid progress in that period is the role that x-ray crystallography played in the meeting series on copper proteins that we have followed above. At the 1979 meeting we all listened with awe to the only crystallographer present, Hans Freeman of Sydney, who showed the structure of poplar plastocyanin, one of the smallest blue copper proteins containing a single copper ion. The data on the immediate environment of the copper confirmed the conclusions drawn by the spectroscopists. At the 1985 meeting, Freeman presented further detail such as structures of reduced plastocyanin and of plastocyanins from different plant sources. Then, at the 1990 meeting, there were five crystallographers in the audience who presented three new structures, namely those of the considerably more complicated multicopper enzyme ascorbate oxidase, bacterial nitrite reductase, and galactose oxidase. Finally, at the 1995 meeting there were presented such impressive accomplishments as the structure of beef heart cytochrome *c* oxidase, of human ceruloplasmin, and amine oxidase of *Escherichia coli*. Of course, it must also be mentioned that it was not only the development of crystallographic methods and of more efficient light sources, it was also the progress in the preparation of proteins in high purity and quantity and the possibility of introducing new groups or exchanging amino acids (all this via molecular genetic procedures) that contributed to the remarkable advances. An example here is the preparation and structure determination of the CuA module of cytochrome *c* oxidase through such approaches (10).

Development and Applications of Spectroscopies

Similar advances were made in other areas using spectroscopy with radiation all over the range of energies from γ rays to radio frequencies. As my personal experience was mainly with spectroscopy, I may be forgiven if, among examples, I will mainly draw on those that I was directly involved in or that are in my field of interest.

Before we leave the realm of high energy radiation, we must mention the relatively recent development of x-ray absorption spectroscopy, which became feasible when sufficiently powerful beam lines became more generally available at the reactor sites. Various features of these spectra have attracted attention: XANES, x-ray absorption near edge structure and more recently also pre-edge structure, and EXAFS, from which distances to neighboring nuclei can be determined or estimated, or certain types of nuclei can be excluded, depending on the quality of the spectra. EXAFS, for instance, has played a decisive role in the discovery and structure determination of the 3Fe cluster of Fe-S proteins (11), and particular attention has been paid recently to the pre-edge features in XANES (12), as it can furnish quantitative information on the degree of covalency of metal-ligand bonds (13). This has been successfully accomplished for Fe-S proteins and has given new insights into the electronic structure of Fe-S proteins.

After this consideration of x-ray spectroscopy in connection with the discussion of the development of x-ray diffraction and crystallography, I will now briefly mention examples of the successful use of spectroscopy at other frequencies, starting from the low energy end. After a slow start, as far as application to proteins goes, NMR has undergone a very impressive development after the introduction of two- and higher-dimensional techniques, in combination with elaborate pulsing techniques and Fourier transform analysis, particularly also by the use of isotopes of a nuclear spin different from that of the naturally occurring atoms, such as ^{2}H, ^{15}N, ^{13}C, ^{17}O, and ^{57}Fe. For use with metal proteins the exploration of "paramagnetic NMR," that is NMR on paramagnetic substances, has had great success (14) and has now become a routine procedure and the method of choice for answering specific questions. When the sequence of a protein is known and preferably also the three-dimensional structure around the metal site, the unpaired spin density on specific atoms can be determined. It has even been possible to observe the migration of spin density between sites (15). Moving on to the milli- meter and centimeter range, EPR has been mentioned above as one of the first decisive tools in approaching the aspects of the function of copper proteins. It has played the decisive role in the discovery of Fe-S proteins and the exploration of the electronic structure and other properties of these proteins (16). The hybrid methods such as ENDOR and ESEEM or optical detection of magnetic resonance are making use of the relatively slow relaxation of electron spins, so that saturation with incident radiation (microwaves in EPR) may occur, which can then be relieved through energy transfer by exciting neighboring atoms with other frequencies (radiowaves in ENDOR or ESEEM). Again, by the use of isotopes of different nuclear spin, very specific information can be obtained on the kind of neighboring atoms, on interatomic dis- tances, and even on the mutual orientation of interacting species. Thus, for instance, we have been able to determine that in the 4Fe cluster of aconitase the specific iron atom (Fe_a) that has no cysteine ligand has a hydroxyl bound in the absence of substrate, which becomes protonated on addition of substrate to the enzyme (17). We could also show with this enzyme and with substrate labeled with ^{17}O or ^{13}C in different positions that the α-hydroxyl of isocitrate and the β-carboxyl of citrate bind to Fe_a (18).

The ESEEM method is applicable for the detection of more distant neighboring atoms. Again pulse and Fourier transform techniques are required in this instance. An example of the combined use of both ENDOR and electron spin echo envelope modulation (ESEEM) is the identification of the sequence of radicals formed in the conversion of α-lysine to β-lysine by 2,3-lysine aminomutase (19). A condition necessary for all the work mentioned here is that a measurable EPR signal can be observed. In the cases cited it was the EPR signal of a reduced [4Fe-4S] cluster or of a free radical.

Resonance Raman (RR) spectroscopy is based on the enhancement of ordinarily observed Raman lines by a transition metal ion present in a molecule. This technique is therefore able to provide specific information concerning the ligands of the metal center and their position with respect to the metal. Again the use of specific isotopes of different molecular mass, such as ^{2}H, ^{13}C, ^{15}N, ^{18}O, ^{34}S, and ^{54}Fe is very helpful and decisive. For instance it has been argued early on the basis of RR (20) that the newly discovered 3Fe cluster could not have the [3Fe-3S] benzene-like ring structure first assumed but must have a structure closely related to the 4Fe cluster, as was shown by EXAFS and chemical analysis (11).

An impressive example of the analytical power of infrared spectroscopy when applied to proteins was furnished when it was discovered that hydrogenases have CO and CN ligands bound to their 2Fe cluster (21). It has also been possible to detect subtle changes in substrates by infrared (22).

Among the methods relying on magnetism the simplest may seem to be direct measurement of magnetic susceptibility. However, it is technically quite difficult to achieve the desired sensitivity. MCD and more so yet VTMCD, namely variable temperature MCD, has taken a prominent position for discriminating different components in *e.g.* a protein containing a

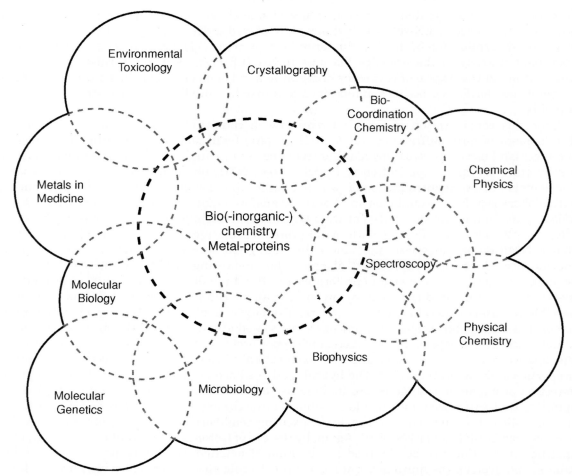

FIG. 1. **Tentative view of adjacent and overlapping fields seen from the horizon of a biochemist.**

number of different heme groups. This technique furnished the clue in the determination of the different Fe-S clusters in succinate dehydrogenase (23). It has also been useful in the determination of the spin state of a substance when EPR is ambiguous. An example here is the determination of the spin state of the reduced $[3Fe-4S]^0$ cluster (24).

At about the middle of the 1960s I was invited to give a lecture at the Max-Planck Institute for Medical Research in Heidelberg. It was there in the Physics Division where Rudolf Mössbauer as a graduate student had discovered the effect now bearing his name. Richard Kuhn, the director of the Institute, introduced me in his unmistakable Viennese accent and his at such occasions usually somewhat pompous way: "Warburg has given us, who are interested in biological oxidations, the heme iron; you have now given us the non-heme iron" (referring to my work on Fe-S proteins). There happened to be in the audience Ekkehard Fluck, a young "Dozent" at the university, who was one of the early explorers of the MB effect in chemistry; he jumped up and commented that I should use MB to find out what these non-heme iron compounds were. When I asked how much iron (and that was to be ^{57}Fe) and in what volume was needed for this, his answer made it clear that this was definitely not the method to use. Nevertheless, it was not even 10 years before my friend Richard H. Sands and others (25) indeed successfully used MB on purified ferredoxins of relatively low molecular weight (though not on mitochondria yet), but it was then 20–30 years later that MB could be applied with success to identify iron in whole bacterial cells (26) and that specific compounds could be recognized and quantitatively determined (27). There was an effect of mutual stimulation, similar to what I described above, when the first EPR data appeared but, of course, at a much more advanced level. Although we biochemists learned something about our proteins and enzymes, so did our challenge stimulate the spectroscopists to optimize the conditions and particularly also to dig out from the literature applicable theoretical concepts that could explain the observations, extend them, or even develop new ones of their own. This led to a closer approach between theoreticians and us at the bench, which turned out to be very productive. Thus, for instance, the concept of "spin-dependent delocalization (SDD)" (also called "double exchange" or "resonance") was so clearly demonstrated, first by the reduced 3Fe cluster [3Fe-4S]^0 (28) and then also for the 4Fe cluster that it is now one of the main features considered important for understanding the electronic structure and reactivity of these clusters. The concept was, of course, not new but was hidden in mathematical equations and under designations that are not easily understood. It is the merit of the colleagues whose names appear in the given references that has brought these concepts to our attention in terms understandable to us (29). The electronic structure of the clusters with more than two iron atoms can now be understood in terms of these interacting forces: 1) SDD, which favors a parallel spin orientation and thus formation of mixed valence (MV) pairs with one shared electron; 2) J, which favors antiparallel coupling as in the 2Fe cluster; and 3) what is called vibronic coupling, which has to do with the symmetry of the surrounding protein environment (*e.g.* a non-Cys ligand) and may favor one or the other spin arrangement. Cases for this are documented, with one of the simplest and most impressive examples being the 2Fe ferredoxin from a mutant of *Clostridium pasteurianum* in which one serine replaces one of the cysteine ligands of the native structure (30).

All the in some way related areas of endeavor mentioned above have, in their own way, become specialty fields, encompassing already a voluminous literature. Thus, definitions of fields are becoming blurred, and we must recognize the fallacy of trying to categorize with any rigidity while still preserving real meaning. Fig. 1 may represent a possible way to depict the situation, as seen from the horizon of a biochemist. The fact that biochemistry occupies a space larger than the others does not mean that it is more important, but it was necessary for practical reasons, namely to provide enough space for demonstrating the overlap.

Address correspondence to: hbeinert@facstaff.wisc.edu.

REFERENCES

1. Beinert, H. (1997) *Eur. J. Biochem.* **245,** 521–532
2. Griffiths, D. E., and Wharton, D. C. (1961) *J. Biol. Chem.* **236,** 1850–1856
3. Beinert, H. (1996) *J. Inorg. Biochem.* **64,** 79–136
4. Ballhaüsen, C. J. (1982) *Introduction to Ligand Field Theory,* McGraw-Hill Inc., New York
5. Sigel, H. (2002) *Chem. Eng. News* **80,** 2
6. Williams, R. J. P., and Fraústo da Silva, J. J. R. (1996) *The Natural Selection of the Elements,* Clarendon Press, Oxford
7. Wallar, B. J., and Lipscomb, J. D. (1996) *Chem. Rev.* **96,** 2625–2657
8. Stubbe, J., and van der Donk, W. A. (1998) *Chem. Rev.* **98,** 705–762
9. Cheek, J., and Broderick, J. B. (2001) *J. Biol. Inorg. Chem.* **6,** 209–226
10. Wilmanns, M., Lappalainen, P., Kelly, M., Dauer-Eriksson, E., and Saraste, M. (1995) *Proc. Natl. Acad. Sci. U. S. A.* **92,** 11955–11959
11. Beinert, H., Emptage, M. H., Scott, R. A., Hahn, J. E., Hodgson, K. O., and Thomson, A. J. (1983) *Proc. Natl. Acad. Sci. U. S. A.* **80,** 393–396
12. Glaser, T., Rose, K., Shadle, S. E., Hedman, B., Hodgson, K. O., and Solomon, E. I. (2001) *J. Am. Chem. Soc.* **123,** 442–454
13. Anxolabéhère-Mallart, E., Glaser, T., Frank, P., Aliverti, A., Zanetti, G., Hedman, B., Hodgson, K. O., and Solomon, E. E. (2001) *J. Am. Chem. Soc.* **123,** 5444–5452
14. Bertini, I., Luchinat, C., and Parigi, G. (2001) *Current Methods in Inorganic Chemistry* Vol. 2, pp. 1–372, Elsevier Science Publishing Co., Inc., New York
15. Banci, L., Bertini, I., Ciurli, S., Ferretti, S., Luchinat, C., and Piccioli, M. (1993) *Biochemistry* **32,** 9387–9397
16. Beinert, H. (2002) *Biochim. Biophys. Acta* **1553,** 7–22
17. Werst, M., Kennedy, M. C., Beinert, H., and Hoffman, B. M. (1990) *Biochemistry* **29,** 10526–10532
18. Kennedy, M. C., Werst, M., Telser, J., Emptage, M. H., Beinert, H., and Hoffman, B. M. (1987) *Proc. Natl. Acad. Sci. U. S. A.* **84,** 8854–8858
19. Magnusson, O. T., Reed, G. H., and Frey, P. A. (1999) *J. Am. Chem. Soc.* **121,** 9764–9765
20. Johnson, M. K., Czernuszewicz, R. S., Spiro, T. G., Fee, J. A., and Sweeney, W. V. (1983) *J. Am. Chem. Soc.* **105,** 6671–6678
21. Pierik, A. J., Roseboom, W., Happe, R. P., Bagley, K. A., and Albracht, S. P. J. (1999) *J. Biol. Chem.* **274,** 3331–3337
22. Lamb, D. C., Nienhaus, K., Arcovito, A., Draghi, F., Miele, A. E., Brunori, M., and Nienhaus, G. U. (2002) *J. Biol. Chem.* **277,** 11636–11644
23. Johnson, M. K., Morningstar, J. E., Bennett, D. E., Ackrell, B. A. C., and Kearney, E. B. (1985) *J. Biol. Chem.* **260,** 7368–7378
24. Thomson, A. J., Robinson, A. E., Johnson, M. K., Moura, J. J. G., Moura, I., Xavier, A. V., and LeGall, J. (1981) *Biochim. Biophys. Acta* **670,** 93–100
25. Dunham, W. R., Bearden, A. J, Salmeen, I. T., Palmer, G., Sands, R. H., Orme-Johnson, W. H., and Beinert, H. (1971) *Biochim. Biophys. Acta* **253,** 134–152
26. Boehnke, R., and Matzanke, B. F. (1995) *Biometals* **8,** 223–230
27. Popescu, C. V., Bates, D. M., Beinert, H., Münck, H., and Kiley, P. J. (1998) *Proc. Natl. Acad. Sci. U. S. A.* **95,** 13431–13435
28. Papaefthymiou, V., Girerd, J.-J., Moura, I., Moura, J. J. G., and Münck, E. (1987) *J. Am. Chem. Soc.* **109,** 4703–4710
29. Beinert, H., Holm, R. H., and Münck, E. (1997) *Science* **277,** 653–659
30. Achim, C., Golinelli, M.-P., Bominaar, E. L., Meyer, J., and Münck, E. (1996) *J. Am. Chem. Soc.* **118,** 8168–8169

THE JOURNAL OF BIOLOGICAL CHEMISTRY
© 2002 by The American Society for Biochemistry and Molecular Biology, Inc.

Vol. 277, No. 42, Issue of October 18, pp. 39045–39061, 2002
Printed in U.S.A.

Reflections

A PAPER IN A SERIES COMMISSIONED TO CELEBRATE THE CENTENARY OF THE JBC IN 2005

JBC Centennial
1905–2005
100 Years of Biochemistry and Molecular Biology

A Research Journey with ATP Synthase

Published, JBC Papers in Press, August 13, 2002, DOI 10.1074/jbc.X200001200

Paul D. Boyer

From the Molecular Biology Institute, UCLA, Los Angeles, California 90095-1570

These reflections present a perspective of how I and my graduate students and postdoctoral fellows, over a span of many years, arrived at the concept that ATP is made by an unusual rotational catalysis of the ATP synthase. A recent sketch of the structure of this remarkable enzyme is given in Fig. 1. Such a depiction is the culmination of the efforts of many investigators.[1] The two portions of the enzyme are the membrane-imbedded F_0 and the attached F_1 that has three catalytic sites, principally on the large β subunits. ATP is formed when protons pass through the F_0, driving the rotation of the ring-shaped cluster of c subunits and the attached ϵ and γ subunits. Other subunits attached to outer portions of the F_0 and F_1 served as a stator. The internal rotary movement of the γ subunit is coupled to sequential changes in the conformation of the catalytic sites. During ATP synthesis these conformational changes promote the binding of ADP and P_i, the formation of tightly bound ATP, and the release of ATP.

Revealing the mechanism of the ATP synthase became a major research goal in the latter part of my long career. This paper recalls how my career developed as related to the remarkable progress in biochemical knowledge. It presents the background and results of fruitful, as well as mistaken, approaches that were explored.

The Early Years

Born and educated through college in Utah, at the age of 21 I entered graduate school in the Department of Biochemistry at the University of Wisconsin in the fall of 1939. The biochemical research and teaching there were excellent. Not until years later did I appreciate all that is necessary to create such a fine scientific environment.

I had had no previous courses or research experience in biochemistry and was uncertain about my career choice. By the end of my first year of graduate study the fascination of biochemical understanding and the addictive effect of experimental attempts to uncover new knowledge had firmly launched me toward a career in biochemical research. The Department of Biochemistry at Wisconsin was at the forefront of research in nutrition and metabolism. Recent achievements included the identification of nicotinic acid as a vitamin, the irradiation of milk to produce vitamin D, the discovery of a vitamin K antagonist (dicoumarin), and the discovery of lipoic acid as a growth factor for bacteria. At that time incoming graduate students were assigned to a mentor professor. Both Henry Lardy, from South Dakota, and I joined the group of Professor Paul Phillips whose major interest was in dairy cattle nutrition. Evidence had been obtained that vitamin C might help prevent reproductive difficulties in cattle, and one of my assignments was to find if vitamin C might ameliorate the reproductive failure that occurred in rats with vitamin E deficiency. No benefits of vitamin C were noted, but the rats

---

[1] Except for a few instances, the mention of important advances in information about the ATP synthase and in related areas of biochemistry is included without specific references. The objective of this contribution is not to provide a review of the field and to recognize priorities for contributions but to note how various advances impacted on studies by my group.

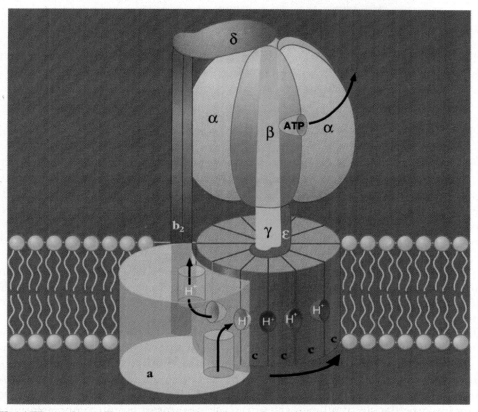

FIG. 1. **The ATP synthase.** The enzyme from *E. coli* has an F_1 portion with subunits designated as $\alpha_3\beta_3\gamma\delta\epsilon$. When separated it acts as an ATPase. The F_0 portion subunits are designated as ab_2c_{9-12}. The passage of protons, at the interface of the a subunit and the ring of c subunits, causes a rotation of the c and attached ϵ and γ subunits relative to the rest of the enzyme. The asymmetric γ subunit (*yellow* and *light green*) extends through the center of the $\alpha_3\beta_3$ cluster. The b_2 and δ subunits serve as a stator. The rotation of the γ subunit results in sequential conformational changes of the catalytic sites that promote ADP and P_i binding, ATP formation, and ATP release. The mitochondrial and chloroplast enzymes are similar, except the F_0 portion has more subunits. The three catalytic sites are principally on the β subunits at an interface with the α subunits. The α subunits also have three non-catalytic sites that bind nucleotides. The figure is from Ref. 112 (copyright 2001, National Academy of Sciences, U. S. A.).

also showed the striking muscular dystrophy characteristic of vitamin E deficiency. Exploration, together with Henry Lardy, of the possible cause of this dystrophy led me into study of ATP-related enzymes. Henry is still active in an exceptionally distinguished career that has included major contributions to the understanding of oxidative phosphorylation.

The milieu at Wisconsin (meetings where students and staff discussed recent research papers, frequent research seminars, and class instructions) introduced me to the wonder of enzyme catalysis. A prominent event was a symposium on respiratory enzymes at which the outstanding biochemists Meyerhof, Cori, Ochoa, Lipmann, Kalckar and others contributed (1). From this and other sources I learned that ATP and phosphorylations were central to the capture and use of energy derived from foodstuffs.

Perhaps defective formation of ATP might underlie the muscle dystrophy in my vitamin E-deficient rats. One approach was to measure the ability of muscle extracts to make phosphocreatine during glycolysis. No definitive defect from vitamin E deficiency was found, but in the course of these experiments, I noted a stimulation of the transfer of phosphate from 3-phosphoglycerate to creatine by K^+ ions. This was traced to a requirement of K^+ for transfer of the phosphoryl group from 2-phosphoenolpyruvate to ADP. The discovery of the K^+ activation of pyruvate kinase was the first demonstration of a K^+ requirement for an enzyme reaction. The two *Journal of Biological Chemistry* publications reporting this were the best of several from my graduate studies (2, 3). An understanding of the K^+ activation was attained at the University of Wisconsin some 50 years later from the x-ray structure of pyruvate kinase (4). The K^+, coordinated to four protein ligands, to an oxygen of the γ-phosphate of ATP, and to a water oxygen, apparently provides a requisite positive charge.

Oxidative phosphorylation was discovered only 7 years before I started graduate studies. As noted in an interesting Prefatory chapter by Englehardt in *Annual Reviews of Biochemistry* (5), ATP was discovered by Lohmann in 1927, and oxidative phosphorylation was first demonstrated by Engelhardt and Liubimova in 1932. These salient contributions at that time seemed far from recent to me, and discoveries such as that of cell-free fermentation by Buchner made about 40 years earlier were relegated to the distant past—science after the escape from the Middle Ages. Now, from my present perspective, research of 30 years ago still seems fairly recent and vibrant. Time seems to go much faster, but it is I who has changed while a unit of time has retained its constant value.

An Introduction to Properties of Proteins

Some 20 amino acids linked in peptide bonds can yield proteins with a truly remarkable diversity of structural properties and the ability for specific combination and catalysis. The versatility of proteins is arguably the most important property of matter that has made life possible. Little was known about protein structure when I was a graduate student. As stated in a 1946 textbook of biochemistry (6): "Since the protein molecule is often built up of hundreds, even thousands, of these amino acids, the problem of protein structure is one of almost insuperable difficulty." In the following years, to be an observer as the wondrous properties of proteins have been revealed is one of the finest rewards provided by my profession.

My appreciation of protein structure and function arose in 1943 when I joined a small group at Stanford University that was supervised by Murray Luck, founder of the *Annual Review of Biochemistry*. Our nation was at war, and Luck's group was asked if they could find how concentrated solutions of human serum albumin, used primarily for the treatment of shock in wounded soldiers, could be heated to inactivate pathogens without denaturing the albumin. The group found that low concentrations of long chain fatty acids or other non-polar anions such as acetyltryptophan would satisfactorily stabilize the albumin. Albumin preparations used militarily and commercially are still stabilized with small concentrations of *N*-acetyl-tryptophan. As part of these studies, I noted that when albumin solutions were exposed to urea or guanidine hydrochloride, the large viscosity increase accompanying denaturation could be reversed by fatty acid addition; a specific combination was markedly influencing the folding of the protein (7). My interest in protein structure was firmly initiated.

Early Studies at Minnesota

In my 17 years at the University of Minnesota, I studied a wide variety of biochemical problems, including such items as the chemistry of α-tocopherol oxidation products, possible formation of antibodies by a refolding of denatured γ-globulins, sulfhydryl groups and enzyme catalysis, and the free energy of hydrolysis of ATP. Mostly my interests have concerned enzymes, and over the years names of some 25 different enzymes have appeared in titles of my publications.

An unsettled problem from my graduate studies at Wisconsin was clarified by the demonstration that mitochondria from the muscles of vitamin E-deficient rats performed oxidative phosphorylation as well as those from as normal muscle (8). Studies in my laboratory (9) and those of my graduate colleague Henry Lardy (10) independently reported that during oxidative phosphorylation oxygen uptake was decreased by the lack of phosphate acceptors. Such respiratory control was the basis for the later development, by Britton Chance and others, of the extensive use of an oxygen electrode to replace the cumbersome Warburg manometric method for measuring rates of oxygen uptake during oxidative phosphorylation.

More importantly, stimulated by the pioneering studies of Mildred Cohn (11), we initiated studies using the heavy oxygen isotope, ^{18}O, for probing phosphorylation reactions. As noted in later sections, insights into ATP synthase catalysis by my group were crucially dependent upon the use of ^{18}O. The ^{18}O isotope and mass spectrometer facilities were made available by physics professor Alfred Nier (a benefit of a research university and a cooperative faculty). Over the years we and others have modified and improved techniques for ^{18}O measurements. Yet studies with ^{18}O remain more laborious than many approaches and have not been widely used. The lack of familiarity with the ^{18}O measurements probably added to the reluctance of the field to accept our concepts, as they were later developed in the 1970s.

In our early studies with ^{18}O we demonstrated that in the glyceraldehyde-3-phosphate dehydrogenase reaction an oxygen from inorganic phosphate appears in the carboxyl group of the 3-phosphoglycerate formed (12). This was explained by a phosphorolysis of an acyl enzyme intermediate demonstrated by studies of Racker's group (13) and mine (14). The phosphorylation accompanying this oxidative step of glycolysis was a prominent basis for the widely adopted paradigm that a phosphorylated intermediate was likely formed during the oxidative phosphorylation of the respiratory chain.

In related experiments my group showed that the enzymic catalyses for formation of phosphocreatine from 3-phosphoglycerate occurred with the retention of all 3 oxygens of the phosphoryl group. Thus such phosphoryl transfers do not involve any steps giving exchange of P_i oxygens with water (12). Also we found that syntheses coupled to ATP cleavage, such as formation of glutamine from glutamate and ammonia, occur with transfer of an oxygen from the substrate to P_i (15). No water oxygen is incorporated into the P_i.

Our initial studies of oxidative phosphorylation with ^{18}O revealed an important characteristic of the oxidative phosphorylation process. We incubated mitochondria with P_i labeled with both ^{18}O and ^{32}P and unlabeled ATP in the presence or absence of substrates or of oxidation inhibitors. We were surprised to discover that, in addition to the strikingly rapid exchange of P_i oxygens with water, a quite rapid $P_i \leftrightarrow$ ATP exchange was occurring (16). The reactions of oxidative phosphorylation appeared to be dynamically reversible. The reversibility continued even when electron carriers were inhibited or nearly fully reduced. This gave evidence for formation of some type of energized compound or state, independent of oxidation-reduction reactions that allowed the ready reversal of the reaction sequence. We thought this likely was some type of chemical intermediate; the idea of an electrochemical gradient across a coupling membrane was far from our thoughts.

Possibilities arose of pursuing interesting aspects of enzyme catalysis not related to ATP formation. For example, in 1955 while on a Guggenheim fellowship for study in Sweden with Nobelist Hugo Theorell, I noted a previously overlooked shift in the fluorescence of NADH upon binding by a dehydrogenase (17). This gave a new basis for measuring combinations of NADH with enzymes. However, the problem was not as interesting as the studies of oxidative phosphorylation that I was also pursuing in the laboratories of Olov Lindberg and Lars Ernster at the Wenner Gren Institute. In an experiment conducted in part in Sweden ^{18}O was used to demonstrate that the terminal bridge oxygen in ATP formed by oxidative phosphorylation came from ADP, not P_i. This and some other research were reported at an International Union of Biochemistry symposium in Japan (18). At that time I was a bit pessimistic about gaining a satisfactory insight into how oxidative phosphorylation occurs. In my contribution I stated: "Our basic knowledge of the chemistry involved does not appear adequate for the task, and the problem is likely to be with us for some time. Researchers who undertake indirect approaches to the problem should do so with recognition that their experiments cannot give final answers, and may not even point the way to final solutions." In retrospect, the pessimism seems appropriate.

During the next several years we undertook experiments looking for intermediates in oxidative phosphorylation, particularly by making use of ^{32}P as a tracer. We learned that radioactively induced reactions of phosphorus compounds with highly labeled $^{32}P_i$ could give rise to radioactive impurities that stick to mitochondrial components but that did not behave like intermediates. Most of my publications during this period were from some worthwhile investigations with other enzymes; one needs to keep research funding available. One of my favorite sayings is that most of what you accomplish in research is the coal that you mine while looking for diamonds.

Some of our studies concerned patterns of isotope exchanges at equilibrium with glutamine synthetase using ^{18}O, ^{32}P, and ^{14}C. It soon became apparent that covalent bond cleaving and formation may not be rate-limiting in enzyme-catalyzed exchanges. Somewhat surprisingly, adequate rate equations governing exchange reactions of enzymes were mostly lacking. I spent a fair effort in a pioneering development of appropriate relationships (19). To some reviewers these relationships were unexpected, and there is an interesting story not told here about what I needed to do to get the publication accepted. Various applications were made by my group. For example, data with glutamine synthetase revealed that the binding of ATP and glutamate was random, and such subtleties as a spatial selectivity of transfer of only one oxygen of the glutamate γ-carboxyl group to phosphate when glutamate and glutamine are readily interconverted at the catalytic site (20). The understanding obtained was useful for later measurements of isotope exchanges that helped in the discovery of compulsory sequential participation of catalytic sites of ATP synthase.

An observation of later interest was that myosin and actomyosin can catalyze an exchange of phosphate oxygens with water oxygens. This can occur with P_i in the medium without added

ATP (21) or with the P_i formed from ATP before it is released to the medium (22). We did not pursue such observations until about a decade later when we belatedly recognized their potential relationship to the mechanism of oxidative phosphorylation.

The Phosphohistidine Story

In 1961 it seemed that our searches with ^{32}P had hit pay dirt. We reported that under oxidative phosphorylation conditions a brief exposure to $^{32}P_i$ and solubilization of the mitochondria with concentrated urea and detergent gave a non-dialyzable ^{32}P-labeled substance. The rate of its formation from P_i or ATP, the disappearance in a cold P_i chase, and the effect of inhibitors and reaction conditions were consistent with its being an intermediate in oxidative phosphorylation. Our interest was heightened when my capable associates identified the substance as a phosphorylated histidine residue in a protein (23). This was the first recognition of a phosphohistidine in biochemical systems. The ability to form the bound phosphohistidine in soluble preparations from mitochondria encouraged the possibility that we could characterize details of the formation process. As the research developed, I became overly enthusiastic in regarding the phosphorylated protein as an intermediate of oxidative phosphorylation (24). In retrospect, I should have been more cautious. It was at this stage that my laboratory group moved to UCLA where we joined the Biochemistry Division of the Chemistry Department.

Our continued studies showed that dialyzable substances from mitochondria could modulate the bound phosphohistidine formation, and this led to the recognition that CoA and succinate were particularly effective. We had overlooked the substrate level phosphorylation accompanying the citric acid cycle. We became aware that a Ph.D. thesis at Illinois by Upper (25) had reported evidence of formation of a phosphoenzyme with the *Escherichia coli* succinyl-CoA synthetase and that such formation had been suggested earlier from catalysis of an ADP $\leftrightarrow$ ATP exchange by the synthetase (26). Our further studies showed that the phosphorylated protein we had detected was indeed an intermediate in the formation of nucleoside triphosphate (ATP or GTP depending on enzyme source) from P_i by succinyl-CoA synthetase (27, 28). Our bound phosphohistidine was clearly not an intermediate in oxidative phosphorylation. In Olympic analogy, we were reaching for a gold but were fortunate to have obtained a bronze.

Another Decade with Little Essential Progress

At this stage I felt that perhaps I could do more for science by accepting an opportunity to become the initial Director of the Molecular Biology Institute at UCLA. Fortunately this did not prevent reasonable continuation of laboratory studies, although I was not encouraged about the progress we and others were making toward elucidation of the major problem of how cells captured energy from oxidations to make ATP. At that time I of course did not know that a decade later we would be fortunate in developing a new concept for oxidative and photosynthetic phosphorylation.

Meanwhile my group pursued some worthwhile studies with other enzymes and continued a few probes of ATP synthesis that were useful but did not yield or point to breakthroughs. In a more sensitive search for the labeling of unidentified components with ^{32}P, a small amount of rapidly labeled lipid fraction was detected (28). However, this labeling was found to continually increase with time, not an expected characteristic of an intermediate. The independence of oxygen exchanges from oxidation-reduction reactions was more firmly established (29). A claim that a localized AMP might be the initial phosphoryl acceptor was refuted and ADP as the initial phosphoryl acceptor more firmly established (30). A sensitive search for possible substances that might transitorily bind an oxygen from P_i on its way to water was negative (31). An exploration of the source of phosphate oxygens in *E. coli* and *Bacillus subtilis* showed that only a few oxygens that entered with the P_i remained (32). Most of them came from water and substrates, undoubtedly by exchange patterns we had been investigating. Other studies gave a welcome observation that laid the base for the later extensive use of chloroplasts by my group; under appropriate conditions chloroplasts catalyzed rapid $P_i \leftrightarrow$ ATP, $P_i \leftrightarrow$ HOH, and ATP $\leftrightarrow$ HOH exchanges. Like oxidative phosphorylation, photophosphorylation was dynamically reversible and its mechanism could be probed by oxygen exchange measurements (33). From later developments the lack of the exchanges noted previously was likely because of the unusual and particularly strong Mg-ADP inhibition of chloroplast ATPase activity that can occur in the dark but is readily reversed by protonmotive force.

In an attempt to gain more insight about energy coupling we also conducted some studies on active transport by *E. coli*. We obtained convincing evidence that a common energized state or intermediate could drive transport or ATP synthesis (34), a view that had been independently developed by Harold (35) and others. However, unlike Harold, we were reluctant at that time to regard that the energized state was a protonmotive force. We were not alone in this reluctance. The field was active, and frequently reviewed. The 1967 (36), 1969 (37), 1971 (38), and 1974 (39) reviews in the *Annual Review of Biochemistry* on electron transport and phosphorylation gave brief and generally negative assessments of Mitchell's proposal that protonmotive force drove ATP synthesis. My hesitation in accepting this proposal came from the lack of a satisfying explanation as to how proton migration could drive ATP formation.

The mechanism of the ATP synthase remained unclear. As noted in the reviews mentioned above, there were a plethora of hypothetical compounds and reactions suggested for participation in ATP formation. A possibility consistent with our various experiments was that an energized state, not involving oxidation-reduction reactions, was used to drive a reaction in which an oxygen from P_i formed water as ADP was phosphorylated to yield ATP. We and others wondered if in some manner energy captured in conformational changes of proteins was involved. Remarkable advances in recognizing the versatility of protein structure were occurring. The x-ray structure of hemoglobin and other proteins and the allosteric properties of enzymes suggested the energy requirements for ATP formation might be accommodated in conformational changes of proteins. But we still had no clear idea about how the conformational changes might function.

A New Concept

In 1972, the first part of what I later called the binding change mechanism of ATP synthesis came from further considerations of past data, not new experimental findings. While attending a seminar that I did not understand, some puzzling aspects of oxygen exchange measurements were occupying my mind. Our thoughts had been that the major use of captured energy was to make the covalent structure of ATP. The realization struck me that past data could be explained if the major use of energy was not to form the ATP but to release a tightly bound ATP from the enzyme. Reversible formation of bound ATP at a catalytic site could explain why the exchange of P_i oxygens was less sensitive to uncouplers than net oxidative phosphorylation. For me it was a rare moment of insight, like suddenly reaching a summit on a mountain climb and seeing a beautiful valley spread below. All enzymes have the capacity for ready reaction reversal at catalytic sites and to bind both products and reactants. The reversal of the hydrolysis of ATP by the ATP synthase is no more remarkable than the reversal of simple hydrolyses by many enzymes, except that with the ATP synthase the product ATP is tightly bound. An additional step or steps must intervene for ATP release. This could logically be an energy-requiring conformational change of the catalytic site.

Richard Cross had joined our laboratory as a postdoctoral fellow. At UCLA he further documented the uncoupler-insensitive oxygen exchange and other aspects. We submitted a paper, "On a New Concept for Energy Coupling in Oxidative Phosphorylation Based on a Molecular Explanation of the Oxygen Exchange Reactions," to the *Journal of Biological Chemistry* for consideration. The publication was declined; at that stage our evidence was not strongly convincing. However, the concept remained appealing. I had recently been elected to the National Academy, and the paper was published in *Proceedings of the National Academy of Sciences* as the first paper I sponsored for the journal (40). A follow-up paper gave additional details (41).

The presence of multiple binding sites for ADP and ATP on the isolated F_1-ATPase and the ATP synthase had been recognized by Slater's group and others. During catalytic turnover some of these nucleotides exchanged with medium nucleotides, and Slater and associates had also suggested the possibility that energy-requiring release of bound ATP might occur in oxidative phosphorylation (42).

The validity of the concept of the role of a tightly bound ATP was strengthened by our finding that myosin ATPase would spontaneously form a tightly bound ATP from medium P_i (43). The estimated $-\Delta G^0$ of the binding of ATP from our and other data was 12–13 kcal/mol. A corresponding tight binding was anticipated for the ATP synthase. In related experiments, Bagshaw and Trentham had recently shown that the apparent ΔG for the hydrolysis of the bound ATP to bound ADP and P_i was only about -1.3 kcal/mol (44); the equilibrium was not far from unity. In a subsequent cooperative study with these investigators an exchange of phosphate oxygens of bound ATP with water was demonstrated to accompany the ATP hydrolysis by myosin (45). The ability to form a bound ATP from P_i by the reversal of ATP hydrolysis readily accounts for the capacity of myosin to catalyze a $P_i \leftrightarrow HOH$ exchange we had observed years earlier (21). Later observations characterized how the combination of myosin with actin promotes the release of the tightly bound ATP, a conformational transition analogous to that proposed for the ATP synthase (46).

At this time I contributed a chapter on "Conformational Coupling in Biological Energy Transductions" in which the possibility that changes with ATP synthase were driven by protonmotive force was recognized. However, my preferred view was still that the conformational changes were driven by some type of interaction with oxidation-reduction enzymes (47).

Recognition of the Role of Protonmotive Force

Peter Mitchell introduced his concept of energy-linked proton translocation in 1961 (48), and in ensuing years he and others continued to present evidence and win converts. By the early 1970s even holdouts like myself were beginning to see the light. It seems probable that the role of protonmotive force would not have been recognized for a long time without Mitchell's contributions.

If proton translocation were coupled to ATP synthesis, I felt it would be accomplished indirectly by protein-linked conformational changes. In contrast, Mitchell proposed that the translocated protons reached the catalytic site and participated directly in the removal of a water molecule. I found his 1974 proposal in *FEBS Letters* (49) unattractive and called attention to some deficiencies in a *FEBS Letters* contribution (50). Without informing me, the journal allowed Mitchell to present a rebuttal following my paper (51). This seemed inappropriate, and the journal agreed to publish my subsequent paper presenting a model of how, through conformational coupling, proton translocation could drive ATP synthesis (52). The suggestions made still seem applicable.

Over the years Peter and I had extensive correspondence and shared a mutual respect. Although we were looking at essentially the same mechanism we tended to present different pictures of our views. Too often in science there is rancor between those who disagree. An important lesson that I have learned is that more will be accomplished if one can maintain cordial relations in an exchange of interpretations.

Other Developments

By the mid-seventies other investigators had provided much welcomed information about the ATP synthase that was quite relevant to mechanism studies. Hatefi and others in David Green's laboratory had shown that the mitochondrial inner membrane could be fractionated to yield separate complexes of the respiratory chain components and the ATP synthase. They (and particularly Racker[2] and associates) had separated and characterized the F_1-ATPase. The knobs visible in electron micrographs of mitochondrial membranes were identified with the F_1-ATPase, connected by a stalk to the membrane portion of the synthase. A similar ATPase had been found in a wide variety of organisms. The ATPase was known to have two or three copies of major α and β subunits and single copies of other smaller subunits. The unusual subunit stoichiometry and observations in a number of laboratories that modification of one β subunit per enzyme essentially stopped catalysis raised intriguing questions about mechanism. The portion of the synthase imbedded in the membrane, F_0, was recognized as being involved in proton transport. The addition of F_1-ATPase to F_0 preparations could restore oxidative phosphorylation or photophosphorylation. Either proton gradients or membrane potential sufficed to drive ATP formation. Beechey had shown that a buried carboxyl group on a small hydrophobic subunit of F_0, present in multiple copies, readily reacted with dicyclohexylcarbodiimide (DCCD)[3] and that this blocked oxidative phosphorylation.

Although information about the ATPase was becoming extensive, how proton translocation could be coupled to ATP formation remained poorly understood. We were encouraged some by the concept that energy-linked binding changes were involved. Fortunately, at this time we obtained evidence for an unusual catalytic site cooperativity displayed by the ATP synthase

---

[2] Racker's contributions were outstanding. One of his former associates, Geoffrey Schatz, has provided a splendid memoir of Racker's career (*Memoirs*, National Academy of Sciences, 1996, available on the internet from www.nationalacademies.org).

[3] The abbreviation used is: DCCD, dicyclohexylcarbodiimide.

and the isolated F_1-ATPase. There was a feeling in my research group that some important secrets about the ATP synthase were being revealed. This created an ambience that stimulated research efforts. Such occasions are an all too infrequent reward of basic research. They help soften the disappointments of the many experiments that yield little or no helpful information.

Alternating Site Participation

Many enzymes have more that one catalytic site, suggesting the possibility of a catalytic cooperativity between sites such that catalytic events at one site are promoted by substrate binding at another site. With most multicatalytic site enzymes, limited or no cooperativity has been observed. In contrast, we found that the ATP synthase showed a nearly complete dependence of continued catalytic steps at one site on the presence of substrate(s) at a second site. This was the first enzyme for which such a striking behavior had been discovered, adding to our interest in the phenomenon.

Our discovery arose from researches by Jan Rosing, a postdoctoral fellow with exceptional experimental skills from Slater's group, and Celik Kayalar, a gifted graduate student. They were symbiotically productive. We devised methods for estimating oxygen exchanges by submitochondrial particles that accompany: (*a*) the binding, exchange, and return to the medium of P_i; (*b*) the binding, exchange, and return to the medium of ATP; (*c*) the binding of P_i, intermediate exchange, and the release of ATP formed; and (*d*) the binding of ATP, intermediate exchange, and the release of the P_i formed. These measurements with ^{18}O were accompanied by measurement of the $P_i \leftrightarrow$ ATP exchange with $^{32}P_i$. The exchange patterns gave evidence that besides promoting ATP release, energy input also increased competent P_i binding. More importantly, the measurements yielded exchange patterns that Kayalar proposed could be explained if the binding of a substrate at one site was necessary for the release of a product from another site.

Whether two or three catalytic sites per enzyme were present was not known at that time. We proposed alternating behavior of two sites, although it was recognized that the results would also be compatible with sequential participation of three sites (53, 54). During net ATP formation or hydrolysis, sites were considered to proceed sequentially through the steps of binding, interconversion of reactants, and release so that at any one time each catalytic site was at a different stage of the catalysis. The concept seemed attractive, but more evaluation was needed.

David Hackney, a talented postdoctoral fellow from Dan Koshland's laboratory, had joined our group and initiated his excellent experimental and theoretical studies of the oxygen exchanges. We were proposing that P_i and ADP can bind and reversibly form bound ATP but that ATP cannot be released until P_i and ADP bind to an additional site. If dynamic reversal of ATP formation at a catalytic site continued in the absence of net reaction, then reductions in the concentration of P_i or ADP should increase the amount of intermediate oxygen exchange per ATP made. We were encouraged by a report from a former postdoctoral fellow of our group, Robert Mitchell, that he and his colleagues observed increased intermediate oxygen exchange accompanying ATP hydrolysis by submitochondrial particles when ATP concentration was lowered (55). Support for the possibility also came from the observation of Wimmer and Rose (56) that when ATP was exposed to chloroplasts in the light, the ATP showed nearly complete exchange of its oxygens before being released. This is as expected if low ADP concentration in the medium prevented the release of the ATP and many reversals occurred before its release.

Hackney observed that during net oxidative phosphorylation as either ADP or P_i concentration was decreased, there was a marked increase in water oxygen incorporation into each ATP formed (57). Additional observations made it unlikely that some type of enzyme heterogeneity or hysteresis could explain the exchange patterns. It deserves emphasis that these experiments were performed with submitochondrial particles during net ATP synthesis, giving them relevance to the actual oxidative phosphorylation process.

An interesting possibility was that catalytic site cooperativity might also be found with the isolated F_1-ATPase. Several years earlier, Ef Racker brought some of his purified F_1-ATPase to our laboratory to find if his enzyme would catalyze an intermediate $P_i \leftrightarrow$ HOH exchange. We tested this at millimolar concentrations of ATP and found that the P_i formed contained only close to the one water oxygen necessary for the hydrolysis. Now, however, with our evidence for cooperativity, it was evident that if reversible ATP formation could occur in the absence of protonmotive force and if participation of alternating sites was necessary, then the extent of intermediate $P_i \leftrightarrow$ HOH exchange with each P_i released should increase as ATP concentrations are lowered. This was found to be so (58) and as ATP concentrations were lowered the number of reversals before the P_i was released approached a limit of over 300 (59). Tightly bound ATP at a single site was undergoing reversible hydrolysis waiting for ATP to bind to another site and promote ADP and P_i release.

The reaction rates and equilibrium characterizing the slow catalysis at a single site were determined in a widely recognized study by Cross together with Grubmeyer and Penefsky (60). They termed this "uni-site catalysis," and their results added considerably to the acceptance by others of alternating site participation. In these studies the K_d for ATP binding to one site of the F_1-ATPase was shown to be near 10^{-12} M (61), indicative of the need for energy input for ATP release and akin to the affinity of ATP for myosin.

The capacity to make bound ATP from medium P_i and ADP/ATP ratio near unity on the enzyme was nicely demonstrated with the chloroplast F_1-ATPase by Feldman and Sigman (62), a contribution that warrants wider recognition. In a slow reaction, needing relatively high P_i concentration, a tightly bound ADP became phosphorylated. Other findings made it probable that this was at the same site as the ADP that was rapidly released in the acid-base transition of thylakoid membranes and thus that this site was likely where covalent bond formation occurred during photophosphorylation.

In addition, results of various investigators established that chemical modification of only one catalytic site effectively stopped catalysis and that each of the three catalytic sites had a different capacity for derivatization. Such behavior agreed with the concept that during catalysis all three catalytic sites were in different conformations and proceeded sequentially through the conformations.

The Basis of ^{18}O Exchange

Our studies with ^{18}O are interpreted on the basis that the exchange results from a reversal of the formation of bound ATP from bound ADP and P_i. As covered in the Appendix of a review there is strong support for this interpretation (63). This includes demonstrations that the P_i oxygen exchanges catalyzed by the sarcoplasmic reticulum ATPase (64, 65) and pyrophosphatase (66, 67), as well as that of myosin ATPase as mentioned above, result from reversible formation of a phosphorylated enzyme or enzyme-bound pyrophosphate or ATP, respectively.

Probes of Initial Reaction Rates

Other evaluations of our postulates were needed. Rapid mixing and quenching techniques yielded essential information. One objective was to find if a tightly bound ADP on the chloroplast ATP synthase might react with medium P_i to form ATP in the first turnover of the enzyme. We used rapid mixing in an acid-base transition of chloroplast thylakoid membranes, as introduced by Jagendorf and colleagues, to start ATP synthesis in a few milliseconds. We found that the tightly bound ADP was not directly phosphorylated but was rapidly released to the medium and that the first ATP formed came from medium P_i and ADP (68). As substantiated in later experiments, the tightly bound ADP in such chloroplast membranes prior to release is tightly bound at a catalytic site without P_i.

The demonstration that exposure to protonmotive force caused the release of a tightly bound ADP from a catalytic site without phosphorylation had important implications for later developments. The tightly bound ADP in the presence of Mg^{2+} causes potent inhibition of ATPase activity of the ATP synthase and F_1-ATPase. Thus such inhibition in the intact synthase is readily and quickly overcome by protonmotive force. When a step of rotational catalysis occurs, the binding site with the tight ADP is opened as if it had an ATP present, while another site is binding ADP and P_i. The properties of the tightly bound ADP also aided interpretation of Walker's 1994 x-ray structure of the major portion of the F_1-ATPase, in which one β subunit has a tightly bound ADP and Mg^{2+} present (69).

Our rapid mixing experiments verified that medium ADP was rapidly bound and phosphorylated as if no phosphorylated intermediates were involved. They provided evidence that during photophosphorylation, in addition to a transitorily bound ATP, about one bound P_i and one bound ADP per enzyme are present and committed to ATP synthesis (70). Such results harmonize with the alternating site model with more than one catalytic site having bound reactants, as required if a tight site is already filled and substrates must initially bind at another site.

Research Conferences and Binding Change Mechanism

Research conferences are important to scientific progress because concepts can be freely discussed, and the publication of proceedings often allows inclusion of material not suited for the usual journals. For example, in my contribution to a 1979 conference honoring Ef Racker, I summarized our concepts and considered how to name our suggested mechanism. A name seemed desirable for ease of discussion and to identify the concept in the field. My contribution entitled "The Binding Change Mechanism for ATP Synthesis" was the first publication in which this nomenclature was used (71).

The binding change mechanism at that time included the following concepts. The first compound made from P_i is ATP itself (no intermediates); a principal requirement of energy is not for the formation but for the release of ATP; energy input also promotes the competent binding of P_i and the sequential participation of catalytic sites so that binding of substrate(s) at one site is necessary for release of product(s) from another site. Two years later, another and even more novel concept of the binding change mechanism was developed, namely the proposal of rotational catalysis. The suggestion that rotation of internal subunit(s) drives the binding changes for catalysis was first published in reports from 1981 and 1983 conferences at the University of Wisconsin (72, 73). How this concept came about is outlined next.

The Proposal of Rotational Catalysis

In the 1970s highly enriched ^{18}O was available, mass spectrometry techniques for ^{18}O analysis had improved, and Mildred Cohn had introduced an NMR method for measuring ^{18}O in phosphate compounds. David Hackney developed theoretical aspects of ^{18}O measurements relevant to observed distributions of ^{18}O isotopomers of P_i with 0 to 4 ^{18}O atoms per P_i or 0 to 3 ^{18}O atoms per ATP molecule. Measurement of the presence of ^{18}O in ATP formed by photophosphorylation showed a pronounced increase in ^{18}O loss at lower ADP and P_i concentrations (74). More importantly, the distribution of ^{18}O isotopomers corresponded to that statistically expected if all the ATP were produced by the same catalytic pathway. This eliminated the possibility that substrate modulation arose from heterogeneity of the enzyme used and made modulation by control sites unlikely. We now regarded the catalytic site cooperativity of ATP synthase to be reasonably well established.

Companion studies with the F_1-ATPase showed that when highly ^{18}O-labeled ATP was hydrolyzed by F_1-ATPase at different ATP concentrations, the distribution of ^{18}O isotopomers was as expected for a single catalytic pathway (58). At appropriate labeling and substrate concentration ranges, the distribution patterns provided a sensitive test for more than one catalytic pathway. A statistically homogeneous distribution meant that every substrate that reacted faced the same possibilities of proceeding through the same reaction steps. This means that rate constants governing the binding and release of substrate(s), their reversible interconversion, and the release of product were the same. To me, the power of this type of ^{18}O use is unusual and indeed a bit awesome.

By now essential contributions of other investigators, including Kagawa and associates in their fine studies with the F_1-ATPase from thermophilic bacteria, had established the presence of three catalytic sites with circular distribution of alternating large α and β subunits around a central core. Catalytic sites were regarded as largely on the β subunits, with the core representing the γ and possibly other small subunits. Observations in McCarty's laboratory demonstrated that modifications of –SH groups on the γ subunit markedly affected catalytic capacity of the chloroplast enzyme (75). The capacity of the F_O component for DCCD-sensitive proton transport had been established. These and other findings strengthened our view that conformational changes in the F_O were in some manner transmitted through the stalk to the catalytic sites on the β subunits to drive the binding changes for ATP synthesis.

Catalytic sites on multisubunit enzymes can be very sensitive to conformational changes in adjacent subunits. Changes in the γ subunit markedly modulated catalysis. How could all three β subunits have identical interactions with the γ subunit? Occurrence of tripartite symmetry of the γ subunit seemed unlikely. The evidence that all three sites conducted catalysis identically was compelling to me. The more I puzzled about these aspects, the more it seemed that there was only one satisfactory answer. This is that the internal asymmetric core, composed of γ and any other tightly associated minor subunits, would need to move rotationally with respect to the outer ring of catalytic subunits. Such movement would allow identical interactions with β subunits as the rotation drove the sequential conformational changes of catalytic sites. When I first presented this concept to my research group, their acceptance was initially quite reserved (they knew all too well that I could be wrong). With further consideration, they became interested and supportive. Much remained to be explored, and some experimental approaches are summarized in the next few sections.

Modulation of Oxygen Exchanges by ATP Concentration

The modulation by ATP concentration of the ^{18}O exchange by the mitochondrial F_1-ATPase was more carefully documented (59). The chloroplast F_1-ATPase showed a similar behavior, and the distribution of the ^{18}O isotopomers in the P_i formed corresponded to a single catalytic pathway (76). Various wild type and mutant *E. coli* F_1-ATPase likewise showed increased exchange of the P_i formed with lower ATP concentrations. However, the distribution of ^{18}O isotopomers with the *E. coli* enzyme revealed more than one reaction pathway, apparently arising in part from the degree of dissociation of the inhibitory ϵ subunit (77). A question had been raised about whether the F_1-ATPase from a thermophile showed catalytic cooperativity because uni-site catalysis was not readily apparent. A cooperative experiment disclosed the expected modulation of the oxygen exchange but at a higher range of ATP concentration (78). The ATPase activity of yeast and *Neurospora* mitochondria showed distinct ATP modulation of the oxygen exchange (79). These various results meant that the increase in the extent of oxygen exchange with each P_i formed (which occurs with a decrease in the ATP concentration) is likely a general property of all F_1-ATPases and supports the probability that all ATP synthases share a common mechanism.

The ATPase of vacuolar membranes has been noted to have a composition resembling that of the ATP synthase. We felt that it should show similar oxygen exchange properties, and measurements demonstrated that this was so (79).

Some Other Assessments

We devised methods to measure bound reactants during steady-state ATP synthesis. A hexokinase accessibility method gave a measure of bound ATP, and a rapid dilution of medium $^{32}P_i$ gave a measure of bound P_i committed to form ATP. Measurements during photophosphorylation showed that even at lower substrate concentrations the total of catalytic site-bound ATP and committed P_i was greater than one per enzyme, as anticipated if the proposed catalytic site cooperativity was occurring. During photophosphorylation, $^{32}P_i$ rapidly labeled catalytic ATP, and then the medium $[^{32}P]$ATP formed was incorporated much more slowly into the non-catalytic sites (80). When illumination ceased, the catalytic site ATP continued to show ^{18}O exchange (81), meaning that reversible formation of bound ADP was still occurring. Within minutes the P_i dropped off, leaving a tightly bound ADP at the catalytic site (82). Such results helped explain labeling patterns we and others had observed and supported our concepts of tightly bound ATP as an intermediate and of catalytic site cooperativity.

The Insidious MgADP Inhibition

Occasionally in biochemical research one encounters a property of a system that seems designed to confuse and thwart the researcher. Such is the case with the inhibition by Mg^{2+}, which is dependent on the presence of an ADP bound without P_i at a catalytic site. Clarification of this unusual role of a tight ADP was necessary for an adequate understanding of the proposed binding change mechanism. The F_1-ATPase as conventionally isolated usually has a considerable portion with tight ADP present. In 1975, Moyle and Mitchell reported that mitochondrial F_1-ATPase was slowly inactivated by Mg^{2+} (83). Hackney noted the inhibition was slowly reversible by ATP addition (84). Observations in Vinogradov's laboratory showed that the inhibition depended on the presence of tightly bound ADP and that the Mg-ADP-inhibited form was stabilized by azide (85). Subsequent studies in our and other laboratories revealed characteristics of the inhibition. F_1-ATPases with tightly bound ADP when exposed to Mg^{2+} shows little or no initial activity upon ATP addition. Added ATP promotes slow release of the inhibitory ADP from a catalytic site as an increase to a steady-state rate is attained. At steady state, a slow interconversion of active and inactive forms continues. The bound ADP required for inhibition may arise from the cleavage of bound ATP or from medium ADP depending upon reaction conditions. P_i and various anions activate by promoting release of the ADP. The inhibitory ADP is at a catalytic site, not at a regulatory site as had been suggested.

Another important result of our continued probing was the recognition that, under some conditions, the presence of ATP at a certain non-catalytic site is necessary for the onset of activity of the chloroplast F_1-ATPase (86). This was the first recognized function for a non-catalytic bound ATP. The action was found to result from acceleration of the release of the inhibitory ADP from catalytic sites that follows the addition of medium ATP (87). With the mitochondrial F_1-ATPase, ATP binding to the non-catalytic site could also accelerate the onset of the Mg-ADP inhibition. Upon addition of ATP and Mg^{2+} to the mitochondrial enzyme, an initial burst of activity declines to a slow rate as the Mg^{2+}-induced inhibition sets in; then the rate increases to a steady state as the non-catalytic sites slowly bind ATP (88).

From the above it is apparent that complicated rate patterns may be found. It is probable that with all F_1-ATPases, and even under favorable conditions, a fair portion of the enzyme may be in the inhibited form. Many reported and planned experiments may be undermined by an unrecognized occurrence of the Mg-ADP inhibition. A procedure for estimating the portion of the enzyme in the inhibited form, as developed by Murataliev (87), deserves wider application.

As mentioned earlier, with the intact ATP synthase the inhibitory MgADP is quickly removed by exposure to protonmotive force. This is akin to the removal of inhibitory imido-ATP that blocks hydrolysis but not synthesis. Chloroplast fragments show a light-activated ATPase that can be maintained by ATP cleavage. For unknown reasons, the activity continues even at higher Mg^{2+} concentrations that would readily result in inhibition of the separated F_1-ATPase (89).

Insights from Use of 2-Azido Nucleotides

By the mid-1980s, the sequence of the ATP synthase subunits was becoming available. An ATP derivative, 2-azido-ATP, which serves as a good substrate and upon photolysis becomes covalently attached, was described in Lardy's laboratory. We embarked on studies to find the number and clarify the location of ATP and ADP binding sites on the F_1-ATPases. That the ADP needed for the Mg^{2+} inhibition was bound at a catalytic site was readily confirmed. The 2-azido-ATP or ADP at catalytic or non-catalytic sites (known to be principally on the β or α subunits, respectively) labeled specific tyrosines not far apart on the β subunit. The sites were thus near subunit interfaces. Sites with similar conserved sequences were noted with the mitochondrial, chloroplast, and *E. coli* enzymes (90–92). Whether the liver (93) and chloroplast enzymes (see Ref. 94 and earlier references) had six nucleotide binding sites remained in question. Our data with the 2-azido nucleotides supported the probability that they, like the mitochondrial enzyme, had six total nucleotide sites (95, 96). Such results added to the already recognized similarity of structure and mechanism of the enzyme from different sources.

We were somewhat surprised to find that derivatization by 2-azido nucleotides of some catalytic or of non-catalytic sites of the chloroplast F_1-ATPase gave rise to multiple catalytic pathways. Measurements of the distribution of ^{18}O isotopomers formed revealed that partially modified enzymes retained some activity that still showed modulation of oxygen exchange by ATP concentration. With more extensive derivatization, the native catalytic pathway disappeared, and two weak, but independent, pathways were noted. Clearly some remaining catalytic sites retained weak activity independent from what neighboring sites are doing (97).

Behavior of ATP Synthase in Intact Mitochondria

Our experiments developing the binding change mechanism had been performed with isolated F_1-ATPases or fragmented membranes. The characteristics of the exchange reactions of the ATP synthase under conditions where mitochondria were capable of a high rate of tightly coupled oxidative phosphorylation were not known. To gain such information, we undertook cooperative experiments with the research group of K. LaNoue, using the ^{32}P and ^{18}O labels (98).

The tightly coupled mitochondria were incubated with oxidizable substrates. When low ADP limited net ATP synthesis, all catalytic steps continued rapidly as concentrations of P_i, ADP, and ATP remained unchanged. The expected rapid exchange of medium P_i with medium ATP with ^{32}P was observed. However, this rate was only about a fourth of the rate of interconversion of bound P_i and ATP at the catalytic site as measured by ^{18}O. Strikingly, the interconversion rate remained high even when the membrane potential was reduced considerably by dinitrophenol addition. The addition of ADP and a hexokinase and glucose trap resulted in rapid formation of glucose 6-phosphate. The distribution of ^{18}O isotopomers in the glucose 6-phosphate showed a single reaction pathway, even when some uncoupler was added. The rapid reversal of bound ATP formation continued, so that about two reversals at the catalytic site occurred for each ATP released to the medium. Even though this reversal was occurring and some medium P_i was being formed from bound ATP, the overall reversal to form medium P_i from medium ATP ceased. This can be explained by the lack of import of ATP by the ADP-ATP translocase. During rapid ATP synthesis, unlike the rapid reaction reversal that is occurring at the catalytic site of the ATP synthase, with high ADP in the medium the translocase is a one-way street.

Another important confirmation of alternating site participation came from these experiments with intact mitochondria. In the dynamic state with no added ADP the forward and reverse rates of all steps are equal, so that there is an equal chance that medium P_i that has formed bound ATP will be released to the medium as P_i or as ATP. If release of the bound ATP can only occur when another ADP and P_i bind, then the rate that medium P_i forms bound ATP will be twice the rate that it forms medium ATP. A ratio of about 2 to 1 for these rates was found when the overall rates were varied up to 10-fold by changes in reactant concentrations or temperature. This provides evidence that alternating site participation is occurring under conditions where rapid oxidative phosphorylation is possible.

One aspect of these experiments may be pointing to an important and unrecognized property of the ATP synthase in its native environment. When the membrane potential was reduced by the addition of some uncoupler while ATP was present not only did net ATP hydrolysis occur but also the rate of reaction reversal at the catalytic site remained high. This was reminiscent of earlier observations with submitochondrial particles that the oxygen exchange accompanying ATP hydrolysis was much greater at higher ATP concentrations than with the separated F_1-ATPase and was relatively insensitive to uncouplers. In some manner, the capacity for rapid interconversion of bound reactants is retained better with the native membrane-bound synthase. I would still like to know how this is accomplished.

Site Filling and Catalysis, an Unfinished Story

It is well recognized that when only one catalytic site on the F_1-ATPase binds ATP or ADP and P_i, a slow interconversion of the substrates occurs. What remains uncertain at the time of this writing is whether a second or a second and a third site must bind ATP for the rapid release of ADP and P_i to occur. For over two decades since slow uni-site catalysis and alternating participation of catalytic sites was recognized, my group and most others felt that the binding of ATP to a second site sufficed for rapid catalytic turnover during net ATP hydrolysis. Because of binding affinities, it was recognized that all three catalytic sites would be filled at millimolar concentrations of ATP, approximating physiological conditions. I proposed that ADP during net synthesis, or ATP during net hydrolysis, entered the catalytic cycle by binding to different sites as indicated in Fig. 2. The critical need under conditions favoring rapid synthesis was regarded as the presence of interconverting, tightly bound substrates at Site 2 of Fig. 2 and ADP and P_i at Site 1. Conversely, under conditions for rapid hydrolysis the critical need was the presence of ATP at Site 3. In each case one rotational step would change the site to the tight conformation where covalent catalysis could occur. For both net synthesis and hydrolysis, the presence or lack of ADP or ATP at a third site was regarded as having a minor influence on the rates.

Several years ago, Senior and Weber and colleagues introduced a fluorometric method for estimating the amount of bound nucleotides at catalytic sites. They replaced a tyrosine at catalytic sites with tryptophan and replaced tryptophans in other locations of the *E. coli* F_1-ATPase (Ref. 99 and earlier references). The binding of nucleotides at the catalytic sites quenched the fluorescence of the tryptophan and allowed an estimation of the number of catalytic sites filled. They and Allison's group with the thermophilic F_1-ATPase (Ref. 100 and earlier references) found that three sites appeared to be filled with nucleotide as near maximal velocity was reached with an increase in the ATP concentration. They then assumed that the binding of ATP to a second and to a third site was necessary for rapid net hydrolysis. This I believe will prove to be incorrect. Instead, it still seems likely that although three sites may become filled (probably mostly with ADP), the essential need for rapid hydrolysis is the binding of ATP to a second site. In other words, bi-site activation probably occurs along with tri-site filling. These issues are considered in more detail elsewhere (101).

Evaluations of Rotational Catalysis

As the research journey proceeded, we attempted some evaluations of whether rotational catalysis indeed occurs. We found that when the chloroplast F_1-ATPase was reacted first with

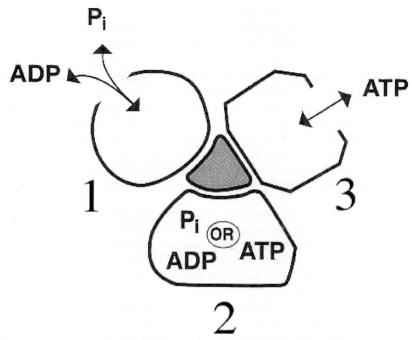

FIG. 2. **A depiction of the three major conformations of catalytic sites for bi-site activation of ATP synthesis or hydrolysis by the ATP synthase.** Three catalytic sites in different conformations are shown with asymmetric interactions to the *shaded* γ subunit. During catalysis sites are converted sequentially into three different states accompanying rotation of the γ subunit. The sequence for synthesis is $1 \rightarrow 2 \rightarrow 3$; for hydrolysis it is $3 \rightarrow 2 \rightarrow 1$. Site *1* binds ADP better than ATP and is the site at which ADP and P_i must be present for rapid synthesis to occur. Site *2* has the ability to catalyze chemical transformation and to be present as a form with ADP and P_i present or with ATP present. ATP can be released from Site *3* during synthesis and must be present at this site for rapid hydrolysis. Figure and legend are reprinted with permission from Ref. 101.

2-azido-ATP and then with $[^{14}C]$DCCD, two different β units were derivatized. Thus the DCCD does not label a subunit with tightly bound nucleotide present. The DCCD-labeled enzyme retained weak catalytic activity. This made it possible for us to find if catalysis changed the conformations of the β subunits that determine their chemical reactivity, as would be expected if rotational movement of the γ relative to the β subunit had occurred. When the enzyme was first reacted with DCCD, allowed to perform catalysis with 2-azido-ATP, and then the azido-ATP photolyzed, the subunits were randomly labeled (102). To us, this made rotational catalysis likely, but the weak catalytic activity of the DCCD-modified enzyme detracted from the result.

In another approach a bifunctional cross-linking agent that reacted with lysine NH_2 groups, and that had a central cleavable –S–S– linkage, was used. About three cross-links, mostly between the γ and δ subunits and the α subunit, caused loss of two-thirds of the activity, and the activity was recovered when the disulfide bonds were cleaved (103). Although the findings were consistent with rotational catalysis, they were not proof.

In contrast, in the same year (1987) Musier and Hammes reported that a cross-linking of the β and γ subunits did not inhibit catalysis and concluded that rotational catalysis did not occur (104). This at first appeared to be a to be a definitive finding. However, examination of their paper suggested some possible experimental uncertainties. Also, possibly the derivatization had uncoupled Ca^{2+}-activated hydrolysis from rotation. A more likely possibility was that the long –CH_2– chains in their cross-linkers may have allowed sufficient freedom of movements to not be restrictive. The catalytically induced movements of β subunits that we had observed with the 2-azido experiments (102) still seemed valid. I thus did not abandon the concept of rotation and looked forward to better evaluations. The concept remained controversial in the field.

It was becoming clear that structural data could provide the base for critical assessment of rotational catalysis. I was aware that Walker's group was attempting to obtain suitable crystals for x-ray analysis. In the meantime, it seemed that my group might accomplish more by studies that were under way with the 2-azido derivatives and by trying to define the location and function of bound nucleotides. As these and related studies progressed I prepared a comprehensive 1993 review of the status of research on how ATP is made under the title "The

Binding Change Mechanism for ATP Synthase—Some Probabilities and Possibilities" (63). The literature at that time was regarded as giving strong support to the concepts proposed in the binding change mechanism, with the exception that rotational catalysis was regarded as likely but definitely not established.

Fortunately progress continued in Walker's laboratory (105). This culminated in the 1994 report of the structure of a major portion of the mitochondrial F_1-ATPase (69). Receipt of an advance copy of the report from Walker was an occasion for gratifying emotion. The reported structure showed that the three β subunits were indeed in different conformations, and one had poor nucleotide affinity. The γ subunit was centrally located with structural associations consistent with its rotation driving sequential conformational changes of the β subunits. The authors interpreted their data as strongly supporting the binding change mechanism. Other x-ray studies interpreted as inconsistent with the binding change mechanism (106) appear mistaken.

The availability of high resolution structural data made more critical assessments of rotational catalysis possible. Richard Cross, my former postdoctoral associate, noted residues in the γ and β subunits that were closely adjacent. When these were replaced with cysteines by mutagenesis good catalytic activity was retained. Oxidation of the –SH groups to form a disulfide cross-link blocked catalytic capacity, which was regained when the disulfide was reduced. With the disulfide linkage present, two β subunits that were not cross-linked were replaced by β subunits from an enzyme labeled with radioactivity during growth of the *E. coli*. Cleavage of the disulfide and catalysis resulted in randomization of the position of the γ subunit relative to the labeled β subunits (107). Similar loss of catalytic capacity upon disulfide cross-linking and related salient findings were reported from Capaldi's laboratory (108). Such results and other related findings were considered by the field to establish the occurrence of rotational catalysis.

In the spring of 1997, a stunning visual conformation of rotational catalysis came from the laboratories of Yoshida and Kinosita in Japan. In a novel experimental approach, they attached a long actin side chain with a fluorescent label to the γ subunit and, through inserted histidine residues, attached the modified enzyme to solid support. Upon hydrolysis of ATP, the rotational movement of γ was observable in the microscope (109). Important characteristics of the catalysis were shown and are still being studied. I remember the thrill when I saw the rotation from a VCR recording that Yoshida kindly sent me. The dramatic experiment has gained wide recognition and removed nearly all doubt about the existence of rotational catalysis. Independently, Junge and associates developed a sophisticated fluorescence polarization technique that showed rotation accompanying ATP cleavage (110). This progress added to the near certainty of rotational catalysis. I was able to include references to their papers in press in a contribution entitled "The ATP Synthase—A Splendid Molecular Machine" that appeared in the 1997 *Annual Review of Biochemistry* (111).

A Life Style Change

By 1994, my research laboratories were essentially closed. ATP synthase and bioenergetics and enzymology had yielded center stage to biochemistry related to genetics and development. Postdoctoral fellows were no longer seeking my laboratory. It was over 50 years since I had received my Ph.D. My mental capacities seemed to have slipped more than my physical capacities. I felt it would be difficult to continue to be at the research forefront and that unfunded U. S. Public Health Service applicants might make better use of funds than I, so I gave 2 years of committed research support back to the U. S. Public Health Service and bought a summer home in a mountain valley in Wyoming with accompanying golf and tennis facilities.

In October of 1997, while on my way to back to my winter haven in a home I love in the hills above UCLA, I received that electrifying early morning call informing me that I had been chosen to share the 1997 Nobel Prize in Chemistry. This of course was personally very gratifying. It increased my stature with my grandchildren. More importantly, it was a recognition of the many fine investigators that had contributed to the unveiling of the ATP synthase mechanism. It gave additional meaning to the careers of postdoctoral fellows and graduate students of my group without whom there would have been no prize, and it has made my life since more vital and interesting. I recommend that if you are going to receive a Nobel prize, have it come late in your career when you no longer have the rewards that come from participation with a fine research group. Also, then you do not need to answer the question, "What research are you going to do now?"

Some Final Comments

The contributions of many scientists were essential for the gaining of our present insights into the ATP synthase catalysis. They should share in the satisfaction that comes from knowing much about how this important biological catalyst appears to operate. As the scientific enterprise grows ever larger, many fine contributors do not receive the appreciation they deserve. They should share in a pride for what has been achieved.

The scientific accomplishment of the Twentieth Century that I admire most is the revealing of the multifaceted capabilities of proteins and of their structures that make these capabilities possible. Perhaps I am a bit more infatuated with enzymes than some. I do not know any enzyme that I could not learn to love, although I will admit that some are more attractive than others.

To all who created our stable and prosperous country and its research universities, which made a career such as mine possible, and mostly to my colleagues, I give my thanks.

Address correspondence to: pdboyer@ucla.edu.

REFERENCES

1. Symposium on Respiratory Enzymes (1942) University of Wisconsin Press, Madison, WI
2. Boyer, P. D., Henry, A., and Phillips, P. H. (1942) *J. Biol. Chem.* **146,** 673–682
3. Boyer, P. D., Lardy, H. A., and Phillips, P. H. (1943) *J. Biol. Chem.* **149,** 529–541
4. Larsen, T. M., Benning, M. M., Rayment, I., and Reed, G. H. (1998) *Biochemistry* **37,** 6247–6255
5. Engelhardt, W. A. (1982) *Annu. Rev. Biochem.* **51,** 1–7
6. Harrow, B. (1946) *Textbook of Biochemistry*, 4th Ed., p. 43, W. B. Saunders Co., Philadelphia, PA
7. Boyer, P. D., Ballou, G. A., and Luck, J. M. (1947) *J. Biol. Chem.* **167,** 407–424
8. Rabinovitz, M., and Boyer, P. D. (1951) *Proc. Soc. Exp. Biol. Med.* **77,** 103–105
9. Rabinovitz, M., Stulberg, M. P., and Boyer, P. D. (1951) *Science* **114,** 641–642
10. Lardy, H. A., and Wellman, H. (1952) *J. Biol. Chem.* **195,** 219–224
11. Cohn, M. (1953) *J. Biol. Chem.* **201,** 735–750
12. Harrison, W. H., Boyer, P. D., and Falcone, A. B. (1955) *J. Biol. Chem.* **215,** 303–317
13. Racker, E., and Krimsky, J. (1952) *J. Biol. Chem.* **198,** 731–743
14. Segal, H. L., and Boyer, P. D. (1953) *J. Biol. Chem.* **204,** 265–287
15. Boyer, P. D., Koeppe, O. J., and Luchsinger, W. W. (1956) *J. Am. Chem. Soc.* **78,** 356–357
16. Boyer, P. D., Falcone, A. S., and Harrison, W. H. (1954) *Nature* **174,** 401–404
17. Boyer, P. D., and Theorell, H. (1956) *Acta Chem. Scand.* **10,** 447–450
18. Boyer, P. D. (1958) *Proc. Int. Symp. Enzyme Chem.* (I. U. B. Symposium) pp. 301–307, Maruzen, Ltd., Tokyo
19. Boyer, P. D. (1959) *Arch. Biochem. Biophys.* **82,** 387–410
20. Graves, D. J., and Boyer, P. D. (1962) *Biochemistry* **1,** 739–747
21. Dempsey, M. E., and Boyer, P. D. (1961) *J. Biol. Chem.* **236,** PC6–PC7
22. Levy, H. M., and Koshland, D. E., Jr. (1959) *J. Biol. Chem.* **234,** 1102–1107
23. DeLuca, M., Ebner, K. E., Hultquist, D. E., Kreil, G., Peter, J. B., Moyer, R. W., and Boyer, P. D. (1963) *Biochem. Z.* **338,** 512–515
24. Peter, J. B., and Boyer, P. D. (1963) *J. Biol. Chem.* **238,** PC1180–PC1182
25. Upper, C. D. (1964) *The Sequence of Reactions Catalyzed by Succinic Thiokinase from Escherichia coli.* Ph.D. thesis, University of Illinois, Urbana
26. Kaufman, S. (1955) *J. Biol. Chem.* **216,** 153–164
27. Mitchell, R. A., Butler, L. G., and Boyer, P. D. (1964) *Biochem. Biophys. Res. Commun.* **16,** 545–550
28. Bieber, L. L., and Boyer, P. D. (1966) *J. Biol. Chem.* **241,** 5375–5383
29. Boyer, P. D., Bieber, L. L., Mitchell, R. A., and Szabolsci, G. (1966) *J. Biol. Chem.* **241,** 5384–5390
30. Hill, R. D., and Boyer, P. D. (1967) *J. Biol. Chem.* **242,** 4320–4323
31. Chaney, S. G., and Boyer, P. D. (1969) *J. Biol. Chem.* **244,** 5773–5776
32. Chaney, S. G., Duffy, J. J., and Boyer, P. D. (1972) *J. Biol. Chem.* **247,** 2145–2150
33. Shavit, N., Skye, G. E., and Boyer, P. D. (1967) *J. Biol. Chem.* **242,** 5125–5130
34. Klein, W. L., and Boyer, P. D. (1972) *J. Biol. Chem.* **247,** 7257–7265
35. Harold, F. M. (1972) *Bacteriol. Rev.* **36,** 172–230
36. Pullman, M. E., and Schatz, G. (1967) *Annu. Rev. Biochem.* **36,** 539–610
37. Lardy, H. A., and Ferguson, S. M. (1969) *Annu. Rev. Biochem.* **38,** 991–1034
38. Van Dam, K., and Meyer, A. J. (1971) *Annu. Rev. Biochem.* **40,** 118–160
39. Baltscheffsky, H., and Baltscheffsky, M. (1974) *Annu. Rev. Biochem.* **43,** 871–897
40. Boyer, P. D., Cross, R. L., and Momsen, W. (1973) *Proc. Natl. Acad. Sci. U. S. A.* **70,** 2837–2938
41. Cross, R. L., and Boyer, P. D. (1975) *Biochemistry* **14,** 392–398
42. Slater, E. C. (1974) in *Dynamics of Energy-transducing Membranes* (Ernster, L., Estabrook, R. W., and Slater, E. C., eds) pp. 1–20, Elsevier Science Publishers B.V., Amsterdam
43. Wolcott, R. G., and Boyer, P. D. (1974) *Biochem. Biophys. Res. Commun.* **57,** 709–716
44. Bagshaw, C. R., and Trentham, D. R. (1974) *Biochem. J.* **141,** 331–349
45. Bagshaw, C. R., Trentham, D. R., Wolcott, R. G., and Boyer, P. D. (1975) *Proc. Natl. Acad. Sci. U. S. A.* **72,** 2592–2596
46. Sleep, J. A., Hackney, D. D., and Boyer, P. D. (1978) *J. Biol. Chem.* **253,** 5235–5238
47. Boyer, P. D. (1974) in *Dynamics of Energy-transducing Membranes* (Ernster, L., Estabrook, R., and Slater, E. C., eds) pp. 289–301, Elsevier Science Publishers B.V., Amsterdam
48. Mitchell, P. (1961) *Nature* **191,** 144–148
49. Mitchell, P. (1974) *FEBS Lett.* **43,** 189–194
50. Boyer, P. D. (1975) *FEBS Lett.* **50,** 91–94
51. Mitchell, P. (1975) *FEBS Lett.* **50,** 95–97
52. Boyer, P. D. (1975) *FEBS Lett.* **58,** 1–6
53. Rosing, J., Kayalar, C., and Boyer, P. D. (1977) *J. Biol. Chem.* **252,** 2478–2485

54. Kayalar, C., Rosing, J., and Boyer, P. D. (1977) *J. Biol. Chem.* **252,** 2486–2491
55. Russo, J. A., Lamos, C. M., and Mitchell, R. A. (1978) *Biochemistry* **17,** 473–480
56. Wimmer, M. J., and Rose, I. A. (1977) *J. Biol. Chem.* **252,** 6769–6775
57. Hackney, D. D., and Boyer, P. D. (1978) *J. Biol. Chem.* **253,** 3164–3170
58. Hutton, R. L., and Boyer, P. D. (1979) *J. Biol. Chem.* **254,** 9990–9993
59. O'Neal, C. C., and Boyer, P. D. (1984) *J. Biol. Chem.* **259,** 5761–5767
60. Cross, R. L., Grubmeyer, C., and Penefsky, H. S. (1982) *J. Biol. Chem.* **257,** 12101–12105
61. Penefsky, H. S. (1985) *J. Biol. Chem.* **260,** 13735–13741
62. Feldman, R. I., and Sigman, D. S. (1982) *J. Biol. Chem.* **257,** 1676–1683
63. Boyer, P. D. (1993) *Biochim. Biophys. Acta* **1140,** 215–250
64. Kanazawa, T., and Boyer, P. D. (1973) *J. Biol. Chem.* **248,** 3163–3172
65. DeMeis, L., and Boyer, P. D. (1978) *J. Biol. Chem.* **253,** 1556–1559
66. Cohn, M. (1958) *J. Biol. Chem.* **230,** 369–379
67. Janson, C. A., Degani, C., and Boyer, P. D. (1979) *J. Biol. Chem.* **254,** 3743–3749
68. Rosing, J., Smith, D. J., Kayalar, C., and Boyer, P. D. (1976) *Biochem. Biophys. Res. Commun.* **72,** 1–8
69. Abrahams, J. P., Leslie, A. G. W., Lutter, R., and Walker, J. E. (1994) *Nature* **370,** 621–628
70. Smith, D. J., and Boyer, P. D. (1976) *Proc. Natl. Acad. Sci. U. S. A.* **73,** 4314–4318
71. Boyer, P. D. (1979) in *Membrane Bioenergetics* (Lee, C. P., Schatz, G., and Ernster, L., eds) pp. 461–479, Addison-Wesley, Reading, MA
72. Boyer, P. D., and Kohlbrenner, W. E. (1981) in *Energy Coupling in Photosynthesis* (Selman, B., and Selman-Reiner, S., eds) pp. 231–240, Elsevier Science Publishing Co., Inc., New York
73. Boyer, P. D. (1983) in *Biochemistry of Metabolic Processes* (Lennon, D. L. F., Stratman, F. W., and Zahlten, R. N., eds) pp. 465–477, Elsevier Biomed, NY
74. Hackney, D. D., Rosen, G., and Boyer, P. D. (1979) *Proc. Natl. Acad. Sci. U. S. A.* **76,** 3646–3650
75. McCarty, R. E., Pittman, P. R., and Tsuchiya, Y. (1972) *J. Biol. Chem.* **247,** 3048–3051
76. Kohlbrenner, W. E., and Boyer, P. D. (1983) *J. Biol. Chem.* **258,** 10881–10886
77. Wood, J. M., Wise, J. G., Senior, A. E., Futai, M., and Boyer, P. D. (1987) *J. Biol. Chem.* **262,** 2180–2186
78. Kasho, V. N., Yoshida, M., and Boyer, P. D. (1989) *Biochemistry* **28,** 6949–6954
79. Kasho, V. N., and Boyer, P. D. (1989) *Proc. Natl. Acad. Sci. U. S. A.* **86,** 8708–8711
80. Rosen, G., Gresser, M., Vinkler, C., and Boyer, P. D. (1979) *J. Biol. Chem.* **254,** 10654–10661
81. Smith, L. T., Rosen, G., and Boyer, P. D. (1983) *J. Biol. Chem.* **258,** 10887–10894
82. Wu, D., and Boyer, P. D. (1986) *Biochemistry* **25,** 3390–3396
83. Moyle, J., and Mitchell, P. (1975) *FEBS Lett.* **56,** 55–61
84. Hackney, D. D. (1979) *Biochem. Biophys. Res. Commun.* **91,** 122–128
85. Vasilyeva, E. A., Minkov, J. B., Fitin, A. F., and Vinogradov, A. D. (1982) *Biochem. J.* **202,** 15–23
86. Milgrom, M. M., Ehler, L. L., and Boyer, P. D. (1990) *J. Biol. Chem.* **265,** 18725–18728
87. Murataliev, M. B., and Boyer, P. D. (1992) *Eur. J. Biochem.* **209,** 681–687
88. Jault, J. M., and Allison, W. S. (1993) *J. Biol. Chem.* **268,** 1558–1566
89. Du, Z., and Boyer, P. D. (1989) *Biochemistry* **28,** 873–879
90. Cross, R. L., Cunningham, D., Miller, C. G., Xue, Z., Zhou, J.-M., and Boyer, P. D. (1987) *Proc. Natl. Acad. Sci. U. S. A.* **84,** 5715–5719
91. Xue, Z., Miller, C. G., Zhou, J.-M., and Boyer, P. D. (1987) *FEBS Lett.* **223,** 391–394
92. Wise, J. G., Hicke, B. J., and Boyer, P. D. (1987) *FEBS Lett.* **223,** 395–401
93. Williams, N., Hullihen, J., and Pedersen, P. L. (1987) *Biochemistry* **26,** 162–169
94. Musier, K. B., and Hammes, G. G. (1988) *Biochemistry* **27,** 7015–7020
95. Guerrero, K. J., and Boyer, P. D. (1988) *Biochim. Biophys. Res. Commun.* **154,** 854–860
96. Xue, Z., Zhou, J.-M., Melese, T., Cross, R. L., and Boyer, P. D. (1987) *Biochemistry* **26,** 3749–3753
97. Melese, T., Xue, Z., Stempel, K. E., and Boyer, P. D. (1988) *J. Biol. Chem.* **263,** 5833–5840
98. Berkich, D. A., Williams, G. D., Masiakos, P. T., Smith, M. B., Boyer, P. D., and LaNoue, K. F. (1991) *J. Biol. Chem.* **266,** 123–129
99. Weber, J., and Senior, A. E. (2001) *J. Biol. Chem.* **276,** 35422–35428
100. Dou, C., Fortes, P. A. G., and Allison, W. S. (1998) *Biochemistry* **37,** 16757–16764
101. Boyer, P. D. (2002) *FEBS Lett.* **512,** 29–32
102. Melese, T., and Boyer, P. D. (1985) *J. Biol. Chem.* **260,** 15398–15401
103. Kandpal, R. P., and Boyer, P. D. (1987) *Biochim. Biophys. Acta* **890,** 97–105
104. Musier, K. M., and Hammes, G. G. (1987) *Biochemistry* **26,** 5982–5988
105. Lutter, R., Abrahams, J. P., van Raiij, M. J., Todd, R. J., Lundquist, T., Buchanan, S. K., Leslie, A. G. W., and Walker, J. E. (1993) *J. Mol. Biol.* **229,** 787–790
106. Bianchet, M., Ysern, X., Hullien, J., Pedersen, P. L., and Amzel, L. M. (1991) *J. Biol. Chem.* **266,** 21197–21201
107. Duncan, T. M., Bulygin, V. V., Zhou, Y., Hutcheon, M. L., and Cross, R. L. (1995) *Proc. Natl. Acad. Sci. U. S. A.* **92,** 10964–10968
108. Aggeler, R., Haughton, M. A., and Capaldi, R. A. (1975) *J. Biol. Chem.* **270,** 9185–9191
109. Noji, H., Yasuda, R., Yoshida, M., and Kinosita, K., Jr. (1997) *Nature* **386,** 299–302
110. Sabbert, D., Engelbrecht, S., and Junge, W. (1998) *Proc. Natl. Acad. Sci. U. S. A.* **94,** 4401–4405
111. Boyer, P. D. (1997) *Annu. Rev. Biochem.* **66,** 717–749
112. Hutcheon, M. L., Duncan, T. M., Ngai, H., and Cross, R. L. (2001) *Proc. Natl. Acad. Sci. U. S. A.* **98,** 8519–8524

THE JOURNAL OF BIOLOGICAL CHEMISTRY
© 2002 by The American Society for Biochemistry and Molecular Biology, Inc.

Vol. 277, No. 50, Issue of December 13, pp. 47965–47971, 2002
Printed in U.S.A.

Reflections

A PAPER IN A SERIES COMMISSIONED TO CELEBRATE THE CENTENARY OF THE JBC IN 2005

JBC Centennial
1905–2005
100 Years of Biochemistry and Molecular Biology

The Pentose Phosphate Pathway

Published, JBC Papers in Press, October 25, 2002, DOI 10.1074/jbc.X200007200

Bernard L. Horecker

From the Department of Biochemistry, Weill Medical College of Cornell University, New York, New York 10021

I received my basic training in enzymology as a graduate student in the laboratory of Professor T. R. Hogness at the University of Chicago from 1936 to 1939. Hogness had constructed a photoelectric spectrophotometer modeled after the one in Otto Warburg's laboratory in Berlin-Dahlem. I was assigned a problem on succinic dehydrogenase from beef heart, using the Warburg manometric apparatus, and did not get to use the spectrophotometer until Erwin Haas arrived from Warburg's laboratory in 1939. Haas asked me to join him in the search for an enzyme that would catalyze the reduction of cytochrome *c* by reduced TPN (now NADP). This reaction was thought to be the missing link in the electron transport chain from substrate to oxygen and marked the beginning of my interest in what was then thought to function as a direct oxidative pathway for the metabolism of carbohydrate but is now known as the pentose phosphate pathway.

After I left Chicago during the Second World War, my experience with the spectrophotometer landed me a job at the National Institute of Health (NIH) in Frederick S. Brackett's group in the Division of Industrial Hygiene. Brackett had assembled an automatic recording spectrophotometer in the basement of Building 2 that I was assigned to use to develop a method for the determination of carbon monoxide hemoglobin in the blood of Navy pilots returning from combat missions. That and a number of other war-related projects kept me occupied for the next 4 years.

In 1945, after the end of the war with Japan, I was advised by the Director of the Laboratory, Dr. Paul Neal, that I was free to return to research in enzymology. I began studies on the reduction of cytochrome *c* by the succinic dehydrogenase system, using what was now my own Beckman spectrophotometer. One day, which I consider to be a turning point in my career, Arthur Kornberg, who had been working in Building 4 on the biological role of folic acid, appeared in my laboratory. Arthur had become convinced that enzymes were the key to an understanding of intracellular biochemical processes and suggested that we work together. We began with studies on the effect of cyanide on the succinic dehydrogenase system, because cyanide was known to bind to and be a general inhibitor of enzymes containing the heme group. An exception was cytochrome *c*, which had been reported to be resistant to the action of cyanide. Contrary to these early reports, we found that cyanide did react with cytochrome *c* and in 1946 published our first paper together, in the *Journal of Biological Chemistry*, entitled "The Cytochrome *c* Cyanide Complex."

Making History in Building 3

Two years later in 1948 when Arthur returned from a study leave in the laboratories of Severo Ochoa in New York and Carl Cori in St. Louis, he invited Leon Heppel and me to join him in setting up a new Section on Enzymes in the Laboratory of Physiology to be housed in Building 3, which was being completely renovated. Leon and I were about to be transferred, it having been discovered that the Industrial Hygiene Research Laboratory in Building 2 had never been officially part of the NIH but was in the Bureau of State Services, which was moving to new headquarters in Cincinnati.

In the fall of 1948 while we waited for the of the renovation of laboratories in Building 3 to be completed, we all three worked in Building 2. Arthur and I, both of whose planned research projects would depend heavily on assays using the "pyridine nucleotide" coenzymes DPN and TPN, collaborated in their isolation. In those early years of American biochemistry there were no vendors that supplied these materials. We isolated them from sheep liver, using the unpublished procedure from Warburg's laboratory that Erwin Haas and I had used in Chicago. In 1948 Arthur and I possessed the world's supply of TPN, and when Warburg visited our laboratory in 1948, we were able to present the discoverer of TPN with a gift of 25 mg of that coenzyme.

The new Enzyme Section in the Division of Physiology in Building 3 provided an exciting and stimulating atmosphere. Together with Herbert Tabor from the Laboratory of Pharmacology in Building 4, we organized a daily lunch hour journal club, during which we reviewed the literature on every facet of enzymology and intermediary metabolism. This was the beginning of a great history for Building 3, continuously occupied by scientists who were to make notable contributions in biomedical science. The first NIH recipients of the Paul Lewis Laboratories Award in Enzyme Chemistry, then one of the most prestigious awards in biological research, were all from Building 3: Arthur Kornberg in 1951, myself in 1952, and Earl Stadtman in 1953. Later, our Section on Enzymes became part of the new Experimental Biology and Medicine Institute, which Henry Sebrell, then the NIH Director, proposed to function as the basic research arm of the NIH. It was later renamed the National Institute of Arthritis and Metabolic Diseases, a change that had no effect on the nature of our research but resulted in increased funding by Congress. We continued to work in the laboratories in Building 3.

Use of the pyridine nucleotides in enzyme assays with the Beckman spectrophotometer required knowledge of the exact extinction coefficients of the 340 nm peaks of the reduced forms. The published values for DPNH showed considerable variation, and there was scant information for TPNH. In the new laboratories in Building 3, Arthur and I designed experiments to determine the true extinction coefficients at 340 nm of both coenzymes, which proved to be identical. That work, published in 1948, made possible quantitative spectrophotometric measurements in reactions involving the pyridine nucleotides and became one of the most frequently cited papers in the biochemical literature.

In the new laboratories in Building 3 Leon Heppel and I also collaborated in the purification of xanthine oxidase from milk after we found that this enzyme could reduce not only methylene blue, a reaction that I had studied in Chicago, but also cytochrome *c*. However, this reduction occurred *only if oxygen was present,* a curious observation that was quickly picked up by Fridovich and Handler, who were working at Duke University on the formation of the superoxide anion. The reduction of cytochrome *c* by superoxide anion became a widely used assay for this species of "active oxygen." I also returned to the study of cytochrome *c* reductase, which Haas and I had isolated from yeast, and accomplished the first isolation of this flavoprotein from mammalian liver. By then it had become apparent that these cytochrome *c* reductases did not function in mitochondrial respiration but rather as components of the cytochrome P-450 system for the metabolism and detoxification of drugs and other xenobiotics.

The Pentose Phosphate Pathway

The Oxidation of Glucose 6-Phosphate—When Otto Warburg discovered TPN as the coenzyme required for the oxidation of glucose 6-phosphate to 6-phosphogluconate, the role of the other pyridine nucleotide, DPN, as the coenzyme required for the fermentation of glucose to ethanol in yeast or the glycolysis of glucose to lactic acid in muscle had been well established. The finding that the new coenzyme was required for the oxidation of glucose 6-phosphate and also for the further oxidation of the product, 6-phosphogluconate, led Warburg and also Frank Dickens in England and Fritz Lipmann, then working in Denmark, to propose that there existed an alternate pathway that functioned as a "direct oxidative pathway." They had obtained evidence that the products formed in the oxidation of 6-phosphogluconate by TPN were carbon dioxide and an unidentified pentose phosphate. Because carbon dioxide was one of the products, it seemed reasonable to regard this alternate pathway as the one responsible for the oxidation of carbohydrate. Haas and I had already shown that TPN could serve as an electron transport link to the cytochromes and therefore to molecular oxygen.

Twenty years after the pioneering work of Warburg, Dickens, and Lipmann, I began studies (with a new laboratory technician, Pauline (Polly) Smyrniotis) on the enzymes involved in the oxidation of 6-phosphogluconate and the metabolic intermediates formed in this pathway. We were joined by J. E. Seegmiller, my first postdoctoral student, and he and I worked out a new method for the preparation of glucose 6-phosphate and 6-phosphogluconate, which were not yet commercially available. We purified the enzyme, 6-phosphogluconate dehydrogenase, from brewers' yeast, the richest source we could find, and by coupling the reduction of TPN to its re-oxidation by pyruvate in the presence of lactic dehydrogenase showed that the first product of the oxidation of 6-phosphogloconate, in addition to carbon dioxide, was a new pentose ester, ribulose 5-phosphate, which was then converted to ribose 5-phosphate by a pentose-phosphate isomerase present in our purified dehydrogenase preparations. The separation of ribulose phosphate from ribose phosphate and the demonstration that their interconversion was catalyzed by a pentose-phosphate isomerase were made possible by the recent development at the Oak Ridge National Laboratory of a separation technique for nucleotides called ion-exchange chromatography.

The identification of the sugar in the new pentose ester as ribulose was based on a number of criteria, including comparison with the authentic sugar, prepared by the method of Glatthaar and Reichstein, using a number of chemical and physical criteria, which included x-ray diffraction of the crystalline nitrophenyl hydrazones. In those days discoveries of new sugar phosphate esters were rare events, and I felt that it was necessary to establish its identity beyond a shadow of doubt. The results were first presented at the American Chemical Society meeting in Boston in 1951 at a symposium honoring Arthur Kornberg's Paul Lewis Laboratories Award, and I recall the warm reaction at that meeting to the work reported from our laboratories in Building 3.

During the following year Jay Seegmiller and I showed that the same products were formed in the metabolism of 6-phosphogluconate by enzymes from mammalian tissues.

The Further Metabolism of the Pentose Phosphates—An important clue to the further steps in what was later to become known as the "pentose phosphate pathway" was already in the literature. In 1938 Zaccharias Dische had demonstrated that red cell lysates catalyzed the conversion of the 5-carbon sugar, ribose 5-phosphate to hexose monophosphate, an observation that Seegmiller and I confirmed in 1952 with rabbit bone marrow extracts. These observations gave rise to the hypothesis that the oxidative pathway was really a cyclic mechanism for the direct oxidation of carbohydrate. With each turn of the cycle one molecule of carbon dioxide would be produced, and the pentose phosphates formed would be metabolized back to hexose phosphates to start another cycle. Six turns of the cycle would result in the complete oxidation of one molecule of glucose.

However, the reactions involved in the conversion of the 5-carbon pentose phosphates to the 6-carbon hexose phosphates were completely unknown. What ensued was a race involving a number of laboratories, including ours at the NIH and those of Ephraim Racker at the New York City Research Laboratories, later at Cornell University in Ithaca, Seymour Cohen at the University of Pennsylvania in Philadelphia, Oliver Lampen at Washington University in St. Louis, and Frank Dickens in England, to identify the reactions and metabolic intermediates involved.

It had already been established from the work of Dische and others that one of the products of pentose phosphate metabolism was the 3-carbon sugar, glyceraldehyde 3-phosphate, which suggested cleavage of a 5-carbon sugar, probably ribulose 5-phosphate, between carbon atoms 2 and 3. The 3-carbon fragment, glyceraldehyde 3-phosphate, was a known intermediate in glycolysis, but what was the fate of the remaining 2-carbon fragment? Polly Smyrniotis and I, now joined by my first foreign postdoctoral fellow, Hans Klenow from Copenhagen, set out to purify the enzyme(s) involved in the cleavage of pentose phosphate, using rat liver as the enzyme source and an assay that measured the appearance of glyceraldehyde 3-phosphate. When we also followed the disappearance of the 5-carbon sugar, using Dische's "orcinol" reaction, we detected the formation of a new product that also reacted with orcinol but produced a different color and a visible absorption spectrum distinctly different from that produced in the reaction with pentoses. Our clue to the identity of this product came from Melvin Calvin's laboratory in Berkeley, where, using radioactive carbon dioxide, they had identified both ribulose diphosphate and a 7-carbon sugar, sedoheptulose monophosphate, as early intermediates in the fixation of carbon dioxide in photosynthesis. Authentic sedoheptulose was available from Nelson Richtmyer's laboratory in Building 4, and on Christmas Eve, 1951, when everybody else had gone home, I sprayed a paper chromatogram with orcinol and up came the blue spot characteristic of sedoheptulose. I rushed up and down the laboratory hallway clutching the paper chromatogram, but there was nobody there to show it to, so I took it home and hung it on the Christmas tree, singing the little ditty: "It's sedoheptulose, it's sedoheptulose, tra la la boom deay, tra la la boom deay," much to the amusement of my young daughters.

We adopted the name "transketolase," first suggested by Racker and his co-workers, because it catalyzed the transfer of a 2-carbon fragment from the ketopentose, ribulose 5-phosphate, to the other 5-carbon sugar, ribose 5-phosphate, to generate the new ketol linkage in the 7-carbon sugar, sedoheptulose 7-phosphate. Thus the unknown 2-carbon fragment never occurred as a free entity. Later, simultaneously with Racker, we showed that the coenzyme carrier for the 2-carbon fragment by transketolase was thiamine pyrophosphate.

Two puzzling observations remained to be explained. One was that the configuration of the hydroxyl group on the third carbon atom of the new product, sedoheptulose 7-phosphate, was opposite that on the third carbon atom of the presumed substrate, ribulose 5-phosphate. This lack of stereospecificity, particularly because we had demonstrated that the reaction was readily reversible, was highly improbable for an enzyme-catalyzed reaction. The other unexplained observation was that the cleavage of pentose phosphate by our purified transketolase preparations from rat liver required the presence of aldolase, a crystalline and supposedly pure enzyme from rabbit muscle that catalyzed the condensation of two triose phosphates to form the hexose, fructose 1,6-bisphosphate. The answer to both of these puzzling observations came from the discovery by Paul Stumpf, while on sabbatical in my laboratory, and reported almost simultaneously from the laboratories of Dickens, Racker, and Ashwell, of another enzyme, an "epimerase," that catalyzed the conversion of ribulose 5-phosphate to its "3-epimer," xylulose 5-phosphate, which had the same stereo-configuratuion at the 3-carbon atom as sedoheptulose phosphate. With this substrate, we confirmed the earlier report by Racker and his co-workers that xylulose phosphate, rather that ribulose phosphate, was the true substrate for cleavage by transketolase and the true donor of the 2-carbon fragment. The requirement for aldolase was explained when we found that crystalline preparations of this enzyme from rabbit muscle contained the epimerase as a contaminant, which could only be removed by many re-crystallizations.

Thus three different pentose phosphates were now shown to be involved in the new pathway: ribulose 5-phosphate, the first product of the oxidation of 6-phosphate gluconate, and xylulose 5-phosphate and ribose 5-phosphate, both formed from ribulose 5-phosphate, one serving as the 2-carbon donor and the other as the acceptor in the reaction catalyzed by transketolase. The addition of any one of these pentose phosphates to crude tissue extracts would result in the formation of an equilibrium mixture of all three.

Completion of the Cycle—Still to be discovered, however, was a mechanism that would convert the products of the transketolase reaction, sedoheptulose phosphate and glyceraldehyde phosphate, to the 6-carbon sugars, fructose 6-phosphate and glucose 6-phosphate, and complete the cycle. In particular, what was the fate of sedoheptulose phosphate? We found that purified enzyme preparations from liver or yeast would catalyze the formation of hexose monophosphate from sedoheptulose monophosphate but only if triose phosphate was also present. When I described this finding at one of our luncheon journal club meetings, Horace ("Nook") Barker, who was visiting from the University of California at Berkeley and working in Kornberg's laboratory, suggested that we consider the possibility of another transfer, this time of a 3-carbon fragment from sedoheptulose phosphate to triose phosphate to generate fructose 6-phosphate. When we carried out an experiment with carbon-14-labeled triose phosphate, we found that, as predicted, the fructose 6-phosphate formed had radioactivity in the last three carbon atoms with the first three unlabeled. We named the enzyme "transaldolase" because it catalyzed the transfer of an aldol linkage rather than the hydrolytic cleavage catalyzed by aldolase.

What remained was to account for the fate of the remaining 4 carbon atoms of sedoheptulose 7-phosphate. For this work Polly Smyrniotis and I were joined by Paul Marks and Howard Hiatt, two young M.D.s working as Clinical Associates in the new Clinical Center in Building

10, who had asked to join my group to learn enzymology in their "spare time," which turned out to be from 5 p.m. to midnight. We identified the missing fragment as another new sugar ester, the 4-carbon sugar erythrose 4-phosphate, in a number of tests, including its conversion to the 7-carbon sugar sedoheptulose 1,7-diphosphate in a condensation with dihydroxyacetone phosphate, catalyzed by fructose bisphosphate aldolase. It was also converted to fructose 6-phosphate in the reaction catalyzed by transketolase.

The elucidation of the pentose phosphate pathway had now been accomplished. It consisted of two branches, an oxidative branch in which the hexose, glucose 6-phosphate, was converted to pentose phosphate and carbon dioxide with the reduction of two molecules of TPN, and a non-oxidative branch, in which three molecules of pentose phosphate (15 carbon atoms) were reconverted to two and one-half molecules of hexose phosphate (15 carbon atoms) in a series of fully reversible reactions. Our contributions included the discovery of three new sugar phosphate esters, ribulose 5-phosphate, sedoheptulose 7-phosphate, and erythrose 4-phosphate, and three new enzymes, transketolase, transaldolase, and pentose-phosphate 3-epimerase. We shared with Racker the discovery of transketolase and confirmed his finding that xylulose 5-phosphate, rather than ribulose 5-phosphate, was the 2-carbon donor in the reaction catalyzed by that enzyme. We also shared with McLean and Dickens, working in England, the discovery that fructose 6-phosphate was also a substrate for transketolase. If the pathway operated as originally envisioned, six turns of the "cycle" would result in the oxidation of one molecule of 6-carbon sugar to six molecules of carbon dioxide.

Functions of the Pentose Phosphate Pathway—The function(s) of the new pathway, however, turned out to be quite different from the pathway for the direct oxidation of carbohydrate that we had expected. It provides two mechanisms for the production of ribose 5-phosphate. One is the "oxidative branch" of the pathway, which also generates 2 eq of TPNH (NADPH). Ribose 5-phosphate can also be formed directly from hexose and triose phosphates by the non-oxidative rearrangements catalyzed by transketolase and transaldolase. Where large quantities of NADPH are required, as in the synthesis of fatty acids or sterols, the excess pentose phosphates produced would be recycled back to hexose monophosphates.

To assist medical students in memorizing the reactions, someone composed the following song.

THE PENTOSE PHOSPHATE SHUNT
(Tune: "MacNamara's Band")

If you're converting carbohydrate into triglyceride,
If you need pentose moieties to make nucleotide,
You'll find that Embden-Meyerhof is not the game to play
And you'll do your biosynthesis the pentose phosphate way.

Chorus: With transaldolase, transketolase, G6PDH too,
Six times six gives five times six plus six of CO_2
Carbons passing to and fro, the back becomes the front,
Did you ever see a pathway like the pentose phosphate shunt?

First G6P is oxidized, NADP reduced
To give gluconolactone (as might have been deduced).
The lactone is then hydrolyzed to make the gluconate
And decarboxylated to its metabolic fate.

There ends the oxidative phase, now multiply by three,
An intermediate balance sheet by way of summary,
Six NADPH are formed, three CO_2 set free,
Three ribulose 5-phosphate formed from three of G6P.

One isomerization from ketose to aldose
Turns ribulose 5-phosphate to the phosphate of ribose
The other two epimerized, inverted at C3,
Two xylulose 5-phosphates formed (hence called Xu5P).

Two carbons from Xu5P transferred from the ketose to aldose
(Transketolase needs TPP as everybody knows),
Thus three plus seven made to meet transaldolase attack,
Three Cs from sedoheptulose the GAP gets back,

Glyceraldehyde 3-phosphate thus becoming F6P
Leaves erythrose 4-phosphate looking for some company,
But Xu5P number two has two top Cs to spare,
Transketolase negotiates their transfer as a pair.

So we've made another F6P, a triose phosphate too,
To see what we have now achieved let's multiply by two,
Four F6Ps, two GAPs, by glycolytic tricks,
Give five glucose 6-phosphates, when we started out with six!

(Author unknown)

The first discovery relevant to the new pentose phosphate pathway, namely the formation of ribulose and ribose phosphates as products of the oxidation of 6-phosphogluconate, was announced in the spring of 1952 at the annual meeting of the American Chemical Society in Chicago. The outline of the complete pentose phosphate cycle, including the reactions catalyzed by the new enzymes transketolase and transaldolase, was published in 1955 in a review written in collaboration with I. C. (Gunny) Gunsalus and W. A. (Woody) Wood for *Bacteriological Reviews* entitled "Pathways of Carbohydrate Metabolism in Microorganisms." The existence of the cycle in mammalian liver and in plant leaves was confirmed in experiments with carbon-labeled ribose 5-phosphate in two papers published with Martin Gibbs of the Brookhaven National Laboratory, describing work carried out there during the summer of 1953.

The Path of Carbon in Photosynthesis

When, in 1952, Calvin's group at the University of California at Berkeley reported evidence for ribulose 1,5-diphosphate as the CO_2 acceptor for the formation of 3-phosphoglyceric acid, the first CO_2 fixation product in photosynthesis, we were excited by the possibility that the pentose phosphate pathway might serve as the mechanism for regenerating this key intermediate from hexose monophosphates. Art Weissbach, a newly arrived postdoctoral student from Columbia, and Polly Smyrniotis carried out the first experiments to identify the enzymatic mechanisms involved. They were able to show that with crude extracts from spinach leaves ribose 5-phosphate was a unique substrate for the formation of phosphoglyceric acid, and they purified a kinase from spinach leaves that they used to prepare the barium salt of ribulose 1,5-bisphosphate (RUDP).

In the fall of 1954 we moved from Building 3 to new laboratories on the 9th floor of the NIH Clinical Center, where, joined by Jerry Hurwitz, we isolated the enzyme phosphoribulokinase, responsible for that reaction, as well as the enzyme ribulose-bisphosphate carboxylase, which catalyzed the formation of 2 mol of phosphoglyceric acid from ribulose bisphosphate and CO_2. Working in laboratories across the hall from each other, Art, Jerry, and I divided responsibilities. Jerry was charged with the purification of phosphoribulokinase, I took on the task of preparing pure ribulose 1,5-bisphosphate, and Art went after the most important enzyme, the ribulose-bisphosphate carboxylase. The last effort deserves a special comment. Although the enzyme was purified only 10-fold from the crude spinach leaf extracts, by all the criteria that we could apply it appeared to be a pure protein, which meant that it constituted about 10% of the soluble protein in the spinach leaf. Later work in other laboratories around the world confirmed this finding, and this enzyme, now known as "Rubisco" for ribulose-bisphosphate carboxylase/oxygenase is now considered to be the most abundant protein on earth.

Our work was published in three back-to-back papers in the February 1956 issue of the *Journal of Biological Chemistry*, entitled: "Spinach Phosphoribulokinase," "The Enzymatic Synthesis and Properties of Ribulose 1,5-Diphosphate," and "The Enzymatic Formation of Phosphoglyceric from Ribulose Diphosphate and Carbon Dioxide." With this work and our earlier demonstration of the reversible reactions for the interconversion of pentose and hexose phosphates, with sedoheptulose phosphate as a prominent intermediate, all of the enzymes for the reactions of the Calvin Cycle were identified.

Conclusion

The pentose phosphate pathway in animals, as discussed earlier, fulfills two important cell requirements: 1) for ribose 5-phosphate for the synthesis of nucleotides and nucleic acids; and 2) for reducing power in the form of NADPH. In photosynthesis, it functions to regenerate the primary CO_2 acceptor, ribulose bisphosphate, from the hexose phosphates produced. Chloroplasts utilize radiant energy to produce ATP, required for the production of ribulose 1,5-bisphosphate from ribulose 5-phosphate and also for the reduction of 3-phosphoglyceric acid to glyceraldehyde 3-phosphate. The reducing agent for the latter reaction, NADPH, is also generated by the action of light in the chloroplasts. In both animals and plants, NADP rather than NAD appears to function as the coenzyme for reductive synthesis.

Comment

Because these were personal "reflections" they have mainly described work from my laboratory. Calvin and his co-workers provided the first clues leading to the development of the photosynthetic cycle and also the conclusive evidence for its function as the path of carbon in intact photosynthesizing cells. These pioneering experiments, as well as important contributions from many other laboratories, are cited in a review that I published in 1957 with Wolf Vishniac and Severo Ochoa in *Advances in Enzymology* (see last entry of the Bibliography).

Address correspondence to: blhorecker@aol.com.

BIBLIOGRAPHY

Horecker, B. L., and Kornberg, A. (1948) The extinction coefficients of the reduced band of the pyridine nucleotides. *J. Biol. Chem.* **175,** 385–390

Horecker, B. L., Smyrniotis, P. Z., and Seegmiller, J. E. (1951) The enzymatic conversion of 6-phosphogluconate to ribulose 5-phosphate and ribose 5-phosphate. *J. Biol. Chem.* **193,** 383–396

Horecker, B. L., and Smyrniotis, P. Z. (1953) The coenzyme function of thiamine pyrophosphate in pentose phosphate metabolism. *J. Am. Chem. Soc.* **75,** 1009–1010

Horecker, B. L., and Smyrniotis, P. Z. (1953) Transaldolase: the formation of fructose 6-phosphate from sedoheptulose 7-phosphate. *J. Am. Chem. Soc.* **75,** 2021

Horecker, B. L., Smyrniotis, P. Z., and Klenow, H. (1955) The formation of sedoheptulose phosphate from pentose phosphate. *J. Biol. Chem.* **205,** 661–682

Weissbach, A., Smyrniotis, P. Z., and Horecker, B. L. (1954) Pentose phosphate and CO_2 fixation with spinach extracts. *J. Am. Chem. Soc.* **76,** 3611

Horecker, B. L., and Smyrniotis, P. Z. (1955) The purification and properties of yeast transaldolase. *J. Biol. Chem.* **212,** 811–825

Horecker, B. L., Smyrniotis, P. Z., Hiatt, H., and Marks, P. (1955) Tetrose phosphate and the formation of sedoheptulose diphosphate. *J. Biol. Chem.* **218,** 827–836

Hurwitz, J., Weissbach, H., Horecker, B. L., and Smyrniotis, P. Z. (1956) Spinach phosphoribulokinase. *J. Biol. Chem.* **218,** 769–783

Horecker, B. L., Hurwitz, J., and Horecker, B. L. (1956) The enzymatic synthesis and properties of ribulose 1,5-diphosphate. *J. Biol. Chem.* **218,** 785–794

Weissbach, A., Horecker, B. L., and Hurwitz, J. (1956) The enzymatic formation of phosphoglyceric acid from ribulose diphosphate and carbon dioxide. *J. Biol. Chem.* **218,** 795–810

Horecker, B. L., Smyrniotis, P. Z., and Hurwitz, J. (1956) The role of xylulose 5-phosphate in the transketolase reaction. *J. Biol. Chem.* **223,** 1009–1019

Vishniac, W., Horecker, B. L., and Ochoa, S. (1957) Enzymatic aspects of photosynthesis. *Adv. Enzymol.* **XIX,** 1–77

Vol. 277, No. 51, Issue of December 20, pp. 49091–49100, 2002
Printed in U.S.A.

Reflections

A PAPER IN A SERIES COMMISSIONED TO CELEBRATE THE CENTENARY OF THE JBC IN 2005

JBC Centennial
1905–2005
100 Years of Biochemistry and Molecular Biology

A Gold Mine of Fascinating Enzymes: Those Remarkable, Strictly Anaerobic Bacteria, *Methanococcus vannielii* and *Clostridium sticklandii*

Published, JBC Papers in Press, October 25, 2002, DOI 10.1074/jbc.X200005200

Thressa Campbell Stadtman

From the Laboratory of Biochemistry, NHLBI, National Institutes of Health, Bethesda, Maryland 20892-8012

Anaerobic Metabolism Background

I was fortunate to have had Dr. H. A. Barker as a mentor for my graduate studies at Berkeley. He had been trained by famous microbiologists from the Delft School of Microbiology, and he instilled in his students a deep interest in the metabolism of anaerobic microorganisms. Members of the Delft School had found that the microbial decomposition of various compounds under anaerobic conditions sometimes involved unusual chemical reactions that were amenable to detailed study because the responsible catalysts were present in exaggerated amounts or subsequent rate-limiting steps allowed intermediates to accumulate. By studying under Barker, who had worked with C. B. van Niel in Pacific Grove and later with A. J. Kluyver in Delft, I became an indirect descendent of the Delft microbiologists.

For my thesis problem, I chose to work on the biosynthesis of methane, an area of research that I knew to be of considerable interest to Barker. Formate, acetate, and various fatty acids were added to simple mineral salts media for selection of organisms able to utilize these substrates for methane production. I used soil samples as inocula that I had dug from San Francisco Bay mud flats. At that time, the bay was heavily contaminated, and the mud flats reeked of hydrogen sulfide at low tide, a clear indication of anaerobic conditions. Microorganisms that grew on acetate, propionate, and short chain fatty acids were obtained, and these were studied using ^{14}C-labeled substrates to determine the source of methane (1). Particularly interesting was the unexpected finding that in the fermentation of acetate methane was derived from the methyl carbon and the carboxyl carbon was the source of the carbon dioxide (2). Barker (Fig. 1) was particularly excited by these results because they were an exception to an earlier hypothesis of van Niel that methane is derived exclusively from carbon dioxide. However, in the other fatty acid fermentations carbon dioxide did serve as oxidant and was reduced to methane.

Formate was actively fermented to a mixture of methane, hydrogen, and carbon dioxide. Two microorganisms were enriched in parallel when formate was supplied as substrate. One proved to be a methane-producing motile coccus that we named *Methanococcus vannielii* in honor of C. B. van Niel (3). The other was a rod-shaped organism that I later named *Clostridium sticklandii* (4).

Detailed studies on the morphology and biochemical properties of *M. vannielii* (3) constituted a major portion of my Ph.D. thesis, and I was very gratified that the results of all of these studies were published with Barker in a series of papers on methane fermentations.

Aerobic Metabolism of Cholesterol

When I first joined the newly formed National Heart Institute at NIH in 1950, I continued working on a project initiated during the year I spent as a postdoctoral fellow at Harvard Medical School. The oxidation of cholesterol using enzymes from an aerobic *Nocardia* species

FIG. 1. **H. A. Barker.**

was investigated. At that time, sterols formed by selective oxidation of the cholesterol side chain would have been useful precursors of cortisone and certain hormones such as progesterone. Unfortunately, cholesterol was degraded completely by the organism under a variety of conditions, and we could not detect any of the desired intermediate products. However, an enzyme that oxidized cholesterol at position 3 of the ring to form Δ-4-cholestene-3-one was identified and partially purified. Later, preparations of this cholesterol oxidase were produced by P-L Biochemicals, Inc. and used clinically for determination of cholesterol.

Amino Acid Fermentation Studies

After my unsuccessful experience with strictly aerobic bacteria as enzyme sources, I was glad to retreat to the anaerobic world and initiated studies on the fermentation of amino acid substrates by the clostridial species I had isolated along with *M. vannielii* from San Francisco Bay mud (4). Initial studies on the anaerobic metabolism of lysine and ornithine (5) and the roles of vitamin B_{12} in these processes (6) provided examples of interesting new reactions and additional roles of B_{12} coenzyme. The degradation of lysine to acetate, butyrate, and ammonia occurred by two distinct processes. In one, acetate was derived from carbon atoms 1 and 2 of the 6-carbon chain of L-lysine, and the residual 4 carbon atoms were converted to butyrate. In the other, acetate was derived from carbon atoms 5 and 6 of D-lysine and butyrate from carbon atoms 1–4. These conversions required the participation of an imposing list of cofactors and involved many distinct enzymic steps (7).

Another amino acid transformation investigated in the early studies was the reductive deamination of glycine by *C. sticklandii*. Significantly, glycine reduction proved to be an energy-conserving process linked eventually to the formation of ATP (8). Thus, in the presence of orthophosphate and ADP, glycine was reduced to acetate and ammonia and ATP was formed with the stoichiometry shown in Equation 1.

$$\text{Glycine} + \text{R(SH)}_2 + \text{P}_i + \text{ADP} \rightarrow \text{acetate} + \text{ammonia} + \text{R-SS} + \text{ATP} \qquad \text{(Eq. 1)}$$

Much later the direct products of the glycine reductase complex were shown to be ammonia and acetyl phosphate (9), and the highly active acetate kinase contaminant in the enzyme preparations converted acetyl phosphate and ADP to acetate and ATP. The key discovery that one of the protein components of the glycine reductase complex is a selenoprotein (10, 11) shifted the emphasis of my later research.

The Selenium Era

Much to my surprise the studies on glycine reductase from *C. sticklandii* led us to the discovery early in May 1972 that the "rich culture medium" containing 2% Tryptone, 1% yeast extract, and formate used for routine growth of the organism was selenium-deficient. When supplemented with 1 μM selenite, the cell population exhibited high glycine reductase activity throughout the entire growth phase, whereas in the absence of added selenite glycine reductase was detected only in early log phase cells. A low molecular weight acidic protein component of the glycine reductase complex (10), termed protein A, that we had isolated previously from early log phase cells proved to be the missing factor in cell-free extracts prepared from end of log phase cell populations that were not supplemented with selenium. A typical dilution curve was exhibited for protein A levels in extracts as a function of growth of *C. sticklandii* in the non-selenite-supplemented medium. In retrospect, I realized that in the 1950s, when the Bethesda tap water could be used for culture of various anaerobic bacteria, the levels of glycine reductase in *C. sticklandii* were considerably higher than they were later when we were forced to use distilled water because of high levels of neutral detergents in the water supply. It is evident that many of the so-called "rich culture media" used by microbiologists are selenium-deficient, and this is true also for various serum-supplemented media used for culture of mammalian cells.

To determine whether selenium was an actual component of protein A, *C. sticklandii* was grown in media containing [^{75}Se]selenite. This resulted in the incorporation of radioactivity in protein A, and the ^{75}Se content of the protein was enriched in parallel with enzyme activity during isolation of the protein in near homogeneous form (11). Thus, by the end of June 1972 we had evidence of the existence of an essential selenium-containing protein, the protein A component of glycine reductase.

There followed a "learning period" for me concerning the chemistry of selenium and its relative, sulfur, to determine the identity of the selenium compound in the labeled protein A. I obtained several organoselenium compounds from the National Cancer Institute library that originally had been collected as potential carcinogens. However, the chemists who had synthesized these compounds had introduced phenyl groups for stability purposes, thus limiting their use as possible model compounds for our studies. Before the identification in 1957 of selenium as an essential nutrient for rats (12) and birds (13), it was known in biology mainly for its toxic properties.

Identification of Selenocysteine in Glycine Reductase Protein A

I had determined previously (10) that reaction of the reduced form of protein A with iodoacetamide inhibited its biological activity as an essential component of the glycine reductase complex and had assumed that one or more essential SH groups had been alkylated. When we treated the ^{75}Se-labeled protein with iodoacetamide or iodoacetate, the biological activity likewise was destroyed, but elimination of radioactive selenium as inorganic forms previously observed during acid hydrolysis was prevented almost completely. Instead, we could recover the radiolabel from the acid hydrolysates in a compound containing an alkyl group attached to the selenium. This derivative was identified as Se-carboxymethyl-selenocysteine by comparison with the corresponding alkyl derivative of authentic selenocysteine (14). We made several other alkyl derivatives of the selenoprotein for further identification and established that the Se-carboxymethyl, Se-carboxyethyl, and Se-aminoethyl forms were the most satisfactory from the standpoint of stability during acid hydrolysis and subsequent chromatographic separation on an amino acid analyzer column. Throughout these studies, my able assistant, Joe Nathan Davis, provided invaluable expertise and together with two post-doctoral fellows, Joyce Cone and Raphael Martin del Rio, we could establish that protein A contains 1 gram atom of selenium per mol and the selenium is present in the form of a selenocysteine residue in the polypeptide (14). The methods we developed for identification of selenocysteine in our bacterial protein were used later by other investigators to isolate and identify the selenium-containing moiety in mammalian glutathione peroxidase, another enzyme that had been reported in 1973 to contain selenium (15).

To determine whether free added selenocysteine could be incorporated into protein A, Gregory Dilworth, a postdoctoral fellow in my laboratory, synthesized selenocysteine labeled either with ^{3}H, ^{75}Se, or ^{14}C, and we grew *C. sticklandii* in the presence of these added labeled substrates. There was no detectable incorporation of the labeled carbon chain of the amino acid into protein A, but the [^{75}Se]selenocysteine was used more efficiently as a selenium source than the normal supplement [^{75}Se]selenite, which is reduced by thiols in the culture medium (16). In retrospect, the facile utilization of selenium from selenocysteine for protein A biosynthesis observed in these experiments is indicative of the participation of a selenocysteine lyase. These lyases, first purified by Kenji Soda and his collaborators in Kyoto from bacteria (17) and from liver (18), convert selenocysteine to an atomic form of selenium and alanine.

$$SeHCH_2CHNH_2COOH \rightarrow Se + CH_3CHNH_2COOH \qquad \text{(Eq. 2)}$$

For several years, we thought these proteins served solely as detoxification agents, but they now are considered to function as selenium transferases or selenium delivery proteins. Much of our current research is directed to elucidation of the chemical properties and biochemical roles of these selenium transferases.

Dr. Richard Glass, a sulfur organic chemist, joined our group in 1987 while on sabbatical leave from the University of Arizona. We had met in 1984 in Lindau, Germany, at a Symposium on the Organic Chemistry of Sulfur. At this meeting the organizers had decided to enlarge the program to include biologically important selenium compounds, and my presentation on the small selenoprotein component of glycine reductase stimulated Dick Glass to become involved in selenium organic chemistry. During his year in Bethesda, we grew *C. sticklandii* in the presence of [77]Se and isolated selenoprotein A labeled with the stable isotope. This was used to investigate conformational properties of the selenoprotein using ^{77}Se NMR spectroscopy as a probe. Later, when we discovered that the biological donor for biosynthesis of selenuridine in tRNAs is selenophosphate (19), the synthesis of this compound was achieved by Glass and his group, and authentic selenophosphate was supplied to us as a reference compound (20). I continue to rely on Dick Glass for advice and assistance concerning a wide variety of problems we encounter in the field of selenium chemistry.

The UGA Codon Is Used for Specific Selenocysteine Incorporation

The presence of an unusual amino acid in two selenoenzymes, glycine reductase and glutathione peroxidase, that was not specified by the genetic code posed the problem of the method of specific incorporation of a selenoamino acid in the proteins. In fact, 13 years elapsed before it was recognized that one of the three stop codons, UGA, is used as the signal for selenocysteine insertion into a growing polypeptide chain. Simultaneously it was shown by August Böck and his collaborators in München that the TGA codon in the *Escherichia coli* formate dehydrogenase H gene directed selenocysteine incorporation into the protein (21) and by P. R. Harrison and his collaborators in Glasgow that the TGA codon in the murine glutathione peroxidase gene corresponded to the position of selenocysteine in bovine glutathione peroxidase (22). The amino acid sequence of bovine glutathione peroxidase had been determined earlier at Grunenthal GmbH in Aachen by Flohé and associates (23). Eventually, I could verify that selenocysteine occurred in the formate dehydrogenase protein in the position predicted by the TGA codon in the gene (24). In a series of elegant experiments by August Böck and his associates, genes were isolated that complemented some of the mutant strains of *E. coli* defective in synthesis of formate dehydrogenase that had been isolated previously by Marie Andre Mandrand-Berthelot (25–27). Four genes that encoded four different products essential for the specific synthesis of selenocysteine and its insertion into protein were cloned and the expressed products characterized. In one step, a serine esterified to a special tRNA (*selC* product, anticodon UCA complementary to UGA) is converted to selenocysteinyl-tRNA by a pyridoxal phosphate-dependent selenocysteine synthase (*selA* gene product) using selenium from selenophosphate, produced by selenophosphate synthetase, the *selD* gene product (19, 27, 28). A unique elongation factor (the *selB* gene product) that binds a secondary stem loop structure located 3′ to the UGA in the *E. coli* fdhF mRNA forms a complex with the selenocysteinyl-tRNA for delivery at the ribosome site and insertion of selenocysteine at UGA (29). Refinements of these groundbreaking discoveries still are being made by many investigators in the field, particularly with respect to the differing modes of recognition of UGA for selenocysteine incorporation in eukaryotes, archae, and *E. coli*. This process that prevents operation of the usual translation termination step and instead directs insertion of selenocysteine at a specific in-frame UGA codon is an important example of a growing list of exceptions to the established stop codon rules (30).

E. coli Formate Dehydrogenase

David Grahame and Milton Axley, working in the anaerobic laboratory at NIH, developed an elegant two-step chromatographic procedure for isolation of the markedly oxygen-sensitive 80-kDa *E. coli* formate dehydrogenase H (31) in highly purified form. This enzyme contains molybdenum in a molybdopterin cofactor in addition to the selenocysteine in the polypeptide. Detailed kinetic analysis of the enzyme (32) and a comparison of the catalytic advantages afforded by selenium over sulfur revealed (33) that the selenocysteine-containing native or wild-type enzyme was about 300 times more active than the selenocysteine/Cys mutant for oxidation of formate with benzyl viologen as the artificial electron acceptor.

A few years later, it was shown in EPR studies that the selenium of the selenocysteine residue in formate dehydrogenase is coordinated directly to the molybdenum in the molybdopterin cofactor (34). The oxidation of formate by this enzyme does not involve a typical molybdenum-dependent hydroxylation mechanism. Instead, formate is converted directly to carbon dioxide without introduction of oxygen from solvent (35). Crystallization of the oxygen-labile enzyme under strictly anaerobic conditions was achieved (36) and based on analysis of the crystal structure (37), it was deduced that the selenium serves as the immediate proton acceptor in the reaction. This would suggest an effect of neighboring protein groups because usually at neutral pH a selenol is almost fully ionized. In contrast, from x-ray absorption spectroscopy (EXAFS) studies of oxidized and reduced forms of the enzyme, a novel selenosulfide ligation to the molybdenum was proposed as the proton acceptor (38). A possible alternative mechanism involving hydride or hydrogen atom transfer from formate to the selenosulfide instead of proton transfer also was suggested. Based on these somewhat differing types of evidence, the exact mechanism of action of the *E. coli* formate dehydrogenase and the precise role of selenium in the enzyme remain to be established. *In vivo*, the reducing equivalents from formate oxidation are transferred via an iron sulfur cluster eventually to a hydrogenase, and hydrogen gas is evolved.

Selenocysteine Incorporation in Clostridia

Despite the dearth of information concerning the genetic makeup of anaerobic spore-forming members of the genus *Clostridium*, Greg Garcia was able to isolate and clone the glycine reductase selenoprotein A gene from two different clostridia (39, 40) and establish that an in-frame TGA codon in each corresponded to selenocysteine at position 44 in the polypeptides (41). However, attempts to express the *C. sticklandii* cloned gene in *E. coli* were only partially successful (40). The full-length, 18-kDa immunologically reactive protein was produced in good yield, but the catalytic activity as a component of glycine reductase was only about 10% that of native selenoprotein. A full-length protein produced in the absence of selenium or in a SelD mutant unable to synthesize selenophosphate was inactive. Detailed analysis showed that read-through and suppression of the UGA codon involved a cysteine-tRNA, and either cysteine or occasionally selenocysteine esterified to the tRNA was inserted. It was concluded that the mRNA secondary stem-loop structure required by *E. coli* for UGA-directed specific selenocysteine insertion was not present in the clostridial mRNA structure. Although details of rules concerning clostridial selenoprotein gene expression are still lacking, the now available genomic sequence of *Clostridium difficile* should provide information on the SECIS stem-loop structure involved and its location in the mRNA. In fact, both glycine reductase and formate dehydrogenase were detected in extracts of a strain of *C. difficile* that we used in our studies in the 1950s, and the corresponding genes have been found in the published genomic structure. It is clear that the statement commonly made in the literature to the effect that in all prokaryotes the SECIS element is identical to that in *E. coli* and is located in the same orientation as in FdhF is incorrect. *E. coli* is not representative of all prokaryotes.

Seleno-tRNAs

Another type of biochemical process in which selenophosphate is utilized as selenium donor is the synthesis of 2-selenouridine in the "wobble position" of the anticodons of certain tRNAs. The 2-selenouridine residue in the form of 5-methylaminomethyl-2-selenouridine had been identified earlier in the lysine and glutamate tRNAs of *E. coli*, *Salmonella typhimurium*,

C. sticklandii, and *M. vannielii* (42). When Dr. Zsuzsanna Veres, a young Hungarian scientist from Budapest, came to my laboratory as a Visiting Fellow she decided to work on the biochemistry of 2-selenouridine. My good luck in having Dr. Veres as a collaborator came about as a result of my visit to Budapest in 1988 as a member of a USA National Academy of Sciences committee commissioned to evaluate the mutual benefits of exchanges between the United States and the Hungarian Academies of Sciences. When my counterpart on the Hungarian Academy committee, Professor Geza Denes, heard that I had an opening in my laboratory for a Foreign Visiting Scientist, he suggested his best student as a possible candidate. Dr. Veres was interested and after the usual formalities she arrived in my laboratory in August 1989. Thus started a very fruitful collaboration of almost 5 years and a deep friendship developed. During Zsuzsa's stay in the laboratory, she demonstrated that the ATP requirement for selenouridine synthesis in tRNAs was explained entirely by its use in the generation of selenophosphate, the biological donor of selenium in the reaction (19, 20, 43). A subsequent step involved the replacement of a sulfur in the 2-thiouridine precursor in tRNA with selenium to form the 2-selenouridine residue, and the responsible enzyme system was partially purified (44). Veres' detailed studies on selenophosphate synthetase and the role of the enzyme in the generation of the new high energy selenium donor compound were very important contributions to the overall field of selenium biochemistry. When Dr. Ick Young Kim, a young investigator from Korea, arrived, he joined Veres in studies on selenophosphate synthetase, and by site-directed mutagenesis he produced several useful mutant forms of the enzyme (45). The Veres-Kim collaboration proved to be very productive in this investigation.

Selenophosphate Synthetase Reaction Mechanism

Later studies in my laboratory on the selenophosphate synthetase reaction mechanism by Dr. Heidi Walker demonstrated that a group on the enzyme first is phosphorylated by reaction with ATP (46). This phosphoryl group derived from the γ-phosphoryl group of ATP subsequently is transferred to selenium to form selenophosphate. The ADP moiety of ATP, which is tightly bound during the initial step, then is cleaved in a hydrolytic step to form orthophosphate (derived from the β-phosphoryl group) and AMP (47). Earlier, we thought that a pyrophosphoryl derivative of the enzyme might be formed in the initial reaction with ATP leaving AMP as the other product. However, Song Liu's experiments showed that retention of ^{32}P from β-^{32}P-labeled ATP was insignificant, whereas when γ-^{32}P-labeled ATP was used up to 0.6 eq of ^{32}P was bound to the enzyme (48). Details of the mechanism of the selenophosphate synthetase reaction are still under investigation.

Selenium-dependent Enzymes That Do Not Contain Selenocysteine

A group of molybdopterin-dependent hydroxylases, nicotinic acid hydroxylase (49, 50), xanthine dehydrogenase, and purine hydroxylase (51), that have been purified from anaerobic bacteria require selenium for activity. However, the selenium in these enzymes is not present in selenocysteine residues in the polypeptides but instead occurs in a labile cofactor. The selenium can be released from the cofactor by treatment with cyanide and thus might be in the form of a perselenide. The mechanism of incorporation of selenium in these enzymes currently is being investigated by Dr. William Self, who discovered purine hydroxylase, the most recent addition to the list of selenium-dependent hydroxylases. It was shown earlier in EPR studies that the selenium in nicotinic hydroxylase is coordinated to the molybdenum of the molybdopterin cofactor (50). In contrast to the hydroxylases from anaerobic bacteria, the corresponding enzymes from eukaryotes have not been shown to be selenoenzymes.

Discovery of a New Mammalian Selenoenzyme

Our studies on thioredoxin reductase were initiated as the result of a serendipitous discovery made by Dr. Takashi Tamura, a young Japanese Visiting Fellow in our laboratory, during his one-year leave of absence from Okayama University. A cytochrome P-450 present in a human lung adenocarcinoma cell line had been predicted to contain selenocysteine based on the occurrence of a TGA codon in the open reading frame of the corresponding gene (52). The possibility that the putative selenocysteine residue, located at some distance from the conserved cysteine at the heme binding site, might have a novel role in the enzyme prompted Dr. Tamura to attempt isolation of the protein. The lung adenocarcinoma cells were cultured in the presence of [^{75}Se]selenite, and the expected 57-kDa protein labeled with ^{75}Se was isolated in near homogeneous form. Two different alkyl derivatives of the protein were prepared, and the corresponding alkyl [^{75}Se]selenocysteines were isolated and identified. The chromophore bound to the protein, however, proved to be FAD instead of a heme group. The FAD could be reduced specifically by NADPH, and various disulfides, including thioredoxin, served as substrates for the enzyme. It was evident that this selenoprotein, a homodimer of 57-kDa subunits, must be thioredoxin reductase, an enzyme that had been purified from various mammalian tissues and studied by other investigators but never suspected to be a selenoenzyme. Although the reported sequence of a putative thioredoxin reductase gene from human placenta (53) contained a TGA codon near the C terminus, this had been interpreted as a termination signal. Subsequently, experiments carried out in my laboratory by Vadim Gladyshev (54) and by Song Liu (55) showed that the selenocysteine in thioredoxin reductase, previously identified by Tamura, occurs at the C terminus in the sequence -Cys-selenocysteine-Gly in a position corresponding to the TGA codon in the placental gene. Thioredoxin reductases purified from human Jurkat T cells (54), from HeLa cells, and from the human adenocarcinoma cells (55) were shown to have the same C-terminal triplet peptide sequences.

The importance of the potential C-terminal redox center for catalytic activity was shown in experiments with the HeLa cell enzyme by Sergey Gorlatov (56). Alkylation of the NADPH-reduced enzyme under conditions that limited alkyl group incorporation to the one ionized selenol per subunit was sufficient to inhibit catalytic activity 99% (56). When HeLa cells were grown at higher than optimal oxygen levels, the isolated enzyme consisted of significant amounts of species that contained an average of 0.5 instead of 1 selenium atom per subunit, and these forms exhibited correspondingly lowered catalytic activities (57). Reduced forms of thioredoxin reductase were very oxygen-labile in the absence of bound pyridine nucleotide, and corresponding losses of selenium and catalytic activity were observed. It now is generally agreed by a number of investigators that premature termination of gene expression at the UGA codon gives rise to a truncated inactive form of the enzyme, and mutant enzyme species in which a cysteine residue replaces the selenocysteine exhibit very low catalytic activity (58). It thus is evident that the additional C-terminal redox center present in fully active mammalian thioredoxin reductases is an important determinant of catalytic activity and is essential in addition to the bound FAD and the redox active cysteine pair near the NADPH binding site in the N-terminal region of the protein.

Selenium Transport Proteins

One of the interesting recent developments in the selenium field comes from the realization of the importance of selenium transport or delivery proteins in selenoprotein biosynthesis. Our specific interest involves the participation of these proteins in supplying selenium for selenophosphate biosynthesis. Even under *in vitro* conditions an atomic form of selenium provided by a delivery protein is used more efficiently as substrate by selenophosphate synthetase than millimolar levels of selenide normally added to reaction mixtures (59). The atomic form of selenium can be derived from free selenocysteine by selenocysteine lyases that are structurally related to the NifS sulfur transferase family of proteins (60) or from inorganic selenium compounds, *i.e.* selenite after reaction with thiols to form RS-Se-SR adducts. Enzymes, such as rhodanese, that can transfer the sulfane sulfur from thiosulfate to cyanide generate a persulfide derivative of an active cysteine residue as the enzyme-bound intermediate (61). In an analogous process, a perselenide derivative of a reactive cysteine residue could be generated by reaction with a selenium substrate (62). An unusual selenium-binding protein that I isolated recently from *M. vannielii* appears to be a candidate for such a role. The gene that encodes this protein was isolated, cloned, and expressed in *E. coli* by Dr. William Self. Several properties of the isolated protein expressed in *E. coli* are identical to those of the native *M. vannielii* protein, and preliminary studies by Dr. Self suggest that the ability to bind selenium may be specific. If so, this could imply a role in supplying the significant levels of selenium required for synthesis of multiple selenoenzymes involved in the energy metabolism of *M. vannielii* (63). The ability to discriminate between selenium present at micromolar concentrations in most biological systems as compared with millimolar levels of sulfur compounds is essential for efficient biosynthesis of specific selenium-containing catalysts.

The Famous NIH Anaerobic Laboratory

An anaerobic laboratory facility (Nitrogen Laboratory) that was constructed in the 1960s in Building 3 at NIH at a cost of $250,000 was used for numerous studies on oxygen-sensitive organic catalysts and oxygen-labile enzymes until March 2001 when the occupants of Building

3 were moved to Building 50. The walls of the anaerobic facility are made of ⅜-inch carbon steel plates that were welded into place and supported by a framework of I-beams. Floor plates were riveted to a concrete floor. All joints were welded and sealed. A nitrogen atmosphere containing hydrogen, introduced to remove the last traces of oxygen by passage through a palladium catalyst bed, was maintained at less than 10 ppm of oxygen.

This laboratory is still the only one of its kind in the world. For one of the first tests of the new anaerobic facility, I inoculated Petri dishes containing a formate-mineral salts agar medium with a culture of *M. vannielii* and placed them in an ordinary 37 °C incubator. When I inspected the plates the next day, I was so delighted to find colonies of this extremely oxygen-sensitive organism on the surface of the agar that I laughed, and this caused enough nitrogen to leak into my mask to set off the alarm system. I then made a rule not to laugh in the anaerobic laboratory. Seriously, over the years, we and investigators from other NIH laboratories and several universities have carried out large scale isolations of oxygen-labile enzymes and characterized oxygen-sensitive flavoproteins, B_{12} coenzyme-dependent enzymes, and selenoproteins in this anaerobic facility (64, 65). To conduct many of these procedures in an anaerobic glove box is either cumbersome or impossible as we are learning to our sorrow. Sadly, this important anaerobic laboratory facility will soon be demolished to convert Building 3 into administrative office space.

Address correspondence to: tcstadtman@nih.gov.

REFERENCES

1. Stadtman, T. C., and Barker, H. A. (1949) Studies on the methane fermentation. VII. Tracer experiments on the mechanism of methane formation. *Arch. Biochem.* **21**, 256–264
2. Stadtman, T. C., and Barker, H. A. (1951) Studies on the methane fermentation. IX. The origin of methane in the acetate and methanol fermentations by *Methanosarcina*. *J. Bacteriol.* **61**, 81–86
3. Stadtman, T. C., and Barker, H. A. (1951) Studies on the methane fermentation X. A new formate-decomposing bacterium, *Methanococcus vannielii*. *J. Bacteriol.* **62**, 269–280
4. Stadtman, T. C. (1954) On the metabolism of an amino acid fermenting *Clostridium*. *J. Bacteriol.* **67**, 314–320
5. Stadtman, T. C. (1962) Lysine fermentation to fatty acids and ammonia: A cobamide coenzyme-dependent process. *J. Biol. Chem.* **237**, 2409–2411
6. Stadtman, T. C. (1972) B_{12} coenzyme-dependent amino group migrations. *The Enzymes* **6**, 539–563
7. Stadtman, T. C. (1983) Some vitamin B_{12}- and selenium-dependent enzymes. *Ann. N. Y. Acad. Sci.* **41**, 233–236
8. Stadtman, T. C., Elliott, P., and Tiemann, L. (1958) Studies on the enzymic reduction of amino acids III. Phosphate esterification coupled with glycine reduction. *J. Biol. Chem.* **231**, 961–973
9. Arkowitz, R. A., and Abeles, R. H. (1989) Identification of acetyl phosphate as the product of clostridial glycine reductase: evidence for an acyl enzyme intermediate. *Biochemistry* **28**, 4639–4644
10. Stadtman, T. C. (1966) Glycine reduction to acetate and ammonia: identification of ferredoxin and another low molecular weight acidic protein as components of the reductase system. *Arch. Biochem. Biophys.* **113**, 9–19
11. Turner, D. C., and Stadtman, T. C. (1973) Purification of protein components of clostridial glycine reductase system and characterization of protein A as a selenoprotein. *Arch. Biochem. Biophys.* **154**, 366–381
12. Schwarz, K., and Foltz, C. M. (1957) Selenium as an integral part of Factor 3 against dietary necrotic liver degeneration. *J. Am. Chem. Soc.* **79**, 3292–3293
13. Patterson, E. L., Milstrey, R., and Stokstad, E. L. R. (1957) Effect of selenium in preventing exudative diathesis in chicks. *Proc. Soc. Exp. Biol. Med.* **95**, 617–620
14. Cone, J. E., Martin del Rio, R., Davis, J. N., and Stadtman, T. C. (1976) Chemical characterization of the selenoprotein component of clostridial glycine reductase: identification of selenocysteine as the organoselenium moiety. *Proc. Natl. Acad. Sci. U. S. A.* **73**, 2659–2663
15. Forstrom, J. W., Zakowski, J. J., and Tappel, A. L. (1978) Identification of the catalytic site of rat liver glutathione peroxidase as selenocysteine. *Biochemistry* **17**, 2639–2644
16. Stadtman, T. C., Dilworth, G. L., and Chen, C. S. (1979) in *Proceedings of the Third International Symposium on Organic Selenium and Tellurium Compounds* (Cagniant, D., and Kirsch, G., eds) Selenium-dependent bacterial enzymes, pp. 115–130, Metz, France
17. Chocat, P., Esaki, N., Tanizawa, K., Nakamura, K., Tanaka, H., and Soda, K. (1985) Purification and characterization of selenocysteine ß-lyase from *Citrobacter freundii*. *J. Bacteriol.* **163**, 669–676
18. Esaki, N., Nakamura, T., Tanaka, H., and Soda, K. (1982) Selenocysteine lyase, a novel enzyme that specifically acts on selenocysteine. Mammalian distribution and purification and properties of pig liver enzyme. *J. Biol. Chem.* **257**, 4386–4391
19. Veres, Z., Tsai, L., Scholz, T. D., Politino, M., Balaban, R. S., and Stadtman, T. C. (1992) Synthesis of 5-methylaminomethyl-2-selenouridine in tRNAs: ^{31}P NMR studies show that the labile selenium donor synthesized by the selD gene product contains selenium bonded to phosphorus. *Proc. Natl. Acad. Sci. U. S. A.* **89**, 2975–2979
20. Glass, R. S., Singh, W. P., Jung, W., Veres, Z., Scholz, T. D., and Stadtman, T. C. (1993) Monoselenophosphate: synthesis, characterization and identity with the prokaryotic biological selenium donor, compound SePX. *Biochemistry* **32**, 12555–12559
21. Zinoni, F., Birkmann, A., Stadtman, T. C., and Böck, A. (1986) Nucleotide sequence and expression of the selenocysteine-containing polypeptide of formate dehydrogenase (formate-hydrogen-lyase-linked) from *Escherichia coli*. *Proc. Natl. Acad. Sci. U. S. A.* **83**, 4650–4654
22. Chambers, I., Frampton, J., Goldfarb, P., Affara, N., McBain, W., and Harrison, P. P. (1986) The structure of the mouse glutathione peroxidase gene: the selenocysteine in the active site is encoded by the "termination codon" TGA. *EMBO J.* **5**, 1221–1227
23. Gunzler, W. A., Steffens, G. J., Grossmann, A., Kim, S.-M. A., Otting, F., Wendel, A., and Flohé, L. (1984) The amino acid sequence of bovine glutathione peroxidase. *Hoppe-Seyler's Z. Physiol. Chem.* **365**, 195–212
24. Stadtman, T. C., Davis, J. N., Ching, W.-M., Zinoni, F., and Böck, A. (1991) Amino acid sequence analysis of

Escherichia coli formate dehydrogenase (FDH$_H$) confirms that TGA in the gene encodes selenocysteine in the gene product. *BioFactors* **3,** 21–27

25. Haddock, B. A., and Mandrand-Berthelot, M.-A. (1982) *Escherichia coli* formate-to-nitrate respiratory chain: genetic analysis. *Biochem. Soc. Trans.* **10,** 478–480

26. Leinfelder, W., Zehelin, E., Mandrand-Berthelot, M.-A., and Böck, A. (1988) Gene for a novel tRNA species that accepts L-serine and cotranslationally inserts selenocysteine. *Nature* **331,** 723–725

27. Leinfelder, W., Forchhammer, K., Zinoni, F., Sawers, G., Mandrand-Berthelot, M.-A., and Böck, A. (1988) *Escherichia coli* genes whose products are involved in selenium metabolism. *J. Bacteriol.* **170,** 540–546

28. Böck, A., Forchhammer, K., Heider, J., Leinfelder, W., Sawers, G., Veprek, B., and Zinoni, F. (1991) Selenocysteine: the 21st amino acid. *Mol. Microbiol.* **5,** 515–520

29. Forchhammer, K., Leinfelder, W., and Böck, A. (1989) Identification of a novel translation factor necessary for the incorporation of selenocysteine into protein. *Nature* **342,** 453–456

30. Hao, B., Gong, W., Ferguson, T. K., James, C. M., Krzycki, J. A., and Chan, M. K. (2002) A new UAG-encoded residue in the structure of a methanogen methyltransferase. *Science* **296,** 1462–1466

31. Axley, M. J., Grahame, D. A., and Stadtman, T. C. (1990) *Escherichia coli* formate-hydrogen lyase. Purification and properties of the selenium-dependent formate dehydrogenase component. *J. Biol. Chem.* **265,** 18213–18218

32. Axley, M. J., and Grahame, D. A. (1991) Kinetics for formate dehydrogenase of *Escherichia coli* formate-hydrogen lyase. *J. Biol. Chem.* **266,** 13731–13736

33. Axley, M. J., Böck, A., and Stadtman, T. C. (1991) Catalytic properties of an *Escherichia coli* formate dehydrogenase mutant in which sulfur replaces selenium. *Proc. Natl. Acad. Sci. U. S. A.* **88,** 8450–8454

34. Gladyshev, V. N., Khangulov, S. V., Axley, M. J., and Stadtman, T. C. (1994) Coordination of selenium to molybdenum in formate dehydrogenase H from *Escherichia coli*. *Proc. Natl. Acad. Sci. U. S. A.* **91,** 7708–7711

35. Khangulov, S. V., Gladyshev, V. N., Dismukes, G. C., and Stadtman, T. C. (1998) Selenium-containing formate dehydrogenase H from *Escherichia coli*: a molybdopterin enzyme that catalyzes formate oxidation without oxygen transfer. *Biochemistry* **37,** 3518–3528

36. Gladyshev, V. N., Boyington, J. C., Khangulov, S. V., Grahame, D. A., Stadtman, T. C., and Sun, P. D. (1996) Characterization of crystalline formate dehydrogenase H from *Escherichia coli*. *J. Biol. Chem.* **271,** 8095–8100

37. Boyington, J. C., Gladyshev, V. N., Khangulov, S. V., Stadtman, T. C., and Sun, P. D. (1997) Crystal structure of formate dehydrogenase H: catalysis involving Mo, molybdopterin, selenocysteine, and an Fe$_4$S$_4$ cluster. *Science* **275,** 1305–1308

38. George, G. N., Colangelo, C. M., Dong, J., Scott, R. A., Khangulov, S. V., Gladyshev, V. N., and Stadtman, T. C. (1998) X-ray absorption spectroscopy of the molybdenum site of *Escherichia coli* formate dehydrogenase. *J. Am. Chem. Soc.* **120,** 1267–1273

39. Garcia, G. E., and Stadtman, T. C. (1991) Selenoprotein A component of the glycine reductase complex from *Clostridium purinolyticum*: nucleotide sequence of the gene shows that selenocysteine is encoded by UGA. *J. Bacteriol.* **173,** 2093–2098

40. Garcia, G. E., and Stadtman, T. C. (1992) *Clostridium sticklandii* glycine reductase selenoprotein A gene: cloning, sequencing and expression in *Escherichia coli*. *J. Bacteriol.* **174,** 7080–7089

41. Sliwkowski, M. X., and Stadtman, T. C. (1988) Selenoprotein A of the clostridial glycine reductase complex: purification and amino acid sequence of the selenocysteine-containing peptide. *Proc. Natl. Acad. Sci. U. S. A.* **85,** 368–371

42. Wittwer, A. J., Tsai, L., Ching, W.-M., and Stadtman, T. C. (1984) Identification and synthesis of a naturally occurring selenonucleoside in bacterial tRNAs: 5-[(methylamino)methyl]-2-selenouridine. *Biochemistry* **23,** 4650–4655

43. Veres, Z., Kim, I. Y., Scholz, T. D., and Stadtman, T. C. (1994) Selenophosphate synthetase. Enzyme properties and catalytic reaction. *J. Biol. Chem.* **269,** 10597–10603

44. Veres, Z., and Stadtman, T. C. (1994) A purified selenophosphate-dependent enzyme from *Salmonella typhimurium* catalyzes the replacement of sulfur in 2-thiouridine in tRNAs with selenium. *Proc. Natl. Acad. Sci. U. S. A.* **91,** 8092–8096

45. Kim, I. Y., Veres, Z., and Stadtman, T. C. (1993) Biochemical analysis of *Escherichia coli* selenophosphate synthetase mutants. *J. Biol. Chem.* **268,** 27020–27025

46. Mullins, L. S., Hong, S.-B., Gibson, G. E., Walker, H., Stadtman, T. C., and Raushel, F. M. (1997) Identification of a phosphorylated enzyme intermediate in the catalytic mechanism for selenophosphate synthetase. *J. Am. Chem. Soc.* **119,** 6684–6685

47. Walker, H., Ferretti, J. A., and Stadtman, T. C. (1998) Isotope exchange studies on the *Escherichia coli* selenophosphate synthetase mechanism. *Proc. Natl. Acad. Sci. U. S. A.* **95,** 2180–2185

48. Liu, S.-Y., and Stadtman, T. C. (1997) Selenophosphate synthetase: enzyme labeling studies with [γ-^{32}P]ATP, [β-^{32}P]ATP, [8-^{14}C]ATP and [^{75}Se]selenide. *Arch. Biochem. Biophys.* **341,** 353–359

49. Dilworth, G. L. (1982) Properties of the selenium-containing nicotinic acid hydroxylase from *Clostridium barkeri*. *Arch. Biochem. Biophys.* **219,** 30–38

50. Gladyshev, V. N., Khangulov, S. V., and Stadtman, T. C. (1994) Nicotinic acid hydroxylase from *Clostridium barkeri*: electron paramagnetic resonance studies show that selenium is coordinated with molybdenum in the catalytically active selenium-dependent enzyme. *Proc. Natl. Acad. Sci. U. S. A.* **91,** 232–236

51. Self, W. T., and Stadtman, T. C. (2000) Selenium-dependent metabolism of purines: a selenium-dependent purine hydroxylase and xanthine dehydrogenase were purified from *Clostridium purinolyticum* and characterized. *Proc. Natl. Acad. Sci. U. S. A.* **97,** 7208–7213

52. Tamura, T., and Stadtman, T. C. (1996) A new selenoprotein from human lung adenocarcinoma cells: purification, properties and thioredoxin reductase activity. *Proc. Natl. Acad. Sci. U. S. A.* **93,** 1006–1011

53. Gasdaska, P. Y., Gasdaska, J. R., Cochran, S., and Powis, G. (1995) Cloning and sequencing of a human thioredoxin reductase. *FEBS Lett.* **373,** 5–9

54. Gladyshev, V. N., Jeang, K.-T., and Stadtman, T. C. (1996) Selenocysteine, identified as the penultimate C-terminal residue in human T-cell thioredoxin reductase, corresponds to TGA in the human placental gene. *Proc. Natl. Acad. Sci. U. S. A.* **93,** 6146–6151

55. Liu, S.-Y., and Stadtman, T. C. (1997) Heparin-binding properties of selenium-containing thioredoxin reductase from HeLa cells and human lung adenocarcinoma cells. *Proc. Natl. Acad. Sci. U. S. A.* **94,** 6138–6141

56. Gorlatov, S. N., and Stadtman, T. C. (1998) Human thioredoxin reductase from HeLa cells: selective alkylation of selenocysteine residue in the protein inhibits enzyme activity and reduction with NADPH influences affinity to heparin. *Proc. Natl. Acad. Sci. U. S. A.* **95,** 8520–8525

57. Gorlatov, S. N., and Stadtman, T. C. (1999) Human selenium-dependent thioredoxin reductase from HeLa cells: properties of forms with differing heparin affinities. *Arch. Biochem. Biophys.* **369,** 133–142

58. Lee, S.-R., Bar-Noy, S., Kwon, J., Levine, R. L., Stadtman, T. C., and Rhee, S. G. (2000) Mammalian thioredoxin reductase: oxidation of the C-terminal cysteine/selenocysteine active site forms a thioselenide, and replacement

of selenium with sulfur markedly reduces catalytic activity. *Proc. Natl. Acad. Sci. U. S. A.* **97,** 2521–2526

59. Lacourciere, G. M., and Stadtman, T. C. (1998) The NIFS protein can function as a selenide delivery protein in the biosynthesis of selenophosphate. *J. Biol. Chem.* **273,** 30921–30926

60. Lacourciere, G. M. (2002) Selenium is mobilized *in vivo* from free selenocysteine and is incorporated specifically into formate dehydrogenase H and tRNA nucleosides. *J. Bacteriol.* **184,** 1940–1946

61. Bordo, D., Forlani, F., Spallarossa, A., Colnaghi, R., Carpen, A., Bolognesi, M., and Pagani, S. (2001) A persufurated cysteine promotes active site reactivity in *Azotobacter vinelandii* rhodanese. *J. Biol. Chem.* **382,** 1245–1252

62. Ogasawara, Y., Lacourciere, G. M., and Stadtman, T. C. (2001) Formation of selenium-substituted rhodanese by reaction with selenite and glutathione: possible role of a protein perselenide in a selenium delivery system. *Proc. Natl. Acad. Sci. U. S. A.* **98,** 9494–9498

63. Yamazaki, S. (1982) A selenium-containing hydrogenase from *Methanococcus vannielii.* Identification of the selenium moiety as a selenocysteine residue. *J. Biol. Chem.* **257,** 7926–7929

64. Stadtman, T. C. (1990) Selenium biochemistry. *Annu. Rev. Biochem.* **59,** 111–127

65. Stadtman, T. C. (1996) Selenocysteine. *Annu. Rev. Biochem.* **65,** 83–100

THE JOURNAL OF BIOLOGICAL CHEMISTRY
© 2002 by The American Society for Biochemistry and Molecular Biology, Inc.

Vol. 277, No. 52, Issue of December 27, pp. 50215–50218, 2002
Printed in U.S.A.

Reflections

A PAPER IN A SERIES COMMISSIONED TO CELEBRATE THE CENTENARY OF THE JBC IN 2005

JBC Centennial
1905–2005
100 Years of Biochemistry and Molecular Biology

The Early Influence of the Institut Pasteur on the Emergence of Molecular Biology

Published, JBC Papers in Press, October 25, 2002, DOI 10.1074/jbc.X200006200

Georges N. Cohen

From the Institut Pasteur, 28 rue du Docteur Roux, 75724 Paris, France

I met Jacques Monod for the first time in September 1944. The 4 years of the hellish Nazi occupation of France were over. Jacques was still wearing the uniform of an officer of the French Army. I was 24 years old and had a relatively limited research experience: six months in the Laboratory of Animal Physiology at the Sorbonne (1939–1940), a few months in the Laboratory of Pharmacology at the Pharmacy School of the University of Montpellier (1941), a few months in the Department of Biochemistry of the Medical School in Marseille (1942), and a year in the Department of Biochemistry of the Institut Pasteur (1943–1944). These activities were interrupted by the military service, a few weeks of captivity, an escape, my marriage, and the birth of my first child. This should explain my lack of professional training and my great desire to find a person who could help me. Jacques Monod became rapidly my mentor.

In 1946, Lwoff and Monod went together to the Cold Spring Harbor Symposium on Heredity and Variation in Microorganisms. This symposium reinitiated a series after a 3-year interruption imposed by the war emergency. It could have been held in the summer of 1945 but was postponed for a year because of travel restrictions. This delay was a fortunate one because whereas the genetics and physiology of microorganisms had made remarkable progress in the laboratories of the United States, when the contacts were reestablished it was found that many discoveries in the same field had been made in Western Europe. As a consequence, the scope of the program was considerably broadened. In addition to Lwoff and Monod, the French contingent included Latarjet and Ephrussi. The symposium presented several important discoveries such as the findings of Anderson, Delbrück, Bailey, and Hershey in phage genetics; those of Lindegren and Pontecorvo on yeast and fungal genetics; and those of Luria, Lwoff, Tatum, Demerec, Latarjet, and Ryan on bacterial mutability. There was also a two-page report by Joshua Lederberg in which bacterial recombination was elegantly demonstrated. However, above all the meeting represented, to echo Seymour Cohen, the emergence of a major young and new scientific community after World War II.

The origin of the β-galactosidase saga can be traced back to the doctoral thesis of Jacques Monod, published 60 years ago, and devoted to the study of bacterial growth. During these studies begun in 1937, Monod had observed that when *Bacillus subtilis* or *Escherichia coli* were grown on a mixture of two particular sugars, growth occurred in two distinct phases separated by a lag time. During the first phase only one of the two sugars was metabolized, and the second began to be degraded only when the first sugar had totally disappeared. Glucose was found to belong to the first category and lactose to the second (1, 2).

A few days after I first met Jacques Monod, he described to me his experiments on this diauxic growth and told me that it might take 20 years or more before this observation receives a molecular explanation, but he was determined to accept the challenge (Fig. 1). During the 1940s, several theories tried to explain the phenomenon of enzymatic adaptation such as the functional hypothesis, where the inducer acts as a substrate, or the equilibrium hypothesis, where it displaces the equilibrium between an inactive precursor and the active enzyme.

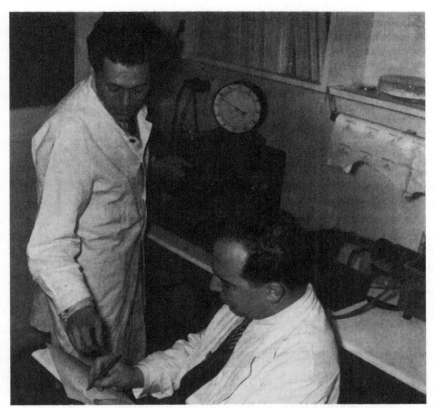

FIG. 1. Jacques Monod (*left*) and Georges Cohen (*right*) measuring β-galactosidase activity spectrophotometrically (circa 1954).

Monod and his colleagues Annamaria Torriani, Melvin Cohn, and Germaine Cohen-Bazire eliminated these theories by a series of convincing experiments. With Melvin and David Hogness, he demonstrated that the induced enzyme is synthesized *de novo* from free amino acids, themselves deriving from the carbon source.

I joined Monod's laboratory in 1954 after having spent my first research years on the mechanism of bacterial fermentations and contributing to the elucidation of some amino acid biosynthetic pathways in *E. coli*. Jacques asked me to see whether after addition of labeled thiomethylgalactoside, a non-metabolizable inducer, radioactivity could be found linked to one of the macromolecular components, DNA, RNA, or protein. In retrospect, this naive experiment had no chance of succeeding. It required the concept of a specific Lac repressor, only proposed in 1964 by Pardee, Monod, and Jacob, and a more sophisticated technology than our primitive methods of enzyme activity measurements and the use of Petri dishes to follow the result of bacterial conjugations. Ultimately, Gilbert and Müller-Hill isolated the repressor in 1966, transforming a concept into a bona fide molecule and answering the question Monod had asked me to study. However, the experiments I carried out with Howard Rickenberg and Gérard Buttin brought interesting fringe benefits; the amount of intracellular radioactivity was negligible in non-induced cultures but very high in cultures that had been pre-induced by growth in the presence of a galactoside. We developed with Jacques Monod the concept of a catalytic permease, which was not readily accepted by the establishment (3–5). It was not until many years later that Benno Müller-Hill wrote me with the news that he had cloned and sequenced the lactose permease (6). I think that our work contributed to opening the field of a molecular approach to cellular permeability, so ably continued by E. Kennedy, R. Kaback, S. Roseman, G. Ferro-Luzzi Ames, and many others. During our work we noticed that mutants that were constitutive for β-galactosidase were also constitutive for β-galactoside permease, establishing that the inducible to constitutive mutation was pleiotropic (4, 5). We named the corresponding alleles i^+ and i^-. In 1959, Irving Zabin and Adam Képès added a third member, the gene for thiogalactoside transacetylase to the two genes whose expression was governed by the *i* gene (7). Monod, Jacob, and their associates found that the three genes were linked, forming a coordinate unit of transcription, which they called an operon. They hypothesized that the product of the *i* gene, the repressor, was bound to a DNA structure, the operator, upstream of the operon's structural genes (6). This hypothesis was later totally substantiated by W. Gilbert and B. Müller-Hill in 1966 and 1967, who isolated the Lac repressor (8) and characterized its target operator sequence (9). In 1959, the repressor hypothesis was extended to the regulation of biosynthetic enzymes by myself and Jacob, working on the tryptophan biosynthetic enzymes (10). This work was beautifully extended by Charles Yanofsky in the United States; his studies on the expression of the tryptophan genes led him among other discoveries to unravel the phenomenon of attenuation (11).

In 1968 Ullmann and Monod (12) simultaneously with Perlman and Pastan (13) showed that the catabolic repression exerted by glucose on β-galactosidase synthesis is reversed by cyclic AMP, opening the way to a molecular explanation of diauxy.

The three-dimensional structure of β-galactosidase (14) provides an explanation for the α-complementation first observed by Ullmann, Jacob, and Monod almost 40 years ago (15) and which, apart from its theoretical interest, forms the basis of the familiar blue-white selection process for recombinant DNA routinely used in both prokaryote and eukaryote research.

After my incursion in the field of galactosidase and permease, I returned to the study of the regulation of the activity and of the synthesis of amino acids in *E. coli*, influenced by the intellectual atmosphere present in Monod's laboratory and by a 6-month decisive collaboration with Earl Stadtman who came to Paris during a sabbatical period, during which we started to elucidate the regulation of the synthesis of the amino acids of the aspartic acid family in *E. coli* (16), a subject that was going to keep me busy for the rest of my scientific life.

In 1960, I created the Laboratoire d'Enzymologie of the Centre National de la Recherche Scientifique at Gif sur Yvette near Paris. I was joined by Jekisiel Szulmajster (Kissel) and by his wife Huguette de Robichon-Szulmajster and enjoyed the presence of numerous students, among which I must cite Jean-Claude Patte, Paolo Truffa-Bachi, Joel Janin, and Michel Véron and of distinguished visitors, in particular Gordon Tomkins, Ed Adelberg, Mike Doudoroff, and Roger Stanier. I continued, however, to maintain close relationships with the Pasteur Institute, where I returned in 1969 to take over the Laboratoire de Physiologie Microbienne when André Lwoff retired. When Jacques Monod became the Director of the Institut Pasteur, he asked me to become his successor as Head of the Laboratoire de Biochimie Cellulaire, where I worked until my official retirement in September 1989 at the age of 70.

During the period between 1947 and 1960, the laboratories of Lwoff, Jacob, and Monod enjoyed the presence of many foreign visitors who came to one of the meccas of modern biology. The first American visitor to come to the Institut Pasteur was Seymour Cohen in 1947, followed by Michael Doudoroff and Melvin Cohn. Other visitors in Monod's laboratory were Martin Pollock, Alvin Pappenheimer, Aaron Novick, Bernard Davis, Athur Koch, Stuart Edelstein, David Hogness, Howard Rickenberg, Leonard Herzenberg, Bernard Horecker, Frederick Neidhardt, Maurice Sussman, Donald Brown, Boris Magasanik, Edmond Fischer, Roger Stanier, Harlyn Halvorson, Arthur Pardee, Earl Stadtman, John Beckwith, Irving Zabin, Dean Cowie, and Robert Rownd. The discovery of lysogeny by Lwoff and the classical analysis of sexuality by his young colleagues, Wollman and Jacob, brought to our laboratory a host of bright scientists among whom I remember Lane Barksdale, Louis Siminovitch, Niels Kjeldgaard, Dale Kaiser, Julius Marmur, Cyrus Levinthal, Seymour Benzer, Gunther Stent, David Shemin, Allan Campbell, Edwin Lennox, Walter Gilbert, Jerard Hurwitz, Edward Adelberg, C. B. van Niel, Jim Darnell, Sol Goodgal, Neal Groman, Bruce and Giovanna Ames, and Ethan Signer. All contributed their knowledge and took advantage of ours.

It was during that period that the concept of messenger RNA originated with the experiments carried out by Brenner, Jacob, and Meselson (18) and those performed by the group of Gros and Hiatt at the Institut Pasteur in collaboration with Gilbert, Kurland, and Watson at Harvard (17).

Personally, I have been present in Monod's laboratory from 1954 to 1960, but I sincerely think that a few individuals only have witnessed the birth of as many fundamental biological concepts in such a short period and in a single laboratory. This was due in great part to the outstanding personality of Jacques Monod and to the atmosphere he was creating around him, generating a climate of constant stimulation and fruitful discussions.

If one is interested in the phylogeny of ideas, it can be said that the early findings at the Institut Pasteur recalled above lie at the origin of present day interest in molecular interactions. These studies have led in other laboratories to the determination of the structure of many DNA-protein and DNA-protein-effector binary and ternary complexes, which have provided or will provide a rational explanation for the regulation of transcription in both prokaryotic and eukaryotic organisms.

Time has elapsed; today promoters, operons, messenger RNA, repressors, and allosteric enzymes are part of our scientific culture. The majority of the present day biologists started their work after 1980 when genetic engineering allowed the isolation and characterization of genes. The period between 1940 and 1963, where the concepts of molecular biology were painfully born, belongs for the new generation of biologists to another world where the tools of investigation were totally different. Still, although being conscious of the evolution of science, I look backwards with nostalgia to these exceptional decades.

Address correspondence to: gncohen@pasteur.fr.

REFERENCES

1. Monod, J. (1941) Sur un phénomène nouveau de croissance complexe dans les cultures bactériennes. *C. R. Acad. Sci. (Paris)* **212,** 934–936
2. Monod, J. (1942) *Recherches sur la croissance des cellules bactériennes.* Ph.D. thesis, Actualités scientifiques et industrielles, Hermann Paris
3. Cohen, G. N., and Rickenberg, H. V. (1955) *C. R. Acad. Sci. (Paris)* **240,** 466–468
4. Rickenberg, H. V., Cohen, G. N., Buttin, G., and Monod, J. (1956) *Ann. Inst. Pasteur* **91,** 829–855
5. Cohen, G. N., and Monod, J. (1957) *Bacteriol. Rev.* **21,** 169–194
6. Büchel, D. E., Gronenborn, B., and Müller-Hill, B. (1980) *Nature* **283,** 542–545
7. Zabin, I., Képès, A., and Monod, J. (1959) *Biochem. Biophys. Res. Commun.* **1,** 289–292
8. Gilbert, W., and Müller-Hill, B. (1966) *Proc. Natl. Acad. Sci. U. S. A.* **56,** 1891–1898
9. Gilbert, W., and Müller-Hill, B. (1967) *Proc. Natl. Acad. Sci. U. S. A.* **58,** 2415–2421
10. Cohen, G. N., and Jacob, F. (1959) *C. R. Acad. Sci. (Paris)* **248,** 3490–3492
11. Yanofsky, C. (1981) *Nature* **289,** 751–758
12. Ullmann, A., and Monod, J. (1968) *FEBS Lett.* **2,** 57–60
13. Perlman, R., and Pastan, I. (1968) *Biochem. Biophys. Res. Commun.* **30,** 656–664
14. Juers, D. H., Jacobson, R. H., Wigley, D., Zhang, X-J., Huber, R. E., Tronrud, D. E., and Matthews, B. W. (2000) *Protein Sci.* **9,** 1685–1699
15. Ullmann, A. (1992) *Bioessays* **14,** 201–205
16. Stadtman, E. R., Cohen, G. N., LeBras, G., and de Robichon-Szulmajster, H. (1961) *J. Biol. Chem.* **235,** 2033–2038
17. Gros, F., Gilbert, W., Hiatt, H. H., Attardi, G., Spahr, P. F., and Watson, J. D. (1961) *Cold Spring Harbor Symp. Quant. Biol.* **26,** 111–132
18. Brenner, S., Jacob, F., and Meselson, M. (1961) *Nature* **190,** 576–581

THE JOURNAL OF BIOLOGICAL CHEMISTRY

Vol. 278, No. 1, Issue of January 3, pp. 1–13, 2003
Printed in U.S.A.

Reflections

A PAPER IN A SERIES COMMISSIONED TO CELEBRATE THE CENTENARY OF THE JBC IN 2005

JBC Centennial
1905–2005
100 Years of Biochemistry and Molecular Biology

Journey of a Late Blooming Biochemical Neuroscientist

Published, JBC Papers in Press, October 31, 2002, DOI 10.1074/jbc.X200004200

Julius Axelrod

From the National Institutes of Health, Bethesda, Maryland 20892

I graduated from tuition-free College of the City of New York (CCNY) in 1933. At that time the country was in the depths of the Great Depression, and there were few positions available for City College graduates. Its students were mainly children of immigrants who were bright and highly motivated. CCNY graduates included eight future Nobel Prize awardees and several distinguished biochemists.

After graduating from City College, I obtained a position at the Harriman Research Laboratories at New York University. Though it paid $25 a month, I was delighted to work in a laboratory. I assisted Dr. K. G. Falk in his research on enzymes in malignant tumors. Dr. Falk was trained as a biochemist in the laboratories in Europe. In 1924, Falk wrote a monograph on "The Chemistry of Enzyme Action." Falk was greatly influenced by Richard Willstäter, an eminent German biochemist. Willstäter believed that enzymes were catalysts of low molecular weight adsorbed on colloidal carriers such as proteins.

In 1935 I was lucky to get a position as a chemist in the Laboratory of Industrial Hygiene for $40 a week. This laboratory was a nonprofit organization and was set up by the New York City Department of Health to test the amount of vitamin supplements added to foods. In the 1930s vitamins were a hot subject in biochemistry. My duties were to modify published methods for vitamins so that they could be assayed in various food products. It required some ingenuity to modify methods for the measurement of vitamins from the literature. This experience proved useful in my later research.

First Experience in Research: The Metabolism of Analgesic Drugs

In 1946, there was an unexpected change in my career. At that time, analgesic drugs such as acetanilide and phenacetin were widely used. Some people who used excessive amounts of these drugs became habituated and developed methemoglobinemia. An independent organization, the Institute for the Study of Analgesic and Sedative Drugs, approached Dr. George B. Wallace, then president of the Laboratory of Industrial Hygiene and retired Chairman of the Department of Pharmacology at New York University, for advice. Dr. Wallace asked me if I would like to work on this problem and he suggested that I consult Dr. Bernard B. Brodie.

Bernard Brodie (Fig. 1) was a professor in the Pharmacology Department at New York University doing research at Goldwater Memorial Hospital in New York City. Goldwater Memorial Hospital was set up during World War II to clinically test newly synthesized antimalaria drugs. Brodie was responsible for developing methods for measuring blood levels of these drugs to establish the most effective dosage regimen. Soon after the end of the war, Brodie and his assistant Sidney Udenfriend published a series of influential papers in the *Journal of Biological Chemistry* on "The Estimation of Basic Organic Compounds in Biological Materials."

I met with Brodie in February 1946 to discuss the cause of toxicity of acetanilide. It was a fateful meeting for me. Brodie invited me to spend time in his laboratory to work on this problem. One of the possible transformation products of ingested acetanilide causing the toxic

FIG. 1. **Bernard B. Brodie (1907–1989).**

effects could be aniline (Fig. 2). One important lesson I learned from my discussions with Brodie was to ask the right questions at the right time and devise the means to answer these questions.

From my previous experience, I learned how to develop methods. Within a few weeks I developed a colorimetric method to measure aniline in blood and urine by diazotizing the amino group and coupling with a dye. After taking acetanilide orally, I identified aniline in my urine. This was one of the most exhilarating experiences in my life, making an important new discovery.

Experiments in dogs showed that there was a direct relationship between the concentration of plasma aniline and methemoglobinemia after the administration of acetanilide. After the oral administration of acetanilide to humans acetanilide was almost completely metabolized. Aniline represented only about 4% of the ingested acetanilide.

A common transformation of compounds containing a benzene ring is hydroxylation on the *para* position. Thus a possible metabolic product after the ingestion of acetanilide could be *N*-acetyl-*p*-aminophenol. Within a few weeks we identified the major metabolic product in humans after the oral administration of acetanilide as *N*-acetyl-*p*-aminophenol and its conjugates, sulfate and glucuronide. The route of metabolism of acetanilide in humans was found to proceed as shown in Fig. 2. *N*-Acetyl-*p*-aminophenol was found to be as potent as acetanilide in analgesic activity. By taking serial plasma samples, acetanilide was rapidly transformed to *N*-acetyl-*p*-aminophenol. After the administration of *N*-acetyl-*p*-aminophenol, negligible amounts of methemoglobin were formed.

In our paper published in 1948 (1), Brodie and I stated "the results are compatible with the assumption that acetanilide exerts its actions through *N-acetyl-p-aminophen*ol (now known as acetaminophen); it is possible, therefore, that it might have distinct advantages over acetanilide as an analgesic." This was my first taste of research and I loved it. "The Fate of Acetanilide in Man" (1) was my first paper and I was determined to continue doing research.

Several pharmaceutical companies subsequently began to sell products containing *N-acetyl-p-*aminoph*enol*. However, aspirin still dominated the analgesic market. In the early 1970s Johnson & Johnson marketed *N-*ace*tyl-p-*aminoph*enol* as Tylenol. Because aspirin might produce gastrointestinal ulcers, Tylenol became one of the best selling analgesics.

Brodie invited me to stay on at Goldwater Memorial Hospital to study the fate of other analgesic drugs. We received a small grant from the Institute for the Study of Analgesic and Sedative Drugs. Another analgesic drug we studied was antipyrine. We found that this drug distributes like body water. The first paper I published as coauthor in the *Journal of Biological Chemistry* in 1949 was "The Use of the Antipyrine in the Measurement of Total Body Water in Man" (2).

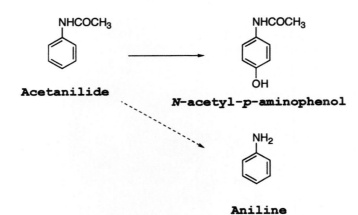

Fig. 2. **Metabolism of acetanilide.**

Move to the National Institutes of Health

Because I did not have a doctoral degree, advancement was unlikely in a hospital associated with an academic institution. In 1949, James Shannon was appointed director for intramural research at the newly formed National Heart Institute in Bethesda, Maryland. I applied for a position at the National Heart Institute and Shannon accepted me. In 1949 the government expanded the original National Institute of Health to a number of medical institutes to form the National Institutes of Health.

At that time, many scientists believed that medical research in government laboratories was mediocre. When Sid Udenfriend, a postdoctoral fellow at Washington University, was offered a position in the National Heart Institute, he asked Carl Cori, his laboratory chief, for advice. Cori told Udenfriend that working in a government laboratory would be the end of his research career.

Shannon persuaded Brodie to come to Bethesda as the Chief of the Laboratory of Chemical Pharmacology at the National Heart Institute. I was assigned to the Laboratory of Chemical Pharmacology in Building 3. This three-story building on the Bethesda campus of the NIH became one of the most fertile research settings in the world. Among the scientists working in Building 3 in the early 1950s, more than half became members of the National Academy of Science, five became Nobel laureates, and three were appointed directors of the NIH.

The ambience in Building 3 was highly stimulating. Everyone knew each other and their research. As the immunologist and essayist Lewis Thomas so eloquently stated, "The National Institutes of Health is not only the largest institution for biomedical science on earth, it is one of the nation's great treasures. As social interventions for human betterment go, this is one standing proof that, at least once in a while, government possesses the capacity to do something unique, imaginative, useful, and altogether right."

Metabolism of Caffeine, Amphetamines, and Ephedrine

The first problem I chose was the physiological disposition of the widely used compound caffeine in man. I developed a sensitive and specific method for measuring caffeine in biological material. The plasma half-life of caffeine in man and the distribution in dog tissues were determined (3).

I soon became intrigued with the sympathomimetic amines. In 1910, Barger and Dale (4) found that β-phenylethanolamine derivatives simulated the effects of sympathetic nerve stimulation with varying degrees of intensity and precision, and they coined the term sympathomimetic amines. Some sympathomimetic amines produced unusual behavioral effects. Amphetamine and methamphetamine in large doses produced symptoms of paranoia. Mescaline, the active principle of peyote, caused hallucinations.

In 1952 little was known about the metabolism of these amines. Because of my experience in drug metabolism, I decided to study the metabolism of ephedrine and amphetamine in a number of animal species. The first amine I examined was ephedrine. Ephedrine, the active principle of Ma Huang, an herb used by ancient Chinese physicians, was introduced to modern medicine by Chen and Schmidt (5) in 1930 to elevate blood pressure. I soon found that ephedrine was metabolized in animals (dogs, guinea pigs, rats) by two pathways, demethylation and hydroxylation on the benzene ring, to yield metabolites that had pressor activity (6).

I then examined the metabolism of amphetamine and methamphetamine (7). These compounds were transformed by a variety of pathways including hydroxylation, demethylation, deamination, and conjugation. Marked species variations in the transformation of these drugs were also found.

Microsomal Drug-metabolizing Enzymes

Over the past 150 years biochemists and pharmacologists have observed that almost all chemical compounds ingested are metabolized by a variety of biochemical changes. Depending on the chemical structure, the body can inactivate or activate drugs and foreign compounds by chemical transformation. In some cases toxic as well as pharmacologically active metabolites can be formed. In 1953 little was known about the enzymes involved in metabolizing drugs and foreign compounds. The ability of animals to metabolize amphetamines and ephedrine by a variety of metabolic pathways stimulated my interest in finding the enzymes involved in these transformations.

I was hesitant to do enzymology; I believed it required special training and aptitude. Gordon Tomkins, then a postdoctoral fellow who shared my laboratory, gave me good advice. He told me all I needed to start was a method for measuring amphetamine and ephedrine, an animal liver, and a razor blade.

In January, 1953 I did my first *in vitro* experiment. To my great pleasure, amphetamine almost completely disappeared when I incubated this drug with rabbit liver slices in a Krebs-Ringer solution. In the following experiment I homogenized the rabbit liver and found that the metabolism of amphetamine was increased when a cofactor, TPN (NADP), was added. I decided to examine which subcellular fraction was transforming amphetamine. Schneider (8) had developed a method for separating the various subcellular fractions by homogenizing tissues in isotonic sucrose and subjecting the homogenate to differential centrifugation. After separation of the nuclei, mitochondria, microsomes (homogenized endoplasmic reticulum), and the cytosol, none of these fractions were able to metabolize amphetamine even in the presence of added TPN. However, when microsomes and the cytosolic fractions were combined, amphetamine rapidly disappeared upon the addition of TPN.

Before going any further I decided to identify the metabolic products of amphetamine. When the combined microsomal and cytosolic fractions were incubated with amphetamine and TPN, ammonia and phenylacetone were identified (9). These results indicated that amphetamine was deaminated by an oxidative enzyme in rabbit liver requiring TPN. This experiment also suggested that the enzyme was present either in the microsomes or the cytosol, and one subcellular fraction supplied factors to the other fraction containing the enzyme. Because of the structure of amphetamine and the requirement of TPN, it was apparent that this enzyme was different from monoamine oxidase.

An approach that I thought was likely to give me a clue to the intracellular location of the amphetamine-deaminating enzyme was to subject each subcellular fraction to elevated temperatures. When I heated the cytosolic fraction to 55 °C for 10 min and then added unheated microsomes, amphetamine, and TPN, amphetamine was metabolized. However, after heating the microsomes to 55 °C and then adding unheated cytosolic fraction and TPN, amphetamine was no longer metabolized. This experiment told me that a heat-labile enzyme was located in the microsomes, and the cytosol provided factors necessary for the deamination of amphetamine.

I suspected that the cytosolic fraction was involved in the action of TPN. Bernard Horecker (then at the NIH) had prepared several substrates for his classic experiments on the pentose phosphate pathway. These enzymes required TPN. He generously supplied me with several substrates that I could test. The addition of glucose 6-phosphate, isocitric acid, or phosphogluconate together with TPN and dialyzed cytosol fraction to microsomes resulted in the metabolism of amphetamine. These substrates had one thing in common: they all generated TPNH (NADPH) even in the presence of oxygen. It became obvious that the cytosolic fraction was supplying a dehydrogenase and substrates to reduce TPN to TPNH. When microsomes were incubated in air with glucose-6-phosphate dehydrogenase, glucose 6-phosphate, TPN, and amphetamine, ammonia and phenylacetone were generated. To confirm that the deaminating enzyme was in the microsomes and that TPNH was a necessary cofactor, I incubated TPNH, microsomes, and amphetamine. Ammonia and phenylacetone were formed in stoichiometric amounts. DPNH could not be substituted for TPNH. In the absence of air there was no metabolism of amphetamine. By 1954 I felt quite confident that I had found an enzyme localized in rabbit liver microsomes that deaminated amphetamine in the presence of TPNH and O_2.

At about the same time I also found that ephedrine was demethylated to norephedrine and formaldehyde by an enzyme present in rabbit microsomes that required TPNH and oxygen. I reported these finding in 1954 at the fall meeting of the American Society of Pharmacology and Experimental Therapeutics. Complete papers appeared in the *Journal of Biological Chemistry* (amphetamine) and the *Journal of Pharmacology and Experimental Therapeutics* (ephedrine) in 1955 (9, 10). Soon after my report on the TPNH-dependent microsomal enzymes was published many drugs that are metabolized by a similar enzyme system were described.

In 1957, it was found that enzymes in the microsomes that required TPNH and oxygen could also catalyze the oxidative metabolism of normally occurring compounds such as androgens to estrogen (11). In studies on the *N*-demethylation of narcotic drugs in a variety of species, it became apparent that there were several microsomal enzymes involved in the metabolism of foreign and normally occurring compounds (12, 13).

In 1965 Omura *et al.* (14) reported that cytochrome P450 was present in liver rat microsomes, and about the same time Estabrook and co-workers demonstrated that this hemoprotein was responsible for the oxidative metabolism of drugs and steroids (14). After many years of intensive work in several laboratories, many cytochrome P450 enzymes were purified (15).

By 1954 I had published about 25 papers, most of them independently and many of them as a solo author. I applied for a promotion at the National Heart Institute and was turned down because I did not have a doctorate. I decided to get a Ph.D. in pharmacology at George Washington University and in 1955 at the age of 42, I received a Ph.D. I decided to leave the National Heart Institute and soon was appointed to a position at the National Institute of Mental Health.

Glucuronides and Jaundice

Just before I left the National Heart Institute, I was intrigued by a paper that found that uridine diphosphate glucuronic acid (UDPGA) was a necessary cofactor for the formation of phenolic glucuronides in a cell-free preparation of liver (16). In a chance meeting with Jack Strominger, then a biochemist at the NIH, we discussed the possible mechanisms for the enzymatic synthesis of UDPGA. We suspected it would be formed by the oxidation of uridine diphosphate glucose (UDPG) by either TPN or DPN. In a preliminary experiment we measured the formation of morphine glucuronide after incubating microsomes and the cytosolic fraction of rat liver with UDPG and either TPN or DPN. Morphine glucuronide was formed in the presence of DPN but not TPN. An enzyme, uridine diphosphate glucose dehydrogenase (17), was purified 180-fold which carried out the following reaction: $UDPG + 2DPN^+ \rightarrow UDPGA + 2DPNH + H^+$.

The work on glucuronide conjugation led to studies on the role of bilirubin glucuronide formation in jaundice. Rudi Schmidt, then at the NIH, and I observed that bilirubin was detoxified by enzymatic transformation to bilirubin glucuronide in the liver, a reaction requiring UDPGA. This led to an interesting clinical observation relating glucuronide formation and jaundice. In patients with congenital jaundice there is a marked increase in free bilirubin in the blood. This suggested to us that there must be a defect in a glucuronide-forming enzyme in this disease. The availability of a mutant strain of rats (Gunn rats) that were jaundiced made it possible to examine whether these animals had a defective glucuronide-forming enzyme (18). We showed that the Gunn rats had a low glucuronide-forming enzyme activity as compared with normal rats. Brodie and I previously showed the *N*-acetyl-*p*-aminophenol was mainly metabolized by glucuronide formation in humans (1). Plasma levels of *N*-acetyl-*p*-aminophenol and its glucuronide were then examined in patients with jaundice. Plasma levels of free *N*-acetyl-*p*-aminophenol were markedly elevated in jaundiced patients as compared with normal subjects (18).

Move to the National Institute of Mental Health (NIMH)

In 1955 I changed the direction of my research to the biochemistry of the nervous system and the effect of psychoactive drugs. The advice and encouragement of Seymour Kety (Fig. 3) influenced my subsequent career to a considerable degree. Seymour Kety was the first director of the intramural program of the NIMH in 1951. He established a program in Bethesda that was world class. His vision, wisdom, and integrity had an important impact on the develop-

Fig. 3. **Seymour S. Kety (1915–2000).**

ment of basic neuroscience and biological psychiatry. In 1948 at the University of Pennsylvania, Kety developed the nitrous oxide method for the measurement of cerebral blood flow. This germinal contribution had a profound influence on our understanding of how the brain uses oxygen and glucose in a variety of normal and abnormal conditions. Together with his student Louis Sokoloff, Kety developed methods for the measurement of brain regional blood flow based on exchanges of non-metabolized diffusible molecules between capillaries and tissues. These investigations led to the development of brain imaging by positive emission tomography.

In the mid-sixties, Kety and co-workers initiated a major study on the genetics of schizophrenia. Using the Danish population registry, Kety and Fini Schulsinger used adoption as a means of separating environmental and genetic factors in the transmission of schizophrenia among family members. From these studies they concluded that about 50% of schizophrenia was of genetic origin, and the mode of transmission appeared to be polygenic.

In addition to his scientific achievements, Kety was an outstanding administrator. When Kety stepped down as director, he became head of the Laboratory of Clinical Science at the NIMH in 1956. This laboratory became a fertile scientific organization integrating basic and clinical research related to psychiatric problems. Scientific excellence and freedom rather than conspicuous relevance were the guiding principles of the Laboratory of Clinical Science under Kety's leadership.

When I joined the Laboratory of Clinical Science in 1955, there was no such discipline as neuroscience. There had been an intellectual and technical separation among scientists working in neurophysiology, neurochemistry, neuroanatomy, neuropharmacology, psychiatry, and neurology. During the 1960s, the barriers among these fields began to break down. Neuroscientists borrowed heavily from molecular biology, biochemistry, biophysics, genetics, and immunology. The ingenious application of new technologies made it possible to ask more sophisticated and penetrating questions regarding the nervous system and the brain. In 1968 a Society of Neuroscience was established. At the first national meeting in 1968 there were about 700 attendees; in 2001 there were 29,000.

When I joined the NIMH, I was given a small laboratory with a technician. Ed Evarts, my laboratory chief, allowed me to work on any problem that was potentially productive and important. I thought that a study on the metabolism and tissue distribution of LSD would be an appropriate problem for my new laboratory. LSD was then used as an experimental drug by psychiatrists to produce abnormal behavior. Bob Bowman at the NIH was in the process of building a spectrofluorimeter. He was kind enough to let me use his experimental model, which made it possible to develop a sensitive fluorometric assay for LSD. This instrument later became the well known Aminco-Bowman spectrofluorimeter. The availability of this instrument made it possible for many laboratories to devise sensitive methods for the measurement of endogenous epinephrine, norepinephrine, dopamine, and serotonin in the brain and other tissues. These newly developed methods for monoamines played an important role in the subsequent rapid expansion in neurotransmitter research.

In a seminar, Kety gave an account of the observations of two Canadian psychiatrists. They found that when epinephrine was exposed to air it was converted to adrenochrome. When adrenochrome was ingested, it produced schizophrenia-like hallucinations. Because of these behavioral effects, they proposed that schizophrenia might be caused by an abnormal metabolism of epinephrine to adrenochrome.

In searching the literature, I was surprised to find that little was known about the metabolism of epinephrine at that time (1957). Because of the provocative hypothesis about the abnormal metabolism of epinephrine in schizophrenia and my previous experience in research on compounds related in structure to epinephrine such as amphetamine, I decided to work on the metabolism of epinephrine and norepinephrine. Epinephrine was then believed to be metabolized and inactivated by monoamine oxidase. However, it was previously shown that after the administration of a monoamine oxidase inhibitor the blood pressure elevation induced by epinephrine to cats was still rapidly reversed. This indicated that enzymes other than monoamine oxidase metabolize and inactivate epinephrine. An abstract in the March 1957 issue of the *Federation Proceedings* gave me a clue. Armstrong and McMillan (19) reported that patients with epinephrine-forming tumors (pheochromocytomas) excreted large amounts of an *O*-methylated product 3-methoxy-4-hydroxyvanillic acid (VMA). This suggested that VMA could be formed by *O*-methylation and deamination of epinephrine or norepinephrine. A potential methyl donor could be *S*-adenosylmethionine. When I incubated *S*-adenosylmethionine, epinephrine, and homogenized rat liver, epinephrine was metabolized.

According to the structure of VMA the most likely site of methylation would be in the metahydroxy group of epinephrine to form 3-*O*-methylepinephrine (metanephrine). The metabolite formed by incubating epinephrine with *S*-adenosylmethionine was identified as metanephrine (20). The *O*-methylating enzyme was purified and was found to *O*-methylate norepinephrine, dopamine, L-DOPA, and catechol but not monophenols. Because of its substrate specificity we named the enzyme catechol-*O*-methyltransferase (COMT). The enzyme was widely distributed in tissues including the brain. Pyrogallol was found to inhibit COMT both *in vitro* and *in vivo* (21). It was observed that COMT mainly *O*-methylated norepinephrine that had been released from nerves. Injecting catecholamines into animal resulted in the excretion of the respective *O*-methylated metabolites.

Irv Kopin, then a postdoctoral fellow, and I soon identified normally occurring metabolites of catecholamines such as normetanephrine, metanephrine, 3-methoxytyramine, and 3-methoxy-4-hydroxyphenylglycol in liver and brain. As a result of the discovery of the *O*-methylated metabolites, metabolic pathways of catecholamine metabolism were clarified. Catecholamines were metabolized by deamination, *O*-methylation, glycol formation, oxidation, and conjugation to glucuronides and sulfates.

The work on COMT gave me a long lasting interest in methylation reactions. The metabolites of catecholamines have been used as a marker for many studies in biological psychiatry. Inhibitors of COMT are used in the treatment of Parkinson's disease with L-DOPA.

Methyltransferase Enzymes

With the discovery of catechol-*O*-methyltransferase I became involved in describing several methyltransferase enzymes. To make methyltransferases more easy to detect, Donald Brown, then a postdoctoral fellow in the laboratory of a colleague, and I synthesized [^{14}C-*methyl*]*S*-adenosylmethionine enzymatically from rabbit liver. Thus the transfer of the labeled methyl group would make the product of a potential methyltransferase radioactive. The first enzyme described by this procedure was histamine *N*-methyltransferase (22).

Other methyltransferases discovered using [^{14}C-*methyl*]S-adenosylmethionine were phenylethanolamine *N*-methyltransferase (the enzyme that converts norepinephrine to epinephrine), protein carboxyl methyltransferase, and tryptamine *N*-methyltransferase. This latter enzyme was found to convert tryptamine, a compound found in the brain, to *N*,*N*-dimethyltryptamine, a psychotomimetic agent.

The methyltransferase enzymes together with [^{3}H-*methyl*]S-adenosylmethionine of high specific activity were used to develop sensitive methods to measure trace biogenic amines in tissues. We were able to detect, localize, and measure octopamine, tryptamine, phenylethylamine, phenylethanolamine, and tyramine in the brain and other tissues (23). Because of the sensitivity of the enzymatic micromethods, my colleagues and I were able to show the coexistence of several neurotransmitters in single identified neurones of *Aplysia* (24). Later Tomas Hökfelt, using immunohistofluorescent techniques, demonstrated the coexistence of more than one neurotransmitter in single neurons in mammalian brain (25).

Chemical Neurotransmission

The experiments on epinephrine stimulated my subsequent research on neurotransmitters and chemical neurotransmission. Chemical neurotransmission has a colorful and unusual history. In 1895 the British physician George Oliver injected an extract of the adrenal medulla into a dog and noted a market elevation in blood pressure (26). When the British physiologist J. N. Langley, in 1901, injected an extract of the adrenal medulla *in vivo*, organs responded as if they were stimulated by the sympathetic nerves. John Jacob Abel in 1897 isolated the active principle of the adrenal medulla as L-epinephrine (61). Abel was one of the founders of the *Journal of Biological Chemistry*.

Langley's observation prompted his student T. R. Elliot at the Cambridge University to inject epinephrine into a dog. Elliot noted that epinephrine produced a response in organs that was similar to that evoked by electrical stimulation of the sympathetic nerves. In an abstract to the British Physiological Society in 1904 (27), Elliot made the brilliant suggestion that epinephrine is released from sympathetic nerves to induce a physiological response in organs with which the nerves form junctions. Elliot was thus the first to propose that nerves communicate by the release of a chemical. Langley, who disliked theories, discouraged Elliot from publishing this idea until more facts were available. The concept of chemical neurotransmissions was not mentioned in the paper published by Elliot in the British *Journal of Physiology* (28).

The idea of chemical neurotransmission influenced the thinking of Otto Loewi, a pharmacologist at the University of Graz. In an autobiographical sketch, Loewi describes a dream, which he had in 1921, of an experiment that would prove chemical neurotransmissions (29). It was an elegant and crucial experiment. Loewi placed a frog heart with an attached vagus nerve in a bath in which the heart could be kept beating and then stimulated the vagus nerve (a nerve that reduces the heart rate). When he collected the fluid of the stimulated heart and transferred it to a denervated second heart, it slowed its beating (30). This demonstrated that the stimulated heart released a compound from the vagus nerve that slowed the unstimulated heart beat. The substance was later identified by Henry Dale as acetylcholine, the first neurotransmitter to be identified (31).

In a similar experiment, Loewi stimulated the accelerans nerve (the sympathetic nerve that increases the heart rate), and the fluid increased the beat of an unstimulated frog heart. For many years it was believed that this neurotransmitter was epinephrine. In 1946, the Swedish physiologist Ulf Von Euler isolated the neurotransmitter of the sympathetic nervous system and identified it as norepinephrine.

Inactivation of Neurotransmitters by Uptake in Nerve Terminals

For many years it was believed that the actions of neurotransmitters are terminated by enzymatic transformation. The neurotransmitter acetylcholine was known to be rapidly inactivated by acetylcholinesterase. Because monoamine oxidase had already been shown not to inactivate norepinephrine, I thought that norepinephrine might be inactivated by COMT. When pyrogallol, a COMT inhibitor (21), was administered to a dog it almost completely inhibited this enzyme. Despite the inhibition of COMT, the blood pressure-elevating action of injected norepinephrine was rapidly ended. This experiment indicated that there were other mechanisms for the inactivation of norepinephrine.

The answer to how catecholamines and other neurotransmitters are inactivated came in an unexpected way. When the metabolic pathway for epinephrine was described, Seymour Kety and co-workers were in a position to test the hypothesis of an abnormal metabolism of epinephrine in patients with schizophrenia. Because of the low endogenous levels of epinephrine and norepinephrine in urine, it was necessary to use [^{3}H]epinephrine and [^{3}H]norepinephrine of high specific activity. Using [^{3}H]epinephrine, Kety and co-workers found no difference in the metabolism of epinephrine between schizophrenic and normal subjects.

Kety was kind enough to give me some [^{3}H]epinephrine for my studies. At that time Hans Weil-Malherbe, a British biochemist, spent several months in my laboratory, and we developed methods for measuring [^{3}H]epinephrine and its metabolites in tissues and plasma. When we injected [^{3}H]epinephrine into cats, it persisted unchanged for at least 2 h in heart, spleen, and salivary gland long after the physiological effects were ended (32). We also found the [^{3}H]epinephrine did not cross the blood-brain barrier (33). [^{3}H]Epinephrine and [^{3}H]norepinephrine were concentrated in organs rich in sympathetic nerves (heart, spleen, and salivary gland). This unexpected phenomenon puzzled us, but it gave us a clue regarding the inactivation of the neurotransmitter norepinephrine. This catecholamine might be taken up and sequestered in sympathetic nerves.

The crucial experiment proving that norepinephrine was taken up and inactivated by sympathetic nerves was suggested by Georg Hertting, a visiting scientist in my laboratory. In this experiment, the superior cervical ganglia of cats were removed on one side resulting in the unilateral degeneration of nerves in the eye muscles and salivary gland. Upon the injection of [^{3}H]norepinephrine the radioactive catecholamine accumulated on the innervated side, but very little appeared on the denervated side (34). This experiment clearly indicated that the neurotransmitter norepinephrine was inactivated by uptake into sympathetic nerves.

The ability of sympathetic nerves to take up [^{3}H]norepinephrine made it possible to label these nerves with the radioactive norepinephrine and to examine whether it can be released on nerve stimulation. Hertting and I found that injected [^{3}H]norepinephrine taken up by sympathetic nerves was released when these nerves were stimulated (35). As a result of these experiments, we proposed that norepinephrine is inactivated by reuptake into sympathetic nerves. Other slower mechanisms for inactivation of catecholamines were by removal by the bloodstream, metabolism by *O*-methylation, and deamination in effector tissues, liver, or kidney.

In another experiment demonstrating uptake of norepinephrine, we injected rats with [^{3}H]norepinephrine. Pineal glands, which are rich in sympathetic nerves, were prepared for electron microscopic autoradiography. Electron microscopy showed a striking localization of photographic grains in non-myelinated axons (36). Grain concentrations appeared only in non-myelinated axons containing dense core 500-Å vesicles. Soon after the reuptake of norepinephrine by nerves was established, the monoamine neurotransmitters, serotonin (37) and dopamine (38), were also found to be inactivated by uptake into nerves. Later it was reported that the amino acid neurotransmitters GABA (γ-aminobutyric acid), glycine, proline, and L-glutamate are taken up by neurons and inactivated (39).

About 40 years after the discovery of the uptake of neurotransmitters in nerves, the uptake sites were cloned and characterized as sodium/chloride-dependent transporters (40). Sodium provides the thermodynamic energy to pump neurotransmitters from low concentrations outside the cell to the much higher concentrations inside the cell. Chloride ions prevent changes in the resting potential of the cell. The molecular characteristics of several neurotransmitter transporter families have been described (40).

Soon after the phenomenon of reuptake was demonstrated, a study on the effect of psychoactive drugs on the uptake of norepinephrine was initiated (41). To do these experiments, we first administered the drug to cats and then measured the concentration of injected [^{3}H]norepinephrine in various tissues. Amphetamine, imipramine, and reserpine block the uptake of [^{3}H]norepinephrine. We also examined the effect of cocaine because this drug was found to cause supersensitivity to epinephrine. After pretreatment of cats with cocaine there was more than 80% reduction of injected [^{3}H]norepinephrine in tissues innervated by sympathetic nerves. This experiment indicated that cocaine blocked the uptake of norepinephrine in sympathetic nerves (42). This allowed greater amounts of the neurotransmitter to remain in the synaptic cleft after cocaine and act on the post-synaptic receptors more intensely and for longer periods of time. It was later shown that cocaine, amphetamines, and antidepressants also blocked the uptake of dopamine and serotonin (43).

Most of the early work on uptake was done in the peripheral nervous system. Because catecholamines do not cross the blood-brain barrier (33) it was impossible to study the uptake, metabolism, storage, and release of catecholamine in the brain. Jacques Glowinski, a postdoctoral fellow, devised a technique to introduce [^{3}H]norepinephrine directly into the rat brain by injection into the lateral ventricle. It was shown that injected [^{3}H]norepinephrine entered the endogenous pool of catecholamines in the brain.

With the labeling of brain noradrenergic neurons with [^{3}H]norepinephrine, Glowinski and I examined the effect of antidepressant drugs. We found that only the clinically effective tricyclic antidepressant drugs block the uptake of [^{3}H]norepinephrine into brain neurons (44). Amphetamine blocked the uptake as well as the release of [^{3}H]norepinephrine in the brain (45). The discovery of the reuptake of neurotransmitters into nerve terminals and the ability of antidepressant drugs to block reuptake of monoamine neurotransmitters led to the rapid development of more effective drugs to treat depression.

About twenty million Americans suffer from depression in any one year. It is one of the most disabling diseases, causing considerable suffering, and one of the major causes of suicide. There was no effective treatment for depression until the Swiss psychiatrist Roland Kuhn observed that imipramine, a tricyclic compound, can relieve depression in many patients (46). These findings led to the rapid screening of potential antidepressant drugs by measuring the ability of a compound to block the uptake of tritium-labeled dopamine, serotonin, and norepinephrine into synaptosomes (pinched off nerve endings) (47).

The discovery process to find an effective drug by a pharmaceutical industry takes about 6 years. Numerous potential synthetic antidepressant compounds can now be measured in a day for their ability to block the uptake of ^{3}H-labeled monoamine neurotransmitters. This procedure saves the pharmaceutical industry many millions of dollars and several years of development. The most well known drug developed in this manner is fluoxetine (Prozac), an SSRI (specific serotonin uptake inhibitor). There are many other SSRI drugs available as well as antidepressant drugs that inhibit the uptake of norepinephrine.

The Pineal Gland as a Neurochemical Transducer

In 1958 Aaron Lerner and co-workers described the isolation of melatonin (5-methyoxy-*N*-acetyltryptamine), a compound that blanched the skin of tadpoles, from the bovine pineal gland (48). Lerner, a dermatologist and biochemist, undertook this problem because he thought that melatonin might be useful in treating skin diseases. Melatonin attracted my attention because it had a methyl group and a serotonin nucleus.

I decided to work on the biosynthetic pathway to melatonin in collaboration with Herb Weissbach. The availability of radioactive *S*-adenosylmethionine provided an opportunity to examine whether the pineal gland can form melatonin from a potential precursor compound. When we incubated bovine pineal extracts with [^{14}C-*methyl*]*S*-adenosylmethionine and *N*-acetylserotonin, a radioactive product was formed that we identified as melatonin. We purified the melatonin-forming enzyme, hydroxyindole-*O*-methyltransferase (HIOMT) from the bovine pineal gland (49). *N*-Acetylserotonin was found to be the best substrate for HIOMT. We also found the enzyme that converts serotonin to *N*-acetylserotonin in the pineal gland (50). We proposed that the synthesis of melatonin in the pineal gland proceeds as follows: serotonin → *N*-acetylserotonin → melatonin.

HIOMT was found to be highly localized in the pineal gland. Small amounts of HIOMT were also found in the retina. These observations convinced me that the pineal gland is a biochemically active organ containing an unusual enzyme and product and was worth further study.

In 1962, Richard Wurtman joined my laboratory as a postdoctoral fellow. As a medical student Wurtman had found that bovine pineal extracts blocked the growth of the rat gonads induced by environmental light. Because research on the pineal gland was a neglected subject and because of our mutual interest in this organ, Wurtman and I decided to spend some time working on the pineal gland. We thought that a good place to start was to isolate the gonad inhibitory factor from the pineal gland. Neither of us wanted to go through the tiresome isolation and bioassay procedure and we decided to study the effects of melatonin. We soon found that melatonin reduced ovary weight and decreased the incidence of estrus in the rat.

The next question that our laboratory was concerned with was how does information about environmental lighting reach the pineal gland located between the two cerebral hemispheres.

In 1960, Virginia Fiske found that exposure to environmental light for several weeks caused a decrease in pineal gland weight (51). We found that keeping rats in continuous light decreased HIOMT activity as compared with those kept in continuous darkness.

Ariens-Kappers reported that the pineal gland is innervated by sympathetic nerves arising from the superior cervical ganglia (52). When the superior cervical ganglia of rats were removed, the effect of light on HIOMT was abolished. This experiment told us that the action of light on melatonin synthesis in the pineal gland was mediated via sympathetic nerves. Quay had just made an important observation that levels of serotonin, a precursor of melatonin, are high during daylight and low at night (53). Together with Sol Snyder, a postdoctoral fellow in my laboratory, we developed a highly sensitive method to measure serotonin in a single pineal gland. This gave us the opportunity to examine the serotonin rhythm. Using serotonin as a marker, we could examine how the melatonin rhythm is regulated by light and dark in a tiny (1 mg) rat pineal gland. We found that in rats kept in continuous darkness or in blinded rats, the 24-h serotonin rhythm persisted (54). This indicated that the indoleamine rhythms are controlled by an internal clock. Keeping rats in constant light abolished the serotonin circadian rhythm. These experiments demonstrated that rhythms of indoleamines in the pineal gland were endogenous and were regulated by environmental light. We found that the circadian rhythm of serotonin was abolished after ganglionectomy or by cutting the nerves from the brain to the superior cervical ganglia. These experiments indicated that the source of messages for the circadian rhythm of melatonin resides somewhere in the brain.

In 1970, Klein and Weller (55) described a robust circadian rhythm in pineal gland serotonin N-acetyltransferase, which is 180^0 out of phase with that of serotonin. One hour after the onset of darkness there was a 30–50-fold rise in serotonin N-acetyltransferase activity. A circadian rhythm in pineal gland melatonin had the same phasing as that of serotonin N-acetyltransferase: high during darkness and low during daytime. Like the serotonin rhythm the serotonin N-acetyltransferase rhythm was abolished by denervation of the sympathetic nerves to the pineal gland or by interrupting nerve impulses from the brain. Bilateral lesions in the suprachiasmatic nucleus in the hypothalamus abolished the circadian rhythm of serotonin N-acetyltransferase and melatonin (56). This and other experiments established that the suprachiasmatic nucleus is the biological clock of the brain. Brownstein and I found a 24-h rhythm in the turnover of norepinephrine in the sympathetic nerves innervating the pineal gland (57). This rhythm in turnover of norepinephrine was abolished in continuous light but persisted in darkness or in blinded rats. This indicated that circadian rhythm in the pineal gland is generated by the rhythmic release of the neurotransmitter norepinephrine. This rhythm in sympathetic nerve activity is driven by the circadian pacemaker in the suprachiasmatic nucleus of the hypothalamus.

Experiments indicated that norepinephrine released from sympathetic nerves innervating the pineal gland stimulated a β−adrenergic receptor, which then activated the cellular machinery for the synthesis of serotonin N-acetyltransferase. Martin Zatz, a postdoctoral fellow, and I (58) showed that the regulation of serotonin N-acetyltransferase and the subsequent synthesis of melatonin consist of a complex series of steps involving the β-adrenergic receptor, cyclic AMP, protein kinase, and synthesis of serotonin N-acetyltransferase mRNA and protein (58).

The link whereby environmental lighting sends its message to the pineal gland and organs outside the brain has been recently clarified. Provencio and co-workers (59) described an unusual opsin-like photosensitive pigment, melanopsin, in the mouse retina residing in a small subset of retinal ganglia cells. The stimulation of melanopsin by light does not require the visual photoreceptors of the rods and cones of the retina.

In 2002 (60), it was reported that the retinal ganglion cells containing the photosensitive pigment melanopsin are connected through the retinohypothalamic tract to the suprachiasmatic nucleus, the primary circadian pacemaker of the brain. Then, as described above, the suprachiasmatic nucleus sends its signal to the superior cervical ganglia, which in turn innervates the pineal gland via norepinephrine-containing (sympathetic) nerves.

Afterthoughts

Despite a late start in my research career, it spanned 50 years. Forty-six of these years were spent at the NIH. The NIH supported my research and gave me full independence in choosing my problem and provided excellent physical and intellectual resources. It spared me the time writing grant proposals and relieved me of the anxieties of soliciting financial support. My freewheeling style might have made it difficult to obtain grants had I been at a university instead of the NIH.

I always maintained a small laboratory with no more than three postdoctoral fellows and an occasional visiting scientist. It gave me great pleasure to interact with my postdoctoral fellows, who were to a considerable degree responsible for my contributions. Offers to head large departments were resisted because it would have involved considerable time in administration. I enjoyed working at the laboratory bench and interacting with my bright postdoctoral fellows.

Joining the NIMH in 1955 was propitious. The field of neuroscience was beginning to explode. This gave me an opportunity to apply a biochemist's approach to study the nervous system and brain. I soon learned that the brain cannot be treated like a liver. The brain has numerous areas with special chemistry and functions. This made the study of the biochemistry of the brain highly complex and challenging.

During my career in biomedical research, the work was largely its own reward. In retrospect, however, a great satisfaction that I have about my work is that it led to treatments for the relief of pain and depression.

Acknowledgments—I thank Lee Eiden for helping me prepare this manuscript and Martin Zatz for comments on the manuscript.

Address correspondence to: eiden@codon.nih.gov.

REFERENCES

1. Brodie, B. B., and Axelrod, J. (1948) *J. Pharmacol. Exp. Ther.* **94,** 29–38
2. Soberman, R., Brodie, B. B., Levy, B. B., Axelrod, J., and Steele, J. M. (1949) *J. Biol. Chem.* **179,** 31–42
3. Axelrod, J., and Reichenthal, J. (1953) *J. Pharmacol. Exp. Ther.* **107,** 519–523
4. Barger, G., and Dale, H. H. (1910) *J. Physiol. (Lond.)* **41,** 19–59
5. Chen, K. K., and Schmidt, F. (1930) *Medicine (Baltimore)* **9,** 1–117
6. Axelrod, J. (1953) *J. Pharmacol. Exp. Ther.* **109,** 62–73
7. Axelrod, J. (1954) *J. Pharmacol. Exp. Ther.* **110,** 315–326
8. Schneider, W. C. (1948) *J. Biol. Chem.* **176,** 259–265
9. Axelrod, J. (1955) *J. Biol. Chem.* **214,** 753–763
10. Axelrod, J. (1955) *J. Pharmacol. Exp. Ther.* **114,** 430–438
11. Ryan, K. G., and Engel, L. (1957) *J. Biol. Chem.* **225,** 103–114
12. Axelrod, J. (1956) *J. Pharmacol. Exp. Ther.* **117,** 322–330
13. Lu, A. Y. H. (1979) *Pharmacol. Rev.* **31,** 277–295
14. Omura, T., Sato, R., Cooper, D. Y., Rosenthal, O., and Estabrook, R. W. (1965) *Fed. Proc. Am. Soc. Exp. Biol.* **24,** 1181–1189
15. Nebert, W., and Gonzalez, F. (1987) *Annu. Rev. Biochem.* **56,** 945–993
16. Dutton, G. J., and Storey, I. D. E. (1954) *Biochem. J.* **57,** 275–283
17. Strominger, J. L., Maxwell, E. S., Axelrod, J., and Kalckar, H. M. (1954) *J. Am. Chem. Sec.* **76,** 6411–6412
18. Axelrod, J. J., Schmid, R., and Hammaker, L. (1957) *Nature* **180,** 1426–1427
19. Armstrong, M. D., and McMillan, A. (1957) *Fed. Proc.* **16,** 146
20. Axelrod, J., and Tomchick, R. (1958) *J. Biol. Chem.* **233,** 702–705
21. Axelrod, J., and La Roche, M. J. (1959) *Science* **130,** 800–801
22. Brown, D. D., Axelrod, J., and Tomchick, R. (1959) *J. Biol. Chem.* **234,** 2948–2950
23. Saavedra, J. M., and Axelrod, J. (1974) *J. Psychiatr. Res.* **11,** 289–291
24. Brownstein, M. J., Saavedra, J. M., Axelrod, J., Zeman, H. H., and Carpenter, D. O. (1974) *Proc. Natl. Acad. Sci. U. S. A.* **71,** 4662–4665
25. Hokfelt, T., Johansson, A., Lungdahl, A., Lindberg, H. M., and Schultzberg, M. (1980) *Nature* **284,** 515–521
26. Oliver, G., and Schaefer, E. A. (1895) *J. Physiol (Lond.)* **18,** 230–280
27. Eliott, T. R. (1904) *J. Physiol. (Lond.)* **31,** XX–XXI
28. Eliott, T. R. (1905) *J. Physiol. (Lond.)* **32,** 401–467
29. Loewi, O. (1960/1961) *Perspect. Biol. Med.* **4,** 3–25
30. Loewi, O. (1921) *Pfluegers Arch. Gesamte Physiol.* **189,** 239–242
31. Dale, H. H. (1929) *J. Physiol. (Lond.)* **68,** 97–123
32. Axelrod, J., Weil-Malherbe, H., and Tomchick, R. (1958) *J. Pharmacol. Exp. Ther.* **127,** 251–256
33. Weil-Malherbe, H., Axelrod, J., and Tomchick, R. (1959) *Science* **129,** 1226–1227
34. Hertting, G., Axelrod, J., Kopin, I., and Whitby, L. G. (1961) *Nature* **189,** 66–68
35. Hertting, G., and Axelrod, J. (1961) *Nature* **192,** 172–173
36. Wolfe, D. E., Potter, L. T., Richardson, K. C., and Axelrod, J. (1962) *Science* **138,** 440–442
37. Hoffman, B. J., Mezey, E., and Brownstein, M. (1991) *Science* **154,** 79–80
38. Ritz, M. C., Lamb, R. J., Goldberg, S. R., and Kuhar, M. J. (1981) *Science* **237,** 1219–1223
39. Iversen, L. (2000) *Mol. Psychiatry* **5,** 357–362
40. Reith, M. E. A. (1997) *Neurotransmitter Transporters*, Humana Press, Totowa, NJ
41. Axelrod, J., Whitby, L. G., and Hertting, G. (1961) *Science* **133,** 383–384
42. Whitby, L. G., Hertting, G., and Axelrod, J. (1960) *Nature* **187,** 604–605
43. Amara, S. G., and Kuhar, M. (1993) *Annu. Rev. Neurosci.* **16,** 73–93
44. Glowinski, J., and Axelrod, J. (1964) *Nature* **204,** 1318–1319
45. Axelrod, J. (1971) *Science* **173,** 598–606
46. Kuhn, R. (1957) *Schweiz. Med. Wochenschr.* **87,** 1135–1140

47. Coyle, J. T., and Snyder, S. H. (1969) *J. Pharmacol. Exp. Ther.* **170,** 221–231
48. Lerner, A. B., Case, J. D., Takahashi, Y., Lee, T. H., and Mori, W. (1958) *J. Am. Chem. Soc.* **80,** 25–87
49. Axelrod, J., and Weissbach, H. (1961) *J. Biol. Chem.* **236,** 211–213
50. Weissbach, H., Redfield, B. G., and Axelrod, J. (1961) *Biochim. Biophys. Acta* **54,** 190–192
51. Fiske, V. M., Bryant, G. K., and Putnam, J. (1960) *Endocrinology* **66,** 489–491
52. Ariens-Kappers, J. (1960) *Anat. Rec.* **136,** 220–221
53. Quay, W. B. (1963) *Gen. Comp. Endocrinol.* **3,** 473–479
54. Snyder, S. H., Zweig, M., Axelrod, J., and Fischer, S. E. (1965) *Proc. Natl. Acad. Sci. U. S. A.* **53,** 301–360
55. Klein, D. C., and Weller, J. L. (1970) *Science* **169,** 348–353
56. Moore, R. Y., and Eichler, V. B. (1972) *Brain Res.* **42,** 201–206
57. Brownstein, M. J., and Axelrod, J. (1974) *Science* **184,** 163–165
58. Zatz, M., and Axelrod, J. (1978) in *Neuronal Information Transfer* (Karlin, A., Tennyson, M., and Vogel, H. J., eds) pp. 47–57, Academic Press, New York
59. Provencio, I., Jiang, G., Grip, W. J., and Rollag, M. D. (1998) *Proc. Natl. Acad. Sci. U. S. A.* **95,** 340–345
60. Hatar, S., Liao, H-W., Takao, M., Benson, D. M., Yan, K-W., Berson, D. M., and Yan, K. W. (2002) *Science* **95,** 1065–1070
61. Abel, J. J., and Crawford, R. C. (1897) *Bull. Johns Hopkins Hosp.* **8,** 151–154

THE JOURNAL OF BIOLOGICAL CHEMISTRY
© 2003 by The American Society for Biochemistry and Molecular Biology, Inc.

Vol. 278, No. 6, Issue of February 7, pp. 3499–3509, 2003
Printed in U.S.A.

Reflections

A PAPER IN A SERIES COMMISSIONED TO CELEBRATE THE CENTENARY OF THE JBC IN 2005

JBC Centennial
1905–2005
100 Years of Biochemistry and Molecular Biology

Happily at Work

Published, JBC Papers in Press, December 18, 2002, DOI 10.1074/jbc.X200003200

Henry Lardy

From the Institute for Enzyme Research, Department of Biochemistry, University of Wisconsin, Madison, Wisconsin 53726

It is a great privilege to be asked for a "Reflections" essay; I admire those prepared by my predecessors. My teachers were less prestigious than Arthur Kornberg's (1), and there was no single major theme in my research as was the case with several previous contributors to this series. Instead we studied a wide variety of metabolic phenomena that I have described in a summary of my first 50 years of biochemical research (2).

Our findings included a treatment for selenium poisoning in livestock (undergraduate thesis; selenium-containing mercapturic acids are excreted in the urine) that was applied successfully to a human case; our studies of spermatozoa will be described in a following section. We elucidated the mechanism by which L-glyceraldehyde inhibits glycolysis (3). That disproved Needham's non-phosphorylating glycolysis in embryos and tumors. Could that have encouraged him to drop experiments and to devote his talents to prepare his magnificent history of Chinese science instead? We found that the function of biotin was to fix CO_2 in heterotrophic organisms (4); cellular respiration rates varied with the availability of inorganic P and phosphate acceptor (5, 6); propionate was metabolized by CO_2 addition to ultimately yield succinate (7, 8). My students purified and crystallized some 10 phosphate-transferring enzymes, and we demonstrated that most of them required MgATP as substrate and were inhibited by free ATP; we found 16 different antibiotics that affected oxidative phosphorylation (9, 10) and a dozen that acted as ionophores (11), some of which are still being used in experiments. We also found that caffeine increased respiration and dramatically induced whiplash-type motility in sperm by increasing cyclic AMP (12, 13); the respiratory response was dependent on the utilization of acetylcarnitine (14). Thyroid hormone and also dehydroepiandrosterone induced the synthesis of mitochondrial glycerol-3-phosphate dehydrogenase to as much as 20 times the normal concentration (15–17) and formed part of a thermogenic system (17, 18). The path of carbon in gluconeogenesis was found to involve carboxylation of pyruvate (Utter reaction) in mitochondria, reduction of oxalacetate to malate, malate transport to cytosol in exchange for pyruvate, oxidation of malate to oxalacetate (the precursor of phosphopyruvate) together with the generation of the NADH required to reduce 3-phosphoglycerate to triose phosphate (19, 20); serine was found to be converted to glucose by an entirely different pathway, probably the reverse of its synthesis from hydroxypyruvate (21). We also found that levels of liver cytosolic phosphoenolpyruvate carboxykinase (PEPCK) are regulated by the need for gluconeogenesis; they are increased by fasting and decreased in well fed animals; PEPCK is activated by ferrous ion, and in liver free calcium activates PEPCK by releasing Fe^{2+} from mitochondria to the cytosol (22); feeding tryptophan inhibits gluconeogenesis because its metabolite, quinolinate, forms a complex with ferrous ion that blocks PEPCK (23, 24). The widely reported enhancement of liver mitochondrial respiration following exercise or the administration of glucagon or adrenaline to rats was found to be mediated by elevated malate concentration in the liver (25, 26). Malate is known to facilitate mitochondrial uptake of substrates by exchange across the mitochondrial membranes.

Naturally there was also an abundance of studies that yielded useful facts but not new concepts and many experiments undertaken to test hypotheses that turned out to be without merit! One reason for the diversity of research is that we wanted graduate students to have their own thesis research problems. Sixty-four candidates earned their Ph.D. degree in our group between 1945 and 1989 and more than 100 postdoctorate fellows conducted their research in our laboratories at the Institute for Enzyme Research. Relationships with these scholars and friends have always meant a great deal to me.

At the time my research history was written (2), we were studying an intriguing class of Janus-like proteins, caltrins, that function in fertilization. Because the work was in progress it was not described in that essay. The caltrins have not been widely publicized and therefore are probably not familiar to most biochemists. The caltrins of different species have widely different structures and their multiple functions are achieved by disparate mechanisms.

The Caltrin Story

No aspect of living processes is more awe-inspiring than the union of a microscopic spermatozoon with an egg of the same species to initiate a new life. In this process the contribution of the male is to present a set of haploid chromosomes to join those of the egg. However, this presentation is a complex ceremony involving "capacitation," *i.e.* alteration of sperm plasma membranes to permit penetration by Ca^{2+}. Calcium uptake is followed by disruption of the acrosome, a sac containing hyaluronidase and proproteinases that autocatalytically are converted to active acrosins. The sperm attach to the protective layer of the egg, a glycoprotein matrix (zona pellucida), and the calcium-activated acrosomal enzymes attack the zona to provide a path for sperm entry. Calcium uptake by the contractile components in the sperm tail facilitates the acquisition of "hyperactivated" motility characterized by rapid lashing and wider excursion of the sperm tail. This causes the sperm to swim in tight arcs to drive through the zona and then penetrate the egg. The role of caltrins in regulating each of these processes is complex and fascinating.

Our work with spermatozoa had been continuous since 1939 when my professor, Paul Phillips, and I developed a medium for the preservation of animal sperm (27). It permitted the retention of motility and fertility for 8–12 days and launched the artificial insemination industry in livestock. Because we had solved the practical problem, I was free to study basic aspects of sperm metabolism and the regulation of energy capture for motility. The findings during that period included the first clear statement concerning the mechanism by which 2,4-dinitrophenol functions: "the fact that DNP decreased the motility of the spermatozoa, while the processes of glycolysis and oxidation are increased, indicates an interference of the energy-coupling mechanism with the result that oxidation and glycolysis run rampant, while the energy is lost as heat rather than as work" (28).

During that same period we discovered that, unlike most substrates that increased both respiration and motility (29, 30), "β-hydroxybutyrate was unusual in that it depressed endogenous respiration slightly, but supported an excellent degree of motility. It is possible that the oxidation of this metabolite, in spermatozoa, is more efficiently coupled with phosphorylation than is the oxidation of the endogenous lipid reserve" (29). This explanation seems also to apply to the working heart (31) and may have therapeutic implications (32).

Nearly a century ago the eminent physiologist Jacques Loeb demonstrated that fertilization of sea urchin eggs does not occur in the absence of Ca^{2+} (33, 90). This failure is based on the need for Ca^{2+} to promote the lysis of the acrosomal membranes on the sperm head (acrosomal reaction) of both invertebrates (34) and vertebrates (35, 36).

We had been investigating the role of calcium transport in the regulation of sperm behavior, including the acrosome reaction and enhancement of motility for some years (35, 37, 91) when Donner Babcock found that the rapid uptake of calcium by bovine epididymal sperm did not occur in sperm separated from ejaculates (38). Epididymal sperm contain 6 ± 1 nmol of calcium/10^8 cells and will accumulate up to 50 nmol/10^8 sperm when incubated in a medium containing 0.2 mM calcium and an oxidizable energy source such as β-hydroxybutyrate (37, 38, 91). Ejaculated bovine sperm have the same low calcium content despite being bathed in 9 mM calcium in seminal fluid. When washed free of seminal fluid and suspended in media containing calcium, ejaculated sperm still do not take up this divalent cation. The obvious next experiment was to add seminal fluid to epididymal sperm, which demonstrated the presence of a <u>cal</u>cium <u>tr</u>ansport <u>in</u>hibitor that we termed caltrin. The inhibitor was purified to homo-

Bovine Caltrin 10 20

Ser.Asp.Glu.Lys.Ala.Ser.Pro.Asp.Lys.His.His.Arg.Phe.Ser.Leu.Ser.Arg.Tyr.Ala.Lys.Leu.Ala.Asn.Arg.Leu.
Ala.Asn.Pro.Lys.Leu.Leu.Glu.Thr.Phe.Leu.Ser.Lys.Trp.Ile.Gly.Asp.Arg.**Gly.Asn.Arg.Ser.**Val

Rat Caltrin 10 20

Lys.Val.Ile.Gly.Lys.Lys.Ala.Asn.Cys.Pro.Asn.Thr.Leu.Val.Gly.Cys.Pro.Arg.Asp.Tyr.<u>Asp.Pro.Val.Cys.Gly</u>.
<u>Thr.Asp.Gly.</u>Lys.<u>Thr.Tyr.</u>Ala.<u>Asn.</u>Glu.Cys.Ile.Leu.Cys.Phe.Glu.Asn.Arg.Lys.Phe.Gly.Thr.Ser.Ilu.Arg.Ile.Gl
n.Arg.Arg.Gly.Leu.Cys

Guinea Pig Caltrin I 10 20

Ala.Phe.Ala.Pro.Ser.Lys.Val.Asp.Ser.Asp.Arg.Pro.Asn.Cys.Ser.Arg.Tyr.Val.Gln.His.Leu.Tyr.Met.Cys.Thr.
Lys.Glu.Leu.<u>Asp.Pro.Val.Cys.Gly</u> <u>Thr.Asp.Gly.</u>His.<u>Thr.Tyr.</u>**Gly.Asn.Arg.Ser.**Ile.Phe

Guinea Pig Caltrin II 10 20

Arg.Arg.Leu.His.Gly.Gln.Ala.Ile.Asn.Arg.Pro.Gly.Ser.Cys.Pro.Arg.Val.Met.Ile.Tyr.Cys.Pro.Ala.Arg.His.Pro
.Pro.Asn.Lys.Cys.Thr.Ser.Asp.Tyr.Asp.Cys.Pro.Lys.Pro.Gln.Lys.Cys.Cys.Pro.Gly.Tyr.Cys.Gly.Lys.Gln.
Cys.Tyr.Gln.Pro.Glu

Mouse Caltrin 10 20

Leu.Ile.Cys.Asn.Ser.Cys.Glu.Lys.Ser.Arg.Asp.Ser.Arg.Cys.Thr.Met.Ser.Gln.Ser.Arg.Cys.Val.Ala.Lys.Pro.
Gly.Glu.Ser.Cys.Ser.Thr.Val.Ser.His.Phe.Val.Gly.Thr.Lys.His.Val.Tyr.Ser.Lys.Gln.Met.Cys.Ser.Pro.Gln.
Cys.Lys.Glu.Lys.Gln.Leu.Asn.Thr.Gly.Lys.Lys.Leu.Ile.Tyr.Ile.Met.Phe.Gly.Glu.Lys.Asn.Leu.Met.Asn.Phe

Stallion Caltrin (very preliminary) 10 20
Ala.Leu.Leu.Ser.Pro.Gly.Thr.Ala.Pro.Asp.xxx.His.Val.Tyr.Lys.Asp.Arg.Leu.His.Leu.xxx.Asn.Arg.Glu.Arg.
Lys.Leu.Ile.Cys.Ala.Thr.Asn.Gly.GlnThr.Tyr.Arg.Asn.Pro.Cys.Ile.Phe.Cys.Arg.Glu.Cys.Ile.Ala.Ser------

Bold: Bovine vs Guinea Pig I

Underlined : Rat vs Guinea Pig I

FIG. 1. **The amino acid sequences of caltrins from bull, rat, guinea pig, and mouse.**

geneity (39) and the amino acid sequence was determined (Fig. 1) (40). A protein with the properties of caltrin was demonstrated to be bound to plasma membranes of ejaculated sperm and was not detected on the membranes of epididymal sperm (41). The sequence also disclosed that a similar protein, termed bovine seminal plasmin, had been isolated from bovine semen and was described as having antimicrobial activity (42). Errors in the sequencing of seminal plasmin (43) were later corrected (44), thus confirming our structure and the identity of seminal plasmin and caltrin. Analyses for bovine caltrin based on inhibition of calcium uptake by epididymal bull sperm indicated that bull seminal fluid contained about twice as much caltrin as was required to inhibit calcium uptake 90% by the sperm present in an ejaculate.

On storage, caltrin lost activity as a blocker of calcium transport and became an *enhancer* of calcium uptake (45). This transformation could be accomplished rapidly by binding the fresh inhibitory caltrin to a cation exchanger. The recovered caltrin *increased* both the rate and extent of calcium uptake. The acidic components of the eluate contained ether-extractable phospholipids that restored calcium transport inhibition to the enhancer caltrin protein. Among the pure phospholipids tested only phosphatidylserine converted enhancer caltrin to a calcium transport inhibitor. Phosphatidylcholine, phosphatidylinositol, and citrate abolished the stimulation of calcium uptake but did not change the enhancer to an inhibitor (46).

With the aid of anti-bovine caltrin antiserum, two caltrin proteins were detected and isolated from guinea pig seminal vesicle secretions (47, 92). There were no common amino acid sequences in these peptides designated G.P. caltrins I and II, and the only identity with bovine caltrin was a group of four (Gly-Asn-Arg-Ser) near the carboxyl terminus of bovine caltrin and G.P. caltrin I (Fig. 1); nonetheless, the anti-bovine caltrin antiserum recognizes these guinea pig proteins. Both G.P. caltrins contain carbohydrate residues as detected with concanavalin A (47, 92); bovine caltrin does not (39). The molecular weights of the peptide portion of G.P. caltrins I and II are 5082 and 6255, respectively. The maximal inhibition of calcium uptake into guinea pig sperm by each of the G.P. caltrins approached 50%. Deglycosylation of G.P. caltrins using trifluoromethanesulfonic acid caused both I and II to enhance the rate of calcium uptake by guinea pig epididymal sperm, *i.e.* they become enhancer caltrins (48).

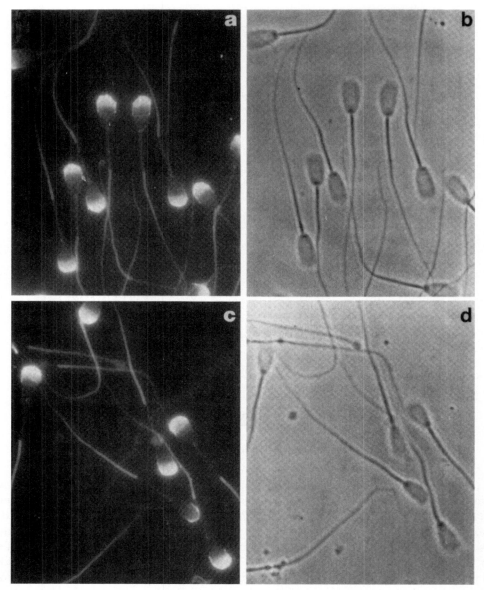

FIG. 2. **Bull sperm bind caltrin to the tail and over the acrosome.** *a*, epididymal sperm treated with 0.40 mg of caltrin/10⁸ cells in 1 ml and washed. *c*, ejaculated sperm washed free of seminal fluid and not exposed to purified caltrin. Sperm were spread and dried on glass slides, treated in succession with rabbit monospecific caltrin antiserum and goat anti-rabbit IgG that had been labeled with fluorescein isothiocyanate. Slides were washed to remove excess protein and viewed with a Zeiss fluorescence microscope (*a* and *c*); *b* and *d* are corresponding phase contrast photomicrographs. Epididymal sperm not exposed to caltrin did not bind the fluorescent-labeled antibody.

The seminal vesicles of rats and mice contain caltrins that have been purified and sequenced (Fig. 1) (49). Their calculated molecular weights are 6217 and 8476, respectively. Rat caltrin is derived from a 54-kDa inactive precursor produced in the seminal vesicles (50); the biosynthesis of rat caltrin and its precursor is androgen-dependent (51). The active rat protein has a sequence of 13 amino acids nearly identical with a segment of G.P. caltrin I. Neither rat nor mouse caltrins have any significant sequence similarity to G.P. caltrin II or bovine caltrin. Each of the caltrins, with the exception of the bovine, contains cysteine residues that are not reactive with thiol reagents until the protein has been treated with reducing agents such as dithiothreitol. Reducing the cystine disulfide bonds of rat caltrin and carboxymethylating the protein diminishes, but does not eliminate, the effect on calcium transport. The locations of the disulfide bonds are known (52). In the case of mouse caltrin, which contains 7 cysteine residues, the protein appears to be a disulfide dimer formed between the odd cysteines. Reduction converts the 17-kDa native mouse caltrin to 8.5 kDa. Bovine caltrin also behaves as a dimer of M_r 9600–10,500 by gel permeation and gel electrophoresis, but from its amino acid content we found a M_r of 5411 and no cysteine.

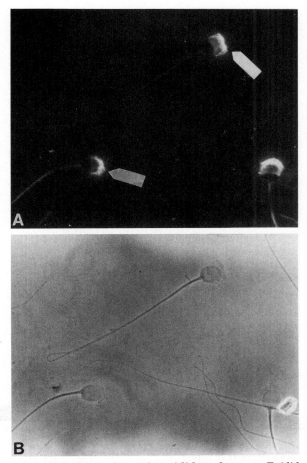

FIG. 3. **Binding of guinea pig caltrin I to guinea pig epididymal sperm.** Epididymal sperm was treated with 0.5 mg of caltrin I/10^8 cells in 1 ml for 1 h and then washed twice with phosphate-buffered saline. Further treatments are described in the legend to Fig. 1 except that the antiserum had been prepared from rabbits treated with caltrin I. *A*, immunofluorescence photomicrograph. *Arrows* designate caltrin binding to the acrosome. *B*, corresponding phase-contrast photomicrograph.

A caltrin protein designated SVS VII has been purified from mouse seminal vesicles by Yee-Hsiung Chen and co-workers (53). It has 76 amino acids, 71 of which are identical with our sequence for mouse caltrin (49). Luo *et al.* (53) determined the sequence of their protein from the corresponding cDNA and the first 18 amino acids by automated Edman degradation; they ascribe the differences to errors in our structure. Our sequence was determined by the Edman procedure applied to five different peptides isolated from caltrin subjected to partial proteolysis. Four of the peptides contained the amino acids in question; each of these fragments contained the same sequence. Therefore we are confident of our structural assignment and assume that there are genetic differences between CD-1 and Swiss white mice. Three of the differences can be explained by single base changes. The Chen group (54) reported another caltrin-like protein, P12, from mouse seminal vesicles with no appreciable sequence similarity to our mouse caltrin.

Bovine caltrin binds over the acrosome and the entire tail of bull sperm but does not bind to the posterior part of the head nor to the midpiece, which contains the mitochondria (45). Washed sperm separated from bull semen show the same fluorescence staining pattern as epididymal sperm treated with caltrin (Fig. 2), but epididymal sperm not exposed to caltrin do not bind the fluorescence-labeled antibody (45). Caltrin binding at these two sites was assumed to regulate the acrosome reaction and the hyperactivation of motility, respectively. These separate functions were clearly defined in the case of guinea pig sperm (see below).

The immunofluorescence test showed G.P. caltrin I binding to the G.P. sperm over the acrosome but not to other parts of the sperm (Fig. 3). Caltrin I (0.5 mg/10^8 sperm) nearly completely inhibited hyaluronidase release from the acrosome during 30 min of incubation in the presence of 1 mM calcium; many of these sperm were hyperactive but had intact acrosomes (48). Guinea pig epididymal sperm not treated with caltrins released hyaluronidase and were

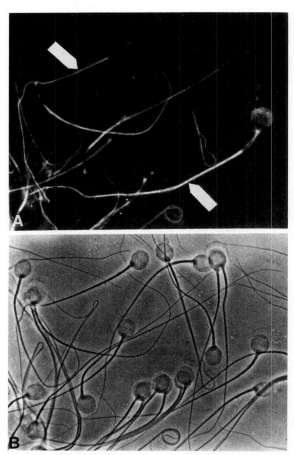

FIG. 4. **Binding of guinea pig caltrin II to guinea pig epididymal sperm.** Conditions are the same as described in the legend to Fig. 3 except that sperm were treated with purified guinea pig caltrin II and the rabbit antiserum had been prepared with caltrin II. *A*, immunofluorescence photomicrograph. *Arrows* designate caltrin binding to the sperm tails. *B*, corresponding phase-contrast photomicrograph. Reprinted with permission from Ref. 48.

hyperactive, indicating calcium access to both the acrosome and the tail. Guinea pig caltrin II (0.5 mg/10^8 sperm) bound to the sperm tail and very sparingly to the head (Fig. 4). It depressed hyaluronidase release from the acrosome only partially, and during 2 h of incubation the sperm maintained linear motility because calcium access to the contractile mechanism was blocked (47, 92). These separate sites of binding and function account for the fact that each of the GP caltrins inhibits about 50% of the calcium uptake that occurs in the absence of these seminal vesicle proteins (48).

The "Eureka!" announcement (55) that "observations of differences in the effect of seminal plasma contamination on hyperactivation and capacitation made in the present study provide further evidence for the existence of functionally separated, distinct regions in the spermatozoon" in effect confirmed for the human sperm what had been demonstrated much earlier in guinea pig sperm (48).

Some years ago Tschesche *et al.* (56) reported the presence of proteolytic inhibitory proteins in mammalian seminal plasma, and their observation has been confirmed by several laboratory groups. Rat caltrin and guinea pig caltrin I are also trypsin inhibitors (52), and the former is identical with the inhibitors from the pancreas isolated by Uda *et al.* (57) and from liver by Kido *et al.* (58). There is extensive homology between rat caltrin and trypsin inhibitors isolated from pancreatic secretions of many different mammalian species. Guinea pig caltrin II, bovine, and mouse caltrins are not trypsin inhibitors (50). The gene for caltrin (seminal plasmin) has been characterized (59) and, remarkably, has been shown to be a member of the extensive neuropeptide Y gene family (60). Seminal plasmin/caltrin was the subject of an excellent review (61).

In summary, the role of caltrins in fertilization can be postulated from their known functions. On ejaculation, spermatozoa bind caltrins as well as other seminal vesicle products. Bound caltrins prevent calcium movement into the acrosome and thus prevent a premature acrosome reaction. The hydrolytic and proteolytic enzymes are retained until needed. By

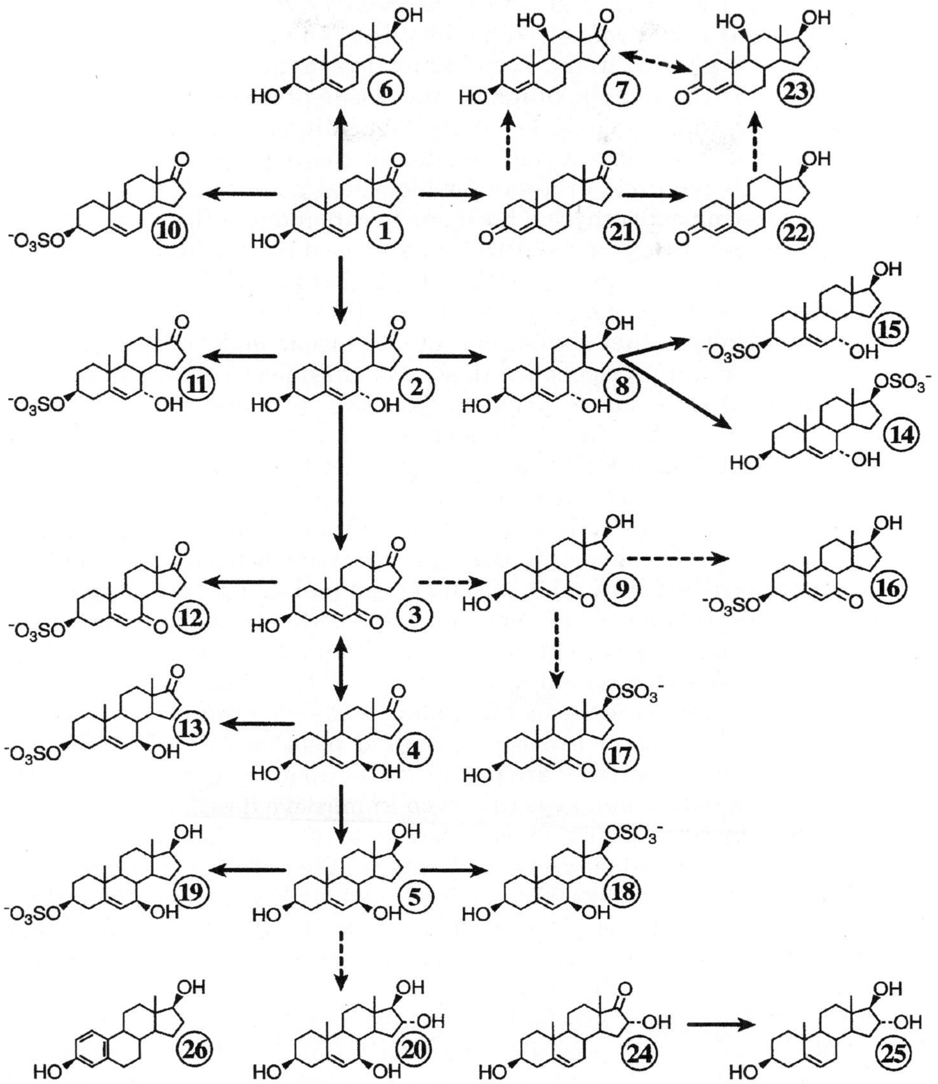

FIG. 5. **Steroids produced from DHEA (1) in liver homogenate fortified with ATP, NADPH, and malate.** The *broken arrows* are postulated enzyme-catalyzed reactions.

preventing calcium uptake by the tail, caltrins keep the sperm moving forward. After some time the sperm will have moved up the female reproductive tract and encountered the egg(s); the phosphatidylserine will have been dissociated from the caltrin protein in the case of bovine and the carbohydrate residues hydrolytically removed in the case of rodents. The enhancer forms of caltrin then stimulate calcium uptake at the acrosome where it activates membrane discomposition and at the tail where it induces whiplash movement of the sperm tail. Species that produce two caltrins have one that acts at the acrosome and controls hyaluronidase and acrosin release; the other binds to the sperm tail and regulates motility.

Investigation of these proteins in our laboratory was dropped for lack of laboratory space on my reaching emeritus status in 1988 but is being continued by Carlos Coronel in Argentina.

Dehydroepiandrosterone—A New Chapter

The University of Wisconsin treats its retirees more hospitably than Columbia treated Professor Chargaff (62); I was allowed to retain a small laboratory, enough for chemistry but not for extensive metabolic research.

A problem that was inviting concerned possible active steroid hormones derived metabolically from dehydroepiandrosterone (DHEA). This steroid was known as an intermediate in the conversion of cholesterol to testosterone and estrogens. Administered in large amounts, it caused fat and weight loss in obese mice (63), rats, and dogs, decreased blood sugar in diabetic mice (64), decreased the incidence of spontaneous and carcinogen-induced tumors in mice (65), enhanced immune responses (66), and improved memory in old mice (67). We, like some others, assumed that DHEA was converted metabolically to more active steroids that exerted these beneficial effects. Beginning in the 1960s many investigators had studied the conversion of DHEA to other steroids by animals, humans, and tissue preparations, but only a few of the products were tested for any biological activity. We initiated a program of synthesizing derivatives of DHEA that were logical metabolites in the hope of finding one or more new hormones. Such a search requires an assay for biological activity, and our earlier research provided one. Administering extra thyroid hormone to rats induces the formation of mitochondrial glycerophosphate dehydrogenase (GPDH) to 20 times the normal level in liver (15, 16) and somewhat less in other tissues (16). After Tagliaferro *et al.* (68) reported that DHEA enhanced metabolism and thermogenesis, we found this steroid induced the formation of hepatic GPDH but not that of other tissues (17, 69). Cytosolic malic enzyme is also increased by these hormones (70), and the response of these two enzymes to administered steroids thus provides a semiquantitative assay of activity. The two enzymes comprise a thermogenic system regulated by calcium and other factors (17, 18, 71, 72).

We found that hydroxylation of DHEA at any position other than 7 abolished the ability to increase the thermogenic enzymes (73). 7α-Hydroxy-, 7-oxo-, and 7β-hydroxy-DHEA were more active than DHEA. Because activity increased in that sequence we postulated that the same sequence was involved in converting DHEA to an active hormone. By incubating DHEA with liver homogenate fortified with ATP, NADPH, and malate and assaying the products at short time intervals, that sequence was indeed established (74) and is shown in Fig. 5. The detection and quantitative measurement of the many products formed from DHEA (Fig. 5, **1**) by liver were possible because of the analytical prowess of Dr. Ashok Marwah (75–79). Several additional products remain to be identified including some glucuronides.

DHEA derivatives bearing oxo- or hydroxyl groups at position 7 do not serve as precursors of androgens or estrogens and therefore are potential therapeutic agents. 7-Oxo-DHEA had no detectable toxicity in rats (80) or monkeys (81) even in massive doses and in a phase I clinical trial was well tolerated by normal men given doses up to 200 mg/day for 28 days (82). Tested at that dose for 8 weeks in obese subjects (body mass index of 31.9 ± 6.2 kg/m^2) who were restricted to 1800 calories/day, subjects receiving 7-oxo-DHEA lost significantly more body weight and fat than those receiving placebos (83). 7-Oxo-DHEA was far more effective than DHEA as an enhancer of memory in old mice and in restoring memory in mice treated with scopolamine (84). Androstenediol (Fig. 5, **6**), one of the main products of DHEA metabolism in liver, has been known for many years to have estrogen activity. It also activates androgen receptor transcriptional activity in prostate cancer cells (85). This function is not inhibited by hydroxyflutamide or bicalutamide, two agents used for treating prostate cancer (86). This raises the question whether androstenediol, produced in adrenals and liver, accounts for the failure of orchidectomy to be an effective long term treatment for prostatic cancer. In a collaborative study, we have also found that DHEA has activity in adipose cells not displayed by its metabolites (87).

Structure/activity comparisons show that ring D of DHEA can be altered in several different ways without abolition of activity. The ring can be expanded by insertion of oxygen at 17a (88) with retention of the ability to induce the formation of both GPDH and malic enzyme. Hydroxylation at position 15 or introduction of 15–16 unsaturation, nearly abolishes the response of GPDH, but induction of malic enzyme is retained (89). Substitutions at position 16 yield steroids with varying activity; some are highly active and point the way to possible routes to true hormones. The search goes on.

Address correspondence to: halardy@facstaff.wisc.edu.

REFERENCES

1. Kornberg, A. (2001) Remembering our teachers. *J. Biol. Chem.* **276,** 3–11
2. Lardy, H. A. (1985) A half century of biochemistry. In *A History of Biochemistry* (Semenza, G., ed) pp. 297–325, Elsevier Science Publishing Co., Inc., New York
3. Lardy, H., Wiebelhaus, V., and Mann, K. (1950) The mechanism by which glyceraldehyde inhibits glycolysis. *J. Biol. Chem.* **187,** 325–337
4. Lardy, H., Potter, R., and Elvehjem, C. (1947) The role of biotin in bicarbonate utilization by bacteria. *J. Biol. Chem.* **169,** 451–452
5. Lardy, H. (1952) The role of phosphate in metabolic control mechanisms. In *The Biology of Phosphorus*, pp. 287–294, Michigan State College Press, East Lansing, MI
6. Lardy, H., and Wellman, H. (1952) Oxidative phosphorylations: role of inorganic phosphate and acceptor systems

in control of metabolic rates. *J. Biol. Chem.* **195**, 215–224

7. Lardy, H., and Peanasky, R. (1953) Metabolic effects of biotin. *Physiol. Rev.* **33**, 560–565

8. Lardy, H., and Adler, J. (1956) Synthesis of succinate from propionate and bicarbonate by soluble enzymes from liver mitochondria. *J. Biol. Chem.* **219**, 933–942

9. Lardy, H., Reed, P., and Lin, C.-H. (1975) Antibiotic inhibitors of mitochondrial ATP synthesis. *Fed. Proc.* **34**, 1707–1710

10. Lardy, H. (1980) Antibiotic inhibitors of mitochondrial energy transfer. *Pharmacol. Ther.* **11**, 649–660

11. Lardy, H., Graven, S., and Estrada-O, S. (1967) Specific induction and inhibition of cation and anion transport in mitochondria. *Fed. Proc.* **26**, 1355–1360

12. Garbers, D., Lust, W., First, N., and Lardy, H. (1971) Effects of phosphodiesterase inhibitors and cyclic nucleotides on sperm respiration and motility. *Biochemistry* **10**, 1825–1831

13. Garbers, D., First, N., and Lardy, H. (1973) The stimulation of bovine sperm metabolism by cyclic nucleotide phosphodiesterase inhibitors. *Biol. Reprod.* **8**, 589–598

14. Milkowski, A., Babcock, D., and Lardy, H. (1976) Activation of bovine epididymal sperm respiration by caffeine. *Arch. Biochem. Biophys.* **176**, 250–256

15. Lee, Y.-P., Takemori, A., and Lardy, H. (1959) Enhanced oxidation of α-glycerophosphate by mitochondria of thyroid-fed rats. *J. Biol. Chem.* **234**, 3051–3054

16. Lee, Y.-P., and Lardy, H. (1965) Influence of thyroid hormones on L-α-glycerophosphate dehydrogenasees and other dehydrogenases in various organs of the rat. *J. Biol. Chem.* **240**, 1427–1436

17. Lardy, H., Su, C.-Y., Kneer, N., and Wielgus, S. (1989) Dehydroepiandrosterone induces enzymes that permit thermogenesis and decrease metabolic efficiency. In *Hormones, Thermogenesis, and Obesity* (Lardy, H., and Stratman, F., eds) pp. 415–426, Elsevier Science Publishers B.V., Amsterdam

18. Lardy, H. (1999) Dehydroepiandrosterone and ergosteroids affect energy expenditure. In *Health Promotion and Aging* (Watson, R. R., ed) pp. 33–42, Harwood, Amsterdam

19. Lardy, H., Paetkau, V., and Walter, P. (1965) Paths of carbon in gluconeogenesis and lipogenesis: I. The role of mitochondria in supplying precursors of phosphoenolpyruvate. *Proc. Natl. Acad. Sci. U. S. A.* **53**, 1410–1415

20. Walter, P., Paetkau, V., and Lardy, H. (1966) Paths of carbon in gluconeogenesis and lipogenesis: III. *J. Biol. Chem.* **241**, 2523–2532

21. Lardy, H., Veneziale, C., and Gabrielli, F. (1969) Paths of carbon in gluconeogenesis. *FEBS Symp.* **19**, 55–62

22. Merryfield, M., and Lardy, H. (1982) Ca^{2+}-mediated activation of phosphoenolpyruvate carboxykinase occurs via the release of Fe^{2+} from rat liver mitochondria. *J. Biol. Chem.* **257**, 3628–3635

23. Veneziale, C., Walter, P., Kneer, N., and Lardy, H. (1967) Influence of tryptophan and its metabolites on gluconeogenesis in the isolated, perfused liver. *Biochemistry* **6**, 2129–2138

24. Snoke, R., Johnston, J., and Lardy, H. (1971) Response of phosphopyruvate carboxylase to tryptophan metabolites and metal ions. *Eur. J. Biochem.* **24**, 342–346

25. Bobyleva, V., and Lardy, H. (1986) The role of malate in exercise-induced enhancement of mitochondrial respiration. *Arch. Biochem. Biophys.* **245**, 470–476

26. Bobyleva, V., Wehbie, R., and Lardy, H. (1986) The role of malate in hormone-induced enhancement of mitochondrial respiration. *Arch. Biochem. Biophys.* **245**, 477–482

27. Lardy, H. A., and Phillips, P. H. (1939) Preservation of spermatozoa. *Proc. Am. Soc. Animal Production* **32**, 219–221

28. Lardy, H. A., and Phillips, P. H. (1943) The effect of thyroxine and dinitrophenol on sperm metabolism. *J. Biol. Chem.* **149**, 177–182

29. Lardy, H. A., Hansen, R. G., and Phillips, P. H. (1945) The metabolism of bovine epididymal spermatozoa. *Arch. Biochem.* **6**, 41–51

30. Lardy, H. A., and Phillips, P. H. (1945) Studies of fat and carbohydrate oxidation in mammalian spermatozoa. *Arch. Biochem.* **6**, 53–61

31. Sato, K., Kashiwaya, Y., Keon, C. A., Tsuchiya, N., King, M. T., Radda, G. K., Chance, B., Clarke, K., and Veech, R. L. (1995) Insulin, ketone bodies and mitochondrial energy transduction. *FASEB J.* **9**, 651–658

32. Veech, R., Chance, B., Kashiwaya, Y., Lardy, H. A., and Cahill, G. F. (2001) Ketone bodies, potential therapeutic uses. *IUBMB Life* **51**, 241–247

33. Loeb, J. (1915) On the nature of the conditions which determine or prevent the entrance of the spermatozoan into the egg. *Am. Natur.* **49**, 257–285

34. Dan, J. C. (1954) Studies on the acrosome. III. Effect of calcium deficiency. *Biol. Bull.* **107**, 335–349

35. Babcock, D. F., First, N. L., and Lardy, H. A. (1976) Action of the ionophore A 23187 at the cellular level. *J. Biol. Chem.* **251**, 3881–3886

36. Yanagimachi, R. (1978) Calcium requirement for sperm-egg fusion in mammals. *Biol. Reprod.* **19**, 949–958

37. Singh, J. P., Babcock, D. F., and Lardy, H. A. (1978) Increased calcium-ion influx is a component of capacitation of spermatozoa. *Biochem. J.* **172**, 549–556

38. Babcock, D. E., Singh, J. P., and Lardy, H. A. (1979) Alteration of membrane permeability to calcium ions during maturation of bovine spermatozoa. *Dev. Biol.* **69**, 85–93

39. Rufo, G. A., Singh, J. B., Babcock, D. E., and Lardy, H. A. (1982) Purification and characterization of a calcium transport inhibitor protein from bovine seminal plasma. *J. Biol. Chem.* **257**, 4627–4632

40. Lewis, R. V., San Agustin, J., Kruggel, W., and Lardy, H. A. (1985) The structure of caltrin, the calcium-transport inhibitor of bovine seminal plasma. *Proc. Natl. Acad. Sci. U. S. A.* **82**, 6490–6491

41. Rufo, G. A., Schoff, P. K., and Lardy, H. A. (1984) Regulation of calcium content in bovine spermatozoa. *J. Biol. Chem.* **259**, 2547–2552

42. Reddy, E. S. P., and Bhargava, P. M. (1979) Seminal plasmin—an antimicrobial protein from bovine seminal plasma which acts in *E. coli* by specific inhibition of rRNA synthesis. *Nature* **279**, 725–728

43. Theil, R., and Scheit, K. H. (1983) Amino acid sequence of seminal plasmin, an antimicrobial protein from bull semen. *EMBO J.* **12**, 1159–1163

44. Sitaram, N., Kumari, V. K., and Bhargava, P. M. (1986) Seminal plasmin and caltrin are the same protein. *FEBS Lett.* **201**, 233–236

45. San Agustin, J., Hughes, P., and Lardy, H. A. (1987) Properties and function of caltrin, the calcium-transport inhibitor of bull seminal plasma. *FASEB J.* **1**, 60–66

46. San Agustin, J., and Lardy, H. A. (1990) Bovine seminal plasma constituents modulate the activity of caltrin, the calcium-transport regulating protein of bovine spermatozoa. *J. Biol. Chem.* **265**, 6860–6867

47. Coronel, C. E., San Agustin, J., and Lardy, H. A. (1988) Identification and partial characterization of caltrin-like proteins in the reproductive tract of the guinea pig. *Biol. Reprod.* **38**, 713–722

48. Coronel, C. E., and Lardy, H. A. (1992) Functional properties of caltrin proteins from seminal vesicles of the guinea pig. *Mol. Reprod. Dev.* **33**, 74–80

49. Coronel, C. E., Winnica, D. E., Novella, M. L., and Lardy, H. A. (1992) Purification, structure, and characterization

of caltrin proteins from seminal vesicle of the rat and mouse. *J. Biol. Chem.* **267,** 20909–20915

50. Coronel, C. E., Novella, M. L., Winnica, D. E., and Lardy, H. (1993) Isolation and characterization of a 54-kilodalton precursor of caltrin, the calcium transport inhibitor protein from seminal vesicles of the rat. *Biol. Reprod.* **48,** 1326–1333

51. Novella, M. L., Maldonado, C., Aoki, A., and Coronel, C. E. (1999) Androgen-dependent synthesis/secretion of caltrin, calcium transport inhibitor protein of mammalian seminal vesicle. *Arch. Androl.* **42,** 1–12

52. Winnica, D. E., Novella, M. L., Dematteis, A., and Coronel, C. E. (2000) Trypsin/acrosin inhibitor activity of rat and guinea pig caltrin proteins. Structural and functional studies. *Biol. Reprod.* **63,** 42–48

53. Luo, C-W., Lin, H-J., and Chen, Y-H. (2001) A novel heat-labile phospholipid-binding protein, SVS VII, in mouse seminal vesicle as a sperm motility enhancer. *J. Biol. Chem.* **276,** 6913–6921

54. Chen, L.-Y., Lin, Y.-H., Lai, M.-L., and Chen, Y.-H. (1998) Developmental profile of a caltrin-like protease inhibitor, P12, in mouse seminal vesicle and characterization of its binding sites on sperm surface. *Biol. Reprod.* **59,** 1498–1505

55. Mortimore, S. T., Swan, M. A., and Mortimore, D. (1998) Effect of seminal plasma on capacitation and hyperactivation in human spermatozoa. *Hum. Reprod.* **13,** 2139–2146

56. Tschesche, H., Kupfer, S., Lengel, O., Klauser, R., Meier, M., and Fritz, H. (1974) Proteinase inhibitors. *Second International Research Conference. Bayer Symposium V,* pp. 164–187, Springer-Verlag, Berlin

57. Uda, K., Ogawa, M., Shibata, T., Murata, A., Mori, T., Kikuchi, N., Toshida, N., Tsunasawa, S., and Sakiyama, F. (1988) Purification, characterization and amino-acid sequencing of two pancreatic secretory trypsin inhibitors in rat pancreatic juice. *Biol. Chem. Hoppe-Seyler* **369,** (suppl.) 55–61

58. Kido, H., Yokogoshi, Y., and Katunuma, N. (1990) A low-molecular-mass Kazal-type protease inhibitor isolated from rat hepatocytes is identical to rat pancreatic secretory trypsin inhibitor. II. *Eur. J. Biochem.* **188,** 501–506

59. Kuhlmann, J. K., and Scheit, K. H. (1993) Characterization of the gene for seminal plasmin, a secretory protein of the bovine seminal vesicle. *Biochim. Biophys. Acta* **1173,** 85–86

60. Herzog, H., Hort, Y., Schneider, R., and Shine, J. (1995) Seminal plasmin: recent evolution of another member of the neuropeptide Y gene family. *Proc. Natl. Acad. Sci. U. S. A.* **92,** 594–598

61. Sitaram, N., and Nagara, R. (1995) Seminal plasmin. *Bioessays* **17,** 415–421

62. Chargaff, E. (1978) *Heraclitean Fire,* Rockefeller University Press, New York

63. Yen, T. T., Allen, J. A., Pearson, D. V., Acton, J., and Greenberg, M. M. (1977) *Lipids* **12,** 409–413

64. Coleman, D. L., Schwizer, R., and Leiter, E. (1984) Effect of genetic background on the therapeutic effects of dehydroepiandrosterone (DHEA) in diabetes-obesity mutants and in aged normal mice. *Diabetes* **33,** 26–32

65. Schwartz, A. G., and Tannen, R. H. (1981) Inhibition of 7,12-dimethylbenzanthracene and urethane-induced lung tumor formation in A/J mice by long-term treatment with dehydroepiandrosterone. *Carcinogenesis* **2,** 1335–1337

66. Loria, R., Inge, T., Cook, S. S., Szakal, A., and Regelson, W. (1988) Protection against acute lethal viral infections with the native steroid dehydroepiandrosterone(DHEA). *Med. Virol.* **26,** 301–314

67. Flood, J. F., Morley, J. E., and Roberts, E. (1992) Memory enhancing effects in male mice of pregnenolone and steroids metabolically derived from it. *Proc. Natl. Acad. Sci. U. S. A.* **89,** 1567–1571

68. Tagliaferro, A., Davis, J. R., Truchon, S., and Van Hamont, N. (1986) Effects of dehydroepiandrosterone acetate on metabolism, body weight and composition of male and female rats. *J. Nutr.* **116,** 1977–1983

69. Su, C.-Y., and Lardy, H. (1991) Induction of hepatic mitochondrial glycerophosphate dehydrogenase in rats by dehydroepiandrosterone. *J. Biochem. (Tokyo)* **110,** 207–213

70. Tepperman, H., de la Garza, S., and Tepperman, J. (1968) Effect of dehydroepiandrosterone and diet protein on liver enzymes and lipogenesis. *Am. J. Physiol.* **214,** 1126–1132

71. Wernette, M., Ochs, R. S., and Lardy, H. (1981) Ca^{2+} stimulation of rat liver mitochondrial glycerophosphate dehydrogenase. *J. Biol. Chem.* **256,** 12767–12771

72. Lardy, H., Kneer, N., Bellei, M., and Bobyleva, V. (1995) Induction of thermogenic enzymes by DHEA and its metabolites. *Ann. N. Y. Acad. Sci.* **774,** 171–179

73. Lardy, H., Kneer, N., Wei, Y., Partridge, B., and Marwah, P. (1998) Ergosteroids II: biologically active metabolites and synthetic derivatives of dehydroepiandrosterone. *Steroids* **63,** 158–165

74. Marwah, A., Marwah, P., and Lardy, H. (2002) Ergosteroids VI: metabolism of dehydroepiandrosterone by rat liver *in vitro*: a liquid chromatographic-mass spectrometric study. *J. Chromatogr. B Biomed. Appl.* **767,** 285–299

75. Marwah, A., Marwah, P., and Lardy, H. (1999) Development and validation of a high-performance liquid chromatography assay for the quantitative determination of 7-oxo-dehydroepiandrosterone in human plasma. *J. Chromatogr. B Biomed. Appl.* **721,** 197–205

76. Marwah, A., Marwah, P., and Lardy, H. (2001) Liquid chromatography-electrospray ionization mass spectrometric analysis of corticosterone in rat plasma using selected ion monitoring. *J. Chromatog. B Biomed. Appl.* **757,** 333–342

77. Marwah, A., Marwah, P., and Lardy, H. (2001) High performance liquid chromatographic analysis of dehydroepiandrosterone. *J. Chromatogr. A* **935,** 279–296

78. Marwah, A., Marwah, P., and Lardy, H. (2002) Ergosteroids VII: perchloric acid induced transformations of 7-oxygenated steroids and their bio-analytical applications; a liquid chromatographic-mass spectrometry study. *J. Bioorganic Chem.* **30,** 233–248

79. Marwah, A., Marwah, P., and Lardy, H. (2002) Ergosteroids VIII. Enhancement of signal response of neutral steroidal compounds in liquid chromatographic-electrospray ionization mass spectrometric analysis by mobile phase additives. *J. Chromatogr. A* **964,** 137–151

80. Lardy, H., Henwood, S., and Weeks, C. (1999) An acute oral gavage study of 3β-acetoxyandrost-5-ene-7,17-dione in rats. *Biochem. Biophys. Res. Commun.* **254,** 120–123

81. Henwood, S., Weeks, C., and Lardy, H. (1999) An escalating dose oral gavage study of 3β-acetoxyandrost-5-ene-7,17-dione in Rhesus monkeys. *Biochem. Biophys. Res. Commun.* **254,** 124–126

82. Davidson, M., Marwah, A., Sawchuk, R., Maki, K., Marwah, P., Weeks, C., and Lardy, H. (2002) Safety and pharmacokinetic study with escalating doses of 3-acetyl-7-oxo-dehydroepiandrosterone in healthy male volunteers. *Clin. Invest. Med.* **23,** 300–310

83. Kalman, D., Colker, C., Swain, M., Torina, G., and Shi, Q. (2002) A randomized double-blind, placebo-controlled study of 3-acetyl-7-oxo-dehydroepiandrosterone in healthy overweight adults. *Curr. Ther. Res.* **61,** 435–442

84. Shi, J., Schulze, S., and Lardy, H. (2000) The effect of 7-oxoDHEA acetate on memory in young and old 57BL/6 mice. *Steroids* **63,** 124–129

85. Miyamoto, H., Yeh, S., Lardy, H., Messing, E., and Chang, C. (1998) Δ^5-Androstenediol is a natural hormone with androgenic activity in human prostate cancer cells. *Proc. Natl. Acad. Sci. U. S. A.* **95,** 11083–11088

86. Prostate Cancer Trialists' Collaborative Group (1995) *Lancet* **346,** 265–269

87. Gomez, F. E., Miyazaki, M., Kim, Y.-C., Marwah, P., Lardy, H., Ntambi, J., and Fox, B. G. (2002) Molecular differences caused by differentiation of 3T3-L1 preadipocytes in the presence of either dehydroepiandrosterone

(DHEA) or 7-oxo-DHEA. *Biochemistry* **41,** 5473–5482

88. Reich, I., Lardy, H., Wei, Y., Marwah, P., Kneer, N., Powell, D. R., and Reich, H. J. (1998) Ergosteroids III. Synthesis and biological activity of seco-steroids related to dehydroepiandrosterone. *Steroids* **63,** 542–553

89. Reich, I., Reich, H., Kneer, N., and Lardy, H. (2002) Ergosteroids V: preparation and biological activity of various D-ring derivatives in the 7-oxo-dehydroepiandrosterone series. *Steroids* **67,** 221–233

90. Loeb, J. (1913) *Artificial Parthenogenesis and Fertilization*, University of Chicago Press, Chicago, IL

91. Singh, J. P., Babcock, D. F., and Lardy, H. A. (1980) Induction of accelerated acrosome reaction in guinea pig sperm. *Biol. Reprod.* **22,** 566–570

92. Coronel, C. E., San Agustin, J., and Lardy, H. A. (1990) Purification and structure of caltrin-like proteins from seminal vesicle of the guinea pig. *J. Biol. Chem.* **265,** 6854–6859

THE JOURNAL OF BIOLOGICAL CHEMISTRY
Vol. 278, No. 7, Issue of February 14, pp. 4369–4380, 2003

Reflections

A PAPER IN A SERIES COMMISSIONED TO CELEBRATE THE CENTENARY OF THE JBC IN 2005

JBC Centennial
1905–2005
100 Years of Biochemistry and Molecular Biology

An Enthusiasm for Metabolism

Published, JBC Papers in Press, December 20, 2002, DOI 10.1074/jbc.X200010200

Bruce N. Ames

From the Children's Hospital of Oakland Research Institute, Oakland, California 94609-1673

Becoming a Scientist

I was born on December 16, 1928 in New York City. My father, Maurice U. Ames, who was born in 1900 in New York City, had a J.D. in law and an M.A. in chemistry. He had originally planned to practice law, but when the depression hit, he became a high school chemistry teacher, which he viewed as a less risky occupation. He later became a high school principal, then supervisor of science for the New York City public school system, and eventually Assistant Superintendent of Schools. My father was very smart, not eager to try new things, and quite placid by nature. My mother, Dorothy Andres Ames, had come to New York as a young child from Poland. My mother had a tremendous *joie de vivre*, and I think I inherited my ebullience and creativity from her. Despite their very different personalities my parents got on marvelously well. Someone once remarked to my mother that my father "has such a wonderful disposition." My mother replied, "Oh he doesn't have a wonderful disposition. He has no disposition."

I grew up in the Washington Heights area of Manhattan. Every summer during my childhood I went with my family to Warrensburg in the Adirondack Mountains, where my father and a group of other New York City school teachers rented houses on Echo Lake. Those were wonderful summers. I would collect and study most of the creatures that existed in the woods around the lake, though my mother never was too enthusiastic about the mice and the snakes. Every week I would go and get another stack of books to read from the town library. I was always curious about the world and loved digging into still another subject, and my reading interests have remained quite eclectic to this day. I attended the Bronx High School of Science where I became immersed in biology and chemistry. I did my first scientific experiments there; I grew tomato root tips in culture to determine the effect of plant hormones on their growth. The picture of those white roots growing on their own when stimulated by hormones stays in my mind. The pleasures of doing those experiments set me on the path to becoming a scientist.

Cornell

I attended Cornell University from 1946 to 1950 and received my B.A. degree with a major in chemistry/biochemistry. I never was a top student, either in high school or college. I had only a so-so memory and was easily distracted by some new enthusiasm (reading all of Tolstoy or mastering some new folk dance) when I should have been studying for an exam. Taking required courses was not a thing I could get very excited about (I am too undisciplined and driven by my own enthusiasms) though I did well in those few that sparked my interest. Two such courses from my Cornell days stay in my memory. One was a history class taught by Professor Marcham in which we investigated historical incidents by reading all of the original documents, which of course were quite contradictory, and then tried to determine what was the most likely reality. The other was a course in biochemical genetics taught by Adrian Srb. I had already taken several genetics courses, as I was interested in the subject, and Srb's course got me all excited because of my background in biochemistry. I applied to various graduate schools as I was finishing up but was somewhat apprehensive because of my less than stellar grades. I was, in fact, turned down by Wisconsin, but luckily I was accepted by Cal Tech, perhaps because Srb, or one of my other references, saw potential in me.

Cal Tech

I arrived at Cal Tech in August 1950. I chose Professor Herschel K. Mitchell, a former postdoctoral fellow of George Beadle, as a mentor and was doing experiments within a few weeks of arriving. Finally I was in my element, lots of research and relatively few courses. Beadle was chairman of the biology department; he and Tatum had previously pioneered the use of biochemical genetic techniques in the mold *Neurospora,* which led to their Nobel prize.

I studied the biosynthesis of histidine in *Neurospora,* using mutant histidine-requiring strains involving at least 4 different genes that Mitchell had isolated. A few months after I got to Cal Tech, I adapted a sensitive reagent for the imidazole ring, which is the heterocyclic ring in histidine, to be used as a spray reagent for paper chromatograms (1). This was the key to elucidating the biosynthetic pathway. I grew a culture of each mutant strain in low histidine medium and chromatographed the supernatant. There were about six different imidazoles in the collection of mutants, though each defective gene had a unique imidazole set, and one had none (2). My next task was to identify these imidazole intermediates. I had one very lucky break. While searching the literature on imidazoles I came across an old German paper that reported cooking up glucose, ammonia, and formaldehyde to form an imidazole with a side chain of four carbons, each containing a hydroxyl group. My intuition told me this was the solution to my problem. I then cooked up ribose, ammonia, and formaldehyde, chromatographed the mixture, and found an imidazole-containing compound with the same mobility and properties as one of the compounds accumulated by one of the histidine-requiring mutants. I guessed, and soon showed, that it was imidazole glycerol (2).

The rest of my thesis went very quickly. While I was doing all of this, Bernie Davis' laboratory published a paper showing that histidinol was a precursor of histidine. That turned out to be another of our imidazoles. A pathway of imidazole glycerol, imidazole acetol, histidinol, and finally histidine seemed to make biochemical sense. We also made the double mutants from all of the genes that were involved, and I determined which imidazole intermediate accumulated. Using this trick I was able to order the steps in the pathway and found that this fit with the biochemistry (3). I made the same compounds from the various pentoses and showed that the substance from ribose, the D-*erythro* isomer, was the right one as it was the same as the accumulated compound from the mutant (4). I soon found that some minor, slow moving, imidazole-containing spots on the chromatograms were the true intermediates; these were the phosphate esters of the compounds. I synthesized imidazole glycerol phosphate by cooking up ammonia, formaldehyde, and ribose 5-phosphate. I suggested that the first step of the pathway involved ribose phosphate. Later at NIH Bob Martin and I showed that phosphoribosyl pyrophosphate was in fact the precursor of imidazole glycerol phosphate and that it condensed with ATP, which donated the nitrogen and carbon of the imidazole ring (5). I worked out a good part of the pathway of histidine biosynthesis and finished most of the work for my doctoral thesis during my first year at Cal Tech.

Cal Tech was an exciting place for a budding scientist. I became part of the group revolving around Max and Manny Delbruck, who had a salon of sorts, which included play readings, dinners, musicals (I played the alto recorder, though not very well), and camping trips into the desert. While at Cal Tech I took both summers off; one summer I took C. B. van Niel's bacterial physiology course at Stanford University's Hopkins Marine Station in Pacific Grove, CA and the next the physiology course at Woods Hole, MA. Both laboratory courses were extraordinary and expanded my interests. I completed my Ph.D. degree in June 1953 at the age of 24. I had arrived at Cal Tech as a very green, very young researcher who was very uncertain that my memory and focus were good enough to make it in the competitive world of science. I left with at least some conviction that my curiosity and creativity might carry me through and that with a little luck I might make it.

NIH

I knew I needed to learn enzymology, so after completing my Ph.D. degree, I took a postdoctoral position in September 1953 in Bernard Horecker's laboratory at the National Institutes of Health (NIH). At NIH I fished out the enzymes of the histidine pathway using the intermediates I had isolated and synthesized at Cal Tech. I had switched from *Neurospora* to *Salmonella typhimurium* as a result of a collaboration with Phil Hartman at Johns Hopkins, who was studying the genetics of the histidine mutants of *Salmonella*. In 1954, as an independent investigator at NIH, I began work on gene regulation in histidine biosynthesis using *Salmonella*. We showed that the histidine genes, which were in a cluster in *Salmonella*, could be overexpressed if histidine availability limited the growth rate; we also showed that the enzymes were controlled as a group, "coordinate repression" (6). We became interested in a mutant found by Hartman, which had a short region at one end of the cluster deleted, but turned off the function of all of the intact histidine genes. We concluded that the cluster of genes was controlled together as a unit by a regulatory sequence.

NIH was a wonderful place to do science. There was enough money for research and no teaching or committee duties. I interacted with outstanding scientists and formed many lasting friendships: Gordon Tomkins, Earl and Terry Stadtman, Maxine Singer, Ira Pastan, Herb and Celia Tabor, Leon Heppel, David Davies, Marty Gellert, Gary Felsenfeld, and many more.

I married Giovanna Ferro-Luzzi in 1960. She had come from Rome to do postdoctoral work at Johns Hopkins University in 1958, and I met her at the Baltimore-Washington Enzyme Club. We are still remarkably happily married some 40 years later. When she finished at Hopkins, Gordon Tomkins gave her a position in his laboratory.

Cambridge/Paris

In l961, I took a year of sabbatical leave from NIH. Giovanna and I divided our time between Francis Crick's laboratory in Cambridge and Francois Jacob's laboratory at the Pasteur Institute in Paris. It was a honeymoon year, both personally and intellectually. This was an exciting time in Cambridge with Crick, Brenner, Perutz, Kendrew, and innumerable distinguished visitors in the incubator for what would become molecular biology. The Institut Pasteur was also an exciting place where Jacob, Monod, Lwoff, Francois Gros, Jean-Pierre Changeux, Giuseppe Attardi, and numerous bright young people worked in a ferment of activity.

NIH Again

I returned to Bethesda in 1962 to become a section chief at NIH in a group Gordon Tomkins had formed, the Laboratory of Molecular Biology. My research focused on the regulation of the histidine operon (the cluster of genes involved with the biosynthesis of histidine in *Salmonella*) and the role of transfer ribonucleic acid (tRNA) in this regulation. I was very lucky in that the first three postdoctoral fellows who came to my laboratory were Gerry Fink, John Roth, and Robert G. Martin, a tremendously talented and enthusiastic group. Among the significant contributions during this period was a paper Bob Martin and I wrote on using sucrose gradient centrifugation to determine the molecular weight of enzymes (7). Bob was a medical student at Harvard who had come to my laboratory for a semester as part of an NIH program for medical students interested in biomedical research. I was enamored of the idea that the histidine biosynthetic enzymes were in a complex in the cell, and I encouraged Bob to see if this was true, using sucrose gradient centrifugation, a method that had been developed for analyzing ribosomes and larger molecules. He worked out a method for doing this during his semester at NIH. Though there was not much to the idea of a complex of histidine biosynthetic enzymes, our paper on the method became one of the most cited papers in biochemistry. Bob enjoyed his time at NIH so much that he came back after he finished medical school and stayed on with me as a postdoctoral fellow. He later showed that the histidine biosynthetic genes were turned on and off as a unit and that a single mRNA was produced from the cluster of genes. His wife, Judith Martin, got a job as a reporter at the *Washington Post*, and she eventually became "Miss Manners," the columnist.

The Test for Mutagens

Sometime in 1964, I read the list of ingredients on a box of potato chips and began to wonder whether preservatives and other chemicals could cause genetic damage to humans. I had been working on some aspects of mutagenesis with Harvey Whitfield (8, 9). I thought it would be useful to have a test for chemical mutagens and so I decided to develop one. Because we had thousands of mutants of *Salmonella* that required histidine for growth, mainly isolated by Phil Hartman over the years, I made use of them in my experiments. The experiments involve placing a few hundred million bacteria onto a Petri dish containing agar medium with a trace amount of histidine. This small amount of histidine allows all of the plated histidine-dependent bacteria to undergo a few cell divisions. After the histidine is depleted from the medium only those bacteria that have mutated back to wild type continue to grow and form visible colonies on a light lawn of the mutant. The spontaneous mutation rate for each strain is relatively constant. However, when a mutagen is added to the assay mixture, there is an increase in the number of histidine-independent colonies and a dose-response curve can be obtained. During the next few years I developed a set of the most sensitive tester strains using all of the known mutagens I could get my hands on; I further improved the sensitivity of the test by eliminating some DNA repair systems in the strains (10).

Leaving NIH

I was happy at NIH; Giovanna and I had two children, and we liked the area. NIH was a great place to work, and we had a wide circle of friends. What prompted my moving was that Gordon Tomkins, the director of the Laboratory of Molecular Biology in which I worked, started looking at job offers. Tomkins, who had both an M.D. and a Ph.D., was an immensely bright polymath with extraordinary charisma, charm, breadth, and intelligence. He was making a mark in science and was known to everyone at NIH. Among the section chiefs in his laboratory were David Davies, Marty Gellert, Gary Felsenfeld, Todd Miles, and myself. Tomkins was at the center of our little universe, but he was getting offers to become department chair at one university or medical school after another and was seriously thinking about moving. I became convinced that he was likely to accept one of these offers and that our tight and compatible group would likely break up. I mentioned to my friend, Jesse Rabinowitz at the University of California, Berkeley that I might be on the market. Berkeley offered me a job soon after, and as I always had a soft spot for California since graduate school, Giovanna and I decided to move. I had been at NIH for 15 years. Tomkins moved to the University of California, San Francisco soon afterward and we were close friends with Gordon and his wife Millicent until his tragic early death. I felt privileged to have known such an extraordinary fellow, as did almost everyone who knew him. I have discussed his life in a commemorative essay (11).

Berkeley

I arrived at the University of California at Berkeley in December 1967 as a Professor of Biochemistry. I continued to work on regulation of the histidine operon with a series of graduate students and postdoctoral fellows. I was particularly interested in the role of histidine transfer RNA and its modified bases, which we had shown were important in the regulation. In later years I also worked on the regulatory system for defense against oxidants. I also continued my work on mutagen detection, though for many years I considered it more of a hobby until it became a major research focus. In trying to get funding for the mutagen project I was turned down by the National Cancer Institute (they did not think bacteria could teach us much about cancer), but I finally got funded by the Atomic Energy Commission, as they were interested in mutation.

My 30 some years at Berkeley were remarkably happy ones, and despite some shiny job offers I never was tempted to leave. I enjoyed and respected my colleagues, who were an amazingly responsible and competent crew. I was fortunate in attracting excellent graduate students and a series of first rate postdoctoral fellows from all over the world, aided no doubt by the allure of the San Francisco Bay Area.

The Biochemistry Department had a rotating chairmanship, and though I tried to avoid the job for as long as I could, I served as the department chairman from 1983 to 1989 out of a sense of duty. I am not particularly good at administration (I am incorrigibly distractable and find myself drifting off in committee meetings and thinking about experiments) so I try to avoid administration whenever I can. I did, however, form the National Institute of Environmental Health Science Center at University of California, Berkeley in 1979 and served as the director until 2002. There are now 22 such centers. I heard we were known as the Center with poor administration but great science.

Mutagens Again

Because the mutagen project was viewed as more applied research and was not basic enough for the graduate students and postdoctoral fellows who came to my laboratory, I utilized mostly a succession of wonderful undergraduate students who did honors work in my laboratory. I have always had the policy of having about six or so undergraduate students in the laboratory at any one time; I particularly enjoy their youthful enthusiasm. The word must have gotten around that my laboratory was a good place to work so I think I attracted some of the best undergraduates. Each undergraduate student normally chooses a postdoctoral fellow to work with based on their interest in the project. A high percentage of my papers from Berkeley have undergraduate students as coauthors.

In the early 1970s we continued to improve the sensitivity of the tester strains (12) and added to the mixture a liver homogenate fraction from rodents, which contains various metabolic enzymes (13). Some chemicals are not mutagens themselves but become mutagens in the presence of the liver homogenate, which can metabolize the chemicals to an active form, which then mutates the bacteria.

I also became more and more interested in the relation of mutagens to carcinogens. We showed that cigarette smoke was highly mutagenic (14) and that we could detect most common chemical carcinogens with the test, particularly after we added the liver homogenate (15). Having had a background in genetics as well as biochemistry, all of my intuition told me that mutagens ought to be carcinogens, though this was not the prevailing view at the time or for many years. I became a proselytizer for this view, though in retrospect I should have also emphasized the role of cell division rates in mutation and carcinogenesis; I tried to make up for this later (16–19). It now seems obvious that increasing either DNA damage or cell division rates, *e.g.* by hormones, increases cancer rates.

In contrast to the expensive and time-consuming rodent cancer test, our method of assaying the mutagenicity of chemicals was simple, rapid, and inexpensive. As a result, it was quickly adopted by thousands of laboratories worldwide, particularly by drug and chemical companies, for the detection of mutagens and potential carcinogens. Our method made it possible to weed out mutagenic chemicals inexpensively early in their development before they were introduced into commerce. I never patented the test, in part because I thought it might detract from my effectiveness in promoting mutagen testing, though I did have a brief pang of regret when it seemed that almost every industry in the world was asking for the strains. I started with the notion that industry would be reluctant to use the test and that regulators would force them to. I soon realized that industry was eager to adopt the test, in part, I concluded, because they had a huge incentive to weed out nasty chemicals. Regulatory agencies only took notice of the test years afterward, perhaps because a lack of competition created no incentive to change their routine way of doing things. This experience, together with subsequent interactions with bureaucracies such as the Environmental Protection Agency and my readings in economics, reinforced a growing conviction that to accomplish anything of importance incentives matter.

Two major conclusions from our work were that mutation is one aspect of the mechanism of cancer causation and that a high percentage of carcinogens are detectable as mutagens. A series of wonderful students did the work, especially Frank Lee and Bill Durston, particularly brilliant undergraduates; David Levin, a graduate student; and Joyce McCann, a postdoctoral fellow, who made a major contribution. An extraordinarily competent and devoted laboratory technician, Edie Yamasaki, also was a major contributor. I gradually drifted out of bacterial work and into rats and humans. In recent years when people ask me "Are you the Ames of the Ames test?" our work on the test seems so long ago that I reply "Oh no, it was my father."

In the early 1990s we made one more improvement in mutagen testing. A postdoctoral fellow, Pauline Gee, some students, and Dorothy Maron, a laboratory technician, developed a new set of six strains that were at least as sensitive as the old tester strains and also diagnosed the 6 possible base pair mutations (20). These strains not only showed whether the test chemicals were mutagenic, they also indicated the type of mutation. The University of California did take out a patent on this improved test. In the beginning I thought that the mutagenicity test would be outmoded in a few years, and I still find it surprising that people are using it 30 years later, despite all of the new genetic tools that have come along.

Carcinogens

My interests in cancer prevention and toxicology stemmed from the mutagen test, and I soon became deeply immersed in both fields. I enjoy learning new fields and I always seem to be in the midst of learning a new one. I can often bring a fresh perspective to a new area because of my broad interests in science. My laboratory at the time was researching gene regulation and later regulation of antioxidant defenses in *Salmonella*. I was helped enormously in entering these new fields by finding a few extraordinarily intelligent and competent associates who could help with the scholarship. A major find was Lois Gold, who walked into my office after she saw a story in the newspaper about a paper we had published in *Science* (21) that Tris-BP was a mutagen. Tris-BP was one of the major flame retardants, which a government agency had decreed were to be in all children's pajamas. She was a mother with a young daughter and wanted to know everything about flame retardants, burn statistics, risk, evidence, etc. She was clearly unusually smart and thorough. After an exhausting hour answering questions, I asked her what her background was. She had a Ph.D. from Stanford and had a background in statistical methods; she had taught at Berkeley and Stanford and was taking a few years off to be with her child. She also had an interest in public health policy. In my excitement about innovative ideas in new fields there is a danger in getting carried away by enthusiasm, so I am always looking for smart, tough minded associates who are willing to challenge my assumptions and data. I hired Lois on the spot to work whatever hours she could put in on various projects, including the Carcinogenic Potency Database I had started.

I had started the Carcinogenic Potency Database after I realized, in trying to compare mutagenic potency with carcinogenic potency, that no one had ever systematized the literature on the quantitative aspects of animal cancer tests. We also found that carcinogens could vary by a million-fold in potency. I applied for a grant to set up the database, but it was turned down as I did not have any experience in animal cancer tests, statistics, or pathology. This was all true, but we thought it was important to do, wanted to do it, and knew we would do it as well as it could be done if we consulted the best people in the various fields, so we decided to go ahead anyway. Lois Gold stayed on to develop the database, which is now the definitive quantitative database in the world on animal cancer tests. Together Gold and I have written over 100 papers based on our analyses of the database. We have challenged most of the assumptions in the field, so we have engendered reams of controversy.

One important finding to come out of our analysis was that over half of all the chemicals tested, whether natural or synthetic, were carcinogenic when tested chronically in rodents at the maximum tolerated dose (MTD), the standard procedure in the rodent cancer bioassay (22). Our analysis suggested that carcinogenesis in the high dose rodent tests was due to the use of a high dose and that the high dose could cause chronic cell killing, inflammation, and cell proliferation, which could account for the carcinogenic effects. We concluded, therefore, that the tests did not provide information to calculate low dose risks (18). These conclusions did not endear us to scientists who have spent their lives testing synthetic chemicals at the MTD, or environmental activists who have tried to purge the world of tiny traces of synthetic chemicals, or regulators whose jobs depend on eliminating traces of "toxic chemicals." I have become inured to *ad hominem* attacks on Gold and myself that allege we are a tool of industry, despite the fact Gold and I have always had a policy not to accept money from industry, or to testify in lawsuits, or to consult. It is clear that our critics do not like our conclusions, but we have seen no convincing rebuttal of our science.

Natural Chemicals, the Forgotten Control

One observation that struck me fairly soon after our mutagenicity test became widely used was the high rate at which we and others were finding mutagens in the natural world of plant chemicals. That got me thinking about the natural chemicals that humans ingest, such as the natural pesticides plants produce to kill off insects and other predators (23) and the burnt material in cups of coffee (24). Because almost all of the chemicals that humans are ingesting are natural (23, 25) it seemed very improbable that synthetic chemicals were likely to be more than a tiny fraction of our total exposure to mutagens/carcinogens, other than from high dose occupational exposures or medicinal drugs.

To put synthetic carcinogens in perspective, Gold and I thought it necessary to examine the carcinogenicity of the natural background of chemicals as an appropriate control for synthetic chemicals. We estimated that 99.9% of all chemical exposure is from ingesting natural chemicals in food, *e.g.* 99.99% of exposure to pesticides is from ingesting natural pesticides produced by plants (23). We published a paper entitled "Ranking Carcinogenic Hazards" in *Science* in 1987 (17). To compare the average daily dose of chemicals which humans might receive with the dose that induced cancer in rodents, we created an index called HERP (human exposure dose/rodent potency dose). The results of HERP showed that the possible cancer hazard of traces of synthetic chemicals such as pesticide residues are tiny compared with natural chemicals in the diet. Even the possible hazards from "rodent carcinogens" in natural chemicals should be viewed with skepticism because of the problem of high dose testing.

We also pointed out that diversion of resources and attention from programs that focus on major risks to those that focus on minor hypothetical risks might hurt public health. As I have become more and more concerned with cancer prevention, I have concluded that we must concentrate on major risks if we are to make any progress and that concern with hundreds of minor, hypothetical risks is a distraction from major risks, such as unbalanced diets and cigarette smoking. Epidemiology is fraught with difficulties. "In Miami, study finds everyone born Hispanic, dies Jewish." Epidemiology is useful when there are large risks, but lacks the power to provide convincing evidence that traces of synthetic chemicals cause small amounts of human cancer. Though I am passionate about cancer prevention, I remain skeptical of the purported dangers from traces of synthetic chemicals, such as pesticides, and do not see much plausibility from either toxicological or epidemiological analysis. Spending time debunking the dubious assumptions (26) behind the environmentalist fervor against traces of industrial chemicals does not prevent any cancer. Having demonstrated the implausibility of such assumptions, I turned to finding more effective ways to prevent cancer.

Diet and Health

In reading what was known about cancer prevention I was attracted to the idea that unbalanced diets are a major contributor to cancer because all the leading epidemiologists thought dietary factors were likely to be in the same league as smoking. My intuition told me there was a lot of interesting science in the diet-cancer area and that the field was murky enough so there were not many people exploring it (27). When I enter a new field, which I seem to do fairly often, I always spend a fair amount of time getting an overview to see where the least amount of effort will bring the maximum return, *i.e.* exploring several different approaches with potentially high payoffs. I am reluctant to enter, or stay in, a field that is very active, as I find it too difficult to focus on just one thing. I think that my talents lie in my finding new ways of looking at a problem and opening up new fields, which is a result of my broad scientific reading and interests. This, of course, makes it much harder to get grants. I was fortunate to have received a large NCI Outstanding Investigator Grant for 15 years, at which point NCI stopped that type of grant. The grant was made for me as it permitted me to do work on whatever interested me, and that saved my neck. I am enormously grateful someone had the vision to fund such a program, at least for a while.

I was intrigued by the reviews of Potter and Block on 200 or so epidemiological studies, which showed that the quarter of the population eating the fewest fruits and vegetables had about double the cancer rate for most types of cancer, compared with the quarter eating the most. Our work on endogenous oxidants as a major source of DNA damage had interested me in antioxidants, and I began to view vitamin C, vitamin E, selenium, and other vitamins and minerals, many of which came from the fruits and vegetables in the diet, as anti-mutagens and anti-carcinogens (27). I began to think that much cancer in certain human populations might be because of the less than optimal amounts of anti-carcinogens and protective vitamins and minerals consumed in the diet.

The work that finally got me seriously involved in this area was the research of Jim MacGregor on folic acid. Jim was a cytogeneticist who spent a year in my laboratory (28). While assaying chromosome breaks in humans and in mice, he stumbled on the fact that folic acid deficiency breaks chromosomes in mice, just as radiation does. He then showed that a person with a very high level of chromosome breaks was folate-deficient and that a folate intervention lowered the level of breaks. Folic acid comes from the Latin word *folia* (*i.e.* leaf); one gets it from green leafy vegetables. (My graduate mentor, H. K. Mitchell, first discovered folic acid and isolated it from 4 tons of spinach.)

Because low folate levels were very common in the population of the United States, I talked a graduate student, Ben Blount, and then a postdoctoral fellow, Matt Mack, into investigating the mechanism. They showed that folate deficiency causes a block in the methylation of dUMP to dTMP, which results in the misincorporation of millions of uracils into the DNA of each rat cell, which causes chromosome breaks (29). Removal of the uracil by uracil glycosylase causes a transient single strand break (nick) in the DNA. Two opposing nicks, *e.g.* from repair of a uracil across from an oxidative lesion, cause a double strand break, the most serious DNA lesion. The chromosome breaks from radiation are made by an analogous mechanism, the repair of opposing oxidative lesions.

This prompted me to look into the whole array of vitamins and essential minerals, as I think it likely that when one input in the metabolic network is inadequate, repercussions will be felt on a large number of systems and lead to degenerative disease. For example, deficiencies of folate, B_{12}, or B_6 lead to an increase in DNA damage and cancer (30); iron deficiency leads to neuron decay and cognitive dysfunction (31) and mitochondrial decay and premature aging (32). We have shown that inadequate levels of many vitamins or minerals, such as iron, zinc, folate, B_{12}, and B_6, result in DNA, mitochondrial, and other types of damage (30–35). Emily Ho, a postdoctoral fellow in my laboratory has shown, for example, that zinc deficiency in human cells in culture not only fills the cell up with oxidants that damage DNA but disables p53, a zinc enzyme, and also various other components of the DNA defense network (33). Low intake of each of these vitamins and minerals is found in 10% or more of the population, particularly in the poor (30).

I am convinced that by tuning up metabolism by ensuring vitamin and mineral adequacy we can effect a major improvement in public health (35), particularly for the poor. Numerous efforts and programs to convince people to change their diets have not been particularly successful. Fortification, *e.g.* the folic acid fortification of flour, has a role to play. Vitamins and minerals are amazingly inexpensive; a multivitamin/mineral pill containing the recommended daily allowance (RDA) for the essential vitamins and minerals costs less than a penny to make. In fact, I think that everyone should take one every day as "insurance" (35), though of course efforts to encourage eating a balanced diet should continue. Vitamin and mineral adequacy is important but is not the only part of our dietary needs, which also include fiber, essential fatty acids, and other components not found in a multivitamin/mineral pill (36).

Oxidants

I became interested in the early 1980s in oxidants from metabolism, smoking, and chronic inflammation as a major source of mutagens; I started working in this area both in *Salmonella* and in higher organisms (37–41). With some wonderful graduate students, particularly Gigi Storz, Lou Tartaglia, and Mike Christman, and postdoctoral fellows Robin Morgan and Fred Jacobson, we clarified for the first time the strategies employed by bacteria in their response to oxidants such as hydrogen peroxide (42, 43). The discovery of the oxyR regulatory protein, which involved isolating it and determining its sequence and DNA-binding site, provided general insights into which cell constituents are damaged by oxidants and how cells sense and respond to oxidative stress. It also showed that an oxyR thiol operated directly as a sensor of oxidative stress (44). A series of studies showed that oxyR controls a variety of genes, including those that code for catalase and a new enzyme, alkyl hydroperoxide reductase (42, 43, 45, 46), which was later cloned and sequenced. Studies on the oxyR regulon led to the elucidation of the mechanisms by which exposure of bacterial cells to low doses of oxidants allows these cells to adapt to subsequent challenges of higher doses of oxidants. These studies also provided insights in understanding how higher organisms such as mammals adapt to oxidant exposure. Work by Rhee and Stadtman identified the mammalian counterpart to the alkyl hydroperoxide reductase. Other laboratories have since identified similar oxidant-responsive elements in mammals.

We documented that endogenous oxidants from normal metabolism are important in damaging DNA in both bacteria (47) and mammals (41, 48). At one point, I had the vision that the lesions that were excised from DNA by repair enzymes should be excreted in the urine and thus could be analyzed. With the help of several sensational postdoctoral fellows, including Mark Shigenaga, Robert Saul, and Rick Cathcart, we looked for known oxidized DNA bases (the radiation biologists had worked out the chemistry) in rat and human urine as a measure of oxidative DNA damage (41, 48–50). This work suggests that there is a large rate of endogenous oxidative damage to DNA (about 100,000 hits/cell/day in the rat) (51). Moreover, though repair is very effective, some oxidative lesions escape repair, the steady state level of oxidative lesions increases with age, and an old rat has accumulated about 66,000 oxidative DNA lesions per cell (51).

Two extraordinarily good Swiss postdoctoral fellows, Roland Stocker and Balz Frei, came to my laboratory to work on oxidation in the late 1980s. They and other students clarified the role of various antioxidants in human plasma (52, 53) and discovered some major antioxidants that were previously not fully appreciated, including uric acid (37), bilirubin (54–56), and ubiquinol (57, 58). We showed that ascorbate serves as a first line defense in blood plasma against lipid oxidation (53) and as a key protective agent against oxidative damage to sperm DNA (59). In the course of this work we developed many new methods for measuring oxidative damage and defenses in tissues, as well as in biological fluids such as urine and plasma. Throughout my career I have always felt that developing new analytical methods helps to open up a field and is well worth the effort. I take some satisfaction in knowing that many of the methods we have developed are among the most highly cited papers. Because mitochondria are the main source of endogenous oxidants and mitochondria are the main targets of oxidants, this led directly to our work on the mitochondrial decay of aging.

Delaying the Mitochondrial Decay of Aging

Aging has been a major interest of mine for some time, in particular the role of mitochondrial decay as a major contributor to aging and age-related degenerative diseases. Mark Shigenaga and Tory Hagen, two brilliant senior postdoctoral fellows, and I wrote a review in 1994 (60) on why mitochondrial decay due to oxidant leakage from the electron transport chain was likely to be a major factor in aging. This idea was not original with us; Denham Harman and then Jaime Miquel had discussed the free radical theory of aging, but we feel we contributed some insights in the review. Writing the review got us all fired up to work on the subject, and Hagen figured out an experimental approach in rats that worked; we showed that there is a large amount of oxidative damage to the mitochondria and mitochondrial decay during aging (61). Kenny Beckman, another unusually creative postdoctoral fellow, and I also reviewed the free radical theory of aging (62). These radicals can cause oxidative damage, which in turn contributes to mitochondrial decay and degenerative diseases such as cancer, aging, heart disease, cataract, and brain dysfunction.

In a series of experiments by Hagen, and later after he left to go to Oregon State, by another excellent postdoctoral fellow, Jiankang Liu, we made progress in reversing some of this mitochondrial decay in old rats by feeding them the normal mitochondrial metabolites, acetylcarnitine (ALCAR) and lipoic acid (LA), at high levels (63–67). The principle behind this effect appears to be that with age, increased oxidative damage to mitochondrial protein causes a deformation of structure of key enzymes, with a consequent lessening of affinity (K_m) for the enzyme substrate (67). The effect of age on the ALCAR binding affinity of carnitine acetyl-transferase can be mimicked by reacting it with malondialdehyde (a lipid peroxidation product that increases with age). Feeding the substrate ALCAR with LA, a mitochondrial antioxidant, restores the velocity of the reaction, K_m for ALCAR-CoA transferase, and mitochondrial function. In old rats (*versus* young rats) mitochondrial membrane potential, cardiolipin level, respiratory control ratio, and cellular O_2 uptake are lower; oxidants/O_2, neuron RNA oxidation, and mutagenic aldehydes from lipid peroxidation are higher. Ambulatory activity and cognition decline with age. Feeding old rats ALCAR plus LA for a few weeks improves mitochondrial function; lowers oxidants, neuron RNA oxidation, and mutagenic aldehydes; and increases rat ambulatory activity and cognition (as assayed with the Skinner box and Morris water maze). I have been so excited about this work that I am sure it has added (or perhaps subtracted) a year or two to my own life.

Two more outstanding postdoctoral fellows, Hani Atamna and Patrick Walter, have shown that common micronutrient deficiencies accelerate mitochondrial decay. Heme biosynthesis takes place predominantly in the mitochondria. Interfering with heme synthesis causes a specific loss of Complex IV with a consequent release of oxidants (68, 69). Iron deficiency (25% of menstruating women in the United States ingest <50% of the RDA) also causes release of oxidants and mitochondrial decay (32) presumably through lack of heme (69). Vitamin B_6 deficiency (10% of Americans ingest <50% of the RDA) also causes heme deficiency (69). In a beautiful new paper Atamna shows that the consequences are likely to be accelerated aging, neural decay, and Alzheimer's disease (31).

The K_m in Genetic Disease, Polymorphisms, and Aging

One of my great pleasures in the last few years has been working on an innovative, integrative review (70) with an undergraduate student, Ilan Elson-Schwab. We think this review will change thinking in both human genetics and nutrition. As many as one-third of mutations in a gene result in the corresponding enzyme having an increased Michaelis constant/K_m (decreased binding affinity) for a coenzyme, resulting in a lower rate of reaction. We review 50 human genetic diseases due to defective enzymes that can be remedied or ameliorated by the administration of high doses of the B vitamin component of the corresponding coenzyme, which we show raises levels of the coenzyme and at least partially restores enzymatic activity (70).

We also review five single-nucleotide polymorphisms in which the variant amino acid reduces coenzyme binding and thus enzymatic activity; the reduced levels of activity are likely to be remediable by raising cellular concentrations of the cofactor through high dose vitamin therapy (70). Some examples of polymorphisms include the (C677T; Ala-222 → Val) methylenetetrahydrofolate reductase (NADPH) and the cofactor FAD (in relation to cardiovascular disease, migraines, and rages), the (C609T; Pro-187 → Ser) mutation in NAD(P):quinone oxidoreductase 1 (NQO1) and FAD (in relation to cancer), the (C131G; Ala-44 → Gly) mutation in glucose-6-phosphate 1-dehydrogenase and NADP (in relation to favism and hemolytic anemia), and the (Glu-487 → Lys) mutation (present in about half of Asians) in aldehyde dehydrogenase and NAD (in relation to alcohol intolerance, Alzheimer's disease, and cancer). As all of the polymorphisms are sorted out in humans, this K_m concept may be relevant for tuning up the metabolism of much of the population. I suspect this might be one of the first major contributions of genomics to public health. We also are actively working on whether high doses of some of the B vitamins might help delay the mitochondrial decay of aging. To encourage further discussion and new information on this topic we have set up a web site (www.KmMutants.org).

Children's Hospital of Oakland Research Institute (CHORI)

At the end of 1999 our building on campus, Barker Hall, reached the top of the list of buildings that needed to be renovated for earthquake reinforcements. We were asked to vacate the building. I was told to cut my laboratory in half and that the University would figure out where to squeeze me in for 2–3 years until the renovations were completed. Instead, I said goodbye to campus and moved to CHORI, with the encouragement of its director Bert Lubin. CHORI is a nearby research facility that has recently renovated a beautiful old high school and turned it into laboratories. We recently occupied a newly renovated wing, which will be a Nutrition-Genomics Center within CHORI. I have been exceptionally happy here these last few years in the company of first rate colleagues, and I do not plan to ever move again.

I recently told a colleague that I thought I was doing the best work of my scientific career. He replied, "Bruce, you've been telling me that for 30 years." Thus, aging has not damaged my enthusiasm genes, though I am not as certain about my neurons. My current passion, as can be seen from the above sections, is tuning up metabolism in humans, both in the young and the old, by vitamins, minerals, and biochemicals. I think this will lead to a marked improvement in health and an increase in longevity. With so much work to do, I have no plans to retire from science.

Address correspondence to: bames@chori.org.

REFERENCES

1. Ames, B. N., and Mitchell, H. K. (1952) The paper chromatography of imidazoles. *J. Am. Chem. Soc.* **74,** 252–253
2. Ames, B. N., Mitchell, H. K., and Mitchell, M. B. (1953) Some new naturally occurring imidazoles related to the biosynthesis of histidine. *J. Am. Chem. Soc.* **75,** 1015–1018
3. Haas, F., Mitchell, M. B., and Ames, B. N. (1952) A series of histidineless mutants of *Neurospora crassa. Genetics* **37,** 217–226
4. Ames, B. N., and Mitchell, H. K. (1955) The biosynthesis of histidine: imidazoleglycerol phosphate, imidazoleacetol phosphate, and histidinol phosphate. *J. Biol. Chem.* **212,** 687–696
5. Ames, B. N., Martin, R. G., and Garry, B. J. (1961) The first step of histidine biosynthesis. *J. Biol. Chem.* **236,** 2019–2026
6. Ames, B. N., and Garry, B. (1959) Coordinate repression of the synthesis of four histidine biosynthetic enzymes by histidine. *Proc. Natl. Acad. Sci. U. S. A.* **45,** 1453–1461
7. Martin, R. G., and Ames, B. N. (1961) A method for determining the sedimentation behavior of enzymes: application to protein mixtures. *J. Biol. Chem.* **236,** 1372–1379
8. Ames, B. N., and Whitfield, H. J., Jr. (1966) Frameshift mutagenesis in *Salmonella. Cold Spring Harb. Symp. Quant. Biol.* **31,** 221–225
9. Whitfield, H. J., Jr., Martin, R. G., and Ames, B. N. (1966) Classification of aminotransferase (C gene) mutants in the histidine operon. *J. Mol. Biol.* **21,** 335–355
10. Ames, B. N. (1971) The detection of chemical mutagens with enteric bacteria. In *Chemical Mutagens: Principles and Methods for Their Detection* (Hollaender, A., ed) Vol. 1, pp. 267–282, Plenum Press, New York
11. Ames, B. N. (1977) Gordon M. Tomkins (1926–1975). In *Biochemical Actions of Hormones* (Litwack, G., ed) Vol. IV, pp. xvii–xxxvi, Academic Press, New York
12. Ames, B. N., Lee, F. D., and Durston, W. E. (1973) An improved bacterial test system for the detection and classification of mutagens and carcinogens. *Proc. Natl. Acad. Sci. U. S. A.* **70,** 782–786
13. Ames, B. N., Durston, W. E., Yamasaki, E., and Lee, F. D. (1973) Carcinogens are mutagens: a simple test system combining liver homogenates for activation and bacteria for detection. *Proc. Natl. Acad. Sci. U. S. A.* **70,** 2281–2285
14. Kier, L. D., Yamasaki, E., and Ames, B. N. (1974) Detection of mutagenic activity in cigarette smoke condensates.

Proc. Natl. Acad. Sci. U. S. A. **71**, 4159–4163

15. McCann, J., Choi, E., Yamasaki, E., and Ames, B. N. (1975) Detection of carcinogens as mutagens in the *Salmonella*/microsome test: assay of 300 chemicals. *Proc. Natl. Acad. Sci. U. S. A.* **72**, 5135–5139

16. Bernstein, L., Gold, L. S., Ames, B. N., Pike, M. C., and Hoel, D. G. (1985) Toxicity and carcinogenic potency. *Risk Anal.* **5**, 263–264

17. Ames, B. N., Magaw, R., and Gold, L. S. (1987) Ranking possible carcinogenic hazards. *Science* **236**, 271–280

18. Ames, B. N., and Gold, L. S. (1990) Too many rodent carcinogens: mitogenesis increases mutagenesis. *Science* **249**, 970–971

19. Ames, B. N., Shigenaga, M. K., and Gold, L. S. (1993) DNA lesions, inducible DNA repair, and cell division: three key factors in mutagenesis and carcinogenesis. *Environ. Health Perspect.* **101**, Suppl. 5, 35–44

20. Gee, P., Maron, D. M., and Ames, B. N. (1994) Detection and classification of mutagens: a set of base-specific *Salmonella* tester strains. *Proc. Natl. Acad. Sci. U. S. A.* **91**, 11606–11610

21. Blum, A., and Ames, B. N. (1977) Flame-retardant additives as possible cancer hazards: the main flame retardant in children's pajamas is a mutagen and should not be used. *Science* **195**, 17–23

22. Ames, B. N., and Gold, L. S. (1990) Chemical carcinogenesis: too many rodent carcinogens. *Proc. Natl. Acad. Sci. U. S. A.* **87**, 7772–7776

23. Ames, B. N., Profet, M., and Gold, L. S. (1990) Dietary pesticides (99.99% all natural). *Proc. Natl. Acad. Sci. U. S. A.* **87**, 7777–7781

24. Ames, B. N., and Gold, L. S. (2000) Paracelsus to parascience: the environmental cancer distraction. *Mutat. Res.* **447**, 3–13

25. Ames, B. N., Profet, M., and Gold, L. S. (1990) Nature's chemicals and synthetic chemicals: comparative toxicology. *Proc. Natl. Acad. Sci. U. S. A.* **87**, 7782–7786

26. Gold, L. S., Slone, T. H., Manley, N. B., and Ames, B. N. (2003) *Misconceptions About the Causes of Cancer*, The Fraser Institute, Vancouver, BC, Canada

27. Ames, B. N. (1991) Foreword: diet and the prevention of disease. In *Micronutrients in Health and Disease Prevention* (Bendich, A., and Butterworth, C. E., Jr., eds) pp. v–vii, Marcel Dekker, Inc., New York

28. MacGregor, J. T., Schlegel, R., Wehr, C. M., Alperin, P., and Ames, B. N. (1990) Cytogenetic damage induced by folate deficiency in mice is enhanced by caffeine. *Proc. Natl. Acad. Sci. U. S. A.* **87**, 9962–9965

29. Blount, B. C., Mack, M. M., Wehr, C. M., MacGregor, J. T., Hiatt, R. A., Wang, G., Wickramasinghe, S. N., Everson, R. B., and Ames, B. N. (1997) Folate deficiency causes uracil misincorporation into human DNA and chromosome breakage: implications for cancer and neuronal damage. *Proc. Natl. Acad. Sci. U. S. A.* **94**, 3290–3295

30. Ames, B. N., and Wakimoto, P. (2002) Are vitamin and mineral deficiencies a major cancer risk? *Nat. Rev. Cancer* **2**, 694–704

31. Atamna, H., Killilea, D. W., Killilea, A. N., and Ames, B. N. (2002) Heme deficiency may be a factor in the mitochondrial and neuronal decay of aging. *Proc. Natl. Acad. Sci. U. S. A.* **99**, 14807–14812

32. Walter, P. B., Knutson, M. D., Paler-Martinez, A., Lee, S., Xu, Y., Viteri, F. E., and Ames, B. N. (2002) Iron deficiency and iron excess damage mitochondria and mitochondrial DNA in rats. *Proc. Natl. Acad. Sci. U. S. A.* **99**, 2264–2269

33. Ho, E., and Ames, B. N. (2002) Zinc deficiency induces oxidative DNA damage, disrupts p53, NFκB and AP1 binding, and affects DNA repair in a rat glioma cell line. *Proc. Natl. Acad. Sci. U. S. A.* **99**, 16770–16775

34. Wallock, L. M., Tamura, T., Mayr, C. A., Johnston, K. E., Ames, B. N., and Jacob, R. A. (2001) Low seminal plasma folate concentrations are associated with low sperm density and count in male smokers and nonsmokers. *Fertil. Steril.* **75**, 252–259

35. Ames, B. N. (2003) The metabolic tune up: metabolic harmony and disease prevention. *J. Nutr.*, in press

36. Willett, W. C. (2001) *Eat, Drink, and Be Healthy: The Harvard Medical School Guide to Healthy Eating*, Simon and Schuster, New York

37. Ames, B. N., Cathcart, R., Schwiers, E., and Hochstein, P. (1981) Uric acid provides an antioxidant defense in humans against oxidant- and radical-caused aging and cancer: a hypothesis. *Proc. Natl. Acad. Sci. U. S. A.* **78**, 6858–6862

38. Ames, B. N., Hollstein, M. C., and Cathcart, R. (1982) Lipid peroxidation and oxidative damage to DNA. In *Lipid Peroxide in Biology and Medicine* (Yagi, K., ed) pp. 339–351, Academic Press, New York

39. Levin, D. E., Hollstein, M., Christman, M. F., Schwiers, A., and Ames, B. N. (1982) A new *Salmonella* tester strain (TA102) with A·T base pairs at the site of mutation detects oxidative mutagens. *Proc. Natl. Acad. Sci. U. S. A.* **79**, 7445–7449

40. Hollstein, M. C., Brooks, P., Linn, S., and Ames, B. N. (1984) Hydroxymethyluracil DNA glycosylase in mammalian cells. *Proc. Natl. Acad. Sci. U. S. A.* **81**, 4003–4007

41. Cathcart, R., Schwiers, E., Saul, R. L., and Ames, B. N. (1984) Thymine glycol and thymidine glycol in human and rat urine: a possible assay for oxidative DNA damage. *Proc. Natl. Acad. Sci. U. S. A.* **81**, 5633–5637

42. Christman, M. F., Morgan, R. W., Jacobson, F. S., and Ames, B. N. (1985) Positive control of a regulon for defenses against oxidative stress and some heat-shock proteins in *Salmonella typhimurium*. *Cell* **41**, 753–762

43. Morgan, R. W., Christman, M. F., Jacobson, F. S., Storz, G., and Ames, B. N. (1986) Hydrogen peroxide-inducible proteins in *Salmonella typhimurium* overlap with heat shock and other stress proteins. *Proc. Natl. Acad. Sci. U. S. A.* **83**, 8059–8063

44. Storz, G., Tartaglia, L. A., and Ames, B. N. (1990) Transcriptional regulator of oxidative stress-inducible genes: direct activation by oxidation. *Science* **248**, 189–194

45. Jacobson, F. S., Morgan, R. W., Christman, M. F., and Ames, B. N. (1989) An alkyl hydroperoxide reductase from *Salmonella typhimurium* involved in the defense of DNA against oxidative damage. Purification and properties. *J. Biol. Chem.* **264**, 1488–1496

46. Storz, G., Jacobson, F. S., Tartaglia, L. A., Morgan, R. W., Silveira, L. A., and Ames, B. N. (1989) An alkyl hydroperoxide reductase induced by oxidative stress in *Salmonella typhimurium* and *Escherichia coli*: genetic characterization and cloning of ahp. *J. Bacteriol.* **171**, 2049–2055

47. Storz, G., Christman, M. F., Sies, H., and Ames, B. N. (1987) Spontaneous mutagenesis and oxidative damage to DNA in *Salmonella typhimurium*. *Proc. Natl. Acad. Sci. U. S. A.* **84**, 8917–8921

48. Adelman, R., Saul, R. L., and Ames, B. N. (1988) Oxidative damage to DNA: relation to species metabolic rate and life span. *Proc. Natl. Acad. Sci. U. S. A.* **85**, 2706–2708

49. Ames, B. N., Saul, R. L., Schwiers, E., Adelman, R., and Cathcart, R. (1985) Oxidative DNA damage as related to cancer and aging: assay of thymine glycol, thymidine glycol, and hydroxymenthyluracil in human and rat urine. In *Molecular Biology of Aging: Gene Stability and Gene Expression* (Sohal, R. S., Birnbaum, L. S., and Cutler, R. G., eds) pp. 137–144, Raven Press, New York

50. Shigenaga, M. K., and Ames, B. N. (1991) Assays for 8-hydroxy-2′-deoxyguanosine: a biomarker of *in vivo* oxidative DNA damage. *Free Radic. Biol. Med.* **10**, 211–216

51. Helbock, H. J., Beckman, K. B., Shigenaga, M. K., Walter, P. B., Woodall, A. A., Yeo, H. C., and Ames, B. N. (1998)

DNA oxidation matters: the HPLC-electrochemical detection assay of 8-oxo-deoxyguanosine and 8-oxo-guanine. *Proc. Natl. Acad. Sci. U. S. A.* **95,** 288–293

52. Frei, B., Stocker, R., and Ames, B. N. (1988) Antioxidant defenses and lipid peroxidation in human blood plasma. *Proc. Natl. Acad. Sci. U. S. A.* **85,** 9748–9752

53. Frei, B., England, L., and Ames, B. N. (1989) Ascorbate is an outstanding antioxidant in human blood plasma. *Proc. Natl. Acad. Sci. U. S. A.* **86,** 6377–6381

54. Stocker, R., Yamamoto, Y., McDonagh, A. F., Glazer, A. N., and Ames, B. N. (1987) Bilirubin is an antioxidant of possible physiological importance. *Science* **235,** 1043–1046

55. Stocker, R., Glazer, A. N., and Ames, B. N. (1987) Antioxidant activity of albumin-bound bilirubin. *Proc. Natl. Acad. Sci. U. S. A.* **84,** 5918–5922

56. Stocker, R., and Ames, B. N. (1987) Potential role of conjugated bilirubin and copper in the metabolism of lipid peroxides in bile. *Proc. Natl. Acad. Sci. U. S. A.* **84,** 8130–8134

57. Frei, B., Kim, M. C., and Ames, B. N. (1990) Ubiquinol-10 is an effective lipid-soluble antioxidant at physiological concentrations. *Proc. Natl. Acad. Sci. U. S. A.* **87,** 4879–4883

58. Tribble, D. L., van den Berg, J. J., Motchnik, P. A., Ames, B. N., Lewis, D. M., Chait, A., and Krauss, R. M. (1994) Oxidative susceptibility of low density lipoprotein subfractions is related to their ubiquinol-10 and alpha-tocopherol content. *Proc. Natl. Acad. Sci. U. S. A.* **91,** 1183–1187

59. Fraga, C. G., Motchnik, P. A., Shigenaga, M. K., Helbock, H. J., Jacob, R. A., and Ames, B. N. (1991) Ascorbic acid protects against endogenous oxidative DNA damage in human sperm. *Proc. Natl. Acad. Sci. U. S. A.* **88,** 11003–11006

60. Shigenaga, M. K., Hagen, T. M., and Ames, B. N. (1994) Oxidative damage and mitochondrial decay in aging. *Proc. Natl. Acad. Sci. U. S. A.* **91,** 10771–10778

61. Hagen, T. M., Yowe, D. L., Bartholomew, J. C., Wehr, C. M., Do, K. L., Park, J. Y., and Ames, B. N. (1997) Mitochondrial decay in hepatocytes from old rats: membrane potential declines, heterogeneity and oxidants increase. *Proc. Natl. Acad. Sci. U. S. A.* **94,** 3064–3069

62. Beckman, K. B., and Ames, B. N. (1998) The free radical theory of aging matures. *Physiol. Rev.* **78,** 547–581

63. Hagen, T. M., Ingersoll, R. T., Wehr, C. M., Lykkesfeldt, J., Vinarsky, V., Bartholomew, J. C., Song, M. H., and Ames, B. N. (1998) Acetyl-L-carnitine fed to old rats partially restores mitochondrial function and ambulatory activity. *Proc. Natl. Acad. Sci. U. S. A.* **95,** 9562–9566

64. Hagen, T. M., Ingersoll, R. T., Lykkesfeldt, J., Liu, J., Wehr, C. M., Vinarsky, V., Bartholomew, J. C., and Ames, B. N. (1999) (*R*)-α-Lipoic acid-supplemented old rats have improved mitochondrial function, decreased oxidative damage, and increased metabolic rate. *FASEB J.* **13,** 411–418

65. Liu, J., Head, E., Gharib, A. M., Yuan, W., Ingersoll, R. T., Hagen, T. M., Cotman, C. W., and Ames, B. N. (2002) Memory loss in old rats is associated with brain mitochondrial decay and RNA/DNA oxidation: partial reversal by feeding acetyl-L-carnitine and/or R-alpha-lipoic acid. *Proc. Natl. Acad. Sci. U. S. A.* **99,** 2356–2361

66. Hagen, T. M., Liu, J., Lykkesfeldt, J., Wehr, C. M., Ingersoll, R. T., Vinarsky, V., Bartholomew, J. C., and Ames, B. N. (2002) Feeding acetyl-L-carnitine and lipoic acid to old rats significantly improves metabolic function while decreasing oxidative stress. *Proc. Natl. Acad. Sci. U. S. A.* **99,** 1870–1875

67. Liu, J., Killilea, D. W., and Ames, B. N. (2002) Age-associated mitochondrial oxidative decay: improvement of carnitine acetyltransferase substrate-binding affinity and activity in brain by feeding old rats acetyl-L-carnitine and/or R-alpha-lipoic acid. *Proc. Natl. Acad. Sci. U. S. A.* **99,** 1876–1881

68. Atamna, H., Liu, J., and Ames, B. N. (2001) Heme deficiency selectively interrupts assembly of mitochondrial complex IV in human fibroblasts: relevance to aging. *J. Biol. Chem.* **276,** 48410–48416

69. Atamna, H., Walter, P. B., and Ames, B. N. (2002) The role of heme and iron-sulfur clusters in mitochondrial biogenesis, maintenance, and decay with age. *Arch. Biochem. Biophys.* **397,** 345–353

70. Ames, B. N., Elson-Schwab, I., and Silver, E. A. (2002) High-dose vitamin therapy stimulates variant enzymes with decreased coenzyme binding affinity (increased K(m)): relevance to genetic disease and polymorphisms. *Am. J. Clin. Nutr.* **75,** 616–658

THE JOURNAL OF BIOLOGICAL CHEMISTRY
© 2003 by The American Society for Biochemistry and Molecular Biology, Inc.

Vol. 278, No. 12, Issue of March 21, pp. 9993–10001, 2003
Printed in U.S.A.

Reflections

A PAPER IN A SERIES COMMISSIONED TO CELEBRATE THE CENTENARY OF THE JBC IN 2005

JBC Centennial
1905–2005
100 Years of Biochemistry and Molecular Biology

Memoirs of a Biochemical Hod Carrier

Published, JBC Papers in Press, January 29, 2003, DOI 10.1074/jbc.X200008200

Hans L. Kornberg

From the Department of Biology, Boston University, Boston, Massachusetts 02215

An invitation to contribute to a series of articles "authored by biochemists whose contributions have helped mark the many advances in biochemistry and molecular biology since 1905" raises a variety of emotional responses. First is, of course, a feeling of surprised pleasure that I should have been considered worthy to participate in this endeavor; as Lewis and Randall pointed out in their preface to *Thermodynamics and the Free Energy of Chemical Substances* (1), the edifice of science is akin to a cathedral built by the efforts of a few architects and many workers, and I have certainly never regarded myself as anything other than a hod carrier on that construction site. Indeed, I note wryly that the two contributions with which my name is (occasionally) associated, the glyoxylate cycle (2) and the formulation of the concept of anaplerotic sequences (3), occupy less than 0.6% of a widely used textbook of biochemistry (4), and much of that space is used for diagrams rather than text.

Second comes the awesome realization that my own career as a practicing biochemist already spans more than half of the century these articles are intended to celebrate; I echo Horace's lament to his friend Postumus: *"eheu fugaces, Postume, Postume, labuntur anni"* (5). So, what did I do to advance biochemical knowledge in the 54 years since I embarked on obtaining my Ph.D. and my life's work?

The Beginnings

I began my research career under the benevolent (though mostly indirect) eye of my beloved teacher, Hans Krebs. He had stimulated my interest in biochemistry by hiring me as a junior technician when I left the United Kingdom equivalent of high school in 1945 and by encouraging me to take a university degree. Although he offered me a place in his department to work for a Ph.D. after I graduated, he thought it best that I should work with his colleague Robert Davies rather than in his own group; I have recounted this previously elsewhere (6).

My chosen topic was to investigate the nature and physiological role of the urease present in mammalian gastric mucosa. Using (and first synthesizing) ^{15}N- and ^{14}C-labeled urea, I demonstrated that there was indeed a significant breakdown of urea to CO_2 and ammonia if this substrate was injected into cats and that the site of this hydrolysis was confined to the stomach but that it was totally abolished by the prior administration to the animals of a mixture of antibiotics. With the help of a bacteriologist colleague, I isolated acid-resistant bacteria that were rich in urease activity from the mucosa of cats not thus medicated (7), but I did not pursue the matter further and thereby missed the opportunity to be the first to identify *Helicobacter pylori*.

The First Taste of America

Although at the time I failed to perceive the significance of my findings to the etiology of gastric ulcers, my work was adjudged to show sufficient promise to qualify me for the award of a Commonwealth Fund Fellowship, which enabled me to work for 2 years in the United States. I had originally been invited to work at Yale by Joseph Fruton, but after I arrived in his department, he selflessly agreed to my joining Efraim Racker's laboratory rather than his own and after a year to my accompanying Ef on his translocation to the Public Health Research Institute of the City of New York. This move occupied the better part of 3 months. Rather than cart equipment from New Haven to New York, I selfishly utilized this interval to put into effect a requirement of the terms of the Fellowship, which was that the holder travel extensively throughout the United States and write an essay on some topic unconnected with his/her work. I chose to investigate and write about American regional cooking and set off in my newly acquired 1940 Buick to eat my way across 39 states, but I interrupted my odyssey at frequent intervals to spend some time in various centers of biochemical research *en route*. Neatly bisecting my trip was a wonderfully fruitful and enjoyable period of 2 months in the laboratory of Melvin Calvin, who had generously allowed me to foist myself on him (under the impression, I later discovered, that I was *Arthur* Kornberg!). I was warmly welcomed also by his colleagues, particularly Andrew A. Benson, Al Bassham, Clinton Fuller, and J. Rodney Quayle, who taught me the techniques used for the isolation and analysis of labeled products formed after incubating microorganisms with ^{14}C-labeled substrates for very short time periods. These techniques enabled me, in later years, to undertake studies on the metabolism of C_2 compounds in bacteria (8), fungi (9), and algae (10) that also propelled me into paths I still follow.

In New York, I continued work on the pentose phosphate pathway that was then being intensively investigated by Bernard Horecker and his colleagues (as Bernie so elegantly recounted in the *Reflections* article published last year in the *Journal of Biological Chemistry* (83)) and in Ef Racker's laboratory. My friend Paul Srere, with whom I shared a laboratory, isolated and studied yeast transaldolase while I concentrated on transketolase. We were able to demonstrate that these two enzymes, highly purified, were able to effect the conversion of pentose phosphate to hexose phosphate (11) and that erythrose 4-phosphate was an intermediate in that process (12).

The Oxford Years

On returning to England in 1955, I was offered a 1-year appointment by Hans Krebs, who had in the mean time been awarded a Nobel Prize and had moved into the Whitley Chair of Biochemistry at the University of Oxford. After an abortive start (I had been asked to investigate a problem, the solution of which was published shortly after I arrived) I decided (with Krebs' blessing) to investigate a question that had been originally posed to me by Ef Racker. The tricarboxylic acid (TCA) cycle yields oxidative energy by effecting the total combustion of C_2 units (as acetyl-coenzyme A) to CO_2 and water, yet the cycle also provides the precursors of many cell components. How can the cycle fulfill both functions and allow microorganisms to grow on *e.g.* acetate or ethanol as sole carbon source? From my cousin Margot Kogut, who had been working in Sidney Elsden's laboratory in Sheffield, I obtained a culture of a pseudomonad known to grow readily on acetate (13). With some guidance from knowledgeable colleagues, I managed to grow this organism on a defined medium containing acetate as sole carbon source, to harvest and wash the cells, and to expose them to $[2-^{14}C]$acetate for brief times; the products were then analyzed by the techniques I had learned in Calvin's laboratory. The only materials that acquired ^{14}C after even the briefest exposure (3 s) were intermediates of the TCA cycle (mainly citrate and malate) or amino acids directly derived therefrom (such as aspartate and glutamate); phosphorylated products did not become labeled until later, which ruled out the operation of autotrophic pathways (14). However, although these data apparently indicated that only the TCA cycle was involved in acetate utilization, the distribution of isotope among the labeled products was not in accordance with that cycle; after the briefest exposure to $[^{14}C]$acetate, 30% of the radioactivity incorporated appeared in citrate but over 40% in malate, with only 10% in [succinate + fumarate], although once the steady state had been reached, labeled malate contributed less to the total radioactivity than did citrate. This could be explained only by postulating a second point of entry of acetate into the TCA cycle, in which its carbons appeared in malate without first passing through succinate and fumarate (8).

A mechanism that satisfactorily accounted for this was demonstrated by a postdoctoral visitor, Neil Madsen, and myself with cell-free extracts of the acetate-grown pseudomonad which, when supplemented with coenzyme A and ATP, formed $[^{14}C]$acetyl-coenzyme A and produced labeled citrate when oxaloacetate was also added; when either isocitrate or glyoxylate was supplied, labeled malate was produced (16). When incubated in the absence of air,

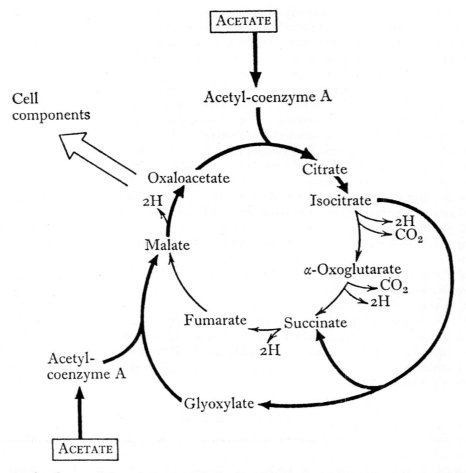

FIG. 1. **Routes for the provision of energy and of cell components during microbial growth on acetate.** The catabolic route (tricarboxylic acid cycle) is shown as *light arrows*; the anaplerotic pathway (glyoxylate cycle) is shown as *heavy arrows*.

extracts supplemented to form acetyl-coenzyme A catalyzed the stoichiometric net formation of malate when glyoxylate was also present, and of malate and succinate when isocitrate was added (17). The enzyme effecting the postulated cleavage of isocitrate to glyoxylate and succinate, then termed isocitritase (18), had been shown previously to be present in extracts of the same pseudomonad (19), and the "malate synthetase" that catalyzed the condensation of acetyl-coenzyme A and glyoxylate to form malate had been discovered in extracts of *Escherichia coli* (20); both were shown to be present and highly active in extracts of the acetate-grown pseudomonad and to be quantitatively capable of accounting for the growth of these bacteria on acetate (21). Moreover, the distribution of label in alanine and aspartate, isolated from cells grown in the presence of labeled CO_2 or specifically labeled acetate, supported the simultaneous operation of the TCA cycle and the "glyoxylate bypass" (22); the joint operation of these routes was therefore termed "the glyoxylate cycle" (2). These two pathways are illustrated in Fig. 1. However, definitive evidence for the necessary and sufficient participation of the key enzymes in microbial growth on C_2 compounds had to await studies on their adaptive formation (23–25) and on the isolation of mutants lacking one or another enzymic activity (26–28).

There are, all too rarely, occasions when a person with a solution but no idea to which problem it might apply meets a person with a problem but no knowledge of the solution. This happy conjunction occurred in 1957 when Harry Beevers was spending a sabbatical in Oxford and told Krebs of his interest in the possible mechanisms that might account for the almost stoichiometric conversion of oil to storage carbohydrates in germinating castor bean seeds. Harry and I met and immediately recognized that the glyoxylate cycle might well provide that route. The next day, Harry appeared with castor beans; we disrupted them in a blender and by late afternoon had demonstrated the presence of a highly active isocitrate lyase (as isocitritase is now more properly called). Incubation of the cell-free extract with [^{14}C]acetate,

ATP, coenzyme A, and isocitrate yielded malate as the sole labeled product; clearly, the sought for mechanism had been found (29, 30). This laid the foundation for Harry's later distinguished work that identified a novel intracellular particle (the "glyoxysome") as the location of these enzymes in plants (31); a similar compartmentation had been observed also in *Tetrahymena* (32) and in a strain of *Chlorella* (10).

Because enzymes of the glyoxylate cycle provided a route for the production of glyoxylate from acetate, the question immediately arose how microorganisms could effect what in principle was the reverse process: to grow on C_2 substrates (such as glycolate, glyoxylate, or glycine) more oxidized than acetate. I was fortunate at this time to be joined by two graduate students, Jack Sadler (who died tragically young in a climbing accident only a few years later) and Tony Gotto (who was to have a distinguished career in medicine after completion of his Ph.D.).

Jack and I were able to show that the provision of energy from glycolate could occur via a dicarboxylic acid cycle, in which an isoform of malate synthetase catalyzed the condensation of glyoxylate and acetyl-coenzyme A as the first step in a sequence of reactions that led from malate via oxaloacetate and pyruvate to the loss of two carbons as CO_2 and to the reformation of the acetyl-coenzyme A acceptor (34). Measurement of the levels of citrate and malate synthetases during growth on acetate or glycolate dramatically illustrated the relative roles of the TCA and dicarboxylic acid cycles in the oxidation of these C_2 compounds (24) and lent confidence to the view that this latter cycle might, under the right circumstances, actually be physiologically significant (35).

However, just as the oxidative TCA cycle could not, on its own, account for growth on acetate, so the dicarboxylic acid cycle could not explain how microorganisms synthesized cell components from glyoxylate or its precursors. Some ancillary route must operate to replenish the intermediates of the TCA and dicarboxylic acid cycles as they are withdrawn in the course of biosyntheses, and it was Tony Gotto and I who were so fortunate as to be able to discern such a pathway (36). It gave us particular pleasure to publish this novel route as one of three adjacent papers, the second of which complemented ours in reporting the reactions that enabled growth to occur on glycine (37) and the third of which explained how organisms grew on oxalate (38), an example of fruitful collegiate collaboration and sharing of information that appears to be regrettably rare nowadays.

The novel biosynthetic pathway we described involves: (*a*) the condensation of 2 mol units of glyoxylate with elimination of 1 mol unit of CO_2 to form tartronic semialdehyde; (*b*) the reduction by NADH + H^+ of this C_3 product to glycerate; and (*c*) the interaction of glycerate and ATP to yield 3-phosphoglycerate, which is then utilized via well established glycolytic and gluconeogenic reactions.

Step (*a*) had been previously described (39, 40), but step (*b*) was catalyzed by a hitherto unknown enzyme, tartronic semialdehyde reductase (41), that we succeeded in crystallizing (42). The two pathways are diagrammed in Fig. 2.

Independence in Leicester

Although my employers, the United Kingdom's Medical Research Council, had tolerantly extended my initial 1-year appointment to 4 and had indeed offered to make this permanent, I felt that the time had come to leave the warm shelter of Hans (since 1958, Sir Hans) Krebs' laboratory and test my wings elsewhere. The University of Leicester, founded as a University College in 1921 and achieving independent university status only after World War II, had only small Departments of Zoology and Botany (the latter hosting one eminent but lone geneticist) to teach the biological sciences but now decided to add a Biochemistry Department. I was offered the Chair in 1960 and together with a colleague (Gareth Morris), who was the first Lecturer to be appointed, a graduate student (John Ashworth), and a secretary I took possession of our laboratories (converted to scientific use from a previous incarnation as wards in the municipal lunatic asylum) late one summer afternoon in 1961 by climbing in through a fortunately open lavatory window; we had been most generously equipped with almost all we needed except a key to the building. I say "almost all" as we had not yet received any incubator shakers that would enable us to grow bacteria in aerated batch cultures; we therefore decided to grow what would grow readily in stationary culture on C_2 compounds in Roux bottles. By a happy accident, we chose a *Micrococcus* species as a test organism and thereby uncovered another novel route for growth on glycolate (43). In this pathway (apparently unique to

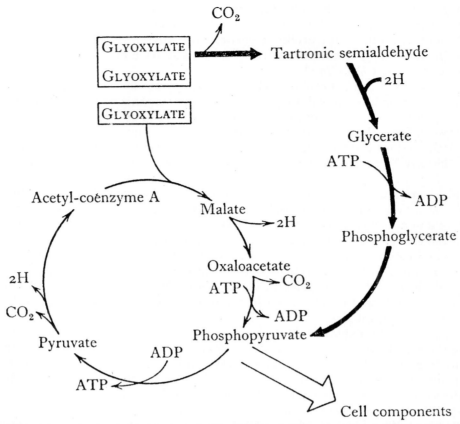

FIG. 2. **Routes for the provision of energy and of cell components during microbial growth on glyoxylate.** The catabolic route (dicarboxylic acid cycle) is shown as *light arrows*; the anaplerotic sequence (glycerate pathway) is shown as *heavy arrows*.

Micrococcus denitrificans), the utilization of glyoxylate proceeds by a sequence involving an initial condensation of this C_2 compound with glycine to form *erythro-β*-hydroxyaspartate, which undergoes transamination with a second molecule of glyoxylate to reform glycine and to yield oxaloacetate (44).

The Concept of Anaplerosis

In October 1964, the *Gesellschaft für Physiologische Chemie* invited me to give a plenary lecture at their fall meeting in Cologne. I chose to discuss the various pathways that serve to maintain the central metabolic routes during the growth of microorganisms on C_2 compounds. Although these pathways differ greatly in their component reactions, they nevertheless serve a common physiological purpose. It was a friend and colleague, Professor A. Wasserstein (then Professor of Classics at Leicester), who suggested the term "anaplerotic" (from the Greek for "filling up again") as a generic term and I gratefully accepted his suggestion (3).

It is seductively easy to write sequences of reactions that might fulfill some desired metabolic function; to demonstrate that they play a necessary and sufficient role requires more than paper chemistry. Fortunately, this is feasible with *E. coli*; the organism has but one chromosome, and a mutation in a gene that specifies some enzyme crucial to the functioning of some metabolic route would be expected to result in a readily distinguishable altered phenotype. An instance of this was provided by a happy collaboration between Ed Adelberg, who was running a summer course at the Marine Biological Laboratory, Woods Hole, and John Ashworth and I, who were running a similar course in an adjacent laboratory. Ed's students isolated a number of auxotrophic mutants of *E. coli* as part of their practical work, and we garnered all that looked biochemically novel. One such mutant was particularly intriguing and together with one of our students (R. L. Ward) we established that although the mutant contained a number of enzymes that in theory might have effected the net synthesis of oxaloacetate or malate from CO_2 and pyruvate or phosphoenolpyruvate (PEP), they were unable to do so because they lacked a specific PEP carboxylase (45, 46).

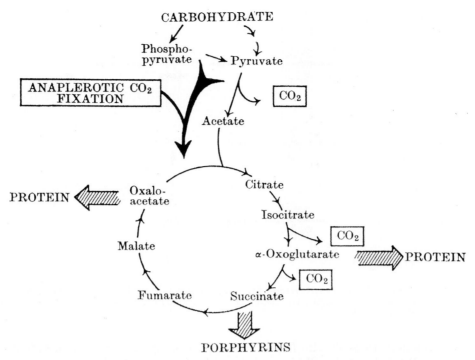

FIG. 3. **Routes for the provision of energy and of cell components during the utilization of carbohydrates.** The catabolic route (Embden-Meyerhof pathway and tricarboxylic acid cycle) is shown by *light arrows*; the anaplerotic sequence (CO_2 fixation) is shown by *heavy arrows*.

In collaboration with the late Jose-Luis Canovas, I demonstrated at a later date that the enzyme required acetyl-coenzyme A as an allosteric activator (Fig. 3) (47), which illustrated beautifully the manner in which a branch point in a metabolic pathway serves also as a site of control.

The realization that the anaplerotic function is exclusively borne by the carboxylation of PEP immediately raised the question of how *E. coli* can grow on C_3 compounds such as alanine, lactate, or pyruvate because direct reversal of the pyruvate kinase reaction is unlikely to occur under physiological conditions. Once again, mutants supplied the answer; my colleague Ron Cooper and I isolated a mutant that, although unimpaired in its ability to utilize glucose or intermediates of the TCA cycle, could not grow on C_3 compounds. This mutant was found to be still rich in pyruvate kinase activity but to lack a hitherto unknown enzyme, PEP synthase, in which the interaction of ATP with pyruvate yields PEP, P_I, and AMP; the energy barrier is surmounted by using two of the "energy-rich" bonds of ATP (48–51).

The dual roles of pyruvate kinase and PEP synthase led us to study also the properties of the former enzyme in *E. coli*. It was known (52) that the pyruvate kinase activity of *E. coli* B was stimulated by fructose 1,6-*bis*phosphate (FBP); what surprised Massimo Malcovati and myself (53) was that there were two forms of this enzyme present in extracts of *E. coli*, K12, one of which was similarly stimulated by FBP but the other one was not. We later showed (54) that this duality was demonstrable in cells rendered permeable by treatment with dilute chloroform in ethanol (55) just as it was in cell-free extracts.

Ad Eundem

In 1973, I was unexpectedly offered the Sir William Dunn Professorship of Biochemistry at the University of Cambridge to succeed the incumbent (Sir Frank Young), who was due to retire in 1975. My immediate response was to refuse; the University of Leicester had treated me with extraordinary generosity, enabling my colleagues and me to build a flourishing School of Biological Sciences in a brand new building and even to initiate a new Medical School, whereas I knew the department in Cambridge to be rich in a great tradition but housed in buildings whose grandeur was not matched by their utility. However, two events changed my mind. One was a simultaneous visit from two giants of British science, Sir Alan Hodgkin and Lord Todd, both of whom were Nobel laureates, Professors in the University of Cambridge, and

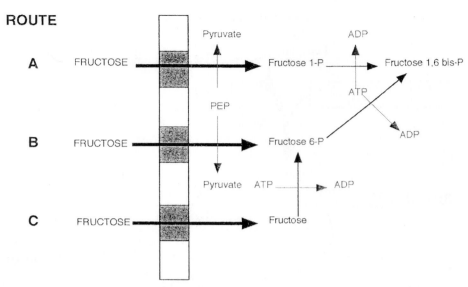

FIG. 4. **Routes for the uptake and utilization of fructose.** Routes A and B necessitate the action of the PTS; in Route C, fructose enters the cells by facilitated diffusion via an isoform of the principal enzyme II for glucose transport but without involvement of the PTS.

President or President-to-be of The Royal Society; I was as clay in their hands and weakly consented after all to accept the Chair, a decision I never regretted.

The second event removed the last scintilla of doubt from my mind: a phone call from Ernest Gale, then Acting Head of the Department, announced that that portion of the department in which I was to occupy laboratory space had burned down overnight! This gave me the opportunity, before I moved, to rebuild the previous warren of little rooms as the large open laboratories to which I had been accustomed in Oxford and in Leicester.

The move to Cambridge marked also a major shift in the main thrust of my work. Although I had retained my interest in microbial metabolic pathways and (with a number of students and postdoctoral fellows) had *inter alia* been able to elucidate the main routes whereby *E. coli* utilize gluconate (56–60) and fructose (61–63) as sole carbon sources for growth, I had also become increasingly aware that considerations of metabolism are incomplete if one ignores the first essential step, the mechanisms whereby substrates cross the cell membrane to enter metabolic sequences and the factors that regulate this process. This awareness had been heightened by analysis of mutants that were impaired specifically in the uptake, but not the catabolism, of C_4 dicarboxylic acids (64, 65) and in the uptake, but not the catabolism, of glucose 6-phosphate (66, 67). It had been given additional impetus by the recognition of a "pecking order" in the sequence in which different hexoses are taken up by *E. coli*. For example, as little as micromolar amounts of glucose will powerfully inhibit the continued uptake of fructose, even though the cells are fully induced for fructose utilization and that ketose is present in great excess (68); however, mutants can be isolated in which this preference for glucose has been abolished (69). The site of one such mutation lay not in a gene for glucose utilization but was co-transducible with the gene(s) specifying the fructose operon, the major route of fructose uptake. We therefore undertook to sequence two of the three genes that comprise this gene cluster, *fruA* (70), which specifies the membrane-spanning transport protein, and *fruK* (71), which codes for a 1-phosphofructokinase, the third member of this operon (*fruB*) having been sequenced by Milton Saier and his colleagues (72). Because the preference for glucose over fructose was also abolished in mutants that formed the proteins of the fructose operon constitutively and in great activities, we (and virtually simultaneously, the late Pieter Postma and his colleagues (73)) also located on the *E. coli* linkage map the regulatory gene involved (74).

Availability of mutants in these and other genes made it feasible to recognize the numerous alternative routes for fructose utilization that can operate in *E. coli* (Fig. 4).

My long time colleague Maurice Jones-Mortimer and I had already shown that mutants unable to use fructose via the proteins of the fructose operon could nonetheless grow by taking up this ketose via a constitutive membrane-spanning protein involved in mannose transport (75), and when that route was also closed, further mutants would arise in which fructose was now taken up via a gene normally involved in the uptake of sorbitol (76); later work showed that the constitutive formation of the mannitol uptake system could likewise facilitate growth on fructose.

Having been raised in the biochemical tradition that it is essential to be able to measure independently both substrates and products of any reaction under study, I had deliberately chosen to study in depth only carbohydrate transport processes that involved the glycose: phosphoenolpyruvate phosphotransferase (PT) system (77), in which the uptake of the hexose was accompanied by its phosphorylation at the expense of PEP. Quantitative measurements could thus be made by a spectrophotometric assay of pyruvate formation in cells rendered permeable by treatment with toluene in ethanol,

$$\text{Sugar}_{out} + \text{PEP} = \text{sugar-phosphate}_{in} + \text{pyruvate} \qquad \text{(Eq. 1)}$$

$$\text{Pyruvate} + \textbf{NADH} + \textbf{H}^+ = \text{lactate} + \textbf{NAD}^+ \qquad \text{(Eq. 2)}$$

which had been worked out by my late friend Dick Reeves, who spent a period of postdoctoral work in my laboratory (54, 78), as well as by techniques involving radioactively labeled materials. The consensus view arising from a variety of investigations was that transport of PT-sugars was necessarily linked to their phosphorylation (79) and that the membrane-spanning proteins could not effect entry of their substrates into the cells by facilitated diffusion. However, this conclusion was not in accord with our finding (80) that, under certain conditions, galactose could enter *E. coli* cells via the principal transport protein for the PT-dependent uptake of glucose but without phosphorylation; this was later observed also with other substrates (81).

In 1995, I reached the mandatory (in the United Kingdom) retirement age and thus had to face the prospect of abandoning research. However, unexpectedly and doubtless undeservedly I was invited to join Boston University as a "University Professor" and Professor of Biology; within a month of arrival and accompanied by my colleague Linda Lambourne, experimental work was once more under way. Being fascinated by the flexibility by which *E. coli* can overcome all manner of metabolic handicaps by evolving alternative routes for fructose utilization, I chose to make this general area the focus of my work, hoping thereby to gain an insight into the mechanisms by which this unicellular organism senses what is "out there" and adjusts its intracellular machinery accordingly. So far, this has shown us that the principal fructose transporter FruA can also admit mannose (82) and that the principal glucose transporter can mutate to effect the facilitated diffusion of fructose (33), this latter process being also the first step in a novel route for fructose utilization that does not involve the PT system (15). I am currently studying further mutants in which fructose supports growth despite the absence of the components of the PT system and of a functioning glucose carrier, profoundly grateful for the opportunity still to carry (and occasionally drop) bricks as small contributions to the grand edifice of biochemistry.

Address correspondence to: hlk@bu.edu.

REFERENCES

1. Lewis, G. N., and Randall, M. (1923) *Thermodynamics and the Free Energy of Chemical Substances*, McGraw-Hill Book Co., New York
2. Kornberg, H. L., and Krebs, H. A. (1957) *Nature* **179,** 988–991
3. Kornberg, H. L. (1965) *Angew. Chem. Int. Ed. Engl.* **4,** 558–565
4. Mathews, C. K., and van Holde, K. E. (1999) *Biochemistry*, 2nd Ed., Benjamin/Cummings, Menlo Park
5. Horace, *Odes 2,* 14
6. Kornberg, H. L. (2002) *IUBMB Life* **54,** 1–2
7. Kornberg, H. L., Davies, R. E., and Wood, D. R. (1954) *Biochem. J.* **56,** 363–372
8. Kornberg, H. L. (1958) *Biochem. J.* **68,** 535–542
9. Collins, J. F., and Kornberg, H. L. (1960) *Biochem. J.* **77,** 430–438
10. Harrop, L. C., and Kornberg, H. L. (1966) *Proc. R. Soc. Lond. B Biol. Sci.* **166,** 11–29
11. Srere, P. A., Kornberg, H. L., and Racker, E. (1955) *Fed. Proc.* **14,** 285–286
12. Kornberg, H. L., and Racker, E. (1955) *Biochem. J.* **61,** iii
13. Kogut, M., and Podoski, E. P. (1953) *Biochem. J.* **55,** 800–811
14. Kornberg, H. L. (1957) *Biochem. J.* **66,** 13P
15. Sproul, A., Lambourne, L. T. M., Jims Jean–Jacques, D., and Kornberg, H. L. (2001) *Proc. Natl. Acad. Sci. U. S. A.* **98,** 15257–15259
16. Kornberg, H. L., and Madsen, N. B. (1957) *Biochem. J.* **66,** 13P
17. Kornberg, H. L., and Madsen, N. B. (1957) *Biochim. Biophys. Acta* **24,** 651–654
18. Smith, R. A., and Gunsalus, I. C. (1954) *J. Am. Chem. Soc.* **76,** 5002–5003
19. Saz, H. J., and Hillary, E. P. (1956) *Biochem. J.* **62,** 563–569

20. Wong, D. T. O., and Ajl, S. J. (1956) *J. Am. Chem. Soc.* **78,** 3230–3231
21. Kornberg, H. L., and Madsen, N. B. (1958) *Biochem. J.* **68,** 549–557
22. Kornberg, H. L., and Quayle, J. R. (1958) *Biochem. J.* **68,** 542–549
23. Kornberg, H. L., and Elsden, S. R. (1961) *Adv. Enzymol.* **23,** 401–470
24. Kornberg, H. L. (1961) *Cold Spring Harbor Symp. Quant. Biol.* **26,** 257–260
25. Kornberg, H. L. (1963) *Biochim. Biophys. Acta* **73,** 517–519
26. Ashworth, J. M., and Kornberg, H. L. (1964) *Biochim. Biophys. Acta* **89,** 383–384
27. Kornberg, H. L., and Smith, J. (1966) *Biochim. Biophys. Acta* **123,** 654–657
28. Brice, C. B., and Kornberg, H. L. (1968) *J. Bacteriol.* **96,** 2185–2186
29. Kornberg, H. L., and Beevers, H. (1957) *Nature* **180,** 35–36
30. Kornberg, H. L., and Beevers, H. (1957) *Biochim. Biophys. Acta* **26,** 531–537
31. Beevers, H. (1980) in *The Biochemistry of Plants: A Comprehensive Treatise* (Stumpf, P. K., and Conn, E. E., eds)
    Vol. 4, pp. 117–130, Academic Press, New York
32. Hogg, J. F., and Kornberg, H. L. (1963) *Biochem. J.* **86,** 462–468
33. Kornberg, H. L., Lambourne, L. T. M., and Sproul, A. (2000) *Proc. Natl. Acad Sci. U. S. A.* **97,** 1808–1812
34. Kornberg, H. L., and Sadler, J. R. (1960) *Nature* **185,** 153–155
35. Kornberg, H. L., and Sadler, J. R. (1961) *Biochem. J.* **81,** 503–513
36. Kornberg, H. L., and Gotto, A. M. (1959) *Nature* **183,** 1791–1795
37. Callely, A. G., and Dagley, S. (1959) *Nature* **183,** 1791–1795
38. Quayle, J. R., and Keech, D. B. (1959) *Nature* **183,** 1791–1795
39. Krakow, G., and Barkulis, S. S. (1956) *Biochim. Biophys. Acta* **21,** 593–594
40. Chow, C. T., and Vennesland, B. (1958) *J. Biol. Chem.* **233,** 997–1002
41. Kornberg, H. L., and Gotto, A. M. (1961) *Biochem. J.* **78,** 69–82
42. Gotto, A. M., and Kornberg, H. L. (1961) *Biochem. J.* **81,** 273–284
43. Kornberg, H. L., and Morris, J. G. (1963) *Nature* **197,** 456–457
44. Kornberg, H. L., and Morris, J. G. (1965) *Biochem. J.* **95,** 577–586
45. Ashworth, J. M., Kornberg, H. L., and Ward, R. L. (1965) *Biochem. J.* **94,** 28P
46. Ashworth, J. M., and Kornberg, H. L. (1966) *Proc. R. Soc. Lond. B Biol. Sci.* **165,** 179–188
47. Canovas, J. L., and Kornberg, H. L. (1966) *Proc. R. Soc. Lond. B Biol. Sci.* **165,** 189–205
48. Cooper, R. A., and Kornberg, H. L. (1965) *Biochim. Biophys. Acta* **104,** 618–620
49. Cooper, R. A., and Kornberg, H. L. (1967) *Biochim. Biophys. Acta* **141,** 211–213
50. Cooper, R. A., and Kornberg, H. L. (1967) *Proc. R. Soc. Lond. B Biol. Sci.* **168,** 263–280
51. Cooper, R. A., and Kornberg, H. L. (1967) *Biochem. J.* **105,** 49C–50C
52. Maeba, P., and Sanwal, B. D. (1968) *J. Biol. Chem.* **243,** 448–450
53. Malcovati, M., and Kornberg, H. L. (1969) *Biochim. Biophys. Acta* **178,** 420–423
54. Kornberg, H. L., and Reeves, R. E. (1972) *Biochem. J.* **126,** 1241–1243
55. Kornberg, H. L., and Malcovati, M. (1973) *FEBS Lett.* **32,** 257–259
56. Kornberg, H. L., and Soutar, A. K. (1973) *Biochem. J.* **134,** 489–498
57. Faik, P., and Kornberg, H. L. (1973) *FEBS Lett.* **32,** 260–264
58. Pouyssegur, J. M., Faik, P., and Kornberg, H. L. (1974) *Biochem. J.* **140,** 193–203
59. Bachi, B., and Kornberg, H. L. (1975) *J. Gen. Microbiol.* **90,** 321–335
60. Bachi, B., and Kornberg, H. L. (1975) *Biochem. J.* **150,** 123–128
61. Ferenci, T., and Kornberg, H. L. (1971) *FEBS Lett.* **13,** 127–130
62. Ferenci, T., and Kornberg, H. L. (1971) *FEBS Lett.* **14,** 360–364
63. Ferenci, T., and Kornberg, H. L. (1973) *Biochem. J.* **132,** 341–347
64. Kay, W. W., and Kornberg, H. L. (1969) *FEBS Lett.* **3,** 93–96
65. Kay, W. W., and Kornberg, H. L (1971) *Eur. J. Biochem.* **18,** 274–281
66. Kornberg, H. L., and Smith, J. (1969) *Nature* **224,** 1261–1262
67. Essenberg, R. C., and Kornberg, H. L. (1977) *J. Gen. Microbiol.* **99,** 157–169
68. Kornberg, H. L. (1973) *Proc. R. Soc. Lond. B Biol. Sci.* **183,** 105–123
69. Amaral, D., and Kornberg, H. L. (1975) *J. Gen. Microbiol.* **90,** 157–168
70. Prior, T. I., and Kornberg, H. L. (1988) *J. Gen. Microbiol.* **134,** 2757–2768
71. Orchard, L. M. D., and Kornberg, H. L. (1990) *Proc. R. Soc. Lond. B Biol. Sci.* **242,** 87–90
72. Reizer, J., Reizer, A., Kornberg, H. L., and Saier, M. H., Jr. (1994) *FEMS Microbiol. Lett.* **118,** 159–162
73. Geerse, R. H., Ruig, C. R., Schuitema, A. R. J., and Postma, P. (1986) *Mol. Gen. Genet.* **203,** 435–444
74. Kornberg, H. L., and Elvin, C. (1987) *J. Gen. Microbiol.* **133,** 341–346
75. Kornberg, H. L., and Jones–Mortimer, M. C. (1975) *FEBS Lett.* **51,** 1–4
76. Jones-Mortimer, M. C., and Kornberg, H. L. (1976) *J. Gen. Microbiol.* **96,** 383–391
77. Kundig, W., Ghosh, S., and Roseman, S. (1964) *Proc. Natl. Acad. Sci. U. S. A.* **52,** 1067–1074
78. Kornberg, H. L., and Reeves, R. E. (1972) *Biochem. J.* **128,** 1339–1344
79. Postma, P., and Stock, J. B. (1980) *J. Bacteriol.* **114,** 476–484
80. Kornberg, H. L., and Riordan, C. (1976) *J. Gen. Microbiol.* **94,** 75–89
81. Postma, P. W. (1981) *J. Bacteriol.* **147,** 382–389
82. Kornberg, H. L., and Lambourne, L. T. M. (1992) *Proc. Roy. Soc. Lond. B Biol. Sci.* **250,** 51–55
83. Horecker, B. (2002) *J. Biol. Chem.* **277,** 47965–47971

THE JOURNAL OF BIOLOGICAL CHEMISTRY
© 2003 by The American Society for Biochemistry and Molecular Biology, Inc.

Vol. 278, No. 13, Issue of March 28, pp. 10859–10878, 2003
Printed in U.S.A.

Reflections

A PAPER IN A SERIES COMMISSIONED TO CELEBRATE THE CENTENARY OF THE JBC IN 2005

JBC Centennial
1905–2005
100 Years of Biochemistry and Molecular Biology

Using Studies on Tryptophan Metabolism to Answer Basic Biological Questions

Published, JBC Papers in Press, January 29, 2003, DOI 10.1074/jbc.X200012200

Charles Yanofsky

From the Department of Biological Sciences, Stanford University, Stanford, California 94305

In my youth I was overwhelmed by the variety of forms of life around me. Yes, while growing up in New York City! As a student at the Bronx High School of Science my teachers made every effort to convince me that no pursuit could be more exciting or rewarding than searching for explanations for the basic processes common to life. I agreed, but I knew this decision was insufficient, for I would have to choose the area of science that was just right for me. I was aware that major unanswered questions existed in all fields of science, particularly regarding the relationship of biochemistry to genetics, the two subjects that interested me most as a high school student. I decided to major in biochemistry, and enrolled at the City College of New York. I completed a year and a half of college study before being drafted into the army in the spring of 1944. I served in the infantry as a cannoneer during World War II. I fought in the Ardennes in the Battle of the Bulge. Understandably this was an awesome experience. Upon returning to college after the war I was more determined than ever to pursue a career in research. When faced with selecting a Ph.D. program to apply to, I received excellent advice from a knowledgeable professor and textbook author, Benjamin Harrow, chairman of the Biochemistry Department at City College of New York. He suggested exploring gene-enzyme relationships with *Neurospora crassa* as the ideal project for me. I agreed and applied to do my graduate work with George Beadle at Caltech or Edward Tatum at Yale. I was rejected by Caltech but fortunately was accepted by Yale.

As it turned out, my mentor in graduate school at Yale was not Edward Tatum; it was David Bonner. Bonner had moved with Tatum from Stanford to Yale and had become his research associate. During the year I applied for admission to Yale, Tatum decided to return to Stanford. Fortunately for me, Bonner stayed on at Yale and took over direction of Tatum's remaining group. Bonner, a wonderful advisor, believed it was in the best interests of both student and advisor to have each student work independently on a well defined project. If successful, he said, we would receive partial credit for our discoveries and would qualify for a faculty position. For most beginning graduate students, selecting a project and deciding how to proceed is relegated to your research mentor and would reflect his or her research preferences. By choosing a specific scientist as your advisor you recognize the importance of his or her contributions. In my initial meeting with Bonner at Yale in June of 1948, as I recall, he handed me a fuzzy culture of a niacin-requiring mutant of *Neurospora* and gave me advice on how to go about identifying the niacin pathway intermediate this mutant was presumed to accumulate. Our ultimate goal, he said, was identifying all the intermediates in the niacin pathway so this knowledge could be exploited in investigations on gene-enzyme relationships. I was the only laboratory member assigned this type of project, probably because Bonner was aware that my background was principally in biochemistry. This project captured my full attention, and fortunately, I was successful. We identified two intermediates accumulated by niacin-requiring mutants, quinolinic acid and a derivative of kynurenine. The knowledge I acquired in these studies served as a valuable resource in decision making throughout the early stages of my career.

Reflections: Questions, Answers, and More Questions

Upon reviewing my research accomplishments and considering what I might emphasize in this article, I was most impressed by the variety of basic biological questions the members of my group have addressed. Early in my career I decided that one of my primary research objectives would be to provide a thorough understanding of all aspects of tryptophan metabolism and to use this knowledge in explaining basic processes of biology. In fact, tryptophan metabolism was the focus of most of my research. However, during the early stages of my career I did not appreciate the variety of scientific questions that I would have the opportunity to address using tryptophan metabolism as my experimental system. Our studies contributed to knowledge on the niacin and tryptophan biosynthetic pathways, enzyme structure/function relationships, organization of genes and operons, the existence of gene-protein colinearity, the molecular basis of suppression, coupling of transcription with translation, regulation of transcription, how tryptophan and tryptophan-tRNA serve as regulatory signals, and the regulatory mechanisms microorganisms use to control tryptophan synthesis and its degradation. The unanticipated role of RNA in regulation, transcription attenuation, was and continues to be one of our major interests. We had no inkling until the 1990s, when bacterial genomes were beginning to be sequenced, that attenuation was so widely used in nature. While we were conducting our investigations on tryptophan metabolism evolutionary questions continually arose. As soon as we understood the features of tryptophan metabolism in one organism we wished to know whether other organisms use the same genes, reactions, and regulatory processes. Despite my personal commitment to tryptophan metabolism, in the early 1980s I returned to studies with *N. crassa* as an experimental organism, addressing other important questions. The lesson to be learned from my experiences, I believe, is to always be on the alert. Important unanswered questions you never anticipated will invariably arise from the results of your current research. It may develop that your chosen experimental system is ideal for answering these questions. Throughout this article I will describe examples taken from my career, where answers led to questions I felt we should address.

The One Gene-One Enzyme Relationship

When I arrived at Yale 1n 1948 most members of the Bonner group were coping with the most significant question then concerning the *Neurospora* scientific community: how to establish the nature of the gene-enzyme relationship. It was some years after Beadle and Tatum (1) had first proposed the one gene, one enzyme, one biochemical reaction hypothesis. Following the pioneering studies of Garrod in the early 1900s, linking heredity with metabolism, there were numerous observations relating metabolic defects with genetic disorders. Beadle and Tatum cemented this relationship in the early 1940s by selecting an organism, *N. crassa*, that could be used to isolate nutritional mutants. These mutants could then be genetically characterized to establish whether their inability to carry out specific biochemical reactions was because of mutations in specific genes. Most importantly, they observed that there was a one to one relationship between gene and biochemical reaction. Despite these findings, when I was completing my graduate studies in 1951 most scientists were skeptical of the validity of the one gene-one enzyme concept. At this time very little was known about the molecular nature and structure of genetic material or the structure of proteins, and virtually nothing was known about protein synthesis. It was not until the early 1950s that the findings of Hershey and Chase (2) and an earlier finding by Avery *et al.* (3) convinced most of us that genetic material was most likely DNA, and it was not until 1953 that Jim Watson and Francis Crick (4) described their elegant structure for DNA. Following these major contributions we accepted as proven that the genetic material of most organisms was double-stranded DNA. Furthermore, it was not until the late 1950s that Seymour Benzer's (5) fine structure genetic analyses with the rII locus of phage T4 equated the genetic map with the structure of DNA. Similarly, it was not until the early 1950s that Sanger's studies (6) with insulin established that proteins consist of linear sequences of amino acids.

While I was in graduate school the goal considered most important by members of the Beadle-Tatum school was to identify a specific enzymatic reaction for which defective mutants could be isolated and then determine whether these mutants lacked that enzymatic activity. Our hope was that studies like these would provide definitive proof for the one gene-one enzyme hypothesis. Several members of the Bonner group were following this approach. Naomi Franklin, Otto Landman, Gabriel Lester, and Howard Rickenberg were examining one of the most popular experimental enzymes during this period, β-galactosidase, from both *Neurospora* and *Escherichia coli*. They were hoping to use the knowledge and techniques being provided by Monod, and subsequently by Jacob and Monod and their exceptional coworkers, to explore the Beadle-Tatum gene-enzyme concept more directly. Impressed by this overriding goal of my mentor and the determination of my fellow students, I decided that I too should follow this path. In my third and last year of graduate study, 1950–1951, I abandoned my niacin pathway studies and initiated a search for the ideal "gene-enzyme" experimental system.

No one in our group at Yale was contemplating what today would be considered the most obvious experimental approach: isolating and sequencing a specific gene and comparing this sequence with the amino acid sequence of its polypeptide product. Neither genes nor proteins could be analyzed in this way; we did not yet know that genetic material was DNA or that proteins consisted of linear sequences of amino acids. At this time the prevailing view in the field of genetics was that chromosomes consist of linear arrays of genes arranged like "beads on a string." It was assumed that each gene was indivisible by genetic recombination. If these views were correct how could we determine the relative positions of independent mutational changes in a specific gene, except by structural analysis, which was not possible? We decided that our next step on the gene-enzyme problem should be to demonstrate convincingly that all mutants altered at a single genetic locus lack the specific enzyme that catalyzes the corresponding reaction.

By the late 1940s numerous nutritional mutants of *N. crassa* had been isolated, many requiring the same metabolite. It was evident that amino acids, vitamins, purines, and pyrimidines are all synthesized by sequential enzyme-catalyzed reactions, mostly in separate pathways. However, these pathways were just beginning to be defined. Genetic analyses with these mutants established a very impressive one-to-one relationship between altered gene and loss of a specific biochemical reaction; this was the experimental basis of the Beadle/Tatum concept. It was also evident that a unique set of genes was associated with each metabolic pathway. However, very few of the enzymes in each newly discovered pathway had been identified, and those that were known did not catalyze reactions that were defective in the nutritional mutants that had been isolated. One of the earliest opportunities to examine mutants lacking a specific enzyme was provided by the findings of Umbreit *et al.* in 1946 (7). They demonstrated that extracts of wild type *Neurospora* contain an enzyme they named tryptophan desmolase, which catalyzes the last reaction in tryptophan synthesis, the covalent joining of indole with L-serine to form L-tryptophan. Tryptophan-requiring mutants of *Neurospora* had been identified that could not grow on indole; therefore these mutants should lack this enzyme activity if the Beadle/Tatum hypothesis were correct. Joseph Lein and Dave Hogness, of Hershell Mitchell's laboratory at Caltech, examined extracts of one such mutant, named *td1*, and reported that yes, it did lack tryptophan desmolase activity (8, 9).

Having spent my first 2 years studying niacin and tryptophan metabolism in *Neurospora*, I decided that tryptophan desmolase was promising as a potential subject for gene-enzyme analyses. I initiated my studies by partially purifying and further characterizing the wild type enzyme and confirming the absence of tryptophan desmolase activity in extracts of mutant *td1*. I also examined a second mutant altered at the same locus, mutant *td2*, and showed that it too lacked tryptophan desmolase activity (10). Excited by the simplicity of this enzyme assay and these positive results, members of the Bonner group turned to isolating 20 additional mutants defective in the conversion of indole to tryptophan. We showed that each was genetically altered at the *td* locus and each lacked tryptophan desmolase activity. These initial findings were very encouraging, and they supported the basic assumption of the Beadle/Tatum concept.

In the course of my studies with mutant *td2* one culture grew in media lacking tryptophan. Instead of discarding this culture, we analyzed it genetically and discovered that its ability to grow without tryptophan was due to an unlinked suppressor mutation. The properties of this suppressed *td* mutant raised a new, then unanswerable, question. *How does a suppressor mutation, a mutation in a gene other than the td gene, restore growth without tryptophan?* My enzyme analyses revealed that the suppressor mutation acted by restoring the organism's ability to form an active tryptophan desmolase (10). Probing still further, I observed that the

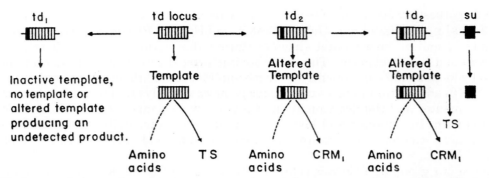

FIG. 1. **Early speculation on how a suppressor mutation might restore synthesis of an active tryptophan synthetase protein (TS) in mutant td2 but not mutant td1.** It was assumed that the *td* gene was altered differently in the two mutants. This allowed the product of a specific suppressor gene to act on the altered template of mutant *td2*, the CRM+ mutant, to produce an active tryptophan synthetase enzyme. Copied with permission from Academic Press (12).

td2 suppressor gene was allele-specific; it had no effect on mutant *td1*. Obviously, then, mutants *td1* and *td2* must have different alterations at the *td* locus. We next performed "reversion" analyses with all our *td* mutants and isolated several additional suppressors. Most of these restored tryptophan desmolase activity only when combined with their respective *td* mutant allele. On the basis of these findings we rephrased our previous question, as follows. *If there is a one-to-one relationship between gene and enzyme and only td mutants lack tryptophan desmolase activity, how does a mutation in a gene distinct from the td locus restore this enzyme activity?* My thoughts on possible explanations temporarily diverted attention from my primary objective, establishing the basis of the one gene-one enzyme relationship. I considered our suppression findings to be extremely interesting and believed that their explanation might provide additional insight into this relationship. This experience, I believe, was largely responsible for many of my subsequent decisions on how to proceed in planning future research. I decided then that our knowledge of basic biological processes was so poor it would be foolish to ignore interesting unexplained observations. Following this line of reasoning I set out to compare the properties of tryptophan desmolase isolated from the wild type strain and from several suppressed mutants.

Throughout this period we were frustrated at how little we could do experimentally. The existing molecular technology was clearly inadequate. With a close friend and former member of the Bonner group, Sigmund Suskind, then a postdoctoral fellow performing immunological research at another institution, we designed a different approach that we thought might provide additional insight into the gene-enzyme relationship, The question we set out to answer was the following. *Does suppressible mutant td2, but not non-suppressible mutant td1, produce an inactive form of the tryptophan desmolase enzyme?* Using my partially purified wild type enzyme as antigen, Suskind prepared a rabbit antiserum that inhibited wild type tryptophan desmolase activity. We used this antiserum in a successful weekend experiment at Yale, analyzing extracts of mutants *td1* and *td2* for an inactive tryptophan desmolase-like protein that would cross-react with our antiserum (11). Mutant *td2* extracts did in fact contain such a cross-reacting material, for which we coined the term "CRM," whereas extracts of mutant *td1* did not. Comparable analyses were then performed with extracts of our other *td* mutants. All our suppressible mutants were shown to be CRM^+, whereas all our non-suppressible mutants were CRM^-. These findings implied, incorrectly, that suppression can restore a functional enzyme only if a mutant produces an inactive form of the wild type enzyme. (There are several reasonable explanations for our inability to isolate suppressors of our CRM^- *Neurospora* mutants, which probably had chain termination mutations in the *td* gene.)

On the basis of our findings I drew a number of interesting conclusions. I presented these at a very exciting symposium entitled "Enzymes, Units of Biological Structure and Function" held at the Henry Ford Hospital in Detroit in 1955 (Fig. 1) (12). My interpretations were of course influenced by new knowledge on DNA and protein structure and the mechanism of protein synthesis. I concluded that "the *td* locus is the only chromosomal area which directly controls tryptophan synthetase formation" (the accepted name had just been changed from desmolase to synthetase). I also concluded that "the *td* locus represents a physiologically indivisible unit, damage to any part of which results in a defect in tryptophan synthetase formation." I stated that "it would seem likely that different portions of the *td* locus are concerned with the synthesis of different parts of the tryptophan synthetase molecule." In attempting to explain how a suppressor mutation restores enzyme activity I postulated that "some product of a suppressor gene cooperates with the altered template in the formation of small amounts of tryptophan synthetase." Looking back on these interpretations, they were all naive guesses, but they proved to be correct. Unfortunately the experimental tools and approaches needed to establish their molecular validity were not available. These studies on missense suppression preceded the enormous interest in suppression aroused by studies on the genetic code and on nonsense mutations. As is so often the case, the significance of a finding is not appreciated until additional relevant knowledge is acquired.

Changing my Experimental Organism

At this stage in my career I was deeply committed to doing everything I could to provide additional insight into the gene-enzyme relationship. I was disappointed at the difficulty I was experiencing attempting to purify the tryptophan synthetase of *Neurospora* and initiated a search for a more suitable experimental enzyme. My first thought was to identify an enzyme in the tryptophan to niacin pathway from *E. coli* or *Bacillus subtilis*, because these organisms were developing as more ideal experimental subjects for biochemical analyses. I performed radioisotope-labeling experiments with these two organisms, hoping to show that one or both synthesizes niacin from tryptophan. My findings provided a disappointing conclusion; neither organism synthesizes niacin from tryptophan (13). This negative result eliminated enzymes of the niacin pathway from my list of possibilities.

While performing these studies I was offered a faculty position in the outstanding Microbiology Department at the Western Reserve University School of Medicine. I decided to accept their offer and left Yale for Cleveland in 1954. As a beginning Assistant Professor I felt it would be wiser to shift my research objectives to a well defined problem, one for which I could foresee obtaining definitive answers. I relied on my prior scientific experience and chose determining the missing reactions in the tryptophan biosynthetic pathway. Although many different classes of tryptophan auxotrophs had been isolated in *Neurospora*, *E. coli*, and other organisms, only two intermediates in the tryptophan pathway had been identified, anthranilate and indole. I chose an enzymological approach in attempting to identify the intermediates in the pathway and initiated my studies by analyzing extracts of wild type and different classes of tryptophan auxotrophs of *E. coli*.

My efforts focused on unidentified intermediates in the tryptophan biosynthetic pathway were successful. Using an enzymological approach we succeeded where others who had employed *in vivo* approaches had failed. The principal reason for this is that the unidentified intermediates in the tryptophan pathway are all phosphorylated. Phosphorylated intermediates accumulated *in vivo* would have been dephosphorylated and therefore inactive when fed to a mutant. With the aid of my graduate student Oliver Smith, the following intermediates were identified: phosphoribosyl anthranilate, carboxyphenylamino-1-deoxyribulose 5-phosphate, and indole-3-glycerol phosphate (IGP). The initial precursor of the tryptophan pathway, chorismic acid, was isolated and identified by Frank Gibson, working with his own group in Australia. Chorismate also serves as precursor of the other aromatic amino acids. With the identification of these additional compounds, the precursor and all the intermediates in the tryptophan biosynthetic pathway were known.

While conducting these studies I made an unanticipated observation that subsequently proved to be of enormous benefit in our colinearity studies. I observed that many tryptophan auxotrophs of *E. coli*, when cultured on growth-limiting levels of tryptophan, produced 20–50 times more tryptophan synthetase than the wild type strain. I thought that the day might come, as it did, when I could exploit this observation to overproduce mutant proteins for purification and analysis. I was aware of the regulatory significance of this observation and concluded that ultimately we should address the regulatory mechanism(s) responsible for this increase.

Despite this temporary diversion in the mid-1950s, I was still committed to establishing the nature of the gene-enzyme relationship. Knowledge about genes, proteins, and protein synthesis was improving, so much so that the gene-enzyme relationship was redefined. The question had matured to the following. *Is the nucleotide sequence of a gene colinear with the amino acid sequence of the corresponding protein?* During this period we learned many new facts about tryptophan synthetase. I thought it might prove to be an ideal enzyme for addressing the colinearity question. Our continuing investigations with this enzyme, from both *Neurospora* and *E. coli*, suggested that it may catalyze the last two reactions in tryptophan formation, the cleavage of IGP to indole and the coupling of indole with serine to form tryptophan. However, there were two observations we could not explain: free indole could not be detected as an intermediate in the conversion of IGP to tryptophan, and the rate of conversion of IGP to indole was lower than its rate of conversion to tryptophan (14). We then had to ask the following question. *Does the enzyme catalyze a third reaction in which IGP and serine react with one another to form tryptophan, or is indole truly the intermediate, and it remains within the enzyme complex?* This puzzle was not satisfactorily solved until the late 1980s. Then, the elegant structural solution for the $\alpha_2\beta_2$ tryptophan synthase (name changed again) enzyme complex of *Salmonella* by Hyde *et al.* (15) revealed that there is a physical tunnel in this enzyme complex connecting the active site of one polypeptide subunit, α, where indole is produced from IGP, to an active site of the second subunit, β_2, where indole reacts with L-serine to form L-tryptophan (15, 16). As you might imagine, it was comforting to have our confusing early observations explained unambiguously by structural and enzymatic studies.

At this stage in my career everything was going well for me at Western Reserve Medical School. I had quality co-workers and I thoroughly enjoyed my interactions with my fellow faculty members, Howard Gest, John Spizizen, David Novelli, Bob Greenberg, and Abe Stavitsky. However, in 1957 I was contacted by Victor Twitty, chairman of the Department of Biological Sciences at Stanford University, and offered a faculty position. Despite my initial disinterest in considering this appointment, I accepted their offer for a variety of reasons, including my learning that Arthur Kornberg's department would be moving to the Stanford campus (to the Stanford Medical School, which was being relocated from San Francisco). Of historical interest, when I arrived at Stanford the laboratory space I was provided was in the basement of old Jordan Hall and was the space previously occupied by Ed Tatum and his research team. I truly was treading in Tatum's footsteps!

Proving or Disproving Gene-Enzyme Colinearity

When setting up my laboratory at Stanford in January of 1958, I decided that the time had come to mount an all out effort to establish or disprove gene-protein colinearity. I was joined in this project by an outstanding young postdoctoral fellow, Irving Crawford, who was recommended to me by Arthur Kornberg. In his exploratory studies with tryptophan synthetase from *E. coli*, Irving was first to establish that the enzyme is a complex composed of nonidentical polypeptide chains. One subunit, TrpA (TSase α), hydrolyzes IGP to indole, whereas the second subunit, TrpB (TSase $\beta2$), covalently joins indole and L-serine to form L-tryptophan (17). However, the enzyme from *Neurospora* is a single polypeptide chain. In what proved to be an extremely valuable observation for our subsequent colinearity studies, Irving found that each *E. coli* subunit activates the other subunit in the reaction that subunit performs alone. This finding suggested that we might be able to detect and assay each inactive TrpA mutant protein enzymatically by measuring its ability to activate the TrpB subunit in the indole plus serine to tryptophan reaction. This expectation proved to be correct; we routinely assayed each mutant TrpA protein during its purification by measuring its activation of TrpB.

We next prepared a set of pure mutant TrpA proteins, each presumably with a single inactivating amino acid change. Good fortune helped us again, for in 1958 Vernon Ingram described an elegant method, "peptide fingerprinting," which he had used to detect peptides with single amino acid changes in mutant human hemoglobins (18). This approach seemed ideal for what we wished to do. If we could identify the single amino acid change in each of our mutant proteins we would then only have to compare the positions of these amino acid changes in TrpA with the order of the corresponding altered sites on a fine structure genetic map of the *trpA* gene to prove or disprove gene-protein colinearity. I knew that we could construct a fine structure genetic map of *trpA* using phage P1, based on a previous genetic study I performed with Ed Lennox (19). I was confident that very shortly we would convincingly prove or disprove gene-protein colinearity.

As one's research accomplishments become better known to the scientific community, increasing numbers of young scientists will apply to join your group. This necessitates making decisions on what size group you consider optimal and how many projects you wish to attack.

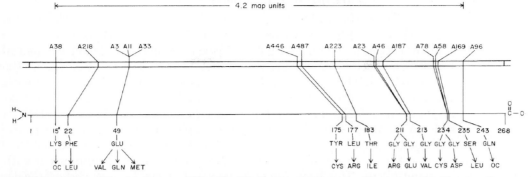

FIG. 2. **Colinearity of the *trpA* gene of *E. coli* with the tryptophan synthase α chain.** The genetic map of *trpA* (*double line above*) reflects the relative positions of the mutationally altered sites examined in the *trpA* gene. This map is based on recombination frequencies observed in mutant by mutant crosses. The corresponding α polypeptide chain is shown below with the numbered position of each amino acid change (and the amino acid change itself) indicated for each mutant. Note that two ochre nonsense changes define the ends of the genetic map. Copied with permission from the *Annual Review of Biochemistry* (101).

Because I enjoyed working at the bench, I felt that I would have sufficient time to serve as advisor to a maximum of about four graduate students and four to six postdoctoral fellows. I had decided sometime earlier to employ two research assistants who would work closely with me, one to perform genetic analyses and the second to carry out biochemical procedures. I was extremely fortunate that an exceptionally bright and competent assistant, Ginny Horn, joined my group in 1958. She performed many of our genetic analyses for over 40 years. A series of talented assistants provided my biochemical "hands."

In the early 1960s the colinearity problem was well publicized. Progress was being made in several laboratories, and it was discussed at many scientific meetings. Outstanding young scientists who joined my group to work on this problem were Don Helinski, Ulf Henning, and Barbara Maling, followed by Bruce Carlton, John Guest, and Gabriel Drapeau. Of considerable aid in our genetic analyses was the use of overlapping *trpA* deletion mutants for initial localization of primary mutations on our fine structure genetic map of the *trpA* gene. Thus we exploited the approach used so successfully by Seymour Benzer. We obtained *trpA* deletion mutants by selecting bacteria resistant to phage T1 and screened for those requiring tryptophan for growth. These arose because the *tonB* locus is close to the *trpA* locus, and *tonB* deletions that confer resistance to phage T1 often extend into *trpA*. The contributions of the individuals mentioned above and those who replaced them established colinearity of the TrpA protein with the *trpA* gene in the early 1960s. I first described our findings supporting colinearity at the Cold Spring Harbor Symposium of 1963 (20). Our complete proof was published in 1964 (21) (Fig. 2). Because thoroughness was an essential element of my strategy, we continued our protein sequencing analyses until the entire amino acid sequence of the 268-residue TrpA protein was completed in 1967 (22). This was by no means a trivial feat, given the technology then available. At that time I believe the TrpA protein was the longest polypeptide to have been completely sequenced.

As mentioned, we were not the only group addressing the colinearity problem. Comparable studies were being performed with the alkaline phosphatase of *E. coli* by Rothman, Garen, and Levinthal, the lysozyme of phage T4 by Streisinger and Dreyer, the rII locus of phage T4 by Benzer and co-workers, and by others working with different gene-protein systems (23). During this period Sydney Brenner and his co-workers also established gene-protein colinearity using a simpler, ingenious strategy (24). They reasoned that the length of a polypeptide chain should be determined by the location of the first in phase stop codon in a coding region. Applying this logic they mapped nonsense mutations to different positions in the head protein gene of phage T4 and demonstrated that the length of the head protein fragments these mutants produced correlated with the locations of the stop codon mutations on the genetic map of the head protein gene.

Despite the many findings in the 1960s supporting gene-protein colinearity, we of course were unaware at the time of the existence of splicing, differential splicing, and trans-slicing, common processes that would have weakened our confidence in our conclusion.

Turning to the Genetic Code

Technology did not exist in the 1960s that would allow us to determine the nucleotide changes in our mutated genes. Fine structure genetic mapping, a la Benzer, was the only effective strategy to characterize a mutated gene. However, much was being learned about mutagenesis and mutagen specificity, primarily, as I recall, from studies by Seymour Benzer and Ernst Freese. One of their objectives was to use mutagens with differing specificities to help in deciphering the genetic code. If the code is a triplet code, as deduced by Crick and co-workers (25), and if chemical mutagens do induce specific nucleotide changes in DNA, then it should be possible to correlate specific amino acid changes in any protein with presumed induced nucleotide changes in the specifying gene. This indirect approach, if applied to all 20 amino acids, should reveal the nature of the genetic code. We felt that we could use it with our system to solve the genetic code. This basic question was as follows. *Can we deduce the genetic code by analyzing the amino acid changes in the TrpA proteins of trpA mutants and their revertants, produced with mutagens with differing known specificities?* The following members of my group adopted this strategy: John Guest, Manny Murgola, Hillard Berger, and Bill Brammer. They successfully used specific mutagens to produce multiple classes of revertants from each of our *trpA* mutants and identified the amino acid changes in many mutant and revertant proteins. This approach also laid the groundwork for impressive subsequent studies on mechanisms of suppression, carried out by Manny Murgola. While these studies were under way the entire scientific world, us included, was startled to learn that Marshall Nirenberg had developed an elegant *in vitro* method that would allow the complete genetic code to be deciphered quickly and unambiguously. Despite our inability to compete with Nirenberg, we did obtain appreciable *in vivo* data supporting his deductions for over 45 codons (26). We also performed mutant by mutant crosses with mutants bearing different amino acid changes at the same TrpA position and showed that genetic recombination can occur within a coding triplet and yield a recombinant amino acid (27).

Other Gene-Protein Issues

While performing studies on the proteins of "revertants" of *trpA* mutants, Don Helinski noticed that some presumed revertants retained the original mutant amino acid change. Prototrophy in these revertants was because of a compensating, second amino acid change. We named this phenomenon "second site reversion" (28). Helinski also observed that the second site amino acid change in one of these "revertants," when introduced alone in TrpA, also inactivated the protein. Thus, two inactivating single amino acid changes, when combined in the same protein, could restore enzyme activity. These findings could not be explained at the time, and it was apparent that they would have to await structural examination. When three-dimensional structure of the tryptophan synthase enzyme complex of *Salmonella* was solved in the late 1980s it was observed that the residues altered in the second site mutants were all in close spatial proximity in the active site of the TrpA subunit (15). Computer graphics modeling predicted that the compensating residue changes acted by restoring the proper geometry of the substrate binding site in TrpA (29).

Returning to Suppression

A familiar question resurfaced in the early 1960s in our studies with *trpA* mutants. *How does a mutation in a specific suppressor gene permit a trpA missense mutant to produce a functional enzyme?* Stu Brody purified the active TrpA protein of one suppressed missense mutant and used peptide fingerprinting analyses to show that the active protein has the wild type residue, Gly, rather than the mutant residue, Arg, at the critical position in the TrpA protein (30). He postulated that suppression causes translational misreading of the mutant Arg codon, leading to the insertion of the wild type amino acid, Gly, at the critical position in the protein. When Brody became aware of the role of transfer RNAs in protein synthesis, he postulated that his missense suppressors, like previously characterized nonsense suppressors, might produce an altered transfer RNA that incorporates the wrong amino acid. This proposal was confirmed experimentally in beautiful studies with transcripts of synthetic DNAs of defined sequences by John Carbon and Paul Berg (31) and N. Gupta and Gobind Khorana (32). Paul has described our personal interactions that led to these successful *in vitro* studies (33).

Opening Pandora's Box

Following completion of our colinearity studies and our foray into deducing the genetic code, there were many unsolved biological problems begging for our attention. The course I followed was conservative; I decided to exploit the knowledge we had recently gathered and attempt to deducing answer what I considered the next set of important questions including the following. *How does each trp enzyme catalyze its respective reaction? What are the three-dimensional structures of the trp enzymes, and how are they related? What are the advantages of forming two enzyme complexes, each containing two different trp polypeptides? What is the purpose of producing two bifunctional trp polypeptides? What is the significance, if any, of the order and organization of the trp genes in the trp operon? What is the explanation for the polar effect of nonsense mutations on downstream gene expression, and what is its significance? What are the important features of transcription, translation, and mRNA degradation for the trp operon of E. coli? What were the ancestral sources of the genes specifying the trp biosynthetic enzymes?* Addressing one of these biochemical questions, graduate student Tom Creighton analyzed the subunit structure of the tryptophan synthetase enzyme complex in the mid-1960s. In a collaborative study with Michel Goldberg and Robert Baldwin of the Biochemistry Department at Stanford, they concluded that this enzyme complex has an $\alpha\beta\beta\alpha$ structure (where α isTrpA and β is TrpB) with α alone existing as a monomer and β alone as a $\beta2$ dimer (34). Convinced that structural information was essential if we were to provide a thorough understanding of this enzyme's action, Ulf Henning grew beautiful crystals of the *E. coli* α chain hoping they would be suitable for crystallographic analysis. In addition, I spent a summer at the University of California in San Diego exploring with members of Joe Kraut's group the possibility of growing α chain crystals satisfactory for structure determination. This approach was pursued by Tom Creighton when he moved to Yale. He had some success, but unfortunately satisfactory crystals of the tryptophan synthase α subunit of *E. coli* could not be grown reproducibly. On a related project, John Hardman of my group initiated studies on the three cysteine residues in the TrpA polypeptide that we thought were essential. His findings on substrate protection of these three cysteines were provocative, but it was evident that without the three-dimensional structure of the protein for reference, these active site studies would be inconclusive. I therefore discontinued work on this project. As I mentioned, the structure of the $\alpha\beta\beta\alpha$ tryptophan synthase enzyme complex from *Salmonella* was eventually solved by Craig Hyde, Edith Miles, David Davies, and their co-workers (15). The structural information they provided served as an invaluable resource for many years, allowing crucial questions to be answered, such as how do the two active sites in the enzyme complex catalyze their respective reactions and how are these sites cross-activated by substrate binding (16, 35).

Ted Cox took a broader view of the consequences of mutations and questioned their impact on organism well being and survival. While with me he began his studies with the *mutT* mutator gene of *E. coli*. In 1967 we showed that *mutT* causes AT to CG mutations preferentially and that continued cultivation of strains with *mutT* led to a uniform shift in the base composition of their total DNA (36). The changes he detected represented about a 0.2–0.5% increase in GC composition. This observation raised additional questions. *What fraction of the residues in each protein is essential? What fraction of the base pairs in the genome of E. coli can be changed without having serious consequences?* I decided not to address these questions at this time.

Turning Our Attention to Organization and Expression of the trp Operon

In the mid 1960s the features of the *trp* operon of *E. coli* that contributed to its expression were poorly understood. The order of the five genes in the operon had been established, but very little was known about operon transcription or how *trp* mRNA translation and degradation proceeded or how these processes were regulated. These basic questions were exciting to young molecular microbiologists, and new members of my group were eager to address one or more of these problems. My co-workers on these subjects from the mid-1960s to the early 1970s were Ron Somerville, Dan Morse, Ray Mosteller, Ron Baker, Robert Baker, Jack Rose, Jun Ito, Fumio Imamoto, Ethel Jackson, Jes Forchhammer, and Sota Hiraga. Of significant aid in our mRNA studies was the use of a temperate bacteriophage, $\phi80$, characterized by A. Matsushiro. This phage genome integrates adjacent to the *trp* operon, allowing one to obtain improperly excised transducing phage that carry different segments of the *trp* operon. The DNAs of these *trp* transducing phage could then be used to detect and measure the relative amounts of labeled mRNA derived from any segment of the operon. A very important, but unrelated project, was carried out with this phage by Naomi Franklin, who was then in my laboratory, with Bill Dove at our Medical School. They provided genetic evidence indicating that during lysogenization the φ80 genome is inserted into the bacterial chromosome. I believe this was the first experimental evidence supporting the Campbell integration model of lysogenization (37).

Using the isolated DNA of *trp* transducing phage bearing different segments of the *trp* operon, RNA hybridization data were gathered for different genes of the operon. It was shown that the operon specifies a single polycistronic *trp* mRNA encoding all five of the *trp* polypeptides and that the transcript was translated as it was being synthesized. It was also observed that nascent *trp* mRNA was generally attacked before its synthesis was completed. Thus most *trp* transcripts isolated from growing cultures were less than full length (38). The last coding region of the *trp* operon transcript, *trpA* mRNA, was found to be degraded in the 3′ to 5′ direction (39). Most nonsense mutations in the first four genes of the operon had a negative, polar effect on downstream gene expression, reducing both *trp* mRNA and protein levels for the downstream genes (40). This "polarity" was a common observation with many bacterial systems. We also found that the untranslated mRNA segment immediately downstream of each introduced nonsense codon was particularly labile (41), consistent with Rho-mediated transcription termination in the untranslated region of the messenger and 3′ to 5′ degradation of each untranslated mRNA segment. Ron Somerville observed continued synthesis of the TrpA polypeptide, but not the TrpB polypeptide, upon prolonged tryptophan starvation (42). His findings were consistent with the presence of a single Trp residue in TrpB but none in TrpA (43). The location of the internal promoter within the *trp* operon, previously identified by Bauerle and Margolin in the *Salmonella trp* operon (44), was determined for *E. coli* by Ethel Jackson of my group by preparing and examining internal deletions in the operon (45). Ultimately its nucleotide sequence (for *E. coli*) was established by Terry Platt's group when Terry had his own laboratory (46). In other studies with the TrpA protein, Dave Jackson observed that he could complement (restore activity to) a mutant TrpA polypeptide *in vitro* by unfolding and refolding the polypeptide in the presence of a second mutant TrpA polypeptide that had an amino acid change elsewhere in the protein (47). Refolding of a mixture of mutant polypeptides allowed this normally monomeric protein to occasionally form an active dimeric species. Restoration of enzyme activity also was observed upon refolding a mutant polypeptide in the presence of a short fragment of wild type polypeptide that corresponds to the mutated segment (47). A model has been proposed explaining these examples of *in vitro* complementation (16). These studies suggested interesting approaches that could be used in studying the mechanism of protein folding.

On to Operon Regulation

Despite these advances, we had not yet begun to address what was becoming the most challenging question for most bacterial physiologists. *How is transcription of your operon regulated?* In early regulatory studies with the *trp* operon of *E. coli*, Georges Cohen and Francois Jacob identified a presumed repressor locus, *trpR*, that appeared to negatively regulate expression of the *trp* operon. In the early 1960s the only additional regulatory observation that concerned tryptophan biosynthesis was the finding that the enzyme catalyzing the initial reaction in the pathway, anthranilate synthase, was feedback-inhibited by tryptophan. Feedback inhibition of the enzyme performing the first reaction in a pathway is common to most biosynthetic pathways. At this time we were reasonably comfortable with the belief that repression plus feedback inhibition for the *trp* operon could deal with all the regulatory needs of the bacterium. To analyze repression more thoroughly, Cathy Squires and Jack Rose of my group partially purified the *trp* repressor and (with the aid of Goeffrey Zubay and H. L. Yang) performed *in vitro* analyses showing that the *trp* repressor is tryptophan-activated and that the repressor does inhibit transcription initiation at the *trp* operon promoter. Follow-up studies by Jack Rose, Cathy Squires, Frank Lee, Rick Kelley, George Bennett, and Rob Gunsalus developed the *trp* repressor-*trp* operator into an excellent experimental system. They showed that the repressor is a dimer, that it has two helix-turn-helix DNA binding domains, and that crucial base pairs in the palindromic *trp* operator are required for repressor binding (48–52). With the aid of Andrzej Joachimiak from Paul Sigler's group, the *trp* repressor was purified and initially characterized. Sigler's group then initiated their elegant studies culminating in determination of the three-dimensional structures of the *trp* aporepressor, the tryptophan-activated *trp* repressor, and the *trp* repressor-*trp* operator complex (53). Their studies represent one of the most thorough analyses of repressor action. Oleg Jardetzky's group at Stanford, using NMR technology, also established the structures of the aporepressor, repressor, and repressor-operator complex (54). Our parallel *in vivo* studies revealed that the activated *trp* repressor reduces transcription initiation at the *trp* operon promoter/operator region about 80-fold (55). The *trp* repressor was also shown to regulate transcription initiation at the promoter/operators of several other operons concerned with tryptophan metabolism, in addition to being autoregulatory. Several of these operator regions have multiple repressor binding sites; for example, the *trp* operon operator region has three (56, 57). Excellent studies on these and other features of *trp* repressor action have been performed by scientists at other institutions: Janette Carey, C. Robert Matthews, C. L. Lawson, K. S. Matthews, C. A. Royer, C. H. Arrowsmith, and others.

A Surprise: the trp Operon Is Also Regulated by Transcription Attenuation!

In the early 1970s we were well aware of the findings by other groups who were conducting regulatory studies with amino acid biosynthetic operons of bacteria. The experimental results of Bruce Ames and his co-workers at the University of California, Berkeley, were of particular interest to us because the *his* operon of *Salmonella* they were studying and our *trp* operon had many similarities. Ames showed that transcription of the *his* operon was not regulated by a histidine-responsive *his* repressor; rather, histidinyl-tRNA was implicated as the molecule that was sensed in the regulatory decision (58). Furthermore, the leader region of the *his* operon, not its promoter, appeared to be the site of regulation. Graduate student Ford Doolittle of my group was persuaded to consider these findings seriously, and he performed a series of regulatory studies with slightly defective *E. coli* tryptophanyl-tRNA synthetase mutants. His results demonstrated that tryptophanyl-tRNA is not involved in *trp* repressor action; thus his findings put our concerns to rest, at least for the moment (59). However, measurements of *trp* mRNA levels carried out during this period by Ron Baker of my group suggested that there may be a second regulatory mechanism, distinct from repression, that regulates transcription of the *trp* operon of *E. coli*. Baker observed that mutants lacking a functional *trp* repressor still responded to tryptophan starvation by increasing their rate of synthesis of *trp* mRNA. Consistent with this observation was the finding by Fumio Imamoto, then back in his own laboratory in Japan, that transcription in progress in the initial segment of the *trp* operon was stopped prematurely upon addition of tryptophan to a tryptophan-starved culture. We wondered: *what is the significance of these regulatory findings?*

Explaining Transcription Attenuation

In the early 1970s Ethel Jackson made the key observation that convinced me to search for a regulatory mechanism distinct from repression that regulates transcription of the *trp* operon (60). As mentioned, Ethel developed a procedure that allowed her to isolate deletions with both end points within the *trp* operon. Her initial objective was locating the internal promoter precisely. During these studies she made the unexpected observation that a class of internal deletions with one end point in the leader region of the operon, the region just following the promoter and before the first structural gene, *trpE*, increased operon expression 6-fold. This increase also was observed in a repressor minus strain! This suggested that there may be a second regulatory site, possibly a site of regulated transcription termination, that can influence *trp* operon expression (60). At about the same time, A. Kasai, at Johns Hopkins University, was performing similar analyses of the effects of deletions that ended in the leader region of the *his* operon of *Salmonella*. Kasai also concluded that the *his* operon leader region may contain a regulated site of transcription termination (61). He introduced the term "transcription attenuation" to describe the mechanism of transcription regulation that presumably occurs at this site. I adopted this term in our studies with the *trp* operon because I felt it was entirely appropriate.

Attenuation Proves to Be a Complex, Multistep Process

In the early and mid-1970s most members of my group were studying features of the *trp* operon and tryptophan metabolism that we believed contributed to operon expression or regulation. We did not appreciate that each was analyzing an event that was crucial to transcription attenuation. The *trp* operon leader region (the genetic segment responsible for transcription attenuation) was isolated and characterized. It is ~160 bp in length and is located between the promoter and the first major structural gene of the operon. This "leader region" was sequenced, first as RNA, and then, when DNA sequencing technology became available, as DNA. This sequence raised several new questions requiring our immediate attention. *What features of the leader region are responsible for transcription attenuation? Is tryptophan or tRNA^{Trp} the signal that is recognized during attenuation in the trp operon? Does the leader region sequence provide any clues that would help us to explain how one of these molecules could act as a regulatory signal?* A potential transcription termination site was located in the leader region just before *trpE*. It had all the features now ascribed to intrinsic transcription termination sites. The members of my group who performed these initial studies were: Kevin Bertrand, Craig Squires, Cathy Squires, Frank Lee, Morley Bronson, Terry Platt, Laurence Korn, George Bennett, Iwona Stroynowski, and Giuseppe Miozzari. Terry Platt had been attempting to identify all the ribosome binding sites in *trp* operon mRNA. He detected one ribosome binding site that was unanticipated; it was located in the leader segment of the transcript. This was an exciting discovery because this site was associated with a 14-residue coding region with two adjacent tryptophan codons. This coding region was located just prior to the terminator sequence. To explore the function of this leader peptide coding region we added the following questions to our "list" of those we felt must be addressed. *What is the role of the transcript's leader peptide coding region, is it regulatory, and does it allow regulation of transcription termination? If it is regulatory, do the Trp codons in the leader peptide coding participate in the regulatory decision? Is the regulatory signal that is sensed uncharged tRNA^{Trp}?* It was evident we were dealing with unfamiliar events in a complex process. Fortunately for us, previous findings with the *his* operon addressed several of these questions; therefore they were extremely helpful. In retrospect, every member of my group contributed to answers to one or more of these questions. We were aided in these studies by Larry Soll, a former student of Paul Berg, who was then at the University of Colorado; Larry performed some of the crucial early experiments implicating tRNA^{Trp} as the regulatory signal (62). Dan Morse, after leaving my laboratory, independently contributed findings establishing the role of uncharged tRNA^{Trp} in *trp* operon attenuation (63). It was becoming clear that transcription attenuation in the *trp* operon involved several sequential events, each dependent upon specific sequences in the transcript of the leader region.

Of particular significance during this period was the finding by graduate student Frank Lee that the *trp* leader transcript could fold to form alternative hairpin structures, each of which plays an essential role in determining whether transcription termination will occur (64). One RNA hairpin serves as a transcription terminator; it directs RNA polymerase to terminate transcription. The second, alternative RNA hairpin functions as an antiterminator. Inspection of the sequence revealed that prior formation of the antiterminator would prevent formation of the terminator. Which of the alternative hairpin structures would form would depend on the cell's ability to translate the two Trp codons in the 14-residue leader peptide coding region. When these two tryptophan codons are translated, the antiterminator would not form; this would allow the terminator to form and terminate transcription (65, 66). When cells are deficient in charged tRNA^{Trp} the translating ribosome would stall at one of the Trp codons. This stalling would promote antiterminator formation, which would then prevent formation of the terminator (65, 66).

Studies over the past 30 years have shown that transcription attenuation is a common regulatory process; variations are used by many bacterial species and their viruses (67). Several transcription attenuation mechanisms are described in a recent review by Henkin and myself (68). In the earliest studied example of regulation by transcription termination/anti-termination, the N protein of bacteriophage λ was shown to prevent Rho-dependent transcription termination during transcription of a region of the phage genome. Attenuation in the *his* operon of *Salmonella*, as mentioned, also was an early studied example; most of its features closely resemble those of attenuation in the *E. coli trp* operon. More recently it has been learned that in addition to ribosome and protein-mediated transcription attenuation decisions, uncharged tRNA (69) and various metabolites can interact directly with leader RNA and regulate transcription termination (70). For example, many of the genes encoding aminoacyl-tRNA synthetases in *B. subtilis* and other Gram-positive bacteria have been shown by Frank Grundy and Tina Henkin and their co-workers to be regulated by direct tRNA-mediated transcription attenuation (71). There are related translational examples where translation of an upstream mRNA coding region influences translation initiation at the adjacent down-

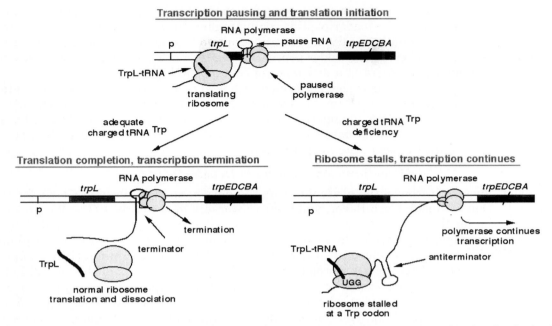

FIG. 3. **A simplified view of the major stages in regulation of transcription termination in the leader region of the *trp* operon of *E. coli*.**

stream coding region (72). Often translation initiation at the downstream coding region is blocked by an appropriate RNA secondary structure; an event occurring during translation of the upstream coding region, such as chloramphenicol binding to the translating ribosome, then exposes the downstream translation initiation region to ribosome loading and translation initiation (72).

Following this initial period of our investigations on transcription attenuation, it was obvious that we would have to establish the role of each segment of the *trp* leader transcript and explain the many events participating in this process. Gerard Zurawski, George Stauffer, and Dirk Elseviers, and sabbatical visitors Keith Brown and Dale Oxender performed important studies that provided a thorough understanding of many of the features of transcription attenuation in the *trp* operon of *E. coli* (65, 66). One obvious, crucial concern that we had not yet addressed was as follows. *How are transcription and translation of the trp leader region coordinated and coupled, as they must be if translation of the leader peptide coding region is to serve as the decision-making event regulating transcription termination?* Postdoctoral fellows Malcolm Winkler, Bob Fisher, Bob Landick, and Jannette Carey answered this question. They established the role of a third hairpin structure that can form in the *trp* leader transcript, a structure that precedes and is an alternative to the antiterminator. This structure, which also serves as an anti-antiterminator, causes the transcribing RNA polymerase to pause during transcription of the leader region (73–76). This pause allows sufficient time for a ribosome to bind to and initiate translation of the leader peptide coding region. Landick and Carey in fact showed that it is this translating ribosome that releases the paused RNA polymerase, allowing transcription and translation to proceed simultaneously (77). This coupling is essential to allow charged or uncharged tRNA^{Trp} to be recognized by the translating ribosome and serve as the regulatory signal. Progress has been made in explaining polymerase-transcript interactions that are responsible for transcription pausing, thanks to thorough studies on this subject by Bob Landick and his group (78) and detailed structural analyses on RNA polymerases and their action provided by Roger Kornberg, Seth Darst, and their co-workers. A simplified view of most of the stages in regulation by transcription attenuation in the *trp* operon of *E. coli* is presented in Fig. 3.

In vivo analyses were also performed to assess the relative contributions of repression and transcription termination in regulating *trp* operon expression (55). We concluded that repression regulates transcription initiation in the *trp* operon about 80-fold, with repression at a minimum during growth with little or no tryptophan. In contrast, transcription attenuation in the *trp* operon of *E. coli* allows only 6-fold regulation, with termination being relieved only when cells are virtually depleted of charged tRNA^{Trp}. The relative insensitivity of attenuation regulation of the *trp* operon to the accumulation of uncharged tRNA^{Trp} reflects the presence of only two Trp codons in the *trp* leader peptide coding region. In the *his* operon of *Salmonella*, for example, where attenuation is the major transcription regulatory mechanism, there are seven contiguous His codons in the leader peptide coding region. This organization makes the *his* operon particularly sensitive to a deficiency of charged tRNA^{His}.

DNA microarray analyses have been performed with wild type *E. coli* and several regulatory mutants under a variety of growth conditions that influence tryptophan metabolism (79). In general the changes in mRNA abundance observed are consistent both qualitatively and quantitatively with expectations based on years of studies of tryptophan metabolism. As expected, many indirect effects were also observed.

Miscellaneous Important Developments

A major advance in conventional cloning was the development of plasmid ColE1 for this purpose by Don Helinski, Herb Boyer, and their co-workers in the early 1970s. We provided the *trp* operon for these studies and analyzed its expression in their classic plasmid cloning/ overexpression paper (80). When DNA cloning and sequencing procedures became available, my group collaborated with several of my former students in determining the complete 7000-base pair sequence of the *trp* operon of *E. coli*; this sequence was published in 1981 (43). Inspection of the nucleotide sequence of the operon revealed many unsuspected features. Among these was the presence of overlapping stop and start codons, UGAUG, joining *trpE* and *trpD*, and *trpB* and *trpA* (43). This punctuation arrangement was intriguing because we already knew that both the TrpE and TrpD polypeptides, and the TrpB and TrpA polypeptides, associate to form enzyme complexes. *We wondered, what is the significance of these stop/start overlaps? Do they allow some form of translational coupling that ensures that the cell synthesizes equal numbers of polypeptides that will form an enzyme complex?* Dan Oppenheim and Anath Das addressed these questions and concluded that translation of these adjacent coding regions is coupled, *i.e.* equal numbers of the two polypeptides encoded by adjacent regions are produced only when the upstream coding region is translated to completion at its overlapping stop codon (81, 82). Translation initiation and termination obviously are very complex processes; transcript sequences can have profound effects on these events.

Studies on Regulation of Tryptophan Degradation

E. coli and many other bacteria have the ability to degrade tryptophan. They produce the enzyme tryptophanase, which degrades tryptophan to indole, pyruvate, and ammonia. Pyruvate and ammonia can be used as carbon and nitrogen sources. Indole's role, other than serving as a tryptophan precursor, is not clear, although recent evidence suggests that it may act as a volatile signal molecule during biofilm formation and quorum sensing (83, 84). The latter observations raise an additional unexpected question. *Is the purpose of the tunnel connecting the two active sites of tryptophan synthase to prevent biosynthetic indole from escaping into the environment?*

Because degradation of tryptophan would be expected to influence regulation of its synthesis, I decided in the early 1980s that it was essential that we thoroughly investigate the tryptophanase (*tna*) operon and how it is regulated. Our initial questions were as follows. *How is the tna operon organized? How is this operon regulated? What are the effects of tna operon expression on trp operon expression and regulation?* Studies on these questions were initiated by Mike Deeley; he was followed on this project by Valley Stewart, Paul Gollnick, Kurt Gish, Ajith Kamath, Vincent Konan, and most recently, Feng Gong. The *tna* operon of *E. coli* has two structural genes, one encoding tryptophanase and the second specifying a tryptophan permease. Transcription initiation in this operon had been shown by others to be regulated by catabolite repression. In our investigations we discovered that transcription of the structural genes of this operon is regulated by a novel mechanism of transcription attenuation. This mechanism is based on features of the nucleotide sequence of the operon's ~300-bp leader region. Tryptophan is the signal molecule that leads to relief from transcription termination. When cultures are growing without excess tryptophan, Rho factor binds to the nascent *tna* operon leader transcript. Bound Rho then contacts the transcribing polymerase that is paused at one of several pause sites in the leader region, and it instructs it to terminate transcription (85, 86). If cultures are growing with high levels of tryptophan, Rho factor's ability to bind to the leader RNA is prevented. Therefore the paused polymerase resumes transcription into the structural genes of the operon (85, 86). Synthesis of a 24-residue tryptophan-containing leader peptide, TnaC, as well as high levels of free tryptophan are required for induction (86). It is thought that the combined action of the nascent uncleaved TnaC-peptidyl-tRNA and bound tryptophan inhibits peptidyl transferase cleavage of the TnaC-peptidyl-tRNA (87, 88). The uncleaved TnaC-peptidyl-tRNA therefore remains associated with the translating ribosome, preventing it from dissociating from the transcript. The stalled ribosome then blocks Rho factor's access to the transcript, thereby allowing the paused polymerase to resume transcription (87). Recent studies suggest that the tryptophan binding/induction site may be the site normally occupied by the aminoacyl moiety of a charged tRNA during translation (88). These findings raise challenging questions about the functional flexibility of the ribosome, questions that become more interesting when they are related to recent exciting structural studies with the ribosome. *What are the structural features of the tryptophan binding site created in the ribosome? How does the tryptophan residue at position 12 of the leader peptide create or modify this binding site? How does bound tryptophan inhibit peptidyl transferase?* The presence of active tryptophanase in a growing culture reduces the tryptophan concentration, which increases *trp* operon expression (89).

Evolutionary Issues

As our gene structure and function studies progressed, many evolutionary questions arose. *Do other organisms use the same genes, proteins, operon organization, and regulatory processes as E. coli in performing tryptophan biosynthesis and its regulation? Can homologous segments of a trp polypeptide from two species be exchanged without loss of enzyme activity? What were the ancestors of the present day genes and proteins of tryptophan biosynthesis?* Members of my group who addressed these questions were Steven Li, Iwona Stroynowski, Bill Schneider, Brian Nichols, Richard Denney, Mike Manson, Joan Hanlon, Eric Selker, and Giuseppe Miozarri. To begin with, the *trp* genes of many organisms were cloned and partially or completely sequenced; the sequences and genetic locations then were compared. Many other laboratories provided comparable information for their favorite genes and operons. Comparative studies with the *trp* genes revealed that all organisms that synthesize tryptophan use the same seven catalytic enzyme domains. The enzymes of the tryptophan biosynthetic pathway therefore probably evolved just once. However, within each polypeptide, when one compares different species, there is appreciable sequence variation. This is typical for most protein evolutionary comparisons. In one beautiful study performed in my laboratory by Bill Schneider and Brian Nichols, segments of the TrpAs of *E. coli* and *Salmonella* were exchanged, generating recombinant TrpA polypeptides. All the recombinant TrpA proteins produced were fully functional despite the fact that 40 of the 268 amino acid residues in the parental homologous TrpA proteins differ (90). This result implies that most of these amino acid differences are tolerable when inserted individually or in clusters.

Evolutionary comparisons of the organization of the seven *trp* genes in different species revealed appreciable variation. In some species the *trp* genes are split in several operons, and often two or more *trp* genes are fused to form multifunctional enzymes. Regulatory mechanisms also vary considerably, possibly reflecting differences in operon organization and participation of one or more pathway intermediates in a second pathway. Nucleotide sequence divergence for the *trp* genes correlated well with predictions of species relatedness based on analyses of ribosomal RNA sequences although there are some hints of horizontal transfer.

Understandably, I was particularly interested in knowing whether the features of repression and transcription attenuation observed with the *trp* operon of *E. coli* are conserved in unrelated species. Among the enteric bacteria we examined the major features were retained, although there was considerable leader sequence variation, presumably reflecting slightly different species-specific objectives (91). Mitzi Kuroda of my group initiated comparative regulatory studies with the *trp* operon of a second well studied prokaryote, *B. subtilis*. We were joined in this effort by Dennis Henner and his group at Genentech when we learned that he too was concerned with this problem. We already knew that there were significant differences in *trp* gene and operon organization in *B. subtilis versus E. coli*. *B. subtilis* has seven distinct *trp* genes, only six of which are clustered as a *trp* operon. Furthermore the six-gene *trp* operon is located within an aromatic supraoperon, which has three additional upstream genes and three additional downstream genes, each concerned with some aspect of aromatic amino acid metabolism (92). The seventh *trp* gene, *trpG*, is located in the folate biosynthetic operon (92). Its location is logical because its polypeptide product, TrpG, is a glutamine amidotransferase that is a component of two similar enzyme complexes, one catalyzing *para*-aminobenzoate synthesis in the folate pathway and the second catalyzing *ortho*-aminobenzoate (anthranilate) formation in the tryptophan pathway. The studies by Mitzi Kuroda and the Henner group were followed by investigations in my laboratory by Paul Gollnick, Paul Babitzke, Joe Sarsero, Enrique Merino, and most recently, by Angela Valbuzzi and Guang-nan Chen. The basic features of attenuation regulation of *trp* operon expression in *B. subtilis* were established; they were quite different from those used for the *trp* operon of *E. coli*. Although alternative antiterminator and terminator hairpin structures also participate in the transcription termination decision, an 11-subunit tryptophan-activated RNA-binding protein, named TRAP, is used by *B. subtilis* to disrupt the antiterminator and promote terminator formation (93–95). We selected TRAP as the name for this protein because it is a t̲rp R̲NA-binding a̲ttenuation p̲rotein (93). Tryptophan-activated TRAP also binds *trpG* mRNA and several other RNAs concerned with tryptophan metabolism. The TRAP binding sites in these transcripts all overlap translation start sites; thus TRAP binding also regulates translation initiation (93). Furthermore, TRAP binding to *trp* operon leader RNA indirectly regulates translation initiation at the *trpE* start site (96). A most interesting recent discovery in my laboratory is that *B. subtilis* contains a previously unidentified regulatory operon, *rtpA-ycbK*, that is designed to sense (and respond to) uncharged tRNA^{Trp} (97). We named the *rtpA* protein AT (Anti-TRAP) because it is designed to bind to and inactivate tryptophan-activated TRAP (98, 99). Transcription of the *rtpA-ycbK* operon is regulated by tRNA^{Trp}-mediated transcription attenuation by the T box antitermination mechanism discovered by Grundy and Henkin (69). We recently observed that uncharged tRNA^{Trp} accumulation has a second regulatory effect on the *rtpA-ycbK* operon; it increases translation of *rtpA*, thereby providing higher levels of AT protein (G. Chen and C. Yanofsky, manuscript in preparation). Thus *B. subtilis* employs two independent mechanisms of sensing uncharged tRNA^{Trp} in this operon; one is transcriptional and the second translational; both regulate AT synthesis (G. Chen and C. Yanofsky, manuscript in preparation). DNA microarray analyses have also been performed with wild type and regulatory mutants of *B. subtilis* to analyze the total genome's transcriptional response during growth under nutritional conditions that affect tryptophan metabolism (R. M. Berka, X. Cui, and C. Yanofsky, manuscript in preparation). The genes we expected to respond did; however, many additional genes responded comparably, suggesting that their expression is closely tied to the genes involved in tryptophan synthesis.

The knowledge we have gathered in our studies on tryptophan metabolism in *E. coli* and *B. subtilis* raise the very tough "why" question. *Why do E. coli and B. subtilis use such dissimilar mechanisms to sense tryptophan and tryptophan tRNA as regulatory signals?* I would love to know the answer!

Enzyme Structural Questions

One particular set of challenging questions was always on my wish list, but I left these questions for other scientists to answer. *What are the three-dimensional structures of the seven protein domains required for tryptophan synthesis? Are any of these domains evolutionarily related? What are the likely ancestral sources of the seven catalytic domains?* I am delighted to report that the three-dimensional structures for all seven protein domains required for tryptophan synthesis have been determined. This knowledge should permit investigators to consider structural as well as catalytic issues when attempting to deduce possible evolutionary origins for these domains. Interestingly, the structures of three of the tryptophan pathway enzymes are 8-fold $\alpha\beta$ barrels. Particularly exciting in this regard is the recent demonstration that an enzyme catalyzing a reaction in histidine biosynthesis (a reaction similar to one catalyzed by an enzyme of the tryptophan pathway) was converted into an active *trp* enzyme by introducing a single amino acid change (100). Given the extraordinary wealth of information being provided by sequence analyses, evolutionary exploration of enzyme origins should be an interesting subject for future investigations.

Returning to Neurospora

Whenever I selected a research project for one of my graduate students I was well aware that this individual might prefer to work on some other problem as a member of my group. Eric Selker, an exceptional graduate student who joined me in the late 1970s, decided that the project I had assigned him, characterizing the genes of the *trp* operon of *Salmonella typhimurium*, would not break new ground, and therefore he preferred to work on a project that was more challenging. He proposed reintroducing *N. crassa* into my laboratory as an experimental organism. As I recall, I resisted Eric's proposal to switch his project only modestly. I knew this organism well, and most importantly, one of my closest colleagues, David Perkins, whose laboratory is just down the hall, was a major contributor to *Neurospora* research. Eric convinced me that the time had come to apply the procedures, technology, and concepts developed in studies with bacteria and yeast to the superb experimental eukaryote selected by Beadle and Tatum as their experimental organism. At a minimum, I thought, we should be able to compare the genes and proteins of tryptophan metabolism and their regulation in *N. crassa* with those in *E. coli*. A few years later a second bright graduate student, Vivian Berlin, also with my approval, switched from her initial bacterial studies to apply modern molecular approaches in analyzing an excellent model developmental process in *Neurospora*, asexual spore formation. Many talented graduate students and postdoctoral fellows subsequently joined my group to perform fungal studies. Their work greatly improved the technology that could be applied in investigations with *Neurospora*. Most of these individuals, after leaving my group, continued to make significant scientific contributions in fungal biochemistry and genetics.

My Treasures

Reflecting on what I would consider our two most impressive contributions, I would select proving gene-protein colinearity and determining the stages and features of regulation by transcription attenuation. The first required our identifying the amino acid changes in a set of TrpA mutant proteins and comparing the relative locations of these amino acid changes with the order of the corresponding mutational changes on the genetic map of the *trpA* gene. Essentially, we verified a relationship, which, at the time, we believed existed. Transcription attenuation, by contrast, was a poorly understood process initially thought to be used only rarely. We were required to break new ground and perform step by step analyses of the roles played by tandem overlapping segments of a transcript, as well as explaining how ribosome stalling at either of two Trp codons selects between alternative RNA structures. I had no reason to suspect that transcription attenuation was such a common regulatory strategy or that so many different mechanisms of attenuation existed. I have illustrated in this article how the answers we obtained while focusing on some specific questions invariably raised new unanswered questions. More often than not, these questions were so challenging they could not be ignored.

Despite the enormous satisfaction I feel personally from what we have accomplished scientifically, I believe my greatest pleasure in practicing science has come from the give and take of daily interactions with members of my group and from thoughtful and stimulating discussions with fellow scientists. My journey in science has been great fun! I was very fortunate to have had Dave Bonner as my mentor and lucky that I "grew up" with a wonderful group of smart graduate students. Learning biochemistry from Joseph Fruton was an extraordinary experience. At Western Reserve, Howard Gest, Bob Greenberg, Abe Stavitsky, and John Spizizen were all special friends who contributed to my development. At Stanford, because of our personal friendship and frequent discussions, Paul Berg put his stamp of approval on virtually everything I have done. I have had many other close friends and colleagues at Stanford, including Dave Perkins, Don Kennedy, Norm Wessells, Paul Ehrlich, Bob Schimke, Phil Hanawalt, Bob Simoni, Dale Kaiser, Dave Hogness, Lucy Shapiro, and Bob Lehman. Scientists at other institutions, some of whom spent a sabbatical in my laboratory, also were great friends, including Howard Zalkin, Frank Gibson, Dale Oxender, Ron Bauerle, Kasper Kirschner, Edith Miles, Stan Mills, Michael Chamberlin, and Paul Sigler. Stan Prusiner, an outstanding scientist with completely different interests, became a very close friend. Finally, throughout the past 40+ years of my career Arthur Kornberg's wisdom and commitment have served as models guiding my behavior. There are many other "treasured" individuals who I did not get to mention in this article; I thank you all.

Acknowledgments—I am extremely grateful to Howard Gest, Cathy Squires, Edith Miles, and Robert Simoni for reading a draft of this manuscript and providing many helpful comments. I would also like to acknowledge the support provided for my research activities by the National Institutes of Health, National Science Foundation, American Heart Association, and American Cancer Society. I have previously written a biographical article describing many of our accomplishments (101).

Address correspondence to: yanofsky@cmgm.stanford.edu.

REFERENCES

1. Beadle, G. W., and Tatum, E. L. (1941) Genetic control of biochemical reactions in Neurospora. *Proc. Natl. Acad. Sci. U. S. A.* **27,** 499–506
2. Hershey, A. D., and Chase, M. (1952) Independent functions of viral protein and nucleic acids in growth of bacteriophage. *J. Gen. Physiol.* **36,** 39–56
3. Avery, O. T., MacLeod, C. M., and McCarty, M. (1944) Studies on the chemical nature of the substance inducing transformation of pneumococcal types. *J. Exp. Med.* **79,** 137–157
4. Watson, J. D., and Crick, F. H. C. (1953) Molecular structure of nucleic acids. *Nature* **171,** 737–738
5. Benzer, S. (1957) The elementary units of heredity. In *The Chemical Basis of Heredity*, pp. 70–93, Johns Hopkins University Press, Baltimore, MD
6. Sanger, F. (1952) The arrangement of amino acids in proteins. *Adv. Protein Chem.* **7,** 1–28
7. Umbreit, W. W., Wood, W. A., and Gunsalus, I. C. (1946) The activity of pyridoxal phosphate in tryptophan formation by cell-free enzyme preparations. *J. Biol. Chem.* **165,** 731–732
8. Mitchell, H. K., and Lein, J. (1948) A Neurospora mutant deficient in the enzymatic synthesis of tryptophan. *J. Biol. Chem.* **175,** 481–482
9. Hogness, D. S., and Mitchell, H. K. (1954) Genetic factors influencing the activity of tryptophan desmolase in *Neurospora crassa*. *J. Gen. Microbiol.* **11,** 401–411
10. Yanofsky, C. (1952) The effects of gene change on tryptophan desmolase formation. *Proc. Natl. Acad. Sci. U. S. A.* **38,** 215–226
11. Suskind, S. R., Yanofsky, C., and Bonner, D. M. (1955) Allelic strains of *Neurospora* lacking tryptophan synthetase: a preliminary immunochemical characterization. *Proc. Natl. Acad. Sci. U. S. A.* **41,** 577–582
12. Yanofsky, C. (1956) Gene interactions in enzyme synthesis. *Henry Ford Hospital International Symposium: Enzymes, Units of Biological Structure and Function*, pp. 147–160, Academic Press Inc., New York
13. Yanofsky, C. (1954) The absence of a tryptophan-niacin relationship in *Escherichia coli* and *Bacillus subtilis*. *J. Bacteriol.* **68,** 577–584
14. Yanofsky, C., and Rachmeler, M. (1958) The exclusion of free indole as an intermediate in the biosynthesis of tryptophan in *Neurospora crassa*. *Biochim. Biophys. Acta* **28,** 641–642
15. Hyde, C. C., Ahmed, S. A., Padlan, E. A., Miles, E. W., and Davies, D. R. (1988) Three-dimensional structure of the tryptophan synthase $\alpha_2\beta_2$ multienzyme complex from *Salmonella typhimurium*. *J. Biol. Chem.* **263,** 17857–17871
16. Miles, E. W. (1995) Tryptophan synthase: structure, function, and protein engineering. In *Subcellular Biochemistry, Proteins: Structure, Function, and Protein Engineering* (Biswas, B. B., and Roy, S., eds) Vol. 24, pp. 207–254, Plenum Press, New York
17. Crawford, I. P., and Yanofsky, C. (1958) On the separation of the tryptophan synthetase of *Escherichia coli* into two protein components. *Proc. Natl. Acad. Sci. U. S. A.* **44,** 1161–1170
18. Ingram, V. M. (1958) Abnormal human hemoglobins. 1. The comparison of normal human and sickle-cell hemoglobins by fingerprinting. *Biochim. Biophys. Acta* **28,** 539–545
19. Yanofsky, C., and Lennox, E. S. (1958) Transduction and recombination study of linkage relationships among the genes controlling tryptophan synthesis in *Escherichia coli*. *Virology* **8,** 425–447
20. Yanofsky, C. (1963) Discussion following article by W. Gilbert: Protein Synthesis in *Escherichia coli*. *Cold Spring Harbor Symp. Quant. Biol.* **28,** 296–297
21. Yanofsky, C., Carlton, B. C., Guest, J. R., Helinski, D. R., and Henning, U. (1964) On the colinearity of gene structure and protein structure. *Proc. Natl. Acad. Sci. U. S. A.* **51,** 266–272
22. Yanofsky, C., Drapeau, G. R., Guest, J. R., and Carlton, B. C. (1967) The complete amino acid sequence of the tryptophan synthetase A protein (α subunit) and its colinear relationship with the genetic map of the A gene. *Proc. Natl. Acad. Sci. U. S. A.* **57,** 296–298
23. Rothman, F. G. (1987) Gene-protein relationships in *Escherichia coli* alkaline phosphatase: competition and luck in scientific research. In *Phosphate Metabolism and Cellular Regulation in Microorganisms* (Torriani-Gorini, A., Rothman, F. G., Silver, S., Wright, A., and Yagil, E., eds) pp. 307–311, American Society for Microbiology, Washington, D. C.
24. Sarabhai, A. S., Stretton, A. O. W., Brenner, S., and Bolle, A. (1964) Co-linearity of the gene with the polypeptide chain. *Nature* **201,** 13–17
25. Crick, F. H. C., Barnett, L., Brenner, S., and Watts-Tobin, R. J. (1961) General nature of the genetic code for proteins. *Nature* **192,** 1227–1232
26. Yanofsky, C., Berger, H., and Brammar, W. J. (1969) *In vivo* studies on the genetic code. *Proc. Int. Congr. Genet.* **3,** 155–165
27. Guest, J. R., and Yanofsky, C. (1965) Amino acid replacements associated with reversion and recombination within a coding unit. *J. Mol. Biol.* **12,** 793–804
28. Helinski, D. R., and Yanofsky, C. (1963) A genetic and biochemical analysis of second-site reversion. *J. Biol. Chem.* **238,** 1043–1048
29. Nagata, S., Hyde, C. C., and Miles, E. W. (1989) The α subunit of tryptophan synthase. Evidence that aspartic acid 60 is a catalytic residue and that the double alteration of residues 175 and 211 in a second-site revertant restores the proper geometry of the substrate binding site. *J. Biol. Chem.* **264,** 6288–6296
30. Brody, S., and Yanofsky, C. (1963) Suppressor gene alteration of protein primary structure. *Proc. Natl. Acad. Sci. U. S. A.* **50,** 9–16
31. Carbon, J., Berg, P., and Yanofsky, C. (1966) Missense suppression due to a genetically altered tRNA. *Cold Spring Harbor Symp. Quant. Biol.* **31,** 487–497
32. Gupta, N., and Khorana, H. G. (1966) Missense suppression of the tryptophan synthetase A protein mutant A78. *Proc. Natl. Acad. Sci. U. S. A.* **56,** 772–779
33. Berg, P. (1973) Suppression: a subversion of genetic decoding. *Harvey Lect.* **67,** 247–272
34. Goldberg, M. E., Creighton, T. E., Baldwin, R. L., and Yanofsky, C. (1966) Subunit structure of the tryptophan synthetase of *Escherichia coli*. *J. Mol. Biol.* **21,** 71–82
35. Pan, P., Woehl, E., and Dunn, M. F. (1997) Protein architecture, dynamics and allostery in tryptophan synthase channeling. *Trends Biochem. Sci.* **22,** 22–27
36. Cox, E. C., and Yanofsky, C. (1967) Altered base ratios in the DNA of an *Escherichia coli* mutator strain. *Proc. Natl. Acad. Sci. U. S. A.* **58,** 1895–1902
37. Franklin, N., Dove, W. F., and Yanofsky, C. (1965) The linear insertion of a prophage into the chromosome of *E. coli* shown by deletion mapping. *Biochem. Biophys. Res. Commun.* **18,** 898–909
38. Morse, D. E., Mosteller, R. D., and Yanofsky, C. (1969) Dynamics of synthesis, translation, and degradation of *trp* operon messenger RNA in *E. coli*. *Cold Spring Harbor Symp. Quant. Biol.* **34,** 725–740
39. Baker, R. F., and Yanofsky, C. (1968) Direction of *in vivo* degradation of a messenger RNA. *Nature* **219,** 26–29

40. Imamoto, F., Ito, J., and Yanofsky, C. (1966) Polarity in the tryptophan operon of *E. coli*. *Cold Spring Harbor Symp. Quant. Biol.* **31**, 235–249
41. Imamoto, F., and Yanofsky, C. (1967) Transcription of the tryptophan operon in polarity mutants of *Escherichia coli*. I. Characterization of the tryptophan messenger RNA of polar mutants. *J. Mol. Biol.* **28**, 1–23
42. Somerville, R. L., and Yanofsky, C. (1964) On the translation of the A gene region of tryptophan messenger RNA. *J. Mol. Biol.* **8**, 616–619
43. Yanofsky, C., Platt, T., Crawford, I. P., Nichols, B. P., and Christie, G. E. (1981) Nucleotide sequence of the tryptophan operon of *Escherichia coli*. *Nucleic Acids Res.* **9**, 6647–6668
44. Bauerle, R. H., and Margolin, P. (1967) Evidence for two sites for initiation of gene expression in the tryptophan operon of *Salmonella typhimurium*. *J. Mol. Biol.* **26**, 423–436
45. Jackson, E. N., and Yanofsky, C. (1972) Internal promoter of the tryptophan operon of *Escherichia coli* is located in a structural gene. *J. Mol. Biol.* **69**, 307–313
46. Horowitz, H., and Platt, T. (1982) Identification of *trp-p2*, an internal promoter in the tryptophan operon of *Escherichia coli*. *J. Mol. Biol.* **156**, 257–267
47. Jackson, D. A., and Yanofsky, C. (1969) Restoration of enzymic activity by complementation *in vitro* between mutant α subunits of tryptophan synthetase and between mutant subunits and fragments of the α subunit. *J. Biol. Chem.* **244**, 4539–4546
48. Kelley, R. L., and Yanofsky, C. (1985) Mutational studies with the *trp* repressor of *Escherichia coli* support the helix-turn-helix model of repressor recognition of operator DNA. *Proc. Natl. Acad. Sci. U. S. A.* **82**, 483–487
49. Bennett, G. N., and Yanofsky, C. (1978) Sequence analysis of operator constitutive mutants of the tryptophan operon of *Escherichia coli*. *J. Mol. Biol.* **121**, 179–192
50. Gunsalus, R. P., and Yanofsky, C. (1980) Nucleotide sequence and expression of *Escherichia coli trpR*, the structural gene for the *trp* aporepressor. *Proc. Natl. Acad. Sci. U. S. A.* **77**, 7117–7121
51. Rose, J. K., Squires, C. L., Yanofsky, C., Yang, H. L., and Zubay, G. (1973) Regulation of *in vitro* transcription of the tryptophan operon by purified RNA polymerase in the presence of partially purified repressor and tryptophan. *Nat. New Biol.* **245**, 133–137
52. Squires, C. L., Lee, F. D., and Yanofsky, C. (1975) Interaction of the *trp* repressor and RNA polymerase with the *trp* operon. *J. Mol. Biol.* **92**, 93–111
53. Otwinowski, Z., Schevitz, R. W., Zhang, R. G., Lawson, C. L., Joachimiak, A., Marmorstein, R. Q., Luisi, B. F., and Sigler, P. B. (1988) Crystal structure of *trp* repressor/operator complex at atomic resolution. *Nature* **335**, 321–329
54. Zhang, H., Zhao, D., Revington, M., Lee, W., Jia, X., Arrowsmith, C., and Jardetzky, O. (1994) The solution structures of the *trp* repressor-operator DNA complex. *J. Mol. Biol.* **238**, 592–614
55. Yanofsky, C., Kelley, R. L., and Horn, V. (1984) Repression is relieved before attenuation in the *trp* operon of *Escherichia coli* as tryptophan starvation becomes increasingly severe. *J. Bacteriol.* **158**, 1018–1024
56. Kumamoto, A. A., Miller, W. G., and Gunsalus, R. P. (1987) *Escherichia coli* tryptophan repressor binds multiple sites within the *aroH* and *trp* operators. *Genes Dev.* **1**, 556–564
57. Lawson, C. L., and Carey, J. (1993) Tandem binding in crystals of a *trp* repressor/operator half-site complex. *Nature* **366**, 178–182
58. Roth, J. R., Silbert, D. F., Fink, G. R., Voll, M. J., Anton, D., Hartman, P. E., and Ames, B. N. (1966) Transfer RNA and the control of the histidine operon. *Cold Spring Harbor Symp. Quant. Biol.* **31**, 383–392
59. Doolittle, W. F., and Yanofsky, C. (1968) Mutants of *Escherichia coli* with an altered tryptophanyl-transfer ribonucleic acid synthetase. *J. Bacteriol.* **95**, 1283–1294
60. Jackson, E. N., and Yanofsky, C. (1973) The region between the operator and first structural gene of the tryptophan operon of *Escherichia coli* may have a regulatory function. *J. Mol. Biol.* **76**, 89–101
61. Kasai, T. (1974) Regulation of the expression of the histidine operon in *Salmonella typhimurium*. *Nature* **249**, 523–527
62. Yanofsky, C., and Soll, L. (1977) Mutations affecting tRNA Trp and its charging and their effect on regulation of transcription termination at the attenuator of the tryptophan operon. *J. Mol. Biol.* **113**, 663–677
63. Morse, D. E., and Morse, A. N. (1976) Dual-control of the tryptophan operon is mediated by both tryptophanyl-tRNA synthetase and the repressor. *J. Mol. Biol.* **103**, 209–226
64. Lee, F., Squires, C. L., Squires, C., and Yanofsky, C. (1976) Termination of transcription *in vitro* in the *Escherichia coli* tryptophan operon leader region. *J. Mol. Biol.* **103**, 383–393
65. Yanofsky, C. (2000) Transcription attenuation: once viewed as a novel regulatory strategy. *J. Bacteriol.* **182**, 1–8
66. Yanofsky, C. (1981) Attenuation in the control of expression of bacterial operons. *Nature* **289**, 751–758
67. Merino, E., and Yanofsky, C. (2002) Regulation by termination-antitermination: a genomic approach. In *Bacillus subtilis and Its Closest Relatives: from Genes to Cells* (Sonenshein, A. L., Hoch, J. A., and Losick, R. eds) pp. 323–336, American Society for Microbiology, Washington, D. C.
68. Henkin, T. M., and Yanofsky, C. (2002) Regulation by transcription attenuation in bacteria: how RNA provides instructions for transcription termination/antitermination decisions. *Bioessays* **24**, 700–707
69. Henkin, T. M. (2000) Transcription termination control in bacteria. *Curr. Opin. Microbiol.* **3**, 149–153
70. Winkler, W., Nahvi, A., and Breaker, R. R. (2002) Thiamine derivatives bind messenger RNAs directly to regulate bacterial gene expression. *Nature* **419**, 952–956
71. Grundy, F. J., Winkler, W. C., and Henkin, T. M. (2002) tRNA-mediated transcription antitermination *in vitro*: codon-anticodon pairing independent of the ribosome. *Proc. Natl. Acad. Sci. U. S. A.* **99**, 11121–11126
72. Lovett, M. A., and Rogers, E. (1996) Ribosome regulation by the nascent peptide. *Microbiol. Rev.* **60**, 366–385
73. Landick, R., and Yanofsky, C. (1984) Stability of an RNA secondary structure affects *in vitro* transcription pausing in the *trp* operon leader region. *J. Biol. Chem.* **259**, 11550–11555
74. Fisher, R. F., Das, A., Kolter, R., Winkler, M. E., and Yanofsky, C. (1985) Analysis of the requirements for transcription pausing in the tryptophan operon. *J. Mol. Biol.* **182**, 397–409
75. Winkler, M. E., and Yanofsky, C. (1981) Pausing of RNA polymerase during *in vitro* transcription of the tryptophan operon leader region. *Biochemistry* **20**, 3738–3744
76. Fisher, R., and Yanofsky, C. (1983) A complementary DNA oligomer releases a transcription pause complex. *J. Biol. Chem.* **258**, 9208–9212
77. Landick, R., Carey, J., and Yanofsky, C. (1985) Translation activates the paused transcription complex and restores transcription of the *trp* operon leader region. *Proc. Natl. Acad. Sci. U. S. A.* **82**, 4663–4667
78. Toulokhonov, I., Artsimovitch, I., and Landick, R. (2001) Allosteric control of RNA polymerase by a site that contacts nascent RNA hairpins. *Science* **292**, 730–733
79. Khodursky, A. B., Peter, B. J., Cozzarelli, N. R., Botstein, D., Brown, P. O., and Yanofsky, C. (2000) DNA microarray analysis of gene expression in response to physiological and genetic changes that affect tryptophan metabolism in *Escherichia coli*. *Proc. Natl. Acad. Sci. U. S. A.* **97**, 12170–12175
80. Hershfield, V., Boyer, H. W., Yanofsky, C., Lovett, M. A., and Helinski, D. R. (1974) Plasmid ColEl as a molecular

vehicle for cloning and amplification of DNA. _Proc. Natl. Acad. Sci. U. S. A._ **71,** 3455–3459

81. Oppenheim, D. S., and Yanofsky, C. (1980) Translational coupling during expression of the tryptophan operon of _Escherichia coli._ _Genetics_ **95,** 785–795

82. Das, A., and Yanofsky, C. (1989) Restoration of a translational stop-start overlap reinstates translational coupling in a mutant _trpB-trpA_ gene pair of the _Escherichia coli_ tryptophan operon. _Nucleic Acids Res._ **17,** 9333–9340

83. Di Martino, P., Merieau, A., Phillips, R., Orange, N., and Hulen, C. (2002) Isolation of an _Escherichia coli_ strain mutant unable to form biofilm on polystyrene and to adhere to human pneumocyte cells: involvement of tryptophanase. _Can. J. Microbiol._ **48,** 132–137

84. Wang, D., Ding, X., and Rather, P. N. (2001) Indole can act as an extracellular signal in _Escherichia coli._ _J. Bacteriol._ **183,** 4210–4216

85. Stewart, V., Landick, R., and Yanofsky, C. (1986) Rho-dependent transcription termination in the tryptophanase operon leader region of _Escherichia coli_ K-12. _J. Bacteriol._ **166,** 217–223

86. Stewart, V., and Yanofsky, C. (1985) Evidence for transcription antitermination control of tryptophanase operon expression in _Escherichia coli_ K-12. _J. Bacteriol._ **164,** 731–740

87. Gong, F., and Yanofsky, C. (2002) Analysis of tryptophanase operon expression _in vitro_: accumulation of TnaC-peptidyl-tRNA in a release factor 2-depleted S-30 extract prevents Rho factor action, simulating induction. _J. Biol. Chem._ **277,** 17095–17100

88. Gong, F., and Yanofsky, C. (2002) Instruction of translating ribosome by nascent peptide. _Science_ **297,** 1864–1867

89. Yanofsky, C., Horn, V., and Gollnick, P. (1991) Physiological studies of tryptophan transport and tryptophanase operon induction in _Escherichia coli._ _J. Bacteriol._ **173,** 6009–6017

90. Schneider, W. P., Nichols, B. P., and Yanofsky, C. (1981) Procedure for producing hybrid genes and proteins and its use in assessing the significance of amino acid differences in homologous tryptophan synthetase polypeptides. _Proc. Natl. Acad. Sci. U. S. A._ **78,** 2169–2173

91. Yanofsky, C. (1984) Comparison of regulatory and structural regions of genes of tryptophan metabolism. _Mol. Biol. Evol._ **1,** 143–161

92. Henner, D., and Yanofsky, C. (1993) Biosynthesis of aromatic amino acids. In _Bacillus subtilis and Other Gram Positive Bacteria: Biochemistry, Physiology and Molecular Genetics_ (Losick, R., ed) pp. 269–280, American Society for Microbiology, Washington, D. C.

93. Gollnick, P., Babitzke, P., Merino, E., and Yanofsky, C. (2002) Aromatic amino acid metabolism in _Bacillus subtilis._ In _Bacillus subtilis and Its Closest Relatives: from Genes to Cells_ (Sonenshein, A. L., Hoch, J. A., and Losick, R., eds) pp. 233–244, American Society for Microbiology, Washington, D. C.

94. Antson, A. A., Otridge, J., Brzozowski, A. M., Dodson, E. J., Dodson, G. G., Wilson, K. S., Smith, T. M., Yang, M., Kurecki, T., and Gollnick, P. (1995) The structure of _trp_ RNA-binding attenuation protein. _Nature_ **374,** 693–700

95. Antson, A. A., Dodson, E. J., Dodson, G., Greaves, R. B., Chen, X., and Gollnick, P. (1999) Structure of the _trp_ RNA-binding attenuation protein, TRAP, bound to RNA. _Nature_ **401,** 235–242

96. Du, H., and Babitzke, P. (1998) _trp_ RNA-binding attenuation protein-mediated long distance RNA refolding regulates translation of _trpE_ in _Bacillus subtilis._ _J. Biol. Chem._ **273,** 20494–20503

97. Sarsero, J. P., Merino, E., and Yanofsky, C. (2000) A _Bacillus subtilis_ operon containing genes of unknown function senses tRNA Trp charging and regulates expression of the genes of tryptophan biosynthesis. _Proc. Natl. Acad. Sci. U. S. A._ **97,** 2656–2661

98. Valbuzzi, A., and Yanofsky, C. (2001) Inhibition of the _B. subtilis_ regulatory protein TRAP by the TRAP-inhibitory protein, AT. _Science_ **293,** 2057–2059

99. Valbuzzi, A., Gollnick, P., Babitzke, P., and Yanofsky, C. (2002) The anti-_trp_ RNA-binding attenuation protein (anti-TRAP), AT, recognizes the tryptophan-activated RNA binding domain of the TRAP regulatory protein. _J. Biol. Chem._ **277,** 10608–10613

100. Jurgens, C., Strom, A., Wegener, D., Hettwer, S., Wilmanns, M., and Sterner, R. (2000) Directed evolution of a (beta alpha) 8-barrel enzyme to catalyze related reactions in two different metabolic pathways. _Proc. Natl. Acad. Sci. U. S. A._ **97,** 9925–9930

101. Yanofsky, C. (2001) Advancing our knowledge in biochemistry, genetics, and microbiology through studies on tryptophan metabolism. _Annu. Rev. Biochem._ **70,** 1–37

THE JOURNAL OF BIOLOGICAL CHEMISTRY
© 2003 by The American Society for Biochemistry and Molecular Biology, Inc.

Vol. 278, No. 14, Issue of April 4, pp. 11729–11730, 2003
Printed in U.S.A.

Reflections

A PAPER IN A SERIES COMMISSIONED TO CELEBRATE THE CENTENARY OF THE JBC IN 2005

JBC Centennial
1905–2005
100 Years of Biochemistry and Molecular Biology

Musings

Published, JBC Papers in Press, January 29, 2003, DOI 10.1074/jbc.X300001200

F. H. Westheimer

From the Department of Chemistry and Chemical Biology, Harvard University, Cambridge, Massachusetts 02138

My experience goes back to the time when chemistry and biochemistry were entirely separate disciplines. Actually, chemistry itself was an entirely different discipline from what it is today. I joined the American Chemical Society in 1933, some 70 years ago. The science has undergone several revolutions since then.

The first revolution was instrumental. I used to joke that the only difference between the Harvard chemistry laboratories when I was a graduate student and Emil Fischer's laboratories in Berlin at the turn of the century (the 20th century, that is) was that we had Pyrex glass and he did not. Electronic UV was not available and neither was IR. Neither paper chromatography nor column chromatography had been developed. Of course there was no NMR, which, all by itself, has revolutionized chemistry. (Edward Purcell, the inventor of NMR, visited the chemistry laboratories at Harvard after we had bought a 100-megacycle machine from Varian and remarked that, for the first time, he knew what a chemist was. A chemist was a scientist who did physics with good equipment.) Soon after, we joined the computer age and went on to practice x-ray crystallography as well as NMR.

The next revolution in organic chemistry was intellectual. The British and the Americans developed physical-organic chemistry, and this subdiscipline (which explained how reactions occur) had a practical side effect; it enabled organic chemists to design and perform original syntheses with perhaps only one-tenth the man years required before. A modification of a popular aphorism reads that nothing fails like success. The German synthetic organic chemists and their disciples in the United States were so proud of their achievements, where they relied on prodigious memories and hard work in the laboratory (trial and error) that they ignored new developments. No, that's not right. They scorned these developments. One prominent United States chemist claimed that, except for Morris Kharasch, there were no organic chemists at the University of Chicago. I was one of several physical-organic chemists there, but apparently we didn't count. Robert Woodward, at Harvard, taught everyone by example that synthetic organic chemists could intellectualize their work and could not safely ignore physical-organic chemistry.

Then there was a third revolution in chemistry involving biochemistry. A German dogma stated that *tierchemie ist schmierchemie* (biochemistry is sloppy chemistry). This was at the same time that Otto Warburg in Germany was opening the chemistry of co-enzymes and that Otto Myerhof and others were illuminating the pathway for glycolysis. It is hard to understand the tightly compartmentalized minds of the chemists of that day. (An extreme example of compartmentalization: at the chemistry library at Cambridge University, an imaginary line divided the room into two parts, one for physical chemists and one for organic. The library had two sets of the *Journal of The Chemical Society*, since an organic chemist was not supposed to cross that imaginary line to use the volumes on the physical chemistry side of the library, and vice versa.) Organic chemists did not read the biochemical literature either or attend biochemical seminars. A colloquium set up many years later for my students and those of another professor in the chemistry department at Harvard quickly divided along an imaginary line between chemists and biochemists.

Let me return to my own career and discuss how I became interested in biochemistry. When I was a postdoctoral student at Columbia, I did not know about compartments and so starting reading a biochemical textbook and some of Myerhof's papers. Then I was lost to old fashioned organic chemistry forever. When I got my toehold job at the University of Chicago in 1936, I knew I would try to combine physical-organic chemistry and biochemistry. Because enzymes are proteins and proteins are made of amino acids, I thought that the amino acids themselves might have special catalytic properties. I set up a study of the mutarotation of glucose catalyzed by amino acids to find out if this was so. Of course, there was no special catalysis by amino acids *per se*; enzymic catalysis is not so simple, but I am not ashamed of that failure.

I did better with the application of physical-organic chemistry to biochemistry with a study of the metal-ion catalysis of the decarboxylation of β-ketodicarboxylic acids and much better with a study of the direct and stereospecific transfer of hydrogen in reactions catalyzed by NAD. I am also proud of demonstrating the need for pseudorotation in the hydrolysis of cyclic phosphate esters and of photoaffinity labeling of enzymes. At any rate, I had a wonderful time because I saw the essential unity of chemistry and biochemistry—not a great feat, really, but astonishingly difficult for some chemists at that time.

I was privileged to chair The National Academy of Sciences Committee for the Survey of Chemistry and asked Arthur Kornberg and Dan Koshland to introduce some biochemistry into the mix. When I had completed a rough draft of the report, I sent it to a respected professor at Columbia and asked him for his opinion and suggestions. He wrote back that he did not like the report at all; to begin with, just the summary contained a large number of references to proteins and nucleic acids, work by people who did not even call themselves chemists. So the aspect of the report of which I was most proud, the unification of chemistry and biochemistry, was subject to severe criticism. And this was in 1965. I took this criticism as a badge of honor then and assume that this particular type of criticism has long since vanished.

I wonder what our blind spots are now.

THE JOURNAL OF BIOLOGICAL CHEMISTRY
© 2003 by The American Society for Biochemistry and Molecular Biology, Inc.

Vol. 278, No. 19, Issue of May 9, pp. 16455–16461, 2003
Printed in U.S.A.

Reflections

A PAPER IN A SERIES COMMISSIONED TO CELEBRATE THE CENTENARY OF THE JBC IN 2005

JBC Centennial
1905–2005
100 Years of Biochemistry and Molecular Biology

Keilin, Cytochrome, and the Respiratory Chain

Published, JBC Papers in Press, January 30, 2003, DOI 10.1074/jbc.X200011200

E. C. Slater

From the Laboratory of Biochemistry, University of Amsterdam, The Netherlands

The defining episode in my scientific career was my close association with David Keilin in the nearly 10 years (1946–1955) during which I was a member of the Molteno Institute at the University of Cambridge. Not only did my work in Cambridge determine the direction of my subsequent research, but Keilin's character, way of working and thinking, and his integrity as a scientist and human being were a continuing inspiration. I remained in contact with him until his death, and one of my proudest moments was when, during his first venture abroad since the War for the conferring of an honorary degree in Utrecht, I was able to show him my laboratory in Amsterdam.

David Keilin (1887–1963)

David Keilin was born in Moscow on March 21, 1887, of Polish parentage; his father was a businessman and small landowner. The family returned to Warsaw where he graduated from the Górski High School in 1904. He studied medicine at the University of Liège in Belgium for a year, but in 1905, being advised that his health would not stand the strain of medical studies, moved to Paris to study biology. In 1915, he obtained his doctorate with a thesis on the biology of insect larvae. In the same year he was invited by G. H. F. Nuttall to be his assistant at the Quick Laboratory of Parasitology in Cambridge, England, the forerunner of the Molteno Institute, where he was to spend the rest of his working life. He was appointed Lecturer in Parasitology in 1925 and in 1931 succeeded Nuttall as Professor and Director of the Molteno Institute. He had to relinquish both posts in 1952 upon reaching the compulsory retirement age of 65 but was able to continue working in the Institute until his death in 1963. He received many honors, including election as Fellow of the Royal Society in 1928 and the award in 1952 of the highest honor of the Society, the Copley Medal. Many do not understand why he was never awarded the Nobel Prize.

Keilin's paper in the *Proceedings of the Royal Society* in 1925 with the title "On cytochrome, a respiratory pigment, common to animals, yeast, and higher plants" (1) marked the beginning of studies of what Warburg later called the respiratory chain (atmungskette), many of us called the electron transfer chain, and David Green, with some prescience, the electron transport chain. The story of how Keilin came upon cytochrome when studying hemoglobin in the horse intestinal parasite *Gastrophilus intestinalis* is told in his posthumously published book (2).

Already 75 years ago there was quite a lot known about biological oxidations. The word "oxidase" had already been introduced by Gabriel Bertrand (3) in the 19th century to describe the enzyme responsible for the hardening of lacquer, now known as laccase. In 1910–1912 Battelli and Stern made thorough studies of the oxidation of a number of substances by oxygen in the presence of ground-up tissue and showed the sensitivity of this process to cyanide (4). They referred to the enzyme responsible as indophenol oxidase from the color reaction they used to measure its activity. In the early 1920s, Thunberg (5) showed that the oxidation of a large number of organic compounds such as succinic acid is catalyzed by enzymes, each specific for its substrate, named dehydrases and later dehydrogenases by Wieland (6). As is well

FIG. 1. **David Keilin (1887–1963).**

known, a controversy developed concerning the mechanism of biological oxidations. Wieland and Thunberg, impressed by the ability of dehydrogenases to catalyze the oxidation of organic compounds by artificial acceptors such as methylene blue, proposed that the fundamental action is the activation by the dehydrogenases of hydrogen atoms, otherwise inert, so that they can react with oxygen. Warburg, impressed by the presence of iron in respiring cells and the ability of cyanide both to combine with iron and to inhibit cell respiration, proposed that the fundamental process is the activation of oxygen by an iron-containing respiratory enzyme (atmungsferment) (7).

Keilin's paper made it clear that the electrons derived from the activation of the hydrogen atoms by the dehydrogenase are transferred via three hemoproteins, which he named cytochromes a, b, and c, to an oxygen-activating oxidase. He did not name the oxidase in his 1925 paper, but in 1927 identified it, on the basis of its sensitivity to cyanide, with Battelli and Stern's indophenol oxidase and on the basis of its sensitivity to both cyanide and carbon monoxide with Warburg's atmungsferment (8). Much to Warburg's chagrin he continued to call it indophenol oxidase and, in retaliation perhaps, Warburg refused to accept the role of the cytochromes. This became one of the controversies of the 1930s (see Ref. 9), matching the vigorous confrontations in this field 30 or 40 years later at the annual meetings of the ASBC.

The basic features of our present picture of the respiratory chain were established by Keilin and his co-workers in the 1920s and 1930s. Already in his first paper, he showed that cytochrome b is the first acceptor of electrons from substrate. Making use of the exceptional stability of cytochrome c, Keilin and Hartree (10) extracted it from heart muscle. Most importantly, in 1939 (11) they showed that what had hitherto been thought of as a single cytochrome a consists of two components that they now called cytochromes a and a_3. In contrast to the other cytochromes, including cytochrome a, cytochrome a_3 combines with carbon monoxide and cyanide and has, therefore, all the properties ascribed to Warburg's atmungsferment.

By 1939, it was possible to write the respiratory chain as a simple chain: dehydrogenase $\rightarrow$ cytochrome b $\rightarrow$ cytochrome c $\rightarrow$ cytochrome a $\rightarrow$ cytochrome a_3 $\rightarrow$ oxygen. Strictly speaking the order of cytochrome c $\rightarrow$ cytochrome a had not been established (it could have been reversed), but Keilin was convinced, correctly as it is now known, that cytochromes a and a_3 are closely associated.

Expansion of Keilin's Respiratory Chain

That was still the situation when in 1946 I joined Keilin as a Ph.D. student (rather mature in age by English standards but not in biochemical knowledge (see Ref. 12)), and more than a half-century later, this description of the respiratory chain is still valid although additional electron-transferring components have been added to it. The first of these was cytochrome c_1, already discovered by Okunuki in 1939 (13) but not generally accepted until Keilin and Hartree in 1955 showed that the absorption band initially ascribed to cytochrome c is derived from two components, one the classical cytochrome c and the other Okunuki's cytochrome c_1 (14).[1]

The second addition to Keilin's respiratory chain, proposed in 1948 before cytochrome c_1 was accepted, was an electron-transferring factor acting in the chain between cytochromes b and c that was irreversibly and specifically destroyed by aerobic incubation with a dithiol compound, called BAL (17). After the discovery by Van Potter that the powerful respiratory chain inhibitor antimycin also inhibits electron transfer between cytochromes b and c, which he ascribed (incorrectly as it transpired) to its binding to the factor, he kindly gave it the name Slater factor (18).

In the late 1950s, F. L. Crane (19) in David Green's laboratory discovered ubiquinone (coenzyme Q) as a new hydrogen carrier between the dehydrogenases and the electron transfer chain proper, but it was not until much later that it was recognized that ubiquinone is also involved in electron transfer within the respiratory chain (see below).

After many earlier proposals that copper is involved as well as iron in the oxidation of cytochrome c, this was finally established in the 1960s by Helmut Beinert, using paramagnetic resonance spectrometry (EPR) (20). Bob van Gelder (21) in my Amsterdam laboratory showed that the cytochrome c oxidase takes up 4 electrons per molecule, one each into the hemes of cytochromes a and a_3 and two into the copper atoms.[2]

The application by Beinert of EPR spectrometry revealed also a whole new class of electron carriers, the iron-sulfur centers (22). With one exception, these centers are involved in the transfer of reducing equivalents from the flavin, by then recognized as a component of all ubiquinone-reducing dehydrogenases, to ubiquinone, rather than in Keilin's respiratory chain itself. The one exception was not in fact discovered by Beinert but by his colleague Rieske and is generally known as the Rieske iron-sulfur protein (23). The high redox potential, around about that of cytochrome c_1, made it an attractive site of action of antimycin and a candidate for my old factor. However, there was no experimental evidence for a reaction with antimycin, and for many years in Amsterdam we did not know quite what to do about the Rieske protein until Simon de Vries found that its EPR spectrum is affected by ubiquinone (24). The breakthrough was made after Bernie Trumpower (25) showed that, after extraction of the Rieske protein, antimycin inhibits the *reduction* of cytochrome b, instead of its *oxidation*, as it was supposed to do if it inhibits the chain between cytochromes b and c. This reminded me of an old observation by Deul and Thorn (26) in my laboratory that this is exactly what antimycin does after destruction of the factor, what we called the "double kill" experiment. Sure enough Simon de Vries showed that the treatment I had used in the 1940s to destroy the factor has a drastic effect on the EPR spectrum of Rieske's iron-sulfur protein (27). By establishing the identity of my factor and the Rieske protein, the number of possible components of the respiratory chain was at least reduced by one.

The double kill experiment is nicely explained by Mitchell's Q cycle (26) to which I had paid insufficient attention when it was proposed, despite a friendly letter from Peter saying that it would give him great pleasure if it turned out that the Q cycle explained the Slater factor. It does. According to this cycle, there are two possible entries of electrons from ubiquinol to cytochrome b, one coupled with the reduction of the Rieske iron-sulfur protein and therefore susceptible to BAL treatment and one via a separate antimycin-sensitive ubiquinol-binding site, which (when the cycle is functioning) operates in the opposite direction by accepting electrons from cytochrome b. I soon became an enthusiastic supporter of the ubiquitous Q cycle (29).

---

[1] To my everlasting embarrassment, I had published a paper in 1949 (15) in which I concluded that Okunuki's evidence for the existence of cytochrome c_1 was unsatisfactory (see also Ref. 16).

[2] That it was much later shown that cytochrome c oxidase contains 3 atoms of copper per molecule is not inconsistent with van Gelder's titrations, because two of the copper atoms are coupled and take up only a single electron.

I have now got a bit ahead of myself chronologically. Just as is the case with Keilin's c and a absorption bands, the b band turned out also to be double, but in this case it is derived from two protoheme prosthetic groups bound to a single polypeptide chain. The first clue of the existence of two components came from Britton Chance and was established in his laboratory in a redox titration by Wilson and Dutton (30). There was quite a lot of what turned out to be rather cloudy work on cytochrome b in the 1970s, but the dust settled with Fred Sanger's determination of its molecular weight via DNA (31), which told me that it is a two-heme cytochrome (32). Its function was established by the Q cycle as a transmembrane subunit of ubiquinol-cytochrome c reductase with the lower potential heme, denoted b_{566}, accepting electrons from ubiquinol on the outside of the inner membrane and transferring them to the higher potential heme (b_{562}) on the inside of the membrane and eventually to ubiquinone.

Fractionation of the Respiratory Chain

Keilin and his students used for their studies of the respiratory chain a suspension of small particles obtained by grinding heart muscle with sand in weak phosphate buffer that became known as the Keilin and Hartree heart muscle preparation (33). I do not think that much attention was given in early studies to the nature or origin of these particles. Indeed I think that I was the first to show that they contain about 30% lipid, an accidental observation made when I was looking for a method of determining the dry weight of the preparation, since in those days the activity of a respiratory preparation was expressed by the Q_{O_2} (μl of O_2/h/mg, dry weight). When as a newcomer I asked Ted Hartree how to measure the dry weight of the suspension in the buffer, he suggested that I precipitate it with trichloroacetic acid, centrifuge, wash the precipitate, dry it, and weigh it. This I did, but I decided to speed up the drying process by washing with ethanol. I found that this decreased the weight by 30%, compared with washing with water, and changed my definition of Q_{O_2} to base it on fat-free dry weight. I did observe that the ethanol extract was bright yellow but did not give this any thought, thereby missing the opportunity of discovering ubiquinone.

The significance of the lipid became clear when at about this time Albert Claude (34) showed that the site of intracellular respiration is the mitochondrion and, when the mitochondrion was viewed by thin section electron microscopy by Palade (35), more precisely in the inner membrane or cristae. We now recognize that the Keilin and Hartree preparation consists of submitochondrial particles, or vesicles, derived from the inner membrane.

No attempt was made by the Keilin school to fractionate the chain apart from the isolation of cytochrome c. The first success was obtained by Wainio (36) and Lucile Smith (37) using deoxycholate and cholate, respectively, to disperse the membrane and allow its components to be separated by conventional ammonium sulfate fractionation. David Green's school (38) importantly expanded this technique to the separation of what he called four complexes, catalyzing, respectively, the reduction of ubiquinone by NADH (Complex I) or succinate (Complex II), the reduction of ferricytochrome c by ubiquinol (Complex III), and the oxidation of ferrocytochrome c by oxygen (Complex IV). I have always thought it a pity that he gave the name Complex to these multisubunit proteins, each of which has a clearly defined enzyme function.

Function of the Respiratory Chain

In the 1920s Keilin and Warburg envisaged that the function of the respiratory chain is to catalyze the oxidation of intermediary metabolites by the transfer of electrons derived from hydrogen atoms to oxygen. That it might have an additional function in ion transport was suggested in 1939 by Lundergårdh (39), specifically that in plants the cytochromes act as electron carriers in one direction and as anion carriers in the opposite direction. The primary function of the respiratory chain, oxidative phosphorylation, was discovered by Engelhardt in 1931 (40). Measurements of the stoichiometry (P:O ratio), made independently in 1939–1940 by Belitzer and Tsibakowa (41) in Leningrad in the USSR and Severo Ochoa (42) in Oxford in England, established that phosphorylation must be coupled not, or not only, to the dehydrogenation of substrate but to electron transfer along the respiratory chain.

Oxidative Phosphorylation and Topography of the Respiratory Chain

After completing my Ph.D. in 1948 with a thesis on the succinate oxidase system and a subsequent study of the NADH oxidase system (43), oxidative phosphorylation was the logical next topic for my research, especially after Al Lehninger's paper on oxidative phosphorylation coupled to the oxidation of NADH (44). This was a new field for the Molteno Institute, and given the opportunity by the Rockefeller Foundation to study in the United States, I spent about 6 months working in Severo Ochoa's laboratory at New York University learning the new techniques.[3] Severo's interests were then mainly on carbon dioxide fixation, but in the same building, Ef Racker was developing the concept of an acyl intermediate in the oxidative phosphorylation reaction of glycolysis (46). Adapting an enzyme assay that he had described, I developed a procedure that enabled me to measure oxidative phosphorylation between substrate and cytochrome *c* (47), the first direct demonstration of what later became known as "site 2 oxidative phosphorylation." I continued these studies after returning to the Molteno Institute and in 1953 published what became known as the "chemical hypothesis" of oxidative phosphorylation (48) in which, by analogy with substrate-linked phosphorylation, the energy of electron transfer is conserved primarily in non-phosphorylated high energy forms of components of the chain.

Around this time, the two functions of the respiratory chain, ion movements and oxidative phosphorylation, were beginning to coalesce. Workers on gastric secretion favored a simple redox pump mechanism, according to which the secreted protons were those liberated from hydrogen carriers by transfer of electrons to the cytochromes. In 1951, however, both salt accumulation in plants (49) and gastric secretion (50) were found to be inhibited by 2,4-dinitrophenol, known to uncouple oxidative phosphorylation from electron transfer. This focused attention on ATP instead of electron transfer as the source of charge separation, and Davies and Krebs (51) proposed in 1951 that "ionic concentration differences, *i.e.* osmotic energy ... may play a role in the synthesis of ATP." Williams (52) proposed that protons could bring about condensation reactions such as polyphosphate formation.

These concepts were developed by Mitchell (53) into a coherent hypothesis encompassing a functional link between electron transfer in the respiratory chain and the translocation in the opposite direction of protons across the inner mitochondrial membrane, whereby the energy is conserved as an electrochemical proton gradient. To accommodate experimental evidence of an H^+:e ratio of about 2, in 1966 he introduced the concept of loops in the respiratory chain with two electrons crossing the membrane from one side to the other followed by two hydrogen atoms in the opposite direction (54). This very important concept of the sidedness of the membrane with the specific location of the electron acceptors and donors was not at first generally accepted, not only because many did not at first accept (or possibly understand) the precise role of protons envisaged by Mitchell but also because those of us more specifically interested in the respiratory chain knew that the order of electron transfer originally proposed was wrong. Mitchell's brilliant proposal of the Q cycle (28), made in answer to these criticisms, as a description of how the oxidation of ubiquinol by ferricytochrome *c* is coupled to the net production of protons on one side of the membrane and their consumption on the other side was soon given solid experimental support.

As more became known of the structure of the two large multisubunit proteins involved in the respiratory chain, namely ubiquinol-cytochrome *c* reductase and cytochrome *c* oxidase, as well as of the ubiquinone-reducing dehydrogenases, such as succinate-ubiquinone reductase and NADH-ubiquinone reductase, it became clear that their dimensions are in fact greater than a phospholipid bilayer and that they are embedded and specifically orientated across the phospholipid layer, which confirmed in structural terms Mitchell's sidedness concept.

Mechanism of Electron Transfer

The discovery in the 1960s and early 1970s of more and more electron-transferring centers in the respiratory chain, particularly the multiplicity of iron-sulfur centers, gave a lot of headaches to those of us who found even the 1948 sequence of dehydrogenase $\rightarrow b \rightarrow$ factor $\rightarrow c \rightarrow a \rightarrow a_3 \rightarrow O_2$ longer than necessary to accommodate a P:O ratio of 3 in oxidative phosphorylation. At the time of the International Congress in Switzerland in 1970, I remember that, in desperation, we proposed double chains.

The real function of the multiplicity of electron transfer centers has only recently become understood as a result of the structural information that tells us where the centers are located in the protein, together with a fundamental increase in our understanding of the nature of electron transfer. Dutton and co-workers (55) have demonstrated that, by virtue of electron

---

[3] A biographical note on Severo Ochoa is to be found in Arthur Kornberg's "Reflections" (45).

tunneling, electrons can readily travel through the protein medium a distance of up to 14 Å between redox centers but that transfer over greater distances is facilitated by a chain of electron carriers. Within this distance of 14 Å, rapid electron tunneling takes place even if the electron transfer is endergonic, provided that the centers are sufficiently close. It is the proximity of the redox centers in chains that provides highly directional electron transfer.

The role of distance between the redox centers in controlling the rate and therefore the specificity of electron transfer is beautifully illustrated by the mobility of the Rieske iron-sulfur protein subunit in ubiquinol-cytochrome c reductase, as shown by the x-ray crystallographic studies of Berry, Crofts, and their colleagues (56). In one conformation, stabilized by the ubiquinol inhibitor stigmatellin, the Fe-S cluster is close enough to the ubiquinol-binding site to allow its reduction by ubiquinol. In a second conformation, it is close enough (about 8 Å) to the heme in cytochrome c_1 to permit rapid electron transfer. The important point is that in neither conformation can both reactions occur at a suitable rate. For example, in the stigmatellin-stabilized conformation, the iron-sulfur cluster is about 27 Å from the heme. Thus, the reaction mechanism must involve movement of the Rieske iron-sulfur protein. Keilin would have enjoyed this paper. X-ray crystallography of proteins was not strange to him. He supported Kendrew and Perutz in their work and lived to see the solution of the structures of myoglobin and hemoglobin.

We now know that one of Keilin's cytochromes, cytochrome b, as well as Okunuki's cytochrome c_1, are subunits of a single protein, ubiquinol-cytochrome c reductase, and that his cytochromes a and a_3 are also bound to a single subunit of cytochrome c oxidase. Cytochrome c remains a single polypeptide. In his earlier papers, Keilin often used the singular "cytochrome" to refer to the cytochrome system, and I think that he regarded them as acting as a single unit. In 1947, he and Hartree stated that "the catalysts in the particles, as in the intact cells, are more or less rigidly held together in a framework that assures their mutual accessibility and a consequent high catalytic activity" (33). This idea of an ordered macromolecular assembly, under the name of the "solid state" model of the respiratory chain, seems to be winning favor over the "liquid state" model that envisaged independent free diffusion of the multisubunit proteins in the membrane and of cytochrome c in the space between the inner and outer membranes of the mitochondrion (see *e.g.* Ref. 57).

In any case, the function of the cytochromes is to transfer electrons. It is the function of the protons, freed by this removal of the electrons from the hydrogen atoms of intermediary metabolites, to drive ion transport and the synthesis of ATP. As Mitchell pointed out in the conclusion to his Nobel Lecture in 1978, "David Keilin's chemically simple view of the respiratory chain appears now to have been right all along." (58).

Address correspondence to: ecslater@btinternet.com.

REFERENCES

1. Keilin, D. (1925) *Proc. R. Soc. Lond. B Biol. Sci.* **98**, 312–339
2. Keilin, D. (1966) *The History of Cell Respiration and Cytochrome*, Cambridge University Press, Cambridge, UK
3. Bertrand, G. (1897) *Ann. Chem. (Phys.)* **12**, 115–140
4. Battelli, F., and Stern, L. (1910) *Biochem. Z.* **30**, 172–194
5. Thunberg, T. (1917) *Skand. Arch. Physiol.* **35**, 163
6. Wieland, O. (1912) *Ber. Dtsch. Chem. Ges.* **45**, 484–499; 2606–2615
7. Warburg, O. (1924) *Biochem. Z.* **177**, 471–486
8. Keilin, D. (1927) *Nature* **119**, 670–671
9. Slater, E. C. (1977) *Trends Biochem. Sci.* **21**, 156–157
10. Keilin, D., and Hartree, E. F. (1937) *Proc. R. Soc. Lond. B Biol. Sci.* **122**, 298–308
11. Keilin, D., and Hartree, E. F. (1939) *Proc. R. Soc. Lond. B Biol. Sci.* **127**, 167–191
12. Slater, E. C. (2003) *IUBMB Life* **55**, in press
13. Yakushiji, E., and Okunuki, K. (1940) *Proc. Imp. Acad. Tokyo* **16**, 299–302
14. Keilin, D., and Hartree, E. F. (1955) *Nature* **176**, 200–206
15. Slater, E. C. (1949) *Nature* **163**, 532
16. Slater, E. C. (1986) in *Selected Topics in the History of Biochemistry (Comprehensive Biochemistry)* (Semenza, G., ed) Vol. 36, pp. 197–253, Elsevier Science Publishers B.V., Amsterdam
17. Slater, E. C. (1948) *Nature* **161**, 405–406
18. Potter, V. R., and Reif, A. E. (1952) *J. Biol. Chem.* **294**, 287–297
19. Crane, F. L., Hatefi, Y., Lester, R. L., and Widmer, C. (1967) *Biochim. Biophys. Acta* **25**, 220–221
20. Beinert, H., and Palmer, G. (1964) *J. Biol. Chem.* **239**, 1221–1227
21. van Gelder, B. F. (1966) *Biochim. Biophys. Acta* **118**, 36–46
22. Beinert, H., and Sands, R. H. (1960) *Biochem. Biophys. Res. Commun.* **3**, 41–46
23. Rieske, J. S., Hansen, R. E., and Zaugg, W. S. (1964) *J. Biol. Chem.* **239**, 3017–3022
24. de Vries, S., Albracht, S. P. J., and Leeuwerik, F. J. (1979) *Biochim. Biophys. Acta* **546**, 316–333
25. Trumpower, B. L. (1976) *Biochem. Biophys. Res. Commun.* **70**, 73–78
26. Deul, D. H., and Thorn, M. B. (1962) *Biochim. Biophys. Acta* **59**, 426–436

27. Slater, E. C., and de Vries, S. (1980) *Nature* **288,** 717–718
28. Mitchell, P. D. (1975) *FEBS Lett.* **59,** 1–6
29. Slater, E. C. (1983) *Trends Biochem. Res.* **8,** 239–242
30. Wilson, D. F., and Dutton, P. L. (1970) *Biochem. Biophys. Res. Commun.* **39,** 59–64
31. Anderson, S., Bankier, A. T., Barrell, B. C., De Bruijn, M. H. L., Coulson, A. R., Drouin, J., Eperon, I. C., Nierlich, D. F., Roe, D. P., Sanger, F., Schreier, P. R., Smith, A. J. H., Staden, R., and Young, I. G. (1981) *Nature* **290,** 457–465
32. Slater, E. C. (1981) in *Chemiosmotic Proton Circuits in Biological Membranes* (Skulachev, V. D., and Hinkle, P., eds) pp. 69–104, Addison-Wesley, Reading, MA
33. Keilin, D., and Hartree, E. F. (1947) *Biochem. J.* **41,** 500–502
34. Hogeboom, G. H., Claude, A., and Hotchkiss, R. D. (1946) *J. Biol. Chem.* **165,** 615–629
35. Palade, G. E. (1952) *Anat. Rec.* **114,** 427
36. Wainio, W. W., Cooperstein, S. J., Kollen, S., and Echel, B. (1948) *J. Biol. Chem.* **173,** 145
37. Smith, L., and Stotz, E. H. (1948) *J. Biol. Chem.* **208,** 819
38. Green, D. E. (1966) in *Comprehensive Biochemistry* (Florkin, M., and Stotz, E. H., eds) Vol. 14, pp. 309–326, Elsevier Science Publishers B.V., Amsterdam
39. Lundergårdh, H. (1939) *Nature* **143,** 203
40. Engelhardt, W. A. (1930) *Biochem. Z.* **227,** 16–38
41. Belitzer, V. A., and Tsibakowa, E. T. (1939) *Biokhimiya* **4,** 516
42. Ochoa, S. (1940) *Nature* **146,** 267
43. Slater, E. C. (1950) *Biochem. J.* **46,** 484–499
44. Friedkin, M., and Lehninger, A. L. (1948) *J. Biol. Chem.* **174,** 757–758
45. Kornberg, A. (2001) *J. Biol. Chem.* **276,** 3–11
46. Racker, E. F. (1961) *J. Biol. Chem.* **190,** 685–696
47. Slater, E. C. (1950) *Nature* **166,** 982–984
48. Slater, E. C. (1953) *Nature* **172,** 975–978
49. Robertson, R. N., Wilkins, M. J., and Weeks, D. C. (1951) *Aust. J. Sci. Res. B* **4,** 248–264
50. Davies, R. E. (1951) *Biol. Rev.* **26,** 87–120
51. Davies, R. E., and Krebs, H. A. (1951) *Biochem. Soc. Symp.* **8,** 77–92
52. Williams, R. J. P. (1949) in *The Enzymes* (Boyer, P., Lardy, H., and Myrbäck, H., eds) Vol. 1, pp. 391–441, Academic Press, New York
53. Mitchell, P. (1961) *Nature* **191,** 144–148
54. Mitchell, P. (1966) *Biol. Rev.* **41,** 455–602
55. Page, C. C., Moser, C. C., Chen, X., and Dutton, P. L. (1999) *Nature* **402,** 47–52
56. Zhang, Z., Huang, L., Schulmeister, V. M., Chi, Y. I., Kim, K. K., Hung, L. W., Crofts, A. R., Berry, E. A., and Kim, S. H. (1998) *Nature* **392,** 677–684
57. Schägger, H. (2002) *Biochim. Biophys. Acta* **1555,** 154–159
58. Mitchell, P. (1979) *Les Prix Nobel en 1978.* The Nobel Foundation, 1979, pp. 134–172, Almqvist Wiksell International, Stockholm

THE JOURNAL OF BIOLOGICAL CHEMISTRY
© 2003 by The American Society for Biochemistry and Molecular Biology, Inc.

Vol. 278, No. 20, Issue of May 16, pp. 17581–17588, 2003
Printed in U.S.A.

Reflections

A PAPER IN A SERIES COMMISSIONED TO CELEBRATE THE CENTENARY OF THE JBC IN 2005

JBC Centennial
1905–2005
100 Years of Biochemistry and Molecular Biology

In Search of the Energetic Role of Peptide Hydrogen Bonds

Published, JBC Papers in Press, February 11, 2003, DOI 10.1074/jbc.X200009200

Robert L. Baldwin

From the Department of Biochemistry, Beckman Center, Stanford School of Medicine, Stanford, California 94305

Forming peptide hydrogen bonds was considered to be probably the most important driving force for protein folding in 1951, when Linus Pauling and Robert Corey proposed the hydrogen-bonded structures of the α-helix (1) and two β-sheets (2). Because the peptide CO and NH groups form competing hydrogen bonds (H-bonds) to water when a protein is unfolded it was evident, however, that the net contribution of the peptide H-bond (CO···HN) to protein stability might be small. In 1955 John Schellman (3, 4) made a first analysis of the energetics of peptide H-bonds in protein folding reactions. He listed the factors that should affect the stability of a peptide α-helix in water, and he estimated the strength of the peptide H-bond in water by attributing the unusual thermodynamics of aqueous urea solutions (which had been measured accurately) to H-bonded urea dimers. His analysis indicated that a peptide helix in water should have at most marginal stability. Any observable helix formation should be driven by the net enthalpy change (ΔH) of forming the peptide H-bond in water, and the aqueous urea data gave $\Delta H = -1.5$ kcal/mol. The proposal of Schellman that helix formation should be driven by the enthalpy of the peptide H-bond was adopted by Zimm and Bragg (5) and by Lifson and Roig (6) in their treatments of the statistical mechanics of helix formation. Klotz and Franzen (7) found, however, that the dimerization of N-methylacetamide (NMA) in water was too small to measure, and the energetic significance of peptide H-bonds for protein folding lapsed into uncertainty. Interest in the problem diminished further as support grew for the bold proposal by Walter Kauzmann (8) in 1959 that the hydrophobic interaction provides the major driving force for protein folding.

Hydrogen Bond Inventory

The change in internal energy (ΔE) for forming a hydrogen bond in the gas phase can be calculated by quantum mechanics, and with steady improvement in methods of calculation, calculated values of H-bond energies are now believed to be comparable in accuracy to good experimental values. A recent calculated value for the ΔE of dimerization of NMA in vacuum is -6.6 kcal/mol, which has been used as a model for the peptide H-bond (9). Some older calculated values indicate that the H-bonds formed by amide CO and NH groups to water (W), and also the W···W and CO···NH H-bonds, have roughly equal energies of about -6 ± 1 kcal/mol (10, 11). The conclusion a decade ago was that *a hydrogen bond inventory,* discussed by Alan Fersht (12, 13), is sufficient to describe the net enthalpy of the peptide H-bond in water. In writing the inventory, the number of H-bonds is assumed to be the same, whereas their types are similar on both sides of the equation.

$$CO\cdots W + NH\cdots W = CO\cdots HN + W\cdots W \qquad \text{(Eq. 1)}$$

If the assumptions made in writing Equation 1 are valid, then the net enthalpy of the peptide H-bond in water is 0 ± 1 kcal/mol to a first approximation. In making quantum mechanics calculations to model the peptide H-bond and the NH···W and CO···W H-bonds, the energies found by using different model compounds to estimate one type of H-bond differ by as much as the energies found for different types of H-bond (11). The enthalpy change ΔH and the internal energy change ΔE are considered here to be interchangeable in aqueous solution because any difference between them should be negligible.

Note, however, that even a small net enthalpy change per peptide H-bond could be important because a typical protein forms about 70% of the possible peptide H-bonds. The patterns of peptide H-bonds found in proteins are complex (14), and any average number must be considered as a rough estimate. If ΔH is as large as -1 kcal/mol per H-bond, this projection would contribute -70 kcal/mol to the folding reaction of a protein with 100 peptide groups. The net free energy change ΔG for folding is in the range -5 to -10 kcal/mol for typical small proteins, and a -70 kcal/mol contribution would be highly significant. For comparison, the hydrophobic interaction is estimated to contribute about -126 kcal/mol to the folding reaction of a protein with 100 peptide bonds and 101 residues. The estimate of -1.2_5 kcal/mol residue is based on the average amount of nonpolar surface area buried per residue in the folding reaction of a typical protein (~ 50 Å^2 (15, 16)) and on a conversion factor between free energy and buried nonpolar area of 25 cal/Å^2. If the energy of the H-bond is -6 kcal/mol, it would be highly unfavorable to bury a peptide NH or CO group in the interior of a protein without making its H-bond, and burial of a free NH or CO group rarely occurs (14).

Use of the Alanine Peptide Helix to Analyze H-bond Energetics

A new approach to understanding peptide H-bond energetics became possible with the discovery by Susan Marqusee (17) that the alanine peptide helix is stable by itself in water. Curiously only alanine, of the 20 naturally occurring amino acids, has this property (18). Thus, helices formed by alanine-based peptides can provide absolute helix propensities when the effect of a guest residue is studied, whereas other systems typically give only relative values because the helix must be stabilized by some other interaction(s), such as salt bridges, whose strength is difficult to measure independently. Amino acids with larger nonpolar side chains, such as leucine, form less stable helices than alanine (18), which suggests that alanine helix formation is not driven by the hydrophobic interaction. Because alanine has just a methyl side chain and only a small amount of nonpolar surface area is buried when an alanine peptide forms a helix (19), it is unlikely at first sight that the hydrophobic interaction could be responsible for helix formation. Instead, the peptide H-bond and solvation of the peptide group probably drive alanine helix formation. Recent calorimetric studies (see below) demonstrate that in fact the hydrophobic interaction is not responsible for alanine helix formation. Alanine helices are prone to be water-insoluble, but two charged ornithine residues at either end of a 13-residue alanine sequence are sufficient to solubilize the helix (20).

The stability of a peptide α-helix formed from a single type of amino acid depends on two different equilibrium constants. The first is a nucleation constant for a reaction in which three adjacent peptide groups assume a helical conformation but no peptide H-bonds are formed, and the second is a helix propagation constant (the helix propensity) for a reaction in which a single H-bonded helical residue is added (5). A peptide H-bond is formed between the CO of peptide group i and the NH of peptide group $i + 3$. To find the absolute value of the helix propensity from measurements of helix stability, it is necessary to determine the helix nucleation constant, which is found from measurements of helix stability for a set of peptides of varying chain lengths. The ratio of helical residues formed in the nucleation reaction to those formed in the propagation reaction decreases as the helix becomes longer and more H-bonded residues are added, and so overall helix stability increases with chain length. The nucleation constant for an alanine-based helix was initially determined by Marty Scholtz (21), who used circular dichroism to measure the thermal unfolding curves of a set of peptides of chain lengths varying from 14, 20, 26 . . . to 50 residues. Later, Carol Rohl (22) confirmed the value of the nucleation constant by a new method, based on NMR measurement of the kinetics of hydrogen exchange, using a different peptide series (22). When we analyzed these results by an adaptation (23) of the Lifson-Roig theory (6), which is particularly well suited to analyzing helix formation by peptides with mixed sequences (24), the helix nucleation constant was found to be 0.0013, more than 1000-fold lower than the helix propagation constant for alanine, which is 1.70 at 0 °C (18).

The Enthalpy of Helix Formation

In using the alanine peptide helix as a wedge to pry open the energetics of peptide H-bonds, the first problem was to determine accurately the net enthalpy change for helix formation. Thermal unfolding curves (21) show that alanine helices unfold with increasing temperature, which suggests that that helix formation is enthalpy-driven. A standard method for measuring the enthalpy change on protein unfolding is differential scanning calorimetry (16). Thermal unfolding curves of peptide helices are quite broad, however, and the calorimetrically measured unfolding curve of even a 50-residue alanine-based helix (25) fails to show either 100% helix at 0 °C or 0% helix at 80 °C, the highest temperature reached in this experiment. The broad thermal melting curve prevents fitting the base line reliably, which limits the accuracy of measuring the enthalpy change. Nevertheless, we were able to measure, in collaboration with Wayne Bolen, an approximate value of the enthalpy change, -1.0 kcal/mol residue (25), which agrees with the value found by fitting helix melting curves (21). Unfortunately the broad melting curve is unsuitable for measuring ΔCp, the change in heat capacity on unfolding, which is the critical quantity for determining if the hydrophobic interaction drives folding. If helix formation is driven by the hydrophobic interaction, then a large ΔCp dominates the expression describing the thermal unfolding curve.

Recently, a way around the problem of the broad curves for thermal unfolding was found. In a peptide system developed by Andrzej Bierzynski and his co-workers (26), based on a peptide sequence taken from an EF-hand protein, helix formation occurs on adding La^{3+} so that ΔH can be measured by titration calorimetry. Independent measurements by us, in collaboration with George Makhatadze (27), gave $\Delta H = -0.90 \pm 0.1$ kcal/mol residue, in good agreement with the value of -0.98 ± 0.1 kcal/mol residue measured by Bierzynski and co-workers.[1] Moreover, measurements of ΔH made at two temperatures show that ΔCp is zero within error (27), which confirms that folding is not driven by the hydrophobic interaction. In the following, an average value of ΔH from these two studies is used, $-0.9_5 \pm 0.1$ kcal/mol residue. Using this value as the ΔH for the peptide H-bond in protein folding gives the scenario mentioned above, in which (even though ΔH per H-bond has only a modest value) the large number of peptide H-bonds ($\sim$70 for a protein with 100 peptide bonds) should produce a large enthalpic contribution, -66.5 kcal/mol, to the folding reaction if the assumptions of the H-bond inventory are applicable.

Application of H-bond Inventory to the Alanine Helix and to Amide Solvation

Does the H-bond inventory approach (Equation 1) give a correct prediction of the measured value of ΔH for alanine helix formation, as it should if peptide H-bonds and solvation of the peptide group provide the only important contributions to ΔH? First an important question must be answered: does the free peptide group form one or two H-bonds to water? As written above, Equation 1 implies that the peptide group makes only one H-bond to water, but both the peptide NH and CO groups should be able to form H-bonds to water. According to the H-bond inventory, the answer can be found from the enthalpy of solvation of simple amides, which must first be corrected for the contributions to the solvation enthalpy from van der Waals interactions and from making a cavity in water for the solute. (It is also necessary to use the correct standard state for transfer of a solute from the gas phase to liquid solution.) Calorimetric data for the solvation enthalpy of some amides are available when the starting material is the amide in gaseous form, and Peizhi Luo (29) analyzed the results to give the enthalpy of interaction between water and the amide polar groups. For four different amides, ΔH is close to -12 kcal/mol; the value for N-methylacetamide is -11.65 kcal/mol (29). Thus, following the rule discussed above in which ΔH for making one H-bond of this type is -6 ± 1 kcal/mol, we might at first conclude that the free peptide group makes two H-bonds to water (however, see below).

In any case, if we use the solvation enthalpy found with amides to predict the enthalpy of interaction between the free peptide group and water, then a simple enthalpy balance combined with the H-bond inventory gives ΔH for forming the alanine peptide helix as follows: ΔH(pred) = 12 (breaking H-bond(s) to water) $-$ 6.6 (forming the peptide H-bond) $-$ 6 (forming a W$\cdots$W H-bond) = -0.6 ± 1, which agrees satisfactorily with the observed ΔH value for the alanine helix of $-0.9_5 \pm 0.1$ kcal/mol residue.

---

[1] G. Goch, M. Maciejczyk, M. Oleszczuk, D. Stachowiak, J. Malicka, and A. Bierzynski, submitted for publication.

However, when we use the H-bond inventory approach to predict the enthalpy of solvation of amides, we encounter a paradox, which I have discussed elsewhere (30). The solvation reaction, starting with the unsolvated amide (Am) in the gas phase (g), can be written as follows.

$$\text{HN-Am-CO (g)} + \text{W}\cdots\text{W (l)} = \text{W}\cdots\text{HN-Am-CO}\cdots\text{W (l)} \qquad \text{(Eq. 2)}$$

According to the H-bond inventory, the unsolvated amide breaks one W⋯W H-bond as it dissolves in liquid (l) water. Thus, the predicted enthalpy of solvating the two amide polar groups is −12 (making two H-bonds to water) + 6 (breaking one W⋯W H-bond) = −6 kcal/mol, but the observed value is −12 kcal/mol. If the assumptions of the H-bond inventory are used to argue that the dry amide makes only one H-bond when it dissolves in water, then the contradiction with the observed value of −12 kcal/mol is even worse. The predicted value then is −6 (making one H-bond to water) + 6 (breaking one W⋯W H-bond) = 0 kcal/mol. Because the H-bond inventory approach fails when applied to this simple problem, its validity is doubtful. Probably the main reason for its failure is that the role of water is not as simple as written in Equations 1 and 2, in which one W⋯W H-bond is broken per peptide H-bond when a protein unfolds or when a dry amide molecule is solvated (see the critique of the H-bond inventory by Ben-Naim (31)). A different approach to understanding the solvation enthalpies of amides is discussed next.

Electrostatic Approach to Understanding Amide Solvation

The standard approach used by chemists to understand the solvation of polar groups in model compounds is based on electrostatics (32, 33). The properties of the Born equation (1920) (34) provide a background for explaining why electrostatics are all important. Atom-splitting experiments were still a novelty in 1920, and Max Born was interested in why Wilson's cloud chamber can be used to see the tracks of charged particles in supersaturated water vapor. The path of a charged particle is visualized by the trail of water droplets it leaves behind. Born calculated the free energy ΔG of transferring an ion (with radius r, charge q) from vacuum to a continuum solvent (water) that has a dielectric constant D.

$$\Delta G = -(q^2/2r)[1 - (1/D)] \qquad \text{(Eq. 3)}$$

He found that the free energy change enormously favors transfer of the ion from vacuum to water, regardless of whether the ion has a positive or negative charge, and consequently the ion induces the formation of water droplets. Chemists soon began to use Born's equation to analyze the solvation thermodynamics of ions in water. The enthalpy of electrostatic solvation can be predicted from Born's analysis and, in a solvent with a high dielectric constant such as water, the electrostatic solvation enthalpy of an ion is predicted to be almost equal to its electrostatic solvation free energy (35, 36). For amides, experimental values are available for both the enthalpy and free energy of solvating the amide polar groups, and the two quantities are nearly equal, probably within error (29). Consequently, the electrostatic solvation of the peptide CO and NH groups may be considered to be enthalpic when the solvation is correctly given by the electrostatic solvation free energy (ESF).

The solvation enthalpy of NaCl (infinite dilution) has the large value of −184 kcal/mol (35)! It is not surprising then that polar molecules such as amides, which contain large partial charges on the amide oxygen and nitrogen, have substantial solvation enthalpies associated with their partial charges, nor is it surprising that chemists have devised schemes for using electrostatics to compute the solvation free energies associated with polar groups. The calculation scheme devised by Barry Honig and his co-workers (32) has the attractive feature that the partial charges and atomic radii of the PARSE parameter set are calibrated from data for the solvation free energies of a large base of model compounds, including amides. The electrostatic algorithm DelPhi is used to compute the ESF. As discussed above, ESF values for the solvation of amide polar groups agree within error with the corresponding solvation enthalpies so long as the solvent is water.

Electrostatic Approach to Analyzing the Role of Solvation in Forming the Alanine Helix

The use of experimental solvation free energies to calibrate the parameters employed in calculating ESF values guarantees that the calculated ESF values will fit the experimental solvation free energies when applied to polar groups of the same type used for calibration. Will electrostatic calculations also give meaningful ESF values when applied to related but different polar groups such as the peptide NH and CO groups in an alanine helix? The only groups that have significant partial charges in an alanine peptide with blocked end groups are the polar CO and NH groups. The ESF value of the central peptide group in a solvent-exposed, 15-residue alanine helix was computed by Franc Avbelj in collaboration with us (29) to be -2.5 kcal/mol, most of which (-2.0 kcal/mol) results from the interaction with water of the peptide CO group. Avbelj and I later found a similar result for peptide H-bonds in a β-structure, an alanine β-hairpin (37), namely that the H-bonded peptide group is solvated and its ESF value is about -2.5 kcal/mol. This calculated interaction between the H-bonded peptide group and water is a basic contradiction of the H-bond inventory.

Solvation of the peptide H-bond should have major energetic consequences for steps in the process of protein folding (i). There is a desolvation penalty for burying an H-bonded peptide group because the ESF value drops to zero when the peptide H-bond is buried out of contact with water (37). Thus, for an alanine helix, the desolvation penalty is exactly the opposite of the ESF of the peptide group in a solvent-exposed helix or 2.5 kcal/mol. The peptide H-bond in an alanine helix changes from being favorable for folding ($\Delta H = -0.9_5$ kcal/mol residue) when the H-bond is solvent-exposed to being unfavorable ($\Delta H = 1.5_5$ kcal/mol residue) when the helix is buried. Consequently, solvent-exposed peptide H-bonds should stabilize but buried H-bonds should destabilize (ii). The size of the calculated desolvation penalty (2.5 kcal/mol) is remarkably large compared with the numerically smaller free energy change per residue for burying the nonpolar surface during folding (-1.4 kcal/mol for an average residue). Consequently, the desolvation penalty ought to be a major factor limiting domain size in globular proteins, because the ratio of solvent-exposed H-bonds to buried H-bonds must then affect the overall stability in a critical manner. The large size of the desolvation penalty suggests that burial of peptide H-bonds must be coupled to a process that provides a favorable free energy change, most likely burial of nonpolar surface area. Coupling has been reported recently (38) between formation of peptide H-bonds and burial of nonpolar surface area when the folding transition state is formed (iii). Side chains larger than alanine hinder the access of water to the helix backbone and substantially reduce the ESF values of peptide groups in a helix (29). Thus, larger nonpolar side chains should give smaller desolvation penalties when H-bonds are buried through folding.

Do calculated ESF values yield the known value for the ΔH of alanine helix formation? The answer to this question is not yet known reliably because it depends critically on the ESF values of peptide groups in the unfolded peptide, which are sensitive both to backbone conformation and to the access of water. Neither is known accurately at present. Until recently, unfolded peptides were assumed to adopt the "random coil" conformation of polymer chemistry, in which there is no preferred backbone conformation and the peptide chain follows a random flight description. However, a recent NMR study of a 7-residue alanine sequence by Neville Kallenbach and co-workers (39) showed surprisingly that the alanine sequence has predominantly the polyproline II backbone conformation. Moreover, the tendency of the unfolded peptide to bend back on itself is important in determining the ESF values of the peptide groups, and little is known about this. I recently compared predicted and observed values for the ΔH of alanine helix formation, based on ESF values, and concluded that they agree within error (30), but the uncertainty associated with ESF values in the unfolded peptide is uncomfortably large.

Some ESF values of a peptide group in structures representative of characteristic stages of protein folding are given for an all alanine peptide in Table I. These ESF values and structures may also be used to consider the process of alanine helix formation. Note that the major uncertainty in representing alanine helix formation lies in the unknown structure of the "unfolded" peptide.

A Paradigm Shift from the H-bond Inventory to Electrostatic Solvation

Adoption of the electrostatic approach to solvation by protein chemists will require a major change in their thinking about peptide H-bonds. The traditional view has been governed by the assumptions of the H-bond inventory in which the H-bonded peptide group does not interact with water, and the net energy of the peptide H-bond depends only on its geometry, not on its exposure to water.

Pressure for change in this traditional view has been building for some time. In 1979 Shneior Lifson and co-workers in their pioneering development of a molecular force field found that the

TABLE I
Predicted ESF values of a peptide group (-NHCO-) in an all alanine peptide with conformations characteristic of stages in the protein folding process

ESF represents electrostatic solvation free energy. A negative value means a stabilizing interaction with the solvent (water), which is treated as a continuum when ESF is calculated with DelPhi and the PARSE parameter set (32). The PARSE parameters (partial charges and atomic radii) are calibrated against experimental values of solvation free energies for a data base of model compounds that includes amides. The structure of a compound must be specified accurately in order to compute its ESF value. This table emphasizes that ESF values depend strongly on backbone conformation as well as on exposure to solvent. The peptide NH and CO dipoles change from being anti-parallel in the extended β-conformation to being parallel in the α_R conformation.

Structure	ESF
	kcal/mol
Solvent-exposed helix[a]	−2.5
Buried helix[b]	0
Extended β-strand (solvent-exposed)[c]	−7.9
Polyproline II (solvent-exposed)[d]	−9.1
Short helix (not H-bonded, solvent-exposed)[e]	−9.5

[a] The ESF value of a fully H-bonded peptide group belonging to residue 8 in the interior of a 15-residue alanine helix (taken from Ref. 29).

[b] The helix is buried out of contact with water. ESF calculations for a variety of structures given in Ref. 37 show that the ESF value drops to zero when exposure of the peptide group to solvent is completely eliminated.

[c] This value, and also the two following values below, represent possible conformations for the unfolded, solvent-exposed alanine peptide. The ESF of a peptide group at an interior position ($\geq$ residue 3) of a solvent-exposed, all-alanine β-strand ($\phi, \psi = -120°, 120°$) is independent of residue number (taken from Ref. 29). The number of peptide groups equals the number of alanine residues with the numbering scheme used here for peptides with blocked end groups (see Ref. 29).

[d] This value is given for a single alanine residue (number 5) in the polyproline II conformation ($\phi, \psi = -70°, 150°$) when all other residues in the 9-residue alanine peptide are in the extended β-strand conformation (taken from unpublished work of F. Avbelj and R. L. Baldwin (manuscript in preparation).

[e] This is a rough value because the ESF value of a peptide group in the α_R conformation ($\phi, \psi = -65°, -40°$) depends strongly on the number of neighboring helical residues and on any peptide H-bonds present (see examples in Ref. 29). This value is representative of the first three helical residues of a 5-residue helical sequence with blocked end groups (taken from Ref. 29).

peptide H-bond is represented to a good first approximation by placing dipoles on the peptide NH and CO groups (40) (see Ref. 41 for a recent treatment). If the peptide H-bond can be represented by peptide dipoles, then it is logical to use an electrostatic approach to analyze the solvation free energy associated with the dipoles. In his 1990 review of "dominant forces in protein folding," Ken Dill observed that "transferring a hydrogen bond into a nonpolar medium is generally disfavored" (42), and he gives references to earlier work on the subject. In a 1991 critique of the H-bond inventory, Ben-Naim (31) also discusses the interaction of water with H-bonded polar groups. The desolvation penalty for burying a peptide H-bond was reviewed in 1995 (43) and again later (9) by Barry Honig and co-workers. Modern work on the electrostatic approach to peptide solvation relies particularly on Honig's framework for calculating electrostatic solvation free energy (32) by an algorithm applicable to peptides and proteins.

My own interest in the electrostatic solvation approach was aroused in 1999 with the observation by Peizhi Luo (44) that helix melting curves of peptides differing by only one nonpolar amino acid cross each other at high temperatures. His results indicate that differences in helix propensity among the nonpolar amino acids must be chiefly enthalpic, rather than being entropic as believed. Luo's observation can be explained if nonpolar amino acids with bulky side chains reduce the access of water to the helix backbone (29), as argued earlier by Franc Avbelj and John Moult (45) and elaborated on later by Franc Avbelj (46). A change in solvation of the peptide CO group, when leucine is substituted by alanine, cannot be detected by Fourier-transform infrared measurements (47), however. Avbelj and I found that β-structure propensities, like helix propensities, depend on backbone solvation as judged by a strong correlation between ESF values (37) and unfolding free energies (48) for mutants of a zinc finger protein. Scientists who make electrostatic calculations on proteins generally agree there is a desolvation penalty when polar groups are wholly or partly buried in proteins. Time will tell whether protein chemists will accept that there is a desolvation penalty for burial of peptide H-bonds.

Historical Footnote

I have been asked how I first became interested in this problem. My interest goes back a long time. John Schellman and I became close friends in the 1950s when I was at the University of Wisconsin and he was at the University of Minnesota. As I studied John's classic paper (3) predicting the factors that should control the stability of a peptide helix in water, I often pondered the question: is the α-helix stable in water or not? When our laboratory took up the study of the mechanism of protein folding in 1970, a central question was whether the peptide H-bond is sufficient to stabilize an isolated secondary structure such as an α-helix. In 1970 it was commonly believed that the answer was known, namely that the peptide H-bond cannot by itself stabilize a helix in water because studies of peptides from helical segments of myoglobin (49) and staphylococcal nuclease (50) failed to detect any helix formation. Moreover, helix propensities and helix nucleation constants measured in a host-guest system (51), using a non-natural amino acid as the host (hydroxypropyl- or hydroxybutyl-L-glutamine), gave results indicating that the peptide H-bond will not stabilize a short peptide helix in water. There was, however, a different result reported in 1971 by James Brown and Werner Klee (52), who found marginal helix formation (but only near 0 °C) for the N-terminal helix of ribonuclease A studied in the "C-peptide," which contains the first 13 residues of RNase A. That the C-peptide does indeed form some helix near 0 °C was confirmed in 1982 by Andrzej Bierzynski and Peter Kim in our laboratory (53), and we then began a search for the factors stabilizing this anomalous C-peptide helix. Today many peptides from helical segments of proteins are known to show some helix formation in water.

The search for the origin of helix stability in C-peptide, which was begun both in our laboratory and that of Professor Manuel Rico in Madrid, uncovered one interaction that had been seen in the structure of RNase S (the $Glu-2^- \cdots Arg-10^+$ salt bridge) and another interaction that was visible in the RNase S structure but not recognized (the $Phe-8 \cdots His~12^+$ amino-aromatic interaction). The search also found the interaction between the helix dipole and a charged group at either end of the helix, which can be either stabilizing or destabilizing. Finally in 1989 the search led to the discovery by Susan Marqusee (17) that alanine by itself forms a stable peptide helix, although no other natural amino acid has this ability. Therefore, the peptide H-bond must be sufficient to stabilize a helix in water, because very little nonpolar surface area is buried in an alanine helix. The stabilizing effect of the peptide H-bond is still disputed, and it has been proposed (28) that the charged residues needed to solubilize an alanine helix are instead responsible for its stability, although uninterrupted alanine sequences as long as 9 residues (44) or even 13 residues (20) are found to have the high helix propensity characteristic of alanine.

Acknowledgments—I thank Franc Avbelj, John Brauman, Bob Lehman, and an anonymous reviewer for discussion.

Address correspondence to: bbaldwin@cmgm.stanford.edu.

REFERENCES

1. Pauling, L., Corey, R. B., and Branson, H. R. (1951) *Proc. Natl. Acad. Sci. U. S. A.* **37,** 205–211
2. Pauling, L., and Corey, R. B. (1951) *Proc. Natl. Acad. Sci. U. S. A.* **37,** 729–740
3. Schellman, J. A. (1955) *C. R. Trav. Lab. Carlsberg Ser. Chim.* **29,** 230–259
4. Schellman, J. A. (1955) *C. R. Trav. Lab. Carlsberg Ser. Chim.* **29,** 223–229
5. Zimm, B. H., and Bragg, J. K. (1959) *J. Chem. Phys.* **31,** 526–535
6. Lifson, S., and Roig, A. (1961) *J. Chem. Phys.* **34,** 1963–1974
7. Klotz, I. M., and Franzen, J. S. (1962) *J. Am. Chem. Soc.* **84,** 3461–3466
8. Kauzmann, W. (1959) *Adv. Protein Chem.* **14,** 1–63
9. Ben-Tal, N., Sitkoff, D., Topol, I. A., Yang, A.-S., Burt, S. K., and Honig, B. (1997) *J. Phys. Chem. B* **101,** 450–457
10. Mitchell, J. B. O., and Price, S. L. (1990) *J. Comput. Chem.* **11,** 1217–1233
11. Mitchell, J. B. O., and Price, S. L. (1991) *Chem. Phys. Lett.* **180,** 517–523
12. Fersht, A. R., Shi, J.-P., Knill-Jones, J., Lowe, D. M., Wilkinson, A. J., Blow, D. M., Brick, P., Carter, P., Waye, M. M. Y., and Winter, G. (1985) *Nature* **314,** 235–238
13. Fersht, A. R. (1987) *Trends Biochem. Sci.* **12,** 301–304
14. Stickle, D. F., Presta, L. G., Dill, K. A., and Rose, G. D. (1992) *J. Mol. Biol.* **226,** 1143–1159
15. Livingstone, J. R., Spolar, R. S., and Record, M. T., Jr. (1992) *Biochemistry* **30,** 4237–4244
16. Robertson, A. D., and Murphy, K. P. (1997) *Chem. Rev.* **97,** 1251–1267
17. Marqusee, S., Robbins, V. H., and Baldwin, R. L. (1989) *Proc. Natl. Acad. Sci. U. S. A.* **86,** 5286–5290
18. Rohl, C. A., Chakrabartty, A., and Baldwin, R. L. (1996) *Protein Sci.* **5,** 2623–2637
19. Richards, F. M., and Richmond, T. (1978) *CIBA Found. Symp.* **60,** 23–45
20. Spek, E. J., Olson, C. A., Shi, Z. S., and Kallenbach, N. R. (1999) *J. Am. Chem. Soc.* **121,** 5571–5572
21. Scholtz, J. M., Qian, H., York, E. J., Stewart, J. M., and Baldwin, R. L. (1991) *Biopolymers* **31,** 1463–1470
22. Rohl, C. A., Scholtz, J. M., York, E. J., Stewart, J. M., and Baldwin, R. L. (1992) *Biochemistry* **31,** 1263–1269
23. Doig, A. J., Chakrabartty, A., Klingler, T. M., and Baldwin, R. L. (1994) *Biochemistry* **33,** 3396–3403
24. Qian, H., and Schellman, J. A. (1992) *J. Phys. Chem.* **96,** 3987–3994

25. Scholtz, J. M., Marqusee, S., Baldwin, R. L., York, E. J., Stewart, J. M., Santoro, M., and Bolen, D. W. (1991) *Proc. Natl. Acad. Sci. U. S. A.* **88,** 2854–2858
26. Siedlecka, M., Goch, G., Ejchart, A., Sticht, H., and Bierzynski, A. (1999) *Proc. Natl. Acad. Sci. U. S. A.* **96,** 903–908
27. Lopez, M. M., Chin, D.-H., Baldwin, R. L., and Makhatadze, G. I. (2002) *Proc. Natl. Acad. Sci. U. S. A.* **99,** 1298–1302
28. Vila, J. A., Ripoll, D. R., and Scheraga, H. A. (2000) *Proc. Natl. Acad. Sci. U. S. A.* **97,** 13075–13079
29. Avbelj, F., Luo, P., and Baldwin, R. L. (2000) *Proc. Natl. Acad. Sci. U. S. A.* **97,** 10786–10791
30. Baldwin, R. L. (2002) *Biophys. Chem.* **101–102,** 203–210
31. Ben-Naim, A. (1991) *J. Phys. Chem.* **95,** 1437–1444
32. Sitkoff, D., Sharp, K. A., and Honig, B. (1994) *J. Phys. Chem.* **98,** 1978–1988
33. Florian, J., and Warshel, A. (1997) *J. Phys. Chem. B* **101,** 5583–5595
34. Born, M. (1920) *Z. Phys.* **1,** 45–48
35. Rashin, A. A., and Honig, B. (1985) *J. Phys. Chem.* **89,** 5588–5593
36. Hirata, F., Redfern, P., and Levy, R. M. (1988) *Comp. J. Quantum Chem. Quantum Biology Symp.* **15,** 179–190
37. Avbelj, F., and Baldwin, R. L. (2002) *Proc. Natl. Acad. Sci. U. S. A.* **99,** 1309–1313
38. Krantz, B. A., Srivastava, A. K., Nauli, S., Baker, D., Sauer, R. T., and Sosnick, T. R. (2002) *Nat. Struct. Biol.* **9,** 1–6
39. Shi, Z., Olson, C. A., Rose, G. D., Baldwin, R. L., and Kallenbach, N. R. (2002) *Proc. Natl. Acad. Sci. U. S. A.* **99,** 9190–9195
40. Lifson, S., Hagler, A. T., and Dauber, P. (1979) *J. Am. Chem. Soc.* **101,** 5111–5121
41. Park, C., and Goddard, W. A., III (2000) *J. Phys. Chem. B* **104,** 7784–7789
42. Dill, K. A. (1990) *Biochemistry* **29,** 7133–7155
43. Honig, B., and Yang, A.-S. (1995) *Adv. Protein Chem.* **46,** 27–58
44. Luo, P., and Baldwin, R. L. (1999) *Proc. Natl. Acad. Sci. U. S. A.* **96,** 4930–4935
45. Avbelj, F., and Moult, J. (1995) *Biochemistry* **34,** 755–764
46. Avbelj, F. (2000) *J. Mol. Biol.* **300,** 1335–1359
47. Gangani, R. A., Silva, D., Nguyen, J. Y., and Decatur, S. M. (2002) *Biochemistry* **41,** 15296–15303
48. Kim, C. A., and Berg, J. M. (1993) *Nature* **362,** 267–270
49. Epand, R. M., and Scheraga, H. A. (1968) *Biochemistry* **7,** 2864–2872
50. Taniuchi, J. H., and Anfinsen, C. B. (1969) *J. Biol. Chem.* **244,** 3864–3875
51. Scheraga, H. A. (1978) *Pure Appl. Chem.* **50,** 315–324
52. Brown, J. E., and Klee, W. A. (1971) *Biochemistry* **8,** 470–476
53. Bierzynski, A., Kim, P. S., and Baldwin, R. L. (1982) *Proc. Natl. Acad. Sci. U. S. A.* **79,** 2470–2474

THE JOURNAL OF BIOLOGICAL CHEMISTRY
© 2003 by The American Society for Biochemistry and Molecular Biology, Inc.

Vol. 278, No. 37, Issue of September 12, pp. 34733–34738, 2003
Printed in U.S.A.

Reflections

A PAPER IN A SERIES COMMISSIONED TO CELEBRATE THE CENTENARY OF THE JBC IN 2005

JBC Centennial
1905–2005
100 Years of Biochemistry and Molecular Biology

Discovery of DNA Polymerase

Published, JBC Papers in Press, June 5, 2003, DOI 10.1074/jbc.X300002200

I. R. Lehman

From the Department of Biochemistry, Beckman Center, Stanford University, Stanford, California 94305

DNA polymerase, an enzyme discovered in 1955, has the remarkable capacity to catalyze the template-directed synthesis of DNA (1, 2). The discovery of DNA polymerase has contributed in major ways to our present day understanding of how DNA is replicated and repaired and how it is transcribed. It also permitted the development of PCR and DNA sequencing, upon which much of modern biotechnology is based. In this article, I wish to recount how the discovery of the first DNA polymerase, DNA polymerase I of *Escherichia coli*, came about. I will say at the outset that although I am the author of this "Reflections" article, the discovery of DNA polymerase and the revelation that it is a template-directed enzyme resulted from the collective efforts of a small group that initially consisted of Maurice Bessman, Ernie Simms, and myself working with Arthur Kornberg in the Department of Microbiology at the Washington University School of Medicine. We were later joined by Julius Adler and Steve Zimmerman. The approach that we took reflected Arthur's strong conviction that once a simple and quantitative assay could be established in a cellular extract, enzyme purification would reveal the enzymes involved and ultimately lead to the elucidation of the reaction(s) that they catalyzed. This approach, taken by Otto Warburg and the other great German biochemists in the 1920s and 1930s, had inspired Arthur Kornberg in the elucidation of coenzyme and nucleotide biosynthesis (3, 4). Bessman, Adler, and I were postdoctoral fellows, Zimmerman was a graduate student, and Simms was a technician.

Incorporation of [14C]Thymidine into Acid-insoluble, DNase-sensitive Product

The story begins with Arthur's discovery in December 1955 that [14C]thymidine, which he had obtained from Morris Friedkin in the Pharmacology Department at Washington University, could be converted in the presence of ATP to a cold trichloroacetic acid-insoluble product by an extract of log phase *E. coli*. The specific radioactivity of the 14C-labeled thymidine was low, and fewer than 100 cpm above background were incorporated out of about 10^6 cpm added to the reaction. However, treatment of the product with crystalline pancreatic DNase, which had just then become available, rendered all of the radioactivity acid-soluble.

I had joined Arthur Kornberg's laboratory in September of 1955 and had begun work on the purification of an enzyme in extracts of bacteriophage T2-infected cells that added a hydroxymethyl group to dCMP to form hydroxymethyl-dCMP. (In the T-even phages, cytosine is entirely replaced by hydroxymethylcytosine, which is present in various states of glucosylation (5, 6).) When Arthur showed me his results, I was tremendously excited by the possibility that they represented the first demonstration of DNA synthesis *in vitro* and I asked if I could put my project on hold and join him. He agreed. We learned later of Seymour Cohen's discovery of dCMP hydroxymethylase, a discovery that opened up the whole field of virus-induced enzymes (7). I have never regretted my decision. Several months later Maurice Bessman arrived, and together with Ernie Simms, the four of us began to fractionate the activities responsible for the incorporation of the labeled thymidine into an acid-insoluble, DNase I-sensitive product.

Earlier that year, Arthur Kornberg and Ernie Simms had begun work on the purification of an activity in *E. coli* that converted thymidine in the presence of ATP to what was referred to as thymidine-X, later identified as dTMP. The activity was thymidine kinase. Additional products presumed to be dTDP and dTTP were also observed. The ability to make ^{32}P-labeled dTMP was a significant step forward because we were not limited by the low radioactivity of the [^{14}C]thymidine that was available, and the [^{32}P]dTMP incorporated into the acid-insoluble product was now in the hundreds and occasionally in the thousands of counts/min. We bet that dTTP was the true substrate for our enzyme rather than dTMP or dTDP, although the latter was a distinct possibility because of the finding a year earlier by Grunberg-Manago and Ochoa that the nucleoside diphosphates rather than the triphosphates were the substrates for their ribonucleotide-polymerizing enzyme from *Azotobacter* (8), which later turned out to be polynucleotide phosphorylase, an enzyme involved in messenger RNA degradation. Once we had [^{32}P]dTMP, we prepared α-[^{32}P]dTTP by incubating our ^{32}P-labeled dTMP with a partially purified nucleoside-diphosphate kinase and ATP and isolating the dTTP, which we carefully analyzed for thymidine, deoxyribose, and phosphate. These were present in the ratio of 1:1:3. Our assay mixture now consisted of a crude sonic extract of *E. coli*, α-[^{32}P]dTTP, ATP, Mg^{2+}, and buffer. As in the original experiment, acid-insoluble ^{32}P was measured. With this assay, we began to fractionate the crude extract for dTTP incorporation into "DNA."

Purification of DNA Polymerase and Discovery of Deoxynucleoside Triphosphates

To begin the fractionation we added streptomycin sulfate to the extract to produce a precipitate that contained the cellular nucleic acids and a nucleic acid-free supernatant. Streptomycin sulfate was used frequently at the time to remove nucleic acids, often a hindrance to protein purification in bacterial extracts. Assay of the nucleic acid-free supernatant (S-fraction) and the nucleic acid-containing precipitate (P-fraction) showed them to be devoid of dTTP incorporation activity. However, when the two fractions were combined, activity was restored. We also observed that prior incubation of the extract or the P-fraction for a few minutes at 37 °C substantially increased activity. Clearly more than one enzyme was required for the incorporation of dTTP into an acid-insoluble product. The complexity of the system became even more apparent when we began to fractionate S and P. The P-fraction could be subfractionated into two fractions, one heat-labile and the other heat-stable, both of which (in combination with the S-fraction) were necessary for activity. The S-fraction could be separated into a heat-labile fraction and a heat-stable fraction that could pass through a dialysis membrane, *i.e.* was dialyzable. The latter could be further fractionated by Dowex-1 chromatography into three discrete fractions. (Dowex-1, an anion exchange resin used at the time, separated low molecular weight acidic compounds.) Thus, incorporation of dTTP into an acid-insoluble product required: (i) two heat-labile fractions; (ii) a heat-stable fraction; (iii) three heat-stable, dialyzable, chromatographically distinct fractions; and (iv) ATP. In the absence of any one of these components, the activity was significantly diminished. Clearly, a lot was going on. The heat-labile component in the P-fraction turned out to be the enzyme that catalyzed phosphodiester bond synthesis and which we named DNA polymerase. The heat-stable, non-dialyzable component in the P-fraction was DNA. The heat-labile, non-dialyzable component of the S-fraction was a mixture of deoxynucleotide kinases, which together with nucleoside-diphosphate kinase produced the heat-stable, dialyzable mixture of dCTP, dATP, and dGTP (Fig. 1).

Multiple Functions of DNA in Reaction

We reconciled these complex requirements for the incorporation of ^{32}P-labeled dTTP into an acid-insoluble product as follows. The DNA in the extract and the P-fraction was degraded by endogenous nucleases to the deoxynucleoside monophosphates (dNMPs). (Recall that preincubation of the extract or the P-fraction significantly enhanced activity.) These were converted to the corresponding deoxynucleoside triphosphates (dNTPs) by the kinases in the S-fraction and ATP to generate dCTP, dATP, and dGTP. The heat-labile component of the P-fraction was the DNA polymerase. What about the DNA in the P-fraction? We speculated that the DNA served two functions in addition to being the source of the deoxynucleoside monophosphates. First, it protected the miniscule amount of the labeled DNA that was synthesized from degradation by the nucleases in the extract. Second, Arthur Kornberg had been strongly influenced by the work on glycogen phosphorylase in the Cori laboratory. In the case of glycogen phosphorylase, glycogen served as a "primer" for the addition of glucosyl units from

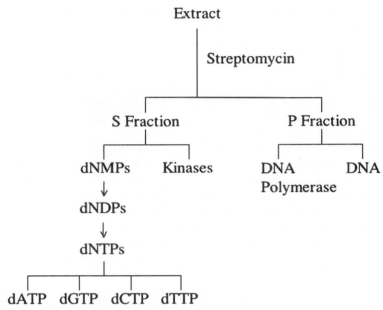

FIG. 1. **Scheme for the separation of components required for synthesis of DNA by DNA polymerase.**

glucose 1-phosphate to extend the glycogen chain (9). Similarly, he felt that dTMP from dTTP was being added to pre-existing DNA chains.

Reconstruction of DNA Synthesis

Once the outlines of the reaction became clear, we set about the task of reconstituting the reaction with purified components. We partially purified each of the deoxynucleotide kinases in the S-fraction and with these kinases and nucleoside-diphosphate kinase synthesized and characterized the four dNTPs (dTTP, dCTP, dGTP, and dATP). This alone was a substantial advance, because with the exception of dTTP (10), none of the other dNTPs had previously been described.

To prepare the four ^{32}P-labeled dNTPs we started with ^{32}P-labeled DNA, isolated from ^{32}P-labeled *E. coli*, from which we generated the four ^{32}P-labeled dNMPs (dAMP, dCMP, dTMP, and dGMP) by treatment with pancreatic DNase and snake venom phosphodiesterase. The dNMPs were individually purified and converted enzymatically to the corresponding ^{32}P-labeled dNTPs. Because the procedure usually consumed 2–3 weeks, the 14-day half-life of ^{32}P necessitated the use of large quantities of ^{32}P (50–100 mCi) in the 100-ml low phosphate culture medium that we used for the growth of *E. coli*.

Isolation of DNA Polymerase

Purification of the DNA polymerase was a difficult and demanding task. The enzyme was present in relatively small amounts even in rapidly growing *E. coli* (about 300 molecules/cell). Fortunately, a fermentor for the large scale growth of *E. coli* that had been installed in the department supplied hundreds of grams of log phase *E. coli*. Later 100-pound batches of *E. coli* cell paste were obtained from the Grain Processing Corporation in Muscatine, IA. DEAE-cellulose and phosphocellulose, invented by Herbert Sober at the NIH, liberated us from the sole reliance on the ammonium sulfate, alumina Cγ, and acetone fractionations that were the major protein fractionation tools at the time. With the aid of chromatography with these ion exchangers, we were able to obtain a several thousand-fold purified but not yet homogeneous preparation of the DNA polymerase. A vexing problem at the time was our inability to remove deoxyribonuclease activity from the enzyme. It was found later that there is a $3' \rightarrow 5'$-exonuclease activity associated with our *E. coli* DNA polymerase and indeed virtually all DNA polymerases, which serves a vital proofreading function, excising incorrectly incorporated nucleotides as replication proceeds (11).

DNA Polymerase Takes Direction from a DNA Template

With the progress in fractionation the reaction requirements were now considerably simplified. Conversion of α-[^{32}P]dTTP into an acid-insoluble product, *i.e.* DNA, required only the partially purified DNA polymerase, Mg^{2+}, DNA, dCTP, dGTP, and dATP. We further found that *all four* dNTPs were absolutely required. With omission of any one of the other three dNTPs, incorporation of α-[^{32}P]dTTP fell to background levels. Here is how Kornberg put it in a symposium held in 1956 at Johns Hopkins University on "The Chemical Basis of Heredity": "In our current studies of DNA synthesis, we are dealing with a moderately purified protein fraction which appears to increase the size of a DNA chain. It does so only under the remarkable condition that all four of the deoxynucleoside triphosphates be present." (12).

The requirement for all four dNTPs was puzzling. If the DNA that we added was simply serving as a primer, why would all four dNTPs be needed? Was it possible that the DNA polymerase was performing the template-directed replication proposed by Watson and Crick for their double-stranded structure of DNA (13)? To test this idea we used DNAs with A+T/G+C ratios ranging from 0.5 to 1.9 as "primers." The result was stunning. The ratio in the product corresponded closely to that of the added DNA throughout the synthesis and was independent of the relative concentrations of the individual dNTPs. Even widely different relative concentrations of the dNTPs did not affect the base ratios of the DNA product. Clearly, the added DNA was serving as a template to direct the polymerase as it synthesized new DNA chains, or as we cautiously put it in our initial publication, "These results suggest that enzymatic synthesis of DNA by the "polymerase" of *E. coli* represents the replication of a DNA template." (2).

Having referred to the DNA added to the reaction as the "primer," by analogy to glycogen phosphorylase it was now clear that it also was serving as a template. However, we now know that all DNA polymerases require a primer to initiate a DNA chain. Various priming mechanisms (short RNA chains, proteins) have evolved to make up for this shortcoming in an otherwise magnificent enzyme (14–16).

Initial Papers Rejected by the Journal of Biological Chemistry

The two reports describing the preparation and characterization of the four dNTPs, the partial purification of the deoxynucleotide kinases required for their synthesis, the partial purification of the newly named "DNA polymerase," and the general properties of the polymerase reaction were declined by the *Journal of Biological Chemistry* when submitted in the Fall of 1957. Among the critical comments were: "It is very doubtful that the authors are entitled to speak of the enzymatic synthesis of DNA"; "Polymerase is a poor name"; "Perhaps as important as the elimination of certain banalities . . . " etc. Through the fortunate intervention of the late John Edsall, who had just assumed the position of Editor-in-Chief in May 1958, the two papers were accepted and appeared in the July 1958 issue (17, 18). Our paper which demonstrated that the polymerase copies the DNA template appeared in the *Proceedings of the National Academy of Sciences* in December of that year (2).

Synthesis of a Copolymer of dAMP and dTMP "de Novo"

By 1958, we had established that a DNA primer and template and all four dNTPs were required by our DNA polymerase for the synthesis of DNA. However, we received a rude shock one day when we observed, to our surprise, that with our most highly purified enzyme, DNA synthesis could proceed in the apparent absence of DNA. This episode is worth recounting in more detail. As I mentioned earlier, an important aim in purifying the DNA polymerase was to remove the contaminating DNase activity, which destroyed the product that we synthesized. Howard Schachman, the distinguished physical chemist, had come from Berkeley to spend a sabbatical year in the laboratory to analyze the DNA product of the polymerase reaction. Using the tools of the polymer chemist, the ultracentrifuge and the viscometer, Howard quickly demonstrated that the product of the reaction was indeed a large polymer. It then occurred to us that viscometry might be a very sensitive method to assay for nuclease activity in our most purified DNA polymerase preparations. I set up a nuclease reaction that contained calf thymus DNA, Mg^{2+}, and the DNA polymerase. At Howard's suggestion, dCTP, dTTP, and dATP were added to closely mimic the standard synthetic reaction conditions. dGTP (which was the most difficult of the triphosphates to prepare) was omitted to prevent DNA synthesis. The viscosity of the reaction mixture was then measured over an extended period. To my disappointment, the viscosity of the solution fell to that of the reaction buffer within about an hour. Obviously, the DNA was completely degraded; our best polymerase preparation was still contaminated with nuclease(s). This experiment was being performed on a Saturday morning at the same time that I was proctoring a microbiology exam for second year medical students down the hall from the physical chemistry laboratory that Arthur Kornberg had set up for Howard. (All of us in the department, including postdoctoral fellows, participated in medical school teaching). After spending some time answering student questions and collecting exams, I returned to the laboratory to discard the reaction mixture and clean the viscometer. Before doing so, I absentmindedly took one last reading. To my amazement the viscosity of the solution had actually increased, and with repeated readings, the viscosity of the solution increased even further but then eventually fell back to that of the buffer. Could we be observing template-independent DNA synthesis? A number of control experiments were hastily performed that ruled out bacterial growth and contamination of the three dNTPs with dGTP. Howard Schachman and Julius Adler quickly found that the increase in viscosity required only the DNA polymerase, Mg^{2+}, dATP, and dTTP and occurred only after a lengthy lag. The product was a copolymer of alternating dAMP and dTMP, d(A-T) (19). Work several years later by Arthur Kornberg and Gobind Khorana showed that the rules had not been violated. The synthesis of the d(A-T) copolymer was indeed template-directed, but the template consisted of trace amounts of DNA present in the DNA polymerase preparation. The polymer was the result of a reiterative mode of DNA replication in which slippage of one stretch of alternating As and Ts within the contaminating DNA generated overlapping ends, which when filled in by the polymerase increased the chain length; ultimately, the high molecular weight d(A-T) copolymer was produced in quantity (20).

Many Families of DNA Polymerases Have Been Discovered

The DNA polymerase that we discovered is now called DNA polymerase I. In the intervening years, four additional DNA polymerases, DNA polymerase II, DNA polymerase III holoenzyme, and DNA polymerases IV and V, have been identified in *E. coli* and purified. The multisubunit DNA polymerase III holoenzyme is actually the enzyme that catalyzes the synthesis of the *E. coli* chromosome. DNA polymerase I, by virtue of its intrinsic ribonuclease H activity, together with its DNA polymerase activity plays an essential role in processing the nascent Okazaki fragments produced during the discontinuous replication of the lagging strand at the replication fork to prepare them for ligation. DNA polymerases II, IV, and V serve in the repair of DNA (reviewed in Ref. 21).

In eukaryotes the situation is even more complex. Fifteen distinct cellular DNA polymerases have been identified, and the list continues to grow (22). Three of these are devoted to replication of the genome (DNA polymerases α, δ, and ϵ); DNA polymerase γ replicates the mitochondrial genome. The rest are all devoted to the repair of specific lesions in DNA. There are, in addition, virally encoded polymerases that replicate viral DNA genomes and in the case of the retroviruses reverse transcribe their RNA genomes into DNA. Despite the number and diversity of DNA polymerases, all of these enzymes show the same requirements that we observed nearly 50 years ago for the "polymerase" of *E. coli*: a template (DNA or RNA) to guide the polymerase in its base selection, a primer onto which deoxynucleotides are added, the four dNTPs, and Mg^{2+}. There are factors associated with DNA polymerases, *e.g.* clamps and clamp loaders, exonucleases, etc., which increase the efficiency and fidelity of DNA replication, but the basic mechanisms of replicating a DNA chain are all the same.

With the crystallization of many DNA polymerases, the determination of their three-dimensional structures (23), and the application of pre-steady state kinetic analyses (24), much is now known about the detailed chemical mechanism of the polymerase reaction. This information has been invaluable in the design of effective chemotherapeutic agents, in particular antiviral drugs.

Envoi

I view those days in the mid-1950s in the Department of Microbiology on the fourth floor of the old Clinic Building at Washington University to be among the most thrilling and enjoyable of my scientific career. There were new and unexpected findings being made virtually every day, and all of us in our small group shared in the joy and excitement of those discoveries. I feel terribly fortunate to have been part of that extraordinary moment in time.

Address correspondence to: blehman@cmgm.stanford.edu.

REFERENCES

1. Kornberg, A., Lehman, I. R., Bessman, M. J., and Simms, E. S. (1956) *Biochim. Biophys. Acta* **21,** 197–198
2. Lehman, I. R., Zimmerman, S. B., Adler, J., Bessman, M. J., Simms, E. S., and Kornberg, A. (1958) *Proc. Natl. Acad. Sci. U. S. A.* **44,** 1191–1196
3. Kornberg, A. (1948) *J. Biol. Chem.* **176,** 1475–1488
4. Kornberg, A., Lieberman, I., and Simms, E. S. (1955) *J. Biol. Chem.* **215,** 389–402
5. Wyatt, G. R., and Cohen, S. S. (1953) *Biochem. J.* **55,** 774–782
6. Lehman, I. R., and Pratt, E. A. (1960) *J. Biol. Chem.* **235,** 3254–3259
7. Flaks, J. G., and Cohen, S. S. (1957) *Biochim. Biophys. Acta* **25,** 667–672
8. Grunberg-Manago, M., and Ochoa, S. (1955) *J. Am. Chem. Soc.* **77,** 3165–3166
9. Cori, G. T., and Cori, C. F. (1943) *J. Biol. Chem.* **151,** 57–72
10. Potter, R. L., and Schlesinger, S. (1955) *J. Am. Chem. Soc.* **77,** 6714
11. Brutlag, D., and Kornberg, A. (1972) *J. Biol. Chem.* **247,** 241–248
12. Kornberg, A. (1957) in *The Chemical Basis of Heredity* (McElroy, W. D., and Glass, B., eds) pp. 579–608, Johns Hopkins University Press, Baltimore, MD
13. Watson, J. D., and Crick, F. H. C. (1953) *Nature* **171,** 737–738
14. Chalberg, M. D., and Kelly, T. J., Jr. (1979) *Proc. Natl. Acad. Sci. U. S. A.* **76,** 655–659
15. Salas, M., Martin, G., Bernad, A., Garmendia, C., Lazaro, J. M., Zaballos, A., Serrano, M., Otero, M. J., Gutierrez, J., and Pares, E. (1988) *Biochim. Biophys. Acta* **951,** 419–424
16. Schekman, R., Wickner, W., Westergaard, O., Brutlag, D., Geider, K., Bertsch, L., and Kornberg, A. (1972) *Proc. Natl. Acad. Sci. U. S. A.* **69,** 2691–2695
17. Lehman, I. R., Bessman, M. J., Simms, E. S., and Kornberg, A. (1958) *J. Biol. Chem.* **233,** 163–170
18. Bessman, M. J., Lehman, I. R., Simms, E. S., and Kornberg, A. (1958) *J. Biol. Chem.* **233,** 171–177
19. Schachman, H. K., Adler, J., Radding C. M., Lehman, I. R., and Kornberg, A. (1960) *J. Biol. Chem.* **235,** 3242–3249
20. Kornberg, A., Bertsch, L. L., Jackson, J. F., and Khorana, H. G. (1964) *Proc. Natl. Acad. Sci. U. S. A.* **51,** 315–323
21. Goodman, M. F. (2002) *Annu. Rev. Biochem.* **71,** 17–50
22. Burgers, P. M. J., Koonin, E. V., Bruford, E., Blanco, L., Burtis, K. C., Christman, M. F., Copeland, W. C., Friedberg, E. C., Hanaoka, F., Hinkle, D. C., Lawrence, C. W., Nakanishi, M., Ohmori, H., Prakash, L., Prakash, S., Reynaud, C-A., Sugino, A., Todo, T., Wang, Z., Weill, J-C., and Woodgate, R. (2001) *J. Biol. Chem.* **276,** 43487–43490
23. Ollis, D. L., Brick, P., Hamlin, R., Xuong, N. G., and Steitz, T. A. (1985) *Nature* **313,** 762–766
24. Kuchta, R. D., Mizrahi, V., Benkovic, P. A., Johnson, K. A., and Benkovic, S. J. (1987) *Biochemistry* **26,** 8410–8417

THE JOURNAL OF BIOLOGICAL CHEMISTRY
© 2003 by The American Society for Biochemistry and Molecular Biology, Inc.

Vol. 278, No. 42, Issue of October 17, pp. 40417–40424, 2003
Printed in U.S.A.

Reflections

A PAPER IN A SERIES COMMISSIONED TO CELEBRATE THE CENTENARY OF THE JBC IN 2005

JBC Centennial
1905–2005
100 Years of Biochemistry and Molecular Biology

Moments of Discovery: My Favorite Experiments

Published, JBC Papers in Press, July 31, 2003, DOI 10.1074/jbc.X300004200

Paul Berg

From the Stanford University School of Medicine, Stanford, California 94305

Even before completing my undergraduate stay at Penn State University, I had decided to get a Ph.D. in biochemistry to help me get a good job in the pharmaceutical or food technology industry. However, sometime during my last year I came across a series of papers from the Biochemistry Department at Western Reserve University in Cleveland, Ohio, an institution I had not previously considered as a place to do graduate work. Those reports described the use of radioisotopes to track metabolic reactions *in vivo* and *in vitro*. Reading further, one name, Harland Wood, dominated the list of authors (Fig. 1). Soon after World War II ended, Wood had been recruited to the Western Reserve University medical school from the University of Minnesota to resurrect a virtually moribund biochemistry department. Intrigued by the new technology, I decided to explore this new approach. By 1948 when I arrived as a graduate student, Wood's carefully chosen group of younger faculty constituted one of the top departments in the country.

Because of an unfortunate miscommunication, I found that I had inadvertently applied to and been accepted into the remnant of the defunct biochemistry department. Although keenly disappointed, I tried to make the best of it by teaming up with two former members of the department, Leonard Skeggs and Jack Leonard, to develop a new kind of artificial kidney. During the ensuing 2 years, I became pretty adept at surgical removal of dog kidneys and keeping the animals alive by dialysis. Recognizing my frustration during one of the biochemistry graduate courses I was obliged to take, Wood asked if I was interested in joining his department and completing my thesis research there. It was a break that changed my life. During the next 2 years, I completed my thesis research on the mechanism by which one-carbon compounds, formate, formaldehyde, and methanol, are converted to the methyl group of methionine. Although Warwick Sakami, one of the young professors in the department, was my nominal adviser, it was Wood who provided the inspiration that set the tone of my career in research.

Wood's scientific exploits as a graduate student and postdoctoral fellow were legendary among members of the department. While working for his Ph.D. at Iowa State University, he made the startling discovery that heterotrophic organisms (those that live on complex carbon compounds for their source of energy and biosynthetic needs) incorporated carbon dioxide into their cellular substituents. This property, previously believed to exist only in photosynthetic plants and autotrophic microbes, was met with considerable disbelief. Characteristically, Wood was not about to let the doubts persist and he turned to isotopes to prove his point. After a brief fling with radioactive carbon-11, whose incredibly short half-life made it difficult to use, he chose the stable carbon-13 isotope to trace the metabolic utilization of carbon dioxide. Because an enriched source of carbon-13 was not readily available in the late 1930s and early 1940s, he proceeded to prepare some himself. He built a water-cooled thermal diffusion column in a five-story abandoned elevator shaft that enabled him to separate sufficient quantities of carbon-13 for his experiments. However, he also needed a way to measure the abundance of carbon-13 in the metabolic products. Getting advice from Alfred Nier, a physicist at the

FIG. 1. **Harland Goff Wood.**

university, he built a mass spectrophotometer from scratch. This display of dogged self-sufficiency reflects his early experiences on the family's Iowa farm and the remarkable work ethic he and his brothers and sisters acquired from their parents and the community in which they were raised.

Wood's devotion to research and to those who shared his commitment to science showed through his outwardly gruff manner. "Hanging out" with the graduate students during the many late evenings when he lingered in the laboratory before heading home were the times I treasured most. His unremitting honesty and forthrightness in the way he practiced science provided the model we all tried to emulate. Wood's response to criticism showed through during a visit from the legendary Hans Krebs. Some years before, Wood had concluded that citric acid could not be one of the intermediates in the Krebs cycle for metabolizing dicarboxylic acids. He based his conclusion on the finding of an unanticipated isotope distribution in the glucose portion of liver glycogen and in intermediates of the cycle after feeding a variety of ^{14}C-labeled metabolic precursors. He concluded that citric acid, a chemically symmetric molecule, could not be an obligatory intermediate in the cycle. For a period, Krebs' original formulation of the cycle stood amended with *cis*-aconitic acid replacing citric acid. Krebs' lecture during that visit provided a wholly novel way to explain how citric acid could be metabolized in an asymmetric way, thereby accounting for Wood's findings. Alexander Ogston had pointed out that citric acid was asymmetric with respect to its chirality and that the enzyme aconitase could bind and metabolize citric acid in an asymmetric manner. Entirely free from any apparent pique, defensiveness, or embarrassment, Wood was forthright in acknowledging Krebs' ingenious explanation and admitted that in this instance the isotope result had been misleading, and he stressed the necessity of understanding the enzyme mechanisms. The magnanimity and generosity of his praise and the unself-conscious manner in which he responded brought home to me his often repeated admonition that criticism focused on the science was not meant to diminish one as a person. It was important for me to keep that in mind when he vigorously contested what I thought were clever interpretations or speculations. David A. Goldthwait and Richard W. Hanson captured the essence of the man in their National Academy of Sciences Biographical Memoir: " . . . as a man without pretensions, whose opinions and decisions were always based on principles and not on personal factors, a man whose mind was open to new ideas and concepts, a man who by his example and encouragement got the best out of his associates, and a man who, once he made up his mind, would drive straight toward his goal. In him one felt the warmth, strength and integrity that made him unique" (1).

Much to the benefit of the students and faculty, Wood's reputation enticed many of the world's leading biochemists to visit and present their latest findings. Besides Krebs, the ones I recall as being most influential were Carl Cori, Severo Ochoa, Fritz Lipmann, Feodor Lynen,

FIG. 2. **Laboratory group at the Institute of Cytophysiology.** Kneeling from *left* to *right*: E. Scarano, W. (Bill) Joklik, P. Berg, H. Klenow; second row from *left* to *right*: V. Hubscher, Jytte Kjeldgaard, A. Munch-Petersen; top row from *left* to *right*: unidentified, H. Kalckar, unidentified, M. Saffran.

Albert Lehninger, Herman Kalckar, and Arthur Kornberg. The latter two made a special impression. Aside from the fact that I and most others could barely understand Kalckar's heavily Danish-inflected English, his almost childish, joyous personality made his still novel use of spectrophotometry for studying nucleotide enzymology seem all the more exciting. Arthur Kornberg was one of the rising "stars" in enzymology but equally notable for me at the time was that he and I graduated from the same Brooklyn High School, Abraham Lincoln, albeit about 10 years apart.

As I was finishing the research for my thesis, I decided that it would be important for me get more intensive training in enzymology. Aware of that decision, Wood arranged for me to have a postdoctoral position with Carl and Gerty Cori at Washington University. Much to his chagrin, I told him that I preferred not to live in St. Louis because of its vestiges of racial segregation and notoriously torrid summers; perhaps apocryphal, foreign consular officials were said to receive a "tropical pay bonus" during their assignment in St. Louis. Turning down what was possibly a career-making opportunity because of an aversion to living in St. Louis was in Wood's mind shortsighted, if not foolish. Disappointing Wood in his aspirations for my future was painful, but in time my decision was forgiven, perhaps because he appreciated my independence. Having thought hard about what I would do instead, I decided to spend the first of two planned postdoctoral years working with Herman Kalckar in Copenhagen, Denmark and to spend the second year in Arthur Kornberg's laboratory at the National Institutes of Health.

Herman Kalckar came to the United States in the late 1930s and was forced to remain throughout World War II. During the eight or so years he spent in the United States he was among the earliest to formulate the concept of high energy bonds as the form in which free energy was captured and stored during oxidative metabolism. Most people were captivated by his charmingly buoyant and fun-loving manner despite their inability to understand what he was saying. As I learned later, it was not just his Danish-like English that confused people, for even the Danes found him difficult to follow when he spoke his native language. Soon after the war ended and the situation in Denmark was near normal, Kalckar returned to Copenhagen and established an active laboratory at the university's Institute of Cytophysiology (Fig. 2).

When I arrived in the fall of 1952, he had already assembled an interesting collection of fellows from Sweden, India, Italy, Scotland, Australia, and Canada. The international makeup of the laboratory made English the *lingua franca* for our scientific and social discourse. The locals in the laboratory were amused and tolerant as they listened to our futile promises to refrain from speaking English in the laboratory; their references to Danish as a "throat disease" made us feel less inadequate. James D. Watson had been in the laboratory the year before I arrived to learn some nucleic acid chemistry, ostensibly on the advice of his graduate professor, Salvador Luria. His stay, however, was brief probably because of his outspoken disdain for biochemistry and his belief that Kalckar had little interest in genes or DNA. That assessment was probably a result of Kalckar's inattention to the laboratory that year, for when I learned to translate Kalckar's mutterings, it was apparent that his interests in biology were wide ranging and most often stimulating and provocative.

Although still not fully recovered from the Nazi occupation, the Danes were welcoming and extraordinarily hospitable, occasionally to our embarrassment. Living in Taarbaek, a small upscale fishing village bordering on the King's private deer park on the outskirts of Copenhagen, was a welcome relief from 4 years in Cleveland and from my wife Millie's 4 years of nursing at the university's hospital. My daily commute to and from the institute and the bike ride home through the woods to our "villa" provided the quiet time for preparing and thinking about the experiments of the day. My American Cancer Society fellowship stipend ($3600 per year), which one of our Danish friends speculated might have been more than the King's allowance, allowed us to live well and to sample the sights and culture of the Europe we had only read about.

Kalckar was a dreamer, often seeking novel explanations for paradoxical observations. One of these originated from a suggestion by Thomas Rosenberg, a physicist friend from the nearby Niels Bohr Institute. Responding to a proposal that insulin acted on the phosphorylation of glucose by hexokinase, they speculated that the hexokinase reaction occurred in two steps; the first product was a high energy glucose 6-metaphosphate that was then hydrated to form glucose 6-phosphate; insulin was presumed to stimulate the hydration step. Commonly, such musings formed the basis for discussions during afternoon tea. At one discussion, I outlined a way to test that possibility. Presuming that the first step was reversible and being aware that ITP was also a substrate for hexokinase, it seemed plausible to expect a glucose-dependent transfer of phosphate from ATP to IDP or from ITP to ADP. At the time, Wolfgang (Bill) Joklik, a postdoctoral fellow from Australia via a Ph.D. at Oxford, joined the laboratory and we agreed to test that idea. Because ^{32}P-labeled ATP and ITP were unavailable commercially at the time, we made our own. A rabbit was injected with ^{32}P-labeled phosphate and ATP was harvested from the skeletal muscles, an exercise Bill and I still chortle over when we recall how the rabbit nearly sabotaged our effort.

The experiment to test the Rosenberg-Kalckar hypothesis led to a serendipitous and more interesting result. The terminal phosphate of ATP was transferred to IDP and from ITP to ADP, but neither reaction was influenced by the presence of glucose. Clearly this finding was inconsistent with the hypothesis' predicted key role for glucose. Following up on that result, Joklik and I discovered that the transphosphorylation activity was because of a previously unknown enzyme that uses ATP to phosphorylate the four ribo- and deoxyribonucleoside diphosphates to the respective triphosphates; we dubbed the enzyme nucleoside diphosphokinase or Nudiki for short (2). Although the new activity was first detected in vertebrate muscle, we purified it from yeast. Subsequently the enzyme was found to be widely distributed in pro-and eukaryotes, not surprisingly because it plays a critical role in generating the "building blocks" for RNA and DNA synthesis.

One of the papers that got lots of discussion at our tea times was a report from Fritz Lipmann, Feodor Lynen, and their respective collaborators Mary Ellen Jones and Helmut Hilz (3). That report alleged that the long standing puzzle of how eukaryotic organisms make acetyl-CoA had been solved. Lipmann's and Lynen's towering reputations and the novelty of their proposal were enough to capture my attention. At the time, the synthesis of acetyl-CoA in bacteria was known to occur via two separate enzymatic reactions. For acetokinase,

$$ATP + acetate \leftrightarrow acetyl\ phosphate + ADP$$

and for phosphotransacetylase

$$Acetyl\ phosphate + CoA \leftrightarrow acetyl\text{-}CoA + P_i$$

By contrast, in yeast and animal cells, acetyl-CoA appeared to be made by a single enzyme (acetyl-CoA synthetase), seemingly in a single reaction.

$$ATP + acetate + CoA \leftrightarrow acetyl\text{-}CoA + AMP + PP_i$$

FIG. 3. **Arthur Kornberg.**

The authors' claim that the reaction proceeds in discrete steps involving successive enzyme-bound intermediates was particularly provocative.

$$\text{ATP} + \text{enzyme} \leftrightarrow \text{enzyme-adenylate} + \text{PP}_i$$

$$\text{Enzyme-adenylate} + \text{CoA} \leftrightarrow \text{enzyme-CoA} + \text{AMP}$$

$$\text{Enzyme-CoA} + \text{acetate} \leftrightarrow \text{acetyl-CoA} + \text{enzyme}$$

The evidence supporting their proposal relied on observations that the enzyme alone catalyzed an exchange of ^{32}P-labeled PP$_i$ with the pyrophosphoryl moiety of ATP, as well as an exchange of ^{14}C-labeled acetate with the acetyl group of acetyl-CoA. Both of these findings were consistent with their formulation of three partial reactions and accounted for the energetics and stoichiometry of the overall conversions. Although enzyme-bound intermediates had previously been suspected as intermediates in certain protease reactions, to my knowledge none had been isolated and characterized. Were analogous enzyme-bound nucleotides formed with other nucleoside triphosphates? Could they be, I wondered, activated substrates for nucleic acid synthesis? As a start, it seemed worth trying to isolate the enzyme-AMP compound when I got to Kornberg's laboratory.

The voyage back to the United States was filled with regrets at leaving the idyllic stay in Denmark. However, there was also the excitement of a new laboratory and a chance to do something different. Ironically, although I had earlier turned down the opportunity to work at Washington University, Kornberg (Fig. 3) informed me about halfway through the year that he had decided to move from the National Institutes of Health to St. Louis to rebuild Washington University's department of microbiology. Later, I learned from him that of the several post-doctoral applicants he had accepted to join his laboratory I was the only one who agreed to the change in location.

It was a typical fall day in mid-November, 1953, when I arrived at Washington University Medical School to join Kornberg's laboratory. Located at the top of an antiquated clinic building, the only way to reach the microbiology department was by passing down a long corridor lined with patients in various states of despair waiting their turn to see a doctor. The final ascent was via a somewhat "ancient" elevator, which, after the sliding gate was secured, inched and lurched its way upward to the fourth floor. On my arrival, the shabbiness of the surroundings was plainly evident. The main corridor's bare bulb lighting, suspended from the unusually high ceilings characteristic of buildings of that vintage, could well have been installed when gas lights went out of fashion. It was hard to realize that that department had been where Sol Spiegelman and Al Hershey had helped usher in molecular biology and where some notable work in medical immunology had been done. However, Kornberg's enthusiasm at my arrival, his excitement about those who would follow, and the prospects for the soon to be completed renovations lessened the importance of the shabby surroundings. Kornberg's escorted tour of the laboratories that had been newly done over, including the one I was to work in, assured me that I had made the right choice for the second year of my postdoctoral fellowship. After settling on a place to live, I was ready to get to the laboratory.

In our meeting to discuss what I would work on, I told Kornberg of my keenness on trying to isolate the enzyme-AMP compound proposed by the Lipmann-Lynen team. He was decidedly cool to my suggestion, expressing considerable skepticism of their claim. Indeed, he believed that the ATP-PP$_i$ exchange reactions offered to support the model could be explained in other ways. For example, the reversible reactions leading to the synthesis of the coenzymes nicotinamide adenine dinucleotide (NAD) and flavin adenine dinucleotide (FAD) (4, 5) result in the production of PP$_i$ and, therefore, even trace amounts of NAD or FAD in their enzyme preparation could account for the observed ATP-PP$_i$ exchange. Nevertheless, despite Kornberg's reservations, I was "unleashed" to explore my hunch with only the admonition to purify the enzyme before testing whether their observations and predictions held up.

Within a relatively short time, using the formation of acetyl-CoA as the assay, I had a substantially purified enzyme. Much to my dismay neither of the two kinds of exchange reactions were detectable. Setting about to determine what was needed to reconstitute the ATP-PP$_i$ exchange, I confirmed that with all the reactants present there was a robust exchange of labeled PP$_i$ with ATP but none when acetate and CoA were omitted. Surprisingly, acetate alone was able to completely restore the enzyme's ability to promote the exchange of ATP with PP$_i$. I inferred that ATP reacted with acetate to produce acetyl adenylate, a nucleotidyl analogue of acetyl phosphate, with the concomitant formation of PP$_i$ (6). It was also plausible that like acetyl phosphate, acetyl adenylate could serve as the acetyl donor to CoA. However, my attempts to isolate the putative acetyl adenylate from the reaction failed.

Seeking to verify my conjecture, I decided to synthesize acetyl adenylate chemically. Being a novel compound, I contacted David Lipkin, a specialist in phosphate chemistry on the Washington University campus a few miles away, on how to proceed. It's easy, he advised: mix acetyl chloride and the silver salt of adenylic acid, remove the insoluble silver chloride, and collect the mixed anhydride from the fluid. Within a week or so the first ever batch of pure acetyl adenylate was available and I could verify that the enzyme converted it rapidly and quantitatively to ATP in the presence of only PP$_i$ and to acetyl-CoA with added CoA. The overall reaction could then be explained as the result of two successive steps.

$$\text{ATP} + \text{acetate} \leftrightarrow \text{acetyl adenylate} + \text{PP}_i$$

$$\text{Acetyl adenylate} + \text{CoA} \leftrightarrow \text{acetyl-CoA} + \text{AMP}$$

A nagging concern was my inability to detect or accumulate acetyl adenylate with only ATP and acetate as the substrates. Perhaps, I thought, it remained bound to the enzyme and existed only in amounts stoichiometric with the amount of enzyme. To test that surmise, I resorted to the use of hydroxamic acid. Acetyl phosphate was known to react with that reagent to form acetyl hydroxamate, and I confirmed that a similar reaction occurred with synthetic acetyl adenylate. I was elated to detect an accumulation of acetyl hydroxamate and PP$_i$ when the enzyme was incubated with ATP, acetate, and hydroxamic acid. Evidently, acetyl adenylate formed in the reaction remains tightly bound to the enzyme when the acetyl acceptor, CoA, is absent.

The novelty of acetyl adenylate as the intermediate in the formation of the acetyl-CoA reaction caused a stir when I reported it at the annual Federation meeting in 1955. Lipmann and Lynen were considerably embarrassed, as they confessed to me later. More than likely the problem with their experiments was the impure state of the enzyme. Having obtained their relatively crude enzyme from yeast grown with acetate as the carbon source, it's likely that acetate contaminated their preparations. Kornberg's reminder of Efraim Racker's dictum not to waste clean thoughts on dirty enzymes was vindicated.

Soon thereafter, the formation of acyl adenylates accounted for the production of the longer chain fatty acyl-CoAs as well as of other carboxylates, *e.g.* lipoic acid. However, I was curious about another ATP-PP$_i$ exchange activity encountered in the earlier fractions of the acetyl-CoA synthetase, one stimulated by methionine (7). It appeared not to be related to the enzyme discovered by GiulioCantoni that forms *S*-adenosylmethionine because of the relative irreversibility of that reaction. Soon other enzymes catalyzing amino acid-dependent exchanges of ATP with PP$_i$ were detected, and their purification revealed that each was specific for a different amino acid. The ability to trap aminoacyl hydroxamates with hydroxamic acid in the reaction was consistent with the likelihood that these enzymes also catalyzed the formation of enzyme-bound aminoacyl adenylates. Reasoning by analogy with the mechanism of the acetyl-CoA synthetase, it seemed probable that there was a naturally occurring acceptor for the aminoacyl moiety, a counterpart to CoA. I asked Jim Offengand, my first graduate student, to search for such an acceptor.

To our surprise, his search led to the discovery of RNA as the aminoacyl acceptor (8). Purification of the acceptor RNA revealed that it was relatively small and probably identical to the sRNA that Zamecnik and Hoagland had found to stimulate the *in vitro* incorporation of amino acids into protein (9). Further work by Offengand and Jack Preiss, my first postdoctoral fellow, established that a single and highly specific enzyme converts each amino acid to an enzyme-bound aminoacyl adenylate and then transfers the aminoacyl group to a specific RNA molecule, now referred to as tRNA. At Gobind Khorana's invitation, I spent the delightful summer of 1956 at his British Columbia Research Council laboratory in Vancouver, Canada learning to synthesize aminoacyl adenylates chemically. With those in hand, each of the purified enzymes was shown to convert the cognate synthetic aminoacyl adenylate to ATP with PP(i) and to aminoacyl tRNAs in the presence of tRNA (10). Because the aminoacyl acceptor property of the tRNA preparation could be successively saturated by each amino acid, we inferred that each amino acid is transferred to only a limited set of tRNA molecules. It took other experiments to establish that each tRNA molecule had a single acceptor site, somewhat surprisingly one of the two 3′-terminal hydroxyl groups. This stoichiometry (one amino acid per tRNA) squared with Francis Crick's surmise that the aminoacyl tRNAs serve as "adaptors" for matching amino acids to their cognate mRNA codons during ribosome-mediated assembly of polypeptide chains (11).

Adenylylation of the acyl groups of fatty acids and amino acids by ATP proved to be the first discovered of a general class of enzymatic reactions. Proteins (for example, DNA ligase and glutamine synthetase) are also adenylylated by ATP. In the case of the ligase, adenylylation of the protein enables it to catalyze the covalent joining of DNA ends, and adenylylation of glutamine synthetase regulates the responsiveness of the enzyme to feedback regulation. In each case, the rapid hydrolysis of the eliminated PP$_i$ to P$_i$ drives the adenylylation reactions to completion.

These discoveries, spaced over a period of about 5–6 years, were most satisfying because they happened at the beginning of my career when I still performed many of the experiments with my own hands. Coincidentally, they also provided the confidence that I could do creditable research independently. Despite my earlier aversion to living in St. Louis, I learned that interacting with remarkable colleagues in a stimulating setting trumped the occasionally unpleasant summer and winter weather, and over the 6 years of my stay there, the city overcame its legacy of racial prejudice and revealed a vibrant social and cultural life.

Address correspondence to: pberg@cmgm.stanford.edu.

REFERENCES

1. Goldthwait, D. A., and Hanson, R. W. (1996) Harland Goff Wood. *Biogr. Mem. Natl. Acad. Sci.* **69,** 3–36
2. Berg, P., and Joklik, W. K. (1954) Enzymatic phosphorylation of nucleoside diphosphates. *J. Biol. Chem.* **210,** 657–672
3. Jones, M. E., Lipmann, F., Hilz, H., and Lynen, F. (1953) On the enzymatic mechanism of coenzyme A acetylation with adenosine triphosphate and acetate. *J. Am. Chem. Soc.* **75,** 3285–3286
4. Kornberg, A. (1950) Reversible enzymatic synthesis of diphosphopyridine nucleotide and inorganic phosphate. *J.*

Biol. Chem. **182,** 779–785

5. Schrecker, A. W., and Kornberg, A. (1950) Reversible enzymatic synthesis of flavin-adenine dinucleotide. *J. Biol. Chem.* **182,** 795–803

6. Berg, P. (1956) Acyl adenylates: an enzymatic mechanism of acetate activation. *J. Biol. Chem.* **222,** 991–1013; Acyl adenylates: the synthesis and properties of adenyl acetate. *J. Biol. Chem.* **222,** 1015–1023

7. Berg, P. (1956) Acyl adenylates: the interaction of adenosine triphosphate and methionine. *J. Biol. Chem.* **222,** 1025–1034

8. Berg, P., and Ofengand, E. J. (1958) An enzymatic mechanism for linking amino acids to RNA. *Proc. Natl. Acad. Sci. U. S. A.* **44,** 78–86

9. Hoagland, M. B., Stephenson, M. L., Scott, J. F., Hecht, L. I., and Zamecnik, P. C. (1958) A soluble ribonucleic acid intermediate in protein synthesis. *J. Biol. Chem.* **231,** 241–257

10. Berg, P. (1958) The chemical synthesis of amino acyl adenylates. *J. Biol. Chem.* **233,** 608–611; Studies on the enzymatic utilization of amino acyl adenylates: the formation of adenosine triphosphate. *J. Biol. Chem.* **233,** 601–607

11. Crick, F. H. C. (1958) On protein synthesis. *Symp. Soc. Exp. Biol.* **12,** 138–163

THE JOURNAL OF BIOLOGICAL CHEMISTRY
Vol. 278, No. 48, Issue of November 28, pp. 47351–47356, 2003

Reflections

A PAPER IN A SERIES COMMISSIONED TO CELEBRATE THE CENTENARY OF THE JBC IN 2005

JBC Centennial
1905–2005
100 Years of Biochemistry and Molecular Biology

Leon Heppel and the Early Days of RNA Biochemistry

Published, JBC Papers in Press, September 15, 2003, DOI 10.1074/jbc.X300008200

Maxine Singer

From the Carnegie Institution of Washington, Washington, D. C. 20005

Today, machines turn out the sequence of a million DNA bases in a day. Fifty years ago, when the chemical and biochemical tools for studying DNA and RNA were at best rudimentary, such a machine was unimaginable. Then, the cutting edge was Erwin Chargaff's demonstration, in 1948, that the base composition of DNA could be reliably determined. His discovery that all DNAs contain equal amounts of adenine and thymine and similarly of guanine and cytosine depended on applying two recent developments: partition chromatography and the absorption spectra of nucleic acid constituents. DNA chemistry took a huge step forward when James D. Watson and Francis Crick, using Chargaff's data, constructed the double helical model of DNA. In contrast, insights into RNA structure lagged behind, thus hampering progress in understanding how DNA carries out its genetic function.

At the beginning of the 1950s, studies on RNA structure in the United States came mainly from the laboratories of Waldo Cohn and C. E. Carter. Progress was slow because of the difficulty of determining whether the internucleotide bond was 5′ to 3′ or 5′ to 2′, because the primitive methods available could not cope with the instability of RNA compared with DNA, and because of the still unrecognized existence of several types of RNA.

The impetus for further advances in DNA and RNA biochemistry emerged not from structural investigations but from studies of the enzymology of phosphate-containing coenzymes and nucleotides. Much of that activity was spurred by a group of extraordinary biomedical scientists, who partly through the accidents of World War II assignments to the United States Public Health Service found themselves at war's end together at the still fledgling National Institutes of Health (NIH) (1). At the time NIH had little prestige compared with academic institutions. What it did offer was regular support and a great deal of scientific freedom. Leon Heppel, Arthur Kornberg, Herbert Tabor, and Bernard Horecker used part of their freedom to learn biochemistry. Horecker, already an experienced enzymologist, helped them find their way. Their primary educational tool was a private, daily, lunchtime journal club; according to legend, the only day off was Christmas. Kornberg was the dominant personality. Years later, long after he had left the NIH and the club was open to other colleagues and even postdoctoral fellows, any proposed change in the lunch club format elicited the question: "What would Arthur think?"

The biochemistry of phosphate-containing compounds became a central interest of several in the original lunch club group. Horecker's work led to a description of the pentose phosphate pathway (2). Kornberg began working on the enzymatic synthesis of pyrophosphate, coenzymes, and nucleotides, and he has told the story about how these investigations led to the discovery of DNA polymerase I in the three years after he left the NIH for Washington University in 1953 (1, 3).

Heppel (Fig. 1) had earned a Ph.D. in biochemistry from the University of California at Berkeley in 1937 and an M.D. in 1941 from the University of Rochester. After completing a medical internship at Strong Memorial in Rochester, he carried out toxicology research at the NIH during the war years. By 1950 he, together with his long time colleague Russell J. Hilmoe,

FIG. 1. **A youthful Leon Heppel.** Courtesy of the Office of NIH History, National Institutes of Health and Dr. Buhm Soon Park.

had begun experiments on enzymes that catalyze the hydrolysis and phosphorolysis of polyribonucleotides and their derivatives. They studied 5'-nucleotidase (4), inorganic pyrophosphatase (5), and the hydrolysis and phosphorolysis of purine ribosides and ATP (6, 7). One of their main interests was a phosphodiesterase found in bovine spleen (8). Although they purified the enzyme to some extent, they were unable to characterize satisfactorily the products of digestion of polynucleotides. Heppel, then just over 40 years old, decided to take a leave from NIH and spend 1953 in Roy Markham's laboratory in Cambridge, England, where he hoped to solve the problem of the structure of the products. Markham could teach Heppel his innovative techniques for partition chromatography on paper strips as well as pioneering paper electrophoresis methods for nucleic acid components. With the support of a Guggenheim Fellowship and a travel grant from the American Cancer Society, Heppel, his wife Adelaide, and their two sons (ages 5 and 1) sailed across the Atlantic on the S.S. United States.

Markham, a few years younger than Heppel, was at the Molteno Institute in the Plant Virus Research Unit of the Agricultural Research Council. Then, as now, the name of a research department need not reflect the most exciting ongoing science. Markham and his associates were mainly concerned with nailing down the structure of the internucleotide bonds in RNA. Did they go from a 5'-hydroxyl to a 2'-hydroxyl on the ribose moiety or, in analogy with DNA, to a 3'-hydroxyl? Both acid and alkaline hydrolysis yielded 2',3'-cyclic phosphodiester intermediates and a mixture of 2'- and 3'-mononucleotides as final products. Similarly, RNase A digestion went through the 2',3'-cyclic intermediates although it eventually gave only 3'-mononucleotides. Neither of these methods could unequivocally establish which kind of bond was in the RNA itself. The analogy with the 5',3' bond in DNA and the fact that RNase A hydrolyzed pyrimidine 3'-benzyl but not pyrimidine 2'-benzyl phosphodiester favored the 3'-hydroxyl link, at least for pyrimidine nucleotides in RNA (9). However, the standard of proof required by biochemists of the day demanded a more direct demonstration. The primary tool at hand was ingenious use of highly specific enzymes. Thus, a specific phosphodiesterase from snake venom that yielded 5'-mononucleotides from RNA had established the link on one side of the internucleotide bond (10).

By April of 1953, Markham's laboratory with Heppel's help had settled the issue; the bond was 5' to 3'. Markham and P. R. Whitfeld, an Australian postdoctoral fellow, reported that when the dinucleotide monophosphates GpC, GpU, ApC, and ApU (separated from RNase A digests after dephosphorylation) were oxidized to dialdehydes by periodate (with cleavage between the 2'- and 3'-hydroxyls of the pyrimidine ribose) and treated at pH 10, 3'-GMP and 3'-AMP were produced (11). In the accompanying paper, Heppel, along with Markham and Hilmoe, showed that the partly fractionated phosphodiesterase from bovine spleen that he had brought to England yielded 3'-purine mononucleotides from compounds such as ApApU with no intermediary formation of cyclic nucleotides (8, 12, 13). Further, the enzyme could not hydrolyze purine 2'-benzyl phosphodiesters (14).

Heppel worked as prodigiously in England as he did at home. And as at home, he and Adelaide enjoyed the sites and life around them despite the difficulties of living with two small children in postwar England. Food rationing was still in place, and the standard of living was not what they had left behind in the United States. Careful and sensitive observers, the Heppels could make a short walk or a single painting into a world of experience. Besides pinning down the internucleotide bond in RNA, Heppel that year also demonstrated that RNase A and the spleen phosphodiesterase could catalyze nucleotide transfer reactions; for example, incubation of 2',3'-cyclic AMP, methanol, and enzyme yielded adenosine 3'-methyl phosphodiester (15). RNase A would even use a nucleoside or nucleotide as acceptor and catalyze the synthesis of polyribonucleotides (16). In this paper, the authors proposed a modification of the abbreviations for polynucleotides then in use, and these became the conventions that we use to this day (*e.g.* putting the 5'-end at the left). Although it soon became clear that polyribonucleotides are not synthesized by transphosphorylation (or transnucleotidation) in cells, the work had several consequences. Most importantly, when Severo Ochoa and Marianne Grunberg Manago discovered polynucleotide phosphorylase (PNPase) in extracts of *Azotobacter vinelandii*, they turned to Heppel for collaboration in characterizing the polymer products. More personally, it was the work on transphosphorylation that attracted the interest of Joseph S. Fruton, my Ph.D. professor at Yale, and led him to recommend that I apply to Heppel for postdoctoral training.

By the time I joined Heppel's NIH laboratory in October of 1956 he was deeply involved in analyzing the polyribonucleotides formed from nucleoside 5'-diphosphates by action of PNPase (17). Earlier that year, he and Ochoa (18) had summarized their results at a conference where they also considered whether PNPase could be responsible for RNA synthesis and speculated on possible mechanisms of DNA synthesis. Arthur Kornberg presented some of the early experiments on DNA polymerase I of *Escherichia coli* at the same meeting. It is easy to imagine the excitement in Baltimore during that symposium as participants heard the first clues to the synthesis of polynucleotides. These discoveries opened a new era for biochemistry, although as it turned out PNPase was not responsible for RNA synthesis and DNA polymerase I was not the key enzyme involved in DNA replication. Meanwhile, Heppel was becoming interested in the mechanisms of the PNPase polymerization reaction as well as of the reverse reaction, the phosphorolysis of the polymers. These two areas became the focus of my own research when I joined Heppel's laboratory. In the next few years others at the NIH, notably Dan Bradley, David Davies, Gary Felsenfeld, Marie Lipsett, Todd Miles, Alex Rich, and later Martin Gellert used the polymers produced by PNPase action to study the physical properties of long polyribonucleotides.

At this time, very few biochemists worked with RNA or polyribonucleotides or indeed with DNA. Two brief sections in Volume II of *Methods in Enzymology*, published in 1955, were sufficient to deal with the known enzymes of phosphate and nucleic acid metabolism; Kornberg and Heppel together contributed a significant percentage of the papers. The community was not even large enough to have a Gordon Conference to call its own. Through most of the 1950s, a single annual conference was entitled "Proteins and Nucleic Acids." Then, in 1959, the Gordon Conference organization announced that because the scope of research in both areas had become "so wide" each topic would have its own conference, although only in alternating years. The 1960 conference, still entitled "Proteins and Nucleic Acids," was the first devoted exclusively to nucleic acids. Finally, in 1962, there was a Gordon Conference on "Nucleic Acids" co-chaired by Heppel and Cyrus Levinthal.

In 1958, when Horecker left the NIH, Heppel succeeded him as chief of the Laboratory of Biochemistry and Metabolism, National Institute of Arthritis and Metabolic Diseases. Before he left, Horecker changed my status from postdoctoral fellow to regular employment as a research chemist. This was a notable appointment because it demonstrated that, in contrast to standard practices in university faculties, Horecker, Heppel, and indeed the NIH provided opportunities for women to become independent investigators. Heppel's new responsibilities never slowed his laboratory work. He set a remarkable tone for the group of researchers under his general oversight. He was "careful, meticulous, childish, and screwy, but always calculatedly so" (19), and he was also enormously supportive of the staff including most especially the postdoctoral fellows. Audrey Stevens, who came because she wanted to learn about RNA from Heppel, flourished in the laboratory. In 1960 she was one of the three investigators who simultaneously discovered RNA polymerase. Her paper, like others written by Heppel's postdoctoral fellows, is published under her name alone (20). She recalls that unlike today's laboratory heads he "worked in the lab every day and did not mind someone looking over his shoulder." He too looked over shoulders peering at the protocol attached to a clipboard propped up on the bench. Custom required that the clipboard contain two sheets of loose-leaf paper separated by carbon paper so that both Heppel and the postdoctoral fellow would have copies; copying machines were yet to be invented. Often, he suggested that the carefully planned protocol be changed just as the experiment was being set up. The only excuse for this irksome behavior was that he was usually correct.

Heppel's laboratory had become a magnet for the growing number of investigators interested in learning how to work with polyribonucleotides and RNA. They were attracted by his store of specific enzymes and knowledge of paper electrophoretic and chromatographic methods as well as the spectrophotometric techniques used to analyze the products of nucleic acid synthesis and degradation. They were also attracted by Heppel's generous and selfless cooperation and hospitality. They knew that their time would be efficiently spent as he scurried around days and evenings helping them at the same time that he kept up with his own experiments. Heppel's visits to Kornberg and his colleagues in St. Louis and to Gobind Khorana in Vancouver spread his reputation as what might now be called a workaholic, albeit one with a well honed, almost wacky, wry sense of humor and a huge store of detailed knowledge. Visitors from Ochoa's laboratory were frequent, and Marianne Grunberg Manago came for several summers after she had returned to Paris. Gobind Khorana too made visits to learn nucleic acid enzymology. Uri Littauer, who had independently discovered PNPase (in *E. coli*) while a postdoctoral fellow in Kornberg's laboratory in St. Louis, came to work with Heppel on enzyme purification and characterization of the polymer products; when Littauer returned to the Weizmann Institute he had, from Heppel, a cache of enzymes with which to continue his work. I. R. (Bob) Lehman remembers that when he visited the NIH laboratory for 2 weeks in 1958, Heppel programmed his days from 8 a.m. to 9 p.m. Lehman was exhausted, but he had learned how to separate oligonucleotides on DEAE-cellulose by the method Heppel and Herbert Sober had developed.

Everyone (staff, postdoctoral fellows, and visitors alike) continued to crowd into the 10 by 20 foot library each noon for the brown bag journal club. I attended for 19 years and through the club kept up with the accelerating pace of new discoveries while knitting a lot of sweaters for my children. Everyone also participated in regularly scheduled clean-up days. Heppel began these days with pep talks and even music from an old phonograph, and he was as likely as any of us to be assigned the dismal job of scrubbing the cold room floor. Almost as dreaded but at least warm was the assignment to clear up Heppel's desk. That was where he haphazardly filed his mail, opened and unopened. Periodically, when the accumulated pile was too depressing to contemplate, he covered it all with a clean sheet of brown wrapping paper and began a new layer. This behavior was the one evident breach in Heppel's otherwise fastidious habits such as changing from street clothes to laboratory clothes every morning and putting some clean material between his hands and commonly used door knobs or faucets. On clean-up day, one unlucky person had to sort through the desk piles, discarding advertisements and making neat piles of letters. What he actually did with the piles was never clear. On one famous occasion, however, he rushed down the corridor after opening a letter from Earl Sutherland and excavated the layers on the desk until he found one he had received earlier from David Lipkin. Sutherland's letter was sent to Lipkin and Lipkin's to Sutherland. The result was the identification of Sutherland's unusual nucleotide with the cyclic AMP that Lipkin had isolated after cooking ATP with barium hydroxide (the story is told in Ref. 21).

During the 1950s, studies on nucleic acid biochemistry and genetics were still quite separate enterprises. The two communities rarely spoke to one another, and when they did, barriers of language, modes of thought, and personality differences made communication largely ineffective. Tensions were exacerbated because biochemists thought the geneticists were too prone to speculation and lacked rigor whereas the geneticists thought the biochemists had no sense for biology (see Ref. 22 for a detailed description of the situation). Few people argued as strenuously for a "biochemical genetics" as did George Beadle after he and Edward Tatum learned in 1941 that a gene specifies a polypeptide (23). Heppel, who was totally focused on his experimental work, never entered the fray or even expressed opinions one way or another. It is unlikely that anyone in the phage group knew about him. Bruce Ames made sure that the lunch club heard about phage genetics and the control of bacterial gene expression. However, I do not recall discussion of the ideas about coding or messenger RNA that were brewing among geneticists in the late 1950s. We did know about the work of Elliot Volkin and Lazarus Astrachan showing that after infection with bacteriophage T2, *E. coli* cells synthesized an unstable RNA with base composition similar to that of the phage (24). Also, we followed the various efforts to establish a reliable cell-free system for protein synthesis especially after our NIH colleague Marshall Nirenberg began experimenting with these systems. Then came the day when poly(U) from Heppel's freezer, synthesized with PNPase, was used by Nirenberg and his colleague Heinrich Matthei in the dramatic experiment that defined the genetic code for phenylalanine. By the spring of 1961 we knew a lot about coding and messenger RNA and several of us were hard at work synthesizing polyribonucleotides with known percentages of two or more bases for the experiments on the other codons. These two discoveries by biochemists, unstable RNA in phage-infected cells and the definition of the genetic code, convinced people that genetics and the new biochemistry were really working on the same questions.

In 1967 Heppel left the NIH to become professor of biochemistry at Cornell University. By this time his research had shifted to the question of the localization of various enzymes in bacteria, primarily *E. coli*. At Cornell, he began studying the permeability of animal cell membranes to ATP, work that evolved into an interest in various physiological effects of ATP. He also continued his habit of writing long, marvelous letters to colleagues left behind. The letters picked up on earlier conversations and recorded his observations about science, art, and music. Frequently they included quizzes that challenged the recipients to match his knowledge; what, for example, he asked, is the name of the restaurant pictured in Renoir's painting, The Boating Party? Sometimes he complained that age was slowing him down, that a concert in the evening made the next day in the laboratory difficult. That was more than 30 years ago but in fact it was mainly "talk." It is only in the last few years that Heppel decreased his daily hours in the laboratory.

Address correspondence to: msinger@pst.ciw.edu.

REFERENCES

1. Tabor, H. (1984) in *NIH: An Account of Research in Its Laboratories and Clinics* (Stetten, D., Jr., and Carrigan, W. T., eds) pp. 220–229, Academic Press, New York
2. Horecker, B. L. (2002) The pentose phosphate pathway. *J. Biol. Chem.* **277**, 47965–47971
3. Kornberg, A. (1989) *For the Love of Enzymes*, pp. 121–169, Harvard University Press, Cambridge, MA
4. Heppel, L. A., and Hilmoe, R. J. (1951) Purification and properties of 5'-nucleotidase. *J. Biol. Chem.* **188**, 665–676
5. Heppel, L. A., and Hilmoe, R. J. (1951) Purification of yeast inorganic pyrophosphatase. *J. Biol. Chem.* **192**, 87–94
6. Heppel, L. A., and Hilmoe, R. J. (1952) Phosphorolysis and hydrolysis of purine ribosides by enzymes from yeast. *J. Biol. Chem.* **198**, 683–694
7. Heppel, L. A., and Hilmoe, R. J. (1953) Mechanism of enzymatic hydrolysis of adenosine triphosphate. *J. Biol. Chem.* **202**, 217–226
8. Heppel, L. A., and Hilmoe, R. J. (1955) Spleen and intestinal phosphodiesterases. *Methods Enzymol.* **2**, 565–570
9. Brown, D. M., and Todd, A. R. (1953) Nucleotides. Part XXI. The action of ribonuclease on simple esters of the monoribonucleotides. *J. Chem. Soc.* 2040–2049
10. Cohn, W. E., and Volkin, E. (1953) On the structure of ribonucleic acids. I. Degradation with snake venom diesterase and the isolation of pyrimidine diphosphates. *J. Biol. Chem.* **203**, 319–332
11. Whitfeld, P. R., and Markham, R. (1953) Natural configuration of the purine nucleotides in ribonucleic acids. *Nature* **171**, 1151–1152
12. Heppel, L. A., Markham, R., and Hilmoe, R. J. (1953) Enzymatic splitting of purine internucleotide linkages. *Nature* **171**, 1152
13. Whitfeld, P. R., Heppel, L. A., and Markham, R. (1955) The enzymic hydrolysis of ribonucleoside 2',3'-phosphates. *Biochem. J.* **60**, 15–19
14. Brown, D. M., Heppel, L. A., and Hilmoe, R. J. (1954) Nucleotides. Part XXIV. The action of some nucleases on simple esters of monoribonucleotides. *J. Chem. Soc.* 40–46

15. Heppel, L. A., and Whitfield, P. R. (1954) Synthesis and interconversion of simple esters of ribomononucleotides. *Biochem. J.* **60,** 1–7

16. Heppel, L. A., Whitfield, P. R., and Markham R. (1954) Synthesis of polynucleotides. *Biochem. J.* **60,** 8–15

17. Heppel, L. A., Ortiz, P. J., and Ochoa, S. (1957) Studies on polynucleotides synthesized by polynucleotide phosphorylase. *J. Biol. Chem.* **229,** 679–694; 695–710

18. Ochoa, S., and Heppel, L. A. (1957) Polynucleotide synthesis. In *The Chemical Basis of Heredity* (McElroy, W. D., and Glass, B., eds) pp. 615–638, The Johns Hopkins University Press, Baltimore, MD

19. Martin, R. G. (1984) A revisionist view of the breaking of the genetic code. In *NIH: An Account of Research in Its Laboratories and Clinics* (Stetten, D., Jr., and Carrigan, W. T., eds) pp. 281–296, Academic Press, New York

20. Stevens, A. (1960) Incorporation of the adenine ribonucleotide into RNA by cell fractions from *E. coli. Biochem. Biophys. Res. Commun.* **3,** 92–96

21. Pastan, I. (1972) Cyclic AMP. *Sci. Am.* **227,** 97–105

22. Judson, H. F. (1996) *The Eighth Day of Creation*, 2nd Ed., Cold Spring Harbor Press, New York

23. Berg, P., and Singer, M. (2003) *George Beadle, An Uncommon Farmer*, pp. 171–173, Cold Spring Harbor Press, New York

24. Volkin, E., and Astrachan, L. (1956) Intracellular distribution of labeled ribonucleic acid after phage infection of *Escherichia coli. Virology* **2,** 433–437

THE JOURNAL OF BIOLOGICAL CHEMISTRY
© 2003 by The American Society for Biochemistry and Molecular Biology, Inc.

Vol. 278, No. 49, Issue of December 5, pp. 48507–48519, 2003
Printed in U.S.A.

Reflections

A PAPER IN A SERIES COMMISSIONED TO CELEBRATE THE CENTENARY OF THE JBC IN 2005

JBC Centennial
1905–2005
100 Years of Biochemistry and Molecular Biology

From Proteins and Protein Models to Their Use in Immunology and Immunotherapy

Published, JBC Papers in Press, September 17, 2003, DOI 10.1074/jbc.X300007200

Michael Sela

From the Department of Immunology, The Weizmann Institute of Science, Rehovot, Israel 76100

The two leitmotifs of my scientific research were synthetic polymeric models of proteins and the structure of proteins as reflected by the three-dimensional conformation controlled by their amino acid sequence. This in turn led me to synthetic polypeptide antigens and to investigation of antibodies, ultimately resulting in the discovery of the determinant-specific genetic control of immune response and to the development of a therapeutic vaccine against the exacerbating-remitting form of multiple sclerosis. In protein chemistry I had two great teachers who became very close friends, Ephraim Katchalski-Katzir and Christian B. Anfinsen (Fig. 1), but in immunology I lacked the benefit of a great mentor, and so to some extent I was self-taught. Thus, I had to "figure out" many things myself.

My Attraction to Polymers

In my childhood I grew up in the courtyard of a textile factory, and I later intended to study fibers, mainly the new synthetic ones. However, I first started studying macromolecules when, as a Ph.D. student, in 1950 I joined the laboratory of Ephraim Katchalski at the Weizmann Institute of Science. Ephraim first synthesized polylysine in the early 1940s and was successfully exploring the use of polyamino acids as protein models. With his collaborators he prepared and studied many physical, chemical, and biological properties of several polymers of trifunctional amino acids such as polyarginine, polyaspartic acid, polyhistidine, and polyserine, as well as the polyamino acids polyproline and polyhydroxyproline (1, 2). Among the early syntheses was the one of poly-L-tyrosine, which was part of the subject of my Ph.D. thesis. My thesis research included also the synthesis of poly-3,5-diiodotyrosine and poly-*p*-amino-L-phenylalanine. Later on I was directly involved with the synthesis of polytryptophan and polycyclohexylalanine. Of special interest was the spectrophotometric titration of polytyrosine and of copolymers of tyrosine with positively or negatively charged amino acids; this showed the influence of the vicinal electrostatic field on the ease of ionization of the phenolic hydroxyl groups (2, 3). We were very touched when John Edsall included figures from this study in his book *Biophysical Chemistry* with Jeffreys Wyman. Actually *Proteins, Peptides and Amino Acids as Dipolar Ions* (Cohn and Edsall's book) served as a basis for intense seminars with both of the Katchalski-Katzir brothers, Ephraim and Aharon. The accent was on physicochemical properties of proteins, polyamino acids, and polyelectrolytes in general. Ephraim was a remarkable teacher—stimulating, inspiring, patient, and always friendly. Today I still cherish his friendship.

For the preparation of poly-L-tyrosine, I remember that I tried 40 times to synthesize the monomer, *N*-carboxy-*O*-benzyloxycarbonyl-L-tyrosine anhydride, before I was successful. This taught me the need for perseverance and optimism in research. Of course, serendipity (defined as luck meeting the prepared mind) also helps. I mention this because much of the story that follows actually depended on the availability of this monomer (4).

FIG. 1. **Christian B. Anfinsen, Ephraim Katzir-Katchalski, and Michael Sela (1986).**

My first paper was on the titration of *N*-carboxy-α-amino acid anhydrides in nonaqueous solvents (5). These are the monomers in the synthesis of amino acid polymers, and the titration was useful for the determination of unreacted anhydride at any instant. My Ph.D. thesis was on the azo derivatives of some aromatic poly-α-amino acids (6). One could even diazotize poly-*p*-aminophenylalanine and couple it to polymers containing tyrosine, resulting in colored water-insoluble compounds.

I shall describe later how the work with polyamino acids brought me into immunology. What I would like to mention here is that we could use as initiators of polymerization of *N*-carboxyamino acid anhydrides (the monomers from which polyamino acids were built) not only monofunctional small molecules but also macromolecules possessing several amino groups. If proteins were used as such polyvalent initiators, we ended up with polypeptidyl proteins, whereas when polylysine or polyornithine were used, we had for the first time multichain polyamino acids, which became so important for me later as synthetic antigens. Mark Stahmann also prepared such polypeptidyl proteins in Wisconsin. We summarized in *Advances in Protein Chemistry* in 1958 (1) and 1959 (2) the early studies on the synthesis and the chemical and biological properties of poly-α-amino acids.

In 1955 I was back in Europe as a young scientist presenting the work on multichain polyamino acids at the International Congress of Chemistry in Zurich, and a week later, the work on spectrophotometric titration of polymers and copolymers of amino acids at the International Congress of Biochemistry in Bruxelles. This was a wonderful occasion to meet scientists whom until then I had known only by reputation and through their papers. Among the many I want to mention two, Hans Neurath and Bill Harrington, who later became close friends of mine. During the same trip I went to see Sir Charles Harington in London. Harington was the man who elucidated the structure of thyroxine and predicted that it is formed from two diiodotyrosine residues by oxidation rather than simple dismutation. I wanted to tell him that the availability of polytyrosine had permitted us (7) to find out that, following alkaline incubation of iodinated polytyrosine, the hydrolysate contained 2% thyroxine and 2% serine. We had, thus, proved the validity of his prediction.

Later I shall discuss our work on linear and multichain polyamino acids as synthetic polypeptide antigens, but now I want to mention that ultimately we developed a therapeutic drug/vaccine against the exacerbating-remitting stage of multiple sclerosis, denoted copolymer 1, named glatiramer acetate and Copaxone by the industry. This drug, approved by the Food and Drug Administration in 1996 and used by tens of thousands of patients, is the first polymeric drug/vaccine in which the active ingredient is the polymer itself, in contrast to polymers used earlier in pharmacopeia for slow release of drugs or for wrapping them.

As a result of studying the mechanism of polymerization of *N*-carboxyamino acid anhydrides with Arieh Berger, I was involved in an interesting story that I want to relate here while discussing polyamino acids. On my second visit to the National Institutes of Health (NIH) in 1960, Marshall Nirenberg came one day and asked me whether I had some poly-L-phenylalanine and whether I knew its solubility properties. I did not have the polymer in Bethesda, but I did ask Nirenberg why he was interested. Through these conversations I became one of the first to know about the breaking of the genetic code, UUU encoding Phe. Although I was somewhat skeptical of the story, I immediately looked for and found, hidden somewhere in an experimental section of a paper in the *Journal of the American Chemical Society,* that poly-L-phenylalanine was insoluble in all the solvents we had tested with the exception of a saturated solution of anhydrous hydrogen bromide in glacial acetic acid (8). Because on that very day I was preparing just such a solution (used to remove carbobenzoxy groups) in the laboratory, I gladly gave the reagent to Nirenberg and was touched and surprised when he acknowledged this in the classical paper that resulted in his receiving the Nobel Prize. The real point of the story lies elsewhere. Why did we try to use such a peculiar solvent? The truth of the matter is that years earlier, together with the late Arieh Berger in Rehovot, we were investigating the mechanism of polymerization leading to linear and multichain polyamino acids. One day I had two test tubes, one with polyphenylalanine and one with polycarbobenzoxylysine, stuck in a beaker on my desk. Arieh came to decarbobenzoxylate the lysine polymer, a reaction with hydrogen bromide in glacial acetic acid during which carbon dioxide is released. He took the wrong test tube away with him and returned, puzzled because the material had dissolved and he could not see any evolution of carbon dioxide. At once we realized the mistake and I noted in my laboratory book that, at long last, we had found a solvent for poly-L-phenylalanine.

Ribonuclease and Other Enzymes

After 5 years of working with protein models, I felt ready to go abroad for a postdoctoral period to work with proteins. Thus, I arrived in 1956 in the laboratory of Chris Anfinsen at the NIH in Bethesda. The friendship between us resulted in prolonged stays in Bethesda in 1956–1957, 1960–1961, and 1973–1974. On his part, Chris came to Rehovot on sabbaticals on several occasions and was an active, extremely valuable member of the Board of Governors of the Weizmann Institute of Science, serving for many years as the Chairman of its Scientific Advisory Committee. His death in May 1995 was for me personally a deeply felt loss. Chris was a great friend, helpful to all those who surrounded him, full of charm and modesty, and actually a great romantic.

From the NIH we sent out our first joint paper, which Chris was in a hurry to prepare for a Festschrift honoring Linderstrom-Lang. The topic was the selective splitting of protein chains by trypsin at arginine residues after lysine residues were reversibly blocked by carbobenzoxy groups. Oxidative opening of the four disulfide bridges of bovine pancreatic ribonuclease to permit its sequencing was possible only because tryptophan was absent in this protein. A more general method, which could be used also for a protein containing tryptophan, such as lysozyme, was reductive cleavage, followed by blocking of the sulfhydryl groups with iodoacetic acid (9). I was fortunate to participate with Chris in these studies and left part of the reduced ribonuclease without blocking its sulfhydryl groups to see if it could reoxidize properly and whether the enzymatic activity would come back. The results of these experiments (10) showed a total recovery of the activity even though statistical considerations pointed to 105 various ways in which the four disulfide bridges could reform. Thus, we demonstrated that no additional information was needed for the correct, unique architecture of a protein molecule and that it is the genetic code dictating the amino acid sequence that is responsible for the conversion of the randomly coiled structure. It is for this most important observation that in 1972 Chris was awarded the Nobel Prize in chemistry, which he shared with Stanford Moore and William Stein, who established the amino acid sequence of ribonuclease. I learned a lot from Chris, a dedicated scientist, who had an incredible flair for attacking the right protein and the most elegant experiment to solve it, a flair matched only by his literary talent.

During my visits to Bethesda, I tried in two ways to combine my previous experience with polyamino acids and research on enzymes. One was the use of copolymers of glutamic acid with aromatic amino acids to efficiently inhibit ribonuclease (11), lysozyme, or trypsin. The other series of studies had to do with poly-DL-alanylation of proteins. In contrast to poly-L-alanine and poly-D-alanine, poly-DL-alanine, which is a random copolymer of L-alanine and D-alanine, is well soluble in water and may serve as a solubilizer. Poly-DL-alanyl ribonuclease could be reduced and reoxidized properly. Poly-DL-alanylation renders gliadin water-soluble (12) and converts myosin into a derivative soluble in distilled water and with all its ATPase activity preserved (13).

On a lighter level, when I arrived in Bethesda everybody was writing the sequences of amino acids in straight lines; the disulfide bridges (at straight angles to the chain) occupied as much space as 10 residues. I found a huge hole puncher with which I made round pieces of paper, wrote the name of 1 residue on each piece of paper, and played with them until the half-cystines of a bridge were able to touch each other. This gave rise to the well known "swan" shape of ribonuclease, and it delights me to see that proteins are still often schematically presented like this.

After returning from my first visit to the NIH (1956–1957), I embarked on a collaboration with Nathan Citri on two conformationally different states of penicillinase. The enzyme changes from an iodine-resistant to an iodine-sensitive state in urea or guanidine hydrochloride. The change in conformation was followed by optical rotatory measurements. This, in 1960, was my first of many papers published in the *Journal of Biological Chemistry* (14).

During my second stay at the NIH (1960–1961), I continued studies on oxidation of reduced ribonuclease (15) and started investigating the enzymatic properties of poly-DL-alanyl derivatives of ribonuclease (16, 17), trypsin, and chymotrypsin (18). Alanylated ribonuclease with as many as 4 or 5 alanine residues per chain kept its enzymatic activity and regenerated its full activity after reduction of its disulfide bridges and subsequent reoxidation (16). We later learned that alanylation affected the enzymatic activity toward RNA but not toward the low molecular weight substrates (17). Poly-DL-alanyl trypsin, with an average polyalanine chain length of 6–9 residues, was resistant to autolysis at temperatures up to 38 °C and reacted normally with soybean and serum inhibitors. Poly-DL-alanyl chymotrypsin had similar stability and activity properties (18). Several years later, Roger Acher visited us from Paris and investigated poly-DL-alanyl Kunitz trypsin inhibitor (19). Only when the alanine residues were attached exclusively to the α-amino group was the inhibitor active. Upon alanylation of all the amino groups, the derivative was virtually inactive, demonstrating the crucial role of ϵ-amino groups for its activity.

While still in Bethesda, I checked the inhibition of ribonuclease by copolymers of glutamic acid and aromatic amino acids (11). Copolymers of tyrosine (or phenylalanine) and glutamic acid are much more efficient inhibitors of ribonuclease than polyaspartic acid, and in this case the attachment to the enzyme occurs not only through electrostatic interactions but also through short range urea-labile bonds. The digestion of ribonucleic acid by pancreatic ribonuclease was stopped completely, at pH 5.0, by relatively small amounts of the inhibitory copolymer. We tested these copolymers also for inhibition of lysozyme (20) and trypsin (21) with similar results.

Immunogenicity and Antigenic Specificity

As my Ph.D. thesis was concerned with polytyrosine (a polymeric chain of phenols) and poly-p-aminophenylalanine (a polymeric chain of anilines), it was natural to produce polypeptidic azo dyes from them. I reasoned that these might serve as synthetic models for azoproteins, of which one rare example, provided by Landsteiner, was the attachment of haptens including peptides, via an azo bond, to proteins. Reading Landsteiner's book *The Specificity of Serological Reactions*, I came across the statement that gelatin probably is not antigenic because it contains no tyrosine. This led me to study the possibility of increasing the antigenicity of gelatin by attachment of tyrosine peptides. To do these studies, the amino groups of the protein were used to initiate the polymerization of the tyrosine monomer, as mentioned earlier. The continuation of this study was the Ph.D. thesis of Ruth Arnon, and we showed that limited tyrosylation enhanced immunogenicity without significantly changing specificity, whereas more extensive tyrosylation converted gelatin into a potent immunogen provoking antibodies mainly to tyrosyl peptides (22). It was at this time that we first promoted the notion of immunogen and immunogenicity and distinguished it from antigenic specificity.

I was delighted to describe the results on the increase in immunogenicity of gelatin upon its polytyrosylation to Sir Charles Harington on the same visit in 1954, as it was in his laboratory that John Humphrey some 15 years earlier had tried to increase the antigenicity of gelatin by attaching it chemically to carbobenzoxy-L-tyrosine. It was several years later that we started collaborating with John Humphrey and his colleagues on several aspects of synthetic polypeptide antigens, contributing to a better understanding of immunology.

As a result of the studies on tyrosylated gelatin, we assumed that gelatin was not necessary for immunogenicity. We, therefore, replaced the gelatin with multichain poly-DL-alanine (23, 24) as the carrier for peptides of tyrosine and glutamic acid and showed that the resulting copolymer, denoted (T,G)-A-L, led to specific, precipitable antibodies in experimental animals. At that stage Sara Fuchs joined us, and we synthesized numerous linear and multichain polyamino acids and tested them for immunogenicity. Our preliminary communication on a "synthetic antigen" was rejected by *Nature* under the pretext that the journal does not publish papers that are part of a series, so we published it elsewhere (25). The final paper (26) became a Citation Classic (*Current Contents*, 1986). The availability of synthetic antigens permitted a systematic elucidation of the molecular basis of antigenicity (27–29). We could learn a lot about the role of size, composition, and shape as well as about the accessibility of those parts of the molecule crucial for immunogenicity. As a matter of fact, we learned that it was possible (provided one was prepared to invest the necessary effort) to prepare synthetic immunogens leading to antibodies of essentially any specificity.

Although in most cases a good immunogen had a molecular mass of at least several thousand daltons, dinitrophenyl-hexalysine and arsanil-trityrosine were by themselves capable of triggering an efficient immune response. The minimal size for a molecule to be immunogenic depends, therefore, largely on its chemical nature.

Although electrical charge may be important in defining the antigenic specificity of an epitope, charge is not a minimum necessary cause for immunogenicity; we could prepare water-soluble amino acid copolymers devoid of charge that were immunogenic. Polymers of D-amino acids were immunogenic only when they were administered in minute amounts and they led to no secondary response. Their immunogenicity was thymus-independent, as was that of several other polymers such as linear (Pro-Gly-Pro)$_n$ and multichain polymers of L-proline locked in with terminal polymeric side chains of D-Phe and D-Glu. The common denominator of all these "thymus-independent" antigens was that they not only possessed repeating antigenic determinants but they also were metabolized slowly, if at all. Even though polymers composed exclusively of D-amino acids are "thymus independent," we were able to show more recently that they are capable of inducing the formation of T cell hybridomas. The different roles of D-amino acids had intrigued me for many years, and I summarized the topic recently (30). Most of the above studies on the molecular basis of antigenicity were carried out before the crucial role of T lymphocytes in immune response was realized. Only later the central question of immunology became: T-B or not T-B?

In the early days there was a wonderful feeling working on synthetic antigens because practically nobody else was working on the subject, but later on it was as pleasant and satisfying to know that so many laboratories had become interested in the synthetic approach to immunological phenomena. One of the most fascinating aspects of our studies with synthetic antigens had to do with the steric conformation of the immunogen and of its epitopes. We distinguished between conformational (conformation-dependent) and sequential determinants (31) and showed how the same peptide (Tyr-Ala-Glu) may lead to antibodies recognizing the sequence (when attached to multichain poly-DL-alanine) or recognizing an epitope defined by conformation (when the tripeptide was polymerized to give an α-helical structure). In addition, we could demonstrate for the first time, by circular dichroism, how antibodies to the α-helical polymer could help transconform into a helical shape a small polymer that was not yet helical (32). These studies led us directly to study proteins and to synthesize a macromolecule in which a synthetic "loop" peptide derived from hen egg white lysozyme was attached to branched polyalanine (33). The resulting antibodies reacted with intact lysozyme through the "loop" region, but the reaction was totally abolished when the disulfide bond within the "loop" was opened, and thus the three-dimensional structure was collapsed. In this connection, it should be remembered that partial degradation products of proteins may still be immunogenic. Furthermore, the sera we were investigating might have contained a myriad of antibodies against degradation products derived from the original immunogen.

In later years we showed that a peptide of 20 amino acid residues derived from the coat protein of MS2 bacteriophage induced, after conjugation with an appropriate carrier, the formation of antibodies that cross-reacted with the intact virus (34). More recently, tens of peptides analogous to segments of proteins have been prepared that may lead to antibodies cross-reactive with the intact protein. Nevertheless, one should remember that many similar peptides have been prepared that were not capable of provoking anti-protein responses. The extent of cross-reactivity will depend entirely on the probability that the free peptide will be able to attain the conformation that it possesses in the native protein. This capability may be prevented either when the segment is too short, not yet able to possess a stabilized correct conformation, or when it is too long and possesses a preferred stabilized conformation different from the one capable of cross-reaction. If the protein segment is more flexible, the chance of cross-reaction is higher, even though there will be cases when a small peptide is capable of manifesting a relatively rigid conformation similar to the one it possesses within a native protein. Thus, antibodies to the rigid helix $(Pro-Gly-Pro)_n$ cross-reacted with collagen (35). The exposure to the outside (hydrophilicity) is also very important to immunopotency: "Whatever sticks out most, is most immunopotent."

Synthetic antigens allowed the study of antibody specificity, immunological tolerance, the role of net electrical charge in defining the nature of antibodies, and delayed hypersensitivity. The results led us to the inevitable conclusion that an immunogen is much more than an antigenic determinant attached to an inert carrier. Unfortunately, we did not know that the separate recognition of antigen by T and B cells was the explanation for our results. However, we did clearly state that the "carrier" had a crucial role in defining the nature of the immune response toward an epitope. Similar to the cooperation between T and B cells for antibody formation, delayed hypersensitivity might be the result, we suggested, of cooperation between two distinct sets of T cells. Recently, I came back to this problem when reviewing together with Israel Pecht, "The Nature of Antigen" (36).

Antibodies

Being interested in methods for isolating antibodies we purified antibodies to gelatin from antigen-antibody complex by proteolysis (37). In another case (38), we isolated on columns of Sephadex antibodies to such low molecular weight antigens as lysozyme and a synthetic polypeptide. With Ruth Arnon we succeeded in preparing an analog of the Fab dimer by splitting the IgG molecule with cyanogen bromide rather than with proteolytic enzymes (39, 40).

Poly-DL-alanylation of immunoglobulin because of its great solubilization effect permitted the total reduction of all the disulfide bridges within the molecule without insolubilizing the light and heavy chain products. This allowed for controlled reoxidation, leading to the correct association of light and heavy chains and the recovery of both antigenic and antibody activity (41, 42). It also confirmed the hypothesis that no genetic information other than that present in the amino acid sequence of the polypeptide chains is required for the correct conformation of a protein molecule as complex as immunoglobulin G.

When Israel Pecht returned to Rehovot from Manfred Eigen's laboratory, he extended the interest in the antibody-combining site to its kinetic aspects. Using temperature-jump methodologies, Pecht was able to resolve the hapten-recognition process with the first homogeneous antibody available at that time, namely a dinitrophenyl specific IgA myeloma (43).

Of great interest to me was the observation we made with Edna Mozes on the inverse electrical net charge relationship between an antigen and the antibodies it provoked (44, 45). The more positively charged the antigen, the more negatively charged was the antibody. We showed that this depended on the net charge of the intact antigen, not on local clustering of charges around the epitope. Thus, we proved that the epitope is recognized while the antigen is still intact. The phenomenon holds for different classes of antibodies and is also valid at the cellular level but not for thymus-independent antigens.

In those early days we used antibodies attached to bromoacetylcellulose for the purification of antigens, and we used antigens (similarly insolubilized) for the isolation of antibodies (46, 47). We did not call it as yet "affinity chromatography," but these were among the first examples of this approach to purification. A detailed study of antibody-combining sites to a series of peptide determinants of increasing size and defined structure led us to the conclusion that the size of the combining sites was in all cases such as to accommodate four amino acid residues and that the most exposed portion of the epitope plays an immunodominant role (48, 49). In two interesting studies, we could show how the combining site of the antibody can transconform the structure of the antigen. I mentioned earlier how antibodies to the α-helical polymer could help transconform a small polymer that was not yet helical into a helical shape (32). We could also demonstrate that the Fab of an antibody to *p*-azobenzenearsonate hapten may "suck out" the *p*-azobenzenearsonate moiety from its unavailable conformation within an ordered copolymer and convert it into another conformation, recognized by Fab (50).

Genetic Control of Immune Response

Even though some hints could be found in earlier literature, the actual establishment of the genetic control of the immune response became possible only through the study of synthetic antigens, simple chemically, in inbred strains of mice and guinea pigs, simple genetically.

In our studies (51, 52), we first showed determinant-specific (antigen-specific) genetic control of immune responses by making use of multichain polyamino acids as antigens and inbred mice as experimental animals. The multichain synthetic polypeptides we investigated, possessed small amounts of tyrosine, histidine, or phenylalanine at the tips of their polymeric side chains. These antigens were denoted (T,G)-A-L, (H,G)-A-L, and (Phe,G)-A-L. We noted that when histidine was substituted for tyrosine, genetic control was completely reversed, whereas replacement with phenylalanine led to a material strongly immunogenic in both strains investigated.

Some time later, using these multichain polypeptides, Hugh McDevitt was able to show for the first time the link between the immune response and the major histocompatibility locus of the mouse, which in turn led to our present day understanding of immune response genes and their products. Of all the contributions of synthetic polypeptides toward our present day understanding of immunology, none has been more important than the discovery and the definition of the genetic control of the immune response, which in turn was a crucial trigger toward a better understanding of the cellular basis of immunological responsiveness. Not surprisingly, a very large proportion of studies using synthetic polypeptides in immunology has been devoted to this field of research. As is apparent from the above story, my contribution has been mainly chemical and immunochemical, whereas McDevitt contributed the major part of the genetic aspects of this study. He described it in detail in his recent scientific autobiography (53).

Synthetic Vaccines

I mentioned earlier, while discussing the role of steric conformation in defining antigenic specificity, that we had prepared a totally synthetic antigen capable of provoking antibodies reacting with native lysozyme. These studies led to the inevitable conclusion that a new approach to vaccination was possible. We reasoned that synthetic vaccines might be a reality in the future (54) for the simple reason that if these conclusions held for one protein, they may hold for others, including viral coat proteins and bacterial toxins. Of course, it is not sufficient to have just a synthetic epitope that will provoke antibodies to the protein. I shall not repeat here the arguments I have made before as to why there is a place for improvement of vaccines today, but for a synthetic vaccine to be successful, it should contain at least five ingredients: (*a*) specificity; (*b*) built-in adjuvanticity; (*c*) the correct genetic background; (*d*) the capacity to cope with antigenic competition; and (*e*) the correct "texture," *i.e.* a form that will give persistent and long lasting immune protection. Much of the experimental work was done in collaboration with Ruth Arnon and various other colleagues.

We first synthesized a peptide from the amino terminus of the carcinoembryonic antigen of the colon; this showed a weak cross-reaction with the intact antigen (55). The first study related to viruses was the synthesis of a peptide from the envelope of the MS2 bacteriophage (34). The synthetic peptide inhibited phage neutralization by antiphage antibodies, and the same peptide elicited antibodies capable of neutralizing the virus after attachment to multichain poly-DL-alanine. Similarly, Ruth Arnon succeeded in preparing a conjugate of a synthetic peptide derived from influenza hemagglutinin, and it provoked antibodies and protected mice against influenza challenge. With Chaim Jacob, we showed that tetanus toxoid coupled with synthetic peptides of the B subunit of cholera toxin led to the formation of antibodies capable of neutralizing the toxic activity of the native cholera toxin (56). Actually, some antibodies inhibited the entire spectrum of activities of the intact cholera toxin, including adenylate cyclase induction and intestinal fluid secretion. Attachment of a peptide composed of residues 50–64 within the sequence of the B subunit of cholera toxin to our multichain polymer (T,G)-A-L produced a totally synthetic vaccine, which elicited in rabbits antibodies with neutralizing capacity (57).

In the above studies, we used Freund's adjuvant or water-soluble peptidoglycan as an adjuvant. A short while later, in collaboration with Louis Chedid and Francoise Audibert, we used their synthetic muramyl dipeptides to prepare totally synthetic conjugates in which a synthetic antigenic determinant and a synthetic adjuvant were covalently linked to a synthetic carrier (58). The resulting conjugate, when administered in aqueous solution into experimental animals, provoked the formation of protective antibodies. When the muramyl dipeptide was bound covalently, it was much more efficient than when it was first mixed with the antigen. We prepared, with Ruth Arnon, such totally synthetic antigens, and these led to neutralization of a virus, MS2 (59), as well as to protection against diphtheria and cholera (60).

Copolymer 1 and Multiple Sclerosis

In our early studies with Ruth Arnon, of special interest was the immune response to lipid components, which was not easy to either elicit or investigate because of solubility problems. However, conjugates in which synthetic lipid compounds were attached onto synthetic copolymers of amino acids elicited a specific response to lipids such as cytolipin H, which is a tumor-associated glycolipid (61), or sphingomyelin (62). Furthermore, we demonstrated that both the sugar and lipid components of such molecules contributed to their immunological specificity. The resultant anti-lipid antibodies were capable of detecting the corresponding lipids both in water-soluble systems and in their physiological milieu. This was fascinating because it gave us a glimpse into some disorders involving lipid-containing tissue and consequently led to our interest in demyelinating diseases, namely disorders in which the myelin sheath, which constitutes the lipid-rich coating of all axons, is damaged, resulting in various neurological dysfunctions. We thus thought that EAE (experimental allergic encephalomyelitis) caused by MBP (myelin basic protein) might actually be induced by a demyelinating lipid and that the positively charged MBP might serve only as a schlepper (carrier) for an acidic lipid (*e.g.* phospholipid). We prepared several positively charged copolymers of amino acids and tested whether we could induce EAE when the copolymers were administered into experimental animals (guinea pigs and rabbits) in complete Freund's adjuvant, similarly to the successful administration of MBP, but we failed. On the other hand, the injection of several positively charged amino acid copolymers in aqueous solution into mice, rabbits, and guinea pigs resulted in efficient suppression of the onset of the disease, experimental allergic encephalomyelitis (63–65). Later on, we could suppress the actual disease in rhesus monkeys and baboons (65, 66). The copolymer 1 we primarily used, denoted Cop 1, now called glatiramer acetate, and by industry "Copaxone," is composed of a small amount of glutamic acid, a much larger amount of lysine, some tyrosine, and a major share of alanine. To our pleasant surprise, there is a significant immunological cross-reaction (both at the antibody level (67, 68) and at the T cell level (69, 70)) between Cop 1 and the myelin basic protein. Interestingly, when an analog of Cop 1 made from D-amino acids was tested, it had no suppressing capacity nor did it cross-react immunologically with the basic protein (71). Cop 1 is not generally immunosuppressive; it is not toxic; actually it is not helpful in any other autoimmune disease except in multiple sclerosis and its animal model, experimental allergic encephalomyelitis.

The clinical trials with Cop 1 have included two preliminary open trials and two double-blind phase II trials, one involving exacerbating-remitting patients (72) and another one in chronic progressive patients (73). The results of the phase II trial in exacerbating-remitting patients demonstrated a remarkable decrease in the number of relapses and in the rate of progression in Cop 1-treated patients compared with the placebo control. Cop 1 is a promising, low risk multiple sclerosis-specific drug for treatment of the relapsing disease. As an antigen-specific intervention, Cop 1 has the advantage of reduced probability of long term damage to the immune system.

After a successful, pivotal multicenter phase III clinical trial conducted in 11 medical centers in the United States (74), Cop 1 was approved by the United States Food and Drug Administration as a drug for multiple sclerosis. This was a moment of gratification and deep emotion for my colleagues and myself as well as for our industrial partners, Teva Pharmaceutical Industries.

We were obviously very interested in the mode of action of Cop 1. We know that the effect was specific for the disease, and we assumed that it has to do with the immunological cross-reaction between the "villain" (myelin basic protein) and the drug (Cop 1). What we have learned later is that Cop 1 binds almost immediately and strongly to the groove of major histocompatibility complex (MHC) class II antigens of most genetic backgrounds, and it displaces efficiently from the groove any peptides derived from the myelin basic protein (75). This promiscuity is probably because of its polymeric character permitting microheterogeneity in the amino acid sequence. The extensive and promiscuous binding to class II MHC molecules, without prior processing, leads to clustering of these molecules on the antigen-presenting cells, which may explain their high affinity binding (76).

This is the first necessary but not sufficient step in its mechanism of action. The binding, which is the least specific step, is a prerequisite for its later effects. Following this interaction, two mechanisms were clearly shown to be effective. 1) Cop 1 binding to the relevant MHC leads to the activation of T suppressor cells because of suppressive determinants shared between myelin basic protein and Cop 1. 2) Successful competition between the complex of Cop 1-MHC class II antigen with the complex of myelin basic protein-MHC class II antigen for the myelin basic protein-specific T cell receptor (a phenomenon called by immunologists the "T receptor antagonism") is shown (77).

An important step in our understanding of the mode of action of Cop 1 was the observation that copolymer 1 induces T cells of the T helper type 2 that cross-react with myelin basic protein and suppress experimental autoimmune encephalomyelitis (78). This was corroborated by clinical studies in multiple sclerosis patients (79). It was of interest to observe that Th2 suppressor lines and clones induced by Copolymer 1 cross-reacted at the level of Th2 cytokine secretion with myelin basic protein but not with other myelin antigens (80). This bystander suppression may explain the therapeutic effect of Cop 1 in EAE and multiple sclerosis (MS).

Cop 1 binds promiscuously to many different cells regardless of their DR restriction. It binds avidly and fast and can also displace already bound antigens, and this holds for all the myelin antigens that may be involved in MS; and yet, Cop 1 exerts its activity in an antigen-specific manner (it is not a general immunosuppressive agent and does not affect other experimental autoimmune diseases). Its specificity must, therefore, be envisaged in the context of the trimolecular complex MHC-Ag-T-cell receptor ("the immunological synapse"), namely as interference with the presentation of the encephalitogenic antigen to the T-cell receptor, which is a specific interaction.

I summarized recently the story of specific vaccines against autoimmune diseases (81) as well as the successful use of Cop 1 (glatiramer acetate, Copaxone) in the treatment of multiple sclerosis for exacerbating-remitting patients (82). The majority of the patients in the great clinical trial continue to be followed in an organized fashion for more than 7 years. Their risk of an MS relapse was over 1.5 per year at onset and is now less than 1 every 6 years. On average, these patients have experienced no increase in neurological disability, whereas natural history profiles would have predicted substantial worsening. The accumulated experience with glatiramer acetate (Cop 1) indicates that its efficiency is apparently increased as a function of usage time while the favorable side effect profile is sustained.

Personally, the whole odyssey of Cop 1 and its use in MS has been a source of great satisfaction and emotion. The awareness that tens of thousands of MS patients feel better because of a drug/vaccine that we conceived and developed moves me deeply. Twenty-eight years passed from the moment of the idea to the approval of Cop 1 by the Food and Drug Administration. I have a feeling that discoveries resulting from basic research take a longer time to fruition, but on the other hand, they are probably more original in terms of concept.

I shall not describe here recent results on the use of Cop 1 to inhibit the progression of secondary degeneration after crush injury of the rat optic nerve (83). Cop 1 also offered protection from retinal ganglion cell loss resulting from a direct biochemical insult caused by glutamate and in a rat model of ocular hypertension (84). This study may point the way to a therapy for glaucoma, a neurodegenerative disease of the optic nerve often associated with increased intraocular pressure as well as for acute and chronic degenerative diseases in which glutamate is a prominent participant.

Therapeutic Vaccines and Autoimmunity

Vaccines are prophylactic in the sense that they are administered to healthy individuals to prevent a disease. Nevertheless, there is a growing trend to use vaccines to alleviate the suffering of those already having a disease. Great effort is being devoted to develop vaccines against tumors, AIDS, hepatitis, tuberculosis, Alzheimer's disease, Huntington disease, etc.

Copolymer 1, used today as a vaccine against MS, is a good example of a beneficial treatment for this autoimmune disease based on its similarity to MBP, one of the putative causes of MS (82). This finding could lead to therapeutic vaccines against other autoimmune diseases such as myasthenia gravis (MG), juvenile diabetes, systemic lupus erythematosus, and rheumatoid arthritis. Furthermore, antibodies prepared against prions raise hopes for a vaccine against bovine spongiform encephalitis and Creutzfeldt-Jakob disease, and antibodies to a peptide derived from β-amyloid plaques could degrade plaques and be used as a therapeutic vaccine against Alzheimer's disease.

By its definition, a preventive vaccine is sufficiently similar in its chemistry to the molecule that provokes the disease so that the immune response directed against it can act against the causative agent. This situation is analogous in the case of therapeutic vaccines. At least one "therapeutic vaccine," copolymer 1 (glatiramer acetate) for the relapsing-remitting form of multiple sclerosis, is being used by many thousands of patients. Another vaccine for type I diabetes has recently completed a phase II trial successfully, and several vaccines against cancer are already being studied, some of which are planned to enter (or have just begun) clinical trials. Therapeutic vaccine preparations against infectious diseases such as HIV, tuberculosis, and malaria are in phase II clinical trials to evaluate their efficacy in patients. In most cases the therapy is based on the resemblance between the etiological agent causing the disease and the therapeutic vaccine.

What is characteristic for a vaccine is its specificity. You do not have one vaccine against all kinds of different viruses or bacteria. For every troublemaker, there is a "molecular cousin," close enough in its chemical composition to lead to an immune response cross-reactive with the troublemaker but harmless biologically because the danger of the original virus or bacterial toxin has been knocked out.

Myasthenia Gravis

Multiple sclerosis is mainly a T cell-mediated disease, whereas in myasthenia gravis the attack of specific antibodies on the acetylcholine receptor (AChR) is the accepted cause of disease. Nevertheless, assuming that most antibody responses need helper T cells, we have synthesized two immunodominant myasthenogenic T cell epitopes (p195–212 and p259–271) derived from an α-subunit of the nicotinic AChR (85). Ideally, the goal of therapy for MG should be the elimination of autoimmune responses to the AChR specifically, without interfering with immune responses to other antigens. To this end, the dual analog composed of the tandemly, reciprocally arranged two single analogs of p195–212 and p259–271, namely Lys-262–Ala-207, was prepared and shown to efficiently inhibit the proliferation of T cell lines specific to the myasthenogenic peptides and of lymph node cells primed *in vivo* to either of these peptides. The dual analog specifically inhibited *in vitro* T cell stimulation to either myasthenogenic peptide in >90% of the responding MG patients (86). The dual analog interferes with specific autoimmune responses (87), and when administered orally, the dual analog could treat experimental allergic myasthenia gravis (EAMG) induced in mice by immunization with the multideterminant native *Torpedo* AChR (88). Moreover, it had beneficial effects on the clinical manifestations characterizing EAMG. Thus, the dual analog is an efficient immunomodulator of EAMG in mice and could be of specific therapeutic potential for MG.

Cancer Research

The idea of binding anti-cancer therapeutic drugs covalently to antibodies reacting with cancerous cells has appealed to me from an early time. Instead of having the drugs, given systemically, spread throughout the whole body, immunotargeting would focus the supply of the drug exclusively to the cancer area. However, we did not get to immunotargeting until many years later when we bound daunomycin and adriamycin via a dextran bridge to antibodies against antigens of leukemia, lymphoma, and plasmacytoma cells. We showed that these are effective as "guided missiles" both *in vitro* and *in vivo* (89). The Fab dimers were almost as effective as intact antibodies. Daunomycin linked to anti-tumor antibodies penetrated the cell membrane at a higher rate than daunomycin linked to dextran or to normal immunoglobulin (90). Together with Japanese colleagues we could show a chemotherapeutic effect against hepatoma in rat (91).

With Meir Wilchek we showed indirect immunotargeting of cis-platinum to a human epidermoid carcinoma using the avidin-biotin system (92). The biotinylated antibody was attached to the cancer cell, and this was followed by cis-platinum attached to avidin. We moved to monoclonal antibody against the extracellular domain of the epidermal growth factor receptor, denoted today ErbB1, and found that its conjugate with daunomycin was quite efficient but so was the antibody by itself (93). A strong synergistic effect was observed when the anti-ErbB1 antibodies were administered together with cis-platin. This observation became of great interest because of its therapeutic potential (*e.g.* in the review article by Mendelsohn and Baselga (94)). Over the years I became more and more convinced that what matters most is the nature of monoclonal antibodies.

In the last dozen years I have been collaborating with Yossi Yarden, who has been working on the family of ErbB receptors and their ligands. We produced and investigated antibodies against these interesting protooncogene products. ErbB2 (also known as HER-2/Neu) is a tyrosine kinase, and its dense appearance is correlated with a poor prognosis in breast cancer. The antibodies formed either inhibited or accelerated the tumorigenic growth of ErbB2-transfected fibroblasts in athymic mice (95). Suppression and promotion of tumor growth by monoclonal antibodies to ErbB2 differentially correlated with cellular uptake (96). ErbB2 has no known efficient ligand but has tyrosine kinase activity. On the other hand, ErbB3 has a ligand, heregulin, but has no tyrosine kinase activity. When they heterodimerize, the dimer is an efficient and active receptor. ErbB2 heterodimerizes also with ErbB1 (epidermal growth factor receptor) and with ErbB4. Based on this information, we investigated (97) a large battery of monoclonal antibodies to ErbB2 and could divide them into several subclasses according to their biological activity. The inhibitory effect of one subclass was due to the acceleration of ligand dissociation by the blocking of heterodimerization. These observations may help us to understand the molecular mechanisms involved in the potential therapeutic effect of anti-ErbB2 antibodies.

Concluding Remarks

I have always been driven by curiosity and search. I know that there are individuals who prefer to be alone all the time, and maybe through daydreaming they reach all their working hypotheses, but I am a great believer in the interaction and in the fertilization of ideas. I have been collaborating with many colleagues around the world, and I have always been keen on having many visiting scientists spending extended periods of time in my laboratory. As for theories, they are very good as working hypotheses as long as you do not take them too seriously, but they are dangerous when they become dogmatic. Since I became involved with research, I have always had two precepts. If something is not worth doing at all, it is not worth doing very well; and if something is worth doing but is obvious, why should I do it? Only if I thought it is not obvious, I would embark on it.

I published my first paper in the *Journal of Biological Chemistry* in 1960 and the last one in 2000, a span of 40 years, including 17 publications.

Address correspondence to: michael.sela@weizmann.ac.il.

REFERENCES

1. Katchalski, E., and Sela, M. (1958) *Adv. Protein Chem.* **13**, 243–492
2. Sela, M., and Katchalski, E. (1959) *Adv. Protein Chem.* **14**, 391–478
3. Sela, M., and Katchalski, E. (1956) *J. Am. Chem. Soc.* **78**, 3986–3989
4. Katchalski, E., and Sela, M. (1953) *J. Am. Chem. Soc.* **75**, 5284–5289
5. Berger, A., Sela, M., and Katchalski, E. (1953) *Anal. Chem.* **25**, 1554–1555
6. Sela, M., and Katchalski, E. (1955) *J. Am. Chem. Soc.* **77**, 3662–3663
7. Sela, M., and Sarid, S. (1956) *Nature* **178**, 540–541
8. Sela, M., and Berger, A. (1955) *J. Am. Chem. Soc.* **77**, 1893–1898
9. Sela, M., White, F. H., Jr., and Anfinsen, C. B. (1959) *Biochim. Biophys. Acta* **31**, 417–426
10. Sela, M., White, F. H., Jr., and Anfinsen, C. B. (1957) *Science* **125**, 691–692
11. Sela, M. (1962) *J. Biol. Chem.* **237**, 418–421
12. Sela, M., Lupu, N., Yaron, A., and Berger, A. (1962) *Biochim. Biophys. Acta* **62**, 594–596
13. Edelman, I. S., Hoffer, E., Bauminger, S., and Sela, M. (1968) *Arch. Biochem. Biophys.* **123**, 211–221
14. Citri, N., Garber, N., and Sela, M. (1960) *J. Biol. Chem.* **235**, 3454–3459
15. Anfinsen, C. B., Haber, E., Sela, M., and White, F. H., Jr. (1961) *Proc. Natl. Acad. Sci. U. S. A.* **47**, 1309–1314
16. Anfinsen, C. B., Sela, M., and Cooke, J. P. (1962) *J. Biol. Chem.* **237**, 1825–1831
17. Wellner, D., Silman, J. I., and Sela, M. (1963) *J. Biol. Chem.* **238**, 1324–1331
18. Epstein, C. J., Anfinsen, C. B., and Sela, M. (1962) *J. Biol. Chem.* **237**, 3458–3463
19. Acher, R., Chauvet, J., Arnon, R., and Sela, M. (1968) *Eur. J. Biochem.* **3**, 476–482
20. Sela, M., and Steiner, L. A. (1963) *Biochemistry* **2**, 416–421
21. Rigby, M., and Sela, M. (1964) *Biochemistry* **3**, 629–636
22. Sela, M., and Arnon, R. (1960) *Biochem. J.* **75**, 91–102

23. Sela, M. (1954) *Bull. Res. Counc. Isr.* **4,** 109–110
24. Sela, M., Katchalski, E., and Gehatia, M. (1956) *J. Am. Chem. Soc.* **78,** 746–751
25. Sela, M., and Arnon, R. (1960) *Biochim. Biophys. Acta* **40,** 382–384
26. Sela, M., Fuchs, S., and Arnon, R. (1962) *Biochem. J.* **85,** 223–235
27. Fuchs, S., and Sela, M. (1963) *Biochem. J.* **87,** 70–79
28. Sela, M. (1966) *Adv. Immunol.* **5,** 29–129
29. Sela, M. (1969) *Science* **166,** 1365–1374
30. Sela, M., and Zisman, E. (1997) *FASEB J.* **11,** 449–456
31. Sela, M., Schechter, B., Schechter, I., and Borek, F. (1967) *Cold Spring Harbor Symp. Quant. Biol.* **32** 537–545
32. Schechter, B., Conway-Jacobs, A., and Sela, M. (1971) *Eur. J. Biochem.* **20,** 321–324
33. Arnon, R., Maron, E., Sela, M., and Anfinsen, C. B. (1971) *Proc. Natl. Acad. Sci. U. S. A.* **68,** 1450–1455
34. Langbeheim, H., Arnon, R., and Sela, M. (1976) *Proc. Natl. Acad. Sci. U. S. A.* **73,** 4636–4640
35. Maoz, A., Fuchs, S., and Sela, M. (1973) *Biochemistry* **9,** 4246–4252
36. Sela, M., and Pecht, I. (1996) *Adv. Protein Chem.* **49,** 289–328
37. Arnon, R., and Sela, M. (1960) *Science* **132,** 86–87
38. Givol, D., Fuchs, S., and Sela, M. (1962) *Biochim. Biophys. Acta* **63,** 222–224
39. Cahnmann, H. J., Arnon, R., and Sela, M. (1966) *J. Biol. Chem.* **241,** 3247–3255
40. Lahav, M., Arnon, R., and Sela, M. (1967) *J. Exp. Med.* **125,** 787–805
41. Freedman, M. H., and Sela, M. (1966) *J. Biol. Chem.* **241,** 2383–2396
42. Freedman, M. H., and Sela, M. (1966) *J. Biol. Chem.* **241,** 5225–5232
43. Pecht, I., Givol, D., and Sela, M. (1972) *J. Mol. Biol.* **68,** 241–247
44. Sela, M., and Mozes, E. (1966) *Proc. Natl. Acad. Sci. U. S. A.* **55,** 445–452
45. Sela, M., Mozes, E., Shearer, G. M., and Karniely, Y. (1970) *Proc. Natl. Acad. Sci. U. S. A.* **67,** 1288–1293
46. Jagendorf, A. T., Patchornik, A., and Sela, M. (1963) *Biochim. Biophys. Acta* **78,** 516–527
47. Robbins, J. B., Haimovich, J., and Sela, M. (1967) *Immunochemistry* **4,** 11–22
48. Schechter, B., Schechter, I., and Sela, M. (1970) *J. Biol. Chem.* **245,** 1438–1447
49. Schechter, B., Schechter, I., and Sela, M. (1970) *Immunochemistry* **7,** 587–597
50. Conway-Jacobs, A., Schechter, B., and Sela, M. (1970) *Biochemistry* **9,** 4870–4875
51. McDevitt, H. O., and Sela, M. (1965) *J. Exp. Med.* **122,** 517–531
52. McDevitt, H. O., and Sela, M. (1967) *J. Exp. Med.* **126,** 969–978
53. McDevitt, H. O. (2000) *Annu. Rev. Immunol.* **18,** 1–17
54. Sela, M. (1972) *Bull. Inst. Pasteur* **2,** 73–86
55. Arnon, R., Bustin, M., Calef, E., Chaitchik, S., Haimovich, J., Novik, N., and Sela, M. (1976) *Proc. Natl. Acad. Sci. U. S. A.* **73,** 2123–2127
56. Jacob, C. O., Sela, M., and Arnon, R. (1983) *Proc. Natl. Acad. Sci. U. S. A.* **80,** 7611–7615
57. Jacob, C. O., Arnon, R., and Sela, M. (1986) *Immunol. Lett.* **14,** 43–48
58. Mozes, E., Sela, M., and Chedid, L. (1980) *Proc. Natl. Acad. Sci. U. S. A.* **77,** 4933–4937
59. Arnon, R., Sela, M., Parant, M., and Chedid, L. (1980) *Proc. Natl. Acad. Sci. U. S. A.* **77,** 6769–6772
60. Audibert, F., Jolivet, M., Chedid, L., Arnon, R., and Sela, M. (1982) *Proc. Natl. Acad. Sci. U. S. A.* **79,** 5042–5046
61. Arnon, R., Sela, M., Rachaman, E. S., and Shapiro, D. (1967) *Eur. J. Biochem.* **2,** 79–83
62. Teitelbaum, D., Arnon, R., Rabinsohn, Y., and Shapiro, D. (1973) *Immunochemistry* **10,** 735–743
63. Teitelbaum, D., Meshorer, A., Hirshfeld, T., Arnon, R., and Sela, M. (1971) *Eur. J. Immunol.* **1,** 242–248
64. Teitelbaum, D., Webb, C., Meshorer, A., Arnon, R., and Sela, M. (1973) *Eur. J. Immunol.* **3,** 273–279
65. Sela, M., Arnon, R., and Teitelbaum, D. (1990) *Bull. Inst. Pasteur* **88,** 303–314
66. Teitelbaum, D., Webb, C., Bree, M., Meshorer, A., Arnon, R., and Sela, M. (1974) *Clin. Immunol. Immunopathol.* **3,** 256–262
67. Webb, C., Teitelbaum, D., Arnon, R., and Sela, M. (1973) *Eur. J. Immunol.* **3,** 279–286
68. Teitelbaum, D., Aharoni, R., Sela, M., and Arnon, R. (1991) *Proc. Natl. Acad. Sci. U. S. A.* **88,** 9528–9532
69. Teitelbaum, D., Aharoni, R., Arnon, R., and Sela, M. (1988) *Proc. Natl. Acad. Sci. U. S. A.* **85,** 9724–9728
70. Teitelbaum, D., Milo, R., Arnon, R., and Sela, M. (1992) *Proc. Natl. Acad. Sci. U. S. A.* **89,** 137–141
71. Webb, C., Teitelbaum, D., Herz, A., Arnon, R., and Sela, M. (1976) *Immunochemistry* **13,** 333–337
72. Bornstein, M. B., Miller, A., Slagle, S., Weitzmann, M., Crystal, H., Drexler, E., Keilson, M., Merriam, A., Wassertheil-Smoller, S., Spada, V., Weiss, W., Arnon, R., Jacobsohn, I., Teitelbaum, D., and Sela, M. (1987) *N. Engl. J. Med.* **37,** 408–414
73. Bornstein, M. B., Miller, A., Slagle, S., Weitzmann, M., Drexler, E., Keilson, M., Spada, V., Weiss, W., Appel, S., Rolak, L., Harati, Y., Brown, S., Arnon, R., Jacobsohn, I., Teitelbaum, D., and Sela, M. (1991) *Neurology* **41,** 533–539
74. Johnson, K. P., Brooks, B. R., Cohen, J. A., Ford, C. C., Goldstein, J., Lisak, R. P., Myers, L. W., Panitch, H. S., Rose, J. W., Schiffer, R. B., Vollner, T., Weiner, L. P., Wolinsky, J. S., and the Copolymer 1 MS Study Group (1995) *Neurology* **45,** 1268–1276
75. Fridkis-Hareli, M., Teitelbaum, D., Gurevich, E., Pecht, I., Brautbar, C., Kwon, O. J., Brenner, T., Arnon, R., and Sela, M. (1994) *Proc. Natl. Acad. Sci. U. S. A.* **91,** 4872–4876
76. Fridkis-Hareli, M., Teitelbaum, D., Pecht, I., Arnon, R., and Sela, M. (1997) *Int. Immunol.* **7,** 925–934
77. Aharoni, R., Teitelbaum, D., Arnon, R., and Sela, M. (1999) *Proc. Natl. Acad. Sci. U. S. A.* **96,** 634–639
78. Aharoni, R., Teitelbaum, D., Sela, M., and Arnon, R. (1997) *Proc. Natl. Acad. Sci. U. S. A.* **94,** 10821–10826
79. Neuhaus, O., Farina, C., Yassouridis, A., Wiendl, H., Bergh, F. T., Dose, T., Wekerle, H., and Hohlfeld, R. (2000) *Proc. Natl. Acad. Sci. U. S. A.* **97,** 7452–7457
80. Aharoni, R., Teitelbaum, D., Sela, M., and Arnon, R. (1998) *J. Neuroimmunol.* **91,** 135–146
81. Sela, M. (1999) *C. R. Acad. Sci. Paris Life Sci.* **322,** 933–939
82. Sela, M., and Teitelbaum, D. (2001) *Expert Opin. Pharmacother.* **2,** 1149–1165
83. Kipnis, J., Yoles, E., Porat, Z., Cohen, A., Mor, F., Sela, M., Cohen, I. R., and Schwartz, M. (2000) *Proc. Natl. Acad. Sci. U. S. A.* **97,** 7446–7451
84. Schori, H., Kipnis, J., Yoles, E., WoldeMussie, E., Ruiz, G., Wheeler, L. A., and Schwartz, M. (2001) *Proc. Natl. Acad. Sci. U. S. A.* **98,** 3398–3403
85. Katz-Levy, Y., Kirshner, S. L., Sela, M., and Mozes, E. (1993) *Proc. Natl. Acad. Sci. U. S. A.* **90,** 7000–7004
86. Zisman, E., Katz-Levy, Y., Dayan, M., Kirshner, S. L., Paas-Rozner, M., Karni, A., Abramsky, O., Bautbar, C., Fridkin, M., Sela, M., and Mozes, E. (1996) *Proc. Natl. Acad. Sci. U. S. A.* **93,** 4492–4497
87. Katz-Levy, Y., Paas-Rozner, M., Kirshner, S. L., Dayan, M., Zisman, E., Fridkin, M., Wirguin, I., Sela, M., and Mozes, E. (1997) *Proc. Natl. Acad. Sci. U. S. A.* **94,** 3200–3205
88. Paas-Rozner, M., Dayan, M., Paas, Y., Changeux, J.-P., Wirguin, I., Sela, M., and Mozes, E. (2000) *Proc. Natl. Acad. Sci. U. S. A.* **97,** 2168–2173
89. Levy, R., Hurwitz, E., Maron, R., Arnon, R., and Sela, M. (1975) *Cancer Res.* **35,** 1182–1191

90. Hurwitz, E., Maron, R., Arnon, R., Wilchek, M., and Sela, M. (1978) *Eur. J. Cancer* **14,** 1213–1220
91. Tsukada, Y., Hurwitz, E., Kashi, R., Sela, M., Hibi, N., Hara, A., and Hirai, H. (1982) *Proc. Natl. Acad. Sci. U. S. A.* **79,** 7896–7899
92. Schechter, B., Arnon, R., Wilchek, M., Schlessinger, J., Hurwitz, E., Aboud-Pirak, E., and Sela, M. (1991) *Int. J. Cancer* **48,** 167–172
93. Aboud-Pirak, E., Hurwitz, E., Pirak, M. E., Bellot, F., Schlessinger, J., and Sela, M. (1988) *J. Natl. Cancer Inst.* **80,** 1605–1611
94. Mendelsohn, J., and Baselga, J. (2000) *Oncogene* **19,** 6550–6565
95. Stancovski, I., Hurwitz, E., Leitner, O., Ullrich, A., Yarden, Y., and Sela, M. (1991) *Proc. Natl. Acad. Sci. U. S. A.* **88,** 8691–8695
96. Hurwitz, E., Stancovski, I., Sela, M., and Yarden, Y. (1995) *Proc. Natl. Acad. Sci. U. S. A.* **92,** 3353–3357
97. Klapper, L. N., Vaisman, N., Hurwitz, E., Pinkas-Kramarski, R., Yarden, Y., and Sela, M. (1997) *Oncogene* **14,** 2099–2109

THE JOURNAL OF BIOLOGICAL CHEMISTRY
Vol. 278, No. 51, Issue of December 19, pp. 50819–50832, 2003

Reflections

A PAPER IN A SERIES COMMISSIONED TO CELEBRATE THE CENTENARY OF THE JBC IN 2005

JBC Centennial
1905–2005
100 Years of Biochemistry and Molecular Biology

A Brief Historical Review of the Waterfall/Cascade of Blood Coagulation

Published, JBC Papers in Press, October 21, 2003, DOI 10.1074/jbc.X300009200

Earl W. Davie

From the Department of Biochemistry, University of Washington, Seattle, Washington 98195-7350

This article explores some of the events and people involved in unraveling the basic mechanisms leading to the clotting of blood. It also brings to focus the important role that my teachers and colleagues had on my career in research. When I entered college majoring in chemistry I had little idea that I would have an opportunity to become a professor of biochemistry at a major university. This was clearly the result of the excellent advice and encouragement that I received, particularly from my teachers early in my career.

As a senior at the University of Washington, I took a course in biochemistry to complete my credit requirements for a B.S. in chemistry. The biochemistry course was taught by Donald Hanahan, an excellent lipid biochemist who understood the importance of a quantitative measurement. I was fascinated by the biochemistry class that Hanahan taught, as well as by a course dealing with the chemistry of natural products. When Hanahan invited me to work in his laboratory on a senior project, I got my first real experience of what it was like to do laboratory research and I enjoyed it. In the fall of 1950, I entered graduate school at the University of Washington and decided to do my thesis research with Hans Neurath to learn something about protein structure and function. Neurath was an excellent teacher, a distinguished protein chemist, and a leader in his field (Fig. 1). He also had high standards and was very demanding of his students. Neurath was originally trained as a colloid chemist at the University of Vienna. Following his postdoctoral training at the University of London in the chemistry department headed by Frederick Donnan, he immigrated to the United States in 1935, where his research interests shifted to protein structure. He then held positions at the University of Minnesota, Cornell University, and Duke University, and in 1950, he joined the University of Washington School of Medicine as chairman of a newly established Department of Biochemistry. His research interest then focused almost entirely on proteases, particularly pancreatic trypsin, chymotrypsin, and carboxypeptidase, because these proteins were available in sizable amounts and could be prepared in high purity. Much of his career then dealt with their structure and function, including their active sites, substrate specificity, their kinetics, amino acid sequence, interaction with inhibitors, and their mechanism of activation. Over the years, Neurath also became well known for his leadership in the publication of scientific literature, having founded and served as Editor-in-Chief of *Biochemistry* for 30 years. In 1990, he founded another new journal, *Protein Science*, as well as editing several excellent volumes, such as *The Proteins* initially with Kenneth Bailey and later with Robert Hill.

For my Ph.D. thesis research, Neurath suggested that I should compare trypsinogen and trypsin to gain some insight as to the mechanism of zymogen activation. Little difference between the two proteins was anticipated because Cunningham and other postdoctoral fellows in Neurath's laboratory had shown that trypsinogen and trypsin had essentially identical molecular weights of 23,800 as measured in the ultracentrifuge (1). In my initial studies, I was unable to detect any difference between the two proteins at their carboxyl-terminal end. This suggested that no peptides or amino acids were removed or peptide bonds cleaved at the

FIG. 1. **Professor Hans Neurath (1909–2002).**

carboxyl end of trypsinogen during its conversion to trypsin. However, in France Rovery and co-workers (2) found that trypsinogen contained an amino-terminal valine, whereas trypsin contained an amino-terminal isoleucine. Shortly thereafter, I isolated an acidic peptide (Val-$(Asp)_4$-Lys) that was generated by limited proteolysis during the activation of trypsinogen (3). Most importantly, the appearance of this peptide correlated exactly with the formation of the enzymatic activity of trypsin. This finding was consistent with the loss of a small amino-terminal valyl peptide from trypsinogen as well as a slight increase in the isoionic point of the protein during its conversion to trypsin (9.3–10.01). As a graduate student, I was very excited by the fact that we were the first to make this observation. Little did we realize at the time that "limited proteolysis" would be a common mechanism seen over and over again in biological systems. This mechanism included the activation of other proteases such as those participating in blood coagulation (4), fibrinolysis (5), and complement activation (6). Furthermore, limited proteolysis is now known to occur in a wide range of biological reactions such as the processing of prohormones (7), the activation of cells via their protease-activated receptors (PARs) (8), the cleavage of signal peptides from proteins destined for secretion (9, 10), and the cleavage of ubiquitin from proteins on their way to endosomes or proteosomes (11). Additional examples are the removal of small or large fragments from proteins such as fibrinogen prior to polymerization (12) and the removal of small propeptides that are signals for protein modification such as carboxylation (13). Also, regulated intramembrane proteolysis (RIP) plays an important role in determining the level of cholesterol in membranes via the sterol regulatory element-binding proteins (SREBPs) (14). Other examples include signaling receptors such as Notch, a single transmembrane protein that is activated by proteolytic cleavage at three specific sites generating an intracellular domain of the protein (15). Notch is then translocated to the nucleus where it binds to transcription factors that play a role in devel-

Fig. 2. **Dr. Bert L. Vallee, Edgar M. Bronfman Distinguished Senior Professor (1919–).**

opment. Thus, proteases have many functions in addition to the digestion of proteins in the gut.

Being in the Neurath laboratory gave me an excellent chance to interact with his other graduate students and postdoctoral fellows. Individuals such as Leon Cunningham gave me considerable guidance during those early years. I also had the chance to meet and visit with many outstanding visitors and collaborators of Hans Neurath. Visitors such as Fred Sanger presented the amino acid sequence of the two chains of insulin, a milestone in amino acid sequence analysis (16).

Another distinguished visitor was Bert Vallee from Boston (Fig. 2). His visit to Seattle led to the discovery of zinc in carboxypeptidase (17). Vallee received his early education at the University of Berne and then immigrated to the United States in 1938 where he entered New York University School of Medicine. In 1946, he moved to Boston for his studies at MIT and Harvard. Vallee developed a highly sensitive flame and spark emission spectrometer for the detection of trace metals in proteins, and this technique led to the development of the field of metalloproteins in his laboratory. Following the discovery of carboxypeptidase A as a zinc metalloenzyme, he then identified dozens of other zinc-containing enzymes employing atomic absorption spectroscopy (18). These enzymes participate in lipid, protein, carbohydrate, and nucleic acid metabolism as well as gene transcription, cell division, and development. Zinc plays a structural as well as a catalytic or cocatalytic role in these proteins. When zinc is associated with DNA-binding proteins, it is bound to three distinct motifs referred to as zinc fingers, twists, and clusters (19). More than 300 metalloenzymes have now been identified and include metallothionein, a small protein that Vallee found in horse kidney (20). This small protein has a unique structure, amino acid composition, and metal binding characteristics. Vallee made many other important contributions such as the discovery and role of angiogenin in blood vessel formation. These visitors made the Neurath laboratory a very stimulating place for a graduate student.

When I received my Ph.D. in 1954, Neurath recommended Fritz Lipmann's laboratory in Boston for postdoctoral study (see "Hitler's Gift and the Era of Biosynthesis" by E. P. Kennedy (21)). Lipmann's laboratory was another very exciting place to work because Mary Ellen Jones and Leonard Spector were close to identifying carbamoyl phosphate as an intermediate in the formation of citrulline (22), while Helmuth Hilz and Phil Robbins were characterizing "active sulfate" (3'-phosphoadenosyl 5'-phosphosulfate) (23, 24), an intermediate employed in the biosynthesis of tyrosine sulfate in proteins and other molecules such as chondroitin sulfate. Lipmann suggested that I should try to isolate one of the amino acid carboxyl-activating enzymes that were thought to be involved in protein biosynthesis (25). Hopefully a pure activating enzyme might provide an approach to finding the natural acceptor for this family of enzymes, something equivalent to the role that CoA played in the activation of acetate. At the time, the biological acceptor tRNA was not known. These studies were carried out with Victor Koningsberg, a postdoctoral fellow from The Netherlands. We employed beef pancreas as an enzyme source because this tissue was very active in protein biosynthesis. These studies led to the isolation and characterization of a tryptophanyl carboxyl-activating enzyme that catalyzed the exchange of pyrophosphate into ATP in the presence of tryptophan and the formation of tryptophan hydroxymate when hydroxylamine was added to the reaction mixture (26).

After two very enjoyable years in Lipmann's laboratory, I learned about a faculty position at Western Reserve University in Cleveland, Ohio in Harland Wood's Department of Biochemistry. Wood had built a first rate department with an outstanding reputation for its research in intermediary metabolism. The biochemistry faculty included distinguished scientists such as Mert Utter, Robert Greenberg, Warwick Sakami, and many others. Wood had talked to Lipmann about this position, and Lipmann had suggested me for the job. At the time, academic positions were rarely advertised as is presently done.

Harland Wood was a very talented and productive scientist who was a giant in the field of intermediary metabolism (Fig. 3). He received his undergraduate training in chemistry and bacteriology at MacAlaster College in Minnesota. In 1931, he became a Ph.D. student in microbiology in the laboratory of Charles Werkman at Iowa State University. As a graduate student, he made the monumental discovery that carbon dioxide fixation occurred in heterotrophic bacteria (27). At the time, CO_2 was thought to be an end product for all cells except for photosynthetic autotrophs. The fixation of CO_2 was discovered long before its role was established in other important reactions such as a building block for purines, amino acids, and fatty acids. The reaction in which pyruvate and CO_2 would generate oxalacetate in bacteria soon became known as the "Wood-Werkman reaction." In collaboration with Alfred Nier and co-workers at the University of Minnesota, Wood was able to show that $^{13}CO_2$ was incorporated into succinate in bacteria (28). This was in complete agreement with the proposal that CO_2 and pyruvate would generate oxalacetate followed by reduction to succinate.

In 1946 Harland Wood moved to Western Reserve University where he was appointed chairman of the Department of Biochemistry. In Cleveland, he continued his studies with ^{13}C to study metabolic pathways employing a mass spectrometer that he built from scratch (29). He then turned much of his efforts to enzyme isolation and characterization. One of his favorite enzymes was a biotin-containing transcarboxylase from *Propionibacterium shermani* (29). This very large protein (M_r ~1,200,000) forms propionyl-CoA and oxalacetate from methylmalonyl-CoA and pyruvate. It consists of a hexameric central subunit attached to 12 biotinyl subunits and 6 dimeric outer subunits. Wood referred to this enzyme as the "Mickey Mouse" enzyme because of its appearance in the electron microscope and its multiple subunits.

Wood was a wonderful boss and I admired him a great deal. He had phenomenal physical stamina and loved to work at the bench throughout his life. Furthermore, he had a strong passion for good science and was very supportive of the research programs of his faculty. He was also unusually frank and honest with his colleagues. When I first visited Cleveland for an interview for a faculty position, he informed me that there was only one tenure position in the department and that was his as Chairman. He assured me, however, that tenure wasn't too important anyway because if he and I didn't get along, one of us would have to leave and it wouldn't be him. This was not a threat, however—just a simple and honest fact of life.

My initial studies in Cleveland dealt with the isolation and identification of aminoacyl adenylates that had been proposed as intermediates by Hoagland and co-workers (25) and DeMoss and coworkers (30) in the carboxyl activation of amino acids. These intermediates, however, had not been isolated from an enzymatic reaction. They were analogous, however, to

FIG. 3. **Professor Harland G. Wood (1907–1991).** Photograph kindly provided by The Plain Dealer Publishing Co., Cleveland, OH and reprinted with permission.

adenylyl acetate suggested earlier by Berg in the formation of acetyl-CoA (31). Experiments carried out in our laboratory with Henry Kingdon and Les Webster in Cleveland led to the isolation and characterization of adenylyl tryptophan and adenylyl serine and demonstrated that these elusive intermediates could be identified in reactions that included amino acid, ATP, Mg^{2+}, activating enzyme, as well as pyrophosphatase to shift the equilibrium of the reaction toward the enzyme-bound intermediate (32, 33).

In 1957, Wood introduced me to Oscar Ratnoff, a distinguished Professor of Medicine at Western Reserve University (Fig. 4). This introduction to Ratnoff started much of my career in a new direction, mainly research in blood coagulation. Ratnoff received his medical training from Columbia University College of Physicians and Surgeons and then worked with C. Lockard Conley and Robert Hartmann in the Department of Hematology at Johns Hopkins University in Baltimore (34). He joined the Department of Medicine at Western Reserve University in Cleveland in 1953 and soon developed an outstanding reputation in blood coagulation. Working on a project in collaboration with Ratnoff seemed like a good idea because he was well known for his great intellect, hard work, and an uncanny ability to relate a large pool of clinical information to basic research. Furthermore, I had developed a few skills in protein chemistry, and it was quite clear that they would be helpful to unravel some of the complex reactions leading to fibrin formation.

One of the most unusual and remarkable properties of blood is its ability to solidify or clot. In humans, this physical change is initiated by tissue injury and destruction and involves plasma proteins, platelets, and tissue components. In invertebrates, the clotting reaction is primarily because of cell aggregation and agglutination. In higher organisms, however, the vascular pressures are high and this increases the risk of bleeding. Thus, the mechanisms for initiating and regulating blood coagulation in humans are far more complex and include the following three general processes: (*a*) the immediate contraction of blood vessels at the site of

Fig. 4. **Professor Oscar D. Ratnoff (1916–).**

vascular injury, (*b*) formation of a platelet plug, and (*c*) the generation of a fibrin clot to stabilize the platelet plug. The latter reaction results from the interaction of tissue and plasma proteins in a series of reactions that occur primarily on the surface of the activated platelets and other cells. These cells provide phosphatidylserine, a membrane phospholipid that is essential for clotting and becomes exposed when cells are activated or damaged.

Ratnoff had many interesting patients who had abnormal blood coagulation. One of Ratnoff's most unusual patients was John Hageman, who had a rather strange clotting abnormality in that his blood didn't clot when added to a glass test tube (35). This could be corrected, however, by the addition of a small amount of plasma or serum from normal individuals or from patients with other known coagulation disorders such as hemophilia. Surprisingly, however, John Hageman had not experienced any bleeding tendency. Ratnoff inquired as to whether I might be able to help him in the isolation of this plasma protein that he called Hageman factor. I suggested that column chromatography on DEAE or carboxymethylcellulose (CMC) might be useful because Peterson and Sober had just published a novel method by which one could separate plasma or serum proteins with these resins (36). Because these reagents were not available commercially, I prepared small amounts and started the purification of Hageman factor from normal pooled human plasma. In these studies, plasma was separated into 50 or 60 fractions, and these were given to Ratnoff for assay of their clot accelerating activity. A few days later he informed me that all the clotting activity was present in a few tubes that contained little or no detectable protein.

It was clear from the earlier studies of Ratnoff and Rosenblum that Hageman factor (now called factor XII) was present in plasma in an inactive form and was activated in a test tube when bound to a glass surface or crushed glass or kaolin (37). This was consistent with the idea that Hageman factor activation could trigger fibrin formation in blood collected in a glass container. In contrast, blood collected in paraffin-lined or silicone-coated bottles would clot very slowly or not at all. After several purification steps, we were able to show that Hageman factor was a plasma protein capable of initiating blood coagulation in the test tube and did so in the absence of tissue extracts (38). Thus, it was participating in the intrinsic pathway of blood coagulation in contrast to the extrinsic pathway that also required tissue extracts. Little was known, however, about the mechanism by which Hageman factor could activate the clotting process. Ratnoff and I then had a number of discussions about the early phases of blood coagulation because I had little knowledge of the field other than the conversion of prothrombin to thrombin by thrombokinase, and fibrinogen to fibrin by thrombin in reactions requiring calcium. This pathway had been proposed in the early 1900s by Morawitz, who described thrombokinase as a coagulant activity from platelets or damaged tissue (39). Howell (40) called the clot-accelerating activity from tissue, thromboplastin, a complex that converted prothrombin to thrombin. Some investigators, however, thought the activity from tissue was because of phospholipid or lipoprotein. Purification was then carried out in a number of laboratories, including Chargaff and co-workers (41), Williams and Norris (42), and Nemerson and Pitlick (43) who identified thromboplastin as a combination of clotting activities. One was a protein now known as tissue factor present in most tissues except platelets and the other as phospholipid. Since then, tissue factor has been purified extensively from bovine (44) and human (45) tissue.

Over the years a number of clinicians identified many patients with different coagulation disorders. In 1936, Patek and Stetson (46) had found that patients with hemophilia were lacking a factor present in normal plasma. The following year it was partially enriched by Patek and Taylor who called it anti-hemophilic factor (AHF) or anti-hemophilic globulin (AHG) (47). This deficiency now called hemophilia A (or factor VIII deficiency) is found almost exclusively in males and is one of the most common of the hereditary coagulation disorders. This clotting abnormality was corrected by the addition of a small sample of normal plasma to the hemophilic plasma restoring the generation of a fibrin clot in the presence of calcium. Hemophilia has been of considerable historical interest since the son of Tsar Nicholas II of Russia had hemophilia and his care occupied much of the time and effort of his parents distracting them from the political problems that were developing (48). Consequently, hemophilia played a significant role in the Bolshevik Revolution in 1917 that led to the execution of Nicholas, his wife, and their children following the October revolution.

In 1944, Robbins (49) made the interesting observation that fibrin formed in the presence of a plasma protein and calcium became rather insoluble in urea. In further studies, Laki and Lorand (50) partially purified this plasma protein that became known as the Laki-Lorand factor, fibrin-stabilizing factor, and presently as factor XIII. Years later, Chen and Doolittle (51) showed that activated factor XIII cross-links fibrin monomers by forming $\epsilon(\gamma$-glutamyl) lysine bonds between two adjacent fibrin molecules. In 1947, shortly after World War II, Owren in Norway (52) described another hemorrhagic disease in a young woman lacking a plasma protein that was called proaccelerin. This disease, referred to as parahemophilia (factor V deficiency), was a rare disorder resulting in bruising and bleeding after minor lacerations or dental extraction. In 1949 Alexander and co-workers (53) described another factor in serum that accelerated the conversion of prothrombin to thrombin. This factor was called serum prothrombin conversion accelerator (SPCA), and the defect was named factor VII deficiency. Another clotting disorder, called hemophilia B, was described in 1952 by Aggeler and co-workers (54), Biggs and co-workers (55), and Schulmann and Smith (56). The protein lacking in these patients was known as plasma thromboplastin component (PTC), Christmas factor, or factor IX. Patients with hemophilia B had clinical symptoms essentially identical to those with classic hemophilia. Furthermore, like classic hemophilia, the disease occurred only in males.

In 1953 Rosenthal and co-workers (57) described a clotting abnormality that they called plasma thromboplastin antecedent (PTA) deficiency or factor XI deficiency. Individuals with PTA deficiency had mild or moderate bleeding symptoms that often became evident only after injury or surgery, such as dental extractions and tonsillectomies. This coagulation deficiency found mainly in Ashkenazi Jews was readily corrected by the addition of small amounts of normal plasma or plasma from patients with Hageman factor deficiency or hemophilia A. Mixing or complementation experiments have been very useful for identifying new coagulation proteins, and this has been nicely illustrated in a recent article by Graham (58). Additional experiments with PTA-deficient plasma were consistent with the concept that patients with this deficiency lack a protein that participates in an early phase of the coagulation pathway. The concept that clotting might involve enzymes or proteins other than thrombin, however, was not universally accepted. Some investigators, particularly Seegers and co-workers (59), felt that thrombin was the only enzyme involved in clot acceleration and the other clotting activities were primarily degradation products of prothrombin and probably artifacts. The clinical and genetic evidence for additional clotting factors, however, continued to strengthen and expand. Shortly thereafter in 1957, Stuart factor deficiency was described by Hougie and

A

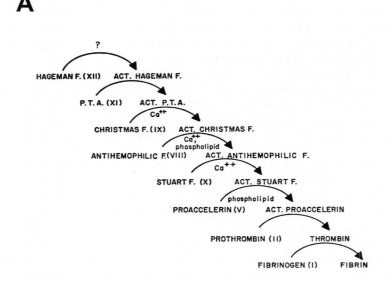

B

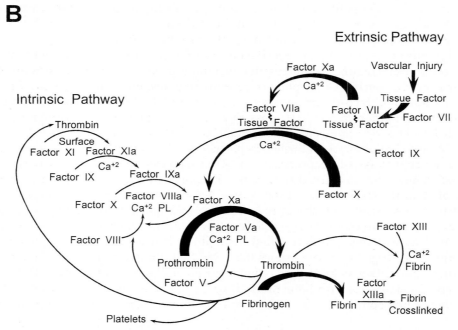

FIG. 5. *A,* "waterfall sequence for intrinsic blood clotting" from Ref. 68. *B,* "coagulation cascade and fibrin formation by the intrinsic and extrinsic pathways" modified from Ref. 4.

co-workers (60). This bleeding disorder occurred in both men and women. Like most other clotting deficiencies, individuals lacking Stuart factor (factor X) fail to readily convert pro-thrombin to thrombin, resulting in the formation of an abnormal or delayed fibrin clot.

With so many different patients being identified with clotting disorders apparently due to the absence of a functional plasma protein, it was clear that an understanding of how these proteins interacted to generate fibrin would require substantial protein purification. Accordingly, Ratnoff and I continued the purification of Hageman as well as PTA and Christmas factor from normal human plasma or in some cases from human deficient plasma. These studies with partially purified preparations provided clear evidence for the activation of PTA by activated Hageman factor (61), a reaction suggested earlier by Hardisty and Margolis (62). This reaction was followed by the activation of Christmas factor by activated PTA (63) as suggested by Soulier and co-workers (64). These reactions are illustrated in the *top half* of Fig. 5A.

An important concept that began to develop in these early studies was that clotting factors were present in blood in an inactive or precursor form and were converted to active enzymes in a step-by-step manner most likely via limited proteolysis. This was supported by the fact that activated PTA was inhibited by diisopropylphosphorofluoridate (DFP), a potent inhibitor of serine proteases (65). With activated PTA, the inhibitor was bound to a serine residue in the active site sequence of -Gly-Asp-Ser-Gly-. These experiments provided good evidence that activated PTA was a trypsin-like serine protease that probably converted Christmas factor to an active enzyme by "limited proteolysis" analogous to our earlier studies on the conversion of trypsinogen to trypsin (3). The activation of Christmas factor also required calcium ions (63). This was the first strong evidence for the role of calcium in the early phases of blood clotting. Thus, the inhibition of clotting by calcium-binding reagents such as oxalate or citrate became clear. The next step in the coagulation pathway was unclear, but it seemed likely that activated Christmas factor could in turn convert anti-hemophilic factor to an active form.

In 1962, I received a letter from Hans Neurath inviting me to join the faculty in the Department of Biochemistry at the University of Washington in Seattle. In just a few years this department had developed a fine reputation for its excellence in protein chemistry and enzymology as well as its superb faculty. Furthermore, Cecil Hougie had joined the medical school faculty in Seattle and was well known in the field of blood coagulation for his studies at Oxford (66), in addition to those at North Carolina previously mentioned (60). It was a difficult decision to leave Harland Wood's department as well as the close collaboration with Ratnoff and the many good friends that I had at Western Reserve. My wife and I finally decided, however, to move back to Seattle because we had grown up in the Pacific Northwest and loved the area.

At the University of Washington, we continued the purification of clotting factors from human and bovine plasma to enrich fractions for Christmas factor, anti-hemophilic factor, and Stuart factor. Our initial studies with Roger Lundblad suggested that activated Christmas factor converted anti-hemophilic factor to an active form, and it in turn converted Stuart factor to an active form in the presence of phospholipid and calcium (67). Similar studies were carried out by Breckenridge and Ratnoff in Cleveland suggesting that activated Stuart factor converted factor V to factor Va, which in turn converted prothrombin to thrombin. This led to a coagulation scheme that Ratnoff and I called a "waterfall sequence for intrinsic blood clotting" (68) (Fig. 5A). This proposal that began to take form in late 1962 (63) and early 1963 was submitted to *Science* for publication in early 1964. Unfortunately, it was declined by the editors. Shortly thereafter it was resubmitted to *Science* essentially unchanged and was accepted. About the same time a nearly identical scheme that was called a "coagulation cascade" was published in *Nature* by R. G. MacFarlane from Oxford (69). These two proposals clarified the sequence in which clotting factors interacted and provided concepts that were readily tested in the laboratory. Important additions and modifications were made in these two proposals during the following years. One that was particularly important linked the intrinsic pathway with the extrinsic pathway of blood coagulation at the level of Stuart factor (42, 43, 70, 71). The other significant change related to factor VIII and factor V. These two proteins are readily activated by limited proteolysis particularly by thrombin (72–74), but they participate as cofactors rather than enzymes. Activated factor VIII forms a complex with activated factor IX, an enzyme, whereas activated factor V forms a complex with activated factor X, another enzyme (75–77). Both reactions require calcium and phospholipid (PL), the latter being provided primarily by the activated platelets.

It is now generally accepted that the extrinsic pathway plays the major role in the initiation of blood coagulation following vascular injury and platelet plug formation. This is illustrated in Fig. 5B employing the Roman numeral nomenclature for the various clotting factors (4). Tissue factor is an integral membrane glycoprotein located in the tissue adventitia and functions as a receptor for factor VII (or VIIa) circulating in blood (78–81). Factor VII binds to tissue factor only after vascular injury at which time blood comes in contact with the damaged tissue. Tissue factor and factor VII then form a one-to-one complex in the presence of calcium ions. This complex on the damaged cell surface membrane facilitates the conversion of factor VII to factor VIIa by the cleavage of a single internal peptide bond (82). This gives rise to a two-chain factor VIIa held together by a disulfide bond. The active site sequence of -Gly-Asp-Ser-Gly-Gly-Pro- is located in the heavy chain of factor VIIa, a trypsin-like serine protease whose physiological activity occurs only when bound to tissue factor. A number of serine proteases catalyze the activation of factor VII, but factor VIIa and membrane-bound factor Xa probably play the major role *in vivo*.

The next step in the extrinsic pathway is the activation of factor X by the tissue factor-factor VIIa complex (70, 71, 83, 84) due to the cleavage of a single peptide bond in the heavy chain of the molecule (85). The tissue factor-factor VIIa complex also activates some factor IX by limited proteolysis (86). This latter reaction is particularly significant following minor vascular injury that generates a low level of the tissue factor-factor VIIa complex and reduced factor X activation. Under these conditions, the intrinsic pathway becomes involved via activated factor IXa (87). The formation of factor Xa and factor IXa generates two additional trypsin-like serine proteases. In the next step, it appears likely that factor Xa activates some of the factor V to factor Va and forms a complex with this activated protein in the presence of calcium and cell membrane phospholipid (PL). This complex then converts some prothrombin to thrombin. These reactions are referred to as "the initiation and priming phase" in the cell-based model of coagulation of Roberts and colleagues (88). The extrinsic pathway, however, is quickly inhibited by a multivalent Kunitz-type plasma protease inhibitor called tissue factor pathway inhibitor (89–91). This protein is a factor Xa-dependent inhibitor of the tissue factor-factor VIIa complex and blocks additional thrombin generation by the extrinsic pathway. Present evidence suggests that the small amount of thrombin that is generated, however, activates additional platelets attached to the site of vascular injury and also converts factor XI to factor XIa, factor VIII to factor VIIIa, and factor V to factor Va (Fig. 5B). These latter activation reactions all occur by limited proteolysis on the surface of the activated platelets that provides the phospholipid (PL). The activation of factor XI by thrombin triggers the intrinsic pathway of coagulation that also takes place on the surface of the activated platelets (92, 93). Initiation of the intrinsic pathway leads to an increase in the concentration of factor IXa, factor Xa, and a burst in the concentration of thrombin. This is followed by an increase in the conversion of fibrinogen to fibrin and factor XIII to factor XIIIa. Factor XIIIa then cross-links the fibrin monomers forming a tough insoluble clot that stabilizes the platelet plug.

A physiological role for Hageman factor in the coagulation pathway has not been clearly established because individuals lacking this activity have no bleeding complications. Accordingly, Hageman factor has been deleted from most coagulation schemes leading to fibrin formation. A similar situation exists for plasma prekallikrein (94, 95) and high molecular weight kininogen (96–99). Deficiencies of these two plasma proteins do not result in bleeding complications even though the two proteins accelerate blood coagulation *in vitro*.

Important advances in our understanding of the regulation of blood coagulation have also occurred over the years. The generation of fibrin is brought to a halt by plasma inhibitors such as antithrombin III (100, 101), a protease inhibitor that is particularly potent in the presence of heparin. Other plasma inhibitors include α_2-macroglobulin (102, 103) and tissue factor pathway inhibitor recounted earlier (89–91). These plasma proteins form stable inactive complexes with serine proteases such as thrombin. Another important regulatory pathway of the coagulation process results from the inactivation of factor Va (104) and activated factor VIII (105) by activated protein C (106). These reactions also occur by limited proteolysis in the presence of calcium and phospholipid. The inactivation of activated factor V is accelerated by protein S (107), another vitamin K-dependent plasma protein (108). The formation of activated protein C by thrombin (109) requires thrombomodulin, a transmembrane protein discovered by Owen and Esmon (110, 111) that stimulates the activation reaction about 20,000-fold.

Vitamin K was discovered by Dam in 1935 (112), but its biochemical relationship to bleeding became apparent only after the important discovery by Stenflo (113), Nelsestuen (114), and Magnusson (115) and their co-workers of γ-carboxyglutamic acid (Gla) in prothrombin. The Gla residues require vitamin K for their biosynthesis and are clustered in the amino-terminal region of the protein where they bind calcium. Calcium binding leads to a conformational change in the molecule and results in its interaction with phospholipid on the surface of damaged cells or activated platelets (116). The Gla residues are also present in the other vitamin K-dependent plasma proteins including factor VII, factor IX, factor X, protein C, and protein S (117). Coumadin drugs such as dicumarol cause bleeding by interfering with the carboxylation of the Glu residues in the vitamin K-dependent proteins resulting in inactive clotting factors (118). This was discovered in cattle fed fermented sweet clover that was rich in dicumarol (119).

The complete amino acid sequence of all the known coagulation factors has been determined in our laboratory and by others employing amino acid sequence analysis and cloning (120). Thus, the peptide bonds that are cleaved by the various trypsin-like serine proteases when clotting has been initiated are known, and all occur on the carboxyl side of an arginine residue. Furthermore, the structure of many of these proteins has been determined by x-ray diffraction. The three-dimensional structure of fibrinogen by Doolittle (121) and Cohen (122) and their co-workers was a major accomplishment, as well as the structures of thrombin, factor IX, factor X, and protein C by Bode and colleagues (123). In addition, the factor VIIa-tissue factor complex has been determined at 2.0-Å resolution by Banner and co-workers (124) and others (125). These studies have added greatly to our knowledge of these proteins that participate in fibrin formation.

Finally, it is important to mention the fact that the DNA sequences coding for the genes for all the clotting factors have been established in our laboratory (120) and others making it possible to identify the mutations in the clotting factors of thousands of patients with bleeding complications. Indeed, the largest number of mutations occurring in the genes coding for human proteins have been found in factor IX-deficient patients (126). Most importantly, the cloning of the coagulation proteins has made it possible to express and prepare recombinant proteins for the treatment of patients with hemophilia and other clotting disorders without the risk of viral contamination such as HIV and hepatitis (127–129). Last, the availability of recombinant factor VIIa has introduced a new and exciting approach for the treatment of hemophilia patients with inhibitors (antibodies) toward factor VIII, as described by Hedner and Kisiel (130). This recombinant plasma protein has also become extremely important in the treatment of patients undergoing various types of surgery where bleeding becomes life threatening (131–135). Indeed, factor VIIa may be the most important recombinant protein ever developed to assist in the treatment of trauma patients, burn patients, and a vast number of other patients undergoing major surgery.

Acknowledgments—I thank all my students and co-workers who made research exciting and fun. Particular thanks are extended to Kazuo Fujikawa, Dominic Chung, Walter Kisiel, Ko Kurachi, Aki Ichinose, and Savio Woo who introduced us to recombinant DNA technology early in the game.

Address correspondence to: ewd@u.washington.edu.

REFERENCES

1. Cunningham, L. W., Jr., Tietze, F., Green, N. M., and Neurath, H. (1953) Molecular kinetic properties of trypsin and related proteins. *Discuss. Faraday Soc.* **13,** 58–67
2. Rovery, M., Fabre, C., and Desnuelle, P. (1952) Étude des extrémités n-terminales du trypsinogène et de la trypsine de boeuf. *Biochim. Biophys. Acta* **9,** 702
3. Davie, E. W., and Neurath, H. (1955) Identification of a peptide released during autocatalytic activation of trypsinogen. *J. Biol. Chem.* **212,** 515–529
4. Davie, E. W., Fujikawa, K., and Kisiel, W. (1991) The coagulation cascade: initiation, maintenance, and regulation. *Biochemistry* **30,** 10363–10370
5. Collen, D. (1999) The plasminogen (fibrinolytic) system. *Thromb. Haemostasis* **82,** 259–270
6. Kirkitadze, M. D., and Barlow, P. N. (2001) Structure and flexibility of the multiple domain proteins that regulate complement activation. *Immunol. Rev.* **180,** 146–161
7. Steiner, D. V. (1998) The proprotein convertases. *Curr. Opin. Chem. Biol.* **2,** 31–39
8. Coughlin, S. R. (2000) Thrombin signaling and protease-activated receptors. *Nature* **407,** 258–264
9. Stroud, R. M., and Walter, P. (1999) Signal sequence recognition and protein targeting. *Curr. Opin. Struct. Biol.* **9,** 754–759
10. Dalbey, R. E., and Von Heijne, G. (1992) Signal peptidases in prokaryotes and eukaryotes—a new protease family. *Trends Biochem. Sci.* **17,** 474–478
11. Wilkinson, K. D. (2000) Ubiquitination and deubiquitination: targeting of proteins for degradation by the proteasome. *Semin. Cell Dev. Biol.* **11,** 141–148
12. Mosesson, M. W., Siebenlist, K., and Meh, D. A. (2001) The structure and biological features of fibrinogen and fibrin. *Ann. N. Y. Acad. Sci.* **936,** 11–30
13. Furie, B., Bouchard, B. A., and Furie, B. C. (1999) Vitamin K-dependent biosynthesis of gamma-carboxyglutamic acid. *Blood* **93,** 1798–1808
14. Brown, M. S., Ye, J., Rawson, R. B., and Goldstein, J. L. (2000) Regulated intramembrane proteolysis: a control mechanism conserved from bacteria to humans. *Cell* **100,** 191–198
15. Selkoe, D., and Kopan, R. (2003) Notch and presenilin: regulated intramembrane proteolysis links development and degeneration. *Annu. Rev. Neurosci.* **26,** 565–597
16. Sanger, F. (1988) Sequences, sequences, and sequences. *Annu. Rev. Biochem.* **57,** 1–28
17. Vallee, B. L., and Neurath, H. (1955) Carboxypeptidase, a zinc metalloenzyme. *J. Biol. Chem.* **217,** 253–261
18. Vallee, B. L., and Auld, D. S. (1990) Zinc coordination, function, and structure of zinc enzymes and other proteins. *Biochemistry* **29,** 5647–5659
19. Vallee, B. L., and Auld, D. S. (1992) Functional zinc-binding motifs in enzymes and DNA-binding proteins. *Faraday Discuss.* **93,** 47–65
20. Vallee, B. L. (1995) The function of metallothionein. *Neurochem. Int.* **27,** 23–33
21. Kennedy, E. P. (2001) Hitler's gift and the era of biosynthesis. *J. Biol. Chem.* **276,** 42619–42631
22. Jones, M. E., Spector, L., and Lipmann, F. (1955) Carbamoyl phosphate, the carbamoyl donor in enzymatic

citrulline synthesis. *J. Am. Chem. Soc.* **77**, 819–820

23. Hilz, H., and Lipmann F. (1955) The enzymatic activation of sulfate. *Proc. Natl. Acad. Sci. U. S. A.* **41**, 880–890
24. Robbins, P. W., and Lipmann, F. (1957) Isolation and identification of active sulfate. *J. Biol. Chem.* **229**, 837–851
25. Hoagland, M. B., Keller, E. B., and Zamicnik, P. C. (1956) Enzymatic carboxyl activation of amino acids. *J. Biol. Chem.* **218**, 345–358
26. Davie, E. W., Koningsberger, V. V., and Lipmann, F. (1956) The isolation of a tryptophan-activating enzyme from pancreas. *Arch. Biochem. Biophys.* **65**, 21–38
27. Wood, H. G., and Werkman, C. H. (1936) The utilization of CO_2 in the dissimilation of glycerol by the propionic bacteria. *Biochem. J.* **30**, 48–53
28. Wood, H. G., Werkman, C. H., Hemingway, A., and Nier, A. O. (1941) The position of carbon dioxide carbon in succinic acid synthesized by heterotrophic bacteria. *J. Biol. Chem.* **139**, 377–381
29. Wood, H. G. (1985) Then and now. *Annu. Rev. Biochem.* **54**, 1–41
30. DeMoss, J. A., Genuth, S. M., and Novelli, G. D. (1956) The enzymatic activation of amino acids via their acyl-adenylate derivative. *Proc. Natl. Acad. Sci. U. S. A.* **42**, 325–332
31. Berg, P. (1955) Participation of adenyl-acetate in the acetate-activating system. *J. Am. Chem. Soc.* **77**, 3163–3164
32. Kingdon, H. S., Webster, L. T., Jr., and Davie, E. W. (1958) Enzymatic formation of adenyl tryptophan: isolation and identification. *Proc. Natl. Acad. Sci. U. S. A.* **44**, 757–765
33. Webster, L. T., Jr., and Davie, E. W. (1960) Purification and properties of a serine-activating enzyme from beef pancreas. *J. Biol. Chem.* **236**, 91–96
34. Roberts, H. R. (2003) Oscar Ratnoff: his contributions to the golden era of coagulation research. *Br. J. Haematol.* **122**, 180–192
35. Ratnoff, O. D., and Colopy, J. E. (1955) A familial hemorrhagic trait associated with a deficiency of a clot promoting fraction of plasma. *J. Clin. Invest.* **34**, 602–613
36. Peterson, E. A., and Sober, H. A. (1956) Chromatography of proteins. I. Cellulose ion-exchange adsorbents. *J. Am. Chem. Soc.* **78**, 751–755
37. Ratnoff, O. D., and Rosenblum, J. M. (1958) Role of Hageman factor in the initiation of clotting by glass: evidence that glass frees Hageman factor from inhibition. *Am. J. Med.* **25**, 160–168
38. Ratnoff, O. D., and Davie, E. W. (1962) The purification of activated Hageman factor (activated Factor XII). *Biochemistry* **1**, 967–974
39. Morawitz, P. (1958) in *The Chemistry of Blood Coagulation* (translated by R. Hartmann and P. Guenther) pp. 1–194, Charles C. Thomas, Springfield, IL
40. Howell, W. H. (1912) The nature and action of the thromboplastic (zymoplastic) substance of the tissues. *Am. J. Physiol.* **31**, 1–21
41. Chargaff, E., Benedich, A., and Cohen, S. S. (1944) The thromboplastic protein: structure properties, disintegration. *J. Biol. Chem.* **156**, 161–178
42. Williams, W. J., and Norris, D. G. (1966) Purification of a bovine plasma protein (factor VII) which is required for the activity of lung microsomes in blood coagulation. *J. Biol. Chem.* **241**, 1847–1856
43. Nemerson, Y., and Pitlick, F. A. (1970) Purification and characterization of the protein component of tissue factor. *Biochemistry* **9**, 5100–5105
44. Bach, R., Nemerson, Y., and Konigsberg, W. (1981) Purification and characterization of bovine tissue factor. *J. Biol. Chem.* **256**, 8324–8331
45. Broze, G. J., Leykam, J. E., Schwartz, B. D., and Miletich, J. P. (1985) Purification of human brain tissue factor. *J. Biol. Chem.* **260**, 10917–10920
46. Patek, A. J., Jr., and Stetson, R. H. (1936) Hemophilia. I. The abnormal coagulation of the blood and its relation to the blood platelets. *J. Clin. Invest.* **15**, 531–542
47. Patek, A. J., and Taylor, F. H. L. (1937) Hemophilia. II. Some properties of a substance obtained from normal plasma effective in acceleration of the clotting of hemophilic blood. *J. Clin. Invest.* **16**, 113–124
48. Massie, R. K. (1967) *Nicholas and Alexandra*, Atheneum, New York
49. Robbins, K. D. (1944) A study on the conversion of fibrinogen to fibrin. *Am. J. Physiol.* **142**, 581–588
50. Laki, K., and Lorand, L. (1948) On the solubility of fibrin clots. *Science* **108**, 280
51. Chen, R., and Doolittle R. F. (1971) Cross-linking sites in human and bovine fibrin. *Biochemistry* **10**, 4487–4491
52. Owren, P. A. (1947) The coagulation of blood. Investigations on a new clotting factor. *Acta Med. Scand.* **194**, 521–549
53. Alexander, B., Goldstein, R., Ladwehr, G., and Cook, C. D. (1951) Coagulation serum prothrombin conversion accelerator (SPCA) deficiency: a hitherto unrecognized coagulation defect with hemorrhage rectified by serum and serum fraction. *J. Clin. Invest.* **30**, 596–608
54. Aggeler, P. M., White, S. G., Glendenning, M. B., Page, E. W., Leake, T. B., and Bates, G. (1952) Plasman thromboplastin compliment (PTC) deficiency: a new disease resembling hemophilia. *Proc. Soc. Exp. Biol. Med.* **79**, 692–694
55. Biggs, R., Douglas, A. S., Macfarlane, R. G., Dacie, J. V., Pitney, W. R., Merskey, C., and O'Brien, J. R. (1952) Christmas disease: a condition previously mistaken for haemophilia. *Br. Med. J.* **2**, 113–129
56. Schulmann, I., and Smith, C. H. (1952) Hemorrhagic disease in an infant due to deficiency of a previously undescribed clotting factor. *Blood* **7**, 794–807
57. Rosenthal, R. L., Dreskin, O. H., and Rosenthal, N. (1953) New hemophilia-like disease caused by deficiency of a third plasma thromboplastin factor. *Proc. Soc. Exp. Biol. Med.* **82**, 171–174
58. Graham, J. B. (2003) Stuart Factor: discovery and designation as factor X. *J. Thromb. Haemostasis* **1**, 871–877
59. Seegers, W. A., Alkjaersig, M. S., and Johnson, S. A. (1955) On the nature of the blood coagulation mechanisms in certain clinical states. *Am. J. Clin. Pathol.* **25**, 983–987
60. Hougie, C., Barrow, E. M., and Graham, J. M. (1957) Segregation of an hereditary hemorrhagic group heretofore called "stable factor" (SPCA), proconvertin, factor VII deficiency. *J. Clin. Invest.* **36**, 485–496
61. Ratnoff, O. D., Davie, E. W., and Mallett, D. L. (1961) Studies on the action of Hageman factor: evidence that activated Hageman factor in turn activates plasma thromboplastin antecedent. *J. Clin. Invest.* **40**, 803–819
62. Hardisty, R. M., and Margolis, J. (1959) The role of Hageman factor in the initiation of blood coagulation. *Br. J. Haematol.* **5**, 203–211
63. Ratnoff, O. D., and Davie, E. W. (1962) The activation of Christmas factor (factor IX) by activated plasma thromboplastin antecedent (activated factor XI). *Biochemistry* **1**, 677–685
64. Soulier, J. P., Wartelle, O., and Menache, D. (1959) Caractères différentiels de facteurs Hageman et P. T. A.: rôle du contact dans la phase initiale de la coagulation. *Rev. Fr. Etudes. Clin. Biol.* **3**, 263–267
65. Kingdon, H. S., Davie, E. W., and Ratnoff, O. D. (1964) The reaction between activated plasma thromboplastin antecedent and diisopropylphosphofluoridate. *Biochemistry* **3**, 166–173
66. Bergsagel, R. M., and Hougie, C. (1956) Intermediate stages in the formation of blood thromboplastin. *Br. J. Haematol.* **2**, 113–129

67. Lundblad, R. L., and Davie, E. W. (1964) The activation of antihemophilic factor (factor VIII) by activated Christmas factor (activated factor IX). *Biochemistry* **3,** 1720–1725
68. Davie, E. W., and Ratnoff, O. D. (1964) Waterfall sequence for intrinsic blood clotting. *Science* **145,** 1310–1312
69. MacFarland, R. G. (1964) An enzyme cascade in the blood clotting mechanism, and its function as a biochemical amplifier. *Nature* **202,** 498–499
70. Osterud, B., Berre, A., Otnass, A. B., Bjorklid, E., and Prydz, H. (1972) Activation of the coagulation factor VII by tissue thromboplastin and calcium. *Biochemistry* **11,** 2853–2857
71. Fujikawa, K., Coan, M. H., Legaz, M. E., and Davie, E. W. (1974) The mechanism of activation of bovine factor X (Stuart factor) by intrinsic and extrinsic pathways. *Biochemistry* **13,** 5290–5299
72. Rapaport, S. I., Schiffman, S., Patch, M. S., and Amos, S. B. (1963) The importance of activation of antihemophilic globulin and proaccelerin by traces of thrombin in the generation of intrinsic prothrombinase activity. *Blood* **21,** 221–236
73. Eaton, D., Rodriguez, H., and Vehar, G. A. (1986) Proteolytic processing of human factor VIII. Correlation of specific cleavages by thrombin, factor Xa, and activated protein C with activation and inactivation of factor VIII activity. *Biochemistry* **25,** 505–512
74. Nesheim, M. E., and Mann, K. G. (1979) Thrombin-catalyzed activation of single chain bovine factor V. *J. Biol. Chem.* **254,** 1326–1334
75. Hougie, C., Denson, K. W., and Biggs, R. (1967) A study of the reaction product of factor VIII and factor IX by gel filtration. *Thromb. Diath. Haemorrh.* **18,** 211–222
76. Østerud, B., and Rapaport, S. I. (1970) Synthesis of intrinsic factor X activator. Inhibition of the function of formed activator by antibodies to factor VIII and to factor XI. *Biochemistry* **9,** 1854–1861
77. Ahmed, S. S., London, F. S., and Walsh, P. N. (2002) The assembly of the factor X-activation complex on activated human platelets. *J. Thromb. Haemostasis* **1,** 48–59
78. Broze, G. J. (1982) Binding of human factor VII and VIIa to monocytes. *J. Clin. Invest.* **70,** 526–535
79. Bach, R., Gentry, R., and Nemerson, Y. (1986) Factor VII binding to tissue factor in reconstituted phospholipid vesicles: induction of cooperativity by phosphatidylserine. *Biochemistry* **25,** 4007–4020
80. Fair, D. S., and MacDonald, M. J. (1987) Cooperative interaction between factor VII and cell surface-expressed tissue factor. *J. Biol. Chem.* **262,** 11692–11698
81. Sakai, T., Lund-Hansen, T., Paborsky, L., Pederson, A. H., and Kisiel, W. (1989) Binding of human factors VII and VIIa to a human bladder carcinoma cell line (J82). Implications for the initiation of the extrinsic pathway of blood coagulation. *J. Biol. Chem.* **264,** 9980–9988
82. Hagen, F. S., Gray, C. L., O'Hara, P., Grant, F. J., Sarri, G. C., Woodbury, R. G., Hart, C. E., Insley, M., Kisiel, W., Kurachi, K., and Davie, E. W. (1986) Characterization of a cDNA coding for human factor VII. *Proc. Natl. Acad. Sci. U. S. A.* **83,** 2412–2416
83. Nemerson, Y. (1988) Tissue factor and hemostasis. *Blood* **71,** 1–8
84. Nemerson, Y. (1995) Tissue factor: then and now. *Thromb. Haemostasis* **74,** 180–184
85. DiScipio, R. G., Hermonson, M. A., and Davie, E. W. (1977) Activation of human factor X (Stuart Factor) by a protease from Russell's viper venom. *Biochemistry* **16,** 4189–4194
86. Østerud, B., and Rapaport, S. (1977) Activation of factor IX by the reaction product of tissue factor and Factor VII. *Proc. Natl. Acad. Sci. U. S. A.* **74,** 5260–5264
87. Marlar, R. A., Kleiss, A. J., and Griffin, J. H. (1982) An alternative extrinsic pathway of human blood coagulation. *Blood* **60,** 1353–1358
88. Roberts, H. R., Monroe, D. M., Oliver, J. A., Chang, J. Y., and Hoffman, M. (1998) Newer concepts of blood coagulation. *Haemophilia* **4,** 331–334
89. Sanders, N. L., Bajaj, S. P., Zivelin, A., and Rapaport, S. I. (1985) Inhibition of tissue factor/factor VIIa activity in plasma requires factor X and an additional plasma component. *Blood* **66,** 204–212
90. Broze, G. J., Jr., Girand, T. J., and Novotny, W. F. (1990) Regulation of coagulation by a multivalent Kunitz-type inhibitor. *Biochemistry* **29,** 7539–7546
91. Baugh, R. J., Broze, G. J., and Krishnaswamy, S. (1998) Regulation of extrinsic pathway factor Xa formation by tissue factor pathway inhibitor. *J. Biol. Chem.* **237,** 4378–4386
92. Naito, K., and Fujikawa, K. (1991) Activation of human blood coagulation factor XI independent of Factor XII. Factor XI is activated by thrombin and factor XIa in the presence of negatively charged surfaces. *J. Biol. Chem.* **266,** 7353–7358
93. Gailani, D., and Broze, G. J., Jr. (1991) Factor XI activation in a revised model of blood coagulation. *Science* **253,** 909–912
94. Hathaway, W. E., Belhasen, L. P., and Hathaway, H. S. (1965) Evidence for a new plasma thromboplastin factor. I. Case report, coagulation studies and physicochemical properties. *Blood* **26,** 521–532
95. Wuepper, K. D. (1973) Prekallikrein deficiency in man. *J. Exp. Med.* **138,** 1345–1355
96. Webster, M. E., Guimaraes, J. A., Kaplan, A. P., Colman, R. W., and Pierce, J. V. (1976) Activation of surface-bound Hageman factor: preeminent role of high-molecular-weight kininogen and evidence for a new factor. In *Kinnins: Pharmacodynamics and Biological Roles,* pp. 285–299, Plenum Press, New York
97. Schiffman, S., Lee, P., Feinstein, D. I., and Pecci, R. (1977) Relationship of contact activation cofactor (CAC) procoagulant activity to kininogen. *Blood* **49,** 935–945
98. Colman, R. W., Bagdasarian, A., Talama, R. C., Scott, C. F., Seavey, M., Guimaraes, J. A., Pierce, J. B., and Kaplan, A. P. (1975) Williams trait: human kininogen deficiency with diminished levels of plasminogen proactivator and prekallikrein associated with abnormalities of the Hageman factor-dependent pathways. *J. Clin. Invest.* **56,** 1650–1662
99. Saito, H., Ratnoff, W., Waldmann, A., and Abraham, J. P. (1975) Fitzgerald trait. Deficiency of a hitherto unrecognized agent, Fitzgerald factor, participating in surface-mediated reactions of clotting, fibrinolysis, generation of kinins, and the property of diluted plasma enhancing vascular permeability (PF/dil). *J. Clin. Invest.* **55,** 1082–1089
100. Rosenberg, R. D. (1979) Mechanism of antithrombin action and the structural basis of heparin's anticoagulant function. In *The Chemistry and Physiology of the Human Plasma Proteins,* p. 353, Pergamon Press, New York
101. Kurachi, K., Fujikawa, K., Shmer, G., and Davie, E. W. (1976) Inhibition of bovine factor IX_a and factor X_a by antithrombin III. *Biochemistry* **15,** 373–377
102. Harpel, P. C., and Rosenberg, R. D. (1976) α_2-Macroglobulin and antithrombin-heparin cofactor: modulators of hemostatic and inflammatory reactions. *Prog. Hemostasis Thromb.* **3,** 145–189
103. Rosenberg, R. D., and Rosenberg, J. S. (1984) Natural anticoagulant mechanisms. *J. Clin. Invest.* **74,** 1–6
104. Kiesel, W., Canfield, W. M., Ericsson, L. H., and Davie, E. W. (1977) Anticoagulant properties of bovine plasma protein C following activation by thrombin. *Biochemistry* **16,** 5824–5831
105. Vehar, G. A., and Davie, E. W. (1980) Preparation and properties of bovine factor VIII (antihemophilic factor). *Biochemistry* **19,** 401–410

106. Esmon, C. T. (2000) Regulation of blood coagulation. *Biochim. Biophys. Acta* **1477,** 349–360
107. Walker, F. J. (1980) Regulation of activated protein C by a new protein: a possible function for bovine protein S. *J. Biol. Chem.* **255,** 5521–5524
108. DiScipio, R. G., and Davie, E. W. (1979) Characterization of protein S, a γ-carboxyglutamic acid containing protein from bovine and human plasma. *Biochemistry* **18,** 899–904
109. Kiesel, W., Hermodson, M. A., and Davie, E. W. (1976) Proteolytic activation of protein C from bovine plasma. *Biochemistry* **15,** 4901–4906
110. Esmon, C. T., and Owen, W. G. (1981) Identification of an endothelial cell cofactor for the thrombin-catalyzed activation of protein C. *Proc. Natl. Acad. Sci. U. S. A.* **78,** 2249–2252
111. Owen, W. G., and Esmon, C. C. (1981) Functional properties of an endothelial cell cofactor for thrombin-catalyzed activation of protein. *J. Biol. Chem.* **256,** 5532–5535
112. Dam, H. (1935) The antihaemorrhagic vitamin of the chick. Occurrence and chemical nature. *Nature* **135,** 652–653
113. Stenflo, J., Fernlund, P., Egan, W., and Roepstorff, P. (1974) Vitamin K dependent modifications of glutamic acid residues in prothrombin. *Proc. Natl. Acad. Sci. U. S. A.* **71,** 2730–2733
114. Nelsestuen, G. L., Zytkovicz, T. H., and Howard, J. B. (1974) The mode of action of vitamin K. Identification of gamma-carboxyglutamic acid as a component of prothrombin. *J. Biol. Chem.* **249,** 6347–6350
115. Magnusson, S., Sottrup-Jensen, L., Petersen, T. E., Morris, H. R., and Dell, A. (1974) Primary structure of the vitamin K-dependent part of prothrombin. *FEBS Lett.* **44,** 189–193
116. Sunnerhagen, M., Drakenberg, T., Forsen, S., and Stenflo, J. (1996) Effect of Ca^{2+} on the structure of vitamin K-dependent coagulation factors. *Haemostasis* **26,** Suppl. 1, 45–53
117. Nelsestuen, G. L., Shah, A. M., and Harvey, S. B. (2000) Vitamin K-dependent proteins. *Vitam. Horm.* **58,** 355–389
118. Stenflo, J. (1974) Vitamin K and the biosynthesis of prothrombin. IV. Isolation of peptides containing prosthetic groups from normal prothrombin and the corresponding peptides from dicoumarol-induced prothrombin. *J. Biol. Chem.* **249,** 5527–5535
119. Link, K. P. (1959) The discovery of dicumarol and its sequels. *Circulation* **19,** 97–107
120. Ichinose, A., and Davie, E. W. (1954) The blood coagulation factors: their cDNAs, genes, and expression. In *Hemostasis and Thrombosis: Basic Principals and Clinical Practice,* 3rd Ed., Lippincott Company, Philadelphia
121. Doolittle, R. F. (2003) X-ray crystallographic studies on fibrinogen and fibrin. *J. Thromb. Haemostasis* **1,** 1559–1565
122. Brown, J. H., Volkmann, N., Jun, G., Henschen-Edman, A. H., and Cohen, C. (2001) Crystal structure of the central region of bovine fibrinogen (E5 fragment) at 1.4-Å resolution. *Proc. Natl. Acad. Sci. U. S. A.* **98,** 11967–11972
123. Bode, W., Brandstetter, H., Mather, T., and Stubbs, M. T. (1997) Comparative analysis of haemostatic proteases: structural aspects of thrombin, factor Xa, factor IXa, and protein C. *Thromb. Haemostasis* **78,** 501–511
124. Banner, D. W., D'Arcy, A., Chene, C., Winkler, F. K., Guha, A., Konigsberg, W. H., Nemerson, Y., and Kirchhofer, D. (1996) The crystal structure of the complex of blood coagulation factor VIIa with soluble tissue factor. *Nature* **380,** 41–46
125. Pike, A. C., Brzozowski, A. M., Roberts, S. M., Olsen, O. H., and Persson, E. (1999) Structure of human factor VIIa and its implications for the triggering of blood coagulation. *Proc. Natl. Acad. Sci. U. S. A.* **96,** 8925–8930
126. Giannelli, F., Green, P. M., Sommer, S. S., Poon, M., Ludwig, M., Schwaab, R., Reitsma, P. H., Goossens, M., Yoshioka, A., Figueiredo, M. S., and Brownlee, G. G. (1998) Haemophilia B: database of point mutations and short additions and deletions–eighth edition. *Nucleic Acids Res.* **26,** 265–268
127. Vehar, G. A. (1987) Production of recombinant coagulation proteins. *Ann. N. Y. Acad. Sci.* **509,** 82–88
128. Harrison, S., Adamson, S., Bonam, D., Brodeur, S., Charlebois, T., Clancy, B., Costigan, R., Drapeau, D., Hamilton, M., Hanley, K., Kelley, B., Knight, A., Leonard, M., McCarthy, M., Oakes, P., Sterl, K., Switzer, M., Walsh, R., and Foster, W. (1998) The manufacturing process for recombinant factor IX. *Semin. Hematol.* **35,** Suppl. 2, 4–10
129. Jurlander, B., Thim, L., Klausen, N. K., Persson, E., Kjalke, M., Rexen, P., Jorgensen, T. B., Ostergaard, P. B., Erhardtsen, E., and Bjorn, S. E. (2001) Recombinant activated factor VII (rFVIIa): characterization, manufacturing, and clinical development. *Semin. Thromb. Hemostasis* **27,** 373–384
130. Hedner, U., and Kisiel, W. (1983) Use of human factor VIIa in the treatment of two hemophilia A patients with high-titer inhibitors. *J. Clin. Invest.* **71,** 1836–1841
131. Lusher, J., Ingerslev, J., Roberts, H., and Hedner, U. (1998) Clinical experience with recombinant factor VIIa. *Blood Coagul. Fibrinolysis* **9,** 119–128
132. Aldouri, M. (2002) The use of recombinant factor VIIa in controlling surgical bleeding in non-haemophiliac patients. *Pathophysiol. Haemostasis Thromb.* **32,** Suppl. 1, 41–46
133. Tobias, J. D., Berkenbosch, J. W., and Russo, P. (2003) Recombinant factor VIIa to treat bleeding after cardiac surgery in an infant. *Pediatr. Crit. Care Med.* **4,** 49–51
134. Danilos, J., Goral, A., Paluszkiewicz, P., Przesmycki, K., and Kotarski, J. (2003) Successful treatment with recombinant factor VIIa for intractable bleeding at pelvic surgery. *Obstet. Gynecol.* **101,** 1172–1173
135. Park, P., Fewel, M. E., Thompson, B. G., and Hoff, J. T. (2003) Recombinant activated factor VII for the rapid correction of coagulopathy in nonhemophilic neurosurgical patients. *Neurosurgery* **53,** 34–39

THE JOURNAL OF BIOLOGICAL CHEMISTRY
© 2003 by The American Society for Biochemistry and Molecular Biology, Inc.

Vol. 278, No. 52, Issue of December 26, pp. 51975–51984, 2003
Printed in U.S.A.

Reflections

A PAPER IN A SERIES COMMISSIONED TO CELEBRATE THE CENTENARY OF THE JBC IN 2005

JBC Centennial
1905–2005
100 Years of Biochemistry and Molecular Biology

The Use of Isotope Effects to Determine Enzyme Mechanisms

Published, JBC Papers in Press, October 28, 2003, DOI 10.1074/jbc.X300005200

W. Wallace Cleland

From the Institute for Enzyme Research, Department of Biochemistry, University of Wisconsin, Madison, Wisconsin 53726

When our laboratory started to carry out kinetic experiments on enzyme-catalyzed reactions we focused originally on initial velocity studies in which the concentrations of substrates, products, and inhibitors were varied. The notation and theory for these types of experiments were published as three papers in *Biochimica et Biophysica Acta* that have received many citations over the years (1–3). We used these methods to study various enzymes over the next decade or so. Although we used isotopes to measure isotopic exchanges in creatine kinase (4), galactokinase (5), shikimate dehydrogenase (6), alcohol dehydrogenase (7), and isocitrate dehydrogenase (8) and to measure rates in NDP kinase (9), we did not determine isotope effects.

However, in 1975 Dexter Northrop discovered how to exploit the Swain-Schaad relationship between deuterium and tritium isotope effects (10) to determine intrinsic isotope effects on the isotope-sensitive bond breaking step of an enzymatic reaction (11). The Swain-Schaad relationship says that the effect of tritium on a rate or equilibrium constant is the 1.442 power of the effect of deuterium substitution (this is derived from the relative masses of deuterium and tritium). Northrop assumed that there was no equilibrium isotope effect and thus that effects on V/K, the apparent first order rate constant at low substrate concentration and one of the independent kinetic constants, could be represented by Equation 1,

$$^{D}(V/K) = (V/K)_{H}/(V/K)_{D} = (^{D}k + c)/(1 + c) \qquad \text{(Eq. 1)}$$

where $^{D}k = k_H/k_D$, the intrinsic isotope effect on the bond breaking step, and c is a commitment to catalysis. If the equilibrium isotope effect is unity and there is only one isotope-sensitive step, Equation 1 is valid regardless of how many steps precede or follow the isotope-sensitive one.

Northrop then subtracted one from each side of Equation 1 to get Equation 2.

$$^{D}(V/K) - 1 = (^{D}k - 1)/(1 + c) \qquad \text{(Eq. 2)}$$

The equation for the tritium isotope effect is the same except that the superscripts are T rather than D. Then if one takes the ratios of Equation 2 for deuterium and tritium, one gets Equation 3.

$$[^{D}(V/K) - 1]/[^{T}(V/K) - 1] = (^{D}k - 1)/(^{T}k - 1) \qquad \text{(Eq. 3)}$$

However, because the Swain-Schaad relationship makes $^{T}k = (^{D}k)^{1.442}$, one can substitute this value into Equation 3 to get an equation involving only experimental parameters and ^{D}k.

$$[^{D}(V/K) - 1]/[^{T}(V/K) - 1] = (^{D}k - 1)/[(^{D}k)^{1.442} - 1] \qquad \text{(Eq. 4)}$$

Because this is a transcendental equation, one has to consult a table of values (12) or use a computer program to obtain a solution.

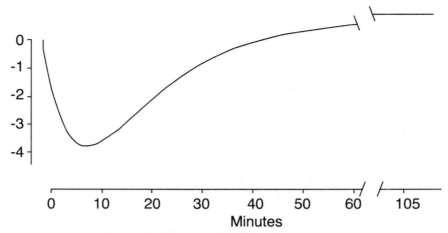

F<small>IG</small>. 1. **Equilibrium perturbation of NADPH level when malate-2-*d* and unlabeled NADPH are used with malic enzyme (13).**

At the time Dexter discovered these relationships, Mike Schimerlik in my laboratory was studying malic enzyme. We wanted to determine whether there was an equilibrium isotope effect on the reaction, so Mike proceeded to determine K_{eq} values with unlabeled and 2-deuterated malate. He used the most accurate way to determine K_{eq}, which is to make up reaction mixtures where the [products]/[reactants] ratio brackets K_{eq} and then add enzyme. The ΔA that results as the reaction reaches equilibrium is plotted *versus* the [products]/[reactants] ratio, and the point where ΔA is zero is K_{eq}. This worked well with unlabeled malate, but when Mike used deuterated malate, the A decreased greatly and then began to increase and returned to the starting point (Fig. 1). What he had forgotten was that he used unlabeled NADPH rather than deuterated nucleotide, which he didn't have. He thus discovered the equilibrium perturbation method for determining isotope effects on reversible reactions (13). The size of the perturbation is a function of the isotope effect although the relationship is only linear for small isotope effects.

$$\text{fractional perturbation} = [\text{isotope effect} - 1]/2.72 \qquad \text{(Eq. 5)}$$

For isotope effects above 1.2, the complete equation must be used (14). The fractional perturbation is the ratio of the perturbation size to the reciprocal of the sum of the concentrations of the perturbants (the molecules between which the label is exchanged). For malic enzyme, Mike was able to determine a deuterium isotope effect of 1.45 by equilibrium perturbation (1.47 on V/K by direct comparison) and also a ^{13}C isotope effect of 1.031, later confirmed by isotope ratio mass spectrometry (15).

Mike determined that there was a sizable equilibrium isotope effect on the malic enzyme reaction (later refined to be 1.18 (16)) and thus that the equation for the isotope effect had to be expanded to allow for this.

$$^D(V/K) = (^Dk + c_f + c_r\,^DK_{eq})/(1 + c_f + c_r) \qquad \text{(Eq. 6)}$$

The constants c_f and c_r are now commitments in forward and reverse directions. Each is the ratio of the rate constant for the bond breaking step to the net rate constant for release from the enzyme of the substrate whose V/K is involved or the first product released. In an equilibrium perturbation experiment, the commitments are for the release of the perturbants.

The equation for the tritium isotope effect is the same except the leading superscripts are T rather than D. When one applies Northrop's method to these equations, the third term in the numerator does not cancel out, and thus one gets only an approximate answer. However, if one divides the experimental $^D(V/K)$ and $^T(V/K)$ isotope effects by the respective equilibrium isotope effects (which gives the values for the reverse reaction) and carries out the Northrop analysis one obtains an approximate value for ^Dk in the back reaction. Then the true ^Dk in the forward direction lies between the value determined in that direction and the one determined in the back reaction multiplied by the equilibrium isotope effect. This approach for malic enzyme gave limits of 5–8 for ^Dk in the forward reaction and 4–6.5 in the reverse direction (17). The true value determined in 1985 by Chuck Grissom is 5.7 in the forward direction (18).

When we first started to work on isotope effects none of us knew very much about them, but Jack Shiner at Indiana University steered us in the right direction, and we discovered that the physical organic chemists knew quite a bit about isotope effects. By attending the Gordon Conferences on isotopes (I have attended every one since 1981) we got to know all of the major players in the field and learned what they knew as well as returning the favor by giving them information about isotope effects on enzymes. This Gordon Conference meets every 2 years in California in the winter (alternating with the ad hoc Enzyme Mechanism Conference, which is convenient) and will meet next in Ventura on February 15–20, 2004. Anyone interested in isotope effects on enzymatic reactions should attend; students and postdoctoral fellows are welcome.

As a result of our increasing interest in isotope effects, Marion O'Leary, Dexter Northrop, and I organized a Steenbock Symposium titled "Isotope Effects on Enzyme-catalyzed Reactions" here in Madison in 1976. This was very successful and the proceedings were published by University Park Press (19). This book includes computer programs for fitting isotope effect data and tables for use of Northrop's method and for equilibrium perturbation analysis.

The year 1980 saw us publishing a number of measured equilibrium deuterium isotope effects (16) as well as kinetic isotope effects by John Blanchard on several enzymes (20, 21). The following year saw the development by Paul Cook in this laboratory of the theory for the variation of observed isotope effects with pH or the concentrations of other substrates (22–24). The forward commitment in Equation 6 represents the ratio of the rate constant for the isotope-sensitive step to the net rate constant for release from the enzyme of the varied substrate in a direct comparison experiment, the labeled substrate in an internal competition experiment, or the perturbant in an equilibrium perturbation one. In an ordered mechanism where the forward commitment is for the first substrate, the observed isotope effect on V/K_a will be unity at infinite concentration of the second substrate, increasing to $^D(V/K_b)$ at very low levels of B. The value of $^D(V/K_b)$ on the other hand is independent of the level of A. In a random mechanism, saturation with one substrate does not eliminate the V/K isotope effect for the other one, although the value may change. This sort of experiment is very useful for determining the kinetic mechanism. Cook used these methods to show that NAD and cyclohexanol added in that order with liver alcohol dehydrogenase, whereas NAD and 2-propanol added randomly to the yeast enzyme (22).

The effect of pH on observed isotope effects depends on whether the isotope-dependent and pH-dependent steps are the same. With a sticky substrate (one that reacts to give products faster than it dissociates), the isotope effect on V/K is reduced by an external forward commitment, but when one goes to a pH where the chemistry becomes rate-limiting, this external part of the forward commitment is eliminated (although any internal commitment remains), and so the V/K isotope effect increases (23). With liver alcohol dehydrogenase, however, the V/K isotope effect for cyclohexanol was 2.5 at low and neutral pH but decreased above a pK of 9.4 to unity. In the reverse direction, the value for cyclohexanone was 2.1 at lower pH values and decreased above the same pK to 0.85 (24). In this mechanism, proton removal from the alcohol to give a zinc-bound alkoxide precedes hydride transfer, and above the pK this proton is lost to the medium, thus committing the reaction to continue. In the reverse direction at high pH hydride transfer comes to equilibrium waiting for a proton to be added from the solvent.

In 1982 I was asked to write a review for *Annual Reviews of Biochemistry* on the use of isotope effects to elucidate enzyme mechanisms. I submitted the review, but it came back all marked up with many changes in wording and meaning, and after an unsatisfactory conversation with the redactor, I withdrew the paper. I then sent it to *Critical Reviews in Biochemistry*, where it was promptly accepted (25).

The next major advance in isotope effect theory was the use of multiple isotope effects by Jeff Hermes (15). When both isotope effects are on the same step, the effect of deuteration on ^{13}C isotope effects allows one to determine intrinsic isotope effects or narrow limits on them. Thus, in Equation 6 where the superscripts are 13, deuteration decreases the rate of the isotope-sensitive step and thus decreases the commitments by the size of the intrinsic deuterium isotope effect in the forward or reverse direction. If one uses both primary and secondary deuterium substitution, one has five equations (^{13}C isotope effect with unlabeled, primary, and secondary deuterated substrates plus primary and secondary deuterium isotope effects) in five unknowns (three intrinsic isotope effects and the two commitments). Jeff applied this tech-

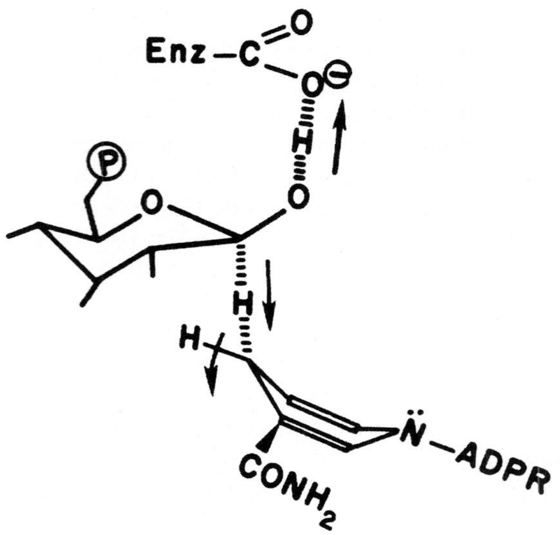

FIG. 2. **Transition state for the glucose-6-P dehydrogenase reaction with *arrows* showing coupled hydrogen motions (26).**

nique to glucose-6-P dehydrogenase both in water and in D_2O (26). The intrinsic ^{13}C isotope effect was 4% in both solvents, but the intrinsic primary deuterium isotope effect was 5.3 in water and 3.7 in D_2O. The α-secondary deuterium isotope effect also decreased in D_2O. However, the surprise was that the sum of forward and reverse commitments increased from 1.24 in water to 2.5 in D_2O with most of the change being in the forward commitment. Thus the major effect of D_2O was on the conformation changes that precede the chemical step rather than on the chemistry itself. However, the decreased intrinsic deuterium isotope effects in D_2O reflect the coupled hydrogen motions in the transition state (proton from the 1-hydroxyl going to aspartate on the enzyme, hydride going from C-1 of glucose-6-P to C-4 of NADP, hydrogen at C-4 of NADP going from trigonal to tetrahedral; Fig. 2). This coupled motion effect, where the first deuterium substitution decreases the effect of further deuteration, shows that tunneling is involved in the hydrogen motions.

This coupled motion effect is very prominent in the formate dehydrogenase reaction (27). The deuterium isotope effect at C-4 of the ring of NAD was 1.23 despite the fact that the equilibrium isotope effect is 0.89. This shows that the motion of this hydrogen from trigonal to tetrahedral is coupled into the reaction coordinate so that there is little or no restoring force at the transition state. However, if deuterated formate is used, this secondary isotope effect decreases to 1.07, showing that the first deuterium substitution decreases the effect of the second deuteration. This is a nice system to study because there are no commitments (the ^{13}C isotope effect in formate is independent of deuteration). When the nucleotide substrate was changed from NAD to thio-NAD and then to acetylpyridine-NAD, the transition state became earlier as the redox potential of the nucleotide became more positive. This led to larger primary deuterium isotope effects (2.17 to 2.60 to 3.32), smaller secondary deuterium isotope effects (1.23 to 1.18 to 1.06) as the coupling of the secondary motion into the reaction coordinate decreased, and smaller ^{13}C isotope effects (4.2 to 3.8 to 3.6%) as the degree of C–C cleavage decreased. The secondary isotope effects decreased halfway to the equilibrium isotope effect with deuterated formate (1.07 to 1.03 to 0.95). Thus with multiple isotope effects one can really determine transition state structure.

When a deuterium and the ^{13}C isotope effect are on different steps, deuteration makes the deuterium-sensitive step more rate-limiting and thus increases one of the commitments for the ^{13}C-sensitive step so that the observed ^{13}C isotope effect decreases. Further, the three measured isotope effects are not independent. In the direction where the deuterium-sensitive step comes first, the equation is,

$$[^{13}(V/K)_H - 1]/[^{13}(V/K)_D - 1] = {}^D(V/K)/{}^D K_{eq} \qquad \text{(Eq. 7)}$$

although in the reverse direction where the ^{13}C-sensitive step comes first,

$$[^{13}(V/K)_H - {}^{13}K_{eq}]/[^{13}(V/K)_D - {}^{13}K_{eq}] = {}^D(V/K) \qquad \text{(Eq. 8)}$$

These equations are really the same except that the first is expressed in terms of the parameters for the forward reaction, and the second one includes the parameters for the reverse reaction. When these equations were applied to data for malic enzyme, the data fitted Equation 7, but not Equation 8, showing that dehydrogenation precedes decarboxylation (15).

6-Phosphogluconate dehydrogenase was also shown to catalyze a stepwise reaction (28), but prephenate dehydrogenase provided some surprises (29). The isotope effects were measured with a substrate lacking the keto group in the side chain but having a V_{max} of 78% and V/K of 18% that of prephenate. The ^{13}C isotope effect in the CO_2 product was 1.03% with deuterated substrate but only 0.33% with unlabeled substrate, whereas the deuterium isotope effect on hydride transfer was 2.34. Thus the reaction is concerted with intrinsic ^{13}C and deuterium isotope effects of 1.0155 and 7.3 and a forward commitment of 3.7, assuming no reverse commitment for the irreversible reaction. The deuterium isotope effect is large, showing considerable C–H cleavage in the transition state, but the 1.55% ^{13}C isotope effect shows that the reaction is asynchronous with little C–C cleavage in the transition state. The reason the reaction is concerted is presumably that the energy of aromatization is so great that the putative keto intermediate has no stability. In fact, if one removes one double bond from the ring of the prephenate analog with no ketone in the side chain the product of the reaction is a ketone and no decarboxylation takes place. The enzyme is thus a secondary alcohol dehydrogenase, and the decarboxylation takes place because of the instability of the keto product.

The multiple isotope method was also applied to ^{15}N and deuterium isotope effects in studies on phenylalanine ammonia lyase (30), adenosine deaminase (31), and aspartate aminotransferase (32) to provide details of the mechanisms of these enzymes. The next development of the theory came with the discovery of intermediate partitioning by Chuck Grissom (18). With malic enzyme one can add oxaloacetate and NADPH and regenerate the putative intermediate on the enzyme. This will then partition both back to malate and NADP and forward to CO_2 and pyruvate. The partitioning ratio (pyruvate/malate = 0.47) is the forward commitment for the decarboxylation step and allowed determination of the intrinsic ^{13}C isotope effect as 1.044. With the deuterium and tritium V/K isotope effects, the equations allow one to determine the intrinsic deuterium isotope effect as 5.7, the forward commitment to hydride transfer as 3.3, and the ratio of reverse hydride transfer to decarboxylation as 10 (18). Thus the tools are available to dissect the entire mechanism.

As the decade of the 90s dawned, we began to determine ^{18}O and other isotope effects to study phosphoryl and acyl transfer. It is very difficult to extract the oxygen out of phosphate quantitatively and insert it into CO_2, so we adopted the use of the remote label method, which had been pioneered by Marion O'Leary (33). For example, to measure the secondary ^{18}O isotope effect on the hydrolysis of glucose-6-P, one prepares two versions of this molecule. One has ^{13}C at C-1 and three ^{18}O's in the phosphate group. The second has ^{12}C at C-1 and no other labels. By ^{12}C we mean carbon that has the 1% natural abundance of ^{13}C removed (it is the by-product of making ^{13}C). One then mixes 1% of the former with 99% of the latter to get a solution of glucose-6-P with the natural abundance of ^{13}C at C-1 but with every ^{13}C accompanied by three ^{18}O's. This remote labeled material is then used in a reaction, and the residual glucose-6-P and the glucose product (phosphorylated back to glucose-6-P by hexokinase) are then degraded by glucose-6-P and 6-P-gluconate dehydrogenases to CO_2 and ribulose-5-P. Analysis of the CO_2 reveals the isotopic discrimination between the two species in the substrate mixture. One then uses glucose-6-P with no special labels in the same experiment, and this determines any ^{13}C isotope effect at C-1. Division of the apparent isotope effect for the remote labeled substrate by the value from natural abundance substrate gives the desired ^{18}O isotope effect.

The remote label method is very powerful and allows one to determine almost any isotope effect in any position of a molecule as long as there is a carbon that can be isolated as CO_2 or a nitrogen that can be isolated and converted to N_2. If there is only one nitrogen in a molecule this is simple as samples can be sealed in quartz tubes with CuO and heated to convert all organic matter to CO_2, H_2O, and N_2, which are readily separated for analysis of N_2 by the isotope ratio mass spectrometer. Convenient remote labels are nitro groups of *p*-nitrophenol or *m*-nitrobenzyl alcohol (inserted by nitration of triphenyl phosphate followed by hydrolysis or benzaldehyde followed by reduction, using either ^{15}N- or ^{14}N-labeled nitrate). Another useful remote label is the exocyclic amino group of adenine, which is readily inserted by the reaction

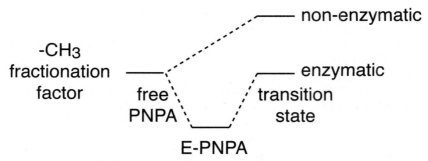

F𝑖𝑔. 3. **Fractionation factors for the methyl protons of *p*-nitrophenyl acetate during non-enzymatic and enzymatic hydrolysis.** The value is lower in free *p*NPA because of hyperconjugation, which is increased upon binding to an enzyme but decreased in the tetrahedral transition states of the reactions (36).

of ammonia with chloropurine riboside and removed later for analysis by adenosine deaminase. This allows ATP, NAD, or other adenine-containing molecules to be remote-labeled.

Al Hengge and others in the laboratory carried out extensive measurements of ^{18}O isotope effects on phosphoryl transfer using the remote label method for analysis. This showed that phosphate monoesters have dissociative transition states for their reactions, diesters have S_n2 reactions, and triesters have associative transition states although they do not form phosphorane intermediates unless geometry requires this (34).

Al Hengge and Rob Hess carried out a thorough study of the reactions of *p*-nitrophenyl acetate with various nucleophiles (35) and with several enzymes (36). In opposition to what most textbooks say, these reactions do not have a tetrahedral intermediate but are concerted. Only when the leaving group has a pK of 16 or higher does a tetrahedral intermediate form and ^{18}O exchange take place during hydrolysis. Al and Rob used five isotope effects to study these reactions. The nitro group was the remote label for measurement of the other isotope effects, and the ^{15}N isotope effect itself told the degree of electron delocalization into the nitro group in the transition state. The other isotope effects were the primary ^{18}O one in the phenolic oxygen, the secondary ^{18}O in the carbonyl oxygen, the primary ^{13}C in the carbonyl carbon, and the deuterium isotope effect from full deuteration of the methyl group. With all five isotope effects, one can really pin down transition state structures!

The major difference between the enzymatic and non-enzymatic cleavages of *p*-nitrophenyl acetate was in the β-deuterium isotope effect in the methyl group. This isotope effect results from decreased hyperconjugation in the tetrahedral transition state and was 4–5% inverse for attack by oxygen nucleophiles (35). However, in the enzymatic reactions this value was 0–2% inverse (36). These data show that in the enzymatic reactions the enzymes polarize the carbonyl group and increase hyperconjugation when the substrate binds (Fig. 3). The fractionation factor then increases as the transition state is approached but not to the degree reached in the non-enzymatic reaction. Thus the isotope effect directly demonstrates the way the enzyme activates the carbonyl group for attack.

In 1992 we published a major study of aspartate transcarbamoylase. This was a collaborative effort by Marion O'Leary, Howie Schachman, and Laura Parmentier, who had been Marion's graduate student before he left for Nebraska and was inherited by me. Laura developed what we called the "dribble-drip" method of measuring an isotope effect. To determine the ^{13}C isotope effect in carbamoyl-P, she needed to start with 12 m𝑀 carbamoyl-P and convert half of it to product. The residual carbamoyl-P was then degraded with acid to liberate CO_2 for analysis. This was no problem when she used high levels of aspartate, but because the isotope effect got larger at lower aspartate, she needed a way to determine the isotope effect at an aspartate level lower than that of carbamoyl-P. The answer was to add the aspartate at the same rate as it was consumed. In practice one adds the aspartate with a pump at a constant rate and uses the calculated level of enzyme. After half of the carbamoyl-P is consumed, the aspartate level is determined. If it has increased, the experiment is repeated with a higher enzyme level, but if it has decreased, the lower enzyme is used. The first reaction mixture is then discarded and the second one analyzed. This procedure allowed determination of the ^{13}C isotope effect at aspartate levels from very low to over 100 m𝑀.

Laura found that the ^{13}C isotope effect with the holoenzyme varied from 1.022 at low aspartate to unity at infinite aspartate with the half-conversion point at 4.8 m𝑀 (37). Thus the kinetic mechanism is ordered with aspartate as the second substrate. With isolated catalytic

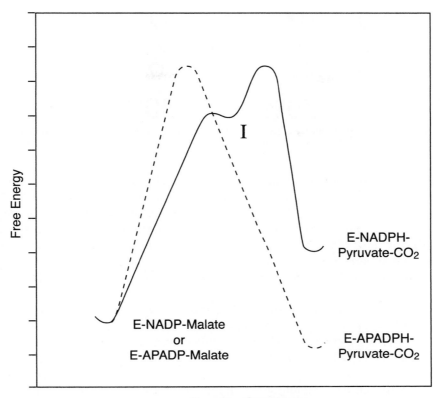

FIG. 4. **Free energy profiles for the malic enzyme-catalyzed conversion of malate to pyruvate, CO_2, and reduced nucleotide.** APADP is the acetylpyridine analog of NADP. I is an E-NADPH-oxaloacetate intermediate. The reaction becomes concerted with acetylpyridine-NADP because the equilibrium constant is more favorable by 2 orders of magnitude (40).

trimeric subunits, which no longer show allosteric kinetics, the ^{13}C isotope effect varied from 1.024 at low aspartate to 1.004 at infinite aspartate (37). The reaction has thus become partly random. With the slow aspartate analog, cysteine sulfinate, the ^{13}C isotope effect was 1.039 at any level of cysteine sulfinate and with both holoenzyme and catalytic subunits. The mechanism has now become completely random, and it appears that the chemistry is fully rate-limiting. The catalytic trimers of the H134A mutant also gave a ^{13}C isotope effect of 1.04 that did not vary with aspartate level, showing a fully random mechanism with rate-limiting chemistry (38). These studies clearly show the power of isotope effects to determine the kinetic mechanism. Presumably the mechanism is ordered only when the complex of enzyme and substrates reacts to give products much faster than carbamoyl-P dissociates. The rate of dissociation of carbamoyl-P relative to forward reaction increases somewhat in the isolated catalytic trimers and much more with the slow alternate substrate or in the slow H134A mutant.

These experiments also gave information about the allosteric behavior of the enzyme. The holoenzyme of aspartate transcarbamoylase shows a highly sigmoid curve of rate *versus* aspartate concentration, which is made more so by the allosteric inhibitor CTP. ATP, on the other hand, activates by restoring Michaelis kinetics. Laura found that the curve of ^{13}C isotope effect *versus* aspartate was identical when high levels of ATP or CTP sufficient to alter the initial velocity curve were present (37). Thus the Monod model of allosteric behavior is valid and there is only one active R form with the same properties regardless of the presence of ATP or CTP. The allosteric control is mediated by the ratio of R to inactive T forms with ATP binding selectively to R and CTP to T.

Our multiple isotope effect studies on malic enzyme with NADP and malate had indicated a stepwise mechanism, but with acetylpyridine-NADP, deuteration increased rather than decreased the ^{13}C isotope effect (39). This suggested that the mechanism may have changed to a concerted one, or there was a large equilibrium isotope effect at C-4 on hydride transfer caused by hyperconjugation with the newly formed keto group. Bill Edens solved this puzzle by showing that the ^{13}C isotope effect at C-3 (which would not be affected by hyperconjugation)

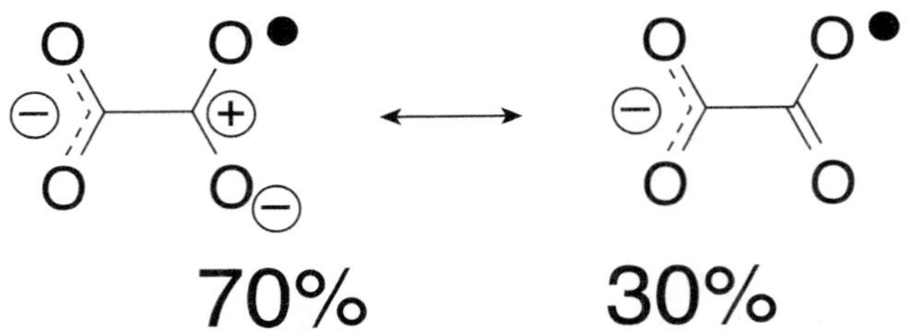

FIG. 5. **Structure of the putative radical intermediate in the oxalate decarboxylase reaction (43).** The radical decarboxylates to give CO_2 from the left carbon and a radical anion of formate from the right carbon.

was also increased by deuteration of malate when acetylpyridine-NADP was the substrate (40). Thus the mechanism truly became concerted. We believe this results from the 2 orders of magnitude more favorable equilibrium constant for the oxidative decarboxylation to pyruvate. The shape of the free energy profile then changes to eliminate the small dip at the top for the oxaloacetate intermediate (Fig. 4). Interestingly, Jeff Urbauer showed that with *erythro*-fluoromalate and acetylpyridine-NADP the mechanism remained stepwise, because the fluorine substitution decreases the equilibrium constant for the reaction by an order of magnitude (41).

Lac Lee showed the power of isotope effects to deduce mechanism in his studies of L-ribulose-5-P 4-epimerase (42). He devised a way to degrade the xylulose-5-P product carbon by carbon and showed that there were over 2% ^{13}C isotope effects at C-3 and C-4. The deuterium isotope effects at these carbons were 4 and 19% for a slow mutant, showing that C–H cleavage was not involved. The mechanism involves an aldol cleavage to the enediolate of dihydroxyacetone and glycolaldehyde-P, followed by rotation of the aldehyde group and condensation.

Our most recent work, a collaborative effort with Nigel Richards in Florida, is a study of the mechanism of oxalate decarboxylase using ^{13}C and ^{18}O isotope effects (43). This enzyme converts one end of oxalate to CO_2 and the other end to formate. The enzyme contains Mn^{2+} and requires catalytic oxygen, which is not consumed during the reaction. Because both oxalate and formate as anhydrous salts are converted to CO_2 by I_2 in dimethyl sulfoxide without exchange of the oxygens, it is possible to determine both the ^{13}C and ^{18}O isotope effects going to each product. At pH 5.7 where the chemistry is rate-limiting, the ^{13}C isotope effects were 1.9% going to formate and 0.8% going to CO_2. The ^{18}O isotope effects were 1.0% going to formate but 0.7% inverse going to CO_2. The large isotope effects during formation of formate and the small ^{13}C one for forming CO_2 suggest that decarboxylation is not rate-limiting, and that in a prior step the C–O bond order is reduced in the end for oxalate going to formate. Application of the appropriate equations for such a model allowed calculation of the C–O bond order in the putative intermediate. This came out 1.16 from the ^{13}C isotope effects and 1.14 from the ^{18}O ones. We suspect that O_2 and Mn^{2+} interact to give a Mn^{3+} species that coordinates the oxalate monoanion, which is the active form of the substrate. In the first step an electron is removed from the coordinated end of oxalate and a proton from the other end. The radical intermediate has ∼70% positive charge in the coordinated end of oxalate (based on a C–O bond order of 1.15; Fig. 5), and this leads to decarboxylation that is four times faster than reversal of the first step. The remaining radical anion picks up an electron from Mn^{2+} and a proton to become formate. The observed isotope effects fit the equations for this mechanism very well.

At this point in time it is obvious that isotope effects are a very powerful tool for determining all aspects of enzyme mechanisms, starting with the kinetic mechanism and ending up with the chemical mechanism and the structure of the transition state. It has been fun seeing the theory and experiment develop together and to have been a part of the process. We are still determining isotope effects on enzymatic reactions and hope to continue doing so for some time in the future. I would like to thank all of the students, postdoctoral fellows, and other visitors who have actually done the work described above and other studies that I have not had space to discuss. They are the real heroes of the tale. Of course I thank the NIH, which has supported all of the work described here (Grant GM 18938).

Address correspondence to: Cleland@enzyme.wisc.edu.

REFERENCES

1. Cleland, W. W. (1963) The kinetics of enzyme-catalyzed reactions with two or more substrates or products. I. Nomenclature and rate equations. *Biochim. Biophys. Acta* **67**, 104–137
2. Cleland, W. W. (1963) The kinetics of enzyme-catalyzed reactions with two or more substrates or products. II. Inhibition: nomenclature and theory. *Biochim. Biophys. Acta* **67**, 173–187
3. Cleland, W. W. (1963) The kinetics of enzyme-catalyzed reactions with two or more substrates or products. III. Prediction of initial velocity and inhibition patterns by inspection. *Biochim. Biophys. Acta* **67**, 188–196
4. Morrison, J. F., and Cleland, W. W. (1966) Isotope exchange studies of the mechanism of the reaction catalyzed by adenosine triphosphate: creatine phosphotransferase. *J. Biol. Chem.* **241**, 673–683
5. Gulbinsky, J. S., and Cleland, W. W. (1968) Kinetic studies of *Escherichia coli* galactokinase. *Biochemistry* **7**, 566–575
6. Balinsky, D., Dennis, A. W., and Cleland, W. W. (1971) Kinetic and isotope-exchange studies on shikimate dehydrogenase from *Pisum sativum*. *Biochemistry* **10**, 1947–1952
7. Ainslie, G. R., Jr., and Cleland, W. W. (1972) Isotope exchange studies on liver alcohol dehydrogenase with cyclohexanol and cyclohexanone as reactants. *J. Biol. Chem.* **247**, 946–951
8. Uhr, M. L., Thompson, V. W., and Cleland, W. W. (1974) The kinetics of pig heart triphosphopyridine nucleotide-isocitrate dehydrogenase. I. Initial velocity, substrate and product inhibition, and isotope exchange. *J. Biol. Chem.* **249**, 2920–2927
9. Garces, E., and Cleland, W. W. (1969) Kinetic studies of yeast nucleoside diphosphate kinase. *Biochemistry* **8**, 633–640
10. Swain, C. G., Stivers, E. C., Reuwer, J. F., Jr., and Schaad, L. J. (1958) Use of hydrogen isotope effects to identify the attacking nucleophile in the enolization of ketones catalyzed by acetic acid. *J. Am. Chem. Soc.* **80**, 5885–5893
11. Northrop, D. B. (1975) Steady-state analysis of kinetic isotope effects in enzymic reactions. *Biochemistry* **14**, 2644–2651
12. Cleland, W. W., O'Leary, M. H., and Northrop, D. B. (eds) (1977) *Isotope Effects on Enzyme-catalyzed Reactions*, pp. 280–283, University Park Press, Baltimore, MD
13. Schimerlik, M. I., Rife, J. E., and Cleland, W. W. (1975) Equilibrium perturbation by isotope substitution. *Biochemistry* **4**, 5347–5354
14. Cleland, W. W. (1980) Measurement of isotope effects by the equilibrium perturbation technique. *Methods Enzymol.* **64**, 104–125
15. Hermes, J. D., Roeske, C. A., O'Leary, M. H., and Cleland, W. W. (1982) Use of multiple isotope effects to determine enzyme mechanisms and intrinsic isotope effects. Malic enzyme and glucose-6-phosphate dehydrogenase. *Biochemistry* **21**, 5106–5114
16. Cook, P. F., Blanchard, J. S., and Cleland, W. W. (1980) Primary and secondary deuterium isotope effects on equilibrium constants for enzyme-catalyzed reactions. *Biochemistry* **21**, 4853–4858
17. Schimerlik, M. I., Grimshaw, C. E., and Cleland, W. W. (1977) Determination of the rate-limiting steps for malic enzyme by the use of isotope effects and other kinetic studies. *Biochemistry* **16**, 571–576
18. Grissom, C. B., and Cleland, W. W. (1985) Use of intermediate partitioning to calculate intrinsic isotope effects for the reaction catalyzed by malic enzyme. *Biochemistry* **24**, 944–948
19. Cleland, W. W., O'Leary, M. H., and Northrop, D. B. (eds) (1977) *Isotope Effects on Enzyme-catalyzed Reactions*, pp. 280–283, University Park Press, Baltimore, MD
20. Blanchard, J. S., and Cleland, W. W. (1980) Use of isotope effects to deduce the chemical mechanism of fumarase. *Biochemistry* **19**, 4506–4513
21. Blanchard, J. S., and Cleland, W. W. (1980) Kinetic and chemical mechanisms of yeast formate dehydrogenase. *Biochemistry* **19**, 3543–3550
22. Cook, P. F., and Cleland, W. W. (1981) Mechanistic deductions from isotope effects in multireactant enzyme mechanisms. *Biochemistry* **20**, 1790–1796
23. Cook, P. F., and Cleland, W. W. (1981) pH variation of isotope effects in enzyme-catalyzed reactions. 1. Isotope- and pH-dependent steps the same. *Biochemistry* **20**, 1797–1805
24. Cook, P. F., and Cleland, W. W. (1981) pH variation of isotope effects in enzyme-catalyzed reactions. 2. Isotope-dependent step not pH dependent. Kinetic mechanism of alcohol dehydrogenase. *Biochemistry* **20**, 1805–1816
25. Cleland, W. W. (1982) Use of isotope effects to elucidate enzyme mechanisms. *CRC Crit. Rev. Biochem.* **13**, 385–428
26. Hermes, J. D., and Cleland, W. W. (1984) Evidence from multiple isotope effect determinations for coupled hydrogen motion and tunneling in the reaction catalyzed by glucose-6-phosphate dehydrogenase. *J. Am. Chem. Soc.* **106**, 7263–7264
27. Hermes, J. D., Morrical, S. W., O'Leary, M. H., and Cleland, W. W. (1984) Variation of transition-state structure as a function of the nucleotide in reactions catalyzed by dehydrogenases. 2. Formate dehydrogenase. *Biochemistry* **23**, 5479–5488
28. Rendina, A. R., Hermes, J. D., and Cleland, W. W. (1984) Use of multiple isotope effects to study the mechanism of 6-phosphogluconate dehydrogenase. *Biochemistry* **23**, 6257–6262
29. Hermes, J. D., Tipton, P. A., Fisher, M. A., O'Leary, M. H., Morrison, J. F., and Cleland, W. W. (1984) Mechanisms of enzymatic and acid-catalyzed decarboxylations of prephenate. *Biochemistry* **23**, 6263–6275
30. Hermes, J. D., Weiss, P. M., and Cleland, W. W. (1985) Use of nitrogen-15 and deuterium isotope effects to determine the chemical mechanism of phenylalanine ammonia-lyase. *Biochemistry* **24**, 2959–2967
31. Weiss, P. M., Cook, P. F., Hermes, J. D., and Cleland, W. W. (1987) Evidence from nitrogen-15 and solvent deuterium isotope effects on the chemical mechanism of adenosine deaminase. *Biochemistry* **26**, 7378–7384
32. Rishavy, M. A., and Cleland, W. W. (2000) ^{13}C and ^{15}N kinetic isotope effects on the reaction of aspartate aminotransferase and the tyrosine-225 to phenylalanine mutant. *Biochemistry* **39**, 7546–7551
33. O'Leary, M. H., and Marlier, J. F. (1979) Heavy-atom isotope effects on the alkaline hydrolysis and hydrazinolysis of methyl benzoate. *J. Am. Chem. Soc.* **101**, 3300–3306
34. Cleland, W. W., and Hengge, A. C. (1995) Mechanisms of phosphoryl and acyl transfer. *FASEB J.* **9**, 1585–1594
35. Hengge, A. C., and Hess, R. A. (1994) Concerted or stepwise mechanisms for acyl transfer reactions of *p*-nitrophenyl acetate? Transition state structures from isotope effects. *J. Am. Chem. Soc.* **116**, 11256–11263
36. Hess, R. A., Hengge, A. C., and Cleland, W. W. (1998) Isotope effects on enzyme-catalyzed acyl transfer from *p*-nitrophenyl acetate: concerted mechanisms and increased hyperconjugation in the transition state. *J. Am. Chem. Soc.* **120**, 2703–2709
37. Parmentier, L. E., O'Leary, M. H., Schachman, H. K., and Cleland, W. W. (1992) ^{13}C isotope effects as a probe of the kinetic mechanism and allosteric properties of *Escherichia coli* aspartate transcarbamylase. *Biochemistry* **31**, 6570–6576
38. Waldrop, G. L., Turnbull, J. L., Parmentier, L. E., O'Leary, M. H., Cleland, W. W., and Schachman, H. K. (1992)

Steady-state kinetics and isotope effects on the mutant catalytic trimer of aspartate transcarbamoylase containing the replacement of histidine 134 by alanine. *Biochemistry* **31,** 6585–6591

39. Weiss, P. M., Gavva, S. R., Harris, B. G., Urbauer, J. L., Cleland, W. W., and Cook, P. F. (1991) Multiple isotope effects with alternative dinucleotide substrates as a probe of the malic enzyme reaction. *Biochemistry* **30,** 5755–5763

40. Edens, W. A., Urbauer, J. L., and Cleland, W. W. (1997) Determination of the chemical mechanism of malic enzyme by isotope effects. *Biochemistry* **36,** 1141–1147

41. Urbauer, J. L., Bradshaw, D. E., and Cleland, W. W. (1998) Determination of the kinetic and chemical mechanism of malic enzyme using (2*R*,3*R*)-*erythro*-fluoromalate as a slow alternate substrate. *Biochemistry* **37,** 18026–18031

42. Lee, L. V., Vu, M. V., and Cleland, W. W. (2000) ^{13}C and deuterium isotope effects suggest an aldol cleavage mechanism for L-ribulose-5-phosphate 4-epimerase. *Biochemistry* **39,** 4808–4820

43. Reinhardt, L. A., Svedruzic, D., Chang, C. H., Cleland, W. W., and Richards, N. G. J. (2003) Heavy atom isotope effects on the reaction catalyzed by the oxalate decarboxylase from *Bacillus subtilis*. *J. Am. Chem. Soc.* **125,** 1244–1252

THE JOURNAL OF BIOLOGICAL CHEMISTRY
Vol. 279, No. 1, Issue of January 2, pp. 1–12, 2004
© 2004 by The American Society for Biochemistry and Molecular Biology, Inc.
Printed in U.S.A.

Reflections

A PAPER IN A SERIES COMMISSIONED TO CELEBRATE THE CENTENARY OF THE JBC IN 2005

JBC Centennial
1905–2005
100 Years of Biochemistry and Molecular Biology

Ligand-Receptor Complexes: Origin and Development of the Concept

Published, JBC Papers in Press, November 6, 2003, DOI 10.1074/jbc.X300006200

Irving M. Klotz

From the Department of Chemistry and Department of Biochemistry, Molecular Biology, and Cell Biology, Northwestern University, Evanston, Illinois 60208-3113

A few years ago I published a small monograph entitled *Ligand-Receptor Energetics* (1) and dedicated it to a number of individuals "whose contributions are no longer remembered." This volume assembles in a logical array the major features of the concepts and procedures developed in the core area of my research interests.

Unlike most of my contemporaries, I did not spend a postdoctoral period or a sabbatical leave in the laboratory of a distinguished scientist. Nevertheless, I have profited enormously from shorter periods of contact with some of the extraordinary individuals of the 20th century, including in my younger days, J. Franck, P. Debye, J. D. Bernal, S. Goudsmit, O. Loewy, E. Chargaff, A. Szent-Gorgyi, and M. Kac. From them and others I obtained numerous valuable insights and wise maxims, of which the following are a sampling.

J. Franck: "always multiply by a factor of 3 an experimenter's claim of the uncertainty of his results."

P. Debye: "even when a very prestigious scientist states a "fact," be cautious." In an early decade of the 20th century, Debye calculated theoretically what the dipole moment of HCl (I think) is and obtained a value of (let us say) 1.85 (Debye units). The then available experimental value was markedly lower (let us say 1.40). New experimental studies were undertaken, therefore, by a succession of physicists, and these yielded dipole moments progressively closer to 1.85. At this point, for reasons that I have forgotten, Debye was prompted to reexamine his theoretical calculation. Lo and behold he discovered he had made an error in his earlier theoretical computation. When corrected, the theory now led to a dipole moment of 1.40, in agreement with the first experiments, which thereafter were widely confirmed.

O. Loewy: "before giving a seminar, it is more important to have an empty bladder than a full mind."

E. Chargaff: "so-called model experiments are carried to incredible lengths prompting one to say that confusion superimposed on complexity may produce papers but not results. [After all] a skunk dipped in chlorophyll is not yet a rose bush."

A. Szent-Gorgyi: "when I first took up fishing, I always used an enormous hook . . . [it is] more exciting not to catch a big fish than not to catch a small one . . . Now I have reduced the size of my hook."

However, these individuals were not the only ones "on whose shoulders I have stood" to attain the understandings I have reached of ligand-receptor interactions. The achievements of the less known men provided the foundations for the creations of their successors, yet their names have largely been lost to succeeding generations.

My interest in ligand-receptor interactions was first aroused in 1942 when I read an article by P. H. Bell and R. A. Roblin (2) on the relative effectiveness of a series of sulfa drugs of different structures. From the late fall of 1940 until the spring of 1945, I was fully engaged in a number of wartime research projects established by the National Defense Research Committee (NDRC) at Northwestern University and was also teaching two courses every term. Nevertheless, I found occasional opportunities to read a few journals, which at that time appeared monthly and were at most a centimeter thick. In the early 1940s penicillin was unknown to the public, but the sulfa drugs, discovered around 1930, were being extensively and effectively used, particularly against pneumonia. Novel structures were being synthesized by pharmaceutical houses.

Bell and Roblin (2) found that the bacteriostatic activity of their hundred sulfonamides at pH 7 increased as the acid of pK of the compound decreased toward 7 but that a further increase in acid strength resulted in declines in activity. Then current opinion attributed sulfonamide activity to binding of the drug by an enzyme within the bacterial cell, which blocked enzymatic activity. It occurred to me that in that case if the relative affinity of the anion of a sulfonamide for the enzyme paralleled its affinity for H$^+$, then I could account for the bell-shaped activity-pK curve for the series of sulfonamides described by Bell and Roblin (2). A full quantitative development of this concept was published in 1944 (3).

One might raise the question at this point, why was it essentially universally accepted at that time that when a substance has a physiological effect on an organism, the effector molecule must be combining with a receptor. This was certainly not self-evident in earlier centuries and millennia. In the Western world the concepts formulated by Galen 2000 years ago (standing on the shoulders of some of his predecessors, such as Hippocrates) dominated medical practice. In essence Galen's foundational premise was that a human being was healthy so long as there was a proper balance between the four humors: phlegm, black bile, yellow bile, and blood. For example, bloodletting was a widely accepted procedure in the treatment of a disturbance in this equilibrium manifested as a disease (including George Washington's final, fatal illness). In the Far East, yin and yang constituted two complementary principles that control health and permeated all features of human life. Medicinals operated by shifting the distribution between yin and yang. Only decades after 1944 did I return to this enigma and try to find when the transition to modern views of effector-receptor combination occurred.

It is often difficult to pinpoint precisely the first appearance of a new insight. As far as I can tell, it was a physicist, not a life scientist, who provided the first vision of a molecular interaction between two substances of physiological impart. G. G. Stokes, in the middle of the 19th century, was Lucasian Professor at Cambridge University, one in the long line of towering theoretical physicists (from Isaac Newton to Stephen Hawking) to hold that appointment. In addition to being a great theorist, he was also a talented experimentalist, particularly in developing spectroscopic methods for examining chemical substances and reactions and for studying blood. It was Stokes who first recognized, from changes in spectra when oxygen (O$_2$) was removed from and subsequently added to blood, that oxygen combined with hemoglobin, *i.e.* that a complex was formed (4).

During the last two decades of the 19th century, J. N. Langley, a British physiologist and histologist, in studies of the effects of extracts of glandular secretions on heart action, concluded that these substances act directly on the cardiac tissue, *i.e.* they are bound (see Ref. 5). Subsequently, from experiments with curare and nicotine, he proposed that these substances competed with each other to form a "chemical compound" with some constituent of muscle tissue. After the turn into the 20th century, he expressed even more general views that "receptive substances" reacted with specific drugs ("chemical bodies").

It was Paul Ehrlich, a contemporary of Langley's, who created the widest and deepest understanding of effector-receptor interactions and used his insights for the systematic development of new drugs. In a sense he was a fortunate beneficiary of fate. Aniline dyes had been introduced into microscopy by Carl Weigert, a cousin of Ehrlich's mother. It was in Weigert's laboratory that Ehrlich initiated his studies of selective staining of dyes on blood cells and on tissues, publishing his first paper in 1877 (see Ref. 5).

Being in a chemistry environment, Ehrlich formulated his ideas in chemical terms, speaking of "chemical affinities" in biological processes (*e.g.* toxin/antitoxin or antigen/antiserum complexes, "magic bullets" seeking specific targets). Some three decades of his experiences were epitomized in his maxim (6),[1] *Corpora non agunt nisi fixata*, which translated becomes "a substance is not (biologically) active unless it is "fixed" (bound by a receptor)."

---

[1] In 1904 Ehrlich received an honorary degree from the University of Chicago and in 1908 was awarded the Nobel Prize.

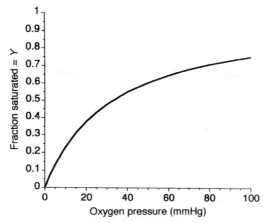

Fig. 1. **Oxygen uptake curve for a hemoglobin that can bind only 1 mol of O_2 at saturation and is half-saturated at an oxygen pressure near 30 mm Hg.**

Returning to my 1944 paper, I recognized then that the molecular, physicochemical approach used to interpret the effects of sulfonamides on bacteriostasis ought to be applicable generally to other pharmacological and physiological effector-receptor interactions. Because I was in no position to carry out appropriate experiments, I focused on searching the literature for such studies with a defined protein rather than an enzyme within a cellular matrix. There were a few publications reporting that some drugs or organic molecules bound to blood serum or plasma. The best of these was one from B. D. Davis (7) who measured the binding of some sulfonamides by serum albumin, but the observations were collated merely as fraction of the drug bound. In the course of these literature searches I did find that two areas had been approached from a molecular physicochemical perspective: hemoglobin-O_2 binding and the binding of H^+ ion by proteins. Oxygenation equilibria had the earlier and longer history.

The concept of effector-receptor complex nurtured by Ehrlich, Langley, and Stokes provided a concrete molecular image, but this was only qualitative in nature. Before a linkage to energetics or thermodynamics could be established, the conception of an equilibrium constant had to emerge. The germ of this idea appeared first in papers by C. M. Guldberg and P. Waage (in the 1860s) whose kinetic studies led them to the formulation of the law of mass action (see Ref. 8). About a decade later, J. W. Gibbs and H. von Helmholtz introduced the free energy function, and from that J. H. Van't Hoff built a bridge to the concept of an equilibrium constant (see Ref. 9).

For hemoglobin, the earliest such studies came from Hüfner (10, 11). Assuming a molecular weight of 16,000 for hemoglobin, corresponding to 1 mol of its content of linked iron, he presented the oxygenation equilibrium in terms of a 1:1 stoichiometric complex. Viewed as a combination of species (Hüfner focused on the dissociation direction), one writes the following.

$$Hb + O_2 \leftrightarrows HbO_2 \qquad \text{(Eq. 1)}$$

Adopting the format of his contemporary physical chemists (Nernst, Ostwald, Arrhenius), Hüfner formulated the appropriate ratio of equilibrium concentrations, which for Equation 1 is

$$\frac{(HbO_2)}{(Hb)(O_2)} = K \qquad \text{(Eq. 2)}$$

where the parentheses represent concentration. The moles of bound O_2, $[HbO_2]$, per mol of total protein, $[Hb] + [HbO_2]$, may be represented by B, which is also the fractional saturation, Y, of the hemoglobin in a one-to-one complex. With some simple algebraic manipulations, one can show, using Equation 2, the following.

$$B = \frac{K(O_2)}{1 + K(O_2)} \qquad \text{(Eq. 3)}$$

In graphical form, this equation corresponds to a rectangular hyperbola (Fig. 1). Hüfner found that his experimental observations fitted a curve of the shape shown in Fig. 1.

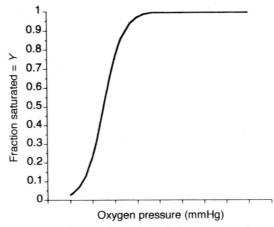

F<small>IG</small>. 2. **Sigmoidal shape of oxygen uptake curve for hemoglobin representative of those described by Bohr *et al.* (12, 13) with dog blood.**

By the beginning of the 20th century, it had become apparent that Hüfner's formulation of the Hb/O_2 equilibrium in terms of a one-to-one complex could not be correct. More careful and extensive measurements by Bohr (12, 13) showed unequivocally (Fig. 2) that the oxygen uptake curve was sigmoidal in shape. An equilibrium constant of the form shown in Equation 2 that can produce a sigmoidal shape in the oxygen uptake curve for hemoglobin is as follows(14).

$$Hb + nO_2 = Hb(O_2)_n \qquad \text{(Eq. 4)}$$

This equation presumes that Hb has a capacity to hold n moles of O_2 and that these moles of O_2 are bound simultaneously, not in a stepwise fashion. Under these circumstances, fractional saturation as a function of O_2 pressure is given by Equation 5.

$$Y = \frac{K(O_2)^n}{1 + K(O_2)^n} \qquad \text{(Eq. 5)}$$

The graphical representation of this equation is indeed of the shape shown in Fig. 2.

From Equation 5 one can also obtain the relation

$$\log\frac{Y}{1 - Y} = \log K + n\log(O_2) \qquad \text{(Eq. 6)}$$

which is known as the Hill equation. The corresponding graph, the Hill plot, should be a straight line with a slope of n, the number of sites for O_2 (or in the general case for the ligand) on the receptor molecule of hemoglobin. Corresponding graphs are often published for other ligand-receptor combinations.

It is not widely recognized that the Hill equation is essentially an empirical one, despite the conjunction of Equation 4 with Equation 5. Even with hemoglobin (a particularly favorable system for its application), experimental measurements (in the range that fit a linear Hill plot) yield a non-integer value for n of 2.5; yet it is now known that hemoglobin has four binding sites for O_2 and not a fractional number.

There are additional problems that arise when more than 1 mol of ligand is bound by a receptor; there are different modes of representation in terms of relevant equilibrium constants. This was first recognized by E. Q. Adams (15) who analyzed an example of the simplest type, a dibasic acid binding H^+ ions. Using more general notation that is applicable to all types of divalent ligand-receptor complexes, we can describe Adams' insight by the diagram in Fig. 3, in which R represents a receptor, L is the ligand, and the *lower left subscripts* on R specify the sites occupied by ligand. The lowercase k's are the site equilibrium constants for the corresponding molecular equilibria. The two stoichiometric equilibrium constants K_1 and K_2 are the phenomenological, thermodynamic ones, which fully describe the binding of ligand to receptor. One can also write an equation for binding of ligand that explicitly includes the four site equilibrium constants.

At that time, I extended Adams' analysis to trivalent and tetravalent receptor complexes and found that the former is described by 3 K_i values or by 12 site constants and the latter by

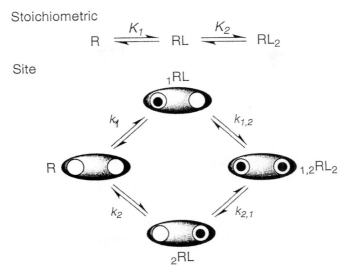

FIG. 3. **Comparison of meanings of stoichiometric and site binding constants.**

$4 K_i$ values or by 32 site constants. Decades later, D. L. Hunston and I published a paper (16) that treated the general case of an n-valent receptor, that is one with n-binding sites. A brief summary of the numbers of stoichiometric and site equilibrium constants for some small values of n is displayed in Table I (1). Clearly there is no practical way to evaluate all the site constants nor would one want a binding equation containing so many parameters.

During the first third of the 20th century, there had also been a number of studies of the acid-base titrations of several proteins. Several investigators had formulated equations for the multiple equilibria involved when many H^+ ions are bound (17–20). The treatment by Simms (18) was the most perceptive and rigorous. It was my archetype when 20 years later I began to formulate equations for ligand-receptor complexes in general.

By the end of spring, 1945, the war in Europe was over. Senior officials in the Federal government and in the National Defense Research Committee (NDRC) knew that the armed forces had three nuclear bombs available, so it was likely that the war in the Pacific would also end soon. Therefore, NDRC began to close and dismantle its projects.

Thus by the beginning of summer, 1945, I had time to outline a research program to assemble data for the binding of an organic molecule by a pure receptor protein. So that we could collect precise data quickly, I wanted a ligand whose concentrations could be measured easily and rapidly (for example, by its absorption of visible light). (During the war, the NDRC had a high priority for purchasing equipment and had obtained one of the first spectrophotometers manufactured by Beckman Instruments.) I picked some azobenzene derivatives whose structures were reminiscent of Ehrlich's famous "compound 606," Salvarsan (an antisyphilitic). During the war, crystallized human serum albumin had been isolated on an industrial scale on the basis of procedures developed by a group "commanded" by E. J. Cohn of the Harvard Medical School. Because this protein served in a front-line first-aid procedure to compensate for trauma and heavy bleeding in injured soldiers and sailors, it was not available. However, in Chicago, Armour and Co., a major slaughterhouse, had also manufactured crystallized bovine albumin, which I knew about from friends who worked at Armour; but its disposition was controlled by Professor Cohn, an authoritarian individual. A request to him produced a favorable response probably because of the intercession of one of the individuals at NDRC, so I received from Armour a treasure of several grams of crystallized bovine serum albumin.

Shortly thereafter, the Abbott Fund awarded me my first research grant for the munificent sum of $300.00. With that money I hired two undergraduates at the then standard wage of 25 cents per hour. By the end of that summer we had created a substantial stock of quantitative ligand-receptor binding information.

In parallel with the experimental work, I began to write out the equations for the multiple equilibria using only stoichiometric, phenomenological binding constants and building on the publications of Adams (15) and of Simms (18). Thereafter, the numerical data were fitted to the equations to obtain values of the binding constants K_i. That was a very tedious process, for in

TABLE I
Number of binding constants for an n-valent receptor

Number of binding sites	Total number of site binding constants	Total number of stoichiometric binding constants
2	4	2
3	12	3
4	32	4
6	192	6
8	1,024	8
12	24,576	12

the absence of any computers every step of arithmetic was done by hand and checked several times to detect computational errors.

During the fall of 1945 I submitted a manuscript on the binding of organic molecules by proteins (with the undergraduates as co-authors) and it was published early in 1946 (21).

The binding curves displayed covered a 1000-fold range of ligand concentrations so that the moles of bound ligand per mol of receptor kept rising. Therefore, the equations for the equilibria and stoichiometric equilibrium constants were written for a n-valent receptor as shown in Equation 7.

$$R + L = RL_1;\ K_1$$

$$RL_1 + L = RL_2;\ K_2$$

$$\vdots \qquad \vdots$$

$$RL_{i-1} + L = RL_i;\ K_i \qquad \text{(Eq. 7)}$$

$$\vdots \qquad \vdots$$

$$RL_{n-1} + L = RL_n;\ K_n$$

From these it follows that B, the moles of bound ligand per mol of receptor, is related to the K_i values by Equation 8.

$$B = \frac{K_1 L + 2K_1 K_2 L^2 + \ldots + (n(K_1 K_2 \ldots K_n)L^n}{1 + K_1 L + K_1 K_2 L^2 + \ldots + (K_1 K_2 \ldots K_n)L^n} \qquad \text{(Eq. 8)}$$

A related companion publication (22) demonstrated that B could also be expressed in terms of the partition function, f, which is the denominator of Equation 8.

$$B = L\frac{d\ln f}{dL} \qquad \text{(Eq. 9)}$$

Sometimes the right-hand side is written $d\ln f/d\ln L$.

For the computation of the successive binding constants K_i, Equation 8 is clearly the more direct one. It was used to evaluate the stoichiometric binding constants for each of the organic molecule-albumin complexes studied in Ref. 21. For azosulfathiazole, the K_i values are shown in Table II. These were based on experimental values of ligand concentration extending over a 300-fold range and B values ranging from 0.2 to 9. This formulation provided a pattern for subsequent studies of ligand-receptor binding.

With this foundation, one could make the connection to thermodynamics through Equation 10,

$$\Delta G^0 = -RT\ln K_i \qquad \text{(Eq. 10)}$$

which provided corresponding free energy changes, $\Delta G_i{}^0$. It was then obvious that one could also obtain the enthalpies, ΔH^0, and entropies, ΔS^0, if one measured the variation of ΔG^0 with temperature.

For the azobenzene ligands of Ref. 21, the thermodynamic parameters were published in 1949 (23). I was very surprised to find that the ΔH^0 of complex formation was small and the ΔS^0 was large. In essence that meant that the favorable free energy of complex formation was not due to a large drop in internal energy (ΔH or ΔE) but rather to an increase in the entropy,

TABLE II
Stoichiometric binding constants for binding of
azosulfathiazole by serum albumin

K_i
$K_1 = 1.25 \times 10^5$
$K_2 = 4.50 \times 10^4$
$K_3 = 2.16 \times 10^4$
$K_4 = 1.17 \times 10^4$
$K_5 = 6.70 \times 10^3$
$K_6 = 3.99 \times 10^3$
$K_7 = 2.43 \times 10^3$
$K_8 = 1.51 \times 10^3$
$K_9 = 9.5 \times 10^2$
$K_{10} = 6.0 \times 10^2$

an unexpected trend when two separate molecular entities combine into a single complex. The suggestion was made, therefore, that the positive ΔS comes from the release of water molecules as ligand and receptor combine. That the solvent could play such a crucial, albeit concealed, role in these interactions was a revelation to me. Subsequently, I learned that a decade earlier J. A. V. Butler (24) had recognized such effects in reactions of organic molecules in water.

Of greater molecular importance, the focus on thermodynamic quantities created a bridge to the broad area of the forces responsible for ligand-receptor stability and ultimately for stabilizing a native protein. We can classify these forces into three groups: (*a*) electrostatic; (*b*) hydrogen bonding; and (*c*) apolar.

Whether electrostatic attraction between a cationic and an anionic entity (in aqueous solution) would lead to a $\oplus\ominus$ combination has been a subject of fluctuating opinion for over a century. Few people today are aware that Svante Arrhenius encountered massive, bitter opposition when he proposed, in the 1880s, that salt dissolved in water becomes separated into two oppositely charged entities, Na^+ and Cl^- (25). And rightly so. After all, as any high school student knows, oppositely charged entities attract each other, as specified by Coulomb's law, with a force proportional to the magnitude of the charges $q+$ and $q-$, respectively, and inversely proportional to the square of the distance, r, between them. True, this relationship applies strictly in a vacuum, but in a solvent the change would be merely the insertion of the dielectric constant, D, in the denominator, not a reversal in the attractive character of the force. For water D is near 80, so the attractive force would be weakened but not abolished. So why should positive Na^+ and negative Cl^- stay apart as separate species?

Arrhenius presented his ideas in his doctoral thesis (which was almost rejected) in 1883. After much discussion, his examiners at the University of Uppsala grudgingly agreed to give him a *fourth class* doctor's degree, perhaps because his earlier performance at the university was a distinguished one. This pass was so low (equivalent to a D grade in the United States) that it did not qualify him to become a beginning faculty member, a docent. Twenty years after receiving his doctorate degree, Arrhenius was awarded the Nobel Prize in chemistry.

Since the 1930s, it has been recognized that there are cationic side chains (Lys, Arg) in proteins and anionic ones (Asp, Glu). Periodically since then it has been assumed that electrostatic bonds such as $Lys^+ \ldots {}^-Glu$ are responsible, at least in part, for the stability of proteins. At other times the possibility of such ion pair formation in an aqueous environment has been dismissed as very unlikely (26). In 1965, Henry DePhillips and I (27) decided to look at a simple model system for such an electrostatic interaction, $C_4H_9NH_3^+ \ldots {}^-OOCC_3H_7$. Changes in infrared spectra in the overtone region indicated that the equilibrium constant for the association of the separate ions to form the ion pair is extremely small, about 0.03. Thus, it is not likely that an ion pair interaction by itself contributes a favorable free energy change to the stabilization of a protein.

The concept of the hydrogen bond was discovered, or invented, in 1919 by M. L. Huggins (28–30)[2] while he was still a student at Berkeley. Huggins named the interaction "hydrogen bridge" and was unhappy with the possible implications of the word "bond." Very few individuals are aware of Huggins contribution. As has been observed (31), "to attract attention it is more important to invent a catchy name for a phenomenon than to discover it."

---

[2] Ref. 28 is based on term paper from Chemistry 120, Berkeley, CA (1919).

$$O \quad \cdots H - O$$
$$\diagup\diagup \qquad\qquad \diagdown$$
$$-C \qquad\qquad\qquad C-$$
$$\diagdown \qquad\qquad \diagup\diagup$$
$$O - H \cdots O$$

STRUCTURE 1

Almost 20 years later, in a classic paper with A. E. Mirsky in 1936 (32) on the structure of proteins, Pauling described the role that peptide hydrogen bonds could play in establishing specific conformations and assigned a value of 5–8 kcal to a hydrogen bond energy, with the N–H···O=C bond being placed near the lower boundary. No reference is given by Pauling to the origin of the 5–8 kcal figure for the hydrogen bond energy. Nevertheless, it was universally accepted for N–H···O=C bonds in polypeptides and used to interpret stability and conformational changes in proteins. Thus if one measured an enthalpy of denaturation of perhaps 50 kcal/mol, one proposed that 8–10 hydrogen bonds had been broken in going from native to the denatured state. Likewise, in the 1950s, when Linderstrom-Lang and his co-workers found that the slow class of hydrogen-deuterium exchanges in protein NCH groups has an activation energy of 20 kcal/mol, they ascribed it to the need to open three adjacent N–H···O=C bonds (each presumably requiring 6–8 kcal) in order to unfold a helical segment.

In a similar vein, Pauling and Mirsky ascribed the denaturing effects of urea to its ability to disrupt hydrogen bonding in proteins because of its "well known hydrogen bonding" properties. This explanation of urea effects persists widely to the present day, although more recently styles have shifted to an explanation in terms of interference with hydrophobic bonding.

Returning to the 5–8 kcal hydrogen bond energy, I do not wish to imply that Pauling had no basis for his suggested values; quite the contrary. Since the early part of this century, apparent molecular weights of compounds such as acetic acid had been measured in the vapor phase and had clearly shown the presence of dimeric molecules. Once hydrogen bonding was appreciated, it became apparent that head-to-head bonds must be present (Structure 1). Studies of the temperature dependence of the vapor phase equilibrium then led to the energy (ΔE^0 or ΔH^0) of the hydrogen bond, around 7 kcal/mol.

However, if we are looking at protein C=O···H–N bonds, this figure is really not pertinent. Strictly speaking, a bond energy refers to the dissociation energy in the gas phase. However, that is not what one needs to know for a peptide hydrogen bond that might be involved in stabilizing a protein conformation. Because the protein is in solution in water, the interpeptide hydrogen bond is exposed to competing bonds with water so the interchange shown in Structure 2 can occur.

It seemed to me at that time that vibrational spectroscopy should provide a probe of the N–H···O=C bond and reflect directly the state of the constant groups. James Franzen and I (33) found that overtone infrared spectroscopy in the 1.5-μm range could be adapted for this purpose with aqueous solutions. Using N-methylacetamide as our prototype for N–H and O=C groups we found the energy (ΔH^0) of N–H···O=C formation to be −4.2, −0.8, and 0.0 in the solvents carbon tetrachloride, dioxane, and water, respectively. This trend from very nonpolar to polar to aqueous solvent, as well as the direct result in water, shows clearly that the amide hydrogen bond energy in an aqueous environment is near zero.

Nevertheless, if there is a high local concentration of N–H and C=O groups, as in a polypeptide, entropic factors contribute to the free energy, ΔG, of formation, and a hydrogen bonded structure may be stabilized.

Although most people think that the concept of a protein helix was revealed to Linus Pauling (34) on Mount Pasadena in 1950, it actually had a tortuous earlier history. The slow evolution of the helix, or the spiral as it was originally called, as a central structural element in proteins also reflects the influential grip of integers. Pioneering structuralists, especially Astbury and Bragg, recognized the potential of two-residue turns for interpreting transitions from α- to β-keratin, but the most incisive early analysis of structure problems came from M. L. Huggins. In 1943 in an article in *Chemical Reviews* (35) that was based on a talk he had given at an American Chemical Society symposium in 1937, Huggins explicitly formulated the necessary constraints of bond distances and angles as well as the requirement for N–H···O hydrogen "bridges." Then he showed that spirals with two residues or three residues per turn (Fig. 4)

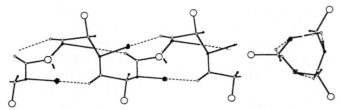

STRUCTURE 2

FIG. 4. **Views of a helix, or spiral, for a polypeptide with three residues per turn showing intrachain hydrogen "bridges" (broken lines), as envisaged by M. L. Huggins.** *Left sketch* is view along axis of spiral; *right sketch* is that down the axis.

could account for the 5.1 Å x-ray reflection characteristic of α-keratin. Furthermore, he pointed out that a 3-fold screw axis of symmetry would give a translation along the axis of the spiral of about 1.7 Å. In a prophetic sentence, he (35) also noted "that there is nothing about this [spiral] structure which requires exactly three residues per turn." Like Moses, Huggins got a glimpse of the Holy Land but never entered it. Ultimately, Pauling, Corey, and Branson (34) broke loose unequivocally from integer constraints and showed, originally by model building, that the 3.7-residue turn best fits interatomic structural and energetic requirements. Thus was the α-helix born.

In contrast to electrostatic bonds and hydrogen bonds, which can be visualized in well defined atomic arrangements, the term apolar bonds encompasses a melange of atomic and molecular interactions. The initial insight into apolar interactions came from J. D. van der Waals (36),[3] who viewed them as including all atomic and molecular forces other than those between + and − charged entities.

Since van der Waals' time, a number of new interactions have been recognized, and their intermolecular bases have been delineated. Early in the 20th century, largely because of P. Debye, dipole moments of molecules (due to partial displacement of charges) were elucidated and measured. Once they were discerned, it became apparent that dipole-dipole and even (single) charge-dipole attractions between molecules must exist. After wave mechanics was developed, F. London discovered dispersion forces (often called London forces), a manifestation of the motion of electrons with time within a molecule (or atom) that produces an electrostatic separation even in spherically symmetric molecules. Subsequently it was also realized that highly conjugated ring structures have π-electron clouds above (and below) their planes. This permits π-π interactions between different aromatic molecules. In recent times it has also been found that the quadrupole moments associated with the π-electron clouds are a basis for formation of complexes with dipolar molecules, such as H_2O or NH_3, or even with cations such as K^+ (see Ref. 1, chapter 9). For most life scientists all of these interactions are (loosely) subsumed within the class van der Waals.

The paragon of an apolar molecule is one of the hydrocarbons. These are insoluble in water so they have also been called hydrophobic. For decades the term hydrophobic bonds has been used as synonymous with van der Waals interactions, and this interpretation still pervades most of the literature. Even the eminent theoretical chemist, H. Eyring, in 1953 used the term "hydrophobic" to describe interfacial energies of apolar molecules in water (37).

---

[3] Ref. 36 is an English translation (with commentary) of his Ph.D. dissertation (Leiden, 1873). He was awarded the Nobel Prize in 1910.

In the field of proteins, recognition of adhesions of apolar groups has led to the metaphor "oil droplet" as a model of a globular protein. In this picture, the interior of the protein is visualized as a very non-polar environment, sometimes even assigned a dielectric constant of 2. Such a view is questionable (26, 38). The polypeptide chains whether in α-helical, β-strand, or idiosyncratic configuration present a

$$
\begin{array}{c}
\text{H} \\
| \\
-\text{C}-\text{N}- \\
\| \\
\text{O}
\end{array}
$$

group every few Å, and each of these introduces a high dipole moment. (For urea the dipole moment is near 8 and for acetamide near 4 (39).) The local concentration of peptide groups within the volume of a globular protein is above 12 M (26). In addition, there are dipoles from Ser, Thr, Tyr, Trp, Gln, and Asn. The term "oil droplet" is deceptive.

Starting in the 1930s, new insights began to appear on the structure of liquid water and of solutions of apolar molecules therein. A pioneering paper was that of J. D. Bernal (eminent x-ray crystallographer) and R. H. Fowler (distinguished theoretician) in 1933 (40). In that essay they presented a picture of the structure of liquid water and interpreted the effects of different solutes therein in terms of "structure making" and "structure breaking" influences. Subsequently, J. A. V. Butler (24) and later H. S. Frank and M. W. Evans (41) pointed out that apolar molecules are insoluble in water because the entropy change is unfavorable or near zero. This observation they interpreted as due to the ordering of water molecules around dissolved apolar groups.

It has also been known for over a century that apolar molecules can form crystalline hydrates, or "ices," with water molecules. Such polyhedral hydrates have been obtained with dozens of "guest" molecules, including Ar, Xe, Cl_2, CH_4, C_3H_8, CH_3Cl, $CHCl_3$, $(CH_3)_3CH$, C_6H_6, CH_3SH, CH_3SCH_3, $CH_2CH_2CH_2CH_2$-O, $(C_5H_{11})_4\ N^+F^-$ (1, 42). Some of these molecules are analogous to protein residue side chains alanine, valine, leucine, cysteine, methionine, and even larger nonpolar groups. Thus it is apparent that solvent water is a remarkably versatile substance in regard to hydrate formation, being capable of forming a large variety of cagelike structures to accommodate a whole gamut of solute structures. These could contribute to the stabilization of a protein molecule and of its complexes with ligands. In recent years, x-ray diffraction has disclosed large numbers of ordered water molecules within and on the surface of protein molecules (43–45).

In 1959, Kauzmann proposed (46) that the term hydrophobic bonding be reserved for interactions between apolar groups that are thermodynamically driven by a favorable (positive) entropy change (ΔS). In ligand-receptor binding, there are many examples of complexes that are stable because of a positive ΔS formation and many others associated with a dominant negative enthalpy change (ΔH) (1). For example, in the series acetate, valerate, caproate, heptanoate, and caprylate, binding by serum albumin is associated with the following thermodynamic parameters: $\Delta S^0 = 9, 12, 10, 4, 1$ cal mol^{-1} deg^{-1}, respectively; $\Delta H^0 = 0, 0, -820, -3,300, -4,700$ cal mol^{-1}. In this series, ΔH^0 becomes the dominant contributor to a negative ΔG^0 as the length of the hydrocarbon chain increases. In many protein-protein interactions also, ΔH^0 is the major contributor to the favorable ΔG^0 (1).

In any event it is essential to recognize that in protein interactions with small or large ligands, there are many different types of bondings present simultaneously that are coupled and intertwined with each other. This enormous complexity in biomolecular interactions has been spelled out only infrequently (1, 47). One must also be aware that the interacting species are embedded in an aqueous environment that also imparts crucial features. Consequently, categorical assignments of net ΔG^0 values of interaction to specific forms of binding are inappropriate. In such highly coupled systems, it is not possible to segregate the contribution of any specific type of force or constituent.

This thermodynamic constraint has been recognized for over a century in analyses of properties of solutions. It can be illustrated in tangible form by asking what is the "volume" of a solute in solution. Generally the molar volume of a pure solute is not a measure of the "effective molecular volume" of a mole of solute molecules in solution. Rather it reflects changes in the entire solution; the solute and solvent molecules are coupled in their interactions. What one can define clearly is the partial molar volume, $\bar{V}_2 = \partial V_{\text{solution}}/\partial n_2$. Thus, $\bar{V}_2$ reflects the change of the *entire* solution when a mole of solute, n_2, is added. For example, hydrogen exhibits a $\bar{V}_2$ of 26 cm^3 mol^{-1} in water, 50 cm^3 mol^{-1} in ether, and 38 cm^3 mol^{-1} in acetone in contrast to 25,000 cm^3 mol^{-1} in the gas phase (at 1 atm and 25 °C). Even more surprising are $\bar{V}_2$ values for some electrolyte solutes dissolved in water. For NaCl, $\bar{V}_2$ is 16.4 cm^3 mol^{-1} compared with 27 cm^3 mol^{-1} for the pure crystal. Particularly striking is the behavior of Na$_2$CO$_3$; $\bar{V}_2$ in water is -6.7 cm^3 mol^{-1} (compared with 42 cm^3 mol^{-1} for the pure solute). Clearly the volume occupied by the atoms of Na$_2$CO$_3$ in water is not negative. What the negative value of $\bar{V}_2$ signifies is that if Na$_2$CO$_3$ is added to water, the volume of the liquid solution shrinks. Clearly there must be a strong interaction of the solvent with the solute. From a molecular perspective, one presumes that this solute actuates a pronounced shrinkage in the volume of the solvent. In solutions with several solutes, the interactions are even more complex.

Similarly, one should not speak of the molar free energy (or ΔG) of, for example, a hydrogen bond within a protein matrix. Because of the coupling of all types of interactions within the protein milieu, one cannot segregate and isolate a single form of bonding. One might speak of the chemical potential $\bar{G}_i$, or partial molar free energy, just as one can define $\bar{G}_i = \partial G_{\text{solution}}/\partial n_i$ for a solute, *e.g.* NaCl, in aqueous solution. However, it is not obvious how one could extract G_i for a single type of interaction within a coupled system.

When it has proved impossible to address a problem with a theory based on analytical closed form, exact equations, scientists have developed approximation methods. Such approaches have been used classically for hundreds of years in celestial mechanics and for almost a century in quantum mechanics. In our times with the development of supercomputers, problems involving very complicated interactions are amenable to solution. Computer simulation approaches are now also widely used to examine molecular dynamics in protein interactions. As these approximation procedures continue to be refined, it behooves us to be cognizant of the advice of Nobelist, theoretical physicist P. W. Anderson: "It is much better to have the simplest theory which fits the observations reasonably well than to have an opaque computer program which spends hours of time getting an exact answer."

Conclusion

In closing, I should also mention that I have profited immensely from "extracurricular" reading of writings of individuals with little or no acquaintance with science. Let me cite just one, James Thurber, America's successor to Mark Twain. The only science course he ever took, as a student at Ohio State University, was the beginning one in zoology. He failed. Nevertheless, this wise and humorous man made one of the most trenchant comments applicable to all science (48): "Do it right or leave it alone, the conclusion you jump to may be only your own."

Address correspondence to: i-klotz@northwestern.edu.

REFERENCES

1. Klotz, I. M. (1997) *Ligand-Receptor Energetics*, John Wiley and Sons, Inc., New York
2. Bell, P. H., and Roblin, R. A. (1942) *J. Am. Chem. Soc.* **64**, 2905–2917
3. Klotz, I. M. (1944) *J. Am. Chem. Soc.* **66**, 459–464
4. Stokes, G. G. (1864) *Proc. R. Soc. Lond. B Biol. Sci.* **13**, 355–369
5. Gillispie, C. C. (1976) *Dictionary of Scientific Biography*, Vol. 4, pp. 295–305; Vol. 8, pp. 14–19, Charles Scribners, New York
6. Ehrlich, P. (1913) *Lancet* **2**, 445–451
7. Davis, B. D. (1943) *J. Clin. Invest.* **22**, 753–762
8. Partington, J. R. (1964) *A History of Chemistry*, Vol. 4, pp. 588–595, Macmillan and Co., London
9. Klotz, I. M., and Rosenberg, R. M. (2000) *Chemical Thermodynamics*, 6th Ed., pp. 154–215; 239–261, John Wiley and Sons, New York
10. Hüfner, G. (1890) *Arch. Anat. Physiol. (Physiol. Abteilung)* 1–27
11. Hüfner, G. (1901) *Arch. Anat. Physiol. (Anat. Abteilung)* 187–217
12. Bohr, C. (1904) *Zeit. Physiol.* **17**, 682–688
13. Bohr, C., Hasselbalch, K. A., and Krogh, A. (1904) *Skand. Arch. Physiol.* **16**, 401–412
14. Hill, A. V. (1910) *J. Physiol. (Lond.)* **40**, iv–vii
15. Adams, E. Q. (1916) *J. Am. Chem. Soc.* **38**, 1503–1510
16. Klotz, I. M., and Hunston, D. L. (1975) *J. Biol. Chem.* **250**, 3001–3009
17. Linderstrom-Lang, K. (1924) *C. R. Trav. Lab. Carlsberg* **15**, No. 7
18. Simms, H. S. (1926) *J. Am. Chem. Soc.* **48**, 1239–1250
19. von Muralt, A. L. (1930) *J. Am. Chem. Soc.* **52**, 3518–3523
20. Cannan, R. K. (1942) *Chem. Rev.* **30**, 395–412

21. Klotz, I. M., Walker, F. M., and Pivan, R. B. (1946) *J. Am. Chem. Soc.* **68,** 1486–1490
22. Klotz, I. M. (1946) *Arch. Biochem.* **9,** 109–117
23. Klotz, I. M., and Urquhart, J. M. (1949) *J. Am. Chem. Soc.* **71,** 847–851
24. Butler, J. A. V. (1937) *Trans. Faraday Soc.* **33,** 229–238
25. Klotz, I. M. (1985) *Diamond Dealers and Feather Merchants: Tales from the Sciences,* Birkhäuser, pp. 83–84, Basel
26. Klotz, I. M. (1960) *Brookhaven Symp. Biol.* **13,** 25–48
27. Klotz, I. M., and DePhillips, H. A. (1965) *J. Phys. Chem.* **69,** 2801–2803
28. Huggins, M. L. (1922) *Science* **55,** 459–460
29. Huggins, M. L. (1936) *J. Phys. Chem.* **40,** 723–731
30. Latimer, W. M., and Rodebush, W. H. (1920) *J. Am. Chem. Soc.* **42,** 1419–1433
31. Klotz, I. M. (1978) *Adv. Chem. Phys.* **39,** 109–176
32. Mirsky, A. E., and Pauling, L. (1936) *Proc. Natl. Acad. Sci. U. S. A.* **32,** 439–447
33. Klotz, I. M., and Franzen, J. S. (1962) *J. Am. Chem. Soc.* **84,** 3461–3466
34. Pauling, L., Corey, R. B., and Branson, H. R. (1951) *Proc. Natl. Acad. Sci. U. S. A.* **37,** 205–240
35. Huggins, M. L. (1943) *Chem. Rev.* **32,** 195–218
36. van der Waals, J. D. (1988) in *On the Continuity of the Gaseous and Liquid States* (Rowlinson, J. S., ed) North-Holland, Amsterdam
37. Eyring, H. (1954) in *The Mechanism of Enzyme Action* (McElroy, W. D., and Glass, B., eds) pp. 123–140, Johns Hopkins University Press, Baltimore
38. Warshel, A. (1978) *Proc. Natl. Acad. Sci. U. S. A.* **75,** 5250–5254
39. Cohn, E. J., and Edsall, J. T. (1943) *Proteins, Amino Acids and Peptides,* p. 144, Reinhold Publishing Co., New York
40. Bernal, J. D., and Fowler, R. H. (1933) *J. Chem. Phys.* **1,** 515–548
41. Frank, H. S., and Evans, M. W. (1945) *J. Chem. Phys.* **13,** 507–532
42. Klotz, I. M. (1970) in *Ciba Foundation Symposium on the Frozen Cell* (Wolstenholme, G. E. W., and O'Connor, M., eds) pp. 5–26, J. and A. Churchill, London
43. Teeter, M. M. (1984) *Proc. Natl. Acad. Sci. U. S. A.* **81,** 604–618
44. Burling, F. T., Weis, W. I., Flaherty, K. M., and Brünger, A. T. (1996) *Science* **271,** 72–77
45. Xu, J., Baase, W. A., Quillin, M. L., Baldwin, E. P., and Matthews, B. W. (2001) *Protein Sci.* **10,** 1067–1078
46. Kauzmann, W. (1959) *Adv. Protein Chem.* **14,** 1–63
47. Finney, J. L., Gellatly, B. J., Golton, I. C., and Goodfellow, J. (1980) *Biophys. J.* **32,** 17–33
48. Thurber, J. G. (1940) *Fables for Our Time and Famous Poems,* Harper, New York

THE JOURNAL OF BIOLOGICAL CHEMISTRY
© 2004 by The American Society for Biochemistry and Molecular Biology, Inc.

Vol. 279, No. 9, Issue of February 27, pp. 7361–7369, 2004
Printed in U.S.A.

Reflections

A PAPER IN A SERIES COMMISSIONED TO CELEBRATE THE CENTENARY OF THE JBC IN 2005

JBC Centennial
1905–2005
100 Years of Biochemistry and Molecular Biology

Biochemistry and the Sciences of Recognition

Published, JBC Papers in Press, January 12, 2004, DOI 10.1074/jbc.X400001200

Gerald M. Edelman

From the Neurosciences Institute and the Scripps Research Institute, San Diego, California 92121

An account of the slow emergence of scientific insight is not in any straightforward way a reliable reflection of a life course. I do not intend here to be explicitly autobiographical but want nevertheless to reflect on whether there is a pattern that has unconsciously guided my scientific work. I believe there is one, if I neglect some noisy interludes. Like Moliere's Monsieur Jourdain, who was astonished to realize that he had been speaking prose all his life, I have come to realize that even when my scientific interests turned to very high levels of organization (organismal, even mental) I had been following the rules of biochemistry. These rules are not just those of organic chemistry itself but also of that chemistry as it emerged under the constraints of genetics and evolution. So although the precision is lent by the syntax of organic chemistry, the semantics or significance of biochemical processes is embedded within the astonishingly rich complexity of cells, organs, and organisms interacting across many layers of organization.

There is a theme that weaves through these layers, which in retrospect I see has shaped my interest. It is the Darwinian approach of population thinking (1), based on the notion that species, categories, and even molecular interactions in living systems arise by selection acting over time on populations consisting of large numbers of variants. The idea that variation is not noise but is rather the substrate for the emergence of biological form and function provides an underlying theme that is central to and defining of what I have called the sciences of recognition. These include evolution itself, embryology (particularly morphogenesis), immunology, and the neurobiology of complex brains. In all these arenas, recognition at molecular, cellular, and organismal levels occurs through selective processes. In each case, the substrate is biochemical although the higher order rules are governed by variation and selection.

I propose to tell a few anecdotes from my early experiences, particularly those that led to molecular immunology. I recount them to point out that scientists can have blind spots and occasionally forget the lesson that one must consider all the levels of organization that emerge from selective events.

Antigen Recognition and Molecular Immunology

In 1958, I was fascinated by the specificity of antigen recognition by antibodies. At the same time I was frustrated as a chemist by the heterogeneity of the γ-globulin fractions containing these antibodies (2). Free boundary electrophoresis by Arne Tiselius and Elvin Kabat (3) revealed a stark contrast between the distribution of net charge of these proteins as compared with that of other serum proteins. I was driven by the hope of resolving this heterogeneity and had the dream, naïve as it was at the time, that by doing the primary structure of antibody molecules, the basis of their specificity would be revealed. In 1959, after cleaving disulfide bonds in so-called 7 S γ-globulins, I decided to examine their behavior by analytical centrifugation. (From now on I will refer to these molecules as immunoglobulins, the modern term.) I was both startled and elated to find that the molecules dissociated into subunits after reduction and alkylation in a denaturing solvent (4). This provided grounds for my first hope:

that one of the polypeptide chains might be small enough to work out its amino acid sequence. At that time, Sanger (5) had completed the sequencing of insulin (molecular weight, 6000), and Stein and Moore (6) were sequencing ribonuclease, which had a molecular weight of about 13,700. My hopes were certainly naïve for the 7 S immunoglobulin had a molecular weight of 150,000.

In any event, the problem of heterogeneity remained to be solved. In the early 1960s, two ideas that were derived from my medical experience proved critical. The first was that perhaps the proteins found in large amounts in the serum of patients with the cancer of plasma cells called multiple myeloma might in fact be pure immunoglobulins. Unlike immunoglobulins from normal persons, they were each homogeneous and each differed from the others in net charge. It was easy to show that these myeloma proteins could be cleaved into polypeptide chains of the same size as that of their supposed normal counterparts.

In some patients with myeloma, the urine contains a smaller protein that is also homogeneous but with a remarkable property. When heated, the urine becomes cloudy in much the same fashion as urine containing albumen. However, on continued heating the urine becomes clear. This so-called Bence Jones protein was the second protein discovered after Liebig first described albumen. Given my hypothesis about myelomas, the thought arose that perhaps Bence Jones protein was one of the chains of the myeloma protein that spilled into the urine because of its relatively low molecular weight (about 22,000). If this were the case, the dream of sequencing an immunoglobulin might be realized.

What about specificity? There was no evidence that myeloma proteins were synthesized as a result of immunization by specific antigens. It was much more likely that the process of neoplasia occurred in a single plasma cell, causing it to overproduce a myeloma protein. This was consistent with the idea (not at all popular at the time) that each myeloma was a single member of a vast preexisting population of immunoglobulin antibodies. These notions were consistent with the proposals of Niels Jerne (7) and Macfarlane Burnet (8) that the immune response was a selectional, not an instructional, process. That is, the various immunoglobulins were synthesized prior to antigen exposure and made up a repertoire of variant proteins; immunization by an antigen stimulated division of those cells with immunoglobulins that happened to bind that antigen and thus make more antibodies (Burnet's process of clonal selection). The most popular theory at the time was, by contrast, an instructional one, the clearest expression of which was that of Linus Pauling (9). The single long chain of the antibody was assumed to fold around the immunizing antigen, providing a complementary fit which after dissociation of the antigen could then bind molecules of similar shape by weak forces. This theory by a great chemist was straightforward and widely accepted but later turned out to be incorrect.

Learning from Theorists

And now, two anecdotes. The first considers events that followed the demonstration with my student, Joseph Gally (10), that the light chains of myeloma proteins and Bence Jones proteins were identical. With M. Poulik, we were able to show that each myeloma protein, when reduced and alkylated and subjected to starch gel electrophoresis, had a unique migration pattern (11). Bence Jones protein obtained from a patient's urine exactly matched the mobility of the light chain from the serum myeloma protein of the same patient. Subsequent experiments on antibodies against defined chemical groups called haptens, purified by B. Benacerraf, revealed light chain patterns that differed for each specificity (12). Within short order we were able to show that the light chains from the different antibodies differed in amino acid composition.

Some months after these discoveries, I was invited to speak in San Francisco at a Kaiser Foundation symposium. I decided that I would show how our findings corroborated selectional rather than instructional theories of antibody formation. When I arrived I saw that the first speaker on the day of my lecture was Linus Pauling, who planned to talk about his instructional theory. I arranged in haste to have a mutual friend set up a dinner with Pauling the night before. Most of the evening was spent on Pauling's concern with nuclear containment and all I could get across was one statement: "Sir, we have found that antibodies are composed of multiple polypeptide chains and those of different specificities have different amino acid compositions." Pauling carried on serenely with no rejoinder. This left me in a bit of a quandary concerning how I would present my conclusions the next day.

I decided to stick closely to the facts. Pauling launched forth in his characteristically brilliant style. When he got to a diagram of the antibody molecule folding around the antigen he said: "This is a diagram of one of the polypeptide chains of the antibody molecule." I realized that he had instantly grasped what I had said at dinner the night before. When I finished presenting my contrary evidence (without polemical confrontation) I returned to my seat. I found a note on the seat. It said: "Edelman, send reprints. Pauling."

Before I deconstruct these events, I want to recount a second anecdote about my encounter with another great scientist. This was Macfarlane Burnet, whose selectional theory, the theory of clonal selection (8), turned out to be correct. While Gally and I were pursuing our work on myelomas, convinced that selectionist ideas were correct, we received a visit by Burnet in our small basement laboratory. He asked: "What are you doing?" I replied, "We are working on the chemistry of antibodies and hope to work out their detailed structure. Like you, we are selectionists."

He replied, "You are wasting your time. Chemistry only makes things more complicated. I don't even call them antibodies. The term recognizers is good enough." I replied, "But Sir, if we don't do the chemistry to show how many variants there are in the antibody repertoire, we won't know if the theory is sound." He said, "Mathematics can make things even worse. Don't worry, young man, my theory is correct."

Well, it turned out that it was correct. Reflecting on the gifts and contributions of Pauling, the chemist, and Burnet, the biologist, I could see hints of blind spots that sooner or later we must all confront. Pauling looked only at the chemical level. He ignored the fact that the body did not produce antibodies to its own antigens, a fact difficult to account for simply by instructional folding. This cellular phenomenon of immune tolerance was a key element in Burnet's thinking. For his part, Burnet was insufficiently respectful of the biochemical rules, the syntax that would ultimately reveal in detail the origins of antibody diversity and specificity.

The Dénouement: Domains and Somatic Variation

The analysis of these rules was to emerge largely from the work of our laboratory and that of Rodney Porter (13, 14) in the mid-1960s. Porter had cleaved the antibody molecule by the protease, papain, yielding one fragment with antigen binding properties and another fragment with other physicochemical characteristics. This early work nicely complemented our studies of chain structure and allowed the formulation of a model consisting of two light chains and two heavy chains. Following upon Hilschmann's demonstration (15) that light chains were composed of variable and constant regions, both laboratories began work to establish the complete amino acid sequence of a myeloma protein, work completed in our laboratory in 1969 (16, 17). The resulting picture was quite beautiful, providing a basis for the assignment of function and for analyses of the origin of antibody diversity. It was also the first demonstration of domain structure in a large protein.

From the mid-1960s on, there was an explosion of theoretical work, which would eventually show that antibody variation at the antigen binding site was largely a somatic process involving somatic mutation and recombination of DNA in antibody-forming cells and their precursors. This was eventually confirmed by the studies of Tonegawa (18), which revealed these processes in fact to be the origin of diversity. Immunology was revealed as a science of recognition having special mechanisms of somatic selection that themselves had evolved by natural selection.

Cell-Cell Recognition and Morphogenesis

By 1970, I concluded that the work in immunology had "scratched my itch" and I decided to move on to developmental biology. I was particularly intrigued with the daunting puzzle of morphogenesis. What kind of recognition does this require at the molecular level? In the classic period of embryology, this question could not have been asked with any reasonable expectation of an answer. Instead, there was the now discredited ontogenetic law of Haeckel (ontogeny recapitulates phylogeny) and the rather more correct view of von Baer which stated that, although early stage embryos of different species resembled each other, as development progressed each species expressed its own idiosyncratic morphological pattern. Later on the German biologists His and Roux (19, 20) concentrated on the mechanics of development, the so-called *"enwicklungsmechanik."* This emphasis is important to this day. However, it did not deal with the equally important problem of how shape is inherited, a central concern of evolutionists and geneticists. How can the genetics (the one-dimensional genetic code) be linked to epigenetic processes to specify a three-dimensional animal in the fourth dimension of time?

Brilliant work had been done by Spemann (21) on embryonic induction, showing that signals from the so-called organizer could set up the embryonic axis. Work by Holtfreter (22) showed that dissociated cells from the different germ layers would sort out to re-form these layers. Despite these and other remarkable achievements of the embryologists, a global explanation of how the genetics and the mechanics worked together to yield form was lacking.

Even during this early work, it was clear that form arose from some combination of the primary processes of development: cell division, cell migration, cell death, cell adhesion, and embryonic induction. It seemed to me in the mid-1970s that cell adhesion was a central candidate process in establishing and maintaining animal form. However, to link it to genetics required that it be mediated by specific protein molecules and not, as the then prevailing view had it, by weak forces at the cell membrane (23). I was stimulated to reach this conclusion by the description of mice that showed abnormal morphogenesis of the cerebellar cortex as a result of point mutations (24).

Given my immunological experience, it was not surprising that I attempted to raise antibodies that, when present in cell cultures, would prevent cell-cell adhesion. My colleagues and I decided to use retinae from embryonic chicks as a source of cells, on the assumption that we would need large numbers of cells. It turned out, in fact, that we used up thousands of fertilized eggs. This effort, which began in earnest in 1974, finally yielded a specific antibody, allowing us to isolate the neural cell adhesion molecule (NCAM), the first cell-cell adhesion molecule to be purified and characterized (25, 26). NCAM is a most unusual intrinsic membrane protein that is expressed at a very early stage of vertebrate development. It is later expressed on all neural tissues and some other tissues in specific patterns that, when perturbed by antibodies, result in distortions of form during embryonic development. At about the same time, we began to isolate CAMS that, unlike NCAM, required calcium for their cell-cell binding activity (27). These calcium-dependent CAMS were also studied extensively by Takeichi and co-workers (28) who named them cadherins.

As is usually the case in such periods of discovery, there was an explosion of work on the differential binding of these CAMS, their location at different sites during development, their down-regulation during cell movement, and their effects on cell division. A key emphasis in my laboratory was on structure and binding. Early on, we found that NCAM had an unusual negatively charged sugar, polysialic acid, which changed in amount and form during development (29). We were also able to show that NCAM binding was homophilic; NCAM on one cell bound NCAM on an apposing cell. High amounts of polysialic acid tended to weaken this binding during cell migration, which, in some locations, was also favored by down-regulation of the CAM at the cell surface.

All of this work was extremely rewarding. However, none of it conveyed the shock I received when Bruce Cunningham and our colleagues analyzed the cDNA and cloned the gene for NCAM (30). When referred back to amino acid sequence, the data indicated that the molecule was made up of domains that were strongly homologous to immunoglobulin domains. This work also revealed the basis for the three spliced forms of the protein. Although to this day the exact assignment of homophilic domain interactions has not been resolved, the binding mode involves complementarity between immunoglobulin-like domains. Confronting the sequence relation between NCAM and immunoglobulin, I could not help recalling T. S. Eliot's line in his "Four Quartets"—"In my end is my beginning."

Adaptive immunity mediated by immunoglobulins is seen only in vertebrate species. The demonstration of molecules homologous to NCAM in invertebrates suggested that immunoglobulins and NCAM were likely to be descendents of a common evolutionary precursor (31, 32). However, unlike antibodies, NCAM did not operate by expressing variable regions in its combining site. Instead, cell-cell recognition operated by place-dependent differential expression of NCAM along with that of other CAMs. By now, over 100 CAMs have been found. Clearly, many different recognition states could be realized by such differential expression without the need to account for morphogenetic patterns by invoking millions of variants of prespecified binding proteins.

Topobiology

This picture is consistent with the notion that cellular dynamics during development operates to give shape by altering interactions among local collectives of cells. These interactions occur epigenetically and not according to a protein code. Of course, differential gene expression is intimately involved. It is now known, for example, that CAM binding sends signals to the cell nucleus and that signaling molecules involved in induction (for example, sonic hedgehog and NF-κB), can affect CAM expression (33). A most exciting discovery was made by Nusslein-Volhard and Wieschaus (34) of genes in *Drosophila* in which local expression is correlated with morphological patterns. These developmental regulatory genes are found in many species, and in later studies (35) we found that a number of CAM genes were targets of the products of, for example, *Hox* and *Pax* genes that belong to this class of regulatory DNA sequences.

It appears that local cell interaction via morphoregulatory molecules such as CAMs and cell substrate adhesion molecules or SAMs alters the mechanochemistry of local cell collectives, collaborating with cell division or cell death to change the shape of these collectives. At the same time, modulation of CAM cell surface expression allows or prevents cell migration. The whole process depends strictly on local signals that are exchanged within and across collectives (36). Borders between collectives are determined by changes in the combinations of CAMs on adjoining cells. To underscore the place-dependent features of these local interactions, I coined the term "topobiology" (37).

Given this picture, how may we place developmental biology within the group of disciplines I have called the sciences of recognition? Clearly all cell-cell recognition is local and dynamic and depends on a series of gene expression events, which are in turn switched on or off depending on the epigenetic history of particular cell collectives. This does not, however, yet account for the overall shape of the developing animal. Inasmuch as there is no prespecified cell-cell binding code in the genome that establishes the position of each cell in an organ or organism, what accounts for final shape and function?

The answer is natural selection, the process we might call the mother of all the sciences of recognition. Natural selection provides the essential link between *entwicklungsmechanik* and genetic inheritance (37). Genetic change can modify the complex suite of interactions among the primary processes of development including the time and place of expression of the morphoregulatory molecules themselves. Thus, although recognition during development is entirely local through the action of such molecules, global form is achieved by natural selection on those developmental sequences that enhance fitness of the organism.

In considering development, one is struck again by the biochemical interactions across many levels of organization. I had the good fortune to learn how to think about such interactions from my several encounters with Pauling and Burnet. Both did not hesitate to embark on theoretical excursions that led to important insights in their respective fields. From Pauling's example, I learned that biochemical rules must be seen in higher level contexts, both cellular and organismal; and from Burnet, I learned that even a correct theory needs to be fleshed out at the level of chemical mechanism, the syntax provided by biochemistry.

Neuroanatomical Recognition and Higher Brain Function

From the mid-1970s on, my interest in systems of recognition drew me almost inexorably into studies of higher brain function. This is an arena in which both morphogenesis and intricate biochemical mechanisms of recognition reach their highest expression. Thirty years ago, psychology and neuroscience were just beginning a cautious exchange. The reasons for caution were clear enough: psychology was emerging from the straitjacket of behaviorism, and neuroscience was just beginning to link developmental anatomy, synaptic biochemistry, and systems physiology into what is now a firm bond. One could begin to ask a series of critical questions. What are the bases of perception, of the various kinds of memory, and of learned behavioral responses? How can these be related to specific biochemical events?

It seemed to me that to make sense of the data in these apparently disparate fields one needed a global theory of brain action that was based on the biology of recognition events rather than on abstract computation. Unfortunately, in freeing itself from behaviorism, cognitive psychology was based on a computer model, a machine model of the mind that tended to ignore the evolutionary facts (38). Driven by my experience in embryology, immunology, and population thinking, I felt that the problem of recognition of environmental and bodily changes by the brain was likely to be solved by a selectionist theory, not by one based on logical instruction.

Accordingly, in 1977 (39) and more extensively in 1987 (40), I proposed the theory called neural Darwinism or the theory of neural group selection (TNGS). It assumed that morphogenesis of the brain with its myriad connections was initially constrained by homeotic genes and the like but then was subject to epigenetic events that resulted in enormous individual variation at the finest ramifications of neuroanatomy. The epigenetic rule was: neurons that fire together wire together. The key was not only in the neuroanatomy but also in the dynamics of the system regulated by biochemical and morphological changes at each synapse, changes that altered synaptic efficacy or strength. The question then became: how could these variations be orchestrated to yield adaptive behavior?

To answer this question, the TNGS put forth three tenets. The first tenet was that the primary processes of development, acting epigenetically, lead to enormous local variation in the repertoires of microcircuits made by branching axons and dendrites. The second tenet states that, overlapping this process and after emergence of more or less defined neuroanatomy, changes in synaptic efficacy across populations of synapses occur as a result of experience. This produces additional enormous variation in the functional connectivity of the brain. In this process, signals from various sensory channels and motor areas select neuronal groups that are made up of excitatory and inhibitory neurons linked by such synaptic change into functioning circuits.

The two linked epigenetic stages of developmental selection and experiential selection cannot, by themselves, coordinate brain responses over space and time. According to the third tenet of the theory, this is accomplished by a process called reentry. The maps of the vertebrate brain are connected by vast numbers of reciprocal axonal fibers. Reentry is an ongoing recursive process of signaling across these fibers that binds the distributed maps together to form spatiotemporally correlated circuits. Such circuits are dynamic and change selectively with signals from the body, the world, and the brain itself. Among the most important processes governing which circuits are selected are signals from the value systems of the brain. These systems release various neurotransmitters and neuromodulators from diffuse ascending neural systems and thereby change synaptic thresholds in a distributed fashion. Thus, adaptive behavior arises from selection at individual synapses coordinated by reentry but also under biasing by evolutionarily selected value systems. The picture that emerges is one of enormous variation in the biochemical profiles of the brain; this variation provides the substrate for selection of those dynamic circuits whose activity leads to adaptive behavior (41).

Of all the sciences of recognition, brain science is the most sophisticated and demanding. Much of my activity in recent years has been dedicated to testing the self-consistency of the TNGS and its ability to tie together the disparate body of data ranging from chemistry to consciousness. In my own laboratory, we have been studying the mechanisms of translation of messenger RNA (42), particularly in neurons (43). Certain messages are carried to individual synapses along with ribosomes and are then translated at dendritic spines after being triggered by synaptic activity. This process may in some cases change synaptic strength. Because there is not enough of each specific messenger RNA to be distributed to every dendritic spine, however, this process inevitably produces additional variance in the synaptic population.

At The Neurosciences Institute, my colleagues and I have been simulating the activity of neuronal populations in supercomputers, and to test the integrative activity ranging from molecules to behavior, we have even constructed brain-based devices (44) that operate according to the principles of the TNGS. Our physiological efforts are focused on the use of magnetoencephalography (MEG) to show that reentry occurs across distributed regions of the human brain when a subject becomes conscious of an object (45). This neural correlate of consciousness is consistent with the supposition of the TNGS that, during evolution of the vertebrate brain, reciprocal connections developed between more posterior regions of the cerebral cortex carrying out perceptual categorization and the more anterior regions involved in memory influenced by value systems. According to the theory, reentry across these connections and those to the thalamus allowed enormously heightened discriminations among different signals to arise from the dynamic activity of the thalamocortical system of a brain so equipped. The phenomenal experiences entailed by these neural activities are these discriminations, the so-called qualia discussed by philosophers. By being able flexibly to plan their responses, animals possessing these abilities would have an adaptive advantage over those unable to make such discriminations (46).

Selection upon Selection and the Sciences of Recognition

The long trail from antibodies to conscious brain events has reinforced my conviction that evolution, immunology, embryology, and neurobiology are all sciences of recognition whose mechanics follow selectional principles. Natural selection is, of course, the governing process, selecting the biochemical mechanisms of those systems that are able to deal with individual recognition events in somatic time.

All selectional systems follow three principles. There must be a generator of diversity, a polling process across the diverse repertoires that ensue, and a means of differential amplification of the selected variants. However, each selectional system employs a different set of mechanisms. In evolution we see mutation, competition, and differential reproduction. In immunology, we have somatic mutation and recombination, antigenic modification and circulation, and clonal expansion of selected lymphocytes. In development, we have variation in local collectives with epigenetic selection of primary processes resulting in form that is subject to natural selection. In neurobiology we add to these morphogenetic principles the polar properties of neurons firing together and wiring together to create an enormous network of functional connectivity within an overall anatomy. This anatomy is characteristic of a species but necessarily shows enormous individual variation. Within this network, synaptic strengths are selected in a value-dependent fashion by behavior. Synchronization of these selective events occurs via the process of reentry, which acts in time periods of milliseconds.

In all cases, although the syntactic rules are given by the biochemistry, the operation of these rules is constrained by the behavior of the higher order organization they help to create. Achieving a deeper understanding of these systems, a project that I like to call completing Darwin's program, will continue to rest on further exploration of the details of their biochemical interactions.

Understanding: The Ultimate Recognition

In reflecting on the tale just told, I realize that I have left out much and that what appears to be a pattern in retrospect was not all that apparent in prospect. I have not mentioned all the colleagues that made it possible to realize the insights I have mentioned here. Claude Bernard, the *doyen* of homeostasis, once said: "Art is I, Science is We." We begin our research as artists but must combine our efforts in a community. In the long reach of scientific truth that we pursue together, we end as a paragraph. That is as it should be.

After 50 years in research, it may be of some use if I make a few remarks about change and organizational style. I have the impression that when I began my work, a central driving force of biochemical research was, above all, the desire to understand. In the enormous technological explosion that has occurred in the last decade that desire is still there but it seems to be muted. We live now in an age of quick publication, fashionable journals, multi-author papers, and the predominance of rather bureaucratic or risk-free criteria for the awarding of grants. We seem to be living in a period dominated by data collecting, a period of molecular natural history.

What has emerged from this effort is a picture of enormous biochemical complexity (47), one only dimly foretold in previous times. On reflection, this is perhaps not surprising, given the fact that not all evolution occurs by natural selection and the fact that correlative variation can occur during selection. The more we see, the more the creatures of our effort seem to grow hair. I suspect that it will take some time before we develop a theory that will allow us to understand the intricate parallel biochemical networks in the eukaryotic cell. As is obvious from my account, I believe that, in this enterprise, thinking is the most important and challenging part of the biochemist's task. Taking this position involves a risk that many large organizations of science are not willing to support. I would hope that some measures are put in place to support scientific monasteries, institutes that are small (less than 50 scientists), freely funded to avoid burdening the young with grant bureaucracy, and diverse across specialties but not too diverse (48). In founding The Neurosciences Institute, I have tried to realize these conditions. The diversity that would be created if there were more such organizations, each arranged around a different focus, might help to encourage young scientists to transform the present mass of data into a general picture that will ultimately relate biological complexity to evolution in a satisfying way. Understanding—the ultimate recognition—remains the name of the game.

Address correspondence to: edelman@nsi.edu.

REFERENCES

1. Mayr, E. (1982) *The Growth of Biological Thought: Diversity, Evolution, and Inheritance*, Harvard University Press, Cambridge, MA
2. Edelman, G. M. (1994) The evolution of somatic selection: the antibody tale. *Genetics* **138**, 975–981
3. Tiselius, A., and Kabat, E. (1939) An electrophoretic study of immune sera and purified antibody preparations. *J. Exp. Med.* **69**, 119–125
4. Edelman, G. M. (1959) Dissociation of γ-globulin. *J. Am. Chem. Soc.* **81**, 3155
5. Stretten, A. (2002) The first sequence. Fred Sanger and insulin. *Genetics* **162**, 527–532
6. Hirs, C. H., Moore, S., and Stein, W. H. (1960) The sequence of the amino acid residues in performic acid-oxidized ribonuclease. *J. Biol. Chem.* **235**, 633–647
7. Jerne, N. K. (1955) The natural selection theory of antibody formation. *Proc. Natl. Acad. Sci. U. S. A.* **41**, 849–857
8. Burnet, F. M. (1959) *The Clonal Selection Theory of Acquired Immunity*, Vanderbilt University Press, Nashville, TN
9. Pauling, L. (1940) A theory of the structure and process of the formation of antibodies. *J. Am. Chem. Soc.* **62**, 2643–2657
10. Edelman, G. M., and Gally, J. A. (1962) The nature of Bence Jones proteins. *J. Exp. Med.* **116**, 207–227
11. Poulik, M. D., and Edelman, G. M. (1961) Comparison of reduced alkylated derivatives of some myeloma globulins and Bence Jones proteins. *Nature* **191**, 1274–1276
12. Edelman, G. M., and Benacerraf, B. (1962) On structural and functional relations between antibodies and proteins of the gamma system. *Proc. Natl. Acad. Sci. U. S. A.* **48**, 1035–1042
13. Porter, R. R. (1959) The hydrolysis of rabbit γ-globulin and antibodies with crystalline papain. *Biochem. J.* **73**, 119–126
14. Porter, R. R. (1973) Structural studies of immunoglobulins (Nobel Prize address). *Science* **180**, 713–716
15. Hilschmann, N., and Craig, L. C. (1965) *Proc. Natl. Acad. Sci. U. S. A.* **53**, 1403–1409
16. Edelman, G. M., Cunningham, B. A., Gall, W. E., Gottlieb, P. D., Rutishauser, U., and Waxdal, M. J. (1969) The covalent structure of an entire γG immunoglobulin molecule. *Proc. Natl. Acad. Sci. U. S. A.* **63**, 78–85
17. Edelman, G. M. (1973) Antibody structure and molecular immunology (Nobel Prize address). *Science* **180**, 830–840
18. Tonegawa, S. (1993) Somatic generation of immune diversity. The Nobel lectures in immunology. *Scand. J. Immunol.* **38**, 303–319
19. His, W. (1874) *Our Body Shape and the Physiological Problem of Its Origin*, Vogel, Leipzig, Germany
20. Roux, W. (1986) The problems, methods, and scope of developmental mechanics. In *Defining Biology: Lectures from the 1890s* (Maienschein, J., ed) pp. 107–148, Harvard University Press, Cambridge, MA
21. Spemann, H. (1938) *Embryonic Development and Induction*, Yale University Press, New Haven, CT
22. Holtfreter, J. (1939) Tissue affinity, a means of embryonic morphogenesis. *Arch. Exp. Zellforsch.* **23**, 169–209
23. Curtis, A. S. G. (1967) *The Cell Surface: Its Molecular Role in Morphogenesis*, Logos Press, London
24. Sidman, R. L., Lane, P. W., and Dickie, M. M. (1962) Staggerer, a new mutation in mice affecting the cerebellum. *Science* **137**, 610–612
25. Brackenbury, R., Thiery, J.-P., Rutishauser, U., and Edelman, G. M. (1977) Adhesion among neural cells of the chick embryo. I. An immunological assay for molecules involved in cell-cell binding. *J. Biol. Chem.* **252**, 6835–6840
26. Thiery, J.-P., Brackenbury, R., Rutishauser, U., and Edelman, G. M. (1977) Adhesion among neural cells of the chick embryo. II. Purification and characterization of a cell adhesion molecule from neural retina. *J. Biol. Chem.* **252**, 6841–6845
27. Gallin, W. J., Edelman, G. M., and Cunningham, B. A. (1983) Characterization of L-CAM, a major cell adhesion molecule from embryonic liver cells. *Proc. Natl. Acad. Sci. U. S. A.* **80**, 1038–1042
28. Takeichi, M. (1991) Cadherin cell adhesion receptors as a morphogenetic regulator. *Science* **251**, 1451–1455
29. Hoffman, S., and Edelman, G. M. (1983) Kinetics of homophilic binding by E and A forms of the neural cell adhesion molecule. *Proc. Natl. Acad. Sci. U. S. A.* **80**, 5762–5766
30. Cunningham, B. A., Hemperly, J. J., Murray, B. A., Prediger, E. A., Brackenbury, R., and Edelman, G. M. (1987) Neural cell adhesion molecule: structure, immunoglobulin-like domains, cell surface modulation, and alternative RNA splicing. *Science* **236**, 799–806
31. Edelman, G. (1987) CAMs and Igs: cell adhesion and the evolutionary origins of immunity. *Immunol. Rev.* **100**, 11–45
32. Edelman, G. M. (1983) Cell adhesion molecules. *Science* **219**, 450–457
33. Krushel, L. A., Cunningham, B. A., Edelman, G. M., and Crossin, K. L. (1999) NF-κB activity is induced by neural cell adhesion molecule binding to neurons and astrocytes. *J. Biol. Chem.* **274**, 2432–2439
34. Nusslein-Volhard, C., and Wieschaus, E. (1980) Mutations affecting segment number and polarity in *Drosophila*. *Nature* **287**, 795–801
35. Edelman, G. M., and Jones, F. S. (1993) Outside and downstream of the homeobox. *J. Biol. Chem.* **268**, 20683–20686
36. Edelman, G. M. (1992) Morphoregulation. *Dev. Dyn.* **193**, 2–10
37. Edelman, G. M. (1988) *Topobiology: an Introduction to Molecular Embryology*, Basic Books, New York
38. Edelman, G. M. (1992) *Bright Air, Brilliant Fire: on the Matter of the Mind.* Basic Books, New York
39. Edelman, G. M., and Mountcastle, V. (1978) *The Mindful Brain: Cortical Organization and the Group Selective Theory of Higher Brain Function*, MIT Press, Cambridge, MA
40. Edelman, G. M. (1987) *Neural Darwinism: the Theory of Neuronal Group Selection*, Basic Books, New York
41. (1993) Neural Darwinism: selection and reentrant signaling in higher brain function. *Neuron* **10**, 1–20
42. Mauro, V. P., and Edelman, G. M. (2002) The ribosome filter hypothesis. *Proc. Natl. Acad Sci. U. S. A.* **99**, 12031–12036
43. Smart, F., Edelman, G. M., and Vanderklish, P. (2003) BDNF induces translocation of initiation factor 4E to mRNA granules: evidence for a role of synaptic microfilaments and integrins. *Proc. Natl. Acad. Sci. U. S. A.* **100**, 14403–14408
44. Krichmar, J. L., and Edelman, G. M. (2002) Machine psychology: autonomous behavior, perceptual categorization, and conditioning in a brain-based device. *Cereb. Cortex* **12**, 818–830
45. Srinivasan, R., Russell, D. P., Edelman, G. M., and Tononi, G. (1999) Increased synchronization of neuromagnetic responses during conscious perception. *J. Neurosci.* **19**, 5435–5448

46. Edelman, G. M. (2003) Naturalizing consciousness: a theoretical framework. *Proc. Natl. Acad. Sci. U. S. A.* **100,** 5520–5524
47. Edelman, G. M., and Gally, J. A. (2001) Degeneracy and complexity in biological systems. *Proc. Natl. Acad. Sci. U. S. A.* **98,** 13763–13768
48. Hollingsworth, J. R., and Hollingsworth, E. J. (2000) Major discoveries and biomedical research organizations: perspectives on interdisciplinarity, nurturing leadership, and integrated structure and culture. In *Practicing Interdisciplinarity* (Weingart, P., and Stehr, N., eds) pp. 215–244, University of Toronto Press, Toronto, Canada

THE JOURNAL OF BIOLOGICAL CHEMISTRY

Vol. 279, No. 10, Issue of March 5, pp. 8517–8525, 2004
Printed in U.S.A.

Reflections

A PAPER IN A SERIES COMMISSIONED TO CELEBRATE THE CENTENARY OF THE JBC IN 2005

JBC Centennial
1905–2005
100 Years of Biochemistry and Molecular Biology

The Discovery of Unconventional Myosins: Serendipity or Luck?

Published, JBC Papers in Press, January 14, 2004, DOI 10.1074/jbc.X300010200

Edward D. Korn

From the Laboratory of Cell Biology, NHLBI, National Institutes of Health, Bethesda, Maryland 20892

When I received an invitation in September 2002 from Herb Tabor to write a Reflections article, I thought there must be some mistake. Reflections are written by old guys like, like, like—and then reality hit—like me. My second thought was "why bother, who'd be interested?" Then, a year later while at dinner in Cambridge, England, Alan Weeds asked me how I had come to work on myosin. My response was interrupted by the waiter's request for our dessert orders after which the conversation turned to other topics. So, to answer Alan's question and because our discovery of the first unconventional myosin (1) and related studies on actin is presumably the reason I was invited to write this article, I accepted the invitation. Tabor's "flexible" guidelines were that the contents should not be biographical but focus on "the evolution of an idea or its consequences or the development of a notable body of work."

Unlikely though it may seem, the unconventional myosin story starts with my initial postdoctoral studies of lipoprotein transport and metabolism. In 1949–1950, John Gofman and his colleagues at the Donner Laboratory at the University of California, Berkeley, developed a centrifugal flotation method for separating plasma lipoproteins and correlated elevated levels of low density lipoproteins and reduced levels of high density lipoproteins with the incidence of coronary artery disease; this was the origin of the concept of "good" and "bad" cholesterol (2). A few years earlier, in 1943, Paul Hahn, University of Rochester, had observed that within 1 min after injection of 250 units of the anticoagulant heparin into lipemic dogs, the lipemia (due principally to chylomicrons, the lowest density lipoproteins in blood) had totally cleared, as observed visually in samples of drawn blood (3). By 1950, Anderson and Fawcett (4) had shown that heparin injection caused the appearance in plasma of a "lipemia clearing factor" that could clear lipemic plasma in vitro. When the intramural program of the National Heart Institute was initiated in 1951, Chris Anfinsen (whose paramount interest was protein folding for which he shared the 1972 Nobel Prize in Chemistry with Stanford Moore and William Stein) agreed to organize a group to study the metabolism of plasma lipoproteins. In addition to Anfinsen, the initial group included Joe Bragdon, Ed Boyle, Dick Havel, Ray Brown, Bob Gordon, and Don Fredrickson.

Before I joined them in 1953 (just having received a Ph.D. from the University of Pennsylvania studying purine biosynthesis in Jack Buchanan's laboratory), Brown, Boyle, and Anfinsen (5) had proposed that heparin and a tissue factor converted a plasma protein precursor into a "clearing factor," which (acting with a plasma coprotein) converted chylomicrons and very low density lipoproteins into smaller (and hence less turbid) low density lipoproteins. Although the possibility that clearing might be related to hydrolysis of ester linkages (chylomicrons and very low density lipoproteins are greatly enriched in triglycerides) was considered, Brown and colleagues concluded that clearing factor catalyzed translipidation or delipidation with any triglyceride hydrolysis by plasma esterases playing a secondary role.

My first contribution was to show that clearing factor was, in fact, a heparin-activated lipoprotein lipase that occurred in and was released by heparin from heart and adipose tissues and which hydrolyzed the triglycerides of lipoproteins but not simple oil emulsions; the latter could, however, be converted to substrate by complexing with a high density lipoprotein (6–8). The cofactor protein was serum albumin, which bound the released unesterified fatty acids that otherwise inhibited lipolysis. The rare genetic disorder Type I hyperlipoproteinemia results from a deficiency of either functional lipoprotein lipase or apolipoprotein CII, the protein in chylomicrons and very low density lipoproteins.

Hydrolysis of lipoprotein triglycerides by lipoprotein lipase in the circulating plasma is a non-physiological consequence of the release of the enzyme from tissues. Studies by Wes McBride (9) of the uptake of doubly radioactively labeled chylomicrons ($[^3H]$cholesterol/$[^{14}C]$palmitate and $[^{14}C]$glycerol/$[^3H]$palmitate) by mammary tissue and liver extended earlier reports that chylomicrons and low density lipoproteins are removed from the circulation prior to any significant hydrolysis of their triglycerides. This, presumably, could occur only through pinocytosis, an obscure process in the early 1960s. When the focus of my research shifted from plasma lipoprotein transport to endocytosis generally, I decided to use amoebae as the experimental system because amoebae are nutritionally dependent on endocytosis, which, I therefore reasoned, should be a major activity of the amoebae. As I wanted to study the effect of endocytosis on the turnover of plasma membrane phospholipids (the membrane fusion and fission events necessary for endocytosis were thought to involve the reversible conversion of membrane phospholipids to lysophospholipids), I sought an amoeba that could be grown in sufficient quantities for biochemical analyses and axenically, so as not to be confused by the lipid metabolism of another organism on which the amoebae fed. Initially, we used a strain of *Dictyostelium* that could be grown on dead, lipid-extracted yeast. Our first efforts were to characterize *Dictyostelium* phospholipids, which led Frank Davidoff to the surprising discovery (10) that these amoebae contain no fatty acids with more than two double bonds and that their diunsaturated fatty acids (which comprise about 40% of the phospholipid fatty acids) are exclusively 5,9-hexadienoic, 5,9-octadienoic, and 5,11-octadienoic. Other than *Dictyostelium*, non-methylene-interrupted polyunsaturated fatty acids are known to occur, in substantial amounts, only in the seeds of certain plants (*e.g.* Sierra meadow rue) and trees (*e.g.* ginkgo) and in marine sponges and, in trace amounts, in some slime molds.

Because, at that time, no strain of *Dictyostelium* could be grown on a soluble, let alone a defined, medium, there were limitations to the use of *Dictyostelium* in studying endocytosis. While on a sabbatical year (1958–1959) at the University of Cambridge, I learned that Robert Neff had recently isolated a strain of *Acanthamoeba castellanii* (from the soil of a park in Pacific Grove, CA) that seemed to be just what we needed (11). This amoeba can be grown axenically in unlimited quantities on a soluble medium of proteose-peptone and glucose, which it ingests only by pinocytosis. Interestingly, the polyunsaturated fatty acids of *Acanthamoeba* proved to be similar to those of higher animals up to and including arachidonic acid (12) and not at all like those of *Dictyostelium*. However, although the amoebae were extremely active phagocytically, we could find no effect of the phagocytic uptake of large amounts of latex beads on membrane phospholipid turnover; by hindsight, perhaps this was because the basal, nonspecific pinocytic activity was so high.

In 1967, I acquired an electron microscope and was instructed in its use by Jack Dalton, who had rediscovered the Golgi complex at the electron microscopic level, and his talented assistant Artrice Valentine. Bob Weisman and I attempted to correlate biochemical events of phagocytosis of latex beads with morphological events at high resolution (13, 14). The decision to combine biochemical and morphological approaches, unusual at that time, is what led to the discovery of the first "unconventional" myosin 6 years later. In 1968, morphological studies with Blair Bowers (15) showed the unmistakable presence in *Acanthamoeba* of microfilaments with a strong resemblance to actin filaments, and by the next year, Bob Weihing (16) had purified *Acanthamoeba* actin. Although this was not the first definitive proof for actin in a nonmuscle cell (in particular several laboratories had purified actin from the slime mold *Physarum polycephalum*) our discovery of *Acanthamoeba* actin resulted in a total re-direction of my research.

The contractile properties of preparations of muscle proteins had been studied for at least 80 years when, in 1943, Straub (17), working in Albert Szent-Gyorgyi's laboratory in Hungary, separated the active component into actin and myosin. This is not the place to review the ensuing 60 years of research that have led to the understanding at the atomic level of the mechanochemical events by which the energy of hydrolysis of ATP drives the relative movements of actin and myosin filaments. It is sufficient for our present purposes to say that we were certain, around 1970, that the actin filaments in *Acanthamoeba* must be involved in cell motility processes and equally certain that where there was actin there must be myosin. After all, myosin is the ATPase that provides the energy for the coupled movement of this protein pair, which is the basis of muscle contraction and, we assumed, all actin-based motile processes. Although little was known about myosins from nonmuscle cells, a myosin similar to muscle myosin had been purified from *Physarum* (18) and Bob Adelstein, just across the hall, was characterizing similar myosins from human platelets (19) and mouse macrophages (20).

We were, however, singularly unsuccessful in purifying myosin from *Acanthamoeba* by the procedures that had worked for other cells. Then, Evan Eisenberg, a postdoctoral fellow in Wayne Kielley's laboratory, suggested to Tom Pollard, a recently arrived postdoctoral fellow in my laboratory, that we make use of the fact that myosins, unique among ATPases, are active at high ionic strength in the absence of any divalent cation (K-EDTA ATPase activity), although their physiologically relevant actin-activated ATPase activity requires magnesium ions. Pollard set about purifying the K-EDTA ATPase from a pyrophosphate extract of amoebae utilizing DEAE chromatography, ammonium sulfate fractionation, and adsorption chromatography on agarose and hydroxyapatite columns (1). At low ionic strength, the MgATPase activity of the enzyme was activated by F-actin until the last purification step when the ATPase activity was separated from a cofactor protein that restored actin-activated MgATPase activity when the two fractions were mixed (21). Pollard's recollection (22) is that Ed Taylor suggested he seek an activator protein by combining fractions from the hydroxyapatite column with the fraction containing MgATPase activity.

I now go rapidly through the subsequent 25 years of research in my laboratory by a number of postdoctoral fellows. In 1977, Hiroshi Maruta found that the cofactor was a kinase that phosphorylated the myosin heavy chain (23), the first example of regulation of myosin activity by heavy chain phosphorylation; in 1983, John Hammer and Joe Albanesi purified the kinase (24); in 1989–1990, Hanna Brzeska and Tom Lynch identified the phosphorylation site (in the motor domain of the heavy chain) and showed that the myosin heavy chain kinase was activated by acidic phospholipid-stimulated autophosphorylation (25, 26); between 1996 and 1999, Brzeska, Joanna Szczepanowska, and John Hoey showed sequence homology of the myosin heavy chain kinase to p21-activated kinases and activation of the kinase by Rac and Cdc42 (27, 28). Unknowingly, and before small GTPases had been discovered, we had purified the first p21-activated kinase.

In the original 1973 papers (1, 21), Pollard and I reported that the MgATPase activity of the amoeba myosin was not a simple hyperbolic function of actin concentration, as for all previously studied myosins, but showed a triphasic dependence with high activity at very low actin concentrations, lower activity as the actin concentration was increased, and then rising activity at still higher actin concentrations. Myosin monomers also aggregated actin filaments into parallel bundles as if the myosin had two actin-binding sites: one, as in all myosins, in the head domain and another, which previously studied myosins apparently did not have, presumably in the tail domain. That the triphasic actin dependence was a result of this second actin-binding site was proposed by Albanesi and Hisao Fujisaki in 1985 (29) and proved by Brzeska and Lynch in 1988 (30); the domain structure of the tail was more fully defined by Xiong Liu and Brzeska in 2000 (31).

Although the requirement for a cofactor (heavy chain kinase) for actin-activated MgATPase activity and the triphasic dependence on actin concentration were unusual for a myosin, the most surprising feature of this *Acanthamoeba* myosin was that it was a globular protein consisting of a single heavy chain of just 140,000 Da and a single light chain (all known myosins consisted of an asymmetric dimer of two heavy chains of ~200,000 Da joined together through a rodlike, coiled-coil helical tail and two pairs of light chains). Furthermore, the *Acanthamoeba* myosin remained monomeric in $MgCl_2$ at low ionic strength (conditions in which all known myosins formed filaments).

Although Pollard and I thought it reasonable to call the amoeba enzyme a myosin because of its actin-activated MgATPase activity, this was not acceptable, at that time, to the muscle biochemists that had been studying conventional myosins for 30 or more years. In his E. B. Wilson Lecture in 2001, Ed Taylor (32) recalled the general feeling of those in the myosin field at the finding of a small, single-headed myosin: "This was a surprise. Although we were not sure why muscle myosin had two heads, an amoeba with a one-headed myosin must somehow be a defective creature. We did not realize that this was the beginning of the end of the isolation of the muscle community from the rest of cell biology." My own recollection is that it was not so much that *Acanthamoeba* was thought to be a defective creature as that this small myosin was thought to be a degradation product of a conventional myosin (*e.g.* like monomeric subfragment 1, which contains the ATPase and actin-binding sites and catalytic properties of conventional myosin but cannot form filaments) despite the evidence we had to show otherwise.

By 1979, Paul Wagner (33) thought it unlikely, although not entirely ruled out, that the *Acanthamoeba* myosin was a degradation product of a conventional myosin. Wagner's acceptance of this novel myosin was largely prompted by the identification by Hiroshi Maruta in my laboratory in 1977 (34, 35), and almost simultaneously by Pollard's laboratory in 1978 (36), of a conventional *Acanthamoeba* myosin (two heavy chains of 180,000 Da and two pairs of light chains of 17,500 and 17,000 Da), which had substantially different enzymatic and physical properties (35, 36) than the myosin that Pollard and I had discovered in 1973. We called the original myosin *Acanthamoeba* myosin I and the new one *Acanthamoeba* myosin II, appropriate both to the order of their discovery and the number of their heavy chains. Parenthetically, we were unable to show actin activation of the MgATPase of purified *Acanthamoeba* myosin II until 1980 when Jimmy Collins (37) discovered that treatment with phosphatase to dephosphorylate three regulatory serine residues located at the tip of the tail (38) reversed the inhibition of actin-activated MgATPase activity; note that the two *Acanthamoeba* myosins are regulated by heavy chain phosphorylation but in very different ways. Two years after the discovery of the second myosin, Hana Gadasi, Maruta, and Collins (39) showed that peptide maps of *Acanthamoeba* myosin I and II were different, and in 1979–1980, Gadasi showed that antibodies to the two myosins did not cross-react (40) and that the two myosins localized differently within the cell (41), foretelling the convincing evidence we obtained in collaboration with Yoshio Fukui in 1989 that at least one of the *Dictyostelium* myosin I isozymes is at the leading edge of locomoting cells whereas myosin II is at the rear (42). Definitive proof of two *Acanthamoeba* myosins (one conventional, one unconventional) came in 1986 when John Hammer cloned and sequenced the genomic DNA for the myosin I and myosin II heavy chains (43–45).

Probably because muscle/myosin biochemists were still skeptical (*e.g.* as late as 1981, Peter Chantler (46), although accepting the reality of *Acanthamoeba* myosin I, wrote that *Acanthamoeba* myosin I "is regarded as peculiar among myosins") and because most cell biologists were not yet molecularly oriented, discovery of other unconventional myosins was slow. By 1987, 14 years after publication of the paper describing *Acanthamoeba* myosin I, the only nonmuscle myosins described were four (single-heavy chain) myosin Is (two from *Acanthamoeba*, one from *Dictyostelium*, and one from intestinal brush border) and ~20 myosin IIs (47). Thereafter, things changed rapidly. In a 1992 review entitled "Unconventional Myosins" (48), Richard Cheney and Mark Mooseker referenced ~14 unconventional (*i.e.* non-myosin II) myosins, divided by sequence homologies of their motor domains into four groups, and observed that "the number of unconventional myosins being discovered is currently frighteningly large." Three years later, the same authors (49) reviewed a myosin superfamily that then consisted of 11 different classes by phylogenetic analysis based on the sequences of the myosin head domains obtained by PCR-based DNA sequencing; class I, alone, contained about 26 entries. By 2001, at least 150 myosin heavy chain sequences had been identified falling into 18 classes in phylogenetic trees based on sequences of their head domains (50); phylogenetic trees based on tail sequences are almost identical suggesting co-evolution of the heads and tails from the original myosin (51). The myosin superfamily is a super-superfamily.

Given the extensive genomic sequences now available, there are probably relatively few myosin DNAs yet to be discovered. Class II, followed by class I, has the most members and occurs in the most species. All species contain multiple myosins but some many more than others, *e.g.* the human genome contains 39–40 myosins falling into 12 classes whereas yeast has only five myosins in three classes (50). Paradoxically, there are many more "unconventional" than "conventional" (class II) myosins.

There is a tremendous amount of work yet to be done to determine the biochemical and biophysical properties and the biological functions of all of these myosins (especially of their tail domains, which are much more diverse than the motor domains and probably the principal determinants of localization and function within the cell). Most myosins are known only by the

DNA sequences of their heavy chains (very few light chains have been identified) with the proteins yet to be purified and studied. Those that have been characterized at the protein level have one or two heavy chains and one to six light chains per heavy chain. Only class II myosins form filaments. Myosins are involved in multiple activities in nonmuscle cells including, but not limited to, cell movement, cytokinesis, pseudopod formation and chemotaxis, cell adhesion, organization of actin filaments and cortical tension, endocytosis and exocytosis, organelle transport, and vision and hearing (at least six different myosin classes). We know that mutations in unconventional myosins can result in loss of pigmentation, blindness, and deafness (52, 53); and it all began with *Acanthamoeba*!

Now let's return to actin. By 1977, Dave Gordon, Jim Boyer, and I (54) had found, contrary to previous observations of others, that the polymerization properties of actins purified from amoebae, brain, platelets, and liver were very similar to those of muscle actin; this is not surprising in retrospect because, as Joel Vandekerckhove later showed (55), the amino acid sequence of *Acanthamoeba* actin, for example, is more than 90% identical to the sequence of rabbit muscle actin and even more similar to the actins of *Dictyostelium*, *Physarum*, and mammalian β-cytoplasmic actins. More interesting, we reported in the 1977 paper (54) that the concentrations of unpolymerized actin in the extracts of the nonmuscle cells could be as much as 10 times higher than the critical concentrations (the concentration of actin monomers when filaments and monomers are at steady state) of the purified actins under physiological conditions. Also, in contrast to muscle actin, we recognized at that time that the polymerization state of actin in nonmuscle cells is dynamically regulated both temporally and spatially, *e.g.* actin filaments accumulate rapidly in close association with the membrane of a newly forming phagocytic cup but disappear equally rapidly when the cup is internalized as a phagosome (56). It followed from these observations that "the dynamic equilibrium between polymerized and nonpolymerized actin in the cell will be regulated . . . by factors that interact with G-actin to keep it nonpolymerized (and) by proteins . . . that interact with and stabilize F-actin filaments" (54). A few such proteins had already been described by 1977 when that was written, and now proteins known to interact with either G-actin or F-actin number in the hundreds.

However, before the effects of all of these proteins on actin assembly and function could be understood, it was necessary to understand the mechanism of actin polymerization in the absence of other proteins, especially the role of ATP hydrolysis (actin-bound ATP is converted to actin-bound ADP during polymerization). Albrecht Wegner described in 1976 (57) how, as a result of the irreversible hydrolysis of ATP, the critical concentration of actin could be different at the two ends of the filament. As a result of Wegner's theory and experimental results and efforts of our laboratory and Carl Frieden and especially Tom Pollard (58), it was found that the association and dissociation rate constants are faster and the critical concentration lower at one end (the plus end) of the filament than the other end (the minus end) and that the critical concentration is higher at both ends for ADP-actin than for ATP-actin. Thus, ATP-actin adds preferentially to the plus end of the filament, and the subsequent hydrolysis of ATP on the filament (59, 60) primes the actin filament for depolymerization, *i.e.* as found later for G-proteins and like the phosphorylated and unphosphorylated forms of a protein, the ATP and ADP forms of actin (and GTP and GDP forms of tubulin) have different properties. At least one actin-binding protein dramatically affects the ATP/ADP-dependent properties of actin. Larry Tobacman and I showed that binding of profilin to monomeric actin amplifies small changes in critical concentration, thereby increasing the concentration of unpolymerized actin (61); Steve Mockrin and I found that profilin accelerates the exchange of ADP for ATP (62), thereby priming the actin for addition to filaments; and Pollard and John Cooper showed that the profilin-actin complex donates the actin monomer exclusively to the plus end of the elongating filament (63), thereby greatly increasing the differential rates of growth at the plus and minus ends of the filament.

In 1982, Terrell Hill and Marc Kirschner (64) described how the free energy of hydrolysis of ATP could be converted into mechanical work if actin polymerized against a resisting force. This has elegantly been shown to account both for the extension of the leading edge of motile cells and the intracellular motility of *Listeria* and other infectious organisms that capture the cell's actin-based motility apparatus (reviewed in Ref. 65). The key to this mechanism is the ubiquitous Arp2/3 complex of seven proteins that was purified from *Acanthamoeba* extracts in 1994 by Laura Machesky in Tom Pollard's laboratory (66). The Arp2/3 complex initiates actin polymerization *de novo* and also induces branching of growing filaments. Julie Theriot (67) demonstrated that the motility of *Listeria* could be quantitatively explained by the rate of polymerization of an actin "comet tail" attached to the rear of the bacterium, and elegant work in the laboratory of Marie-France Carlier and Dominique Pantaloni (major contributors to our understanding of microtubule and actin filament dynamics) reconstructed this motile system from highly purified proteins: the seven-member Arp2/3 complex plus four actin-binding proteins, actin depolymerizing factor, actin capping protein, profilin, and α-actinin (68). In the cell, this system links to extracellular stimuli through small GTPases and phosphatidylinositol bisphosphate, which activate WASp, which activates the Arp2/3 complex (65). *Most notably, myosin is not required! So, it seems that our discovery of the first unconventional myosin was based on the false premise that actin-based motility must depend on a myosin.* Very recently, however, John Hammer's laboratory (69) discovered an ubiquitous protein, CARMIL, that acts as a scaffold binding the seven-protein Arp2/3 complex, the α and β subunits of capping protein, and myosin I. This implies a role for myosin I at the leading edge of a motile cell, not, as we had originally assumed, as the principal motile force but possibly in the assembly of actin filaments that drives motility at the leading edge of the cell; this may explain our earlier finding of myosin I at the leading edge of *Dictyostelium*.

We have come to the end of the scientific reflections but not to the end of this essay. Although the guidelines for Reflections suggest that they not be biographical, science is done by people who are greatly influenced by other people, and my part in the science I have just described is no exception. I had begun undergraduate studies at the University of Pennsylvania as an economics major, shifted to chemistry (more because I decided economics was not for me than because of a compelling interest in chemistry), and applied to graduate school (because all of the faculty had doctorates) although I had little idea what working scientists did other than teach what they had been taught. Almost totally ignorant of biochemistry, I applied to several biochemistry departments because a family friend, who had just finished medical school, was enthusiastic about his postdoctoral experience in Sam Gurin's laboratory at Penn. As it happened, Penn was the only program that accepted me. I was instantly enraptured by biochemistry, which, given the absence of a good textbook, we learned directly from the journals with student-led seminars covering all of intermediary metabolism (which was biochemistry then at Penn) on a 3–4-year cycle. We discussed the knowledge that led to the research, critiqued the experiments and the interpretation of the results, and discussed what experiments should be done next. Thus, while learning biochemistry, we also learned how to think like scientists. It would be only a slight exaggeration to say that I learned biochemistry from the pages of the *Journal of Biological Chemistry*.

My doctoral research on purine biosynthesis, under the mentorship of Jack Buchanan, brought me immediately into one of the most exciting fields in biochemistry and taught me lessons that have lasted a lifetime. First was the power, indeed the necessity, of biochemistry to understand biology. The physiology department at Penn was still teaching that it was impossible to learn anything useful by grinding up tissues and purifying proteins because in doing so one was destroying the very thing one wanted to understand. But how, I wondered, would I ever understand how 4-amino-5-imidazolecarboxamide was converted to its ribotide, the immediate precursor of adenylic acid, which was my task in Buchanan's laboratory, by analyzing the components of arterial and venous blood from a perfused liver? It was also important to choose the best experimental system and trust to the universality of biochemical processes. Though he was interested in purine biosynthesis as the first step in understanding nucleic acid biosynthesis and because of the importance of ATP in intermediary metabolism, Buchanan had used pigeon liver for the painstaking task of identifying the precursor of each of the carbon and nitrogen atoms of the purine ring to take advantage of the fact that uric acid, a purine, is made in abundance in bird liver as the excretory end product of nitrogen metabolism. I also learned the importance of using purified enzymes whenever possible (much more difficult then than now) and the many ways in which isotopically labeled compounds could be exploited. Those lessons learned are four of Kornberg's *Ten Commandments of Enzymology* (70). I also learned the value of hard work; Jack told me (although I think he may not remember this), and I paraphrase, "If the other guy is smarter than you, there's nothing you can do about it, but you can work harder than anyone else if you want to" (this was probably a comment about my work habits rather than my intelligence or at least so I'd like to think). Also important was the not unrelated advice, which may also have come from Jack:

"Don't think too much about what to do. Just do the first experiment, almost any experiment, and it will tell you what to do next."

Impressed by Earl Stadtman's papers when he was a graduate student in H. A. Barker's laboratory at the University of California, Berkeley, and not incidentally by the opportunity to travel across the vast country that I had never seen, I made arrangements for a postdoctoral fellowship in Barker's laboratory. Just a few months before I was to leave, health problems forced Barker to reduce his activities. In a letter informing me that he would not be able to accept me into his laboratory, Barker wrote that he had already contacted Arthur Kornberg who had agreed that I could join him at Washington University. Despite his outstanding accomplishments, I wrote to Kornberg declining his very kind and generous offer, in part because St. Louis held little attraction especially in comparison to my visions of California, but more importantly because the Kornberg and Buchanan laboratories were doing very similar research and I wanted a different scientific experience. When I met Arthur 15 years later in Alec Bangham's laboratory in Babraham, England, Arthur remembered the incident saying that Paul Berg was to come to his laboratory that same year and he (Kornberg) had envisioned a paper authored by Korn, Berg, and Kornberg, which was never to be. Instead, arrangements were made for me to join Chris Anfinsen, a long time friend and colleague of Buchanan's, at the National Heart Institute where the intramural research program had been initiated just a few years earlier by James Shannon, who later became the most important Director of NIH.

And now, finally, I get to the title of this essay. The word "serendipity" was invented by Horace Walpole at the end of the 18th century to describe the events in the fairy tale *The Three Princes of Serendip* in which the princes "were always making discoveries, by accident and sagacity, of things they were not in quest of" (71). Note that "accidental sagacity" is not the same as "luck," which, though accidental, is not sagacious. So, was it serendipity or just plain dumb luck to have stumbled into biochemistry, to have been accepted as a graduate student in one of the better departments with a history dating back to Dr. Benjamin Rush, a signer of the Declaration of Independence (the medical school of the University of Pennsylvania is the oldest medical school in the United States), to have been accepted into the Buchanan laboratory, and to have had the rare privilege to begin a career in biochemistry in proximity to one of its true pioneers, Otto Meyerhof, who, as I remember it, had been rescued from Nazi-controlled Europe by the Rockefeller Foundation with the understanding that Penn would make a scientific home for him? No question, all of that was dumb luck.

And it was certainly luck and not serendipity that I found myself in Building 3 at NIH where, intending to stay for no more than 3 years, I have spent my entire career. In those days, NIH was small enough that all of the biochemists met at weekly seminars where we took turns discussing our current research, and there were monthly research meetings of the NIH and Johns Hopkins University biochemists, all in addition to daily meetings within each laboratory. How could one not succeed in this environment? Of the 86 scientists in Building 3 between 1950 and 1953, 27 became members of the National Academy of Sciences and three, Chris Anfinsen, Arthur Kornberg, and Julie Axelrod, are Nobel laureates. More specifically, of the nine of us (I include Marty Rodbell, who joined us in 1956) who worked on lipoprotein metabolism, two (Bragdon and Gordon) died prematurely, five were elected to the National Academy of Sciences, and two became Nobel laureates (Anfinsen and, of course, Rodbell, who shared the 1994 Nobel Prize in Medicine with Al Gilman for discovery of G-proteins). It is interesting, at least to me, and probably little known that Rodbell's discovery of G-proteins evolved from studies of lipoprotein lipase (72). Rodbell, with whom I had shared a laboratory when I found lipoprotein lipase in adipose tissue, developed his novel method for preparing isolated fat cells in order to study the synthesis and release of lipoprotein lipase from adipocytes. To demonstrate the functionality of the isolated fat cells, Rodbell showed that they were appropriately responsive to insulin and then found that GTP was required for the hormone response, which led to his discovery of G-proteins.

Perhaps it was serendipity that led me from lipoprotein metabolism to endocytosis to actin to myosin, but it was luck that actin and myosin were being studied in the same laboratory by Wayne Kielley (whom I had known at Penn where he was a postdoctoral fellow of Otto Meyerhof), Bob Adelstein, and Evan Eisenberg, each of whom freely offered the guidance I needed. And it was luck that *Acanthamoeba* myosin I has high K-EDTA ATPase activity, the basis on which we purified it, because we now know that many myosins do not. Indeed, Pollard and I missed conventional myosin II on those first DEAE columns because *Acanthamoeba* myosin II has very low K-EDTA ATPase activity. Had it been otherwise we might never have discovered myosin I. In any case, whether serendipity or dumb luck, there was no road map or strategic plan to my research, just intense interest and a willingness to follow my nose wherever it led, trusting my sense of smell to lead me in the right direction.

Arthur Kornberg recently added an eleventh commandment to his first ten: "thou shalt support basic research" (70), to which I would add "and good applied and clinical research," for each is important in its own right and they cross-fertilize. If permitted, I might suggest a twelfth commandment, "thou shalt support the individual investigator wheresoever he/she goest." Funding organizations and research directors could do worse than paraphrase to scientists what, in the Old Testament, Ruth said to Naomi (73), "Whither thou goest, I shall go; and where thou lodgest, I will lodge; thy science shall be my science."

It is commonplace to say that the era of biochemistry is behind us, that cell biology is the science of the 21st century. Although, in a narrow sense, this may be true, I view contemporary cell biology not as the successor to biochemistry but as the coming together of biochemistry and dynamic morphology. It is consistent with this view that the *Journal of Biological Chemistry* paper by Pollard and me describing the first unconventional myosin (1), the principal subject of this Reflections, was selected as one of 42 *Landmark Papers in Cell Biology* (74). The reductionist (biochemical) approach of identifying, purifying, and characterizing each of the individual components of the cell at the molecular and atomic level was never thought to be the end of biological research but rather the necessary first step for understanding complex cell processes. There are, to be sure, still many proteins to be identified and characterized, but we are now in an exciting new phase of biochemistry, cellular biochemistry (what the *Journal of Biological Chemistry*'s Table of Contents calls the Molecular Basis of Cell and Developmental Biology), in which powerful imaging techniques and genetic manipulations allow us to study the behavior of cells and subcellular organelles at the molecular level. As we approach the 100th anniversary of the *Journal of Biological Chemistry*, there is enough to do to fill its pages (if not its web site) for another 100 years.

Address correspondence to: edk@nih.gov.

REFERENCES

1. Pollard, T. D., and Korn, E. D. (1973) *J. Biol. Chem.* **248,** 4682–4690
2. Gofman, J. W., Lindgren, F., Elliott, H., Mantz, W., Hewitt, J., Strisower, B., and Herring, V. (1950) *Science* **111,** 166–171
3. Hahn, P. F. (1943) *Science* **98,** 19–20
4. Anderson, N. G., and Fawcett, B. (1950) *Proc. Soc. Exp. Biol. Med.* **74,** 768–771
5. Brown, R. K., Boyle, E., and Anfinsen, C. A. (1953) *J. Biol. Chem.* **302,** 423–434
6. Korn, E. D. (1954) *Science* **120,** 399–400
7. Korn, E. D. (1955) *J. Biol. Chem.* **215,** 1–14
8. Korn, E. D. (1955) *J. Biol. Chem.* **215,** 15–26
9. McBride, O. W., and Korn, E. D. (1964) *J. Lipid Res.* **5,** 459–467
10. Davidoff, F., and Korn, E. D. (1963) *J. Biol. Chem.* **238,** 3199–3209
11. Neff, R. J. (1957) *J. Protozool.* **4,** 176–182
12. Korn, E. D. (1963) *J. Biol. Chem.* **238,** 3584–3587
13. Weisman, R. A., and Korn, E. D. (1967) *Biochemistry* **6,** 485–497
14. Korn, E. D., and Weisman, R. A. (1967) *J. Cell Biol.* **34,** 219–227
15. Bowers, B., and Korn, E. D. (1968) *J. Cell Biol.* **39,** 95–111
16. Weihing, R. R., and Korn, E. D. (1969) *Biochem. Biophys. Res. Commun.* **35,** 906–912
17. Straub, F. B. (1943) in *Studies from the Institute of Medical Chemistry University of Szeged* (Szent-Gyorgyi, A., ed) Vol. II, pp. 3–15, S. Krager, Basel
18. Adelman, M. R., and Taylor, E. W. (1969) *Biochemistry* **8,** 4976–4988
19. Adelstein, R. S., Pollard, T. D., and Kuehl, W. M. (1971) *Proc. Natl. Acad. Sci. U. S. A.* **68,** 2703–2707
20. Adelstein, R. S., Conti, M., Johnson, G., Pastan, I., and Pollard, T. D. (1972) *Proc. Natl. Acad. Sci. U. S. A.* **69,** 3693–3697
21. Pollard, T. D., and Korn, E. D. (1973) *J. Biol. Chem.* **248,** 4691–4697
22. Pollard, T. D. (2000) http://www.mrc-lmb.cam.ac.uk/myosin/MyoI.html
23. Maruta, H., and Korn, E. D. (1977) *J. Biol. Chem.* **252,** 8329–8332
24. Hammer, J. A., III, Albanesi, J. P., and Korn, E. D. (1983) *J. Biol. Chem.* **258,** 10168–10175
25. Brzeska, H., Lynch, T. J., and Korn, E. D. (1989) *J. Biol. Chem.* **264,** 19340–19348
26. Brzeska, H., Lynch, T. J., and Korn, E. D. (1990) *J. Biol. Chem.* **265,** 3591–3594
27. Brzeska, H., Szczepanowska, J., Hoey, J., and Korn, E. D. (1996) *J. Biol. Chem.* **271,** 27056–27062
28. Brzeska, H., Young, R., Knaus, U., and Korn, E. D. (1999) *Proc. Natl. Acad. Sci. U. S. A.* **96,** 394–399
29. Albanesi, J. P., Fujisaki, H., and Korn, E. D. (1985) *J. Biol. Chem.* **260,** 11174–11179
30. Brzeska, H., Lynch, T. J., and Korn, E. D. (1988) *J. Biol. Chem.* **263,** 427–435
31. Liu, X., Brzeska, H., and Korn, E. D. (2000) *J. Biol. Chem.* **275,** 24886–24892
32. Taylor, E. W. (2001) *Mol. Biol. Cell* **12,** 251–254
33. Wagner, P. (1978) *Nature* **274,** 846–847
34. Maruta, H., and Korn, E. D. (1977) *J. Biol. Chem.* **252,** 399–402
35. Maruta, H., and Korn, E. D. (1977) *J. Biol. Chem.* **252,** 6501–6509

36. Pollard, T. D., Stafford, W. F., III, and Porter, M. E. (1978) *J. Biol. Chem.* **253,** 4798–4808
37. Collins, J. H., and Korn, E. D. (1980) *J. Biol. Chem.* **255,** 8011–8014
38. Collins, J. H., Coté, G. P., and Korn, E. D. (1982) *J. Biol. Chem.* **257,** 4529–4534
39. Gadasi, H., Maruta, H., Collins, J. H., and Korn, E. D. (1979) *J. Biol. Chem.* **254,** 3631–3636
40. Gadasi, H., and Korn, E. D. (1979) *J. Biol. Chem.* **254,** 8095–8098
41. Gadasi, H., and Korn, E. D. (1980) *Nature* **286,** 452–456
42. Fukui, Y., Lynch, T. J., Brzeska, H., and Korn, E. D. (1989) *Nature* **341,** 328–331
43. Hammer, J. A., III, Jung, G., and Korn, E. D. (1986) *Proc. Natl. Acad. Sci. U. S. A.* **83,** 4655–4659
44. Hammer, J. A., III, Bowers, B., Paterson, B. M., and Korn, E. D. (1987) *J. Cell Biol.* **105,** 913–926
45. Jung, G., Korn, E. D., and Hammer, J. A., III (1987) *Proc. Natl. Acad. Sci. U. S. A.* **84,** 6720–6724
46. Chantler, P. D. (1981) *Nature* **292,** 581–582
47. Korn, E. D., and Hammer, J. A., III (1988) *Annu. Rev. Biophys. Biochem.* **17,** 23–45
48. Cheney, R. E., and Mooseker, M. S. (1992) *Curr. Opin. Cell Biol.* **4,** 27–35
49. Mooseker, M. S., and Cheney, R. E. (1995) *Annu. Rev. Cell Dev. Biol.* **11,** 633–675
50. Berg, J. S., Powell, B. C., and Cheney, R. E. (2001) *Mol. Biol. Cell* **12,** 780–794
51. Korn, E. D. (2000) *Proc. Natl. Acad. Sci. U. S. A.* **97,** 12559–12564
52. Redowicz, M. J. (2002) *Acta Biochim. Pol.* **49,** 789–804
53. Hirakawa, M. J., and Takemura, R. (2003) *Trends Biochem. Sci.* **28,** 558–565
54. Gordon, D. J., Boyer, J. L., and Korn, E. D. (1977) *J. Biol. Chem.* **252,** 8300–8302
55. Vandekerckhove, J., Lal, A. A., and Korn, E. D. (1984) *J. Mol. Biol.* **172,** 141–147
56. Korn, E. D., Bowers, B., Batzri, S., Simmons, S. R., and Victoria, E. J. (1974) *J. Supramol. Struct.* **2,** 517–528
57. Wegner, A. (1976) *J. Mol. Biol.* **108,** 130–150
58. Pollard, T. D. (1986) *J. Cell Biol.* **103,** 2747–2754
59. Carlier, M. F., Pantaloni, D., and Korn, E. D. (1984) *J. Biol. Chem.* **259,** 9983–9986
60. Pollard, T. D., and Weeds, A. G. (1984) *FEBS Lett.* **170,** 94–98
61. Tobacman, L. S., Brenner, S. L., and Korn, E. D. (1983) *J. Biol. Chem.* **258,** 8806–8812
62. Mockrin, S. C., and Korn, E. D. (1980) *Biochemistry* **19,** 5359–5362
63. Pollard, T. D., and Cooper, J. A. (1984) *Biochemistry* **23,** 6631–6641
64. Hill, T. L., and Kirschner, M. W. (1982) *Proc. Natl. Acad. Sci. U. S. A.* **79,** 490–494
65. Pollard, T. D., and Borisy, G. G. (2003) *Cell* **112,** 453–465
66. Machesky, L. M., Atkinson, S. J., Ampe, C., Vandekerckhove, J., and Pollard, T. D. (1994) *J. Cell Biol.* **127,** 107–115
67. Theriot, J. A., Mitchison, T. J., Tilney, L. G., and Portnoy, D. A. (1992) *Nature* **357,** 257–260
68. Loisel, T. P., Boujemaa, R., Pantaloni, D., and Carlier, M. F. (1999) *Nature* **401,** 613–616
69. Jung, G., Remmert, K., Wu, X., Volosky, J. M., and Hammer, J. A., III (2001) *J. Cell Biol.* **153,** 1479–1497
70. Kornberg, A. (2003) *Trends Biochem. Sci.* **28,** 515–517
71. Boyle, R. (2000) http://livingheritage.org/three_princes.html
72. Rodbell, M. (1994) <http://www.nobel.se/medicine/laureates/1994/rodbell-autobio. html>
73. Book of Ruth, Chapter 1, Verse 16
74. Gall, J. G., and McIntosh, J. R. (eds.) (2001) *Landmark Papers in Cell Biology*, pp. 455–464, Cold Spring Harbor Laboratory Press, Cold Spring Harbor, NY

THE JOURNAL OF BIOLOGICAL CHEMISTRY
© 2004 by The American Society for Biochemistry and Molecular Biology, Inc.

Vol. 279, No. 21, Issue of May 21, pp. 21679–21688, 2004
Printed in U.S.A.

Reflections

A PAPER IN A SERIES COMMISSIONED TO CELEBRATE THE CENTENARY OF THE JBC IN 2005

JBC Centennial
1905–2005
100 Years of Biochemistry and Molecular Biology

My Love Affair with Insulin

Published, JBC Papers in Press, March 15, 2004, DOI 10.1074/jbc.X400002200

Christian de Duve

*From the Christian de Duve Institute of Cellular Pathology, B-1200 Brussels, Belgium and
The Rockefeller University, New York, New York 10021*

It all started with a chance encounter in the fall of 1935. As a second year medical student at the Catholic University of Louvain (Belgium) with time on my hands, I conformed to the local tradition according to which "good students" would "do a laboratory," which meant that they joined the laboratory of one of their professors and participated on a voluntary basis in whatever research was going on. This arrangement suited both parties. The professors got free manpower. The students kept out of mischief, gained experience, had fun, and (if they persevered long enough) could write up a dissertation and use it to compete for a traveling fellowship. Many a scientific career was launched in this way.

Pre-war Louvain

The Physiology Laboratory—By pure chance, I became associated with the laboratory of one of the rare, true scientists on the medical faculty. He was Joseph P. Bouckaert, the professor of physiology, who, after spending 1 year in the London laboratory of A. V. Hill, winner of the 1922 Nobel prize in medicine, had, against great odds, created a modest but thriving research laboratory. Not much of a bench worker himself, Bouckaert was greatly helped by his second in command, Pierre-Paul De Nayer, a skillful and multivalent experimenter, who ran the practical classes and supervised much of the research work. Investigators enjoyed considerable freedom under this dual guidance, productively channelled by De Nayer's technical rigor and by Bouckaert's encyclopedic knowledge and keenly analytical mind. Particularly important especially in the academic setting of a university with strong ties to the Catholic Church (I have described this setting elsewhere (1)) were Bouckaert's total dedication to basic research and his strong conviction that all phenomena of life had to be explained in strictly physical and chemical terms without calling on any sort of "vital force." Without his example, I would probably never have embraced a scientific career.

Bouckaert had no pet subject. Dedicated to teaching, he had the strange idea that the research done in his laboratory should cover every major chapter of his physiology course (which he taught single-handed in both French and Flemish, the two official languages of Belgium). Thus, in addition to the energetics of muscle contraction, the specialty of his mentor A. V. Hill, and to basal metabolism, an interest he inherited from his predecessor, the Dutch physiologist A. K. Noyons, he had groups working on the action of insulin, also started under Noyons, on kidney function, on gastric secretion, on cardiac activity, on neurobiology, and even on experimental psychology. As chance would have it, when offered the "menu," I chose to join the insulin group. I knew nothing of the field but had been attracted to it by the lurid sight of a team performing a bloody operation, which I learned later was the removal of the liver from a dog. Thus, very unromantically, started my love affair with insulin, an adventure that was to dominate my life as a budding scientist for close to 20 years.

The Hepatic Action of Insulin—When I entered Bouckaert's laboratory, insulin had been discovered only a dozen years before. Some of the best laboratories in the world were vying to solve the mechanism of action of the hormone. Two schools confronted each other, prolonging a controversy that had divided the field of diabetes research for more than 50 years. On one hand were the advocates of the liver and on the other those of the "periphery," mostly the muscles. The hepatic theory went back to Claude Bernard, the discoverer of the "glycogenic" function of the liver. Partisans of this theory attributed the characteristic hyperglycemia of diabetes to "overproduction" of glucose by the liver and believed that the main effect of insulin was to inhibit this phenomenon. The opposite theory held "underutilization" of glucose responsible for the elevated blood sugar in diabetes and viewed insulin as primarily stimulating the uptake of this sugar by the muscles.

By the time I joined the fray, as no more than a timid onlooker at first, there was general agreement on the peripheral effect, which had been convincingly demonstrated in particular by a famous team (2) that included Sir Henry Dale, who was to win the 1936 Nobel prize in medicine, Charles Best, co-discoverer of insulin with Banting but ignored by Stockholm when this discovery was recognized by the 1923 prize, and a young Belgian investigator from Louvain, Joseph P. Hoet, who had since become a distinguished diabetes specialist and was, for this reason, something of a local competitor to Bouckaert, symbolically opposing clinical to basic research. The role of the liver, however, continued to be hotly debated, with (at the time I am writing about) a distinct majority against it. Many workers, including the team just mentioned, denied any inhibition of hepatic glucose production by insulin. Some even claimed, on the strength of impressive results, that insulin actually enhanced this process, thereby helping to supply the muscles with the extra glucose they were utilizing under the influence of the hormone. Among the more committed defenders of this intellectually appealing theory were Carl and Gerty Cori in the United States, about whom I shall have more to say later.

Bouckaert's contribution to the field was modest but pertinent. He felt that studying the effect of insulin by injecting animals with the hormone was complicated by the animals' reaction to hypoglycemia, which included a discharge of epinephrine, a hormone known to stimulate hepatic glycogenolysis. Thus, it seemed quite possible that the observed enhancement of hepatic glucose production was not because of the injected insulin itself but due to epinephrine secreted by the adrenal glands in response to the elicited hypoglycemia. To avoid such artifacts, Bouckaert had devised a technique known as the "compensation" technique in which animals injected with insulin were given a continuous intravenous infusion of glucose adjusted, by trial and error, to keep the blood sugar level unchanged (3).

Others had done the same thing, of course, but with less precision. Furthermore, in Bouckaert's hands the amount of glucose injected, the so-called "compensation dose," became a quantitative measure of the effect of insulin expressed in terms of glucose consumed. Indeed, except for possible fluid expansion, the amount of glucose injected to maintain a constant blood sugar level was obviously equal to the extra amount of glucose used under the influence of the hormone.

As a first application of this technique, the group had measured the compensation dose needed by rabbits injected subcutaneously with increasing amounts of insulin. A nice hyperbolic relationship was observed, indicating saturation of a receptor and plateauing at a level, called the "maximal effect" of insulin, where further increases in the amount of insulin injected no longer increased the compensation dose (3). Subsequent experiments were all performed on animals injected with a "supramaximal" dose of insulin, thereby avoiding dosage effects. Interestingly, dogs needed considerably more glucose than did rabbits to compensate for the effect of a supramaximal dose of insulin.

As a next step, Bouckaert tackled the liver problem by the simple device of measuring the compensation dose in whole animals and in hepatectomized animals. It is at this stage that I joined the group, taking charge more and more of the conduct of the experiments as older students involved in the project left the laboratory and De Nayer became increasingly preoccupied with other projects. Similar experiments were also performed on totally eviscerated animals and on animals injected with various substances (for example, epinephrine.

The most spectacular finding and the only one of interest for the present account was that hepatectomized dogs needed considerably less glucose to be kept normoglycemic after injection of a supramaximal dose of insulin than did intact, similarly anesthetized animals. The conclusion was drawn, enthusiastically if not very critically, that the liver is the major site of insulin action. Taking our results at face value, it seemed that the hormone not only inhibits hepatic glucose production but even strongly stimulates the uptake of glucose by the liver as it does in muscle. The great controversy was finally solved. The liver was the winner, at least in quantitative terms! Before the triumph could be savored, however, the war had broken out.

Under German Occupation

In this story, which is to remain strictly scientific, I shall skip my personal participation in the conflict, which, in any case, was minimal. Let it simply be said that after some minor adventures and a lucky escape (more comical than heroic) from a prisoners column, I found myself back in Louvain able to complete my clinical training and to take my final examinations. I graduated as an M.D. in the spring of 1941 facing bleak immediate prospects but looking forward to a future that I never doubted was to see the final defeat of the Nazis.

Filling Time, Preparing for the Future—There would be much to tell of those war years, but I must stick to my subject. I did my best to pursue my goals despite the difficulties imposed by the war conditions. Having realized that my ambition to elucidate the mechanism of action of insulin on the liver could not possibly be fulfilled by the simple technologies I had used so far but required more incisive, biochemical approaches, I decided to take advantage of my enforced inactivity in the laboratory and to go back to school to learn chemistry of which I knew only the bits that were taught to medical students. I was able to do this while supporting myself by working as a clinical assistant in the cancer institute, doing mostly night duty.

Despite these demanding activities, my love affair with insulin went on unabated. Experimental work being out of the question, I decided to put our results in order and wrote them up in a series of papers that appeared between 1944 and 1946 in the *Archives Internationales de Pharmacodynamie et Thérapie*, a journal published in Ghent under the direction of Corneille Heymans, who was kind enough to accept my first efforts (4–7). In addition, I still found time for reading, wading through much of the work published until then on diabetes and insulin and organizing it in a 400-page book containing more than 1200 references. This work actually found a publisher. It appeared in 1945, simultaneously in Brussels and Paris, under the title *Glucose, Insuline et Diabète* (8). It was condensed into a dissertation containing mostly the experimental work with which I was able, in 1945, to conquer the degree of "Agrégé de l'Enseignement Supérieur," a sort of glorified Ph.D. that served as a prerequisite for obtaining a professorial position.

I also wrote an English review covering the laboratory's work on insulin as well as some of my thinking on the subject. This paper was published in *Physiological Reviews* in 1947 (9) thanks (as I remember) to the recommendation of Dale, who did not like it but felt that having been isolated during the war we should be allowed special latitude. All this writing, I must say, was very much a solo exercise. Bouckaert, whose name appeared as last author on the experimental papers and as first author on the review, left me an essentially free rein. De Nayer had left the laboratory to take over the directorship of a new sports institute, and my fellow students had disappeared without a trace. Fortunately, links of my family with England, where I was born during the previous war, had made me sufficiently familiar with the English language so that I could write an acceptable text for the review. All these activities did not prevent me from getting married in 1943 to a wonderful lady, who is still my wife today and who gave birth to our first two children in 1944 and 1946.

A central point in my thinking at the time, obviously influenced by Bouckaert's insistence on keeping the blood glucose level constant but also bolstered by much of what I had read, was that the rate of glucose utilization by the tissues, including the liver, is directly proportional to the glucose concentration in the blood independently of any hormonal influences and due simply to a mass action effect. I was particularly impressed, in defending this notion, by the work of an American investigator, Samuel Soskin, who had championed the concept of a "hepatic threshold" for glucose, defined as the blood glucose level at which glucose production and utilization by the liver exactly balance each other (10). According to Soskin, the hepatic threshold for glucose was elevated in diabetes and lowered by insulin. In this, he ran counter to the opinion held by the majority of workers, in particular the Coris, who dominated the field and (as I learned later) had made the controversy into something of a personal feud.

Blissfully unaware of these undercurrents at the time I wrote my thesis, I enthusiastically endorsed the concept of a hepatic threshold for glucose and incorporated it into a general theory of insulin action according to which the hormone has the same effects as hyperglycemia and, therefore, must favor whatever process is subject to the mass action effect of glucose concentration. Not much remains of this theory except for the fact that liver glucokinase, contrary to other hexokinases, has a high enough K_m for the rate of the reaction it catalyzes to be influenced almost linearly by concentration changes in the range of the normal blood glucose level. Theorizing apart, my reflections produced an unexpected side effect that turned out to be of some significance, not only for my career but even for the field. I rediscovered glucagon.

Glucagon, My First (Re)Discovery—Among the various papers that I had read dealing with the possible effects of insulin on the liver, one by Bridge (11) had given me special trouble because it flatly contradicted the theory that I strongly believed for many reasons to be correct. Yet I could find no fault with it as the author had kept his animals constantly hyperglycemic by a continuous infusion of glucose. Nevertheless, addition of insulin to the infused glucose, while furthering the synthesis of muscle glycogen, inhibited liver glycogen formation in a dosage-dependent fashion, offering what appeared as incontrovertible support for the Cori theory that insulin favors the transfer of glucose from the liver to the periphery. This work had worried me to such an extent that I had devoted some 4 pages to its description in the book I was writing.

Then, as told elsewhere (12), a thought suddenly flashed through my mind on a bright day in May 1944 as I was walking through the rubble-strewn streets of Louvain, which two nights before had been devastated by a disastrously misdirected bombing by allied planes. The thought focused on one word: glucagon! I knew of this substance as a hyperglycemic impurity that accompanied insulin through several purification steps but was removed by crystallization of the hormone according to a method devised by Abel (13, 14). After eliciting a flurry of interest in the late 1920s, glucagon had since been largely forgotten even though clear hints existed in the literature, as I found out later, that it may have made a comeback. What happened was that a simpler technique for crystallizing insulin in the presence of zinc had been worked out by Scott (15). Unbeknown to the investigators, the impurity had been reintroduced into insulin preparations.

That something of the kind may have happened was the suspicion that occurred to me on that day in May 1944 as a possible explanation of Bridge's results. It implied that the insulin used by the American investigator, which was made by the Lilly company, must be contaminated with glucagon, whereas the brand we used, which was British (Allan-Hanbury) before the war and Danish (Novo) during the German occupation, had to be free of this contaminant because it had given no sign of a paradoxical effect on the liver. I included this proposed interpretation in my book but had to await the availability of Lilly insulin before I could test it experimentally.

I did not have long to wait. The Allied forces entered Louvain on September 4, 1944. I duly celebrated the event on September 5 and went the next day to the American headquarters, where I managed to see a doctor and to obtain from him a few vials of the precious product. The same afternoon, with a young medical student, Henri-Géry Hers, who became my first co-worker and was to share many of my later scientific adventures, I injected some of the material into one of the rabbits that, fortunately, were still raised in the physiology institute because the institute's garden provided all the food they needed and the caretaker found them to be a profitable source of meat. I shall never forget the telltale, initial rise in blue tinge that preceded its subsequent fading in the row of test tubes containing the blood samples we had taken and had analyzed for glucose by the time-honored Folin-Benedict reaction (which relied on the reduction of cupric to cuprous ions, producing a blue color under the conditions used). Lilly insulin produced an "initial hyperglycemia," the signature of glucagon. The Danish Novo insulin, when tested in the same manner, did not cause an initial hyperglycemia. I felt like the French astronomer Le Verrier when the planet Neptune, which he had calculated must be there, was actually discovered.

Later, at Hers' suggestion, we used the compensation method to verify our prediction, adding increasing amounts of Lilly insulin to the glucose that was injected into animals treated with a supramaximal dose of Novo insulin. As more Lilly insulin (acting mostly through its glucagon because the animals were already saturated with insulin to start with) was added, less glucose had to be infused to keep the blood sugar level constant until a point was reached where *no glucose was needed at all*. A constant infusion of pure Lilly insulin entirely neutralized the combined blood sugar-lowering effects of the Novo insulin given at the start and of the true insulin present in the perfusate! Nothing of the kind happened when Novo insulin was added to the infused glucose. On the contrary, even more glucose had to be provided because the animals were kept continually saturated with the hormone.

Communicated for the first time in May 1945 at a meeting of the Société de Biologie in Brussels (16, 17), these results were included in the *Physiological Reviews* paper (9). They contributed significantly to my later acceptance by experts in the field, including the Coris. However, before coming to that stage I must briefly refer to a temporary infidelity to my beloved insulin, not because of any new infatuation but imposed by the exigencies of my training as a biochemist.

A Brief, Post-war Infidelity

For the 3 years that followed the liberation of Belgium, I had to leave insulin on the back burner and devote myself to the biochemical training I aspired to. This required my completing the dissertation for a master's degree in chemistry. I gained this degree in 1946 with a work dealing with the purification of penicillin. How this came about is a story in itself but irrelevant to the present account.

Next came actual biochemistry, which had not been part of the curriculum I had followed as it was not recognized as a valid discipline by the science faculty at that time. One of the professors of organic chemistry referred to it contemptuously as "kitchen chemistry," (actually not a bad description, historically speaking, though not in the pejorative sense in which it was meant). I acquired my biochemical training in Sweden in the laboratory of Hugo Theorell, a world renowned expert on hemoproteins. My 18-month stay in Theorell's laboratory was a valuable and memorable experience in many respects. It provided me with the basic training I needed and ended with a modest achievement, the crystallization of human myoglobin. I will not dwell on it further because it had nothing to do with insulin, which still remained on the back burner until the spring of 1947, when, nearing the end of my Swedish interlude, I started thinking of a future in which I would be reunited with the object of my passion. My dream was to inaugurate this future with a stay in the Cori laboratory at Washington University, in St. Louis, Missouri, in the United States.

I have already mentioned the Coris as the most forceful proponents of the theory that I myself held to be false. I had, because of this, conceived the naïve project of spending some time in their laboratory, never doubting for one moment that I would make them see the light that was so glaringly evident to me. I had, in the meantime, been offered and had accepted a position as lecturer in physiological chemistry in the medical school of my Louvain alma mater, and my new responsibilities required me to be on duty at the latest at the end of January 1948, which meant that I could spare only a few months for my contemplated stay in the United States.

When I wrote to Carl Cori outlining my request, his answer was coldly negative, alleging that he never accepted anybody for less than a year and adding: "With you, there is the additional difficulty that we do not see eye to eye with respect to the mechanism of action of insulin." I was shattered because our disagreement was the very reason that had motivated my application. Then, a few weeks later came a second letter from Cori: "You may be interested to hear that Dr. Earl Sutherland, in my laboratory, has just discovered that the glycogenolytic effect of insulin on liver slices is due to an impurity. I believe you have also done some work on this subject." There followed an invitation to come over and collaborate with Sutherland.

What this letter alluded to was a paper by Shipley and Humel (18) describing the stimulation of glycogen breakdown in rat liver slices incubated in the presence of insulin. This paper had attracted Cori's attention for obvious reasons, and he had asked Sutherland, who had newly joined his laboratory after a stint in the Army, to investigate the matter. As Cori's letter implied, Sutherland had found that the glycogenolytic effect was not due to insulin itself; it persisted when the hormone added (Lilly's, of course) had been inactivated by cysteine or alkaline treatment (19). I don't know to what extent he was influenced by my findings in doing this experiment, but it is clear from Cori's letters that they were familiar with my work, probably through the *Physiological Reviews* paper (9).

My efforts to secure from Belgian sources the support I needed for my projected trip were unsuccessful, but the problem was finally solved with the help of Theorell, who obtained a fellowship for me from the Rockefeller Foundation, which was supporting his laboratory. My Belgian failure thereby turned into a blessing, because my own laboratory in Belgium was later to benefit greatly from my early association with this powerful foundation.

St. Louis

I spent only four months in the Cori laboratory, from the beginning of September to the end of December 1947. I did not see much of the Coris and never had my projected discussion with them. One reason for this was that 1 month after our arrival the Coris had received news that they were jointly awarded one half of the 1947 Nobel prize in medicine (the other half went to the Argentinian Bernardo Houssay) for their "discovery of the catalytic conversion of glycogen." I hasten to add that we met many times after that and became great personal friends.

The announcement from Stockholm created much excitement in the laboratory. Having been privileged to attend the Nobel ceremonies the year before (through Theorell, who was a member of the Nobel Committee for medicine), my wife and I became something of experts on the topic. My wife, in particular, was able to give Gerty, who paid little attention to her attire, some valuable advice concerning dresses. I myself remembered (although it had not struck me at the time) how a few months earlier Theorell had quizzed me on the Cori achievements, which were not in his personal field of expertise.

My disagreement with the famous couple with respect to the hepatic action of insulin did not, of course, blind me to their enormous merits. They were among the founders of metabolic biochemistry. In particular, their discovery of *phosphorolysis*, the splitting of a bond with inorganic phosphate, had been an illuminating key to the understanding of bioenergetics, showing how the energy that would normally be dissipated by hydrolysis could be conserved in the generated phosphate ester bond. This finding paved the way for the discovery of RNA phosphorylase by Marianne Grunberg-Manago and Severo Ochoa (a Cori pupil), which played a major role in the unraveling of the genetic code, and to the discovery by Arthur Kornberg (another Cori pupil) of DPN (NAD) *pyrophosphorolysis*, a reaction that, reversed, was to account for the biosynthesis of the coenzyme and in due course for that of DNA.

Interestingly, a Cori finding that had particularly caught the attention of the Nobel Committee was the observation that purified glycogen phosphorylase, when incubated with glucose 1-phosphate (the "Cori ester") and a glycogen primer, catalyzed the synthesis of glycogen or, to be more precise, of an amylose-like, linear glucose polymer (branching had not yet been discovered) that gave a blue color with iodine instead of the normal mahogany tinge (the so-called "blue" glycogen). For the first time, it was hailed, a biological macromolecule had been synthesized in the test tube. What was not known at the time is that this feat was a pure artifact. Phosphorylase never synthesizes glycogen in living cells, the local concentration of inorganic phosphate being such that the phosphorolytic direction is always favored. It befell the Argentinian Luis Leloir (yet another Cori pupil) to identify the true mechanism of glycogen synthesis (from UDP-glucose). Needless to say, this historical detail in no way detracts from the monumental importance of the Cori contributions.

My memories of the Cori laboratory bring up the image of a beehive in which small individual groups worked in separate laboratories on distinct problems, which they were not encouraged to discuss with each other. Already in those days, competition weighed on personal relations and fraud was not absent. The Coris themselves were victims of fraud by one of their co-workers and had to rescind a paper. The "omerta" law was poorly observed; we were all members of a happy family and freely talked science when we met on social occasions.

Because of the pressure of time, my personal contacts were largely restricted to Earl Sutherland. He was very different from me in temperament. Outwardly jovial and easygoing, he rarely betrayed (behind a deceptively casual and self-deprecating attitude) the intensity of the passion that drove him. Only when he was opposed and convinced he was right did he become obstinately unyielding. Anything but a Cartesian, he had a keen mind but a baffling, circumlocutory way of expressing himself, often voicing only the final conclusion of some long internal monologue that was left to be guessed but, when divined, often proved strikingly pertinent. His approach to research was essentially pragmatic and intuitive, seeming to rely more on instinct and flair than on rational reasoning. Typically, when we later independently tried to elucidate the mechanism of the glycogenolytic effect of glucagon and epinephrine, he unerringly picked on phosphorylase as the target of the hormonal action, a finding that eventually led him to discover cyclic AMP. On my part, I had tried every possibility I could think of but had excluded phosphorylase *a priori* because the enzyme was believed (see above) to catalyze the synthesis as well as the breakdown of glycogen and I knew that "the activity of a catalyst is without influence on the equilibrium of the reaction it catalyzes." Earl knew it too, but the knowledge did not constrain him.

Despite our differences in personality, we made an excellent team and became close friends. We shared a burning interest in our problem, a concern for quality, and an almost untiring capacity for work, often laboring until late at night before ending for a snack in the only diner of the neighborhood that was still open, a hovel called "The Pig's Ear." A skillful experimenter, Earl taught me much, including his gift for cutting thin liver slices that continued to perform beautifully when incubated *in vitro*.

Our partnership proved fruitful. In four hectic months, we showed that glucagon is made by no other tissue than the pancreas except, surprisingly, the gastric mucosa and certain other parts of the digestive tract. Using a variety of approaches, we obtained strong evidence indicating that pancreatic glucagon was probably a hormone made in the endocrine islets by cells different from the insulin-producing beta cells, presumably the alpha cells (20). Incidentally, we did not call the substance "glucagon." Earl had taken a strange dislike to this term and insisted on the cumbersome name of hyperglycemic-glycogenolytic factor or H-G factor. Several years later I decided to reinstate the old name (21) after having read Warburg's memoirs, in which the great German biochemist recalled an old dispute with David Keilin concerning the name of the "respiratory enzyme," settling the matter by categorically stating that "it is the right of the discoverer to name his discovery." It seemed to me that this right belonged to the original discoverer of glucagon, an American named J. R. Murlin, and that we had no right to change his chosen term just because we didn't like the sound of it.

This is as far as we could go. Only after I returned to Belgium was I able to bolster the alpha cell hypothesis further by showing, in collaboration with Charles Vuylsteke, that treating guinea pigs with cobalt (which my colleague, the anatomy professor Ernest Van Campenhout, had found to selectively damage the islet alpha cells) caused a drastic lowering of the glucagon content of the pancreas (22). We also found that the pancreas of birds, which is particularly rich in alpha cells, has a correspondingly high content of glucagon (23).

Our St. Louis findings were published under the names of Sutherland and de Duve (20). The Coris generously refused to add their names on the paper, which they could have done but felt they had no right to do, not having participated in the work in any way. My suggestion that the credit be shared equally between Earl and myself by splitting the publication into two papers, with each of us appearing as first author on one, was adamantly turned down by Earl. It was one of the rare occasions when his inner ego was allowed to surface.

My stay in St. Louis yielded other dividends. First, it brought me in contact with the Lilly company, which, far from penalizing me for showing their product to be impure, actually took over the purification and sequencing of glucagon (24, 25) and, in addition, generously added me to the small, privileged network of investigators (including, prominently, the Coris) they supported financially and invited regularly to their annual "Insulin Conferences" in Indianapolis. Without this invaluable support, I would never have been able to start a successful laboratory after my return to Belgium or to establish the many early links with American investigators that greatly helped me to put our work "on the map." Note that this no-strings-attached bounty even continued for a while after I had left the insulin field. The 1955 paper in which the word "lysosome" first appeared acknowledges the generous support of the Lilly Research Laboratories (26)!

My return journey from St. Louis was also rewarding. It took me to Toronto, where I was kindly received by Charles Best; to Chicago, where I met Rachmiel Levine, a former associate of Soskin who, himself, was no longer active in the field; to Boston, where I called on Baird Hastings, a leader in the study of carbohydrate metabolism, and, especially, on Fritz Lipmann, one of my heroes, with whom I formed a lasting relationship; and, finally, to New York, where I paid my first visit to the legendary Rockefeller Institute for Medical Research to call on my famous countryman Albert Claude. He received me with great friendliness and gave me some of his reprints, which turned out to be of crucial importance in my later research. He also took time to introduce me to "a young man you may like to meet," George Palade. Little did we suspect at that time that I would myself join Rockefeller some 15 years later; even less did we suspect that the three of us would one day be invited to Stockholm together. I owe an immense debt to that day in May 1944, when, amid the rubble of fuming ruins, inspiration whispered the word "glucagon" into my brain.

Back in Belgium

The rest of my story has been told elsewhere (27). Briefly summarized, it starts with the efforts made by the little team of outstanding young co-workers I had the good fortune to assemble right from the start (Henri-Géry Hers, already mentioned, and two medical students, Jacques Berthet and Lucie Dupret, soon to become Mrs. Berthet) to characterize the hexose phosphatase shown by the Coris to account for the unique ability of the liver to form free glucose. The rationale for this work was that this enzyme might be responsible for the difficulties experienced in attempts to demonstrate an effect of insulin on isolated liver tissue and, thus, that more needed to be known about its properties and regulation.

Identified as a specific glucose 6-phosphatase, different from the unspecific acid phosphatase, the enzyme was found to be irreversibly precipitated at acid pH, a property that my acquaintance with Claude's work allowed me to interpret as evidence that the enzyme was attached to some intracellular structure. This surmise, in turn, led to our using Claude's technique of differential centrifugation, as modified by his pupil Walter Schneider, to identify the structure in question, which was found to accompany the fraction called "small granules" or "microsomes" by Claude (28).

Further work carried out largely by a medical student, Henri Beaufay, who had joined the group by then, showed glucose 6-phosphatase to be firmly attached to a lipoprotein structure (now identified with endoplasmic reticulum membranes) (29). Given the technologies of the day, it is doubtful that we would have progressed much further, let alone solved the problem, because even today the control of glucose 6-phosphatase activity in the liver is still poorly understood. However, serendipity knocked on our door with the complicity of an enzyme, acid phosphatase, that held not the slightest interest for us but was included in our assays because of earlier work in which it had served as background for the characterization of glucose 6-phosphatase (see above).

To cut a long story short, acid phosphatase revealed itself as both particle-bound and "latent" in fresh liver preparations, losing both properties simultaneously upon aging of the preparations under mild conditions. The "hidden enzyme" proved an irresistible attraction. Insulin, my beloved, was ignominiously dropped, and all my energies were spent chasing after the elusive new particles. They turned out to be digestive bodies or "lysosomes" (26) and close by were hidden other particles, the "peroxisomes" (30). With apologies for putting further strain on an already exhausted metaphor, these two particles became my paramour and remained so for most of the years that followed. They kept me and a large number of collaborators on both sides of the Atlantic wholly engaged for the remainder of my scientific career.

The break with my former love was not brutal. That affair dragged along for a few more years, during which I tried to keep insulin and glucagon alive in the laboratory and enjoyed the satisfaction of witnessing the demonstration that the conversion of labeled glucose to hepatic glycogen, both in intact rabbits and in isolated rabbit liver slices, is enhanced, modestly but significantly, both by an increase in glucose concentration and by adequately compensated insulin, while being inhibited by glucagon (31). Two lectures, my insulin swan songs, landmark that period for me. In 1952, I was invited to give the Banting Memorial Lecture of the British Diabetic Association at the First Congress of the International Diabetes Federation in Leiden. I spoke on glucagon (21). In 1956, I attended a meeting at the CIBA Foundation in London, where I last met Gerty Cori a few months before her indomitable spirit finally succumbed to the fatal disease that first declared itself at the very time of my stay in St. Louis, as recalled in this journal by Kornberg (32). I spoke on the hepatic action of insulin, receiving a sympathetic reception from Gerty and Carl, both of whom I recall with deep emotion (33).

Fortunately for the field, Hers did not, unlike my other co-workers, follow me in my new research direction. He remained faithful to carbohydrate metabolism to which he contributed a number of valuable findings, starting with the elucidation of the pathway of fructose metabolism, the "Hers pathway," which he found to involve the aldolase-mediated splitting of fructose 1-phosphate rather than the conversion of this ester to fructose 6-phosphate by a mutase, as postulated by the Coris, once more crossing paths with the famous pair. Later, he made many detailed contributions to our understanding of glycogen metabolism and its control culminating in his discovery (with Emile Van Schaftingen and Louis Hue, who brilliantly follow in his footsteps today) of fructose 2,6-bisphosphate (34). Who would have thought that a hexose phosphate ester was still waiting to be discovered 50 years after the isolation of glucose 1-phosphate by the Coris?

In his work on glycogen, Hers had become interested in the congenital anomalies of glycogen metabolism, and in particular the glycogen storage diseases, which had been Gerty Cori's last research interest. After her death, he pursued her work and undertook a systematic search for the missing enzyme, using pathological specimens of these rare conditions collected from various clinical centers. This is how he ran into the mysterious type II glycogenosis (Pompe's disease) in which all the known enzymes of glycogen breakdown showed normal levels and the patients even responded normally to glucagon and epinephrine. However, the liver, muscles, and heart of these patients showed grossly elevated glycogen contents, leading to the death of the victims at an early age. Eventually Hers succeeded in identifying the deficient enzyme, which turned out to be an α-glucosidase with an acid pH optimum, not previously known to have anything to do with glycogen metabolism.

In another laboratory such a finding might long have remained unexplained. In ours, an acid hydrolase immediately called to mind lysosomes. The technology was available, and the enzyme was rapidly identified as, indeed, belonging to lysosomes. On the strength of this discovery, Hers proposed his concept of inborn lysosomal disease (35), an enormously fruitful notion that turned out to apply successfully to most polysaccharidoses, lipidoses, and other storage diseases (36). Thus was elucidated, with important consequences for diagnosis, prevention, and therapy, a vast chapter of pathology that had remained totally mysterious until then, and thus had the unpredictable fortuities of research brought Hers and myself back together years after our paths had diverged.

The Moral of the Story

It may seem inappropriate to use the term "moral" in connection with a love affair that ended in betrayal, but I should like to formulate three recommendations derived from the experience.

First, choose your mentors well. The art of scientific research is not learned in books. It is, like the crafts in the Middle Ages, learned at the bench under the direction of a master. It has been my good fortune to work under and with a number of such masters, each of whom has taught the importance of technical excellence, rigorous reasoning, and intellectual honesty.

I should add, for the benefit of those who are becoming mentors themselves, that it is equally important to choose one's co-workers well. I have been blessed with a number of outstanding collaborators without whom I would never have accomplished the work that is credited to me.

Second, keep your eyes open for the odd or unexpected and never dismiss it simply because it does not fit within your program. If chance offers you a clue, follow the trail. You may not discover what you were looking for, but what you discover may be more interesting than what you were looking for. In retrospect, I find that my greatest luck came from the unforeseen: insulin that wasn't and mitochondria that weren't.

My last recommendation is for the powers that be. Fund the investigator, not the investigation. Do please remember, I beseech you, this self-evident yet rarely recognized truth that science, at least its spearhead called basic research, explores the unknown and is therefore unable, by definition, to predict how useful or profitable its discoveries will be. Rather than demanding assurances on this account that cannot possibly be honestly provided, put your trust in the investigator's skill, instinct, curiosity, and motivation. This will produce the best research contributing best to the advancement of knowledge, the true aim of science. Whether useful or profitable applications arise from new knowledge will be revealed only after the fact.

Acknowledgments—I am indebted to Émile Van Schaftingen for fruitful discussions and to Neil Patterson for valuable help in making this paper readable. This article is dedicated to the memory of Carl and Gerty Cori.

Address correspondence to: deduve@icp.ucl.ac.be.

REFERENCES

1. de Duve, C. (2002) *Life Evolving*, Oxford University Press, New York
2. Best, C. H., Dale, H. H., Hoet, J. P., and Marks, H. P. (1926) Oxidation and storage of glucose under the action of insulin. *Proc. R. Soc. Lond. B* **100,** 55–71
3. Bouckaert, J. P., De Nayer, P. P., and Krekels, R. (1929) Équilibre glucose-insuline. *Arch. Int. Physiol.* **31,** 180–193
4. de Duve, C., and Bouckaert, J. P. (1944) Nouvelles recherches concernant l'action de l'insuline. I. Influence de la hauteur de glycémie sur l'action de l'insuline chez l'animal normal. *Arch. Int. Pharmacodyn. Thér.* **69,** 486–501
5. de Duve, C., De Nayer, P. P., Van Oostveldt, M., and Bouckaert, J. P. (1945) Nouvelles recherches concernant l'action de l'insuline. II. Influence de l'insuline chez l'animal normal, hépatectomisé et éviscéré. *Arch. Int. Pharmacodyn. Thér.* **70,** 78–98
6. de Duve, C., De Nayer, P. P., De Keyser, J., and Bouckaert, J. P. (1945) Nouvelles recherches concernant l'action de l'insuline. III. Influence de divers facteurs expérimentaux sur l'action hépatique de l'insuline. *Arch. Int.*

Pharmacodyn. Thér. **70**, 383–393

7. de Duve, C., Marin, G., and Bouckaert, J. P. (1946) Nouvelles recherches concernant l'action de l'insuline. V. Influence de l'adrénaline sur l'équilibre glucose-insuline. *Arch. Int. Pharmacodyn. Thér.* **72**, 29–38

8. de Duve, C. (1945) *Glucose, Insuline et Diabète*, Masson et Cie, Paris

9. Bouckaert, J. P., and de Duve, C. (1989) (1947) The action of insulin. *Physiol. Rev.* **27**, 39–71; reprinted in *Nutrition* **5**, 375–409

10. Soskin, S., and Levine, R. (1937) A relationship between blood sugar level and the rate of sugar utilization, affecting the theories of diabetes. *Am. J. Physiol.* **120**, 761–770

11. Bridge, E. M. (1938) The action of insulin on glycogen reserves. *Bull. Johns Hopkins Hosp.* **62**, 408–421

12. de Duve, C. (1994) Born-again glucagon. *FASEB J.* **5**, 979–981

13. Abel, J. J. (1926) Crystalline insulin. *Proc. Natl. Acad. Sci. U. S. A.* **12**, 132–136

14. Geiling, E. M. K., and de Lawder, A. M. (1930) Studies on crystalline insulin; does insulin cause initial hyperglycemia? *J. Pharmacol. Exp. Ther.* **39**, 369–385

15. Scott, D. A. (1934) Crystalline insulin. *Biochem. J.* **28**, 1592–1602

16. de Duve, C., and Hers, H. G. (1947) La prétendue action glycogénolytique de l'insuline. *C. R. Soc. Biol.* **141**, 1147

17. de Duve, C., Hers, H. G., and Bouckaert, J. P. (1946) Nouvelles recherches concernant l'action de l'insuline. VI. Action de l'insuline sur le glycogène du foie. *Arch. Int. Pharmacodyn. Thér.* **72**, 45–61

18. Shipley, R. A., and Humel, E. J., Jr. (1945) Carbohydrate and acetone body metabolism of liver slices and the effect of insulin. *Am. J. Physiol.* **144**, 51–57

19. Sutherland, E. W., and Cori, C. F. (1948) Influence of insulin preparations on glycogenolysis in liver slices. *J. Biol. Chem.* **172**, 737–750

20. Sutherland, E. W., and de Duve, C. (1948) Origin and distribution of the hyperglycemic-glycogenolytic factor of the pancreas. *J. Biol. Chem.* **175**, 663–674

21. de Duve, C. (1953) Glucagon, the hyperglycaemic glycogenolytic factor of the pancreas. *Lancet* **265**, 99–104

22. Vuylsteke, C. A., Cornelis, G., and de Duve, C. (1952) Influence du traitement au cobalt sur le contenu en facteur H-G du pancréas de cobaye. *Arch. Int. Physiol.* **60**, 128–131

23. Vuylsteke, C. A., and de Duve, C. (1953) Le contenu en glucagon du pancréas aviaire. *Arch. Int. Physiol.* **61**, 273–274

24. Staub, A., Sinn, L. G., and Behrens, O. K. (1955) Purification and crystallization of glucagon. *J. Am. Chem. Soc.* **79**, 2807–2810

25. Bromer, W. W., Sinn, L. G., and Behrens, O. K. (1957) The amino acid sequence of glucagon. V. Location of amide groups, acid degradation studies, and summary of sequential evidence. *J. Am. Chem. Soc.* **79**, 3608

26. de Duve, C., Pressman, B. C., Gianetto, R., Wattiaux, R., and Appelmans, F. (1955) Tissue fractionation studies. 6. Intracellular distribution patterns of enzymes in rat-liver tissue. *Biochem. J.* **60**, 604–617

27. de Duve, C. (1969) The lysosome in retrospect. in *Lysosomes in Biology and Pathology, Volume 1* (Dingle, J. T., and Fell, H. B., eds) pp. 3–40, North-Holland Publishing Company, Amsterdam

28. Hers, H. G., Berthet, J., Berthet, L., and de Duve, C. (1951) Le système hexose-phosphatasique. III. Localisation intracellulaire des ferments par centrifugation fractionnée. *Bull. Soc. Chim. Biol.* **33**, 21–41

29. Beaufay, H., and de Duve, C. (1954) Le système hexose-phosphatasique. VI. Essais de démembrement des microsomes porteurs de glucose 6-phosphatase. *Bull. Soc. Chim. Biol.* **36**, 1551–1568

30. de Duve, C. (1996) The peroxisome in retrospect. *Ann. N. Y. Acad. Sci.* **804**, 1–10

31. Berthet, J., Jacques, P., Hers, H. G., and de Duve, C. (1956) Influence de l'insuline et du glucagon sur la synthèse du glycogène hépatique. *Biochim. Biophys. Acta* **20**, 190–200

32. Kornberg, A. (2001) Remembering our teachers. *J. Biol. Chem.* **276**, 3–11

33. de Duve, C. (1956) The hepatic action of insulin. *CIBA Found. Colloq. Endocrinol.* **9**, 203–222

34. Van Schaftingen, E., Hue, L., and Hers, H. G. (1980) Fructose 2,6-bisphosphate, the probable structure of the glucose- and glucagon-sensitive stimulator of phosphofructokinase. *Biochem. J.* **192**, 897–901

35. Hers, H. G. (1965) Inborn lysosomal diseases. *Gastroenterology* **48**, 625–633

36. Hers, H. G., and Van Hoof, F. (eds.) (1973) *Lysosomes and Storage Diseases*, Academic Press, New York

The Journal of Biological Chemistry
© 2004 by The American Society for Biochemistry and Molecular Biology, Inc.

Vol. 279, No. 27, Issue of July 2, pp. 27831–27836, 2004
Printed in U.S.A.

Reflections

A PAPER IN A SERIES COMMISSIONED TO CELEBRATE THE CENTENARY OF THE JBC IN 2005

JBC Centennial
1905–2005
100 Years of Biochemistry and Molecular Biology

A Short History of the Thermodynamics of Enzyme-catalyzed Reactions

Published, JBC Papers in Press, April 8, 2004, DOI 10.1074/jbc.X400003200

Robert A. Alberty

From the Department of Chemistry, Massachusetts Institute of Technology, Cambridge, Massachusetts 02319

The first and second laws of thermodynamics were known before Gibbs wrote his great paper "Equilibrium of Heterogeneous Substances" that was published in the *Transactions of the Connecticut Academy* in 1876 (1), but he completely changed the character of thermodynamics by showing it obeyed all the rules of calculus and introducing the chemical potential μ and what we now call the Gibbs energy, G. Obeying the rules of calculus means that there are many relationships between various thermodynamic properties. The introduction of the chemical potential made it possible to treat chemical reactions. The first law introduces the internal energy U that provides the criterion for spontaneous change and equilibrium at constant volume V and entropy S. The enthalpy H is defined by

$$H = U + PV \qquad \text{(Eq. 1)}$$

and it provides the criterion for spontaneous change and equilibrium at constant pressure and entropy. The Helmholtz energy A is defined by

$$A = U - TS \qquad \text{(Eq. 2)}$$

and it provides the criterion for spontaneous change and equilibrium at constant volume and temperature. This is beginning to look useful in the laboratory except that chemistry is usually carried out at constant pressure and temperature. Gibbs defined the property G, which we now call the Gibbs energy, as follows.

$$G = H - TS \qquad \text{(Eq. 3)}$$

The Gibbs energy provides the criterion for spontaneous change and equilibrium at constant temperature and pressure. These three definitions are what we now refer to as Legendre transforms. Legendre transforms are the most significant concept in this short history. Note that Equations 1–3 each involve a product of conjugate variables that yields energy. Everybody knows that the variables in an equation can be changed by simply substituting an equation for one of the variables in terms of a new variable. Not everybody knows that a derivative can be introduced as a new variable, but Gibbs did. I wrote a review on Legendre transforms in 1994 (2), and later I chaired an IUPAC Committee that wrote a Technical Report on Legendre transforms (3). Two more Legendre transforms will be used in these Reflections.

Before going further, we must be clear about what thermodynamics can tell us about a reaction system. Callen (4) has written: "Prediction of the new equilibrium state is the central problem of thermodynamics." Thermodynamic measurements on systems at equilibrium can be used to calculate properties that can be used to predict whether reactions in a system will go to the right or the left under a given set of conditions in addition to making it possible to calculate the equilibrium composition. It is not necessary to have measurements on the actual reactions in the system to do this because other pathways can be used to calculate the equilibrium composition. Rather than tabulating equilibrium constants of chemical reactions, chemists recognized a long time ago that the most efficient way to store thermodynamic information on chemical reactions was to make tables of the standard Gibbs energies of formation, $\Delta_f G^0$, standard enthalpies of formation, $\Delta_f H^0$, and standard molar entropies, S_m, of species (5).

Early Measurements of Equilibrium Constants of Enzyme-catalyzed Reactions

Robert N. Goldberg has told me that the first reported measurement of the equilibrium constant of an enzyme-catalyzed reaction was published by Quastel and Woolf in 1926 (6) on the aspartate ammonia-lyase reaction.

$$\text{Aspartic acid = fumaric acid + ammonia} \qquad \text{(Eq. 4)}$$

They summarized their experimental data with the following equation.

$$K = \frac{[\text{fumaric acid}][\text{NH}_3]}{[\text{aspartic acid}]} = 0.040 \text{ at pH 7.4 and 37 °C} \qquad \text{(Eq. 5)}$$

Several more equilibrium constants were determined in the 1930s and even more in the 1940s, but it was not until 1953 when Burton joined Krebs (7) that the field began to get organized. In their article about the Gibbs energy changes associated with the individual steps of the tricarboxylic acid cycle, glycolysis, and alcoholic fermentation and with the hydrolysis of the pyrophosphate groups of adenosine triphosphate, they referred to an article by Alberty *et al.* (8), which notes the fact that the ΔG^0 for the hydrolysis of ATP becomes practically independent of pH below 6.3. So how did I get involved with ATP? I was very fortunate to have worked on the wartime Medical Research Council project on plasma proteins centered at Harvard Medical School under the direction of Prof. Edwin Cohn from June 1944 to January 1947. I worked for Prof. J. W. Williams at the University of Wisconsin on plasma fractionation and submitted my Ph.D. thesis on the electrophoresis of plasma proteins in June 1947. As an instructor at the University of Wisconsin I looked for new ways to use the Tiselius moving boundary electrophoresis apparatus and measured amounts of AMP and ADP in commercial preparations of ATP that were just then becoming available. To understand the changes in mobility of ATP with pH, a couple of my first graduate students and I determined the pK values of these substances and the dissociation constants of their magnesium complex ions (8).

I wanted to move into enzyme kinetics and was interested in the ideas of Prof. Pauling, so I arranged to spend the academic year of 1950–1951 at Cal Tech. I chose to work on fumarase because I was able to get one of the first Beckman DU spectrometers equipped with a strip chart recorder. Although I was primarily interested in rates, this research brought me into contact with thermodynamics in a couple of ways. In 1953 Bock and I (9) determined the apparent equilibrium constant for the reaction fumarate + H_2O = L-malate as a function of pH and temperature. Because we were able to determine the Michaelis constants and maximum velocities in both the forward and reverse directions, we were able to confirm the Haldane relation between these kinetic constants and the equilibrium constant. The next year Frieden, Bock, and I were able to crystallize fumarase and to determine its sedimentation coefficient (10). In the same year, Massey joined us as a postdoctoral fellow, and we studied the effects of pH on the kinetic constants and developed ways to represent these effects with simple equations (11). In 1958 Hammes and I showed that the binding of substrates by fumarase was diffusion-controlled (12).

Production of the First Tables of Standard Thermodynamic Properties of Species of Biochemical Reactants

In 1957 Krebs and Kornberg published "Energy Transformations in Living Matter" (13), and Burton was the author of the Appendix "Free Energy Data of Biological Interest." Burton made a table of standard Gibbs energies of formation of species from chemical thermodynamic sources and from measurements of equilibrium constants of enzyme-catalyzed reactions. He used this table to calculate equilibrium constants of a number of reactions using the convention that the "$\Delta G'$ (for the reaction at pH 7) is identical with the ΔG^0 except that the standard condition of H^+ ion is that of the pH specified (usually 7) instead of 1 molal activity (pH 0)." This works fine when the reactants are single species (like fumarate and L-malate at pH 7), but it does not work for a reactant like ATP at pH 7.

I had a wonderful time working on enzyme kinetics with graduate students and postdoctoral fellows, but in 1961, I became Associate Dean of Letters and Science and in 1963 I became Dean of the Graduate School at the University of Wisconsin. At first I carried out a nearly normal research program, but I had less and less time to spend with my graduate students. In 1967 I moved to MIT to be Dean of the School of Science. Although I did not have a laboratory, I wanted to do some research, and the availability of help from the Computer Laboratory led me to write two theoretical papers on the hydrolysis of ATP (14, 15). Phillips and co-workers (16) had published earlier papers, and we were in pretty good agreement. By this time, the problem that Burton had with ATP was avoided by using a balanced reference reaction written in terms of species and a binding polynomial for each reactant. Guynn and Veech (17) carried out a number of interesting studies (for example, studies of the reactions catalyzed by phosphate acetyltransferase and acetate kinase).

In the early 1970s, Edsall and others felt that it was a good time to seek international agreement on nomenclature and symbols for biochemical thermodynamics. A Commission was formed with Gutfreund and Privalov representing the International Union of Biochemistry (IUB), Edsall and Jencks representing the International Union of Pure and Applied Biophysics (IUPAB), Wadsö (Chairman) representing the International Union of Pure and Applied Chemistry, and associate member Biltonen. I was invited to join the Commission, but I was too busy to do it. I corresponded with the Commission and was basically in agreement with their recommendations (18). They recommended the symbol K' for the apparent equilibrium constant and $\Delta G^{0'} = -RT\ln K'$ for the standard Gibbs energy of reaction at a specified temperature, pH, and ionic strength. As the field of biochemical thermodynamics continued to grow, four important additions and improvements were made. Wilhoit (19) extended the Burton table by including standard enthalpies of formation of species. Thauer and co-workers (20) included inorganic species and suggested that $\Delta G^{0'}$ can be calculated using $\Delta G^0 + m\Delta G'(H^+)$, where $\Delta G'(H^+)$ is equal to the Gibbs energy of hydrogen ions at the experimental pH and is negative when more protons are consumed than formed. Goldberg and Tewari (21) made a very thorough evaluation of the literature data on the pentoses and hexoses. Miller and Smith-Magowan (22) reviewed and evaluated the data on the Krebs cycle and related compounds.

Learning about Legendre Transforms

Jeffries Wyman had been working on the thermodynamics of the equilibria involving hemoglobin since before 1948, and he and Stanley Gill published their book on binding and linkage in 1990 (23). Ligand binding was considered to be a separate field, but researchers on enzyme-catalyzed reactions recognized that some ideas like linkage $(\partial N_H/\partial pMg) = (\partial N_{Mg}/\partial pH)$ applied in both fields. Wyman understood how to use Legendre transforms, and he and Stanley Gill discussed them in the last chapter of their book. I had heard of Legendre transforms, but I did not learn about them from Wyman. To show how I learned to use Legendre transforms, I have to write about my leaving the Dean's Office in 1982 and going back to teaching physical chemistry.

Except for my papers on ATP hydrolysis in 1968 and 1969, my administrative responsibilities had kept me too busy to do any research or even to stay current with research on enzyme kinetics and the thermodynamic of enzyme-catalyzed reactions. In thinking about starting research again, I knew I wanted to use computers to study complicated reaction systems, but I practically had to start over in research. The oil shock of 1972 made me worry about what the world was going to do when the petroleum supplies began to decrease. I applied to the Department of Energy to work on coal liquefaction, and I was turned down. However, they were willing to support me to work on petroleum processing, and so I began to learn about hydrocarbons and global ways of making calculations on systems with literally millions of different molecules. I learned how to calculate standard Gibbs energies of formation of isomer groups, such as the decanes, assuming the isomers are rapidly interconverted. I learned to use Benson's group additivity method to estimate thermodynamic properties of gas molecules for which there was no experimental data. I also learned how to use matrices in calculations of equilibrium compositions of very large systems of reactions by using computer programs. In 1988 I joined with Irwin Oppenheim to apply statistical mechanics to these systems (24). When the partial pressure of ethylene is held constant, a semigrand ensemble can be used to calculate the equilibrium distribution of alkyl benzenes, and Irwin and I began to realize that in our calculations we were inventing a new thermodynamic potential, that is we were using a Legendre transform. My "eureka" moment came when I realized that these new thermodynamic concepts applied to biochemistry because the pH is treated as an independent variable, and so the Gibbs energy G does not provide the criterion for spontaneous change and equilibrium. I applied to NIH for support and have been funded for the past decade to make a new type of biochemical thermodynamic table and new types of thermodynamic calculations on biochemical reaction systems.

Transformed Thermodynamic Properties of Biochemical Reactants and Reactions

To define a transformed Gibbs energy G' of a biochemical reaction system at specified temperature, pH, and ionic strength that does provide the criterion for spontaneous change and equilibrium, we have to use a Legendre transform, that is we have to continue the process described in Equations 1–3. This time we have to subtract from the Gibbs energy G the product of conjugate variables involved with the pH. The specified chemical potential of hydrogen ions $\mu(H^+)$, which is related to the pH, has to be multiplied by its conjugate variable, the total amount of hydrogen atoms in the system that is represented by $n_c(H)$. Here n_c stands for the amount of a component, which is something that is conserved (25). The transformed Gibbs energy G' is defined as follows (26, 27).

$$G' = G - n_c(H)\mu(H^+) \tag{Eq. 6}$$

The chemical potential of hydrogen ions at a specified pH is given by

$$\mu(H^+) = \mu(H^+) + RT\ln[H^+] = \mu(H^+) - RT\ln(10)\text{pH} \tag{Eq. 7}$$

where $\mu(H^+)$ is the chemical potential of hydrogen ions at unit activity. The amount of the hydrogen component in the system is given by $n_c(H) = \Sigma N_H(j)n(j)$, where $N_H(j)$ is the number of hydrogen atoms in species j and $n(j)$ is the amount of species j. The Gibbs energy of the system is additive as shown by $G = \Sigma\mu n(j)$, and the transformed Gibbs energy is additive as shown by $G' = \Sigma\mu'n(j)$, where $\mu'(j)$ is the transformed chemical potential of species j. Substituting these relations into Equation 6 leads to the following equation.

$$\Delta_f G'^0(j) = \Delta_f G^0(j) + RT\ln[j] - N_H(j)[\Delta_f G^0(H^+) - RT\ln(10)\text{pH}] \tag{Eq. 8}$$

In writing this equation, chemical potentials have been replaced by Gibbs energies of formation $\Delta_f G$, as is customary in dealing with experimental data. The remarkable thing about this equation is that it turns out that the transformed Gibbs energies of formation $\Delta_f G'^0$ for the various protonated forms of a reactant like ATP are equal at a specified pH when the species are at chemical equilibrium! The standard Gibbs energies of formation $\Delta_f G^0$ of the species ATP^{4-}, $HATP^{3-}$, and H_2ATP^{2-} with respect to the elements at 298.15 K and zero ionic strength are -2768.10, -2811.48, and -2838.18 kJ mol^{-1} (28, 29). When these species are at equilibrium at pH 5.90 and 0.25 M ionic strength, their concentrations are 2.133×10^{-3}, 7.806×10^{-3}, and 6.568×10^{-5} M, respectively, in a 0.01 M solution of ATP. The transformed Gibbs energy of formation $\Delta_f G'^0$ calculated using Equation 8 is -2382.35 kJ mol^{-1} for each of the three species. Therefore, we can say that the transformed Gibbs energy of the sum of the three species, referred to as ATP, is -2382.35 kJ mol^{-1} at 298.15 K, pH 5.90, and 0.25 M ionic strength when the ATP concentration is 0.01 M. At equilibrium at a specified pH, the three species of ATP are pseudoisomers, that is they have the same transformed Gibbs energies of formation just like isomers have the same Gibbs energies of formation when they are in equilibrium.

The equation for the standard transformed Gibbs energy of formation of species j is obtained using Equation 8 with $[j] = 1.000$ M.

$$\Delta_f G'^0(j) = \Delta_f G^0(j) - N_H(j)[\Delta_f G^0(H^+) - RT\ln(10)\text{pH}] \tag{Eq. 9}$$

Thus if we know the standard Gibbs energy of formation of a species $\Delta_f G^0(j)$, its standard transformed Gibbs energy of formation $\Delta_f G'^0(j)$ can be calculated at a specified temperature, pH, and ionic strength. The next question is "How do you calculate the standard transformed Gibbs energy of formation $\Delta_f G'^0$ of a reactant i, like ATP, at a specified temperature, pH, and ionic strength?" The answer is

$$\Delta_f G'^0(i) = -RT\ln\sum_{j=1}^{N_s}\exp(-\Delta_f G'^0(j)/RT) \tag{Eq. 10}$$

where N_s is the number of species in the pseudoisomer group. The standard transformed Gibbs energy of formation of a reactant $\Delta_f G'^0(i)$ is a very important property because if it can be expressed as a function of temperature, pH, and ionic strength, the standard transformed enthalpy of formation $\Delta_f H'^0(i)$, standard transformed entropy of formation $\Delta_f S'^0(i)$, and average number of hydrogen ions bound by reactant i can be calculated by simply taking partial derivatives. When $\Delta_f G'^0(i)$ is known for all the reactants in an enzyme-catalyzed reaction, the apparent equilibrium constant K', standard transformed enthalpy of reaction $\Delta_r H'^0$, standard transformed entropy of reaction $\Delta_r S'^0$, and the change in binding of hydrogen ions in the reaction can be calculated at the desired temperatures, pHs, and ionic strengths.

Thus when you specify the pH you open up a whole new world of thermodynamics in which you are dealing with reactants (sums of species) rather than species. Because magnesium ions play a role like hydrogen ions, the definition of G' in Equation 6 can be extended by subtracting a term $n_c(Mg)\mu(Mg^{2+})$ to make pMg also an independent variable. Since I was an officer in IUPAC at the time, I organized a committee to make recommendations about this new nomenclature (30).

Standard transformed Gibbs energies of formation and standard transformed enthalpies of formation can be calculated as functions of temperature, pH, and ionic strength from the species properties in the tables mentioned earlier. Literature data on apparent equilibrium constants and standard transformed enthalpies of enzyme-catalyzed reactions can be used to extend these tables of species data. Goldberg, Tewari, and co-workers have surveyed the literature for measurements of these thermodynamic properties, evaluated them, and published six reports on these valuable thermodynamic data. Their first report was published in 1992 and the most recent in 1999 (31). These reports provide thermodynamic information on about 900 reactants.

The most efficient way to store thermodynamic data on enzyme-catalyzed reactions is to use small matrices with a row for each species containing $\{\Delta_f G^0(j), \Delta_f H^0(j), z(j), N_H(j)\}$, where $z(j)$ is the charge number and $N_H(j)$ is the number of hydrogen atoms in species j. The calculation of standard transformed thermodynamic properties at the specified temperature, pH, and ionic strength is sufficiently complicated that a computer with a mathematical application is required. Mathematica® (32) is excellent for this because of its symbolic capabilities and its facilities for making plots and tables and taking partial derivatives. A table (BasicBiochem-Data2, library.wolfram.com/infocenter/MathSource/797) of the properties of the species of 131 biochemical reactants has been placed on the web so that these data can be downloaded by anyone with Mathematica on their computer. This package also contains programs for using the data.

If the small matrix can be constructed for a reactant, it can be used to express $\Delta_f G'^0(i)$ of reactant i as a function of temperature, pH, and ionic strength. This function is very important because all the other standard transformed thermodynamic properties can be calculated as a function of these variables by simply taking partial derivatives with a computer.

This process of making Legendre transforms can be taken a step further in considering systems of biochemical reactions like glycolysis and the tricarboxylic acid cycle (33). In a living cell, the concentrations of coenzymes tend to be in steady states because they are involved in many reactions. When this is the case, a further transformed Gibbs energy G'' of a reaction system can be defined by use of the following Legendre transform.

$$G'' = G' - \Sigma n_c(\mathrm{coenz}_i)\mu'(\mathrm{coenz}_i) \qquad \text{(Eq. 11)}$$

When this is applied to glycolysis, it can be shown that all the thermodynamics of the system can be represented by $C_6 = 2C_3$, where C_6 is the sum of the reactants with six carbon atoms and C_3 is the sum of the reactants with three carbon atoms. One of the advantages of Legendre transforms is that no information is lost, and so even the equilibrium concentrations of species can be calculated by using this one reaction.

Because thermodynamics can tell us whether a given enzyme-catalyzed reaction will go to the right or the left under specified conditions, we can see which reactions can be coupled with other reactions to store energy or provide energy for synthesis of needed reactants. As thermodynamic tables grow, the number of reactions between reactants in the table grows exponentially. Existing literature data will make it possible to greatly extend current tables, but more equilibrium studies are needed on reactants for which there is currently no literature data.

This essay has been about the most fundamental concepts in the thermodynamics of biochemical reactions, but the actual calculations and results are described in detail in my book "Thermodynamics of Biochemical Reactions" (34).

Conclusion

I feel very fortunate that I worked on petroleum thermodynamics long enough to learn how to use Legendre transforms. When I came back to biochemistry I saw it with new eyes. I could see previously missed opportunities. Some of the new equations look like the equations of chemical thermodynamics, but they are different because they apply to sums of species like ATP rather than species. When the pH is specified there are more thermodynamic properties to consider and more relations between them. I think the moral is that sometimes in research it is a good idea to spend some time in another field because you may come back and see your previous field in a new light.

Address correspondence to: alberty@mit.edu.

REFERENCES

1. Gibbs, J. W. (1948) *The Collected Works of J. Willard Gibbs*, Vol. 1, Yale University Press, New Haven, CT
2. Alberty, R. A. (1994) *Chem. Rev.* **94**, 1457–1482
3. Alberty, R. A., Barthel, J. M. G., Cohen, E. R., Ewing, M. B., Goldberg, R. N., and Wilhelm, E. (2001) *Pure Appl. Chem.* **73**, 1349–1380
4. Callen, H. B. (1985) *Thermodynamics and an Introduction to Thermostatistics*, p. 26, John Wiley & Sons, Inc., New York
5. Wagman, D. D., Evans, W. H., Parker, V. B., Schumm, R. H., Halow, I., Bailey, S. M., Churney, K. L., and Nutall, R. L. (1982) *J. Phys. Chem. Ref. Data* **11**, Suppl. 2, 1–392
6. Quastel, J. H., and Woolf, B. (1926) *Biochem. J.* **20**, 545–555
7. Burton, K., and Krebs, H. A. (1953) *Biochem. J.* **54**, 94–107
8. Alberty, R. A., Smith, R. M., and Bock, R. M. (1951) *J. Biol. Chem.* **193**, 425–434
9. Bock, R. M., and Alberty, R. A. (1953) *J. Am. Chem. Soc.* **75**, 1921–1926
10. Frieden, C., Bock, R. M., and Alberty, R. A. (1954) *J. Am. Chem. Soc.* **76**, 2482–2485
11. Alberty, R. A., Massey, V., Frieden, C., and Fuhlbrigge, A. A. (1954) *J. Am. Chem. Soc.* **76**, 2486–2493
12. Alberty, R. A., and Hammes, G. G. (1958) *J. Phys. Chem.* **52**, 154–159
13. Krebs, H. A., and Kornberg, H. L. (1957) *Energy Transformations in Living Matter*, Springer-Verlag, Berlin (Appendix by K. Burton)
14. Alberty, R. A. (1968) *J. Biol. Chem.* **243**, 1337–1342
15. Alberty, R. A. (1969) *J. Biol. Chem.* **244**, 3290–3302
16. Phillips, R. C., George, P., and Rutman, R. J. (1969) *J. Biol. Chem.* **244**, 3330–3342
17. Guynn, R. W., and Veech, R. L. (1973) *J. Biol. Chem.* **248**, 6966–6972
18. Wadsö, I., Gutfreund, H., Privalov, P., Edsall, J. T., Jencks, W. P., Armstrong, G. T., and Biltonen, R. L. (1976) *J. Biol. Chem.* **251**, 6879–6885
19. Wilhoit, R. C. (1969) in *Biochemical Microcalorimetry* (Brown, H. D., ed) Academic Press, New York
20. Thauer, R. K., Jungermann, K., and Decker, K. (1977) *Bacteriol. Rev.* **41**, 100–179
21. Goldberg, R. N., and Tewari, Y. B. (1989) *J. Phys. Chem. Ref. Data* **18**, 809–880
22. Miller, S. L., and Smith-Magowan, D. (1990) *J. Phys. Chem. Ref. Data* **19**, 1049–1073
23. Wyman, J., and Gill, S. J. (1990) *Binding and Linkage*, University Science Books, Mill Valley, CA
24. Alberty, R. A., and Oppenheim, I. (1988) *J. Chem. Phys.* **89**, 3689–3694
25. Beattie, J. A., and Oppenheim, I. (1979) *Principles of Thermodynamics*, Elsevier, Amsterdam
26. Alberty, R. A. (1992) *Biophys. Chem.* **42**, 117–131
27. Alberty, R. A. (1992) *Biophys. Chem.* **43**, 239–254
28. Alberty, R. A., and Goldberg, R. N. (1992) *Biochemistry* **31**, 10610–10615
29. Boerio-Goates, J., Francis, M. R., Goldberg, R. N., Ribeiro da Silva, M. A. V., Ribeiro da Silva, M. D. M. C., and Tewari, Y. (2001) *J. Chem. Thermodynamics* **33**, 929–947
30. Alberty, R. A., Cornish-Bowden, A., Gibson, Q. H., Goldberg, R. N., Hammes, G. G., Jencks, W., Tipton, K. F., Veech, R., Westerhoff, H. V., and Webb, E. C. (1994) *Pure Appl. Chem.* **66**, 1641–1666
31. Goldberg, R. N. (1999) *J. Phys. Chem. Ref. Data* **28**, 931–965
32. Wolfram, S. (1999) *The Mathematica Book*, 4th Ed., Cambridge University Press, Cambridge, UK
33. Alberty, R. A. (2000) *J. Phys. Chem. B* **104**, 650–657
34. Alberty, R. A. (2003) *Thermodynamics of Biochemical Reactions*, John Wiley & Sons, Inc., New York

THE JOURNAL OF BIOLOGICAL CHEMISTRY
© 2004 by The American Society for Biochemistry and Molecular Biology, Inc.

Vol. 279, No. 38, Issue of September 17, pp. 39187–39194, 2004
Printed in U.S.A.

Reflections

A PAPER IN A SERIES COMMISSIONED TO CELEBRATE THE CENTENARY OF THE JBC IN 2005

JBC Centennial
1905–2005
100 Years of Biochemistry and Molecular Biology

The Biotin Connection: Severo Ochoa, Harland Wood, and Feodor Lynen

Published, JBC Papers in Press, May 27, 2004, DOI 10.1074/jbc.X400005200

M. Daniel Lane

From the Department of Biological Chemistry, The Johns Hopkins University School of Medicine, Baltimore, Maryland 21205

Unique circumstances sometimes bring us into contact with individuals who will profoundly influence us, particularly in our formative years. In this article I would like to reflect on the circumstances that brought me into contact with three great biochemists, Severo Ochoa (1), Harland Wood (2), and Feodor Lynen (3). Each entered the field by a different route: Ochoa as a physician with an interest in physiology, Wood as a bacteriologist trained at Iowa State University, and Lynen as an organic chemist trained in the German tradition with Nobel Prize winner, Heinrich Wieland.

They entered the field of biochemistry in the late 1930s when the race was on to discover new enzymes, cofactors, and metabolic cycles. Hans Krebs had formulated the tricarboxylic acid cycle in 1937 and ornithine cycle (now known as the urea cycle) in 1932, some B vitamins had been found to function as cofactors or prosthetic groups of enzymes, and Rudolf Schoenheimer (Columbia University College of Physicians and Surgeons) had demonstrated the dynamic state of tissue proteins using heavy isotopes of hydrogen and carbon (mid-1930s). This was where the action was and it attracted many of the brightest young minds into the field. This was the arena in which Ochoa, Wood, and Lynen were early participants. Excited by discovery, they transmitted this excitement to their younger colleagues.

I was fortunate to have scientific associations and enduring friendships with each of them. My connection developed through the B vitamin, biotin, and its role in the reactions catalyzed by a family of biotin-dependent enzymes, notably carboxylases. The B vitamin, biotin, has an interesting history not familiar to most scientists who now make use of it. Today, this vitamin is widely used along with avidin (or its cousin, strepavidin), the specific biotin-binding protein from egg white, to probe biochemical phenomena. Biotinylation of proteins and nucleotides and the use of avidin to "fish out" or detect these molecules from/in complex mixtures has found great utility.

It is a curiosity that nature has brought together within the hen's egg the richest source of biotin in the yolk and in the white, a "toxic" factor, avidin, which when fed to animals causes biotin deficiency. In 1936, Kögl and Tönnis isolated 1.1 mg of biotin from more than 500 pounds of egg yolk. Paul György recognized that the distribution, fractionation behavior, and chemical properties of Kögl's yeast growth factor and the anti-egg white injury factor in egg yolk (then called vitamin H) were similar. When Kögl's pure biotin methyl ester became available it was found to be extremely potent in protecting rats against "egg white (*i.e.* avidin) injury." Within a few years Vincent Du Vigneaud and colleagues determined the structure of biotin, which cleared the way for an attack on the role of biotin at the molecular level.

By 1950 biotin had been implicated in a number of seemingly unrelated enzymatic processes including the decarboxylation of oxaloacetate and succinate; the "Wood-Werkman reaction" (discovered by Harland Wood (2)), *i.e.* the carboxylation of pyruvate; the biosynthesis of aspartate; and the biosynthesis of unsaturated fatty acids. Of course, we now know that biotin functions in each of these processes as a mobile "CO_2 carrier" bound covalently to a carboxylase. The long sought after link between biotin and enzymatic function was provided by Henry Lardy at the University of Wisconsin. Lardy showed that liver mitochondrial extracts catalyzed the ATP- and divalent cation-dependent carboxylation of propionate (subsequently shown to be propionyl-CoA) to form succinate (4). Later work in the laboratory of Severo Ochoa found that the initial carboxylation product was methylmalonyl-CoA, an intermediate en route to succinyl-CoA. The connection to biotin was made by Lardy with the finding that the propionate-carboxylating activity was lacking in liver mitochondria from rats made biotin-deficient by being fed egg white, which of course contained avidin ($K_{D(biotin)} \sim 10^{-15}$). Moreover, the failure of mitochondrial extract to catalyze the carboxylation of propionate was quickly cured by injecting the rats with biotin.

Upon joining the faculty at Virginia Polytechnic Institute in Blacksburg, Virginia in 1956, I decided to try to determine how propionate is metabolized in the liver. Because of its unique features, I settled on bovine liver as the tissue source of the enzyme system to address this question, propionate being a major hepatic carbon source in ruminants. Unlike carbohydrate digestion by monogastric animals, ruminants digest carbohydrates in the rumen, the large anaerobic fore compartment of their multi-compartmented "stomach." Virtually all carbohydrate is fermented in the rumen to short chain fatty acids, primarily acetate and propionate. Thus glucose, the major digestion product of carbohydrates in monogastric animals, is not available for absorption in ruminants. Propionate, produced in abundance by fermentation in the rumen, is absorbed directly into the portal system and transported to the liver where it is the major carbon source for gluconeogenesis, the pathway leading to glucose production.

My entry into this area coincided with Lardy's report that propionate was somehow carboxylated to form succinate. I recall writing to Henry Lardy, and he referred me to Severo Ochoa at New York University School of Medicine. He knew that Ochoa was working on propionate metabolism and had found that propionyl-CoA first became carboxylated to form methylmalonyl-CoA and then was converted to succinyl-CoA. With some trepidation about competing with the Ochoa laboratory, I decided to forge ahead and purify propionyl-CoA carboxylase from bovine liver mitochondria. For the reasons mentioned above bovine liver turned out to be an excellent source of the enzyme. At that point I wrote to Severo Ochoa, and he generously gave me a status report on their progress and put me in contact with the people in his laboratory (Alisa Tietz, Martin Flavin, and later, Yoshito Kaziro) who were working on the enzyme. This initiated what was to be a long relationship with Severo Ochoa and also his colleague, Yoshito Kaziro (now in Tokyo).

About that time I applied to the National Science Foundation for a research grant to support my work on propionate metabolism. The grant proposal was rejected because the reviewers felt that I was really "in over my head" competing with the Ochoa laboratory and also because it had been rumored that his laboratory had already crystallized the enzyme from muscle. I knew that this was not true because in my correspondence with Ochoa he had indicated that the crystals turned out to be pyruvate kinase, not propionyl-CoA carboxylase. After much anguish I wrote to the Head of the National Science Foundation Review Committee, Louis Levin, indicating that the Committee was mistaken: "the carboxylase had not been crystallized" and that I thought it was inappropriate for the National Science Foundation to take a position on a grant application based on the size of the laboratory, rather than the merit of the proposal. A few weeks later I received a letter from Lou Levin indicating that the Study Section had reversed its decision and that the grant would be funded. I doubt seriously if that could happen today. Thus began my independent career in research and a developing relationship with Severo Ochoa.

In 1959, a paper by Lynen and Knappe appeared in *Angewandte Chemie* (5) (later published in full in *Biochemische Zeitschrift* (6)) that created tremendous excitement in my laboratory. The paper described the rather remarkable finding that β-methylcrotonyl-CoA carboxylase, a biotin-dependent carboxylase (involved in leucine catabolism in certain bacteria), catalyzed the ATP-dependent carboxylation of "free" biotin in the absence of its acyl-CoA substrate. The product was shown to be a labile carboxylated biotin derivative, later identified as 1'-*N*-carboxybiotin. Because biotin was believed to be a prosthetic group covalently bound to the enzyme and because free biotin exhibited an extremely high K_m, Lynen proposed that the free biotin had accessed the active site of the carboxylase and by mimicking the biotinyl prosthetic group had gotten carboxylated.

FIG. 1. **Harland Wood**, *circa* **1991**. (Reprinted with permission of the Cleveland Plain Dealer newspaper.)

Shortly thereafter Don Halenz and I succeeded in purifying a related enzyme, propionyl-CoA carboxylase, from bovine liver mitochondria. After convincing ourselves that it too was a biotin-dependent enzyme, we turned our attention to how the biotinyl group was attached to the carboxylase and what enzymatic reactions were involved in its becoming attached to the carboxylase. Dave Kosow, also in my laboratory at Virginia Tech, had just found that extracts of liver from biotin-deficient rats contained catalytically inactive propionyl-CoA *apo*carboxylase. Moreover, he demonstrated that a soluble ATP-dependent enzyme system in these extracts from the livers of the biotin-deficient animals catalyzed the covalent attachment of [^{14}C]biotin to the *apo*enzyme, thereby restoring its ability to carboxylate propionyl-CoA (7).

Moreover, Dave Kosow showed (7) that upon treating the ^{14}C-biotinylated carboxylase with *Streptomyces griseus* protease, biocytin (*i.e.* ϵ-N-biotinyl-L-lysine) was released. This meant, of course, that the biotin prosthetic group had been linked to propionyl-CoA carboxylase through an amide linkage to a lysyl ϵ-amino group. A few years later it became evident that this long (~14 Å) side arm facilitates oscillation of the 1'-N-carboxybiotinyl prosthetic group between catalytic centers on the enzyme (7).

After completing those experiments I invited Severo Ochoa to visit Virginia Polytechnic Institute and to present two lectures, which he graciously agreed to do. One of these talks dealt with propionyl-CoA carboxylase and the other with the genetic code, the two major projects under way in the laboratory of Ochoa at the time. While he was in Blacksburg Dave and I showed him our results on the site of attachment of biotin to the enzyme. We gave him some of the protease and within a month of his return to New York City he confirmed our findings with the heart propionyl-CoA carboxylase.

It was at this point in 1962 that I decided to take a sabbatical leave in Munich with Feodor Lynen (known to his colleagues as "Fitzi") at the Max-Planck Institüt Für Zellchemie where I could continue the work on the enzymatic mechanism by which biotin became attached to propionyl-CoA carboxylase. Before leaving for Munich Dave Kosow and I developed another more potent apoenzyme system with which to investigate the "biotin loading" reaction. This system made use of *Propionibacterium shermanii* that expressed huge amounts of methylma-lonyl-CoA:pyruvate transcarboxylase, another biotin-dependent enzyme studied extensively by Harland Wood. Moreover, this organism had an absolute requirement for biotin in the growth medium, which when grown at very low levels of biotin produced large amounts of the apotranscarboxylase. The choice of the *P. shermanii* system turned out to be a good one. It so happened that my stay in Munich coincided with Harland Wood's sabbatical leave in Lynen's Institute. This was a two-fold bonus for me, first because Harland was the world's expert on this enzyme and second because it began a lasting personal relationship with him. He has been a role model for me ever since that period in Munich.

Harland (1907–1991) grew up on a farm near Mankato, Minnesota. He entered Macalester College in Minnesota where he majored in chemistry and worked his way through college. While a student at Macalester, he met Milly Davis and in their third year of college they married (in 1929, the year of the stock market crash and beginning of the great depression of the 1930s). In those days this required a meeting (for approval I presume) with the President of the college, who needn't have been concerned as she was at his side for the next 62 years. They were an amazing couple, a cooperative inseparable team. My wife and I shared their friendship for more than 30 years. In 1931, Harland became a graduate student in bacteriology in the laboratory of C. H. Werkman at Iowa State University in Ames, Iowa, where he made a discovery that was so controversial, although correct, that it was questioned by his thesis adviser Werkman as well as by leaders in the field of microbial metabolism including C. B. van Niel. Harland had discovered (2) that heterotrophic organisms, such as the *Propionibacteria*, were able to fix CO_2. Prior to this it was believed that only auxotrophs, *i.e.* chemosynthetic or photosynthetic auxotrophs, could carry out the net synthesis of organic compounds from CO_2. His discovery truly opened the area of enzymatic carboxylation in higher organisms. After completing his Ph.D. degree Harland (Fig. 1) did postdoctoral work at the University of Wisconsin with W. H. Peterson and then returned to Iowa State as a faculty member. Harland was an innovator and an improviser. While at Iowa State he decided to conduct CO_2 fixation experiments using $^{13}CO_2$, but because of World War II restrictions he could not gain access to a mass spectrometer nor could he obtain "heavy" $^{13}CO_2$. In true Woodsian style, he built his own mass spectrometer and constructed a thermal diffusion column in the Science building at Iowa State College (2). In 1946, Harland became Professor and Director of the Biochemistry Department at Western Reserve (now Case-Western Reserve) University. He ran the most democratic department on record in which faculty salaries were determined by the faculty at a meeting where members voted on one another's salary for the upcoming year!

Upon arriving in Munich in August of 1962, I indicated to Lynen that I would like to investigate the *P. shermanii* "biotin loading" enzyme system, and he agreed with my proposal. Because Harland Wood was already at the Institute, I got his advice on growth conditions and for large scale preparations of the transcarboxylase (actually, the apotranscarboxylase). Both Lynen and Wood were quite enthusiastic about the project. It turned out that by growing *P. shermanii* in biotin-deficient medium the bacteria produced as much of the *apo*transcar-boxylase as the *holo*transcarboxylase when the organism was grown on normal/biotin-contain-ing medium. Within a short time I was able to resolve and purify both the *apo*transcarboxylase and the synthetase that catalyzed loading biotin onto the *apo*enzyme (7). Dave Young, a postdoctoral fellow who had recently completed his medical training at Duke University, and Karl Rominger, a Ph.D. candidate under Lynen's direction, collaborated with me on these studies. Finally, we proved that the synthetase catalyzed a two-step reaction in which the first step involved the ATP-dependent formation of biotinyl-5′-AMP and pyrophosphate after which the biotinyl group was transferred from the AMP derivative to the appropriate lysyl ϵ-amino group of the *apo*transcarboxylase.

While in the midst of these studies, a controversy developed regarding the site at which biotin became carboxylated during catalysis. It was suggested that HCO_3^- became incorpo-rated into the 2′-position of the ureido ring of the covalently bound biotinyl prosthetic group of biotin-dependent enzymes and that the 2′-carbon was then transferred to the acceptor substrate. It was suggested that Lynen's experiments (referred to above) had been done with free biotin and not the biotinyl prosthetic group covalently linked to the carboxylase. Such a mechanism would have necessitated opening and then closing the ureido ring of biotin during the course of the reaction, which to a chemist like Lynen didn't make chemical sense. Moreover, this proposal was inconsistent with the known lability of free 1-*N*-[^{14}C]carboxy-

FIG. 2. **Feodor ("Fitzi") Lynen,** *circa* **1980.** (Reprinted with permission of the Max-Planck Gesellschaft.)

biotin. We knew from my earlier studies that enzyme-$^{14}CO_2^-$, presumably enzyme-biotin-$^{14}CO_2^-$ (prepared by incubating propionyl-CoA carboxylase with $H^{14}CO_3^-$ and ATP-Mg^{2+}), was even less stable than free 1-N-carboxy-[$^{14}CO_2^-$]biotin. so we set out to address the issue head on using propionyl-CoA carboxylase as the source of enzyme-biotin-$^{14}CO_2^-$. The previous spring before going to Munich, I had found that enzyme-$^{14}CO_2^-$ (derived from propionyl-CoA carboxylase) could be stabilized by methylation with diazomethane, *i.e.* enzyme-$^{14}CO_2^-$ was labile to acid before but was stable after methylation. Moreover, digestion of methylated enzyme-$^{14}CO_2^-$ (enzyme-$^{14}CO_2$-CH$_3$) with *S. griseus* protease produced a single radioactive derivative, presumably methoxy-[^{14}C]carbonyl-ϵ-N-biotinyl lysine. This product had chromatographic properties similar, but not identical, to ϵ-N-biotinyl lysine. Because I did not have the authentic compound for comparison, these experiments could not be completed at the time. Fortunately, Joachim Knappe, a former member of Lynen's research group now at the University of Heidelberg, had synthesized the derivative and provided Lynen with a sample. Thus, we were able to verify the presumptive identification. This proved that the covalently bound biotinyl prosthetic group, like free biotin, was carboxylated at the 1'-N position (8). Shortly thereafter, Knappe in Heidelberg and Harland Wood on sabbatical in Lynen's laboratory in Munich showed using a similar approach that the carboxybiotin prosthetic groups of β-methylcrotonyl-CoA and transcarboxylase, respectively, had identical structures (9). Taken together these studies proved unequivocally that the site of carboxylation of biotin was on the 1'-N of the biotinyl prosthetic group.

By this point in my sabbatical in Lynen's Institute, I began to recognize certain habits of "the Chief." For example, he had the habit of working in his office until late in the afternoon. Then, around dusk, *i.e.* 6:00–6:30 p.m., he would emerge to make "rounds" in the Institute, moving from one bench to the next to survey the day's progress or lack of it. Of course not one of the ~30 investigators would consider leaving until after he had passed through. He ran a "tight

FIG. 3. **Severo Ochoa with colleagues viewing an enlargement of an electron micrograph of acetyl-CoA carboxylase (1966).** From right to left: Albrecht Kleinschmidt, Erwin Stoll, Severo Ochoa, and Dan Lane.

ship"! Fitzi had an uncanny memory and could recall details of experiments done weeks earlier.

Lynen (1911–1974) (3) (Fig. 2) was born and spent his entire life in Munich and environs. He received his doctoral training in organic chemistry at the University of Munich with Heinrich Wieland (Nobel Prize in Chemistry in 1927), graduating in 1937. He then married Wieland's daughter, Eva. He was spared the ravages of World War II because of a serious skiing accident, which left him with a persistent limp. Perhaps Lynen's most important contribution was the discovery of acetyl-CoA, the elusive molecule "active acetate," sought after by many investigators including Fritz Lipmann, David Nachmansohn, and Severo Ochoa. Ochoa had discovered "condensing enzyme," now known as citrate synthase, which catalyzed the formation of citrate from "active acetate" and oxaloacetate. These discoveries led to an important collaboration between Lynen and Ochoa in which they proved that citrate synthase used acetyl-CoA, along with oxaloacetate, to form citrate. These findings finally answered the question of how "active acetate" entered the citric acid cycle. In 1964 Lynen received the Nobel Prize (with Konrad Bloch) in Physiology or Medicine for his work on "the mechanism and regulation of cholesterol and fatty acid metabolism."

Lynen had strong connections to the United States. Many Americans came to his Institute to do postdoctoral work or sabbaticals. During the period that Harland Wood and I spent in Munich, the other Americans in the group included Esmond Snell, on sabbatical leave from Berkeley, David Young, Walter Bortz, Dick Himes, Paul Kindel, Martin Stiles, and Ed Wawskiewicz. Although Fitzi Lynen was a hard driving biochemist, he did like to socialize over a beer or a martini. On Friday afternoons Harland would often bring a half-gallon bottle of Gilbey's gin to the Institute and prepare martinis in the second floor laboratory.

Shortly after returning from Munich in the Summer of 1963, I received a phone call from Severo Ochoa, who asked if I might be interested in joining the faculty of his department at New York University School of Medicine in New York City. My wife, Pat, and I had some concern about moving from the bucolic setting of Blacksburg, Virginia (where we could see 20 miles from our living room window) to the big city. Nevertheless, we relished the new challenges ahead and were ready for a change in lifestyle. We loved New York City and never regretted having made the decision. Severo Ochoa helped make it worthwhile.

Severo Ochoa (1905–1993) (1, 10) (Fig. 3) was born in Luarca, Spain, the youngest of seven children. His father was a lawyer and businessman. He completed his M.D. degree (with honors) at the University of Madrid. Though never having studied with him, he was inspired by Ramón y Cajal, the Spanish neuroanatomist and Nobel Prize winner (1906). Following medical school (1929–1931) Ochoa joined Otto Meyerhof's laboratory in Heidelberg where he worked on muscle glycolysis. His early days in science were marked by the upheavals in Europe leading up to World War II. At the time of the Spanish civil war in 1936, he left Spain for Heidelberg for the second and final time. Then in 1938, because of the turmoil in Germany, he moved to Oxford University in England to work in Professor Rudolph Peter's unit. In 1941 he came to the United States where he joined Carl and Gerty Cori at Washington University in St. Louis.

In his comments at the Nobel Prize banquet in 1964, Ochoa spoke of those who had influenced him most.

> I was deeply influenced by my great predecessor Santiago Ramón y Cajal. I entered Medical School too late to receive his teachings directly but, through his writings and his example he did much to arouse my enthusiasm for biology and crystallize my vocation. Among the great names that adorn the roll of Nobel prize-winners in Medicine is that of Otto Meyerhof, my admired teacher and friend, to whose inspiration, guidance and encouragement I owe so very much. I was very fortunate to have worked also under the guidance of other great scientists and I wish to acknowledge my indebtedness to Sir Rudolph Peters and to Nobel prize winners Carl and Gerty Cori who did so much to add new dimensions to my scientific outlook and enlarge my intellectual experience.

The seven years (1964–1970) I spent in Ochoa's department were among the most exciting of my scientific career. It was a small department with only a handful of faculty, which at that time included Charles Weissman, Bob Warner, Bob Chambers, Albrecht Kleinschmidt, and Severo. Upon arriving at New York University Medical School in August of 1962, Severo asked me to give 15 lectures in the first year medical student biochemistry course the next month. This course was Ochoa's pride and joy and he and the faculty attended every lecture. (In retrospect, I feel that this is an excellent way to ensure quality control in teaching.) At the time, however, I hadn't relished the idea of having a Nobel prize winner (1964, with Arthur Kornberg, Ochoa's first postdoctoral fellow) in the audience for the first 15 lectures in my new scientific home. Despite knowing that my first few lectures at New York University were not particularly good, after the lecture Severo put his hand on my shoulder and said, "That was an excellent lecture, Dan." I knew that it hadn't been, but I did appreciate the encouragement. This was typical of Severo's behavior toward young scientists in whom he had confidence. I suspect that his response reflected the encouragement he had received from his mentors during his development.

Every afternoon at 3:00 p.m. we took a break for coffee in the department library where we discussed the latest results of our experiments or a hot new paper. Because the faculty was small, these were informal gatherings, which created a sense of camaraderie. Severo never failed to show up for these sessions. We could always count on Charles Weissman for a good, often slightly "off color" joke. "Have you heard the one about the ——?" Because of his innate ability at story telling, Charles was a favorite lecturer of the medical students. His timing was impeccable.

Severo had a princely presence in part because of his carriage, tall stature, and silver hair. At national/international meetings, when he walked into a room he attracted hushed attention. Despite this, he had a warm personality and showed genuine concern for his colleagues, associates, and students.

It is natural that we feel a closeness to those to whom we are related through research interests. In Hans Krebs book, *Reminiscences and Reflections* (11), he illustrates the scientific genealogy leading to Ochoa.

We talk rather loosely these days about "impact factor" (and citation index) in evaluating the worth of one's publications, but it is the excitement and joy of doing science, rather than the recognition itself, that motivates us.

Research today moves at great speed. Communication is rapid, publication is rapid, and one is left with the impression that everything of importance was done in the past 10 years. However, science is built stepwise on the shoulders of those who came before us. Little is taught today as to how each of our particular areas of the biological sciences developed. For many students the "important stuff" now goes back into the past for only 7–8 years. Most online scientific journals go back only 7–8 years. Fortunately, the *Journal of Biological Chemistry* is the exception and is to be commended, because it is online all the way back to the point of its origin in 1905. These Reflections may be a sign of recognition that the history of discovery still has importance.

Acknowledgment—I thank my wife, Pat Lane, who assisted with this article and shared these friendships and experiences with me.

Address correspondence to: dlane@jhmi.edu.

REFERENCES

1. Ochoa, S. (1980) *Annu. Rev. Biochem.* **49,** 1–30
2. Wood, H. G. (1985) *Annu. Rev. Biochem.* **54,** 1–41
3. Lynen, F. B. (1964) Information available on the Nobel Museum Web Site: www.nobel.se/
4. Lardy, H. A., and Adler, J. (1956) *J. Biol. Chem.* **219,** 933–942
5. Lynen, F., Knappe, J., Lorch, E., Jutting, G., and Ringelmann, E. (1959) *Angew. Chem.* **71,** 481–486
6. Knappe, J., Ringelmann, E., and Lynen, F. (1961) *Biochem. Z.* **335,** 168–176
7. Moss, J., and Lane, M. D. (1971) *Adv. Enzymol. Relat. Areas Mol. Biol.* **35,** 321–442 (a review article)
8. Lane, M. D., and Lynen, F. (1963) *Proc. Natl. Acad. Sci. U. S. A.* **49,** 379–385
9. Lynen, F. (1967) *Biochem. J.* **102,** 381–400
10. Kornberg, A., Horecker, B. L., Cornudella, L., and Oró, J. (eds) (1975) *Reflections on Biochemistry*, pp. 1–14, Pergamon Press, New York
11. Krebs, H. A. (1981) *Reminiscences and Reflections*, Oxford University Press, Oxford, UK

THE JOURNAL OF BIOLOGICAL CHEMISTRY
© 2004 by The American Society for Biochemistry and Molecular Biology, Inc.

Vol. 279, No. 39, Issue of September 24, pp. 40247–40251, 2004
Printed in U.S.A.

Reflections

A PAPER IN A SERIES COMMISSIONED TO CELEBRATE THE CENTENARY OF THE JBC IN 2005

JBC Centennial
1905–2005
100 Years of Biochemistry and Molecular Biology

Early Steps on the DNA Ladder—A Recollection

Published, JBC Papers in Press, May 28, 2004, DOI 10.1074/jbc.X400004200

Robert Sinsheimer

*From the Department of Molecular, Cell, and Developmental Biology, University of California,
Santa Barbara, California 93106-9610*

I have participated in and observed more than 60 years of the "golden age" of biology. What has most impressed me is the cumulative nature of this enterprise: discovery producing discovery producing new techniques producing further discovery, in ever cumulative progression. Our prizes and awards recognize landmarks in this process but most significant is the ever continuing and broadening stream of advances.

Pre-war Years: 1937–1942

In my undergraduate years at MIT, immediately prior to World War II, I enrolled in the newly reformulated program in quantitative biology. Two concepts seized my imagination: viruses and genes. Viruses seemed to occupy some nebulous realm between living and non-living. Genes seemed to be the essential key to biology, much as the atom was to chemistry and the atomic nucleus was to the physics of the day.

To an MIT student, steeped in physics, chemistry, and mathematics, the then intangible nature of the gene seemed a tantalizing problem. By default, genes were hypothesized to be proteins because no other substances seemed to afford the requisite complexity and variety. However, as yet no one knew the complete composition of any one protein, much less its three-dimensional structure.

On the other hand, one of the few clues to the physical nature of the gene (the ultraviolet action spectrum for the induction of mutations) paralleled the absorption spectrum of the nucleic acids (1, 2).

Graduate School Years: 1946–1949

When I returned to biology at the end of the War, two papers from the wartime years stood out for me. The demonstration by Avery, McLeod, and McCarty (3) that the transforming principle is DNA was dramatic, and the brilliant experiments of Beadle and Tatum (4) demonstrated that genes could specify the structure of enzymes (known to be proteins), thereby linking genes directly to the metabolism of the cell.

My graduate mentor was John Loofbourow (5), a physicist with a background in spectroscopy, who had turned his attention to biophysical problems. I learned much from him, including a tradition of venturesome self-reliance.

Iowa State Years: 1949–1957

In my first faculty post at Iowa State, I set out to learn as much as I could about DNA. At Iowa State as a biophysicist in a physics department I was quite isolated, but indeed almost all of the few DNA researchers of the time were isolated. (Isolation was not all bad; it provided time to develop one's own ideas and to work at a steady pace.) In 1950, the first Gordon Conference on Proteins *and* Nucleic Acids drew only some 78 participants from the United States and abroad.

a

FIG. 1. *a*, photo of attendees at the 1951 Gordon Conference on Proteins and Nucleic Acids. *b*, key to 1951 photo.

The summer Gordon Conferences (held in New Hampshire) and the annual FASEB meetings provided the few opportunities to counter the isolation of Iowa. At the summer conferences I met and conferred with, among others, Paul Doty, Rollin Hotchkiss, John Edsall, Erwin Chargaff, and Maurice Wilkins and, later, James Watson and Francis Crick and (as proteins were then included) Fred Sanger, John Kendrew, Max Perutz, and Aaron Klug (Fig. 1, *a* and *b*). The FASEB meetings provided contact with the biochemists including Arthur Kornberg, Paul Berg, Stanford Moore, William Stein, and Paul Zamecnik.

The extant techniques of DNA research were primitive and no ancillary industry existed, as today, to provide components and instruments.

Having very little funds, I took advantage of my location as a biophysicist in the physics department to make use of its excellent machine shop and its sophisticated research equipment. We designed and built a time-controlled fraction collector for column fractionations and a versatile light-scattering instrument for determination of molecular weight and size.

To study the basic components of DNA (the deoxyribonucleotides) I needed to prepare DNA and to devise means to digest it quantitatively. We prepared calf thymus DNA (6) from thymus glands obtained directly from the slaughterhouse in Des Moines. To digest it completely (which had never been done) we used pancreatic deoxyribonuclease (commercially available) and venom phosphodiesterase (for which we devised a method of purification from snake venom (7)). The deoxyribonucleotides were then fractionated quantitatively on an ion exchange column (8) as was pioneered by Waldo Cohn (9). This result in turn permitted us to establish the first spectrophotometric standards for the deoxyribonucleotides.

We obtained infrared spectra of the nucleotides in H_2O and D_2O to determine that they were in the amino and keto forms in solution (10). Seeking to attack the mutation question, we irradiated the deoxyribonucleotides with ultraviolet light and followed the changes in UV absorption and column behavior (11, 12).

We also observed that the deoxyribonuclease digestion alone cleaved just 25% of the phosphodiester bonds. Column fractionation revealed that about 1% of the product was

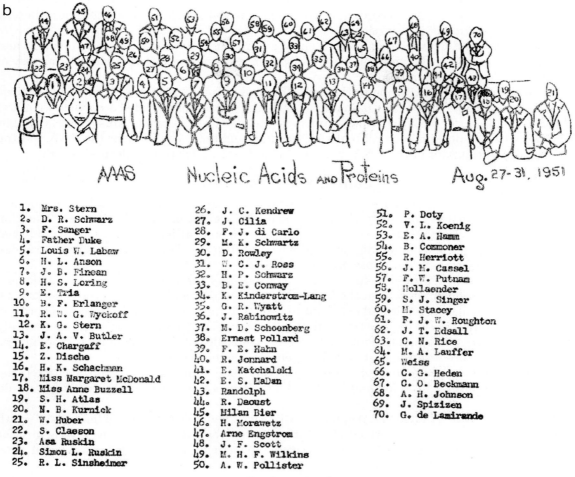

1. Mrs. Stern
2. D. R. Schwarz
3. F. Sanger
4. Father Duke
5. Louis W. Labaw
6. H. L. Anson
7. J. B. Finean
8. H. S. Loring
9. E. Tria
10. B. F. Erlanger
11. R. W. G. Wyckoff
12. K. G. Stern
13. J. A. V. Butler
14. E. Chargaff
15. Z. Dische
16. H. K. Schachman
17. Miss Margaret McDonald
18. Miss Anne Buzzell
19. S. H. Atlas
20. N. B. Kurnick
21. W. Huber
22. S. Claeson
23. Asa Ruskin
24. Simon L. Ruskin
25. R. L. Sinsheimer

26. J. C. Kendrew
27. J. Cilia
28. F. J. di Carlo
29. M. K. Schwartz
30. D. Rowley
31. W. C. J. Ross
32. H. P. Schwarz
33. B. E. Conway
34. K. Kinderstrom-Lang
35. G. R. Wyatt
36. J. Rabinowitz
37. M. D. Schoenberg
38. Ernest Pollard
39. F. E. Hahn
40. R. Jonnard
41. E. Katchalski
42. E. S. LaDan
43. Randolph
44. R. Daoust
45. Milan Bier
46. H. Morawetz
47. Arne Engstrom
48. J. F. Scott
49. M. H. F. Wilkins
50. A. W. Pollister

51. P. Doty
52. V. L. Koenig
53. E. A. Hamm
54. B. Commoner
55. R. Herriott
56. J. M. Cassel
57. F. W. Putnam
58. Hollaender
59. S. J. Singer
60. M. Stacey
61. F. J. W. Roughton
62. J. T. Edsall
63. C. N. Rice
64. M. A. Lauffer
65. Weiss
66. C. G. Heden
67. C. O. Beckmann
68. A. H. Johnson
69. J. Spizizen
70. G. de Lamirande

FIG. 1—*continued*

mononucleotides and about 16% was mixed dinucleotides (13, 14). We were able to column fractionate these into the various possible combinations. We noted that methylcytosine occurred in dinucleotides only in combination with guanine.

Chargaff's data (15) on the molar equalities of A and T and of G and C (plus mC) in DNA were becoming available. Our dinucleotides proved that these equalities were not the result of any simple sequential pairing of A and T or G and C.

To proceed further in nucleic acid research I needed to be able to study function in a biological system. For this I turned to my other long standing interest, viruses. For an RNA virus I used tobacco mosaic virus, which I could grow in the University's greenhouses (to the dismay of the botanists). We grew tobacco mosaic virus in tobacco and purified it, and from this we prepared its RNA. By light scattering we demonstrated that the RNA of the virus comprised one molecule of molecular weight of about 2 million (16, 17). Subsequently we demonstrated that the infectivity of the RNA was associated exclusively with the 2 million molecular weight molecule (18, 19).

For a DNA virus, bacteriophage was the obvious choice. Thanks to Max Delbruck, I was able to spend 6 months at Caltech in the first half of 1953. This was of course the time period of the breakthrough in DNA structure analysis with, first, Pauling's failed proposal of a three-stranded helix (20) and then the Watson-Crick double helix (21). The latter was first known from a letter to Delbruck that spring and then at the Cold Spring Harbor Symposium in June.

At Caltech one met legends like George Beadle and Henry Sturtevant and Linus Pauling and legends to be like Ed Lewis and visitors such as Francois Jacob and Andre Lwoff.

Back at Iowa State, I broadened my DNA studies to include (for comparison) DNA from wheat germ and the phage DNAs. We discovered the glucosylation of cytosine (22) in the DNA of the T-even phages (variant in different strains (23)). However, I focused most of my attention on a small bacteriophage discovered earlier in Paris, φX174 (24). I reasoned that a small phage would have less nucleic acid and thus be more amenable to analysis without fragmentation by the techniques then available and as well would have fewer genes, thereby easing the dissection of its functions.

As with any new virus we had to work out the conditions for growing it and storing it and purifying the particles. Fortunately we had by then acquired an ultracentrifuge (courtesy of the National Science Foundation).

Using the electron microscope in the department, I obtained pictures of the purified virus showing it to be a particle ~25 nm in diameter. Light scattering provided a particle weight of about 6.2 million for the virus and confirmed the particle diameter. This particle weight together with the phosphorous content suggested a weight of 1.7 million for the DNA, but the sedimentation constant of the DNA (23.8 S) was anomalous for that molecular weight.

Caltech Years: 1957–1977

At this time (1957) I moved to a faculty position at Caltech. Once re-established there, I quickly confirmed (by light scattering) the molecular weight of the DNA to be 1.7 million (about 5400 nucleotides). Then, using the techniques we had earlier developed, we established that the nucleotide composition did not fit the Chargaff ratios. The DNA was single-stranded and ϕX was the first of a new class of viruses (25, 26).

With ϕXDNA we had the first intact DNA molecule and the first complete DNA genome.

We went on to demonstrate that the DNA was infective (27) and that it was circular (28, 29, 30), to learn how it was replicated (31), and to ascertain its genetic map (32). In collaboration with Arthur Kornberg we demonstrated that his purified DNA polymerase could successfully replicate the DNA and produce synthetic infective molecules (33). Subsequently, Fred Sanger used ϕX DNA to produce the first complete genome sequence (34).

In 1959 the *Journal of Molecular Biology* began publication, and in 1960, I chaired the Gordon Conference on Proteins and Nucleic Acids. It was the last year the two fields would meet together.

With the double helix and DNA polymerase (35), with Sanger's sequence of insulin (36), with Kendrew's X-ray diffraction-derived structure of myoglobin (37), and Perutz's structure for hemoglobin (38) molecular biology had arrived. The unending wave of progress had been launched. How far we have come!

Address correspondence to: sinsheim@lifesci.ucsb.edu.

REFERENCES

1. Stadler, L. J., and Uber, F. M. (1942) Genetic effects of ultraviolet radiation in maize. IV Comparison of monochromatic radiations. *Genetics* **27,** 84–118
2. Hollaender, A., and Emmons, C. W. (1941) Wavelength dependence of mutation production in ultraviolet with special emphasis on fungi. *Cold Spring Harbor Symp. Quant. Biol.* **9,** 179–186
3. Avery, O. T., McLeod, C. M., and McCarty, M. (1944) Studies on the chemical nature of the substance inducing transformation of pneumococcal types. *J. Exp. Med.* **79,** 137–158
4. Beadle, G. W., and Tatum, E. L. (1941) Genetic control of biochemical reactions in *Neurospora. Proc. Natl. Acad. Sci. U. S. A.* **27,** 499–506
5. Loofbourow, J. R. (1940) Borderland problems in biology and physics. *Rev. Mod. Phys.* **12,** 267–358
6. Mirsky, A. E., and Pollister, A. W. (1946) Chromosin, a desoxyribose nucleoprotein complex of the cell nucleus. *J. Gen. Physiol.* **30,** 117–148
7. Sinsheimer, R. L., and Koerner, J. F. (1952) A purification of venom phosphodiesterase. *J. Biol. Chem.* **198,** 293–296
8. Sinsheimer, R. L., and Koerner, J. F. (1951) Ion exchange separation of deoxyribonucleotides. *Science* **114,** 42–43
9. Cohn, W. E. (1950) The anion-exchange separation of ribonucleotides. *J. Am. Chem. Soc.* **72,** 1471–1478
10. Sinsheimer, R. L., Nutter, R. L., and Hopkins, G. R. (1955) Infrared absorption spectra of pyrimidine nucleotides in H_2O and D_2O solution. *Biochim. Biophys. Acta* **18,** 13–27
11. Sinsheimer, R. L. (1954) The photochemistry of uridylic acid. *Radiat. Res.* **1,** 505–513
12. Sinsheimer, R. L. (1957) The photochemistry of cytidylic acid. *Radiat. Res.* **6,** 121–125
13. Sinsheimer, R. L., and Koerner, J. F. (1952) Di-desoxyribonucleotides. *J. Am. Chem. Soc.* **74,** 283
14. Sinsheimer, R. L. (1954) The action of pancreatic desoxyribonuclease I. Isolation of mono- and dinucleotides. *J. Biol. Chem.* **208,** 445–459
15. Chargaff, E. (1955) Isolation and composition of the deoxypentose nucleic acids and of the corresponding nucleoproteins. In *The Nucleic Acids* (Chargaff, E., and Davidson, J. N., eds) Vol. I, pp. 307–371, Academic Press, New York
16. Northrop, T. G., and Sinsheimer, R. L. (1954) Light scattering by tobacco mosaic virus nucleic acid. *J. Chem. Phys.* **22,** 703–707
17. Hopkins, G. R., and Sinsheimer, R. L. (1955) Visible and ultraviolet light scattering by tobacco mosaic virus nucleic acid. *Biochim. Biophys. Acta* **17,** 470–484
18. Cheo, P. C., Friesen, B. S., and Sinsheimer, R. L. (1959) Biophysical studies of infectious ribonucleic acid from tobacco mosaic virus. *Proc. Natl. Acad. Sci. U. S. A.* **45,** 305–313
19. Friesen, B. S., and Sinsheimer, R. L. (1959) Partition cell analysis of infective tobacco mosaic virus nucleic acid.

J. Mol. Biol. **1,** 321–328

20. Pauling, L., and Corey, R. B. (1953) Proposed structure for the nucleic acids. *Proc. Natl. Acad. Sci. U. S. A.* **39,** 84–97
21. Watson, J. D., and Crick, F. H. C. (1953) Molecular structure of nucleic acids. *Nature* **171,** 737–738
22. Sinsheimer, R. L. (1954) Nucleotides from T2r+ bacteriophage. *Science* **120,** 551–553
23. Sinsheimer, R. L. (1956) The glucose content of the deoxyribonucleic acids of certain bacteriophages. *Proc. Natl. Acad. Sci. U. S. A.* **42,** 502–504
24. Sertic, V., and Bulgakov, N. (1935) Classification et identification des typhi-phages. *Comptes Rendus de la Soc. de Biol.* **119,** 1270–1272
25. Sinsheimer, R. L. (1959) Sedimentation and properties of bacteriophage φX174. *J. Mol. Biol.* **1,** 37–42
26. Sinsheimer, R. L. (1959) A single-stranded deoxyribonucleic acid from bacteriophage φX174. *J. Mol. Biol.* **1,** 43–53
27. Guthrie, G. D., and Sinsheimer, R. L. (1960) Infection of protoplasts of *Escherichia coli* by subviral particles of bacteriophage φX174. *J. Mol. Biol.* **2,** 297–305
28. Fiers, W., and Sinsheimer, R. L. (1962) The structure of the DNA of bacteriophage φX174 III. Ultracentrifugal evidence for a ring structure. *J. Mol. Biol.* **5,** 424–434
29. Kleinschmidt, A. K., Burton, A., and Sinsheimer, R. L. (1963) Electron microscopy of the replicative form of the DNA of bacteriophage φX174. *Science* **142,** 961
30. Freifelder, D., Kleinschmidt, A. K., and Sinsheimer, R. L. (1964) Electron microscopy of single-stranded DNA: circularity of DNA of bacteriophage φX174. *Science* **146,** 254–255
31. Sinsheimer, R. L., Starman, B., Nagler, C., and Guthrie, S. (1962) The process of infection with bacteriophage φX174. I. Evidence for a "replicative form." *J. Mol. Biol.* **4,** 142–160
32. Benbow, R. M., Hutchison, C. A., III, Fabricant, J. D., and Sinsheimer, R. L. (1971) The genetic map of bacteriophage φX174. *J. Virol.* **7,** 549–558
33. Goulian, M., Kornberg, A., and Sinsheimer, R. L. (1967) Enzymatic synthesis of DNA XXIV. Synthesis of infectious phage φX174 DNA. *Proc. Natl. Acad. Sci. U. S. A.* **58,** 2321–2328
34. Sanger, F., Air, G. M., Barrell, B. G., Brown, R. I., Coulson, A. R., Fiddes, J. C., Hutchison, C. A., III, Slocombe, P. M., and Smith, M. (1977) Nucleotide sequence of bacteriophage φX174 DNA. *Nature* **265,** 687–695
35. Lehman, I. R., Zimmerman, S. B., Adler, J., Bessman, M. J., Simms, E. S., and Kornberg, A. (1958) Enzymatic synthesis of deoxyribonucleic acid. 5. Chemical composition of enzymatically synthesized deoxyribonucleic acid. *Proc. Natl. Acad. Sci. U. S. A.* **44,** 1191–1196
36. Sanger, F. (1952) The arrangement of amino acids in proteins. *Adv. Protein Chem.* **7,** 1–28
37. Kendrew, J. C., Dickerson, R. E., Strandberg, B. E., Hart, R. G., Davies, D. R., Phillips, D. C., and Shore, V. C. (1960) Structure of myoglobin: a three-dimensional Fourier synthesis at 2-Å resolution. *Nature* **185,** 422–427
38. Cullis, A. F., Muirhead, H., Perutz, M. F., Rossman, M. G., and North, A. C. T. (1962) The structure of haemoglobin. IX. A three-dimensional Fourier synthesis at 5.5-Å resolution: description of the structure. *Proc. R. Soc. Lond. A* **265,** 161–187

THE JOURNAL OF BIOLOGICAL CHEMISTRY
© 2004 by The American Society for Biochemistry and Molecular Biology, Inc.

Vol. 279, No. 44, Issue of October 29, pp. 45291–45299, 2004
Printed in U.S.A.

Reflections

A PAPER IN A SERIES COMMISSIONED TO CELEBRATE THE CENTENARY OF THE JBC IN 2005

JBC Centennial
1905–2005
100 Years of Biochemistry and Molecular Biology

A Tribute to the *Xenopus laevis* Oocyte and Egg

Published, JBC Papers in Press, August 11, 2004, DOI 10.1074/jbc.X400008200

Donald D. Brown

From the Department of Embryology, Carnegie Institution of Washington, Baltimore, Maryland 21210

When I was asked to reflect as part of the celebration of the 100-year anniversary of the *Journal of Biological Chemistry* I recalled a talk by Seymour Cohen at the Federation meetings in Atlantic City about 1960. He began by thanking bacteriophage for providing him with so many wonderful research problems. I decided in the same spirit to pay homage to the *Xenopus laevis* egg and oocyte, two states of a cell that has played and continues to play a central role in most of the disciplines of modern biology including biochemistry and molecular biology. Many of us owe a debt of gratitude to this cell.

The egg is the most important and interesting cell in the repertoire of any organism. In *X. laevis* this single cell has a diameter of about 1.3 mm. The oocyte is permeable to small molecules, but after it undergoes meiosis and becomes an unfertilized egg it is impermeable to these same molecules. The oocyte is an active site of RNA and protein synthesis but not DNA replication, whereas the unfertilized egg is poised to replicate every 10 min after it is fertilized. During the cleavage period the embryo is transcriptionally silent. An oocyte can be cultured for days, but once ovulated the egg degenerates rapidly if it is not fertilized. The oocyte is the largest single cell in the body yet it has many of the same structures as somatic cells. These compartments are so exaggerated in size that they are accessible to cell biologists for manipulation and visualization. The huge oocyte nucleus is called a germinal vesicle (GV). The premeiotic tetraploid chromosomes are expanded into a "lampbrush" configuration so that they can be studied with a light microscope.

The *X. laevis* egg and its possibilities for experimental manipulation were introduced to modern biology in the late 1950s by John Gurdon (Fig. 1), then a graduate student in the laboratory of Michail Fischberg in the Department of Zoology at Oxford University. Gurdon's thesis was to reproduce with the South African "clawed toad" *X. laevis* the famous nuclear transplantation experiments that Briggs and King had perfected with the American leopard frog, *Rana pipiens* (1). Embryonic nuclei were injected into eggs whose own nuclei had been removed or destroyed. These early cloning experiments addressed the question of whether a differentiated and specialized somatic cell nucleus was still capable of expressing its full genetic repertoire. Briggs and King found that nuclei from *R. pipiens* embryos older than gastrula never promoted normal development, suggesting that the genetic material might change in cells as they specialize during embryonic development. This result was challenged by John Gurdon's demonstration that nuclei from *X. laevis* embryos are more permissive. Even a small fraction of nuclei derived from differentiated intestinal epithelial cells supported normal development (2). This crucial scientific question of whether irreversible changes occur in the genome of highly specialized cells was addressed more precisely by experimental manipulation than by biochemistry or genetics. The concepts behind these experiments have influenced the stem cell field. The topic of whether the genome is altered in specialized somatic cells was revisited just this year by the same strategy of nuclear transplantation. Postmitotic nuclei from olfactory neurons support the development of normal fertile mice when transplanted into enucleated mouse eggs (3).

FIG. 1. **John B. Gurdon.** Photo taken in 2000.

Control of Genes Expressed in Oocytes

A developing amphibian embryo requires no organic nutrients from its rearing medium. The entire development from the single-cell egg to a feeding tadpole of hundreds of thousands of cells occurs using materials stored in the egg. The unique composition of the oocyte and egg has led to many important discoveries that invariably can be traced to this storage function. In the 1950s and early 1960s there were reports that eggs of many species had much more DNA than expected for a single cell. The first person to investigate this by isolating and characterizing the "egg DNA" from *R. pipiens* and *X. laevis* was Igor Dawid (Fig. 2). He came to the Department of Embryology of the Carnegie Institution of Washington in Baltimore in 1963 as an independent investigator after completing his postdoctoral training in biochemistry at MIT. Dawid found that an egg contains orders of magnitude more high molecular DNA than the amount expected of a single cell (4). Using the new DNA hybridization technology that had been developed at the Department of Terrestrial Magnetism of the Carnegie Institution (5), Dawid showed that egg DNA is a select group of sequences rather than representative of the entire frog genome. The first reports had appeared that some cytoplasmic organelles contain DNA, and Dawid demonstrated that the extra egg DNA is mitochondrial DNA (6). Because a single *X. laevis* egg cell has the same abundance of mitochondria as about 100,000 somatic cells the quantity of mitochondrial DNA exceeds the amount of nuclear DNA in an *X. laevis* egg by several hundred-fold. These discoveries led to the realization that an individual's mitochondria are maternally inherited.

In addition to mitochondria each mature *X. laevis* oocyte accumulates the same amount of ribosomes as hundreds of thousands of somatic cells. With the discovery of mRNA in 1960 it became clear that RNA was the direct gene product, and therefore changes in RNA synthesis, not protein content, better reflect gene expression. In 1963 Yankofsky and Spiegelman (7) demonstrated that the two large ribosomal RNAs (rRNA) in *Escherichia coli* were encoded separately in the bacterial DNA. Because they are so abundant in eukaryotic cells these two rRNAs became the first gene products that could be studied in animal cells. Jim Darnell (8) found that the two large rRNAs were derived from the same high molecular weight precursor. The question of how a single cell, the oocyte, could synthesize the RNAs for so many ribosomes became a focus of my own interest in differential gene expression for a decade.

By the time that I graduated from medical school I had decided that ultimately I would study how embryos developed. The field was related to medicine but completely unexplored. Follow-

Fig. 2. **Igor B. Dawid.** Photo taken in 1999.

ing 1 year of internship I had the good fortune to be chosen by Seymour Kety, who directed the laboratory on schizophrenic research at the National Institute of Mental Health, to be in the first class of "research associates" at the National Institutes of Health. This marvelous program that was designed to train newly minted M.D.s in research provided me with 2 years of experience learning biochemistry. Before leaving NIH for an exciting year in the Monod laboratory at the Pasteur Institute I needed to find a laboratory where I could begin my future studies in embryology. Entirely by accident I discovered a small research unit located on the campus of the Johns Hopkins Medical School in Baltimore whose faculty studied embryonic development. The Department of Embryology of the Carnegie Institution of Washington had specialized for 50 years in the descriptive anatomy of human embryos and reproductive biology. I arrived there as an independent fellow in the fall of 1960 indoctrinated with the new operon model of gene expression control determined to study the biochemistry of development. Frog eggs were large and plentiful, and they develop synchronously after fertilization. They seemed perfect for biochemistry.

In 1962 I read about a mutation in the frog *X. laevis* that had been discovered in the Fischberg laboratory (9). This mutation altered the number of nucleoli. The homozygous embryos had no visible nucleoli and died at the time that a normal embryo begins to accumulate new ribosomes. Bob Perry (10) and Edstrom and Gall (11) had shown by cytochemical experiments that nucleoli contain high GC RNA characteristic of rRNA. In 1964 John Gurdon and I found that the homozygous anucleolate mutant of *X. laevis* cannot synthesize either the 18 or 28 S ribosomal RNA molecules (12). This discovery confirmed the nucleolus as the site of rRNA synthesis. The molecular explanation of the mutation came 2 years later from the work of Max Birnstiel (Fig. 3) who developed a method to isolate the rRNA genes (rDNA) from the bulk of the *X. laevis* genomic DNA (13). He reasoned from the known base composition of rRNA that rDNA should have a higher GC content than the average 40% GC genomic DNA of *X. laevis.* Sueoka, Marmur, and Doty (14) had established the relationship of GC content to the density of DNA when banded to equilibrium by centrifugation in CsCl. Wallace and Birnstiel (13) purified the high GC rDNA by repeated cycles of centrifugation. In doing so they demonstrated that the anucleolar mutant lacks rDNA and is therefore a deletion mutation. From the amount of radioactive rRNA that hybridized with genomic DNA they estimated that there are several hundred copies of 18 and 28 S RNA genes per haploid complement of *X. laevis* DNA. These repeated genes must be clustered because a deletion removes all of them. Birnstiel's purification of the *X. laevis* rDNA genes was the first isolation of a specific gene from any organism, and it occurred 10 years before cloning. Max Birnstiel (15) and I (16) have reviewed the research on purified genes that preceded the recombinant DNA era. *X. laevis* oocytes played a prominent role.

FIG. 3. **Max L. Birnstiel.** Photo taken in 2000.

An oocyte is a tetraploid cell, but each *X. laevis* germinal vesicle contains about 1500 rather than the expected 4 nucleoli. At a 1966 meeting on the nucleolus in Montivideo, Oscar Miller showed his spectacular pictures of genes in the act of transcribing RNA. He had unraveled these "Christmas tree" structures from the nucleoli of *X. laevis* oocyte nuclei (17). Joe Gall (Fig. 4), who attended the same meeting, and I realized that these structures must be extra chromosomal tandemly repeated rRNA genes. Soon thereafter Igor Dawid and I (18) and Joe Gall (19) independently showed that the rRNA genes just like the nucleoli are present in a 1000-fold excess in oocyte GVs, a phenomenon that we named specific gene amplification. We had identified a novel regulatory mechanism by which a single cell could ramp up its synthesis of a normal cytoplasmic structure, the ribosome. In those days before cloning, *X. laevis* oocytes became a major source of purified rDNA to study rDNA structure (20). Joe Gall and Mary Lou Pardue (21) studied the early stages of rDNA gene amplification in immature oocytes by hybridizing radioactive rRNA to oocyte sections on slides. This method called "*in situ* hybridization" remains an essential tool of modern molecular biology.

Following the discovery of rDNA gene amplification in oocytes it was logical to look into the genes that encode other RNA components of the ribosome. Along with one molecule of 18 and 28 S RNA there is a molecule of a 5.8 S and a 5 S RNA in each ribosome. Birnstiel (22) demonstrated that the 5.8 S RNA is cleaved from the same precursor as 18 and 28 S RNA, thus accounting for its stoichiometry in the ribosome. However, the 5 S RNA genes are not linked to the rDNA genes in *X. laevis* (23). Although there are several hundred rRNA genes in the *X. laevis* genome we found tens of thousands 5 S RNA genes arranged in tandem and distributed on many chromosomes. In fact 5 S DNA comprises 0.7% of the *X. laevis* genomic DNA. Its unusual nucleotide composition facilitated the purification of 5 S DNA by density gradient methods from *X. laevis* genomic DNA (24). The repeat length is a mere 700 base pairs. In the summer of 1973 I prepared ^{32}P-labeled cRNA from genomic 5 S DNA by transcribing the separated strands with *E. coli* polymerase and then spent 2 months with George Brownlee in Cambridge helping him sequence the ribonuclease-generated ^{32}P-labeled oligonucleotides by the two-dimensional separation method that George had developed with Fred Sanger. From these chromatograms we pieced together the essential features of a repeat of 5 S DNA (25). By 1970 it had been determined that the 5 S RNA stored in oocytes differs by several nucleotides from that found in somatic cell ribosomes (26). We found that each repeat of 5 S DNA has one oocyte-specific 5 S RNA gene, one partial gene that George named a "pseudogene," and an AT-rich spacer. Each spacer consists of varying numbers of a degenerate AT-rich 15-base pair nucleotide repeat. Nina Fedoroff in collaboration with the Brownlee laboratory subsequently sequenced an entire repeat from genomic 5 S DNA (27, 28). This was the first time that a

Fig. 4. **Joseph G. Gall.** Photo taken in 1996.

full-length eukaryotic gene had been sequenced. Subsequently we isolated two other families of 5 S RNA genes from the genomic DNA of *X. laevis*, one of which was the much smaller somatic 5 S RNA gene family (29).

The "dual" 5 S RNA gene system is another mechanism by which the oocyte synthesizes large amounts of a ribosomal component. The thousands of oocyte 5 S RNA genes are active in growing oocytes so that the ribosomes in oocytes contain oocyte-specific 5 S RNA. When embryogenesis begins the amplified rDNA genes are lost and the oocyte 5 S DNA is inactivated. At gastrulation the chromosomal rDNA genes and the smaller gene family encoding the somatic 5 S RNA genes begin to be expressed. In somatic cells the rate of ribosome synthesis correlates with the rate of protein synthesis. In growing oocytes most ribosomes are stored as monosomes for later use during embryogenesis. 5 S RNA accumulates in oocytes stored in cytoplasmic ribonucleoprotein particles before ribosome assembly. One of the proteins in this particle is none other than TFIIIA, the 5 S DNA-specific transcription factor that is stored in large amounts in oocytes (30). I will discuss TFIIIA later in this article.

The Use of Oocytes for mRNA Translation

In 1969 a 9 S RNA was isolated from rabbit reticulocytes and deduced to be the mRNA for globin (31). A cell-free lysate prepared by Jerry Lingrel synthesized recognizable globin for short incubation periods before the extract activity died. This was the first identification of a eukaryotic mRNA. In 1971 John Gurdon and his colleagues injected globin mRNA into the cytoplasm of *X. laevis* oocytes and demonstrated the synthesis of rabbit globin (32). The advantages of this *in vivo* method to assay protein synthesis were immediately clear. The cultured living oocyte synthesizes foreign proteins for days rather than minutes, and the protein accumulates in the oocyte cytoplasm. The ease with which the large oocyte can be injected and then cultured brought this *in vivo* translation assay to the attention of the burgeoning field of molecular biology.

Injection of mRNA into oocytes has provided a successful method to clone genes from complex mixtures of mRNAs. In addition to efficient translation the protein product is transported to its expected location in the cell and then functions correctly. An early example of the power of oocyte molecular biology was its use in interferon research. When poly(A)$^+$ RNA from cultured mammalian cells activated to produce interferon was injected into *X. laevis* oocytes

500 times greater titers of the active molecule were synthesized and secreted than by cultured cell extracts as judged by a sensitive bioassay based on the antiviral effects of interferon (33). Charles Weissmann and his colleagues (34) fractionated poly(A)$^+$ RNA by size on a sucrose gradient and cloned interferon cDNA from the active mRNA fraction assayed by injection into *X. laevis* oocytes. This was the first application of expression cloning. Enzymes encoded by rare mRNAs have been expression-cloned in *X. laevis* oocytes using their enzymatic reaction as an assay. An example is the cloning of deiodinase type 1 (35), a selenocysteine-containing protein from rat liver, by Reed Larsen and his colleagues.

Douglas Melton developed the strategy of injecting synthetic mRNA (36) and then antisense oligonucleotides (37) into fertilized eggs as an assay for the influence of a gene on development. This alternative to traditional forward genetics has made *X. laevis* second only to *Drosophila* as a model system to identify genetic pathways in embryogenesis. The resulting embryos are analyzed in a number of ways to determine the effect of overproducing a gene product, mutations of that product, or antisense oligonucleotides. Many genes crucial to embryonic development have been cloned first from *X. laevis* because their function can be determined by these mRNA injection assays. An extension of expression cloning by Richard Harland (38) has used the effect on embryogenesis as an assay to identify genes that influence development. Recently the Harland laboratory (39) has developed a screening method to identify large numbers of genes important for development based upon the observable phenotype caused by their overexpression in a developing embryo.

The Use of Oocytes in Cell Biology

The injection of labeled proteins into the oocyte cytoplasm results in their transport to the site in the cell where they normally reside (40, 41). Newly translated secretory proteins from many different species cross intracellular membranes of the oocyte (42, 43). Once genes could be cloned and mutated synthetic mRNA was injected into oocyte cytoplasm to delimit the signals on a protein for secretion (44) and nuclear localization (45). The localization of this stored mRNA in the egg is controlled by sequences in the 3′-untranslated region of the mRNA that were identified by an oocyte injection assay (46).

Neurophysiologists and biochemists have taken advantage of the *X. laevis* oocyte to clone and investigate receptors and ion channel proteins. The oocyte has some endogenous receptors. For example, it contains muscarinic acetylcholine receptors but no nicotinic receptors. Injection of mRNA from the electric organ of the ray (47) or skeletal muscle of the cat (48) produces functional nicotinic acetylcholine receptors. The multisubunit functional protein is assembled in oocytes, glycosylated correctly, and sequestered into the plasma membrane. Peter Agre (49) developed a striking assay for his Nobel Prize-winning discovery of a water channel gene. He prepared synthetic mRNA from the previously unknown cDNA, injected it into *X. laevis* oocytes, and then watched them swell and rupture.

The Use of Oocytes for Transcription

An early indication that *X. laevis* eggs would be rich in the molecules needed for RNA transcription was Bob Roeder's quantification of the three isoforms of eukaryotic RNA polymerase that he had previously discovered in sea urchin embryos. One *X. laevis* egg contains 4 orders of magnitude more of these RNA polymerases than does one somatic cell (50). In 1977 Mertz and Gurdon (51) demonstrated that SV40 DNA injected into *X. laevis* oocyte nuclei produced SV40 mRNA, and this mRNA was translated into recognizable SV40 proteins. We had purified the oocyte-specific 5 S DNA from *X. laevis* genomic DNA and had been studying its structure. This prompted John Gurdon and me to collaborate on another of our transatlantic experiments. I sent John the 5 S DNA. He injected the DNA into oocyte nuclei with a radioactive precursor and mailed the radioactive extract back to me for electrophoretic analysis. The newly synthesized 5 S RNA was accurately initiated and terminated (52). Then Ed Birkenmeier (53) prepared an extract from hand-isolated germinal vesicles that was competent to transcribe accurately added 5 S DNA. By that time repeating units of 5 S DNA had been cloned by the new recombinant DNA technology. Having a fully characterized cloned gene and an oocyte extract that faithfully transcribed it allowed us to identify the DNA-controlling regions that specify accurate initiation and termination of 5 S RNA synthesis. As Shigeru Sakonju and Dan Bogenhagen deleted the spacer regions adjacent to the 5 S gene we were astonished that the gene kept making 5 S RNA in our *in vitro* oocyte nuclear extract. When Shige deleted into the 5′-end of the gene's coding region and recloned the construct it continued to make 5 S-like RNA. Two of us independently sequenced this construct to confirm this remarkable fact. Before specific RNA synthesis stopped, about one-third of the coding region had been replaced with plasmid sequences (54, 55). Deletions from the 3′ end altered termination as soon as one of the four Ts that encode the Us at the 3′ end of the mature 5 S RNA had been removed (56). However, these constructs continued to initiate transcription correctly. This set of experiments delimited a region of about 50 base pairs within the coding region of the 5 S RNA gene that we named the "internal control region."

Meanwhile Bob Roeder and his colleagues (57) purified a protein from *X. laevis* oocytes that bound tightly to 5 S DNA and was required for accurate transcription. Our laboratories joined forces to show that this protein, which Roeder had named TFIIIA, complexed specifically with the internal control region of the 5 S DNA gene (58). Roeder's group (59) cloned the cDNA for TFIIIA from oocyte mRNA. Aaron Klug (60) recognized in the sequence 9 repeating peptide regions that he predicted must complex zinc. This was the discovery of "zinc finger" transcription factors. Active TFIIIA protein was purified easily for biochemistry because of its accumulation in huge amounts in *X. laevis* oocytes within the RNP particle. TFIIIA has the unusual feature of binding specifically to the 5 S RNA gene and 5 S RNA (30). The gene encoding TFIIIA is transcribed from a different start site in oocytes than it is in somatic cells, undoubtedly using one or more oocyte-specific transcription factors (yet another mechanism devised for enhanced ribosome synthesis). For many years the simple dual 5 S RNA gene system provided novel insights into the molecular aspects of differential gene expression (61).

In 1980 Grosschedl and Birnstiel (62) delimited regulatory elements in the sea urchin histone H2A gene by injecting mutant constructs into the *X. laevis* oocyte. Steve McKnight (63) originated the linker scanning method to mutate systematically the promoter region and assayed the transcripts after injecting the DNA constructs into the oocyte nucleus. In the early days of recombinant DNA technology the *X. laevis* oocyte played an important role in the new "reverse" genetics or as we called it "genetics by DNA isolation."

The Use of X. laevis Eggs for Cell Cycle Research

In 1971 Masui and Markert (64) and Smith and Ecker (65) found that cytoplasm from an oocyte that had been induced to undergo meiosis with progesterone could induce GV breakdown in an untreated oocyte. The factor was named maturation promoting factor or MPF. Its identity and how it acted catalytically remained a mystery for decades, but it ushered in a new career for *X. laevis* oocytes and eggs, which was their role in unraveling the intricacies of the cell cycle. An oocyte is arrested in prophase of its first meiotic division and has not undergone DNA synthesis for months, yet hours after completing meiosis and fertilization it divides every 10 min throughout its cleavage stages. Laskey and Gurdon (66) found that eggs but not oocytes could replicate injected double-stranded DNA. The realization that eggs have stored nuclear components including a huge excess of histones (67, 68) led to the development of *X. laevis* egg extracts for the assembly of chromatin (69) and nuclei (70). *X. laevis* egg extracts initiate and complete efficient semiconservative DNA replication (71). Progress on the molecular details of the cell cycle including DNA replication and chromatin, nuclear, and mitotic spindle assembly in the past 10 years has been remarkable due in no small degree to the *X. laevis* egg and oocyte.

Lampbrush Chromosomes and the Oocyte Nucleus

The GVs of amphibian oocytes have expanded chromosomes that resemble the brushes used to clean the dirt from lamps in the days before electricity. The larger the genome the greater is the size of the loops of these "lampbrush" chromosomes. Two scientists often working together over a period of decades have elucidated the structure of these huge chromosomes. Joe Gall and H. G. (Mick) Callan began their cytogenetic experiments over 50 years ago with salamander lampbrush chromosomes. In 1987 (72) they published the first physical maps of the *X. laevis* lampbrush chromosomes. With the accumulation of *X. laevis* sequence data it is possible that these chromosomes can be mapped with the degree of accuracy previously reserved for the giant polytene chromosomes of *Drosophila*. Joe Gall has demonstrated that the GV contains the same structures as somatic nuclei but so exaggerated in number and size that they are especially suited for analysis (73).

In Summary

The value of the *X. laevis* egg and oocyte for biology is an ongoing story, which is the reason that this article became part reminiscence and part manual review. In a recent paper Miledi and his colleagues (74) demonstrated that membranes from frozen tissues could be shown to contain functional receptors and channels when injected into *X. laevis* oocytes. They observed that this powerful and versatile assay has barely been explored for the study of human diseases. Judging from the central role that the *X. laevis* egg and oocyte continue to play in so many biological disciplines I suspect that a new generation of biologists will have reason to pay their tributes to this remarkable cell.

Address correspondence to: brown@ciwemb.edu.

REFERENCES

1. Briggs, R., and King, T. J. (1952) *Proc. Natl. Acad. Sci. U. S. A.* **38**, 455–463
2. Gurdon, J. (1960) *J. Embryol. Exp. Morphol.* **8**, 505–526
3. Eggan, K., Baldwin, K., Tackett, M., Osborne, J., Gogos, J., Chess, A., Axel, R., and Jaenisch, R. (2004) *Nature* **428**, 44–49
4. Dawid, I. B. (1965) *J. Mol. Biol.* **12**, 581–599
5. Bolton, E. T., and McCarthy, B. J. (1962) *Proc. Natl. Acad. Sci. U. S. A.* **48**, 1390–1397
6. Dawid, I. B. (1965) *Proc. Natl. Acad. Sci. U. S. A.* **56**, 269–276
7. Yankofsky, S. A., and Spiegelman, S. (1962) *Proc. Natl. Acad. Sci. U. S. A.* **48**, 1069–1078
8. Scherrer, K., Latham, H., and Darnell, J. E. (1963) *Proc. Natl. Acad. Sci. U. S. A.* **49**, 240–248
9. Elsdale, T. R., Fischberg, M., and Smith, S. (1958) *Exp. Cell Res.* **14**, 642–643
10. Perry, R. P. (1962) *Proc. Natl. Acad. Sci. U. S. A.* **48**, 2179–2186
11. Edstrom, J. E., and Gall, J. G. (1963) *J. Cell Biol.* **19**, 279–284
12. Brown, D. D., and Gurdon, J. B. (1964) *Proc. Natl. Acad. Sci. U. S. A.* **51**, 139–146
13. Wallace, H., and Birnstiel, M. L. (1966) *Biochim. Biophys. Acta* **114**, 296–310
14. Sueoka, N., Marmur, J., and Doty, P. (1959) *Nature* **183**, 1429–1433
15. Birnstiel, M. L. (2002) *Gene (Amst.)* **300**, 3–11
16. Brown, D. D. (1994) *BioEssays* **16**, 139–143
17. Miller, O. L., and Beatty, B. R. (1969) *Science* **164**, 955–957
18. Brown, D. D., and Dawid, I. B. (1968) *Science* **160**, 272–280
19. Gall, J. G. (1968) *Proc. Natl. Acad. Sci. U. S. A.* **60**, 553–560
20. Dawid, I. B., Brown, D. D., and Reeder, R. H. (1970) *J. Mol. Biol.* **51**, 341–360
21. Gall, J. G., and Pardue, M. L. (1969) *Proc. Natl. Acad. Sci. U. S. A.* **63**, 378–383
22. Speirs, J., and Birnstiel, M. L. (1974) *J. Mol. Biol.* **87**, 237–256
23. Brown, D. D., and Weber C. S. (1968) *J. Mol. Biol.* **34**, 661–680
24. Brown, D. D., Wensink, P. C., and Jordan, E. (1971) *Proc. Natl. Acad. Sci. U. S. A.* **68**, 3175–3179
25. Brownlee, G. G., Cartwright, E. M., and Brown, D. D. (1974) *J. Mol. Biol.* **89**, 703–718
26. Wegnez, M., Monier, R., and Denis, H. (1972) *FEBS Lett.* **25**, 13–18
27. Fedoroff, N. V., and Brown, D. D. (1978) *Cell* **13**, 701–716
28. Miller, J. R., Cartwright, E. M., Brownlee, G. G., Fedoroff, N. V., and Brown, D. D. (1978) *Cell* **13**, 717–725
29. Peterson, R. C., Doering, J. L., and Brown, D. D. (1980) *Cell* **20**, 131–141
30. Pelham, H. R. B., and Brown, D. D. (1980) *Proc. Natl. Acad. Sci. U. S. A.* **77**, 4170–4174
31. Lockard, R. E., and Lingrel, J. B. (1969) *Biochem. Biophys. Res. Commun.* **37**, 204–212
32. Gurdon, J. B., Lane, C. D., Woodland, H. R., and Marbaix, G. (1971) *Nature* **233**, 177–182
33. Reynolds, F. H., Premkumar, E., and Pitha, P. M. (1975) *Proc. Natl. Acad. Sci. U. S. A.* **72**, 4881–4885
34. Weissmann, C., Nagata, S., Boll, W., Fountoulakis, M., Fujisawa, A., Fujisawa, J-I., Haynes, J., Henco, K., Mantei, N., Ragg, H., Schein, C., Schmid, J., Shaw, G., Streuli, M., Taira, H., Todokoro, K., and Weidle, U. (1982) *Philos. Trans. R. Soc. Lond. B Biol. Sci.* **299**, 7–28
35. Berry, M. J., Banu, L., and Larsen, P. R. (1991) *Nature* **349**, 438–440
36. Krieg, P. A., and Melton, D. A. (1984) *Nucleic Acids Res.* **12**, 7057–7070
37. Melton, D. A. (1985) *Proc. Natl. Acad. Sci. U. S. A.* **82**, 144–148
38. Smith, W. C., and Harland, R. M. (1992) *Cell* **70**, 829–840
39. Grammer, T. C., Liu, K. J., Mariani, F. V., and Harland, R. M. (2000) *Dev. Biol.* **228**, 197–210
40. Gurdon, J. B. (1970) *Philos. Trans. R. Soc. Lond. B Biol. Sci.* **176**, 303–314
41. Bonner, W. M. (1975) *J. Cell Biol.* **64**, 431–437
42. Zehavi-Willner, T., and Lane, C. (1977) *Cell* **11**, 683–693
43. Colman, A., and Morser, J. (1979) *Cell* **17**, 517–526
44. Krieg, P. A., Strachen, R., Wallis, E., Tabe, L., and Colman, A. (1984) *J. Mol. Biol.* **180**, 615–643
45. Dingwall, C., Sharnick, S. V., and Laskey, R. A. (1982) *Cell* **30**, 449–458
46. Yisraeli, J. K., and Melton, D. A. (1988) *Nature* **336**, 592–595
47. Sumikawa, K., Houghton, M., Emtage, J. S., Richards, B. M., and Barnard, E. A. (1981) *Nature* **292**, 862–864
48. Miledi, R., Parker, I., and Sumikawa, K. (1982) *EMBO J.* **1**, 1307–1312
49. Preston, G. M., Carroll, T. P., Guggino, W. B., and Agre, P. (1992) *Science* **256**, 385–387
50. Roeder, R. G. (1974) *J. Biol. Chem.* **249**, 249–256
51. Mertz, J. E., and Gurdon, J. B. (1977) *Proc. Natl. Acad. Sci. U. S. A.* **74**, 1502–1506
52. Brown, D. D., and Gurdon, J. B. (1977) *Proc. Natl. Acad. Sci. U. S. A.* **74**, 2064–2068
53. Birkenmeier, E. H., Brown, D. D., and Jordan, E. (1978) *Cell* **15**, 1077–1086
54. Sakonju, S., Bogenhagen, D. F., and Brown, D. D. (1980) *Cell* **19**, 13–25
55. Bogenhagen, D. F., Sakonju, S., and Brown, D. D. (1980) *Cell* **19**, 27–35
56. Bogenhagen, D. F., and Brown, D. D. (1981) *Cell* **24**, 261–270
57. Engelke, D. R., Ng, S., Shastry, B. S., and Roeder, R. G. (1980) *Cell* **19**, 717–728
58. Sakonju, S., Brown, D. D., Engelke, D., Ng, S-Y., Shastry, B. S., and Roeder, R. G. (1981) *Cell* **23**, 665–669
59. Ginsberg, A. M., King, B. O., and Roeder, R. G. (1984) *Cell* **39**, 479–489
60. Miller, J., McLachlan, A. D., and Klug, A. (1985) *EMBO J.* **4**, 1609–1614
61. Wolffe, A. P., and Brown, D. D. (1988) *Science* **241**, 1626–1632
62. Grosschedl, R., and Birnstiel, H. L. (1980) *Proc. Natl. Acad. Sci. U. S. A.* **77**, 7102–7106
63. McKnight, S. L., Gavis, E., Kingsbury, R., and Axel, R. (1981) *Cell* **25**, 385–398
64. Masui, Y., and Markert, C. L. (1971) *J. Exp. Zool.* **177**, 129–145
65. Smith, L. D., and Ecker, R. E. (1971) *Dev. Biol.* **25**, 232–247

66. Laskey, R. A., and Gurdon, J. B. (1973) Eur. *J. Biochem.* **37,** 467–471
67. Adamson, E. D., and Woodland, H. R. (1974) *J. Mol. Biol.* **88,** 263–285
68. Laskey, R. A., Mills, R. A., and Morris, N. R. (1977) *Cell* **10,** 237–243
69. Wyllie, A. H., Laskey, R. A., Finch, J., and Gurdon, J. B. (1978) *Dev. Biol.* **64,** 178–188
70. Forbes, D. J., Kirschner, M. W., and Newport, J. W. (1983) *Cell* **34,** 13–23
71. Blow, J. J., and Laskey, R. A. (1986) *Cell* **47,** 577–587
72. Callan, H. G., Gall, J. G., and Berg, C. A. (1987) *Chromosoma* **95,** 236–250
73. Gall, J. G., Wu, Z., Murphy, C., and Gao, H. (2004) *Exp. Cell Res.* **296,** 28–34
74. Miledi, R., Duenas, Z., Martinez-Torres, A., Kawas, C. H., and Eusebi, F. (2004) *Proc. Natl. Acad. Sci. U. S. A.* **101,** 1760–1763

The Journal of Biological Chemistry
© 2004 by The American Society for Biochemistry and Molecular Biology, Inc.

Vol. 279, No. 51, Issue of December 17, pp. 52807–52811, 2004
Printed in U.S.A.

Reflections

A PAPER IN A SERIES COMMISSIONED TO CELEBRATE THE CENTENARY OF THE JBC IN 2005

JBC Centennial
1905–2005
100 Years of Biochemistry and Molecular Biology

Reminiscences of Leon A. Heppel

Published, JBC Papers in Press, September 14, 2004, DOI 10.1074/jbc.X400007200

Leon A. Heppel

From the Department of Molecular Biology and Genetics, Cornell University, Ithaca, New York 14853

My parents were converted Mormons who had emigrated from Germany to Utah planning to live on a farm. The oldest of five children, I was born in Granger, Utah, in 1912. Farm life proved difficult and after 10 years our family moved to San Francisco. There, the city encouraged interesting local activities particularly for poor people, and life was more pleasant than in Utah.

In school, I became interested in chemistry. While a high school student, my mother, who was ambitious on my behalf, persuaded John Stauffer, president of Stauffer Chemical Company, to give me a job doing analytical work at the American Cream Tartar Company in San Francisco. This supported me through high school and afterward when I enrolled at the University of California, Berkeley to major in chemistry and chemical engineering.

At Berkeley

Unhappily, my job at the American Cream Tartar Company and the support it provided did not last. In 1931, the Stauffer Chemical Company merged with the Schilling Spice Corporation and the combined company owned American Cream Tartar. A vice president of Schilling Spice undertook to effect economies, but the only economy he could find was getting rid of me. Shocked and urged by my mother to plead my case, I told the vice president how much I depended on the job. His cold reply was, "You need Schilling Spice Company but does Schilling Spice need you?" I never forgot those cruel words. Because of them, I abandoned my plan to be a chemical engineer turning instead to physiological biochemistry, which I thought would be a gentler profession. Fortunately I received a fellowship that allowed me to complete a B.S. degree in 1933. That same year I entered Berkeley's graduate school as a biochemistry student.

Living in midtown San Francisco and commuting each day to Berkeley was a tiring chore. The Bay Bridges had not been built. In early morning, I took a streetcar to the Ferry Building where I boarded a boat for Oakland; on good days this took half an hour, but if the fog was intense, it was a much longer trip. From Oakland an electric train went to Berkeley and the university. In midafternoon, I returned across the Bay and spent a few hours working in one of the several Stauffer Chemical factories. Aside from the commute, however, life and science in Berkeley were exciting. During this period, Ernest O. Lawrence and others were doing great work and were anxious to talk about it. I made good friends among the chemists, one of whom discovered ^{14}C (Martin D. Kamen in 1940).

Nutrition was a major subfield of biochemistry in the 1930s, and I decided to do my thesis in that subject under Professor C. L. A. Schmidt. Schmidt was harsh and domineering but helpful. In later years when he became dean of the College of Pharmacy at the University of California, San Francisco, he hired my mother to take charge of equipment and supplies.

For my thesis research, I decided to work on potassium (K^+) metabolism in white rats. The experiments showed that K^+ was essential for the growth and survival of young rats, and there was some evidence that sodium (Na^+) could partially replace K^+. Rubidium (Rb^+) supported good growth in K^+-free diets for a month, but thereafter the rats developed sudden tremors and died. My Ph.D. degree in biochemistry was awarded in 1937, a year when there were no jobs available for a biochemist. Luckily, Schmidt came to my rescue. He remembered a promise that George Whipple had made when he left Berkeley to start a new medical school in Rochester, New York. Whipple had told Schmidt that if he ever had a Ph.D. student who decided to come to medical school in Rochester, the student would receive partial support from the school. Right after receiving the Ph.D., I boarded a train for Rochester.

At Rochester

Good fortune in the shape of a mentor came my way in Rochester. My work at Berkeley had attracted the attention of W. O. Fenn, a brilliant young physiologist who was a very quiet person and unusually kind. Fenn spent much of the day doing experiments with the help of a cheerful but somewhat talkative young woman. He gave me a position and suggested that I continue to study K^+ metabolism in young rats. My initial results replicated my earlier finding that the rats grew well for a while when Rb^+ replaced dietary K^+ but then quickly developed tremors and died. In the early phase, although the rats appeared to be healthy, 7.5% of their muscle K^+ was replaced by rubidium. Other experiments demonstrated that Na^+ could replace K^+ to some extent, and studies with radioisotopes confirmed that K^+ and Na^+ were able to cross an animal cell membrane. This was an astonishing finding, as German physiologists believed that the lipid cell membrane prevented passage of hydrophilic metal ions. Thanks to the generous spirit of Fenn, I was the sole author on three papers describing this work (1–3).

The War Years

By 1942 when I completed the M.D. degree and internship at Rochester, my work there had drawn considerable attention, and I received three offers for assistant residency positions from schools where interest in electrolytes was great: Yale Medical School with John Peters, Columbia University with Robert Loeb, and San Francisco Medical School. However, the entry of the United States into World War II interrupted normal, peacetime activities. Arthur Kornberg, a close medical school friend, and I joined the United States Public Health Service. Kornberg received sea duty while I was assigned to the National Institutes of Health (NIH). At NIH under orders from the Navy, I carried out tedious studies on the toxicity of halogenated hydrocarbons. Most importantly, the future began to take shape when I made a new friend, the enzymologist Bernard Horecker. Also, I persuaded Rolla E. Dyer, Director of NIH, to bring Kornberg to Bethesda. Together with Kornberg and Herbert Tabor and with the help of Horecker, I began to learn enzymology. Kornberg then left to spend a year (1946) in the laboratory of Severo Ochoa in New York and another (1947) with Gerty and Carl Cori in St. Louis. When he returned to NIH, he started a new research section for the study of enzymes and invited Horecker and me to join.

Enzymology at NIH

Leaning on my background in toxicology, I began to examine the behavior of enzymes in toxic situations. Also, I investigated the metabolic reactions that convert inorganic nitrite to nitrate and nitroglycerines. I also purified inorganic pyrophosphatase and crystallized it with the help of Moses Kunitz (of the Rockefeller Institute (now University)) and purified 5′-nucleotidase.

A Sabbatical Year in England

Then, in about 1951, my attention turned more generally to the phosphorylation and hydrolysis of purine ribonucleosides. This led, quite naturally, to an interest in enzymes that might hydrolyze RNA. Accordingly, my technician, Russell Hilmoe, and I purified from spleen an enzyme that partially solubilized RNA. The next step was to determine which linkages in RNA were split and which were resistant to the enzyme action. Roy Markham and J. D. Smith in Cambridge, England had demonstrated that fragments produced by RNA hydrolysis could be separated using paper chromatography and paper electrophoresis. Fortunately, I succeeded in obtaining a year's leave of absence from NIH, one of the first sabbaticals to be offered there, and spent a profitable year abroad in the laboratory of Markham. My work in England included the demonstration that the natural configuration of purine nucleotides in RNA was 3′–5′ rather than the alternative 2′–5′ (4). Further evidence for this linkage was obtained from a study of the action of nucleases on mononucleotide esters carried out with Daniel Brown and

Lord Alexander Todd (5). Also, the early steps in the hydrolysis of RNA by pancreatic ribonuclease were worked out in a collaboration with Paul R. Whitfeld (6). This work lead to the isolation, by paper chromatography and paper electrophoresis, of cyclic terminal oligonucleotides. Whitfield, an Australian graduate student in the laboratory, was an excellent colleague in research and deserving of the credit he received when his name appeared on five of our publications (for example, Refs. 6–8).

Later on, I had an interesting interaction with Markham and Sutherland. Dr. Markham found that heating ATP with dilute alkali caused the formation of substantial quantities of a new compound whose properties puzzled him, as he related in a letter to me. At a later date, Dr. Sutherland wrote about a compound isolated from liver in minute quantities. It was biologically active. The two letters ended up in different parts of a pile of mail. However, one day I chanced to re-read both letters and I figured that these compounds were the same. This turned out to be so, and thus cyclic adenylic acid became readily available.

Nucleic Acid Biochemistry at NIH

I returned to NIH in January of 1954. Interesting and stimulating visitors began to come to the laboratory to learn techniques and collaborate. Henry Kaplan, a very distinguished Professor of Radiology at Stanford spent a sabbatical in the laboratory. Three joint papers were published with Horecker and Jerard Hurwitz, then a beginning researcher and now a distinguished biochemist. Jack Strominger was also a welcome visitor; the two of us, together with Elizabeth Maxwell, studied the phosphorylation of nucleoside monophosphates by nucleoside triphosphates. At this time, there was considerable interest in the results and methods I had obtained during my stay in England. A good deal of attention was being paid in particular to the demonstration that "synthetic" oligonucleotides could be synthesized by enzyme-catalyzed nucleotide exchange reactions (7). Before long, I learned about the discovery of polynucleotide phosphorylase in *Azotobacter vinelandii* by Marianne Grunberg-Manago and Ochoa at New York University. The same enzyme was independently discovered in *Escherichia coli* by Uri Littauer and Kornberg.

At the time, I was one of only a few individuals who had the knowledge and experience required to study this enzyme and its products. Ochoa proposed that we collaborate and I accepted. Early in the course of the collaboration, a very able and pleasant postdoctoral fellow, Maxine Singer, joined my laboratory. She contributed greatly to the studies and made the association enjoyable. We put to good use all that I had learned in England about polyribonucleotides. One of our important findings was that short oligonucleotides could serve as primers for polynucleotide phosphorylase (9). Some time later, Singer and I used polynucleotide phosphorylase to prepare polyribonucleotides and oligoribonucleotides that Nirenberg used in his work on the genetic code. Singer continued to work on polynucleotide phosphorylase when she became an independent investigator.

The elegant organic synthesis of oligonucleotides by Khorana was not available until a later period. Therefore, when working on the genetic code, it was an advantage to be able to use enzymatic methods.

Russell Hilmoe remained my able and intelligent technician for many productive years; he was particularly good at adapting to new situations. Marie Lipsett, who had a good grasp of physical chemistry, joined the laboratory group; she collaborated with Dan Bradley on the study of complex formation between oligonucleotides and homopolymers. The flow of visitors continued as many people began to investigate nucleic acid enzymology. Littauer and I. R. (Bob) Lehman visited from Kornberg's department in St. Louis. Gobind Khorana's occasional visits were a joy as they gave me a chance to observe the development of his work and share in his good company as well as collaborate. Several times I also visited in Khorana's laboratory. Audrey Stevens was an especially brilliant postdoctoral fellow; all on her own she was one of the people who simultaneously discovered RNA polymerase. Altogether, it was an enjoyable and exciting time. After some years, however, I decided to turn to a different problem: the properties of bacterial membranes.

New Fields

Harold Neu, a medical postdoctoral fellow, joined me in the new investigations. The first problem he tackled was the location of ribonuclease in *E. coli*. At that time, a ribonuclease had been found associated with the 30 S ribosomes of the bacteria. Neu showed that the ribonuclease was actually in the periplasmic space between the cell membrane and the cell wall but binds to the 30 S ribosomes when the cell is split open (10, 11). With special care, it was possible to obtain ribosomes free of ribonuclease. Thus, the ribonuclease is a periplasmic enzyme with no connection to ribosomes. In the course of this work, Nancy Nossal, a postdoctoral fellow, contributed to the development of Neu's procedure for the osmotic shock of the cells (12). The protocol made it possible to recover enzymes in high yield from the periplasmic space of Gram-negative bacteria. The procedure has since been used in many laboratories. Neu, and later others, discovered a number of other periplasmic enzymes, all located in the space between the cell membrane and cell wall.

Anraku, a visitor from Japan, was very quiet but very effective and productive. He observed that Gram-negative bacteria able to transport D-galactose contain a specific periplasmic protein that can bind that sugar. A similar observation was made in the laboratory of Arthur Pardee. In the next few years, a large number of binding proteins were discovered in my laboratory and elsewhere. At NIH, several additional postdoctoral fellows contributed to this work. H. R. Dvorak, an M.D., had a special interest in metalloproteins. He and R. W. Brockman, a hard worker who visited the laboratory from Alabama, also worked on phosphatases released from *E. coli* by osmotic shock.

The Years at Cornell

In 1967, Efraim Racker induced me to join the Department of Biochemistry at Cornell University. The move was the beginning of more than 30 pleasant and productive years in Ithaca. The first postdoctoral fellow to join the laboratory, George Dietz, was an able and pleasant young man who studied the uptake of hexose phosphates by *E. coli.*

Joel Weiner, a graduate student from Canada, and Clem Furlong, a postdoctoral fellow, worked on amino acid transport in *E. coli* including leucine-specific and glutamine-specific (13) periplasmic binding proteins. Furlong was an especially good experimentalist and was helpful with equipment problems. Weiner later became an outstanding member of the Canadian Biochemical Society. Ed Berger, a graduate student, carried out a landmark study showing that there are different mechanisms of energy coupling for the active transport of proline and glutamine in *E. coli* (14); this work received much favorable attention. Another member of the early group at Cornell was postdoctoral fellow Barry Rosen. He studied basic amino acid transport in *E. coli*, another process that involved a binding protein.

Other students, postdoctoral fellows, and visitors contributed to our growing understanding of the periplasmic space and transport. Susan Curtis looked at the mechanism of ribose uptake, which involved energy from ATP rather than an energized membrane. James Cowell noted a similar result for glycylglycine. Janet Wood, a very able Canadian, worked on L-leucine transport. J. B. Smith and a graduate student, Paul Sternweis, purified the two "minor" subunits of F_1-ATPase and examined their properties (15). I was able to help Smith during a period when jobs were difficult to get and was delighted when he began doing independent work. T. Kitagawa made an interesting finding when he showed that the osmotic shock procedure does not necessarily kill the cells; some cells remain viable. Stanley Dunn and Masamitsu Futai used their time in the laboratory purifying and reconstituting the *E. coli* F_1-ATPase (16). Nizar Makan from India spent several postdoctoral years on exhaustive work that yielded evidence for metabolic processes that might be involved in permeabilization.

In 1975, I decided to gain more experience in animal cell research. A half-year sabbatical was granted and I spent it with Henry Rozengurt in London. In the ensuing years, I made six additional visits of several months each to the Rozengurt laboratory. On one of these visits, I observed that 3T6 cells, which are spontaneously transformed, leaked nucleotides when 50 μM ATP is added to the medium; the effect is highly specific for ATP. Many excellent investigators have since studied this phenomenon, and G. Weisman, I. Friedberg, and I reviewed this work in 1986 (17). Friedberg received his degree for the work in my laboratory in about 1980. The most recent years in my laboratory included Ding-ji Wang and Ning-na Huang. They showed that ATP, in concentrations of a few micromolar, was a mitogen and explored this important effect of extracellular ATP in a series of papers (18).

I want also to mention a few other people who were in my laboratory at various times and whose collaboration I value. They include R. G. Alfonzo from Venezuela, K. Jacobson, a skilled organic chemist, and the productive Fernando Gonzalez, a graduate student and postdoctoral fellow. Barun De was a persistent and hard worker. Ahmed Ahmed came to the United States on a number of occasions to learn modern biology; he is a well known Professor of Plant Science and Toxicology in his native Egypt. I was also fortunate to know Gary Weisman and to watch with pleasure as he developed into a leader in his field.

In the early 1980s I was able to spend 13 months (divided into short periods) back at NIH as a Fogarty Scholar in the laboratory of Claude Klee. It was good to be able to spend the entire day doing experiments at the bench. Klee is remarkable for being able to do experiments at the same time that she was running the Laboratory of Biochemistry in the National Cancer Institute.

Conclusion

These reminiscences cover about 75 years. They are based on what I remember and no claims for accuracy are made. Selected references and reviews are included for the interested reader, and these sources also describe similar work done in other laboratories.

I have never forgotten how Professor W. O. Fenn arranged that I would be sole author on three papers describing work that I carried out in his laboratory. After all, he was the department head and I was only a medical student on a part-time physiology fellowship. On occasion, I tried to do the same for a student or postdoctoral fellow of mine. However, I stopped when a reviewing editor accused me of removing my name because I had no interest in the work.

Wonderful friendships are formed in research laboratories. Bernard Horecker was a friend for many years and a good source of advice; several of our joint papers are still referred to on occasion. Arthur Kornberg gave no end of guidance and inspiration, especially in the early years. My wife Adelaide and I will always have a special place in our hearts for Herb and Celia Tabor.

I have mentioned here nearly all of those who held positions in my laboratory over the years. The list is small. I prefer to work with a small group and always to do some experimental work myself.

I am especially pleased with the performance of women in my laboratory. They had difficulties in obtaining positions in my day.

Address correspondence to: lah9@cornell.edu.

REFERENCES

1. Heppel, L. A. (1939) The electrolytes of muscle and liver in potassium-depleted rats. *Am. J. Physiol.* **127,** 385
2. Heppel, L. A. (1940) The diffusion of radioactive sodium into the muscles of potassium-deprived rats. *Am. J. Physiol.* **128,** 449
3. Heppel, L. A. (1940) Effect of age and diet on electrolyte changes in rat muscle during stimulation. *Am. J. Physiol.* **128,** 440
4. Heppel, L. A., Markham, R., and Hilmoe, R. J. (1953) Natural configuration of the purine nucleotides in ribonucleic acids. *Nature* **171,** 1151
5. Brown, D. M., Heppel, L. A., and Hilmoe, R. D. (1954) The action of some nucleases on simple esters of monoribonucleotides. *J. Chem. Soc.* **4576,** 40
6. Heppel, L. A., and Whitfeld, P. R. (1955) Nucleotide exchange reactions catalyzed by ribonuclease and spleen phosphodiesterase. I. Synthesis and interconversion of simple esters of monoribonucleotides. *Biochem. J.* **60,** 1
7. Heppel, L. A., Whitfeld, P. R., and Markham, R. (1955) Nucleotide exchange reactions catalyzed by ribonuclease and spleen phosphodiesterase. II. Synthesis of polynucleotides. *Biochem. J.* **60,** 8–15
8. Heppel, L. A., Whitfeld, P. R., and Markham, R. (1955) A note on the structure of triphosphopyridine. *Biochem. J.* **60,** 19
9. Singer, M. F., Heppel, L. A., and Hilmoe, R. J. (1957) Oligonucleotides as primers for polynucleotide phosphorylase. *Biochim. Biophys. Acta* **26,** 447
10. Neu, H. C., and Heppel, L. A. (1964) On the surface localization of enzymes in *E. coli. Biochem. Biophys. Res. Commun.* **17,** 215
11. Neu, H. C., and Heppel, L. A. (1964) Some observations on the "latent" ribonuclease of *Escherichia coli. Proc. Natl. Acad. Sci. U. S. A.* **51,** 1267
12. Neu, H. C., and Heppel, L. A. (1965) The release of enzymes from *Escherichia coli* by osmotic shock and during the formation of spheroplasts. *J. Biol. Chem.* **240,** 3685
13. Weiner, J. H., and Heppel, L. A. (1971) A binding protein for glutamine and its relation to active transport in *Escherichia coli. J. Biol. Chem.* **246,** 6933
14. Berger, E. A. (1973) Different mechanisms of energy coupling for the active transport of proline and glutamine in *Escherichia coli. Proc. Natl. Acad. Sci. U. S. A.* **70,** 1514
15. Smith, J. B., and Sternweis, P. C. (1977) Purification of membrane attachment and inhibitory subunits of the proton translocating adenosine triphosphatase from *E. coli. Biochem. J.* **16,** 306–311
16. Dunn, S. D., and Futai, M. (1980) Reconstitution of a functional coupling factor from the isolated subunits of *E. coli* F_1-ATPase. *J. Biol. Chem.* **255,** 113–118
17. Heppel, L. A., Weisman, G. A., and Friedberg, I. (1986) Permeabilization of transformed cells in culture by external ATP. *J. Membr. Biol.* **86,** 189–196
18. Huang, N., Wang, D., and Heppel, L. A. (1989) Extracellular ATP is a mitogen for 3T3, 3T6 and A431 cells and acts synergistically with other growth factors. *Proc. Natl. Acad. Sci. U. S. A.* **86,** 7904–7908

THE JOURNAL OF BIOLOGICAL CHEMISTRY
© 2004 by The American Society for Biochemistry and Molecular Biology, Inc.

Vol. 279, No. 53, Issue of December 31, pp. 54975–54982, 2004
Printed in U.S.A.

Reflections

A PAPER IN A SERIES COMMISSIONED TO CELEBRATE THE CENTENARY OF THE JBC IN 2005

JBC Centennial
1905–2005
100 Years of Biochemistry and Molecular Biology

My Brief Encounter with the Phosphoinositides and IP$_3$

Published, JBC Papers in Press, October 8, 2004, DOI 10.1074/jbc.X400010200

Clinton E. Ballou

From the Department of Molecular and Cell Biology, University of California, Berkeley, California 94720

For my first independent research project after my appointment to the Berkeley faculty, I chose to work on the structures of myoinositol-containing phospholipids, a study that led us eventually to the discovery of D-myoinositol 1,4,5-trisphosphate or IP$_3$. Before describing this research, however, I should say how that choice came about. While in graduate school at the University of Wisconsin, I had had the good fortune to study under Karl Paul Link, who was widely renowned for his discovery of dicumarol and the synthesis of related blood anticoagulants such as warfarin, work that was recognized with two Lasker Awards (1). On the side, however, Link remained a carbohydrate chemist at heart, a hobby that had grown out of his studies on plant polysaccharides and uronic acids while a student and then a young faculty member. In fact, Stanford Moore had completed his doctoral dissertation with Link on a method for characterizing aldo-monosaccharides as benzimidazole derivatives (2).

I arrived at Madison in the fall of 1946, fresh from a stint in the United States Navy, and I found Link's laboratory bursting at the seams with about 15 ex-GIs, all hard at work trying to make up for lost time. During earlier investigations on the structure-function relationship of coumarin anticoagulants, an attempt to synthesize the glucoside of dicumarol had been frustrated because the acetylated intermediate was degraded in alkali under conditions used for deacetylation (3). Because glycosides are acetals, which are typically acid-labile and alkali-stable, I found the anomaly intriguing and decided to study a variety of synthetic compounds in an effort to understand the structural basis for alkali sensitivity (4). This research formed the core of my doctoral dissertation, and although I failed to recognize it at the time, the chance exposure to carbohydrate chemistry was to have a lasting influence on the direction my career would take.

I continued my indoctrination in sugar chemistry during a postdoctoral year in Edinburgh, Scotland, with E. G. V. Percival in the new Department of Chemistry at Kings Buildings headed by Edwin Hirst. This was a time of economic depression in Britain, which was still suffering the aftermath of the war, and I discovered that I had left a well equipped laboratory in Madison to engage an unexpectedly primitive research environment. Wisely I did not let this change in fortunes discourage me. Instead I undertook a project dealing with the structure of maple sapwood starch and did the best that I could with the available facilities (5). My efforts were well rewarded because, in the process, I became adept at the uses of analytical and preparative filter paper and cellulose column chromatography, skills that were to be extremely valuable in my later research. The greatest challenge to my ingenuity, however, was to construct an electric stirring device from a small board-mounted motor, a couple of wooden pulleys, a piece of string, and a glass rod. The speed of the motor was regulated by adjusting light bulbs that were wired in series with the power cord to draw off electricity, a crude but effective method of control. I have always enjoyed working with my hands, so this mundane project even took on a certain appeal.

Living in a new environment always has its fringe benefits. While in Edinburgh, I developed a special affection for the Scots and a better understanding for the lingering resentment that

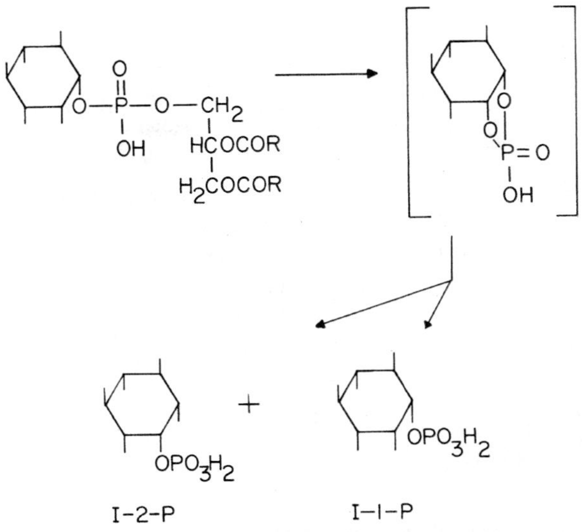

FIG. 1. **Alkaline degradation of soybean monophosphoinositide (15).** The products are D-myoinositol 1-phosphate (*I-1-P*) and myoinositol 2-phosphate (*I-2-P*). *R* is a fatty alkyl chain.

reflects a long history of conflict within the British Isles. Thus, I could understand why one of my graduate student colleagues was proud to proclaim, at every opportunity, that he had never been south of the border! It was also during this year that some Scottish separatists sneaked into Westminster Abbey and made off with the Stone of Scone. This symbol of Scottish nationalism, which was taken from Scotland to England by Edward I, had long rested beneath the chair on which British monarchs were crowned. The incident created quite a stir among the local patriots, but after its recovery the stone was returned to the Abbey. (I was recently informed that the Stone of Scone has since been returned to Scotland.)

Although I enjoyed the time, when the year ended I was ready to move on to Berkeley, where I had arranged to study with Hermann O. L. Fischer. Nicknamed "Hermannol," probably by his friend Claude Hudson as a play on the term "polyol," Fischer was an expatriate German scientist who had experienced a turbulent career that eventually led him to the University of Toronto. Then, when the new Biochemistry and Virus Laboratory was set up in 1948, Wendell Stanley had recruited him to Berkeley. I was attracted to Fischer in part because of his research on phosphorylated sugars but also because during graduate school I had drawn heavily on the published works of his father, Emil Fischer (6). I guess the idea of being associated with the son of Emil Fischer just seemed "real cool" to me. As it turned out, it also proved beneficial that I happened to go to Berkeley just as the University was entering a period of rapid postwar expansion.

This was a time of active research on biosynthetic pathways that involved short chain phosphorylated sugars, as exemplified by the studies of Melvin Calvin on photosynthesis, of P. R. Srinivasan and David Sprinson on shikimic acid biosynthesis, and of Bernard Horecker on transaldolase. With Fischer and his colleague, Donald MacDonald, I undertook the syntheses of several such metabolic intermediates, including D-glyceric acid 2-phosphate, D-glyceraldehyde 3-phosphate, dihydroxyacetone phosphate, hydroxypyruvic acid 3-phosphate, and D-erythrose 4-phosphate (7). The novelty of our approach was to prepare stable dimethyl acetal derivatives of the inherently unstable phosphorylated compounds with aldehydo or keto groups. These could be stored indefinitely and then be converted by mild acid hydrolysis of the acetal to the active metabolites as needed. Our success is documented by the fact that today, 50 years later, samples of the preparations have survived in pure crystalline usable form. During these first years in Berkeley, I also became interested in inositol chemistry as a result of studies on the cyclitols in sugar pine heartwood (8). Then, when Elvin Kabat came to Berkeley from Columbia University to spend a sabbatical with Fischer and learn some carbohydrate chemistry we all collaborated on the methylation analysis of galactinol, an α-D-galactoside of myoinositol. This study established that the galactose was linked to the L-l-position on the inositol ring (9), a fact that I was to put to good use in my later studies.

After my appointment to the faculty in 1955, I was in a position to set up an independent program, and this background led me to undertake a project concerned with the character-

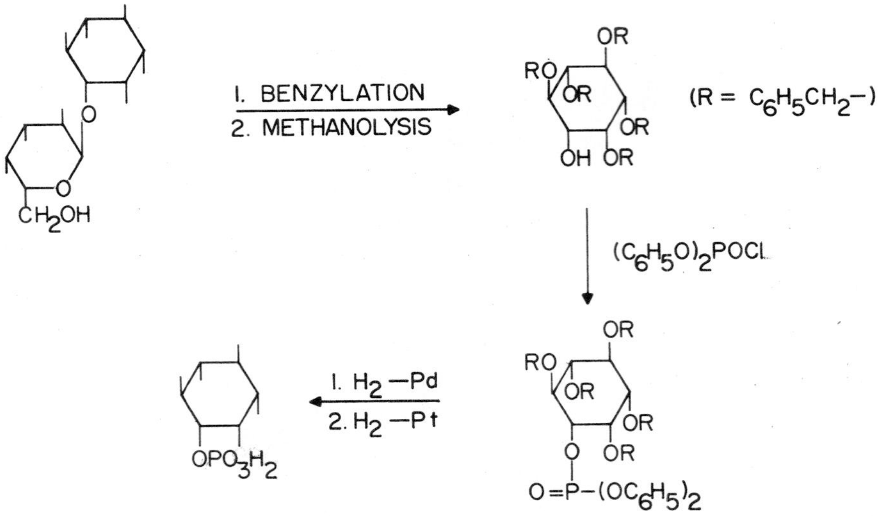

FIG. 2. **Synthesis of L-myoinositol 1-phosphate (16, 17).** The starting material for this synthesis was galactinol, 1-*O*-α-D-galactopyranosyl-L-myoinositol (9).

ization of inositol-containing phospholipids. In so doing, I was fortunate to have Finn Wold, Lewis Pizer, and Francis Lane Pizer as my first graduate students. At the time, there was convincing evidence from a number of studies that the lipid known as "phosphoinositide" was a phosphatidylmyoinositol (10), and as expected for such a structure, acid or alkaline hydrolysis of the phosphodiester bond had yielded myoinositol phosphate as one of the degradation products (11–13). Because the chemical hydrolysis of phosphate diesters with neighboring free hydroxyl groups can lead to phosphate migration, however, the position of attachment of the phosphatidic acid unit to the myoinositol ring was uncertain. Important studies at Cambridge University by Brown and Todd (14), showing that the alkaline hydrolysis of the phosphate diester linkage in nucleic acids proceeds via a cyclic phosphate intermediate, suggested to us a strategy to resolve this uncertainty. We subjected pure soybean phosphoinositide to alkaline hydrolysis and isolated the inositol phosphate fraction. It consisted mainly of myoinositol 1-phosphate along with some myoinositol 2-phosphate and other minor products (15). This result indicated that the putative myoinositol cyclic phosphate intermediate had involved positions 1 and 2 on the ring.

Because position 2 of the myoinositol ring lies between two adjacent *cis*-hydroxyls, called D-1 and L-1, the phosphatidyl group in the lipid could have been attached to position 2 or to one of the adjacent enantiomeric 1-positions.[1] The choice between these alternatives was suggested by the fact that the myoinositol 1-phosphate we isolated was optically active, $[\alpha]$D −9.8° (water, pH 2). This would be expected from the cyclization and reopening of a phosphate diester group originally on the D-1- or L-1-position, because the intermediate cyclic phosphate would be asymmetric if the myoinositol in the starting diester were asymmetrically substituted (Fig. 1). This would not be the result if the original diester involved position 2, which has a plane of symmetry, unless the asymmetry of the glycerol portion were able to exert a directive influence during the reaction.

To complete the characterization, we carried out a definitive synthesis of L-myoinositol 1-phosphate, starting from galactinol (9). For this synthesis, we perbenzylated galactinol, removed the benzylated galactose moiety by acidic methanolysis, and phosphorylated the free L-1-position of the recovered penta-*O*-benzylmyoinositol. Deblocking of the product by hydrogenolysis yielded L-myoinositol 1-phosphate (Fig. 2), which showed $[\alpha]$D +9.3° (water, pH 2) (16, 17). Because this synthetic L-isomer, which later was found to occur naturally (18), showed a rotation equal to that of the lipid-derived product, but of opposite sign, it must be the enantiomer; and consequently, the 1-phosphatidylmyoinositol (15) must have had the

---

[1] For these assignments, the three adjacent *cis*-hydroxyls of myoinositol are numbered one to three, and the direction of numbering is selected to give substituted positions the lowest possible number. When the ring is represented with these three hydroxyls projecting downward and the direction of numbering is clockwise, the myoinositol configuration is D and if counterclockwise it is L. Note that myoinositol 2-phosphate and 5-phosphate have a plane of symmetry and are *meso* compounds.

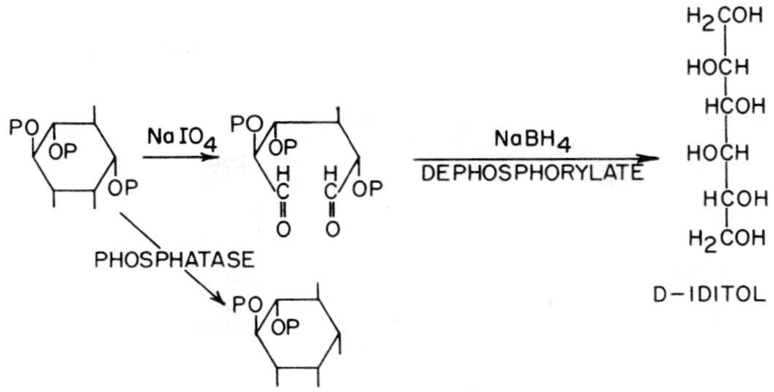

FIG. 3. **Reactions used to characterize D-myoinositol 1,4,5-trisphosphate (22, 25).** P is $-PO_3H_2$.

D-configuration.[2] In an important parallel study, Brown *et al.* (19) degraded horse liver phosphoinositide by the periodate/phenylhydrazine procedure, which avoided the cyclic phosphate intermediate, and they recovered a single myoinositol 1-phosphate with the same optical activity as the isomer we had obtained from the soybean lipid. Together, these studies firmly established that the myoinositol ring was substituted on the D-1-position in phosphatidylmyoinositol from both plants and animals. This was an important result, although it was not surprising because most myoinositol derivatives show chirality.

At the time, I was aware of the important work of Jordi Folch at Harvard Medical School, who had isolated a complex phosphoinositide from beef brain (20, 21). This isolation was based on the facts that phospholipids have low solubility in acetone, but they can be extracted from an acetone powder of brain tissue with chloroform, and the inositides can then be precipitated selectively by adding ethanol or methanol. Because strong acid hydrolysis of the material had yielded an "inositol metadiphosphate," Folch concluded that the original lipid was a polyphosphoinositide. Because it was known, however, that acid treatment could cause phosphate groups to migrate around the inositol ring (15), we decided to reexamine this characterization. A new graduate student from the University of Chile, Carmen Grado, had just joined my group, and I suggested that she should repeat the brain phosphoinositide preparation according to Folch. When Grado subjected this material to strong acid hydrolysis, she observed that the resulting inositol phosphate fraction gave a very diffuse unresolved streak on paper chromatography (22). She then repeated the study, using alkaline degradation of the brain lipid, and found that chromatography of the inositol phosphate fraction gave a well resolved pattern of five components, one mono-, two bis-, and two trisphosphates of myoinositol. This suggested that the Folch brain inositide preparation was a mixture of related substances, and because the myoinositol trisphosphates predominated, we proposed that "the lipid might more accurately be called a triphosphoinositide" (22). At about the same time, Dittmer and Dawson, at Cambridge University, reported the isolation from ox brain of a lipid fraction with the composition expected for a triphosphoinositide (23).

Grado then went on to characterize each inositol polyphosphate in the mixture, using a sequence of periodate oxidation to cleave the inositol ring between free glycol groups, borohydride reduction of the resulting dialdehyde, and dephosphorylation to yield a free polyalcohol. From an inositol bisphosphate, one could expect a tetritol if the phosphate groups were next to each other. If they were in a 1,3-position, a pentitol would result; and if they were in a 1,4-position, the ring would be cleaved in two places to give two molecules of malondialdehyde phosphate, which would be oxidized further by excess periodate to yield inorganic phosphate, formate, and carbon dioxide. From an inositol trisphosphate with the phosphates adjacent to each other, a pentitol would be formed; if in a 1,2,4 arrangement, a hexitol would result; and if in 1,3,5 arrangement, the inositol ring would survive the treatment. Besides indicating the phosphate positions, the identity and optical activity of the resulting polyol would also reveal the chirality of the inositol derivative. Using these methods, Grado characterized the two bisphosphates as D-myoinositol 1,4- and 4,5-bisphosphate and the major trisphosphate fraction as either the D-1,4,5-isomer or the D-1,4,6-isomer, the uncertainty arising because both of these trisphosphates would yield the same D-iditol in the above analytical procedure (22). The

---

[2] The convention for assigning configurations to substituted myoinositols was changed during the 1970s, so that what we designated L-myoinositol 1-phosphate in 1959 (16, 17) was later renamed D-myoinositol 1-phosphate. In this article, I have assigned all configurations in agreement with the convention now used.

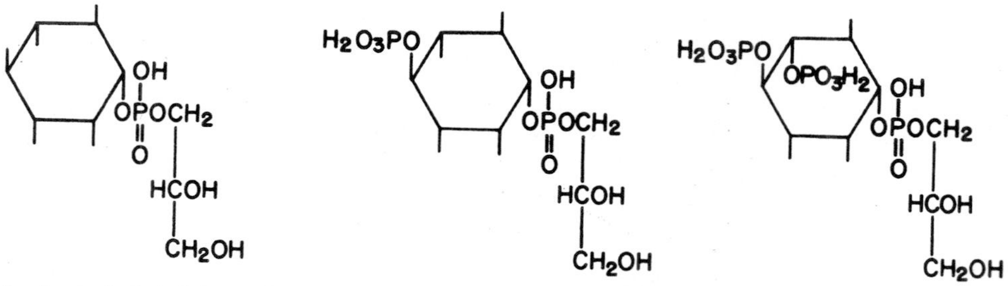

FIG. 4. **Products isolated from deacylated brain polyphosphoinositide (27).** The intact lipids were found to be acylated by a mixture of stearic, oleic, and arachidonic acids (28).

uncertainty was resolved by Raymond Tomlinson, a graduate student who had made a detailed study of the dephosphorylation of phytic acid (myoinositol hexaphosphate) by wheat bran phytase (24). He observed that alkaline phosphomonoesterase selectively removed phosphate groups flanked by unsubstituted hydroxyls, and he found that the myoinositol trisphosphate isolated by Grado was converted to D-myoinositol 4,5-bisphosphate by this treatment (25). Thus, the complete characterization of D-myoinositol 1,4,5-trisphosphate can be summarized as shown in Fig. 3.

These studies still left open the question of the true nature of the apparently heterogeneous brain phosphoinositide. From the composition of his preparation, Folch (21) had postulated that it could be represented as a *meta*-diphosphatidylmyoinositol, whereas Hawthorne (26) proposed a cyclic structure of myoinositol *meta*-diphosphate with monoacylglycerol. I was fortunate at the time to be joined by a postdoctoral co-worker, Hans Brockerhoff, who had studied with Donald Hanahan at the University of Washington. To obtain the water-soluble component(s) of the brain lipid complex with intact phosphodiester linkages, Brockerhoff deacylated the phosphoinositide preparation with hydroxylamine and separated the products on an ion exchange column (27). This yielded three fractions with compositions corresponding to glycerol myoinositol phosphate (20%), glycerol myoinositol diphosphate (22%), and glycerol myoinositol triphosphate (58%) (Fig. 4). Further analysis suggested that these products could be derived from three lipids: l-phosphatidyl-D-myoinositol, 1-phosphatidyl-D-myoinositol 4-phosphate, and 1-phosphatidyl-D-myoinositol 4,5-bisphosphate. This conclusion was confirmed when Stewart Hendrickson, a postdoctoral fellow who had studied with Herbert Carter at the University of Illinois, developed an ion exchange procedure using a homogeneous chloroform/methanol/water solvent. This solvent dissolved the intact brain phosphoinositide preparation and allowed its separation into three homologs (28), analysis of which agreed with Brockerhoff's assignments (27). Hendrickson also found that the three lipids were closely related in that each was predominantly acylated by the same mixture of stearic, oleic, and arachidonic acids. Later, Brown and Stewart (29) also characterized purified triphosphoinositide, using the selective degradation procedure Brown and co-workers had exploited so effectively earlier (19).

During the 1960s when we were conducting the above studies, very little was known about the cellular function(s) of the inositol phospholipids. Mabel and Lowell Hokin at the University of Wisconsin had investigated the possible role of these lipids in cellular secretion (30), and they, along with others, had studied the incorporation of ^{32}P$_i$ into the brain lipids (31, 32). These studies had yielded only limited information owing, in part, to uncertainty about the actual structure of the brain inositide. From the insight we had gained by our structural work, it appeared to us likely that the three components would be interconvertible in cells by an enzyme-catalyzed process of cyclic phosphorylation-dephosphorylation. When Brockerhoff investigated the incorporation of [^{32}P]phosphate, [^{3}H]myoinositol, and [^{14}C]glycerol into the individual inositides in brain tissue slices, the results proved to be consistent with such a pathway (33, 34). Thus, the monoester phosphate groups turned over rapidly, whereas the glycerol, myoinositol, and phosphodiester groups were much more stable. Moreover, turnover of the monoester phosphate groups was not random, because partial enzymic dephosphorylation of 1-phosphatidylmyoinositol 4,5-bisphosphate to the next lower homolog occurred by the selective removal of the 5-phosphate group, indicative of a specific 5-phosphomonoesterase in brain tissue (35).

I became eligible for a sabbatical leave in 1961, and because our work on the brain polyphosphoinositides was going well, I asked Edgar Lederer if I could spend a year with him to study the glycophosphoinositides of mycobacteria. He welcomed me in his very gracious

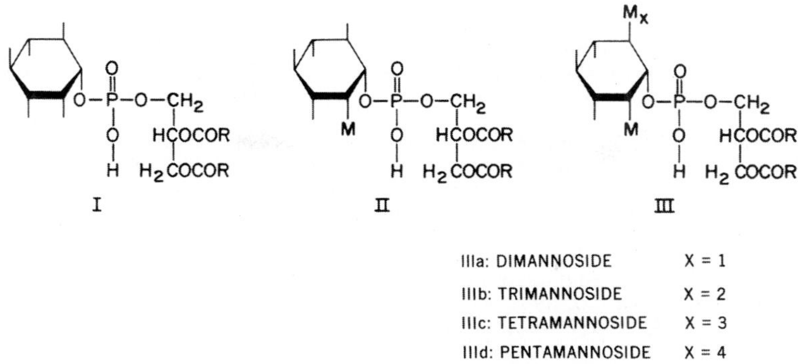

FIG. 5. **Structures of mycobacterial mannophosphoinositides (40).** M is α-D-mannopyranosyl.

manner, and he even arranged the rental of a spacious apartment in Paris on rue Pierre Curie (later renamed rue Pierre et Marie Curie). Thus, I had only a short stroll to catch the Ligne de Sceaux at Luxembourg Station for the daily ride to his CNRS laboratory at Gif-sur-Yvette. Myoinositol, as a lipid constituent, was first reported by R. J. Anderson to occur in the phospholipids of mycobacteria (36), and Lederer subsequently described a dimannosyl phosphoinositide from the same source (37). While at Gif, I collaborated with his colleague, Erna Vilkas, on experiments to establish the linkages of both the phosphatidyl and the mannosyl groups to the myoinositol ring (38). In later investigations by Yuan Chuan Lee, a postdoctoral student from the University of Iowa, we determined the structures of the family of mannosyl phosphoinositides in *Mycobacterium smegmatis* (39, 40). Like the other phosphoinositides, the phosphatidyl group was found attached to the D-1-position of myoinositol, whereas a single mannose was linked to position 2 and one to four mannoses were linked to the D-6-position (Fig. 5). This phospholipid was later found to serve as an anchor for the lipoarabinomannan in mycobacteria (41), and it is interesting that the glycophosphoinositide protein anchor has the analogous structure in which a carbohydrate chain is also attached to position 6 of myoinositol (42).

In a report to the International Congress of Biochemistry on the "Structure of Myoinositol Phospholipids" (43), I summarized the results of our studies and observed that: "In attempting to assess the role of phospholipids in cellular metabolism, one can place primary emphasis on the lipid end of the molecule and its modification according to the type of fatty acid there esterified. Or, one can direct attention to the hydrophilic end. In the case of the inositol phospholipids, we find, in the great structural variability of the inositol part, evidence that herein may lie the prime functional center of these molecules." I have never considered myself a clairvoyant, and as it turned out, both the polar and nonpolar ends of the inositides have important regulatory functions. Today, we can look back and see that our earlier studies were significant mainly in helping to prepare the groundwork for the explosive developments concerning the cellular functions of the phosphoinositides that followed upon the important discoveries described in the review by Berridge and Irvine (44).

In these Reflections, I have limited myself to that early period of the 1960s in which I was directly involved, and I have referred only peripherally to the many subsequent important developments. I can't avoid reference, however, to the role that has been discovered for 1-phosphatidylmyoinositol 3-phosphate and its derivatives (45), substances we never encountered in our investigations. I should also admit that I am a little disappointed that I never encouraged my co-workers to pursue a detailed study of the enzymes involved in the metabolism of the polyphosphoinositides. My only excuse is that we were drawn in other directions by our discovery of the mycobacterial polymethylpolysaccharides (46, 47), which were found later to act as regulators of fatty acid synthesis in this microorganism (48), and to investigations on the genetic control of yeast mannoprotein structure (49). Both of these developments are traceable to the sabbatical leave I spent at Gif in 1961, a testament to the unpredictable influence such an experience can have. Despite the minor doubt expressed above, I must say that I enjoyed a wonderful ride with the phosphoinositides, and it was all great fun! I am especially grateful to the many co-workers who shared this journey with me.

Address correspondence to: ceba@berkeley.edu.

REFERENCES

1. Link, K. P. (1959) The discovery of dicumarol and its sequels. *Circulation* **XIX,** 97–107
2. Moore, S., and Link, K. P. (1940) Carbohydrate characterization. I. The oxidation of aldoses by hypoiodite in methanol. II. The identification of seven aldo-monosaccharides as benzimidazole derivatives. *J. Biol. Chem.* **133,** 293–311
3. Huebner, C. F., Karjala, S. A., Sullivan, W. R., and Link, K. P. (1944) Studies on the hemorrhagic sweet clover disease. VI. Glucosides of 4-hydroxycoumarins. *J. Am. Chem. Soc.* **66,** 906–909
4. Ballou, C. E. (1954) Alkali-sensitive glycosides. *Adv. Carbohydr. Chem.* **9,** 59–95
5. Ballou, C. E., and Percival, E. G. V. (1952) Wood starches: the structure of the sapwood starch of the maple (*Acer* spp.). *J. Chem. Soc.* 1054–1056
6. Fischer, E., and Beensch, L. (1894) Über einige synthetische glucoside. *Ber. Dtsch. Chem. Ges.* **27,** 2478–2486
7. Ballou, C. E., Fischer, H. O. L., and MacDonald, D. L. (1955) The synthesis and properties of D-erythrose 4-phosphate. *J. Am. Chem. Soc.* **77,** 5967–5970
8. Ballou, C. E., and Anderson, A. B. (1953) On the cyclitols present in sugar pine (*Pinus lambertiana Dougl.*). *J. Am. Chem. Soc.* **75,** 648–650
9. Kabat, E. A., MacDonald, D. L., Ballou, C. E., and Fischer, H. O. L. (1953) On the structure of galactinol. *J. Am. Chem. Soc.* **75,** 4507–4509
10. Hanahan, D. J., and Olley, J. N. (1958) Chemical nature of monophosphoinositides. *J. Biol. Chem.* **231,** 813–828
11. Wooley, D. W. (1943) Isolation and partial determination of structure of soybean lipositol, a new inositol-containing phospholipid. *J. Biol. Chem.* **147,** 581–591
12. Hawthorne, J. N., and Chargaff, E. (1954) A study of inositol-containing lipids. *J. Biol. Chem.* **206,** 27–37
13. McKibbin, J. M. (1956) A monophosphoinositide of liver. *J. Biol. Chem.* **220,** 537–545
14. Brown, D. M., and Todd, A. R. (1952) Nucleotides. Part X. Some observations on the structure and chemical behavior of the nucleic acids. *J. Chem. Soc.* 52–58
15. Pizer, F. L., and Ballou, C. E. (1959) Studies on myoinositol phosphates of natural origin. *J. Am. Chem. Soc.* **81,** 915–921
16. Ballou, C. E., and Pizer, L. I. (1959) Synthesis of an optically active myoinositol 1-phosphate. *J. Am. Chem. Soc.* **81,** 4745
17. Ballou, C. E., and Pizer, L. I. (1960) The absolute configuration of the myoinositol 1-phosphates and a confirmation of the bornesitol configurations. *J. Am. Chem. Soc.* **82,** 3333–3335
18. Eisenberg, F. (1967) Myoinositol 1-phosphate as product of cyclization of glucose 6-phosphate synthase reaction. *J. Biol. Chem.* **242,** 1375–1382
19. Brown, D. M., Clark, B. F., and Letters, R. (1961) Phospholipids. Part VII. The structure of a monophosphoinositide. *J. Chem. Soc.* 3774–3779
20. Folch, J. (1949) Complete fractionation of brain cephalin: isolation from it of phosphatidylserine, phosphatidylethanolamine, and phosphoinositide. *J. Biol. Chem.* **177,** 497–504
21. Folch, J. (1949) Brain diphosphoinositide, a new phosphoinositide having inositol metadiphosphate as a constituent. *J. Biol. Chem.* **177,** 505–519
22. Grado, C., and Ballou, C. E. (1961) Myoinositol phosphates obtained by alkaline hydrolysis of beef brain phosphoinositide. *J. Biol. Chem.* **236,** 54–60
23. Dittmer, J. C., and Dawson, R. M. C. (1960) The isolation of a new complex lipid: triphosphoinositide from ox brain. *Biochim. Biophys. Acta* **40,** 379–380
24. Tomlinson, R. V., and Ballou, C. E. (1962) Myoinositol polyphosphate intermediates in the dephosphorylation of phytic acid by phytase. *Biochemistry* **1,** 166–171
25. Tomlinson, R. V., and Ballou, C. E. (1961) Complete characterization of the myoinositol polyphosphates from beef brain phosphoinositide. *J. Biol. Chem.* **236,** 1902–1906
26. Hawthorne, J. N. (1955) A further study of inositol-containing phospholipids. *Biochim. Biophys. Acta* **18,** 389–393
27. Brockerhoff, H., and Ballou, C. E. (1961) The structure of the phosphoinositide complex of beef brain. *J. Biol. Chem.* **236,** 1907–1911
28. Hendrickson, H. S., and Ballou, C. E. (1964) Ion exchange chromatography of intact brain phosphoinositides on diethylaminoethyl cellulose by gradient salt elution in a mixed solvent system. *J. Biol. Chem.* **239,** 1369–1373
29. Brown, D. M., and Stewart, J. C. (1966) The structure of triphosphoinositide from beef brain. *Biochim. Biophys. Acta* **125,** 413–421
30. Hokin, L. E., and Hokin, M. R. (1958) Acetylcholine and the exchange of inositol and phosphate in brain phosphoinositide. *J. Biol. Chem.* **233,** 818–821
31. Hokin, L. E., and Hokin, M. R. (1953) Enzyme secretion and the incorporation of ^{32}P into phospholipids of pancreas slices. *J. Biol. Chem.* **203,** 967–977
32. Dawson, R. M. C. (1954) A measurement of ^{32}P labelling of individual kephalins and lecithin in a small sample of tissue. *Biochim. Biophys. Acta* **14,** 374–379
33. Brockerhoff, H., and Ballou, C. E. (1962) Phosphate incorporation in brain phosphoinositides. *J. Biol. Chem.* **237,** 49–52
34. Brockerhoff, H., and Ballou, C. E. (1962) On the metabolism of the brain phosphoinositide complex. *J. Biol. Chem.* **237,** 1764–1766
35. Chang, M., and Ballou, C. E. (1967) Specificity of ox brain triphosphoinositide phosphomonoesterase. *Biochem. Biophys. Res. Commun.* **26,** 199–205
36. Anderson, R. J. (1930) The chemistry of the lipoids of tubercle bacilli. XIV. The occurrence of inosite in the phosphatide of human tubercle bacilli. *J. Am. Chem. Soc.* **52,** 1607–1608
37. Vilkas, E., and Lederer, E. (1961) Sur la structure du phosphatidyl-inositol-dimmanosides de *Mycobacterium tuberculosis*. *Bull. Soc. Chim. Biol.* **42,** 1013–1022
38. Ballou, C. E., Vilkas, E., and Lederer, E. (1963) Structural studies on the myoinositol phospholipids of *Mycobacterium tuberculosis* (var. *bovis* BCG). *J. Biol. Chem.* **238,** 69–76
39. Ballou, C. E., and Lee, Y. C. (1964) The structure of myoinositol mannoside from *Mycobacterium tuberculosis* glycolipid. *Biochemistry* **3,** 682–685
40. Lee, Y. C., and Ballou, C. E. (1965) Complete structures of the glycophospholipids of mycobacteria. *Biochemistry* **4,** 1395–1404
41. Hunter, S. W., and Brennan, P. J. (1990) Evidence for the presence of a phosphatidylinositol anchor on the lipoarabinomannan and lipomannan of *Mycobacterium tuberculosis*. *J. Biol. Chem.* **265,** 9272–9279
42. Ferguson. M. A. J., Homans, S. W., Dwek, R. A., and Rademacher, T. W. (1988) Glycosylphosphatidylinositol moiety that anchors *Trypanosoma bruccii* variant surface glycoprotein to the membrane. *Science* **239,** 753–759
43. Ballou, C. E. (1964) Structure of myoinositol phospholipids. *6th International Congress of Biochemistry*, pp. 547–548, New York

44. Berridge, M. J., and Irvine, R. F. (1989) Inositol phosphates and cell signalling. *Nature* **341,** 197–205
45. Whitman, M., Downes, C. P., Keeler, M., Keller, T., and Cantley, L. C. (1988) Type I phosphatidylinositol kinase makes a novel inositol phospholipid, phosphatidylinositol-3-phosphate. *Nature* **332,** 644–646
46. Ballou, C. E. (1968) Studies on the structure of a lipopolysaccharide from mycobacterium species. *Acc. Chem. Res.* **1,** 366–373
47. Gray, G. R., and Ballou, C. E. (1970) Isolation and characterization of a polysaccharide containing 3-*O*-methyl-D-mannose from *Mycobacterium phlei. J. Biol. Chem.* **246,** 6835–6842
48. Bloch, C. (1977) Control mechanisms for fatty acid synthesis in *Mycobacterium smegmatis. Adv. Enzymol. Relat. Areas Mol. Biol.* **45,** 1–84
49. Ballou, C. E. (1990) Isolation, characterization and properties of *Saccharomyces cerevisiae* mutants with nonconditional protein glycosylation defects. *Methods Enzymol.* **185,** 440–470

THE JOURNAL OF BIOLOGICAL CHEMISTRY
Vol. 280, No. 3, Issue of January 21, pp. 1705–1715, 2005

Reflections

A PAPER IN A SERIES COMMISSIONED TO CELEBRATE THE CENTENARY OF THE JBC IN 2005

JBC Centennial
1905–2005
100 Years of Biochemistry and Molecular Biology

Metabolism in the Era of Molecular Biology

Published, JBC Papers in Press, November 20, 2004, DOI 10.1074/jbc.X400009200

Richard W. Hanson

From the Department of Biochemistry, Case Western Reserve University School of Medicine, Cleveland, Ohio 44106-4935

Prologue

"No profit grows where there is no pleasure taken.
In brief sir, study what you most affect"
Tranio in *The Taming of the Shrew*

I have spent a lifetime in the area of intermediary metabolism and have seen it move from the center of biochemistry to the backwater of our science in a very short period, only to be re-discovered by a new generation of biologists. By 1970, the writing was on the wall for metabolism; it was largely considered a "mature area," lacking excitement; molecular biology was the area of the future. A sure sign of this was that graduate students in biochemistry (always first to spot the trends) almost never selected their thesis research in metabolism. The course in intermediary metabolism that I taught was dropped from the curriculum of our graduate education program; our students were expected to learn all they needed to know about metabolism as undergraduates before they attended graduate school. After all, as a graduate student once said to me, "the great problems in metabolic research have been solved." As one could easily predict, there is currently a shortage of scientists who truly understand metabolism and its regulation.

I subscribe to the *Contrarian* philosophy of investment. When a common stock is too popular with buyers, it is almost always a bad investment. It is better to find a company that has good fundamentals but is underappreciated by the market; in the long term, this is the always the best buy! I have found this to be very true for research. As others turned away from metabolism and toward genetics, the field remains a ripe area for further research. As long as diseases like diabetes, obesity, and atherosclerosis remain to be cured, there will be no shortage of interest in metabolism. To support this contention, I have counted five cover articles in *Time* magazine over the past year (2003–2004) on obesity, diabetes, and the Atkins Diet. Obviously, the general public in the United States still finds metabolism interesting! However, the problem in 1970, when I began my foray into molecular genetics, was how to enter into this virtually foreign field and still be productive enough to sustain my career.

For me personally, the transition from metabolism to molecular biology was a risky one. By planting my research in two fields, I could easily have become a "jack of all trades and master of none." However, I had no choice; it was adapt or perish. My epiphany in this matter occurred in 1971 at a meeting on gluconeogenesis held in Gottingen, Germany. I had been invited to attend because John Ballard and I had mistakenly claimed in a paper on adipose tissue metabolism that pyruvate carboxylase was present in the cytosol (1); the intracellular location of this enzyme was actively discussed at the meeting. Despite my inexperience (I was 35 at the time), I was invited to chair a session at the meeting and, as the chair, was asked to lead a discussion on new approaches to metabolic research. I remember being rather disappointed with the answers, which ranged from developing better cell lines for metabolic studies to improving techniques for the determination of intracellular intermediates. The discussions at this meeting were published as part of the proceedings and still make interesting reading (2).

In stark contrast, at about that time molecular biologists were devising ways to isolate and characterize mammalian genes, an effort that would revolutionize biology. Metabolic research would never be the same again! I am delighted to have lived through this exciting period and to have contributed in some small way to the transition of metabolism into this new era. This Reflections is all about trying to make it doing metabolic research in the "era of molecular biology" or *how I came to love the gene*!

Making Early Choices

For most of us, the area we choose in graduate school is the area in which we find ourselves for the rest of our scientific lives; I chose metabolism and for better or worse have been at it ever since. Like most things in my life, this choice was not planned; it just seemed to happen. While a student at Northeastern University in Boston in the early 1950s, I worked in a small research-based company in Cambridge, Bio-Research Institute, as a co-operative work experience. There I met a young graduate of the Ph.D. program at Brown University, Tom Kelley. Tom had been a student with a member of the faculty in the Biology Department at Brown, Dr. Paul Fenton, and recommended him highly. As fate would have it, I was accepted in the graduate program in biology at Brown in 1959, and I selected Paul as my graduate advisor. For my thesis research, I studied the biochemical basis for the differences between two inbred strains of mice. One strain, the A/Fn, could be made readily obese and showed a relationship between dietary fat intake and carcass fat content. I demonstrated that during fasting these mice accumulated triglyceride in their livers. The I/Fn mice were leaner, oxidized more fatty acids to carbon dioxide, and generated more ketone bodies after an overnight fast. Adipose tissue from the A/Fn mice also had higher rates of fatty acid synthesis *in vitro* than did adipose tissue from the I/Fn mice (3). Isotopically labeled compounds were just beginning to be generally available for metabolic studies, and I adapted and/or developed a variety of experimental techniques to quantify metabolic flux rates in tissues from these mice and in the intact animals. Today, in the age of genomics, the genetic basis of metabolic variations in strains of inbred mice is very much in fashion. Thus, metabolic research has come full circle, but today the key technique is gene arrays to identify the underlying genetic factors that contribute to the metabolic variations leading one strain of mouse to become obese (and develop insulin resistance) whereas the other strain remains lean. The research problems never seem to change, only the techniques we use to address them! Paul Fenton was very much ahead of this time. This experience working with mice taught me a lesson of the importance of integrating metabolic information across physiological levels; from then to now, I have avoided being too much of a reductionist.

The Story of How Phosphoenolpyruvate Carboxykinase Became the Very Modern Model of a Regulated Gene

I began working on the regulation of expression of the gene for the cytosolic form of phosphoenolpyruvate carboxykinase (PEPCK-C) in 1967; that was before those of us in metabolism thought much about genes. I had just finished 2 years as an officer in the United States Army and arrived for a stint as a postdoctoral fellow in the laboratory of Sidney Weinhouse at the Fels Research Institute, Temple University School of Medicine, in Philadelphia (Fig. 1). For me this proved to be an excellent choice.

Sidney Weinhouse had a distinguished career in biochemistry. He was among the first to use isotopes of carbon when they became available immediately after World War II. Through a series of elegant experiments using ^{13}C-labeled octanoic acid, he proved the correctness of Knoop's hypothesis that ketone bodies were synthesized from two carbon fragments that were generated by the β-oxidation of fatty acids in the liver (4). Weinhouse, together with David Dipietro (5) discovered hepatic glucokinase and described many of its kinetic properties as well as its induction by feeding rats a high carbohydrate diet. Sidney was also known for his work on the biochemical characterization of minimal deviation hepatic tumors (6, 7); he was the long-time Editor of *Cancer Research* and a respected leader in cancer biology. Sidney Weinhouse died in 2001 at the age of 94.

Sidney Weinhouse was a very busy man. As the Director of the Fels Research Institute, he had a lot on his plate. Despite being very busy, Sidney had an open door policy and he always seemed to have time to talk to me about science or about life in general. He had what I might characterize as the "if it's not broken don't fix it" approach to mentorship; I could do the research I wanted on a mutually agreed upon topic and if I needed advice, he was available.

FIG. 1. **Sidney Weinhouse, Richard W. Hanson, and Woon Ki Paik at the Fels Research Institute, Temple University School of Medicine, Philadelphia, PA in June of 1978.**

Another postdoctoral fellow, John Ballard, and I began a collaboration on the development of hepatic gluconeogenesis in the rat. John was also working on the kinetic properties of galactokinase, which he purified from porcine liver (6–8), and I was involved in studies of ketone body metabolism by adipose tissue (9). I was quite familiar with the use of isotopes to determine the rate of flux of intermediates over specific metabolic pathways, and I would routinely relate the flux rate to changes in the activities of enzymes in the pathway. At about the time we began our joint research, two of the enzymes involved in hepatic gluconeogenesis, pyruvate carboxylase and the mitochondrial form of PEPCK, had been discovered at Case Western Reserve University (then Western Reserve University) in Cleveland by Bruce Keech and Merton Utter (pyruvate carboxylase) (10) and Kiyoshi Kurahashi and Merton Utter (PEPCK) (11). Later, Robert Nordlie and Henry Lardy demonstrated that there were two isoforms of PEPCK, one in the mitochondria (PEPCK-M) and one in the cytosol (PEPCK-C); pyruvate carboxylase is a mitochondrial enzyme (12). John Ballard and I developed an isotopic assay for PEPCK and pyruvate carboxylase and then used them to study the development of these two enzymes in the liver (13). In an interesting coincidence, 10 years later I became Chair of the Department of Biochemistry at Case Western Reserve University, a position also held by Merton Utter.

With our newly developed enzyme assays for pyruvate carboxylase and PEPCK, we found that there was no detectable PEPCK-C activity in the liver of rats before birth and that the enzyme appeared in a rapid fashion within the first several hours after birth, increasing to adult levels in the first day after birth (13). On the other hand, we noted that pyruvate carboxylase was present in the liver before birth and increased within the first day of life. As we understood in greater detail later, the initial transcription of the gene for PEPCK-C at birth was a key element in the initiation of hepatic gluconeogenesis that occurs in all mammals. Finally, we demonstrated, together with Helen Philippides, a Ph.D. student with John, and Linda Fisher, my first technician, that the administration of glucagon or cAMP to the rats while they were *in utero* would prematurely induce the appearance of PEPCK-C in the liver; insulin could block this induction. Because the induction of PEPCK-C could be inhibited by actinomycin D, we assumed that its rapid appearance at birth was due to the initiation of gene transcription. It would take another decade to definitively prove this point. In retrospect, this research formed the basis for my later venture into molecular biology.

Glyceroneogenesis: the Metabolic Role of Pyruvate Carboxylase and PEPCK-C in Adipose Tissue

By 1967 it had been well established that both pyruvate carboxylase and PEPCK-C were involved in hepatic and renal gluconeogenesis. So it was a real surprise that year when John

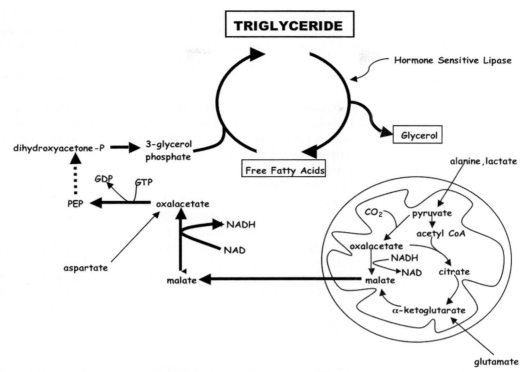

FIG. 2. **The pathway of glyceroneogenesis in adipose tissue.** This figure is adapted from Ref. 78, which presents a detailed discussion of the metabolic significance of glyceroneogenesis in mammals and the research that supports its biological role in the triglyceride/fatty acid cycle. Pyruvate is carboxylated to oxalacetate in the mitochondria via pyruvate carboxylase, and oxalacetate is reduced to malate by NAD malate dehydrogenase. Malate is transported to the cytosol and reduced to oxalacetate by the cytosolic form of NAD malate dehydrogenase. PEPCK-C then decarboxylates oxalacetate to form PEP, which is subsequently converted to dihydroxyacetone phosphate and then to glycerol 3-phosphate via an abbreviated version of the gluconeogenic pathway. This glycerol 3-phosphate is then used for the synthesis of triglyceride.

Ballard and I found pyruvate carboxylase in adipose tissue, a tissue that did not make glucose. We proposed that pyruvate carboxylase played an anaplerotic role (*i.e.* it replenished citric acid cycle anions) during lipogenesis in adipose tissue, because citrate efflux from the mitochondria depletes intermediates of the citric acid cycle (1). This is similar to the function of the enzyme in the liver during gluconeogenesis. We came to the totally *incorrect* conclusion that there were both mitochondrial and cytosolic forms of the pyruvate carboxylase in adipose tissue. It turned out that it is easy to break mitochondria during their isolation from adipose tissue and thus release the enzyme. In the same year, John and I, together with Gilbert Leveille, reported that adipose tissue also contained PEPCK-C (14). What was this gluconeogenic enzyme doing in a tissue that does not make glucose?

Several previous studies had shown that isolated epididymal fat pads could synthesize the glycerol moiety of triglyceride (glyceride-glycerol) from pyruvate in the absence of added glucose, but the authors did not speculate on how this occurred. Using specifically labeled [^{14}C]pyruvate, we demonstrated that glyceride-glycerol was synthesized from pyruvate in adipose tissue via a pathway that involved both pyruvate carboxylase and PEPCK-C (14). Furthermore, the conversion of pyruvate to glyceride-glycerol via this pathway increased when the animal was fasted, due in part to the induction of PEPCK-C activity that occurs in adipose tissue. We proposed that this pathway (Fig. 2), which was later termed *glyceroneogenesis* by Eleazar Shafrir and his colleagues (15), was involved in the re-esterification of fatty acid to triglyceride in adipose tissue during fasting. Most textbooks of biochemistry indicate that 3-phosphoglycerol is synthesized in the fed state from glucose via glycolysis. Our proposed pathway of glyceroneogenesis was clearly not intuitive.

In 1967, Lea Reshef from the Department of Biochemistry, Hebrew University-Hadassah Medical School in Jerusalem, Israel visited Sidney Weinhouse at the Fels Research Institute. Lea was studying the mechanism by which ruminant animals synthesize triglyceride in the absence of dietary glucose (16, 17). It took only a brief discussion for us to realize that we were working on the same pathway and to begin a collaboration that has lasted to this day! In 1970, a collaborative paper appeared in the *Journal of Biological Chemistry* (18) in which we demonstrated the stoichiometry of the process of 3-phosphoglycerol formation from pyruvate for the synthesis of triglyceride in adipose tissue. Martha Vaughan (19) had reported that in isolated adipose tissue 30% of the fatty acid released by lipolysis was re-esterified to glyceride-glycerol in the absence of glucose. We confirmed this finding and proposed that glyceroneogenesis from pyruvate was the source of the 3-phosphoglycerol required for triglyceride synthesis (18).

Lea Reshef, John Ballard, and I published a number of papers on glyceroneogenesis (18, 20). However, the idea of the metabolic role of this pathway never really caught on and, until very recently, it had not been included in a text book of biochemistry; since 1970 there have been only 40 references to glyceroneogenesis in *PubMed*! To our delight, however, things seem to be changing. Labeling studies in mammals, including humans, have demonstrated the striking degree of fatty acid recycling that occurs, even during prolonged fasting. As an example, Jensen *et al.* (21) reported that humans that have fasted for 84 h recycle about 70% of the fatty acids released by lipolysis in adipose tissue back to triglyceride. This so called *triglyceride/ fatty acid cycle* has been shown to occur in a broad number of physiological conditions (22). Because the control of circulating fatty acids is a critical factor in the regulation of glucose oxidation by muscle, the triglyceride/fatty acid cycle has been implicated in Type 2 diabetes. It also turns out that the liver is a critical factor in triglyceride/fatty acid cycling and has a very high rate of glyceroneogenesis (23). Satish Kalhan (24) demonstrated that the liver of overnight fasted humans uses glyceroneogenesis almost exclusively to make the glyceride-glycerol for triglyceride synthesis. To support the general importance of glyceroneogenesis in adipose tissues, Lea Reshef and her student Yael Olswang (25) reported that the tissue-specific ablation of PEPCK-C gene transcription in adipose tissue of mice caused lipodystrophy, and Franckhauser *et al.* (26) found that the overexpression of PEPCK-C in adipose tissue resulted in obesity. Thus, glyceroneogenesis is critical for the control of fatty acid re-esterification during fasting and PEPCK is central to this pathway. In April 2003, a symposium devoted to glyceroneogenesis was held in Paris, France. This event was organized by Claude Forest and Elmus Beale, both of whom have made important contributions to the establishment of glyceroneogenesis in adipose tissue (31, 32). With this renewed interest, glyceroneogenesis is gradually being included in textbooks of biochemistry (27, 28).

Early Forays into Molecular Biology

Our finding of the rapid appearance of PEPCK-C activity in the liver at birth led us to determine whether this was due to the initiation of gene transcription or to regulation of the turnover of either PEPCK-C mRNA or the enzyme itself. By the early 1970s, techniques were becoming available to determine the levels of mRNA for specific proteins. Although the techniques were not available to isolate the gene for PEPCK-C (this came a decade later), it was possible to measure the synthesis rate of the enzyme using an antibody. John Ballard and I purified PEPCK-C from rat liver and developed a polyvalent antibody that we use to this day (29). With the antibody in hand, we carried out pulse-chase experiments to determine the effect of diet and hormones on the synthesis rate of hepatic PEPCK-C and to determine its half-life (about 6 h) (30). We also assessed alterations in the synthesis rate of PEPCK-C in the liver during development. At birth, the synthesis of PEPCK-C increased from negligible levels in rats *in utero* to adult levels within 12 h after birth; we could detect no degradation of the enzyme during this period of rapid enzyme synthesis. A parallel set of experiments with adult animals demonstrated that hormones such as glucagon and glucocorticoids increased the synthesis of PEPCK-C in the liver and that insulin decreased the rate of enzyme synthesis. A major player in this early research on the control of PEPCK-C gene expression was Shirley Tilghman, who was a graduate student in my laboratory (31). Shirley is now the President of Princeton University, no doubt the consequence of working on PEPCK-C early in her career!

From these early studies, it was apparent that the rate of synthesis of PEPCK-C was changed rapidly by diet and hormones and that these changes were very large in magnitude (*i.e.* 10-fold in 30 min). Studying the control of the expression of the gene for this enzyme seems in retrospect to be a "no brainer." However, at the time there were other enzymes in which gene expression was altered equally rapidly by diet and hormones. These include malic enzyme, tyrosine aminotransferase, and glucose-6-phosphatase, to name just a few. Alan Goodridge (32, 33) had demonstrated that in chickens the initial expression of the gene for hepatic malic enzyme was induced at hatching by feeding carbohydrate. Both tyrosine aminotransferase and glucose-6-phosphatase were induced dramatically at birth in the livers of rats, and the expression of the genes for both enzymes was altered in the livers of adult mammals by hormones such as dexamethasone, glucagon, and insulin. We now know that there is a single copy of PEPCK-C in the mammalian genome, that it is a relatively small gene (7 kb), that its mRNA is relatively abundant, and that changes in gene transcription induced by diet and hormones are rapid and very large. The genes for the enzymes mentioned above turned out to be either difficult to isolate (glucose-6-phosphatase) or to have a simpler regulation of their gene transcription (tyrosine aminotransferase and malic enzyme). Our decision to invest the time and effort into the study of the control of transcription of the gene for PEPCK-C was critical in developing what is now *the* model for studying glucose-regulated gene transcription. Why did we choose to study PEPCK-C gene expression? There are two answers to this question: 1) we considered this enzyme to be of exceptional metabolic importance and thus worth the effort or 2) we did not know any better. The latter is no doubt closer to the truth since, as Shakespeare once said, "Fortune brings in some boats that are not steered."

With some trepidation in the mid-1970s we began to isolate and determine the level of what was called at the time "translatable RNA" for PEPCK-C from the livers and kidneys of rats. I had no training in the isolation of RNA and very little understanding of molecular biology in general. My graduate education had been largely compartmentalized; I knew a lot about metabolism but had not a clue about the function of genes. Because there was no cDNA for a gene of interest available at that time, the levels of a specific mRNA involved the isolation of poly(A)$^+$ mRNA from a target tissue and its subsequent translation *in vitro* by a wheat germ extract, using a radioactive amino acid. An antibody was then used to isolate the protein being studied, which was separated by gel electrophoresis and quantified. The amount of label in the isolated protein was equivalent to the amount of mRNA for the protein that has been added to the translation system. This was a laborious process that involved the preparation of wheat gene extract from batches of wheat germ that seemed to have magical properties that were difficult to reproduce from batch to batch. Today, no one ever refers to "translatable RNA" as a method to quantify the level of mRNA in a tissue, but for a time in the early 1970s, preparing a viable wheat germ extract was a skill of importance!

As luck would have it, Patrick Iynedjian, a Swiss physician-scientist, was doing a postdoctoral fellowship in my laboratory at the Fels Research Institute. Patrick's research interest was understanding the regulation of metabolic acidosis and its connection to renal gluconeogenesis, a process that involved the induction of PEPCK-C gene expression (34, 35). He showed clearly for the first time that metabolic acidosis and glucocorticoids increased both the rate of PEPCK-C synthesis and the level of PEPCK-C mRNA in the kidney cortex of rats (36, 37). At about the same time, Dimitris Kioussis (38) and Predez Garcia-Ruiz (39) studied the effect of cAMP on the induction of PEPCK-C mRNA in the liver. They also studied the effect of insulin on changes in hepatic PEPCK-C mRNA during development. What was surprising to me at the time was the rapidity of the changes in PEPCK-C mRNA (10-fold increase in hepatic mRNA in 30 min) and the fact that they paralleled the alterations that we had noted in the synthesis rate of PEPCK-C. Clearly, gene transcription and the rate of PEPCK-C synthesis from its mRNA were coordinated. At about that time, papers began to appear reporting the isolation of cDNAs for specific gene products. It had, at last, became possible to study gene transcription without indirectly measuring the concentration of an mRNA in a functional assay.

Isolation of the Gene for PEPCK-C and the Characterization of the Metabolic Control of Its Transcription: an Ongoing Endeavor

In 1978 I left Temple University to become the Chairman of the Department of Biochemistry at Case Western Reserve University School of Medicine in Cleveland, a position that I held until 1999. As I moved my laboratory to Cleveland, I was acutely aware of the need to clone the cDNA PEPCK-C and to use it to isolate and characterize its gene; without this there would be no progress in determining the mechanism of hormonal control of PEPCK-C gene transcription (and no grants). In retrospect, this was the most critical point in my foray into molecular biology. If we were unable to isolate the cDNA for PEPCK-C over a single granting cycle there would be no chance for renewal; needless to say, the pressure was on us. The approach used to accomplish this in the mid-1970s was to isolate the protein of interest, determine a portion of its amino acid sequence, and from that predict mRNA sequence coding for the protein. With this in hand, it was possible to synthesize a series of probes to be hybridized against a cDNA library prepared by reverse transcribing hepatic mRNA. There were so many places that this procedure could go wrong that it required all of the optimism I could muster to keep from sinking into a state of deep depression when experiment after experiment turned out to be negative. It is hard to imagine the difficulty of this research today when almost any cDNA can be purchased!

We used the PEPCK-C that we had isolated from rat liver and were able to get a partial sequence that we used for the design of our probes. After many tries and a lot of heartache by several postdoctoral fellows, Heeja Yoo-Warren, a graduate student in my laboratory, isolated a putative cDNA for PEPCK-C from a library made from poly(A)$^+$ mRNA from the livers of diabetic rats. This work was published in 1981 (40). The gene was quickly isolated and the number of exons and introns in the PEPCK-C gene was determined by R-loop mapping. We found the number to be 8 (41); there are actually 9 (42). It turned out that this technique was not sensitive enough to detect a small intron at the 3′-end of the gene. At about the same time, Darryl Granner and his colleagues, then at the University of Iowa, published the sequence of the gene for PEPCK-C from the rat (42). Anyone who lived through this period can testify to the frustration in isolating a cDNA for a protein like PEPCK-C. There was no middle ground; you had a cDNA or you did not! It was very much like being in the neck of a bottle; inside the neck your research was totally constrained; once through the neck the possibilities seemed endless.

I have always had an interest in the metabolic role of PEPCK in different vertebrate animals (see Ref. 43 for more details of this interest). To this day, the metabolic roles of the two isoforms of PEPCK are poorly understood. To provide some information on this subject, we set about to characterize the genes for both isoforms of PEPCK-C from the chicken. John Cook isolated and sequenced the cDNA PEPCK-C (44), Sharon Weldon the cDNA PEPCK-M (45) from the chicken, and Yaccov Hod (46) characterized the gene for PEPCK-C from the chicken. The two isoforms of PEPCK have similar molecular masses (about 68 kDa), but they have only 60% sequence identity (45). In addition, transcription of the gene for PEPCK-M is not inducible by factors that stimulate the expression of the gene for PEPCK-C, such as cAMP (45). Clearly more work is needed to improve the characterization of both the biological role of the two isoforms of PEPCK, as well as the factors that control the transcription of PEPCK-M.

Once the gene for PEPCK-C was isolated, the action shifted to the characterization of its regulation by more direct techniques. Wouter Lamers and Herman Meisner (47) determined the effect of diet and hormones on the rate of gene transcription in the liver of rats using "run off" transcription analysis. We were very pleased to see that the rate of change of PEPCK-C gene transcription was rapid and the change was large. The half-time of transcription was 30 min after feeding carbohydrate to the rats, and the injection of Bt$_2$cAMP caused a 10-fold induction of gene transcription in 30 min. Thus, changes in the rate of transcription of the gene for PEPCK-C parallel the changes in the level of its mRNA and in the rate of enzyme synthesis. The rapidity of changes in PEPCK-C gene transcription in response to hormones has been a major asset in studying the control of this process in mammals. In fact, transcription of the gene is more rapid than RNA processing. Maria Hatzoglou (48), then a graduate student in my laboratory, found that the nuclei from rat liver, stimulated by the administration of Bt$_2$cAMP, contained a number of precursor species of PEPCK-C mRNA in various stages of processing; introns could be detected in the nucleus that had not yet been degraded. We even proposed a model for the maturation of PEPCK-C mRNA that involved the splicing of individual exons of the RNA that proceeds from the 5′- to 3′-end of the message.

Transcriptional analysis is often referred to, with some derision, as "promoter bashing." My colleagues and I have spent almost two decades trying to understand the regulation of PEPCK-C gene transcription, so I know well the effort required to follow the every increasing complexity of gene transcription. Our work in this area, much of it in collaboration with Lea Reshef, began when the promoter became available for analysis in 1983. At the time, we had no idea of what to expect of a regulatory domain and where it might reside in the promoter, and no models were available to guide us. In a series of studies in the mid-1980s, we demonstrated that a relatively short segment of the PEPCK-C gene promoter contained all of the information needed to account for the induction of gene transcription from the promoter by cAMP and glucocorticoids and identified the first cAMP regulatory element ever described. I recall at the time being surprised that it was so close to the start site of gene transcription (−80). Jay and

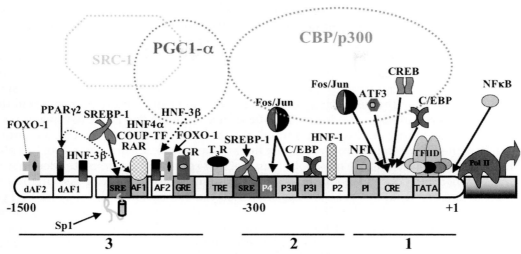

FIG. 3. **The mid-2004 version of PEPCK-C gene promoter showing the transcription factors and co-activators that regulate the transcription of the gene.** This figure is adapted from one published in Ref. 63; the reader is directed to that article for more details on the control of PEPCK-C gene transcription. The abbreviations used are: *CREB*, cAMP regulatory element binding protein; *ATF3*, activating transcription factor 3; *NFκB*, nuclear factor κB; *COUP-TF*, chicken ovalbumin upstream promoter-transcription factor; *PPARγ2*, peroxisome proliferator-activated receptor γ2; *SREBP-1*, sterol regulatory element binding protein; *HNF*, hepatic nuclear factor; *GRU*, glucocorticoid regulatory unit; T_3R, thyroid hormone receptor; *C/EBP*, CAAT/enhance binding protein; *NF1*, nuclear factor 1; *CREM*, cAMP regulatory element modifier; *CBP/p300*, CREB binding protein/p300; *PGC-1α*, peroxisome proliferator-activated receptor γ coactivator 1α; *SRC-1*, sterol receptor coactivator-1, *RAR*, retinoic acid receptor; *AF1*, accessory factor 1; *AF2*, accessory factor 2; *dAF1*, distal accessory factor 1; *dAF2*, distal accessory factor 2; *TRE*, thyroid hormone regulatory element; *Pol II*, RNA polymerase II; *GRE*, glucocorticoid regulatory element; *CRE*, cAMP regulatory element; *P1, P2, P3(I), P3(II),* and *P4* are protein binding sites identified by DNase I footprinting (53).

Heidi Short (49), Tony Wynshaw-Boris (50, 51), and Jin-Song Liu (52) did a great deal of the early research that described the functional organization of the PEPCK-C gene promoter. Of special importance was the demonstration by Bill Roesler of the protein-binding domains in the promoter (53). Bill used DNase I footprinting to analyze ~1 kb of the gene promoter and identified a number of binding sites that are being tested for functional significance to this day. The number and proximity of binding sites and the apparent high affinity of transcription factor binding has made the PEPCK-C gene promoter particularly interesting for transcriptional studies (see Ref. 54 for a review). Dwight Klemm (55) carried out an elegant study that demonstrated the possibilities of using the PEPCK-C gene promoter for studies of *in vitro* transcription, an area still in need of careful study.

This research was quickly followed by a series of studies that identified a number of transcription factors that are involved in the hormonal and dietary control of PEPCK-C gene transcription. Of special importance is the role of C/EBPα in the control of PEPCK-C gene transcription, first described in my laboratory by Bill Roesler and George Vandenbark (53) and Jin-Song Liu (52) and the role of C/EBPβ discovered by Edwards Park (56). Austin Gurney (57) demonstrated that c-Fos inhibited PEPCK-C gene transcription as effectively as insulin, Marta Giralt (58) mapped the thyroid hormone regulatory element in the PEPCK-C gene promoter, and Deborah Crawford and Patrick Leahy (59, 60) studied the inhibitory role of nuclear factor 1 on PEPCK-C gene transcription. More recently, Kaushik Chakravarty (61, 62) has studied the role of SREBP-1c in the insulin control of PEPCK-C gene transcription.

Fig. 3 summarizes the current version of the PEPCK-C gene promoter with the various transcription factors and co-activators that have been shown to bind to the promoter and/or contribute to the control of gene expression. These transcription factors interact with co-activator and co-repressors (SRC-1, PGC-1α, and CBP/p300) to form transcription complexes that control polymerase II activity. The various hormones and/or control factors (*i.e.* acidosis, alkalosis, fatty acids, glucose) initiate signaling cascades that recruit or activate transcription factors, which bind to specific sites on the PEPCK-C gene promoter. The complexity of the tissue-specific and hormonal regulation of PEPCK-C gene transcription is evident from Fig. 3; clearly, more work needs to be done before the control of PEPCK-C gene transcription is fully understood. However, the interested reader is directed to a recently published review of the mechanistic basis for the complex regulation of transcription of this interesting gene (63).

Most of molecular biology is carried out using transformed cell lines to study gene expression. This approach is a powerful one but has its limitations when one attempts to understand the physiological control of a gene involved in metabolism. A great example of this is the control of PEPCK-C gene transcription in liver and adipose tissue by glucocorticoids; transcription of the gene is stimulated by glucocorticoids in the liver but inhibited in adipose tissue. Mary McGrane (64, 65), Yash Patel (66), Jed Friedman (67), and Pam Lechner (68) each carried out important studies of PEPCK-C gene promoter function by linking the promoter to a reporter gene and introducing this gene into transgenic mice. By introducing specific mutations into the gene promoter they tested the function of individual elements and determined the regions required for the tissue-specific transcription of the PEPCK-C gene. We also used this technique to test, in the intact animal, the putative hormone response elements that had been identified by promoter analysis using hepatoma cells in culture. My motto has always been that the intact animal is the metabolic "court of last resort"; if the promoter does not work as predicted when introduced into animals, there is something wrong with the prediction!

Lea Reshef and her student Yael Olswang abolished the expression of the gene for PEPCK-C in adipose tissue by mutating the PPARγ2 binding domain in the gene promoter in the germ line of the mice (25). The resultant tissue-specific ablation of PEPCK-C gene expression only in the adipose tissue stresses the required utilization of this regulatory site in this tissue only. Thirty percent of these mice became lipodystrophic because of the absence of glyceroneogenesis in their adipose tissue, accentuating the central regulatory role of PEPCK-C in this pathway. Colleen Croniger (69, 70) and Parvin Hakimi studied the metabolic consequences of a deletion of the genes for C/EBPα and C/EBPβ and PEPCK-C in mice. At the current time my colleague, Jianqi Yang, has produced a mouse model in which the gene for C/EBPα can be ablated in adult mice within 3 days by the induction of transcription of the gene for Cre recombinase. At 12 days after the ablation of the gene for C/EBPα the mice lose interest in food and have a continuing decrease in weight. They die almost exactly 2 weeks later. Our goal in all of these studies has been to make animal models that provide us with insight into metabolic regulation.

What Goes Around, Comes Around; the Return of Metabolism

A strange thing has happened recently; trendy journals like *Cell* and *Nature* have discovered metabolism. I am pleased to see it, even if it is several decades overdue! With the alarming increase in obesity and diabetes throughout the world (obesity has displaced smoking as the number one health hazard in the United States) and with a diet-conscious public, metabolism is now difficult to avoid. However, the new metabolism is quite a different discipline from the traditional subject that I learned as a graduate student. It is now deeply routed in molecular biology and genetics and has the power of genome-wide analysis to identify candidate genes involved in multigene diseases, such as diabetes. I have been very impressed with the powerful tools for the study of metabolism that have been provided by molecular genetics; the return of metabolism to the "front burner" of the biomedical sciences has very much to do with the new techniques available to study old problems. Metabolism has always been an important part of medical education, and teaching metabolic principles to our medical students and undergraduate biochemistry majors has been an important part of my scientific life.

My Career as an Editor of the Journal of Biological Chemistry

Emerson wrote that: "To genius must always go two gifts, the thought and the publication." My former boss, Emmanuel Farber, then the Director of the Fels Research Institute, said the same thing but more directly; he had a sign over his desk that read, "If it's not published, it's not research." How true that statement is! My first publication was in 1960 in the *Journal of Biological Chemistry* (71), and since that time, I have never wanted to publish my work anywhere else. There is something about the *Journal* that has inspired me (and many others as well) to devote so much of our efforts (in my case 30 years) to its service. Almost every working day for the last 20 years I have spent several hours involved in some aspect of its business. Through all of this, I have always felt that I was involved with something far bigger than myself and that I was part of a great line of biochemists, many long past, who have worked to make the *Journal* a true icon of biochemistry. To me the *Journal* is the greatest institution in all of biochemistry; there is nothing even close to it for its critical contributions to our science. As an Associate Editor for the past 20 years, I have watched with great pride as the *Journal* has led the way in the world of electronic publishing and more recently in the totally electronic submission and review of manuscripts. For the past 40 years the *Journal* has been led by Herb Tabor; he is in the long tradition of dedicated and truly far-sighted individuals who have guided the fate of the *Journal* since its establishment. I have watched with great admiration as Herb has handled all kinds of issues: the difficult kind that always seem to arise when a publication receives 14,000 manuscripts a year and publishes more than 50,000 pages! I can attest to the truth of the statement that the buck always stops with the Senior Editor. If a publication can be said to reflect the personality of its leadership, the *Journal* reflects the wonderful personal values of Herb Tabor. His hallmark is kindness to all (especially to prospective authors of the *Journal*) and a deep-seated decency and respect for the truth and for the power of a truly democratic approach to his job. For me, he has been a beacon of good character in an often troubled world.

Last Words

I have had the great good fortune to have worked for my entire scientific life studying the regulation of metabolism. Much of my work over my entire career has focused on the metabolic role of PEPCK. Early in my career, Mulchand Patel and I were interested in the metabolism of adipose tissue (72); today I still study the role of PEPCK-C in that tissue (22). With Koreshika Ogata, Alan Garber, and Mireille Jomain-Baum, I studied the control of hepatic gluconeogenesis in various species (73, 74), and Ifeayni Arinze and I worked together to determine the pattern of development of the two isoforms of PEPCK in the liver at birth (75, 76). The development of PEPCK-C is still an interest to me, but now I study the role of specific transcription factors in this process. In the 1990s my research turned to the area of gene therapy; my colleague Jose Perales developed a method for introducing genes into mammalian tissues (77). The fact that I am still active in research at the age of 69 is a testimony to the fact that steady, careful work on an important topic can lead to significant contributions; it is not necessary to be flashy, only steady. However, I have also found that nothing worthwhile in research can be accomplished alone. I have been blessed over the years with outstanding colleagues; there are too many to acknowledge in this article, but I thank them all for what they have given me. I especially have a deep debt of gratitude to John Ballard and Lea Reshef; they gave me much more than I ever gave to them. Over the past decade, my collaboration with Satish Kalhan has also shown me the importance of metabolic research with humans and how powerful it can be in studying the true nature of disease. All of my collaborators and students know all too well (as I do) that research is difficult and often discouraging; most experiments fail! I have always ascribed to Winston Churchill's admonition that: "Success is going from failure to failure with enthusiasm."

Acknowledgments—My thanks to Herbert Tabor, David Samols, Martin Snider, Lea Reshef, and Gloria M. Hanson for their very helpful comments during the preparation of this article. A special note of thanks to my colleague Kaushik Chakravatry for electronically rescuing the photograph shown in Fig. 1 and for drawing Fig. 2.

Address correspondence to: rwh@case.edu.

REFERENCES

1. Ballard, F. J., and Hanson, R. W. (1967) *J. Lipid Res.* **8,** 73–79
2. Soling, H.-D., and Willms, B. (eds) (1971) *Regulation of Gluconeogenesis,* Georg Thieme Verlag, Stuttgart, Germany
3. Hanson, R. W., and Fenton, P. F. (1965) *Proc. Soc. Exp. Biol. Med.* **121,** 343–346
4. Weinhouse, S., Medes, G., and Floyd, N. F. (1944) *J. Biol. Chem.* **153,** 143–151
5. Dipietro, D. L., and Weinhouse, S. (1960) *J. Biol. Chem.* **235,** 2542–2545
6. Ballard, F. J. (1975) *Methods Enzymol.* **42,** 43–47
7. Ballard, F. J. (1966) *Biochem. J.* **101,** 70–75
8. Ballard, F. J. (1966) *Biochem. J.* **98,** 347–352
9. Hanson, R. W. (1965) *Arch. Biochem. Biophys.* **109,** 98–103
10. Utter, M. F., and Keech, D. B. (1960) *J. Biol. Chem.* **235,** 17–18
11. Utter, M. F., and Kurahashi, K. (1953) *J. Am. Chem. Soc.* **75,** 785–787
12. Nordlie, R. C., and Lardy, H. A. (1963) *J. Biol. Chem.* **238,** 2259–2263
13. Ballard, F. J., and Hanson, R. W. (1967) *Biochem. J.* **104,** 866–871
14. Ballard, F. J., Hanson, R. W., and Leveille, G. A. (1967) *J. Biol. Chem.* **242,** 2746–2750
15. Gorin, E., Tal-Or, Z., and Shafrir, E. (1969) *Eur. J. Biochem.* **8,** 370–375
16. Reshef, L., Niv, J., and Shapiro, B. (1967) *J. Lipid Res.* **8,** 688–691
17. Reshef, L., Niv, J., and Shapiro, B. (1967) *J. Lipid Res.* **8,** 682–687
18. Reshef, L., Hanson, R. W., and Ballard, F. J. (1970) *J. Biol. Chem.* **245,** 5979–5984
19. Vaughan, M. J. (1962) *J. Biol. Chem.* **237,** 3354–3358
20. Reshef, L., Meyuhas, O., Boshwitz, C., Hanson, R. W., and Ballard, F. J. (1972) *Isr. J. Med. Sci.* **8,** 372–381
21. Jensen, M. D., Ekberg, K., and Landau, B. R. (2001) *Am. J. Physiol.* **281,** E789–E793
22. Reshef, L., Olswang, Y., Cassuto, H., Blum, B., Croniger, C. M., Kalhan, S. C., Tilghman, S. M., and Hanson, R. W. (2003) *J. Biol. Chem.* **278,** 30413–30416
23. Botion, L. M., Brito, M. N., Brito, N. A., Brito, S. R., Kettelhut, I. C., and Migliorini, R. H. (1998) *Metabolism* **47,** 1217–1221

24. Kalhan, S. C., Mahajan, S., Burkett, E., Reshef, L., and Hanson, R. W. (2001) *J. Biol. Chem.* **276,** 12928–12931
25. Olswang, Y., Cohen, H., Papo, O., Cassuto, H., Croniger, C. M., Hakimi, P., Tilghman, S. M., Hanson, R. W., and Reshef, L. (2002) *Proc. Natl. Acad. Sci. U. S. A.* **99,** 625–630
26. Franckhauser, S., Munoz, S., Pujol, A., Casellas, A., Riu, E., Otaegui, P., Su, B., and Bosch, F. (2002) *Diabetes* **51,** 624–630
27. Nelson, D. L., and Cox, M. M. (2005) *Principles of Biochemistry,* pp. 806–808, W. H. Freeman and Co., New York
28. Voet, D., and Voet, J. G. (2004) *Biochemistry,* 3rd Ed., p. 940, John Wiley & Sons, Inc., New York
29. Ballard, F. J., and Hanson, R. W. (1969) *J. Biol. Chem.* **244,** 5625–5630
30. Hopgood, M. F., Ballard, F. J., Reshef, L., and Hanson, R. W. (1973) *Biochem. J.* **134,** 445–453
31. Tilghman, S. M., Hanson, R. W., and Ballard, F. J. (1976) in *Gluconeogenesis: Its Regulation in Mammalian Species* (Hanson, R. W., and Mehlman, M. A., eds) pp. 47–92, John Wiley & Sons, Inc., New York
32. Goodridge, A. G., Garay, A., and Silpananta, P. (1974) *J. Biol. Chem.* **249,** 1469–1475
33. Goodridge, A. G. (1970) *Biochem. J.* **118,** 259–263
34. Longshaw, I. D., Alleyne, G. A., and Pogson, C. I. (1972) *J. Clin. Invest.* **51,** 2284–2291
35. Longshaw, I. D., and Pogson, C. I. (1972) *J. Clin. Invest.* **51,** 2277–2283
36. Iynedjian, P. B., Ballard, F. J., and Hanson, R. W. (1975) *J. Biol. Chem.* **250,** 5596–5603
37. Iynedjian, P. B., and Hanson, R. W. (1977) *J. Biol. Chem.* **252,** 8398–8403
38. Kioussis, D., Reshef, L., Cohen, H., Tilghman, S. M., Iynedjian, P. B., Ballard, F. J., and Hanson, R. W. (1978) *J. Biol. Chem.* **253,** 4327–4335
39. Garcia-Ruiz, J. P., Ingram, R., and Hanson, R. W. (1978) *Proc. Natl. Acad. Sci. U. S. A.* **75,** 4189–4193
40. Yoo-Warren, H., Cimbala, M. A., Felz, K., Monahan, J. E., Leis, J. P., and Hanson, R. W. (1981) *J. Biol. Chem.* **256,** 10224–10229
41. Yoo-Warren, H., Monahan, J. E., Short, J., Short, H., Bruzel, A., Wynshaw-Boris, A., Meisner, H. M., Samols, D., and Hanson, R. W. (1983) *Proc. Natl. Acad. Sci. U. S. A.* **80,** 3656–3660
42. Beale, E. G., Chrapkiewicz, N. B., Scoble, H. A., Metz, R. J., Quick, D. P., Noble, R. L., Donelson, J. E., Biemann, K., and Granner, D. K. (1985) *J. Biol. Chem.* **260,** 10748–10760
43. Hanson, R. W., and Patel, Y. M. (eds) (1994) *Advances in Enzymology* (Meister, A., ed) Vol. 69, pp. 203–281, John Wiley and Sons, Inc., New York
44. Cook, J. S., Weldon, S. L., Garcia-Ruiz, J., Hod, Y., and Hanson, R. W. (1986) *Proc. Natl. Acad. Sci. U. S. A.* **83,** 7583–7587
45. Weldon, S. L., Rando, A., Matathias, A. S., Hod, Y., Kalovic, P. A., Savon, S., Cook, J. S., and Hanson, R. W. (1990) *J. Biol. Chem.* **165,** 7308–7317
46. Hod, Y., Yoo-Warren, H., and Hanson, R. W. (1984) *J. Biol. Chem.* **259,** 15609–15614
47. Lamers, W. H., Hanson, R. W., and Meisner, H. M. (1982) *Proc. Natl. Acad. Sci. U. S. A.* **79,** 5137–5141
48. Hatzoglou, M., Sekeris, C. E., and Hanson, R. W. (1985) *Proc. Natl. Acad. Sci. U. S. A.* **82,** 4346–4350
49. Short, J. M., Wynshaw-Boris, A., Short, H. P., and Hanson, R. W. (1986) *J. Biol. Chem.* **261,** 9721–9726
50. Wynshaw-Boris, A., Lugo, T. G., Short, J. M., Fournier, R. E. K., and Hanson, R. W. (1984) *J. Biol. Chem.* **261,** 12161–12169
51. Wynshaw-Boris, A., Short, J. M., Loose, D. S., and Hanson, R. W. (1986) *J. Biol. Chem.* **261,** 9714–9720
52. Liu, J., Park, E. A., Gurney, A. L., Roesler, W. J., and Hanson, R. W. (1991) *J. Biol. Chem.* **266,** 19095–19102
53. Roesler, W. J., Vandenbark, G. R., and Hanson, R. W. (1989) *J. Biol. Chem.* **264,** 9657–9664
54. Hanson, R. W., and Reshef, L. (1997) *Annu. Rev. Biochem.* **66,** 581–611
55. Klemm, D. J., Roesler, W. J., Liu, J., Park, E. A., and Hanson, R. W. (1990) *Mol. Cell. Biol.* **10,** 480–485
56. Park, E. A., Roesler, W. J., Liu, J., Klemm, D. J., Gurney, A. L., Thatcher, J., Shuman, J., Friedman, A., and Hanson, R. W. (1990) *Mol. Cell. Biol.* **10,** 6264–6272
57. Gurney, A. L., Park, E. A., Giralt, M., Liu, J., and Hanson, R. W. (1992) *J. Biol. Chem.* **267,** 18133–18139
58. Giralt, M., Park, A. E., Gurney, A., Liu, J. S., Hakimi, P., and Hanson, R. W. (1991) *J. Biol. Chem.* **266,** 21991–21996
59. Crawford, D. R., Leahy, P., Hu, C. Y., Gronostajski, R., Grossman, G., Woods, J., Hakimi, P., Roesler, W. J., and Hanson, R. W. (1998) *J. Biol. Chem.* **273,** 13387–13390
60. Leahy, P., Crawford, D. R., Grossman, G., Chaudhry, A., Gronostajski, R., and Hanson, R. W. (1999) *J. Biol. Chem.* **274,** 8813–8822
61. Chakravarty, K., Leahy, P., Becard, D., Hakimi, P., Foretz, M., Ferre, P., Foufelle, F., and Hanson, R. W. (2001) *J. Biol. Chem.* **276,** 34816–34823
62. Chakravarty, K., Wu, S.-Y., Chiang, C.-M., Samols, D., and Hanson, R. W. (2004) *J. Biol. Chem.* **279,** 15385–15395
63. Croniger, C. M., Chakravarty, K., Olswang, Y., Cassuto, H., Reshef, L., and Hanson, R. W. (2002) *Biochem. Mol. Biol. Edu.* **30,** 353–362
64. McGrane, M. M., deVente, J., Yun, J., Bloom, J., Park, E. A., Wynshaw-Boris, A., Wagner, T., Rottman, F. M., and Hanson, R. W. (1988) *J. Biol. Chem.* **263,** 11443–11451
65. McGrane, M. M., Yun, J., Patel, Y. M., and Hanson, R. W. (1991) *Trends Biochem. Sci.* **17,** 40–44
66. Patel, Y. M., Yun, J. S., Liu, J., McGrane, M. M., and Hanson, R. W. (1994) *J. Biol. Chem.* **269,** 5619–5628
67. Friedman, J. E., Yun, J. S., Patel, Y. M., McGrane, M. M., and Hanson, R. W. (1993) *J. Biol. Chem.* **268,** 12952–12957
68. Lechner, P. S., Croniger, C. M., Hakimi, P., Millward, C., Fekter, C., Yun, J. S., and Hanson, R. W. (2001) *J. Biol. Chem.* **276,** 22675–22679
69. Croniger, C., Trus, M., Lysek-Stupp, K., Cohen, H., Liu, Y., Darlington, G. J., Poli, V., Hanson, R. W., and Reshef, L. (1997) *J. Biol. Chem.* **272,** 26306–26312
70. Croniger, C. M., Millward, C., Yang, J., Kawai, Y., Arinze, I. J., Liu, S., Harada-Shiba, M., Chakravarty, K., Friedman, J. E., Poli, V., and Hanson, R. W. (2001) *J. Biol. Chem.* **276,** 629–638
71. Bernfeld, P., Nesselbaum, J. A., Berkeley, B. J., and Hanson, R. W. (1960) *J. Biol. Chem.* **235,** 2852–2859
72. Patel, M. S., Owen, O. E., Goldman, L. I., and Hanson, R. W. (1975) *Metabolism* **24,** 161–173
73. Ogata, E. S., Swanson, S. L., Collins, J. W., and Finley, S. A. (1990) *Pediatr. Res.* **27,** 56–63
74. Ogata, K., Watford, M., Brady, L. J., and Hanson, R. W. (1982) *J. Biol. Chem.* **257,** 5385–5391
75. Arinze, I. J. (1975) *Biochem. Biophys. Res. Commun.* **65,** 184–189
76. Arinze, I. J., Garber, A. J., and Hanson, R. W. (1973) *J. Biol. Chem.* **248,** 2266–2274
77. Perales, J. C., Ferkol, T., Beegen, H., Ratnoff, O. D., and Hanson, R. W. (1994) *Proc. Natl. Acad. Sci. U. S. A.* **91,** 4086–4090
78. Croniger, C. M., Olswang, Y., Reshef, L., Kalhan, S. C., Tilghman, S. M., and Hanson, R. W. (2002) *Biochem. Mol. Biol. Edu.* **30,** 14–20

THE JOURNAL OF BIOLOGICAL CHEMISTRY
© 2005 by The American Society for Biochemistry and Molecular Biology, Inc.

Vol. 280, No. 11, Issue of March 18, pp. 9753–9760, 2005
Printed in U.S.A.

Reflections

A PAPER IN A SERIES COMMISSIONED TO CELEBRATE THE CENTENARY OF THE JBC IN 2005

JBC Centennial
1905–2005
100 Years of Biochemistry and Molecular Biology

My Life in Science, Not the Restaurant Business

Published, JBC Papers in Press, January 4, 2005, DOI 10.1074/jbc.X400011200

George R. Stark

From the Cleveland Clinic Foundation, Lerner Research Institute, Cleveland, Ohio 44195

I begin this essay with a brief account of the personal and social aspects of my career, followed by the science.

Early Years

I was born in New York City in 1933 to Jack and Florence Stark, the third of three children, 5–7 years after my sisters, Edna and Bernyce. Because my father was in the restaurant business and doing well at the time, there was a big party to celebrate the blessed arrival of the long awaited boy child. The restaurant business is treacherous, the silver spoon got bent pretty quickly, and my first career choice was made: not the restaurant business. At the beginning of World War II, Dad moved us to the Washington, D.C. area and opened a luncheonette at 15th and H Sts., N.E., "Stark's Beef and Beans," which sustained us through the war and early postwar years. We lived in semi-rural Maryland, where I went through most of secondary school. Mom worked as a bookkeeper in D.C., and my sisters were away all day in high school, then college, so I had to fend for myself much of the time. Saturdays were spent helping out in the restaurant, perfecting my emerging skills in chemistry and manual dexterity by preparing and flipping pancakes. Between rush hours, I played pool with the streetcar drivers relaxing in the pool hall next door (it was the end of the line) and got a chance to become pals with Albert, the jolly black cook who showed me a very different perspective on life. I have been very fortunate to have made friends with many different people, helping me to appreciate their varied approaches to living and to learn how to adapt to new situations, in life and in science. Angling for catfish in Georgetown with Albert was a highlight. Whites socializing with blacks was not common in D.C. at that time. My dad was devastated when he had to refuse to serve a wounded black veteran in the restaurant. In our segregated nation's capital in 1945, to have done so would have been the end of the restaurant and our livelihood. When I go to D.C. now, usually to visit NIH, I am thrilled to see how well so many black people are doing, with the shame of segregation long gone. How far we have come!

Grammar school was uneventful, but my three years in Hyattsville (Maryland) High School were not. I had inspiring teachers in biology (Mr. Owens) and chemistry (Mr. Lauer) and did a couple of fun projects in science fairs. For "How Dangerous is a Kiss?" I had the school beauty queen press her luscious lips to a Petri dish, causing their imprint to be immortalized as a thriving culture of bacteria and mold. Why she wouldn't dance with me at the prom I have no idea.

In 1950, we moved back to New York. My dad, who had little formal education but read widely and deeply, was determined that I should be a scientist and insisted that I needed to be in the right place for a good education so, with the pull of a relative who was a New York state senator, my way was wangled into the elite Bronx High School of Science for my senior year. After the relative peace and quiet of Hyattsville, here was a challenge!

Columbia and Rockefeller

I managed to survive Bronx Science well enough to gain admission to Columbia College, where I was to spend 8 wonderful years as an undergraduate and graduate student. Earning money was essential at this time, so summers I rented out seat cushions at Lewisohn Stadium (allowing me to enjoy the full program of wonderful classical concerts free), and during the academic year, I perfected my demon touch typing at the Columbia Scholastic Press Association, working for Col. Joseph M. Murphy, one of the kindest people I have ever met. Columbia College was a revelation, from enjoying the physical activity of lightweight crew to eye-opening, life-changing exposures to the humanities, contemporary civilization, the fine arts, and music. I was a premedical student until I took comparative anatomy, which convinced me to find another road. Chemistry was challenging and fun, as was my advisor, Charles Dawson, whose laboratory included both organic chemists and biochemists. I joined them as a graduate student, working on ascorbate oxidase from yellow crook-necked squash. Because the enzyme was concentrated in the skin, we got a great initial purification by peeling many bushels of squash in the cold room, accompanied by lots of graduate student raucous humor. Charles Dawson was the first serious scientist I had encountered up close and personal, and his wisdom and camaraderie with his students and fellows made a deep impression on me. Unfortunately, none of the rock songs I composed with my labmate Eddie Grossman (the brother-in-law of Neil Sedaka) made the hit parade, but I did finish a thesis and went on to become a postdoctoral fellow in a famous laboratory at Rockefeller University.

But before we get to that, let me introduce you to Mary Beck, a winsome physics major at Michigan who lived in New York. We met the summer after her freshman (my sophomore) year in college and got married as soon as we could after she graduated. Mary worked as a radiation physicist, paused to raise our two children, Robert and Janna, and then joined my laboratory for many years. In a short essay, what can one say about the glue that holds one's life together?

When I joined them at Rockefeller, Stanford Moore and William Stein were famous protein chemists, having invented the amino acid analyzer and sequenced bovine pancreatic ribonuclease, work for which they were to be awarded the Nobel Prize. In their laboratory I discovered that cyanate, formed from urea, could carbamylate the amino groups of proteins and, together with Derek Smyth, I used carbamylation as the basis of a new method to determine the amino-terminal residues of proteins. I also worked on the mechanism of action of ribonuclease, and extension of this type of work to aspartate transcarbamylase followed at the beginning of my independent career at Stanford. Bill Stein and Stan Moore were wonderful scientists, wonderful gentlemen, and wonderful to me, and we maintained close friendships until each met an untimely death. I could not have had better teachers.

Dennis Shaw, a labmate at Rockefeller, had come from Fred Sanger's group at Cambridge. Shortly after Dennis left each laboratory in which he had worked, the laboratory head won a Nobel Prize: the first prize to Sanger, Moore, and Stein; the second prize to Sanger, Gerald Edelman. I don't want to think about how much Dennis was offered to work in his fifth laboratory, but the streak was broken.

Stanford

After 4 happy years at Rockefeller, I was recruited to the famous Department of Biochemistry at Stanford by Arthur Kornberg to bring protein organic chemistry to the department, together with Lubert Stryer, who was responsible for protein physical chemistry. There I was to spend 20 wonderful years before moving on. My personal and scientific life was enriched immeasurably, initially by Arthur, Lubert, Paul Berg, Dave Hogness, Dale Kaiser, Bob Lehman, and Buzz Baldwin, joined later by Doug Brutlag, Ron Davis, and Jim Rothman. What a group! What an environment! We worked as individuals but with constant exchanges of ideas and information in a system propelled by Arthur's wisdom, for example, in establishing journal clubs and faculty research meetings several times each week. Space for students and fellows was assigned nearly randomly, so that a single small laboratory might have people working on completely different projects from four different groups. Reagents and ideas were shared freely; we were truly a community of scholars. I learned metabolism and bacterial, phage, and *Drosophila* genetics and was right next door to key discoveries in molecular biology, for example, the creation of the first recombinant DNA in Paul Berg's and Dale Kaiser's laboratories. My own background in chemistry helped us to figure out how to attach RNA and proteins covalently to paper, establishing the Northern and Western methods as derivatives of

Ed Southern's pioneering work in transferring fragments of DNA from gels to nitrocellulose. Two sabbaticals in London, in 1970 with Lionel Crawford at the Imperial Cancer Research Fund (ICRF) and in 1977 with Ian Kerr at the Medical Research Council laboratory at Mill Hill, helped to transform my laboratory from protein chemistry to cell and molecular biology. The Cold Spring Harbor course in animal cells and viruses, taught superbly well in 1970 by Tom Benjamin and Howard Temin, paved the way for my work on SV40, initially with Lionel Crawford in London and later in my own laboratory at Stanford.

Ian Kerr's experiments with 2′,5′-oligoadenylates and interferons led to a collaboration with his laboratory that began with a second sabbatical in London in 1977 and remains in place today, with Ian visiting my laboratory in Cleveland. Ian and I first met in 1963, when he joined Bob Lehman as a postdoctoral fellow, and I have profited enormously from our friendship and scientific association. In 1983, after 20 years at Stanford, I made the difficult decision to move to London, where Ian and I developed a close collaboration to study interferon-dependent signaling.

ICRF

By the time I got to London, Ian had moved to ICRF in the center of the city at Lincoln's Inn Fields. In addition to running my laboratory, I gradually assumed some administrative duties as Associate Director of Research. We were fortunate to be able to have a house, complete with garden, about 2 miles north of the ICRF, in Camden Town. Walking everywhere, including back and forth to work every day, was a pleasure. London is a fairyland, probably my favorite city. Part of the laboratory worked on mechanisms of gene amplification, derived from our previous work on aspartate transcarbamylase (as you will see), and the rest worked on mechanisms of response to interferons, eventually using a genetic approach that we are still developing. The years at ICRF taught me many things. Because the laboratory was fully funded, I had the liberty and luxury to concentrate fully on the science. I appreciated this most after returning to the United States, having to deal again with the nitty gritty of NIH funding. At ICRF, the method of funding facilitated an outstanding system of central services, which provided everything a scientist could wish for to make research easy and productive. In moving to Cleveland, I brought as much of the ICRF-style central services with me as I could, including Derek Duke, who single-handedly and heroically set most of them up at the Cleveland Clinic.

Cleveland

A couple of years short of age 60, I discovered that retirement at age 62 was mandatory at ICRF, meaning that very soon I would have to begin to scale down my laboratory. No way! I had to move on. At the Cleveland Clinic Foundation (CCF), my interferon friends and colleagues Bryan Williams, Ganes Sen, and Bob Silverman were helping to look for a new head of research, a position vacated by Bernadine Healy when she left to become head of NIH under the first President Bush. CCF was anxious to build further upon the excellent foundation that Bernadine had established and offered to provide appropriate resources, including a new building. This new challenge was most attractive, as was the opportunity to join the interferon mafia in Cleveland, and so we moved once again, in 1992. In Cleveland, I spent 10 years helping to build the Lerner Research Institute to its present status and size (eight full departments and about 130 principal investigators), with the tremendous help of the department chairs and Derek Duke, who did the lion's share of the administrative work, leaving me free to help develop the scientific enterprise and to continue my own research. After 10 years, CCF internal politics encouraged me to step down as chairman, but I remain involved in building joint research programs between CCF and its academic partner Case Western Reserve University, where I am currently a Professor of Genetics. The laboratory has maintained a strong interest in mechanisms of interferon action and in the development of novel genetic methods and has explored new projects in interleukin-1-dependent signaling and in other aspects of NFκB-driven gene expression. We also continue to work on aspects of p53 activation and function.

What I Have Learned

Treat everyone with kindness and respect. Learn to work with and get the best from coworkers—bright scientists come with many different personalities, and tolerance for differences in background, cultures, and lifestyles is essential. A good sense of humor helps a lot! Be

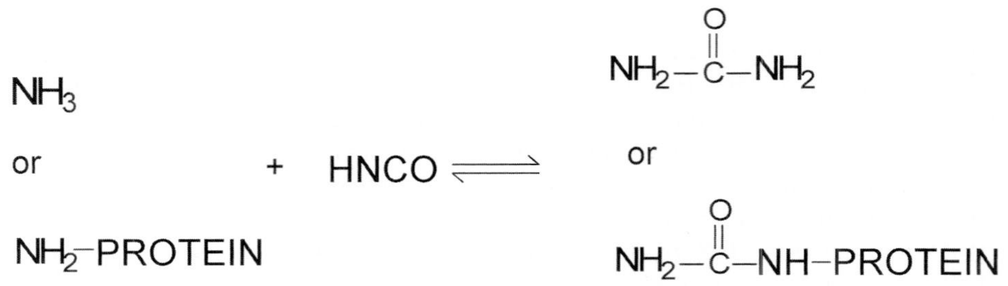

$$NH_3$$

or

$$NH_2-PROTEIN$$

$$+ \quad HNCO \rightleftharpoons$$

$$\begin{matrix} O \\ \| \\ NH_2-C-NH_2 \end{matrix}$$

or

$$\begin{matrix} O \\ \| \\ NH_2-C-NH-PROTEIN \end{matrix}$$

FIG. 1. **Cyanate, formed from urea, carbamylates proteins.**

daring in choosing new scientific projects and stick to them as long as you continue to feel that the direction is positive. (Unfortunately, the current system of NIH funding does not encourage projects that develop slowly or are somewhat risky, no matter how important they may be. Enterprising investigators often figure out a way around this problem and, hopefully, the system will change.) Think mechanistically, not descriptively. Try to discover how things work.

From Urea to Gene Amplification via Aspartate Transcarbamylase

Wohler reported the reaction of ammonia with cyanic acid to give urea (Fig. 1) more than 150 years ago. At Rockefeller, I found that this reaction is reversible and that the cyanate formed in the 8 M urea commonly used to denature proteins reacts with the amino groups of lysine residues to give homocitrulline residues (Fig. 1), with the elimination of positive charges and profound effects on the ability of the protein to refold when the urea is removed, helping to explain the irreversible denaturation of proteins in urea, which was something of a puzzle at the time (1). The α-amino groups of proteins also react with cyanate and, upon exposure to acid, cyclize to give hydantoins, which can be used to identify the amino termini (2). These discoveries, made in the Moore-Stein laboratory, stimulated my interest in cyanate chemistry, leading to later work at Stanford on aspartate transcarbamylase. Work at Rockefeller on the mechanism of ribonuclease action also stimulated my interest in enzyme mechanisms in general, and I began to wonder whether cyanate might be involved as an enzyme-bound intermediate in the transfer of a carbamyl group from carbamyl phosphate to aspartate, catalyzed by *Escherichia coli* aspartate transcarbamylase (ATCase; Fig. 2). However, a variety of approaches showed that cyanate was not an intermediate and that the transfer was likely to be direct, leading Kim Collins and me to think about the structure of the transition state intermediate in this reaction (Fig. 3).

We followed Linus Pauling's reasoning that an analog of the transition state would be a potent reversible inhibitor, binding much more tightly to the enzyme than substrates or products. Thus we synthesized N-phosphonacetyl-L-aspartate (PALA; Fig. 3) and were delighted to find that it was a very specific inhibitor of ATCase at nanomolar concentrations (3). It turns out that, fortuitously, PALA can readily enter mammalian cells to inhibit ATCase potently and specifically and thus block the *de novo* biosynthesis of pyrimidine nucleotides. More of this soon. PALA proved to be useful in helping us to unravel the catalytic mechanism used by *E. coli* ATCase and in helping Howard Schachman's laboratory to unravel the allosteric mechanism. Much productive work on the catalytic mechanism followed in our laboratory, using a variety of methods ranging from chemical modification to nuclear magnetic resonance. Toward the end of this period, my first sabbatical at ICRF put me in contact with mammalian cells in culture, and of course I tried out some of our precious supply of PALA on them. Although significant inhibition of growth was seen, I didn't yet realize that the uridine present in serum allowed the cells to bypass the *de novo* pathway and survive. When I used dialyzed serum, the true power of PALA to kill cells was revealed. However, about 0.001% of the cells survived and formed colonies. These new cell populations stably maintained their resistance to PALA and had elevated levels of ATCase activity. Furthermore, by using higher and higher concentrations of PALA, we could continue to select ever more resistant cell variants, with truly remarkable enzyme levels, up to 5% of the soluble protein (4)! From these cells, we purified mammalian ATCase to homogeneity, leading us to discover that it was one of three enzymes covalently linked in a single giant polypeptide (CAD) that also included the first (carbamyl phosphate synthetase) and third (dihydro-orotase) enzymes of the *de novo* pyrimidine pathway (5). Meanwhile, Geoff Wahl and Rick Padgett undertook to find the cause

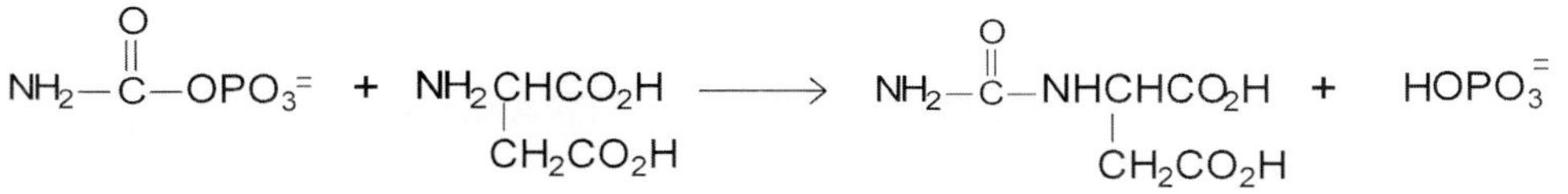

$$NH_2-\overset{\overset{\textstyle O}{\|}}{C}-OPO_3^{=} \ + \ \underset{\underset{\textstyle CH_2CO_2H}{|}}{NH_2CHCO_2H} \ \longrightarrow \ NH_2-\overset{\overset{\textstyle O}{\|}}{C}-\underset{\underset{\textstyle CH_2CO_2H}{|}}{NHCHCO_2H} \ + \ HOPO_3^{=}$$

Fig. 2. **Transfer of a carbamyl group from carbamyl phosphate to L-aspartate, catalyzed by ATCase, the second step of** *de novo* **pyrimidine biosynthesis.**

of CAD overproduction in PALA-resistant cells. These were early days in mammalian molecular biology, and many of the methods had to be developed and adapted along the way. First we found that the levels of CAD mRNA were elevated and then that the number of CAD genes was higher in the resistant cells (6). Together with independent work from Bob Schimke's laboratory showing that methotrexate resistance was due to increased copies of the dihydrofolate reductase gene (published a few months earlier than our paper), the work provided the earliest evidence for gene amplification in mammalian cells. Because increased gene copy number is a hallmark of cancer cells, it seemed important to investigate the mechanism of amplification, which we did for many more years (7–9).

PALA is quite specific for ATCase since, in cell culture and in animals, its toxic effect is completely neutralized by uridine, which provides an alternative route to pyrimidine nucleotides through salvage biosynthesis. Together with Randall Johnson, we initiated tests of PALA as an antitumor agent in mice, with initial spectacular results in which mice bearing two different types of transplanted tumors could be cured by PALA as a single agent (10). Unfortunately, as is often the case with agents that are effective in mouse models, for reasons that are not yet clear, PALA is not effective as a single agent in a variety of human tumors and has seen only very limited therapeutic use, mainly in combination with other drugs.

PALA inhibits the growth of both normal and tumor cells in tissue culture, but only the tumor cells give rise to resistant variants through gene amplification. The tumor suppressor protein p53, required to prevent amplification and functional only in the normal cells, is activated by the DNA strand breaks that accompany amplification, and active p53 prevents the rare normal cells in which this event has occurred from proliferating. We are still pursuing two important mechanistic issues concerning the action of PALA on normal cells. What events follow PALA-mediated arrest of DNA synthesis and cause the activation of p53? What is the basis of the stable protective growth arrest of normal human fibroblasts that allows them to survive many weeks of exposure to PALA, in contrast to tumor cells, which are killed within days? Perhaps a better understanding of how different types of cells are differentially affected will suggest novel therapeutic approaches in which PALA can be used for the treatment of cancer.

Interferons, NFκB, and Mutant Mammalian Cells

My sabbatical in Ian Kerr's laboratory at Mill Hill in 1977 stimulated work on 2′,5′-oligoadenylates that was relatively short lived and on how cells respond to interferons (IFNs), which continues unabated today. While we were still at Stanford, Richard Friedman cloned the first cDNAs corresponding to IFN-stimulated genes and went on to identify the first IFN-responsive elements in the promoters of such genes (11, 12). Following the move to London, the work proceeded as a close collaboration with Ian Kerr's laboratory. We characterized the promoters in more detail and, importantly, described the activation by IFN of a latent DNA-binding protein present in the cytosol of untreated cells (13). What was this protein and how was it activated? Biochemical purification of interferon-stimulated gene factor 3 (ISGF3) in Jim Darnell's laboratory provided the answers to the first question and, eventually, to part of the second. The novel signal transducers and activators of transcription (STATs) 1 and 2 and the associated protein IRF9 constitute ISGF3, and activation was achieved through phosphorylation of specific tyrosine residues on the STATs. The kinase responsible was identified through work initiated in our laboratories by Sandra Pellegrini. We developed a method, described below, for obtaining mutants of human cells that failed to respond to IFN because of the loss of expression of a single protein, caused by chemical mutagenesis (14). In principle such mutants could be complemented with exogenous DNA encoding the missing protein, thus allowing an unknown signaling component to be identified. Sandra obtained the mutant cell line U1A at ICRF and took it with her to her own laboratory at the Pasteur Institute in Paris, where she cloned the missing enzyme (15). Tyk2 is a tyrosine kinase that associates tightly with the cell-surface receptor for type I IFNs. It is a member of a small family of related

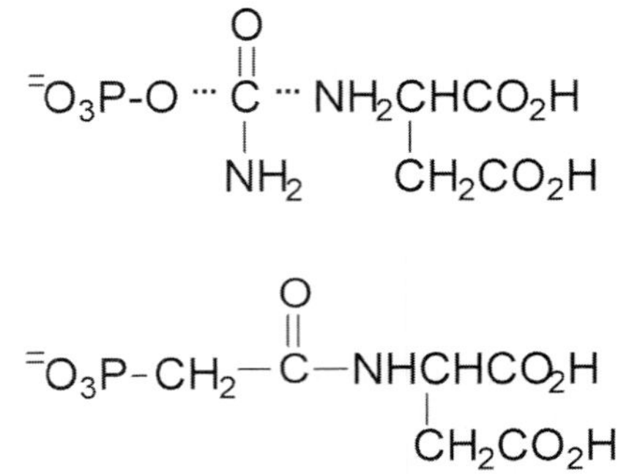

$$\text{}^=O_3P-O \cdots \underset{\underset{NH_2}{|}}{\overset{\overset{O}{\|}}{C}} \cdots \underset{\underset{CH_2CO_2H}{|}}{NH_2CHCO_2H} \qquad \text{TRANSITION STATE}$$

$$\text{}^=O_3P-CH_2-\overset{\overset{O}{\|}}{C}-\underset{\underset{CH_2CO_2H}{|}}{NHCHCO_2H} \qquad \text{PALA}$$

FIG. 3. **Structures of a transition state in the ATCase reaction and of the transition state analog PALA.**

kinases known as JAKs and, together with JAK1, is responsible for the activation of phosphotyrosine binding sites for STATs 1 and 2 on the IFN-α receptor and for the subsequent tyrosine phosphorylation and activation of the STATs themselves. Continuation of the mutant hunt led eventually to the isolation of a set of eight cell lines, each lacking a different single protein required for signaling in response to type I or type II IFNs, namely STAT1, STAT2, IRF9, Tyk2, JAK1, JAK2, and the receptor subunits IFNAR2 and IFNGR2 (see, for example, Refs. 16–18). Because the JAKs and STATs are required for signaling in response to many cytokines (19), these mutant cell lines have been broadly useful to the ~400 different laboratories to which they have been provided so far. Because signaling in response to IFNs involves more than the JAKs and STATs, a major current occupation of the laboratory involves describing the nature and mechanism of action of the additional factors that are required for induction of the full complement of IFN-responsive genes. Furthermore, STATs 1 and 3 can also function as transcription factors in the absence of tyrosine phosphorylation, driving the expression of a set of genes distinct from those activated by dimers of STAT1 or STAT3.

The genetic approach used with IFNs was extended to interleukin-1 (IL-1) by Xiaoxia Li. IL-1 does not activate STATs, using instead another important latent transcription factor, NFκB. Mutants lacking the signaling proteins IRAK or MyD88 were obtained and used to help characterize the pathway (20). In contrast to the simple pathway used by IFNs, mainline signaling in response to IL-1 is unbelievably complicated, requiring over 20 different proteins and still counting! Xiaoxia now continues to unravel this pathway in her own laboratory.

The same cells used to select mutants unresponsive to IL-1 can also be used to select mutants in which, abnormally, NFκB is constitutively active, and chemical mutagenesis was used to generate such mutants (21). Further work revealed that these, and also many cancer cell lines with abnormal constitutive activation of NFκB, achieve this state by secreting factors, including TGFβ, that activate NFκB by binding to cell-surface receptors (22, 23). Because activated NFκB contributes importantly to the resistance of cancer cells to apoptosis, it is important to identify the proteins whose lost expression in the mutant cells allows NFκB activation, and this effort continues in the laboratory today.

Some Methods

I have always tried to find better ways of doing things in the laboratory, and we have been fortunate enough to develop several methods of broad utility. To investigate the oligomeric structure of ATCase, Gregg Davies perfected the use of bifunctional imidoesters to cross-link the lysine residues of proteins. We realized that intra-oligomer cross-linking was highly favored over inter-oligomer cross-linking and that the resulting products could be seen in denaturing gels as a series of bands, with the band of highest molecular weight representing the full oligomer (24). Thus CAD, with three bands, was shown to exist as a trimer (5).

We had learned to couple DNA covalently to diazotized cellulose before attempting to analyze mRNAs by the then current method of running a tube gel, cutting it into many slices, and hybridizing each slice with a radioactive probe. Once through this cumbersome procedure was enough, and we reasoned that RNA could be transferred from a slab gel to diazotized cellulose, where it would be bound covalently and would still be available for hybridization with a labeled probe, as in the Southern procedure in which DNA is bound non-covalently to nitrocellulose, a procedure that did not work for RNA at the time. Thus the Northern procedure was born (25). Perhaps more original was the development of the Western method. Because we knew that diazonium groups would react with proteins as well as nucleic acids, we reasoned that proteins could also be transferred from slab gels to paper, with detection through the binding of tagged antibodies (26). Later, both the Northern and Western methods were improved by others to eliminate the need for covalent linkage to paper.

Finally, I want to discuss the origin and development of methods for forward genetics in mammalian cells, which has the major goal of discovering hitherto unknown components of signaling pathways. In the initial experiments noted earlier, we used an IFN-regulated promoter to drive the expression of the selectable marker protein guanine phosphoribosyl transferase. Xiaoxia Li later developed a more flexible and generally useful selection, using *Herpes* thymidine kinase to select unresponsive mutants with gancyclovir and a protein encoding zeocin resistance to select cells with restored function (20). Chemical mutagenesis gave unresponsive mutants at workable frequencies. All of these were recessive, lacking expression of a single protein required for signaling. Although Sandra Pellegrini's heroic effort led to the complementation of mutant U1A with genomic DNA encoding Tyk2, using the HAT selection, functional complementation of most of the mutants obtained in the IFN and other pathways has been very difficult, with a low rate of success, for reasons that are not completely clear.

Current work in the laboratory aims at eliminating the pesky problem of functional complementation by using retroviral insertion to mark the mutated gene, which can then be identified directly (27). If the retrovirus carries a strong promoter, its insertion into or near a gene can generate dominant mutants, in which the overexpression of a full-length or truncated protein or an antisense RNA from a mutated allele blocks the function of the normal protein or mRNA expressed from the unaffected allele (28). This method and related ones are being used to identify proteins involved in regulating the activation of NFκB or in regulating the activation or function of p53. Forward genetics has contributed immeasurably to our current understanding of pathways in bacteria and yeast. Its potential to contribute similarly to analysis of mammalian systems has hardly been tapped. Hopefully, novel methods being developed in several laboratories, including my own, will soon help to open these new frontiers further.

This account of my career is already too long, and thus I must omit much important work carried out over many years by many bright, hard working, and dedicated students, fellows, and technicians. I hope you are all willing to forgive me the omissions and to remain friends. I have been unbelievably fortunate to have been paid well for practicing my main hobby of science, so why would I want to stop? Hopefully, the fun and fulfillment can continue for at least a few more years.

This article is dedicated to my teachers and friends in science who have passed on: Charles Dawson, Bill Stein, Stanford Moore, and Ernesto Scoffone.

Address correspondence to: starkg@ccf.org.

REFERENCES

1. Stark, G. R., Stein, W. H., and Moore, S. (1960) *J. Biol. Chem.* **235,** 3177–3181
2. Stark, G. R., and Smyth, D. G. (1963) *J. Biol. Chem.* **238,** 214–226
3. Collins, K. D., and Stark, G. R. (1971) *J. Biol. Chem.* **246,** 6599–6605
4. Kempe, T. D., Swyryd, E. A., Bruist, M., and Stark, G. R. (1976) *Cell* **9,** 541–550
5. Coleman, P. F., Suttle, D. P., and Stark, G. R. (1977) *J. Biol. Chem.* **252,** 6379–6385
6. Wahl, G. M., Padgett, R. A., and Stark, G. R. (1979) *J. Biol. Chem.* **254,** 8679–8689
7. Stark, G. R., Debatisse, M., Giulotto, E., and Wahl, G. M. (1989) *Cell* **57,** 901–908
8. Smith, K. A., Gorman, P. A., Stark, M. B., Groves, R. P., and Stark, G. R. (1990) *Cell* **63,** 1219–1227
9. Stark, G. R. (1993) *Adv. Cancer Res.* **61,** 87–113
10. Johnson, R. K., Inouye, T., Goldin, A., and Stark, G. R. (1976) *Cancer Res.* **36,** 2720–2725
11. Friedman, R. L., Manly, S. P., McMahon, M., Kerr, I. M., and Stark, G. R. (1984) *Cell* **38,** 745–755
12. Friedman, R. L., and Stark, G. R. (1985) *Nature* **314,** 637–639
13. Dale, T. C., Imam, A. M., Kerr, I. M., and Stark, G. R. (1989) *Proc. Natl. Acad. Sci. U. S. A.* **86,** 1203–1207
14. Pellegrini, S., John, J., Shearer, M., Kerr, I. M., and Stark, G. R. (1989) *Mol. Cell. Biol.* **9,** 4605–4612
15. Velazquez, L., Fellous, M., Stark, G. R., and Pellegrini, S. (1992) *Cell* **70,** 313–322
16. McKendry, R., John, J., Flavell, D., Muller, M., Kerr, I. M., and Stark, G. R. (1991) *Proc. Natl. Acad. Sci. U. S. A.* **88,** 11455–11459
17. Muller, M., Laxton, C., Briscoe, J., Schindler, C., Improta, T., Darnell, J. E., Jr., Stark, G. R., and Kerr, I. M. (1993) *EMBO J.* **12,** 4221–4228
18. Watling, D., Guschin, D., Muller, M., Silvennoinen, O., Witthuhn, B. A., Quelle, F. W., Rogers, N. C., Schindler, C., Stark, G. R., and Ihle, J. N. (1993) *Nature* **366,** 166–170
19. Darnell, J. E., Jr., Kerr, I. M., and Stark, G. R. (1994) *Science* **264,** 1415–1421
20. Li, X., Commane, M., Burns, C., Vithalani, K., Cao, Z., and Stark, G. R. (1999) *Mol. Cell. Biol.* **19,** 4643–4652
21. Sathe, S. S., Sizemore, N., Li, X., Vithalani, K., Commane, M., Swiatkowski, S. M., and Stark, G. R. (2004) *Proc. Natl. Acad. Sci. U. S. A.* **101,** 192–197

22. Lu, T., Sathe, S. S., Swiatkowski, S. M., Hampole, C. V., and Stark, G. R. (2004) *Oncogene* **23,** 2138–2145
23. Lu, T., Burdelya, L. G., Swiatkowski, S. M., Boiko, A. D., Howe, P. H., Stark, G. R., and Gudkov, A. V. (2004) *Proc. Natl. Acad. Sci. U. S. A.* **101,** 7112–7117
24. Davies, G. E., and Stark, G. R. (1970) *Proc. Natl. Acad. Sci. U. S. A.* **66,** 651–656
25. Alwine, J. C., Kemp, D. J., and Stark, G. R. (1977) *Proc. Natl. Acad. Sci. U. S. A.* **74,** 5350–5354
26. Renart, J., Reiser, J., and Stark, G. R. (1979) *Proc. Natl. Acad. Sci. U. S. A.* **76,** 3116–3120
27. Stark, G. R., and Gudkov, A. V. (1999) *Hum. Mol. Genet.* **8,** 1925–1938
28. Kandel, E. S., and Stark, G. R. (2003) in *Signal Transducers and Activators of Transcription (STATs): Activation and Biology* (Seghal, P. B., Levy, D. E., and Hirano, T., eds) pp. 299–309, Kluwer Academic Publishers, Dordrecht, Netherlands

THE JOURNAL OF BIOLOGICAL CHEMISTRY
© 2005 by The American Society for Biochemistry and Molecular Biology, Inc.

Vol. 280, No. 15, Issue of April 15, pp. 14361–14365, 2005
Printed in U.S.A.

Reflections

A PAPER IN A SERIES COMMISSIONED TO CELEBRATE THE CENTENARY OF THE JBC IN 2005

JBC Centennial
1905–2005
100 Years of Biochemistry and Molecular Biology

Masters of DNA

Published, JBC Papers in Press, February 17, 2005, DOI 10.1074/jbc.X400012200

Sidney Altman

From the Department of Molecular, Cellular, and Developmental Biology, Yale University, New Haven, Connecticut 06520

In many ways, I went from being on the outside with a smattering of techniques to the inside of the world of molecular biology with the study of RNA processing. Much of my current work grew out of what I learned as a graduate student and as a postdoctoral fellow. In that I was very lucky. I studied with masters of DNA starting in the decade that began with the Watson-Crick model of DNA. My graduate work was done with Leonard Lerman as my thesis advisor and my first postdoctoral experience was in Matthew Meselson's laboratory. How I wandered into molecular biology and my second postdoctoral experience with Sydney Brenner and Francis Crick are described elsewhere (1). It is appropriate to begin with my experiences in Lerman's laboratory in the small Department of Biophysics, chaired by T. T. Puck, at the University of Colorado Medical Center in Denver.

Leonard Lerman discovered the intercalation of acridine derivatives in DNA (2–4). In my view, that was an astounding finding, partly because one knew so little about how small molecules bound to DNA in a quite specific manner and also because of the biological relevance of the discovery. Critical experiments that proved that the acridines intercalated occurred when Lerman was on sabbatical at the MRC Laboratory of Molecular Biology in Cambridge, England in 1960. At that time, Crick and Brenner and their colleagues were carrying out the monumental experiment that showed that the genetic code was triplet in nature (5). Actually, Lerman's experiments on intercalation gave them some notion of the kind of mutations that the acridines might produce. Crick and Brenner masterly used the idea of addition and deletion mutations to explain their data. Over the next few years, Lerman proved aspects of the intercalation model in many ways. Originally, he used viscosity and some x-ray diffraction data to confirm the model, and later he also used the lack of reactivity of amino groups on acridine derivatives to further the proof.

I met Lerman, in a serendipitous manner, in the spring of 1962 when I was inquiring about the prospects for a potential graduate student in the University of Colorado department in Denver and a description of the work done there. Shortly after our meeting, I was accepted as a student in Denver. The department had six or seven faculty members and one very active student, Barry Egan. In a way, it was a classic research department: no courses; everybody was in the laboratory working. That was an ideal change for me because I had left a very large physics department in which there was little opportunity for new students to do any laboratory work . . . and so began my education as a student of molecular biology.

Before I continue with my own view, faulty as that can be at this time, it is worthwhile documenting some of the other accomplishments of Lerman's. As a postdoctoral fellow with Leo Szilard, he invented affinity chromatography on columns to purify mushroom tyrosinase (6). Subsequently, he plunged into studies of DNA in the late 1950s. Lerman and Tolmach succeeded in labeling transforming DNA with ^{32}P and demonstrated that the radioactivity was incorporated into a genetically transformed strain of *Pneumococcus* (7, 8). These were bold experiments in a time when DNA was not yet routinely treated as both a biological and physical material at the same time, notwithstanding the earlier Avery *et al.* (9) and Hershey and Chase (10) experiments.

Shortly after I started in work in Lerman's laboratory, some pieces of small equipment had to be purchased. This was a puzzle for me; I was sent out to buy a particular kind of screwdriver. As I recall, there were two prices in the hardware store I visited, $7 and $17. The agony of choice consumed me and forced me to call Lerman. His answer to the question I posed represented his attitude as a teacher perfectly: "You decide."

Fortunately, we agreed on a thesis topic rather soon—the effect of acridine derivatives on T4 DNA replication. The idea behind the topic was to understand how the acridines acted as mutagens. As a consequence, I became extremely familiar both with the acridines and phage T4 over the next few years (11, 12). This was extremely important for both my postdoctoral experiences, and certainly I also became adept at various ultracentrifugation techniques, including buoyant density centrifugation.

An additional and important teacher during my graduate years was Rose Litman, a research associate affiliated with the Lerman laboratory. Rose had characterized the mutagenic effect of bromodeoxyuridine during her thesis work (13) and then went on to study transformation with Harriet Ephrussi-Taylor. Later, she characterized a UV-induced DNA polymerase by an affinity method (14) very similar, and simultaneous with, the method that Alberts devised for studying T4 DNA polymerase (15). Alberts had used DNA cellulose that had been prepared by heating whereas Rose used a DNA cellulose that had been prepared by UV radiation. Rose was a warm and very literate colleague and a good teacher. Several students had come to the department after I joined it, and Rose gave a course essentially on molecular genetics; it was excellent. Indeed, the course was so stimulating that it encouraged me to study genetics, including *Drosophila* genetics, on my own.

My studies of acridine-treated T4 DNA showed very quickly that the DNA was made in foreshortened pieces, possibly because of acridine inhibition of DNA molecules with many single-stranded breaks in preparation for recombination. It became a task to understand how the size of the pieces fit in with what we knew of acridine mutagenesis. There was a correlation between molecular weight of the T4 DNA and the concentration of acridines (12). I did succeed in an interpretation of the experiments, but I think the real explanation of the mutagenic event fell beyond my capabilities at the time. Ripley went further in this regard with respect to the enzymology and function of the acridines during the mutagenic event (16, 17).

Lerman left Colorado in 1965 to join the faculty at Vanderbilt University. A few months later, I joined him (while remaining a student at Colorado) in order to finish up my experiments. I became very friendly with Leonard and his family and our friendship has continued. We became much more than a student-teacher pair. I can only hope that has happened to many graduate students and their advisors. As a final note here, let me also say that when I was applying for a postdoctoral fellowship, after my failure with two private foundations, Leonard suggested that he better take a more liberal attitude toward the truth and, I think, omitted the various faults and warts he could detect in my character.

After I left the laboratory, as a consequence of my outrageous attempt first to join the Brenner-Crick group (no room at that time) and then Meselson's group, Tom Maniatis became a student of Leonard's, and they went on to study a collapsed form of DNA, akin to the structure one finds in phage heads (18). The methods and analysis used were subtle, and the experiments produced a good version of a collapsed DNA. At this time, the intercalation system was used more and more widely, and the name Lerman began to be forgotten by the new experts on DNA and its manipulations. Lerman's ideas were always novel and creative.

With great good fortune, I did succeed in getting a fellowship that enabled me to become a postdoctoral fellow with Matthew Meselson. Matt was, of course, a famous name in molecular biology, having done his great experiment with Frank Stahl (19) when he was a graduate student. He seemed a rather formal person when I first met him at a meeting in Gatlinburg, Tennessee; very few people wore suits and a tie but Matt did. There was a swimming pool where we were staying, and one evening, Matt was at the side of the pool, looking in, fully dressed. Someone shouted, "Go on Matt, you can do it—just step across the water!" It did seem possible.

Matt's description of how he came across buoyant density centrifugation of DNA has been written about extensively (20). It was no accident, it seemed, when he understood the problem of separating pieces of DNA made in different generations in bacteria by density labeling with ^{15}N.

A lecture by Monod on adaptation of enzymes and his own personal education on rare earth salts as a high school student provided some of the clues for the experimental method of buoyant density centrifugation. Both in this case and Lerman's case with acridines, the combined nature of deep intelligence with a true knowledge of the nature of the physical-chemical properties of DNA in solution allowed for the discoveries to be made. Most importantly, in both Lerman's (2) and Meselson and Stahl's experiments (19), unique theories were presented regarding an explanation of the data; in both cases, only one possible model fit the data really well.

It is important to point out that Lerman was a graduate student of one of Pauling's collaborators at Caltech and Meselson was a graduate student of Pauling himself.

Matt Meselson's ideas revolutionized the steps one could take to study DNA (and later RNA and complexes with proteins (21)). This breakthrough certainly dwarfed many new methods we see today. Meselson has said that he was only following what the Watson-Crick model suggested in terms of what he wanted to show: first, how does DNA replicate, and second, does breakage and reunion occur in recombinant molecules? The latter was proved, again with the use of buoyant density centrifugation (22), a few years after the first discovery by Meselson and co-workers.

I came to Matt's laboratory as the outsider from the boondocks. Shortly after I arrived, there was some problem in the laboratory with equipment. I was approached immediately as the person responsible even though I had nothing to do with the equipment. I recognized the situation but it did not repeat itself very often.

The laboratory was populated by several postdoctoral fellows and a few graduate students. Among the postdoctoral fellows were Ray Kaempfer, Marc Rhoades, Toshio Nagata (a senior visitor), and Bob Yuan. I recall that we were a chummy group but very hard working. Ray had just shown that ribosomal subunits went through a cycle of unattached subunits that assembled into a ribosome and recycled through the subunit state after use in the complete ribosome (23). He used a modification of the traditional velocity and buoyant density centrifugation to prove his point. Bob Yuan was working with Matt on the first purification of a restriction enzyme (24). Their method, using velocity sedimentation, proved to be very powerful and became a widely used step in general purification procedures. Both Marc Rhoades and I were working on endonucleases coded for by phages λ and T4 (25, 26). We found such nucleases, although there certainly was more than one produced by T4. The one I characterized, a nuclease that induced single-stranded breaks in native T4 DNA, was made during the mid-phase of T4 infection, but it was not sufficiently characterized to link to any particular gene sequence at that time. We used column chromatography to purify the enzymes with velocity gradients waiting to be employed too. From my point of view, I learned how to assay for and purify an endonuclease, something with which I became very familiar with on my next stop at the MRC laboratory in the England, and I certainly had a good education in biochemical purification.

We had various activities in the laboratory that were amusing. I recall, at the beginning of my stay, trying to calibrate one of Matt's centrifuges with a stroboscope. It required turning all the lights in the laboratory off from time to time. Certainly, not a popular activity. We also had a few sessions of birling on 5-gallon toluene drums. Two reagents added to toluene in the counting of electrons that made the solution fluorescent were poured into the drum and the 5 gallons were mixed, supposedly by hand. With a small amount of balance involved, these drums could be rolled around the floor by someone standing on them and persuading the drums to roll.

Ray and I became very good friends, and when his physician wife, Miep, gave birth (after a heavy Italian dinner loaded down with garlic) to their first child I became his godparent. Matt, whose mind worked at an extremely fast pace and seem to outstrip all of us in thinking about scientific problems, was very involved with activities in chemical and biological warfare at the time. This did not hurt the postdoctoral fellows too much because we were accustomed to fewer interactions with our mentor than were the graduate students. We got along and Matt was a pleasure to be with. Although I was trained mainly as a biochemist, I was deeply impressed by the power of genetics both as a consequence of Matt's own work listening to his lucid lectures in a genetics course and speaking to other friends, Mark Ptashne and Vincent Perrotta. This certainly helped in my talks with Matt. After I left the laboratory, Matt became involved with heat shock genes in *Drosophila* and, more recently, with the evolution of Bdelloid rotifers.

At one point during my stay in Matt's laboratory, Sydney Brenner came by for a visit. He now walked with a cane, the result of a serious motorcycle accident in England. He and I and Matt went to lunch at "Au Bon Pain" in Harvard Square. Sydney commented "That's what I have—bon pain." It was on this visit that Sydney asked if I wanted to come to his laboratory when I finished my time with Matt because there was now room for another postdoctoral fellow. I agreed in a flash. Of course, the topic we had discussed for my work was obsolete (1) when I arrived in Cambridge, England, but I, myself, soon settled on another: the effects of acridine mutagenesis on tRNA structure! I presumed I knew a lot about acridines and how they worked, and it seemed to be one of the few choices I had, given the general topics of research in the Brenner-Crick group and my limited upbringing in molecular biology. In fact, my view on the world certainly had been colored both by Lerman and Meselson, two individuals who had a wide perspective on the DNA world and who chose only to work on topics of undeniable general importance. Their hardheaded view of how to look critically at experiments was uncompromising.

In England, I started making acridine-induced mutations in a suppressor tRNA with the hope that I would generate mutant tRNAs with small additions or deletions in their structure. Although I was not far off from this goal (I made large additions, it seemed), it pushed me on the right road to further, rewarding experiments (27). Initially, I used an acridine half-mustard derivative to make non-suppressing mutants of the tRNA. The mutated tRNA gene products were ultimately examined during infection by phage $\phi80$ carrying these genes (28). In this manner, I discovered the first radioactive tRNA precursor molecule.

In the MRC Laboratory, only wide sample well slots in a slab gel were then used, but after a while when I was investigating cell extracts for enzymes that cleaved the tRNA precursor I isolated, a local machinist quickly made template sample well slots that contained at least 12 wells. In fact, I was so excited that now any number seemed possible. Of course, I soon learned that Bill Studier had already developed such "analytical" slab gels concurrently (29). Nevertheless, my previous experience with small T4 DNA molecules induced by acridines and the biochemistry of a T4 endonuclease led perfectly to the required state of mind for analysis of RNase P and the cleavage of tRNA precursor molecules. In fact, one lesson stayed with me until today: if you want to learn what happens to a large molecule (a tRNA precursor, for example) in biochemical analysis of nucleolytic enzymes, you must always have an assay that displays the effect of enzymes on any part of the large molecule.

Subsequently at Yale, another lesson from my earlier days led to a convincing experiment that RNase P had an RNA component. One of my graduate students, Ben Stark, had purified that enzyme and had shown that micrococcal nuclease could inactivate the RNase P function by attacking, presumably, an RNA component (21). At least one other method of proof was required. To me that meant a physical test in a buoyant density gradient. We were exceedingly lucky that RNase P from *Escherichia coli* did not dissociate in CsCl, and we measured the buoyant density of the complex at 1.71 g/ml, a reasonable compromise between an RNA and a protein component.

Although we were now dealing with an enzyme that had an RNA component, many of the rest of the experiments we did for the next 10 years or so were perfectly straightforward from a biochemical point of view. The enzyme kinetic constants, ion requirements, subunit properties and their function, and the outline of the catalytic center (and nucleotide sequence) became clear as the years passed. What I learned as a graduate student and during my first postdoctoral years was essential in preparing me for what came afterward in the world of science. What I could *not* learn from anyone was the complete variety, good to bad, of human reactions to a novel idea: an enzyme had a catalytic RNA subunit.

Address correspondence to: sidney.altman@yale.edu.

REFERENCES

1. Altman, S. (2003) *Genetics* **165,** 1633–1639
2. Lerman, L. S. (1961) *J. Mol. Biol.* **3,** 18–30
3. Lerman, L. S. (1963) *Proc. Natl. Acad. Sci. U. S. A.* **49,** 94–102
4. Lerman, L. S. (1964) *J. Mol. Biol.* **10,** 367–380
5. Crick, F. H. C., Barnett, L., Brenner, S., and Watts-Tobin, R. J. (1961) *Nature* **192,** 1227–1232
6. Lerman, L. S. (1953) *Nature* **172,** 635–636
7. Lerman, L. S., and Tolmach, L. J. (1957) *Biochim. Biophys. Acta* **26,** 68–82
8. Lerman, L. S., and Tolmach, L. J. (1959) *Biochim. Biophys. Acta* **33,** 371–387

9. Avery, O. T., MacLeod, C. M., and McCarty, M. (1944) *J. Exp. Med.* **98,** 451–460
10. Hershey, A. D., and Chase, M. (1962) *J. Gen. Physiol.* **36,** 39–56
11. Altman, S., and Lerman, L. S. (1970) *J. Mol. Biol.* **50,** 235–261
12. Altman, S., and Lerman, L. S. (1970) *J. Mol. Biol.* **50,** 263–277
13. Litman, R. M., and Pardee, A. B. (1959) *Virology* **8,** 125–127
14. Litman, R. M. (1968) *J. Biol. Chem.* **243,** 6222–6233
15. Alberts, B. M., Amodio, F. J., Jenkins, M., Gutmann, E. D., and Ferris, F. L. (1968) *Cold Spring Harbor Symp. Quant. Biol.* **33,** 289–305
16. Ripley, L. S. (1990) *Annu. Rev. Genet.* **211,** 63–74
17. Kaiser, V. L., and Ripley, L. S. (1995) *Proc. Natl. Acad. Sci. U. S. A.* **92,** 2234–2238
18. Maniatis, T., Venable, J. H., Jr., and Lerman, L. S. (1974) *J. Mol. Biol.* **84,** 37–64
19. Meselson, M., and Stahl, F. W. (1958) *Proc. Natl. Acad. Sci. U. S. A.* **44,** 671–682
20. Holmes, F. L. (2001) *Meselson and Stahl and the Replication of DNA*, Yale University Press, New Haven, CT
21. Stark, B. C., Kole, R., Bowman, E. J., and Altman, S. (1978) *Proc. Natl. Acad. Sci. U. S. A.* **75,** 3717–3721
22. Meselson, M., and Weigle, J. J. (1961) *Proc. Natl. Acad. Sci. U. S. A.* **47,** 857–868
23. Kaempfer, R. O. R., Meselson, M., and Raskas, H. J. (1968) *J. Mol. Biol.* **31,** 277–289
24. Yuan, R., and Meselson, M. (1968) *Nature* **217,** 1110–1114
25. Rhoades, M., and Meselson, M. (1973) *J. Biol. Chem.* **248,** 521–527
26. Altman, S., and Meselson, M. (1970) *Proc. Natl. Acad. Sci. U. S. A.* **66,** 716–721
27. Altman, S., and Kirsebom, L. (1999) in *The RNA World* (Gesteland, R., Cech, T., and Atkins, J., eds) 2nd Ed., Cold Spring Harbor Laboratory Press, Cold Spring Harbor, NY
28. Altman, S. (1971) *Nat. New Biol.* **229,** 19–21
29. Studier, F. W. (1972) *Science* **176,** 367–376

THE JOURNAL OF BIOLOGICAL CHEMISTRY
© 2005 by The American Society for Biochemistry and Molecular Biology, Inc.

Vol. 280, No. 17, Issue of April 29, pp. 16529–16541, 2005
Printed in U.S.A.

Reflections

A PAPER IN A SERIES COMMISSIONED TO CELEBRATE THE CENTENARY OF THE JBC IN 2005

JBC Centennial
1905–2005
100 Years of Biochemistry and Molecular Biology

My Contributions to Science and Society

Published, JBC Papers in Press, February 17, 2005, DOI 10.1074/jbc.X400013200

Ephraim Katchalski-Katzir

From the Department of Biological Chemistry, The Weizmann Institute of Science, 76100 Rehovot, Israel

Not too many of my scientific colleagues have lived, as I have, through the birth pangs of a new state or felt the need to throw themselves into a lifestyle that is critical for their own survival and their nation's future. If this sounds dramatic, it is no more and no less than what it was like to be a scientist in the emerging and newly established State of Israel for the larger part of the 20th century when the local Jewish population and many Zionists living abroad were devoting all their energies to achieving statehood and then building and protecting the new state after its creation in 1948. Perhaps I may therefore be forgiven if these reflections on my scientific activities are inextricably interwoven with recollections of my life outside science. I have participated in the most significant events in my country during the historic period of its emergence and development as a dynamic new state. At the same time, I have derived enormous pleasure and fulfillment from my chosen path of research and teaching in the life sciences.

In 1922, when I was 6 years old and my brother Aharon was 9, my family emigrated to Palestine from Poland. Our first home was Tel Aviv, then a tiny city taking shape on the sand dunes adjacent to ancient Jaffa. After a year we moved to Jerusalem. My brother and I were especially drawn to the natural sciences, and after high school we both decided to continue our studies at the new Hebrew University of Jerusalem. I began in 1932, 2 years after Aharon had enrolled in the university's first group of biology students. The ascent to Mount Scopus each day on my motor bike, one of the few motorized vehicles in Jerusalem in those days, was always an exhilarating experience with the Old City in front of me flanked by the mighty Judean desert to the west and the stone-colored new city shining in the east.

Already in high school it was clear to me that, like all those of our generation, we would have to play our part in activities that had nothing to do with learning but were bound up with the national renaissance. Growing up in Palestine under the British mandate, and especially on the university campus, I was caught up in the ideological and political ferment of that time. Jews were returning to their ancient homeland after 2000 years, filled with the desire to build a democratic state in which we could determine our own future, revive our original language, and revitalize our culture. We were ready to forge a new society, which would be based on the principles of social justice defined by our biblical prophets and would offer a high quality of life enriched by the highest moral and spiritual values. In this exhilarating atmosphere, we threw ourselves with great enthusiasm into activities aimed at fulfilling the Zionist dream.

In the 1930s and 1940s the local Arab population, angered by the increasing Jewish presence, often attacked the Jews. We had to protect ourselves, and this we did by joining the illegal Jewish defense organization, the *Haganah*, which later became the Israel Defense Forces.

Thus, while still a student, I had already formed quite a clear idea of my goals in life. I would do what I could to help establish the State of Israel and contribute to its security and its social and economic development. In addition, I would attempt to do some original research while at the same time playing my part in raising a new generation of Israeli scientists and helping to create the physical and intellectual conditions in which science and technology could flourish in this region. Like Chaim Weizmann, whose life and work served as an inspiration to many young scientists, I believed with all my heart "that science will bring peace to this country, renew its youthful vigor and create the sources for new life, both spiritually and materially." I have been lucky enough to spend my life in pursuit of my goals, with some success and considerable satisfaction.

Study and Work at Hebrew University of Jerusalem

The international tone of Israeli scientific endeavor was set in the early years of the Hebrew University by the excellent teachers, some of them world famous scientists, who had made their way to Palestine from the great centers of learning in England, Europe, and the United States. After years of solitary research before regular teaching activities started at the university, they were delighted that at last they had someone to teach. They treated their small groups of students as their friends and future scientific heirs, doing their best to endow us with all their accumulated knowledge. Professors and students roamed the country together, exploring and recording its flora and fauna, geology, water, and mineral resources.

Our mathematics teacher was Binyamin Amira, who participated in the setting up of the Institute of Mathematics at the university and grew roses in his spare time. Shimon Samburski taught us physics, and Moshe Weizmann, Chaim Weizmann's younger brother, taught us organic chemistry. Leo Picard taught us geology and paleontology. I remember him handing me his book in English, dealing with the formation of the Dead Sea, with instructions to be ready to discuss its contents after 2 weeks.

With Tchorna Reiss, a Romanian botanist who asked me to translate her lectures into Hebrew, I spent many hours at the swampy Lake Huleh near the Sea of Galilee, looking for plankton species, which I then described in my first scientific publication. I was captivated by the variety of exquisite unicellular organisms in the lake, the ordered patterns of their lives, and the wonderfully delicate silicon structures that some of them built for themselves.

Alexander Eig, who headed the Department of Botany, was a self-taught expert on botanical ecology with an astonishing knowledge of the plants of Israel. He would take us into the Judean Desert on lengthy field trips, pointing out plant societies and describing their struggles as they competed with one another for survival. I well remember how the desert came to colorful life after a brief rainstorm, with myriads of plant species springing into flower. My enchantment with those unforgettable vistas led me to study the desert flora, and my second publication, together with my friend Gideon Orshan, was on the plants that survive in this arid area. Together with Haim Shifroni, headmaster of the school in Kibbutz Ein Harod, I also published two volumes on organic chemistry, which were used as high school textbooks for many years.

Michael Evenari introduced my brother and me to plant physiology, a new and fascinating field of study. Gladly putting aside classification and collection and memorization of details, we tried instead to fathom the secrets of biological processes and the physical and chemical mechanisms that cause them. We became close friends of the zoologist Shimon Bodenheimer, with whom Aharon wrote a small book in Hebrew about the butterflies of Israel, called *Children of the Sun*. I can still see my brother running after butterflies and hardly ever catching one.

I soon found myself under the spell of the biological sciences, with botany, zoology, and bacteriology as my major subjects. In trying to learn something about the structure, function, and behavior of these living organisms, however, I realized that I would first have to study chemistry, physics, and mathematics, and so I spent some years in the exact sciences before returning to biology. Here my interest was attracted by the large molecules, the macromolecules of the cell, which play a critical role in determining life processes. I was fascinated by the lectures of our biochemistry professor, Andor Fodor, who introduced me to the world of biopolymers. Most intriguing was the revelation that proteins not only constitute the basic building blocks of elaborate cellular structures but also act as molecular machines that carry out a multitude of complex reactions within cells and tissues.

The research for my M.Sc. and Ph.D. degrees was done in the Department of Theoretical and Macromolecular Chemistry, headed by the late Max Frankel. Aharon, Frankel's laboratory assistant, was using potentiometric techniques to investigate the interaction of amino acids and peptides with aldehydes and sugars. Understandably, he persuaded me that for my master's thesis I should prepare salt-free basic trifunctional amino acids and investigate their electrochemical properties. These amino acids were not available on the market, so I had to prepare them from red blood cells. For about a year I collected blood from the slaughterhouse, separated and hydrolyzed the red cells, and isolated the basic amino acids lysine, arginine, and histidine from the hydrolysate by means of an elaborate electrophoretic technique. I needed amino acids for my doctoral research as well and was greatly relieved to discover that it was now possible to buy them.

We also kept a low profile regarding our activity with the *Haganah*. I became an officer in this underground organization and for a while commanded a field unit but was mainly involved, with Aharon and others, in the establishment of the scientific research team that later became the Israeli army's research and development unit.

One of the most useful books I came across during my graduate studies was *Proteins, Amino Acids and Peptides as Ions and Dipolar Ions* (by Edwin J. Cohn and John T. Edsall, published in 1943), which made me realize that to know something about proteins, I would first need to understand the structure and properties, in the solid state and in solution, of various high molecular weight proteins and polypeptides. Aharon and I spent many pleasant hours together in a small grove of trees outside the laboratory poring over whatever articles on polymer chemistry we could lay our hands on, and soon we could practically recite by heart the pioneer works of Hermann Staudinger, Herman Mark, Kurt Meyer, and Paul Flory. Within a year we were the undisputed experts on macromolecules in Palestine and within another year or two found ourselves leading the field in the Middle East. However, we felt completely isolated from the mainstream of scientific activity in Europe and the United States. Naturally there was a certain satisfaction in having one's own ideas uncontaminated by those of others, but this feeling was rapidly superseded by the need to exchange ideas with colleagues working in related areas.

Staudinger, Meyer, and others had suggested that synthetic high molecular weight compounds might serve as useful models in the study of biopolymers. This idea caught my attention. Israel's plastics industry did not yet exist, and so the only available polymers were the polyethylene, polystyrene, nylons, and bakelite that we had to purchase for our laboratory. Although it was fascinating to realize that the structurally complicated plastic materials appeared to have multiple potential uses, for example as fibers, fabrics, and kitchenware, it was disappointing to find that they were biologically inert and therefore of no interest to biologists. I therefore set out to transform inert synthetic polymers into biopolymers that would be of biological relevance.

Synthesis of Poly-L-lysine

What interested me was the synthesis of the simplest polymer, composed of repeats of one amino acid only. I assumed that if I could synthesize this macromolecule it might be possible, by studying its properties, to learn something about structure-function relationships in proteins. Also, it seemed to me that by covalently attaching amino acids, peptides, and proteins to selected inert synthetic polymers, it should be possible to endow these polymers with specific biological characteristics. The project seemed to be worth a try.

At the start, I believed it would be possible to prepare amino acid polymers by carrying out well chosen polycondensation reactions of the corresponding amino acid esters. My results with this approach were not particularly impressive, and so I looked around for other amino acid derivatives that might yield the desired polymers. To my great satisfaction, I found that α-N-carboxyl amino acid anhydride, which Leuchs had prepared in 1906 and which can by now be readily prepared by interacting amino acids with phosgene, had yielded a reactive labile monomer that readily yielded the desired polyamino acid in the solid state or in solution. As I was particularly interested in preparing a basic polyamino acid, I decided to start with the synthesis of poly-L-lysine. I believed that the synthesis of this basic polyamino acid would shed new light on the chemical, biophysical, and biological properties of basic proteins such as the protamines and histones, which are found in all cell chromosomes in combination with DNA and seem to protect and regulate the activity of genes during development of the cell. The preparation of poly-L-lysine was finally achieved by polymerization of ϵ-N-carbobenzyloxy-α-N-carboxy-L-lysine anhydride to yield poly-ϵ-N-carbobenzyloxy-L-lysine and the removal of the protecting carbobenzyloxy group with phosphonium iodide, work carried out with my student Izhak Grossfeld. At first we assumed that the benzyl groups of the benzyloxycarbonyl residue are reduced by the liberated phosphine; however, as we found ourselves weeping copiously during synthesis, we realized that benzyl iodide was evolving as a result of the HI liberated. Many years later, these findings led Arieh Berger and Dov Ben Ishai in my laboratory at the Weizmann Institute to develop the classic technique for removal of the benzyloxycarbonyl-protecting groups with HBr in glacial acetic acid.

When we sent in our first paper on the synthesis of poly-L-lysine to the *Journal of the American Chemical Society*, it was rejected by the editor, who was not convinced that a polymer had actually been produced. More hard work in the laboratory yielded evidence that persuaded even the most skeptical editor that what we had was indeed a high molecular weight, water-soluble polymer of L-lysine. I was delighted that we now had our synthetic macromolecule that showed all the characteristics of a high molecular weight polymer, and in the case of poly-L-lysine, of a polyelectrolyte as well. It was also gratifying to find that our poly-L-lysine was readily attacked by trypsin and interacted with viruses, bacteria, cells, and tissues in an interesting biological manner. The technique we developed opened the way for the preparation of linear homopolymers of other bi- and trifunctional amino acids, in which the steric configuration of the amino acid monomer was always retained during polymerization.

Transfer to the Weizmann Institute of Science

In the meantime, our work at the Hebrew University was coming to an end as our proposed research budgets, each amounting to about $30 a year, were beyond the means of the university's treasury. Both Aharon and I were therefore in a receptive mood when Chaim Weizmann, the distinguished organic chemist who in 1948 became the first President of the State of Israel, invited us in 1946 to join the academic staff of the new scientific center to be named after him.

The planning committee of the new Weizmann Institute of Science was headed by Ernst David Bergmann, Weizmann's distinguished assistant, and Herman Mark, Head of the Polymer Institute at the Polytechnic Institute of Brooklyn, who in 1947 invited me to spend some time in his world famous Polymer Center. On the way there I spent a few weeks as a Research Fellow at Columbia University with David Rittenberg, learning the new isotopic labeling techniques for identifying and characterizing intermediate metabolites. Rittenberg was aware of my work on poly-L-lysine and drew my attention to a recently published short note by Robert Woodward and C. M. Schramm in the *Journal of the American Chemical Society* (1). The title of their work, "Synthesis of protein analogs," gave me considerable satisfaction, as it clearly showed that Woodward and Schramm thought, just as I did, that poly-α-amino acids would be useful as simple high molecular weight models for proteins.

Herman Mark organized the purchase of the first sophisticated scientific equipment for the Weizmann Institute—an ultracentrifuge, an electron microscope, an electrophoretic apparatus, and an x-ray diffractometer. Palestine at that time (1947) was in turmoil, with the British preparing to leave and our leaders girding themselves for the declaration of the State of Israel. Rather than risk shipping our precious hardware to Rehovot, Mark had it temporarily installed in the laboratories at Brooklyn. He even suggested running the Weizmann Institute as part of the Brooklyn Polytechnic until things settled down, an offer I naturally declined, and within a short time the equipment and I were home in Rehovot.

This was at the beginning of May 1948. Most of my colleagues were by now involved in intensive on-campus research and development activities for the *Haganah*. Other types of research were virtually at a standstill. Aharon and I threw ourselves into whatever had to be done, drawing on all our professional expertise to assist in the defense of the new state. It was painfully clear to all of us that, much as we might aspire to careers in basic research, survival was the first necessity. The State of Israel was established on May 14, 1948. On the same day, the new State was invaded by five Arab armies and found itself fighting for its existence. I was temporarily placed in charge of the Israeli army's science corps, and until the end of the War of Independence we carried out military research, laying the foundations for the army's scientific defense unit, *Hemed* (an acronym for *Cheyl Mada* or Science Unit), which was established by Aharon, Yochanan Ratner (from the Technion in Haifa), Ernst David Bergmann (by then head of the Weizmann Institute), and myself. Most of the scientists at the Institute were in uniform, laboratories were in use day and night, and the formerly tranquil campus resounded with the test explosions of new weapons. What we lacked in arms experience we made up for in motivation and a talent for innovation, and this work prepared the way for

Israel's future defense industry. We designed and produced various items of defensive equipment.

Just prior to the establishment of the State, Ben-Gurion had taken upon himself the position of unofficial defense minister. I remember that while still in Brooklyn I received a letter from my brother describing his meeting with Ben-Gurion, who had summoned him to hear about *Hemed*'s activities and to offer his help. Aharon told him that the unit needed money, whereupon Ben-Gurion reached in his pocket and handed him fifteen English pounds. Aharon was delighted, and wrote that they had hardly known what to do with the unit's new-found wealth!

Nearly 60 years later, *Rafael*, which grew out of *Hemed*, is a billion dollar company producing highly sophisticated military equipment in cooperation with the Israel Defense Forces.

During our War of Independence, some of the American scientists who were supposed to take charge of departments at the Institute became jittery about coming to Israel. Consequently, Aharon was asked to be temporary head of the Department of Polymers, and I was made acting head of the Department of Biophysics. These two appointments soon became permanent.

Shortly afterward, in 1951, at the invitation of John Edsall, I first came to Harvard University and its medical school as a Visiting Scientist and have maintained close contacts with my colleagues there ever since. The department at that time was headed by Edwin Cohn. It took a while, I remember, to become familiar with the Harvard scene and style. After some months, having garnered the courage to come up with my own proposals for research, I would talk them over with John Edsall, who unfailingly encouraged my efforts. Next I would call on Larry Oncley, who unfailingly discouraged them; he would assure me that my ideas could not work or had already been tried without success. My next sounding board was Edwin Cohn, who would enthusiastically collar me and deliver lengthy monologues on his own projects. At Harvard I established lasting friendships with Elkan Blout, Paul Doty, Bob Woodward, and Konrad Bloch, all of whom encouraged me to continue with my original research and offered useful critical comments.

Poly-α-amino Acids as the Simplest of Protein Models—After moving to the Weizmann Institute, I continued to extend my work on polyamino acids as protein models. With my colleagues and students I synthesized several other polyamino acids, as well as amino acid copolymers and multichain polyamino acids, including branched macromolecules.

By this time, other groups were also preparing polyamino acids and studying their properties: Mark Stahmann in Wisconsin (2), Clement Bamford in England, and Elkan Blout and Paul Doty at Harvard. Some of these synthetic polymers could be drawn into fibers whose conformation, as determined by x-ray analysis, resembles that of silk and wool keratin. The information gathered by Bamford's group at the research laboratory of Cortaulds in Maidenhead, Berkshire on the conformation and conformational transitions occurring in polyamino acids prompted the company to build a pilot plant for the production of poly-γ-methyl-L-glutamate fibers and cloth. I still have a piece of cloth made of these fibers, given to me on one of my visits to the British group. Because of the high costs of raw materials and production the project was dropped but not before a film studio had produced a movie starring Alec Guinness in an indestructible white flannel suit made of poly-γ-methyl-L-glutamate.

The availability of high molecular weight polyamino acids opened the way to the x-ray analyses of poly-γ-benzyl-L-glutamate fibers done by Max Perutz in 1951, which confirmed the predictions of Pauling and Corey in connection with the α-helical polypeptide backbone. These data as well as the findings of Elliott and Malcolm in 1959 helped John Kendrew and Max Perutz decipher the x-ray patterns of myoglobin and hemoglobin. In addition, polyamino acids synthesized and studied in my laboratory by Arieh Berger, Joseph Kurtz, and Jurgen Engel served as useful models for elucidating the structure of collagen.

With the availability of poly-α-amino acid models it was possible to clarify, during the 1950s and 1960s, the mechanism and kinetics of polymerization of *N*-carboxyl amino acid anhydrides, determine the α-helical conformation of some of the polyamino acids in the solid state and in solution, detect β-parallel and anti-parallel pleated sheets of polyamino acids, and induce helix-coil transitions in the solid state and in solution under appropriate conditions. Fruitful collaboration between experimentalists and theoreticians like H. Scheraga, J. Schellman, J. R. Tinoko, M. Levitt, and S. Lifson facilitated the successful correlation of the macromolecular conformations of polyamino acids in solution with their hydrodynamic properties, optical properties, dipole moments, and nuclear magnetic properties (3).

Biological Properties of Polyamino Acids—Meanwhile, in Rehovot during the late 1940s, I concentrated on the study of the biological properties of polyamino acids. To my delight, poly-L-lysine and other homopolyamino acids and amino acid copolymers turned out to be excellent models for investigation of the mechanism of enzymatic protein hydrolysis and transpeptidation. I still remember the excitement with which I followed the rapid hydrolysis of poly-L-lysine by trypsin, using the cumbersome old Van Slyke apparatus. We showed that the specificity of an enzyme acting on a high molecular weight polypeptide is often strikingly different from that observed with low molecular weight peptides. Partial hydrolysis of poly-L-lysine yielded, as expected, a mixture of lysine oligomers. These were separated chromatographically and investigated immunologically by my former student Arieh Yaron, in Herb Sober's laboratory at the National Institutes of Health in the United States. Uptake of these oligomers by *Escherichia coli* was studied by Charles Gilvarg of Princeton University, then a visiting scientist at the Weizmann Institute. By using a lysineless mutant of *E. coli*, Gilvarg showed that *E. coli* readily takes up all oligomers up to tetralysine, but not larger polypeptides, and that these oligomers permit growth of the lysine auxotroph.

In our experiments with a prolineless mutant of *E. coli*, my co-worker Sara Sarid observed that the organism can grow on a synthetic medium in which poly-L-proline is substituted for L-proline. Clearly, the polymer was being hydrolyzed by an unknown enzyme. Further investigations by Arieh Yaron of the cleavage of various synthetic proline-containing oligo- and polypeptides led to the identification and characterization of a novel enzyme, aminopeptidase P, in prokaryotes and eukaryotes.

Antigenicity of Poly-α-amino Acids—An important outgrowth of the studies on synthetic polyamino acids was the development in my laboratory of techniques for the preparation of polypeptidyl proteins (proteins to which polypeptide chains are covalently attached via amide bonds to the free amino groups of the protein). The synthesis of polytyrosyl gelatin and the demonstration that it is antigenic, in contrast to the unmodified protein, led in 1960 to the preparation by Michael Sela and Ruth Arnon, then in my department, of the first fully synthetic antigen. In this compound, tyrosine and glutamic acid residues are attached to a multi-poly-DL-alanyl poly-L-lysine. I vividly remember our immunological experiments, in which guinea pigs injected two or three times with polytyrosyl gelatin went into anaphylactic shock. Besides being a nasty experience for the guinea pigs, this was a sobering demonstration to me of how careful one should be in treating living beings with synthetic or even native polymers. Nevertheless, the way was now opened for the fundamental and extensive studies of Sela and his co-workers on the chemical and genetic basis of antigenicity.

Some of the polypeptidyl enzymes we prepared retained full enzymatic activity. This finding was the basis for our subsequent preparation of a great variety of immobilized enzymes (4).

Use of Poly-α-amino Acids in Deciphering of the Genetic Code—Knowledge of the properties of synthetic polypeptides played a decisive role in the work that led in 1961 to the cracking of the genetic code. In their first paper on the subject, Marshall Nirenberg and J. H. Matthei identified the poly-L-phenylalanine, produced enzymatically in a cell-free system in the presence of polyuridylate used as messenger, with the poly-L-phenylalanine we had synthesized in Rehovot. As it happens, Michael Sela was at NIH when Nirenberg was working on the code, and he had informed Nirenberg that the normally insoluble poly-L-phenylalanine could be dissolved in acetic acid saturated with HBr. Soon afterward, Nirenberg and Ochoa identified other homo- and heteropolyamino acids as part of the effort to decipher the genetic code: poly(A) was found to code for poly-L-lysine, poly-C for poly-L-proline, and poly-G for polyglycine.

A Treatment for Multiple Sclerosis—Multiple sclerosis (MS) is a chronic inflammatory demyelinating disease of the central nervous system in which infiltrating lymphocytes, predominantly T cells and macrophages, cause irreversible damage to the myelin sheath. It is thought to be an autoimmune disease associated with an early viral infection. Based on previous clinical information, Michael Sela and Ruth Arnon examined the effect of a copolymer prepared in my laboratory, consisting of L-Ala:L-Glu:L-Lys:L-Tyr (6.0:1.9:4.6:1.0) on rats and mice suffering from experimental allergic encephalomyelitis, an animal model for MS. Their encouraging results led to development of the drug known as copolymer I (Cop-1), termed Copaxone and glatiramer acetate by the industry and widely used today as a therapeutic vaccine to reduce the rate of progress of MS in patients with the exacerbating-remitting form of this disease.

Proteins with Glutamine Repeats and Reiteration of Other Amino Acids—Four neurodegenerative diseases are linked to excessive repeats of glutamine residues near the N terminus of affected proteins. They are Huntington's disease, spinobulbar muscular atrophy, spinocerebral ataxia type 1, and dentatorubral-pallidoluysian atrophy. The more numerous the glutamine repeats, the more severe the disease and the earlier its onset. The repeats tend to lengthen in successive generations of affected individuals, especially in male transmission. These findings prompted Max Perutz and his collaborators to construct molecular models of poly-L-glutamine and study their optical, electron, and x-ray diffraction properties. Their published data disclosed the presence of β-sheets strongly held together by hydrogen bonds, suggesting that glutamine repeats might function as polar zippers by joining specific transcription factors bound in separate DNA segments. In line with these findings an impressive set of data on codon reiteration, published by Green and Wang (5) showed that hydrophobic amino acids, and particularly glutamine, account for a large proportion of the longer reiterants.

It is interesting to note that in vertebrates there are specialized telomeric structures, which are located at the ends of eukaryotic chromosomes and appear to function in chromosome protection, positioning, and replication. The telomeres consist of hundreds or thousands of tandem repeats of the sequence TTAGGG. Remarkably, all immortal cells examined to date show no net loss of telomeric length upon cell division, suggesting that maintenance of telomeres is required in order for cells to escape from replicative senescence.

Immobilized Enzymes and Other Polymer-Biopolymer Conjugates—My interest in enzyme-polymer conjugates was aroused by the growing body of data indicating that many of the enzymes embedded in organelles or biological membranes within cells act as heterogeneous catalysts. I thought it should be feasible to immobilize an enzyme by conjoining it artificially to a non-biological polymer, thereby restricting its free movement, and then to study its properties, especially its kinetic characteristics, under controlled conditions. I believed that the enzyme, once immobilized, could be put to work in novel enzyme reactors, allowing continuous transformation of appropriate substrates into desired products in the laboratory, the clinic, and industry.

My first paper on an immobilized enzyme was published in 1960 (6) when I described the preparation of a water-insoluble trypsin derivative and its use in a trypsin column. Our column indeed showed high activity toward most of the well known synthetic and native trypsin substrates. Of particular interest was the finding that the enzymatic activity of the water-insoluble trypsin remained practically unaltered in dilute HCl at 2 °C. Immobilization prevented autodigestion, and blocking of the ϵ-amino groups of the enzyme led to a marked decrease in the number of peptide bonds susceptible to trypsin.

These encouraging results prompted my group to prepare other immobilized enzymes, including immobilized chymotrypsin, urease, papain, alkaline phosphatase, and carboxypeptidase, in each case by covalent binding of the enzyme via non-essential side groups to water-insoluble carriers. Under well specified conditions many of these conjugates showed higher stability than the enzymes from which they were derived so that they could be employed in the design and utilization of enzyme reactors of various kinds (stirred tank reactors, packed bed reactors, fluidized bed reactors, enzyme tubes, and enzyme films).

Growing interest in immobilized enzymes led to the development by various groups of novel enzyme immobilization techniques in which enzymes were adsorbed or covalently bound to organic or inorganic carriers or entrapped in gels, fibers, or microcapsules and systems in which enzymes remained in solution but functioned in a limited space enclosed by an ultra-filtration membrane. In a novel enzyme immobilization technique that I developed together with my collaborators at Tel Aviv University's Biotechnology Center, immobilized monoclonal antibodies were used as carriers to combine with their corresponding enzyme antigen. With this technique, immobilization did not result in any loss of enzymatic activity. Thus, within a relatively short period, we were able to obtain a great variety of immobilized enzymes as well as enzyme reactors of various types, which opened the way to the use of immobilized enzymes in the food, pharmaceutical, and chemical industries (7). In addition to their more obvious economic and technical advantages, the products of enzymic reactions do not, as a rule, contaminate the environment. Furthermore, thermostable enzymes can be isolated from thermophilic bacteria, and it is possible to modify the characteristics of the enzyme by the use of modern molecular genetic techniques applied to suitable microorganisms.

The first industrial use of immobilized enzymes was reported in 1967 by Chibata and co-workers of the Tanabe Seiyaku Company in Japan, who developed columns of immobilized *Aspergillus oryzae* aminoacylase for the resolution of synthetic racemic DL-amino acids into the corresponding optically active enantiomers. Around 1970, two other immobilized systems were launched on a pilot plant scale (8). In England, immobilized penicillin acylase, also referred to as penicillin amidase, was used to prepare 6-aminopenicillanic acid from penicillin G or V, and in the United States, immobilized glucose isomerase was used to convert glucose into fructose. These successful industrial applications prompted extensive research in enzyme technology, leading to a steady increase in the number of industrial processes based on sophisticated immobilized enzyme reactors.

The use of immobilized enzymes in industry is now well established. I still chuckle when I recall the comment of my good friend, the late Ernst Chain, who told me that I was wasting my time modifying pure, well characterized enzymes and transforming them into heterogeneous catalysts of no use whatsoever. Happily, he was more successful as a scientist than as a prophet. The intermediate compound 6-aminopenicillanic acid, which he employed in the preparation of the semisynthetic penicillin derivatives used as oral antibiotics, is now prepared worldwide by means of an immobilized enzyme process. Many companies produce tons of products, including acrylamide from acetonitrile using immobilized nitrile hydratase and high fructose corn syrup from glucose using immobilized glucose isomerase. The Japanese were somewhat more appreciative of my efforts than Professor Chain. In 1985 I was awarded the first Japan Prize for my work on immobilized enzymes.

Education and Teaching

As a scientist and a teacher, I have always thought it important to make young people aware of the achievements of modern science and technology and their relevance for everyday life. While still a student I ran a program of well attended science lectures for the general public, which were held at the Hebrew University and also at newly established settlements (mainly *kibbutzim*) in different parts of the country. Early in my career I started to arrange for schoolchildren to meet each week on the university campus with scientists who shared their enthusiasm for experimental work and who were able to stimulate those young imaginations. This was the beginning of the tradition of extramural scientific activities for children and youth. Over the years and throughout the country these programs have become an integral feature of all of Israel's institutes of higher learning, with the support of the Ministry of Education and the participation of hundreds of Ph.D. students who serve as instructors and thousands of pupils, many of them new immigrants from culturally disadvantaged backgrounds. Today, some 10,000 children attend courses in astronomy, physics, chemistry, bacteriology, virology, genetics, proteomics, and electronics on our university campuses. At the Weizmann Institute, thanks to the devoted efforts of my friend, the late Amos de Shalit, an international science summer camp has become a prestigious annual event for scientifically gifted high school seniors. Moshe Rishpon, a physicist who ran the Youth Activities Section at the Institute for many years, now presides over a well equipped "hands on" Science Park, which draws many hundreds of children and parents alike.

My interest in popularizing science in Hebrew also led me to coedit, together with the late Shlomo Hestrin, one of the first Israeli Hebrew popular science journals, *Mada* (*Science*), on which a whole generation of youngsters was raised.

From the early 1950s, several unusually talented young men and women came to work with me and my group in the Department of Biophysics at the Weizmann Institute. Having received such inspiring guidance from my own teachers and motivated by my strong desire to help educate young Israeli scientists, I was more than ready to invest time and effort in nurturing these gifted young people. As a result, instead of concentrating strictly on my own specific research interests, I found myself moving in a number of directions, exploring different (though related) ideas with my students. My aim was to guide each one into an area that would enable him or her to tackle specific problems in my laboratory and eventually form independent research groups. Some of my students went on to achieve remarkable success. Our collaborations would often continue even after they had left my team and begun work in other disciplines. At one point, former students of mine headed no less than three scientific departments at the Weizmann Institute: Organic Chemistry (Avraham Patchornik), Chemical Immunology (Michael Sela), and Chemical Physics (Izchak Steinberg).

Serving My Country

As I became more involved in science, I increasingly felt that the academic community had a moral duty to participate in matters of public concern. Because of this sense of obligation, as well as my lifetime involvement with social activities in Israel, in 1966 I accepted the invitation of Prime Minister Levi Eshkol to head a committee charged with advising the government on the organization of its future activities in science and technology. An important result of our work was the appointment, in several government ministries, of Chief Scientists charged with promoting applied research in governmental institutions, in institutes of higher learning, and in industry itself. Our recommendations prompted a marked increase in cooperation between these three sectors. They also led to a dramatic increase in government spending on applied research, leading to a surge in innovative science-based activities, especially in high technology industry and space research.

Serving as Fourth President of the State of Israel

My ongoing involvement as an adviser in government-related activities included participation in various bodies such as the National Councils for Education and for Research and Development and a committee that recommended the legal framework covering the rights and obligations of engineers and technicians. In 1967, during the period that culminated in the Six Day War, I served as Chief Scientist of the Defense Ministry. In view of my close association with all sectors of Israel's government and its prime ministers in the course of the above activities, I was not entirely surprised when Prime Minister Golda Meir approached me to stand for President. I was clearly being offered a unique opportunity to place whatever talents I might possess at the service of my country. In May, 1973, I became the fourth President of the State of Israel and embarked on one of the most interesting periods of my life.

The President is elected by the Knesset, Israel's parliament, for a 5-year term. Israelis look to their President for moral rather than political leadership and choose an individual noted for intellectual activities rather than political experience. Running the country is the responsibility not of the President but of the prime minister and his/her cabinet. The President's function, on the other hand, is to represent the state and the people. He therefore serves, both at home and abroad, as a symbol of the State of Israel.

This description may suggest that being President is a rather pleasant pastime, not overly arduous, and requiring not much more than gracious behavior on official occasions. Nothing could be further from the truth. On becoming President, I frequently found myself thinking of my mentor, Chaim Weizmann. A visitor had once asked him how he spent his time as President, to which Weizmann had replied: "Oh, I'm kept very busy—I symbolize and symbolize all day long." I soon came to understand exactly what he had meant. Symbolizing the state means not only supporting it in its successes but also defending it in its failures. It means being a source of moral strength and inspiration, acting sometimes as a father figure and always as an example. It means raising the national morale in times of trouble. I found that symbolizing my country and representing its people was by no means an easy task. In Israel, the President is relatively accessible to the public, and one of the most demanding (and satisfying) aspects of my office was my contact with hundreds of people from all walks of life who came to Beit Hanassi, the presidential residence, to share their ideas and feelings with their President. In the reception rooms, surrounded by the images and symbols of our ancient past and our national rebirth, people talked to me about the lives they wanted to lead, the country they hoped to build, and the state and society to which they would be proud to belong. They talked of their dreams of peace with our Arab neighbors and their hopes for tranquillity within our own borders, echoing the vision of the prophet Isaiah, whose words are inscribed on the frieze framing the ceiling of the President's study: "Nation shall not lift up sword against nation, neither shall they learn war any more."

My involvement, in the course of my presidential duties, with individuals and families in distress reaffirmed my belief in the power of the President to act as a positive feature in people's lives. A President who has the humanity and compassion to use his influence wisely may find the means of helping afflicted people in a way that could determine the future course of their lives. I should perhaps mention, however, that with all their esteem for the President, Israelis are not in the habit of indulging any self-importance the President might feel. I well remember being invited to address a lunch time meeting of the Israel Association of Architects and Engineers and asking the chairman how long I was expected to talk. "You're the President, sir," he replied. "You can talk for as long as you like. We're leaving at 2 o'clock."

When I accepted the presidential nomination, I realized that I would have to give up my scientific activities for a few years. As any scientist will appreciate, this was a serious sacrifice. I expected that I would miss my work in the laboratory, and my fears turned out to be fully justified. I kept up as far as possible with the literature and attended scientific meetings whenever they could be accommodated in my schedule. I also took advantage of my office to promote science and higher education. All too rarely my colleagues, presumably mindful of my other activities and reluctant to make demands on my time, would approach me to review a scientific article. To their astonishment they usually received my comments within a day or two, never realizing with what relish I had fallen upon the work.

Two of the most momentous events in Israel's modern history occurred when I was President. I refer to the Yom Kippur War and the visit of President Anwar Sadat of Egypt to Jerusalem. The first of these occurred 6 months after I entered office, and the second shortly before I left it, so that the period of my presidency was in one sense defined by those two events.

The Yom Kippur War started on October 6, 1973, when Egypt and Syria launched a surprise attack while Jews were at prayer on Yom Kippur, the holiest day in the Jewish calendar. From the military point of view, Israel gained an impressive victory but at very great cost. We lost more than 2500 soldiers; many more were wounded, and hundreds were taken prisoner. The entire country was in mourning.

It was not until Anwar el-Sadat came to Jerusalem in November 1977 that the way was opened to peace with one of our erstwhile enemies. The visit came at very short notice and took us all by surprise. Its direct outcome was the peace treaty between Egypt and Israel, signed by President Sadat, Prime Minister Menachem Begin, and American President Jimmy Carter at Camp David near Washington, D. C. on March 26, 1979. Twelve years passed before other Arab leaders were ready to follow Sadat's courageous example. The Madrid Peace Talks, held under the auspices of the United States and Russia, and later the talks held in Oslo raised a new spirit of optimism and hope for peace in the region. As a result of those talks, a peace agreement was finally signed in 1994 between the Prime Minister of Israel, Yitzhak Rabin, and the chairman of the Palestine Liberation Organization, Yasir Arafat, and autonomous rule was established, as a first step, in Gaza and Jericho. Also in 1994, Yitzhak Rabin and the Prime Minister of Jordan signed a peace treaty between our two countries in the presence of King Hussein of Jordan and the American President Bill Clinton.

There was a time when I believed, as did many of my friends, that we could find an arrangement with the Palestinians that would allow us to achieve a normal relationship, both nations pursuing their own national, economic, and social aspirations while cooperating on a regional level in matters of concern to us all. I remember with mixed pleasure and sadness the close personal relationship that I developed with President Sadat during his brief but momentous visit to Israel and until his untimely death. This was a valued friendship and one that I had hoped would help establish closer ties between our two countries. It was a bitter disappointment to find that zealots from both sides seemed to have ruined every chance for lasting peace. Sadat was murdered in Egypt by Moslem extremists, and Rabin, whom I greatly respected and admired, was assassinated by a Jewish extremist in Israel.

And yet, even in these difficult and uncertain times, when terrorist outrages occur daily not only in our region but in many places around the world, I have not lost hope. I feel that there is still a chance that in the end the peace seekers among the Israelis, the Palestinians, and the Arab countries in the Middle East will prevail, and a way will be found for all of us to live rather than die together on this tiny piece of the planet.

My Brother Aharon

My beloved elder brother Aharon was murdered in May, 1972, at Ben-Gurion Airport, by Japanese terrorists supported by local Palestinian groups. Of all those who touched my life, the one who had the greatest personal influence on me was my brother. Aharon was my closest friend and colleague, my guide and leader into the world of polymer research. Together we studied quantum mechanics, statistical mechanics, polymer chemistry, thermodynamics, and biophysics. Our decision to move to the Weizmann Institute was taken jointly, and together we worked toward promoting science and technology in the early days for the benefit of Israel's Defense Forces and later in the interest of the wider society.

Aharon Katzir-Katchalsky was one of Israel's most gifted scientists and social leaders, a brilliant speaker, an inspiring lecturer, and a prolific writer who did much to popularize science. Among his many accomplishments was the creation of the Israel National Academy of Sciences. His untimely death was mourned by scientists and non-scientists and indeed by citizens in all sectors of the country. All of us felt ourselves bereft by his loss. Abroad, his many distinguished colleagues were horrified by this blow and came together in Israel to set up a Center in his name to promote scientific activities in areas within his wide range of interests. Aharon will long be remembered by the entire scientific community for his outstanding contributions to many spheres of life and science.

Biotechnology in Israel

When my term as State President ended, I was invited to spend some time at Tel Aviv University before returning to the Weizmann Institute. During my time-out from the laboratory in the 1970s I had kept myself informed of the important advances in the life sciences taking place in the United States, England, and Europe. Particularly impressive was the progress in biotechnology. Therefore, after consulting with colleagues, I decided to try and establish a Department of Biotechnology at Tel Aviv University. It was clear to me that it was only a matter of time before the achievements in genomics and proteomics would have a profound influence on medicine, agriculture, and industry. At that time many young scientists in Israel were interested in research in the basic life sciences, and it seemed to me that it would be good for the economy, as well as for the young scientists, to redirect their work into more practical avenues. With the consent and encouragement of the President of the University, Prof. Yoram Dinstein, I was able to establish a biotechnology department after receiving excellent advice on designing the teaching program and research work from outstanding scientists such as Malcolm Lilly from the United Kingdom and Arnold Demain from the United States.

The Department of Molecular Microbiology and Biotechnology at Tel Aviv University is now well established and is popular with students of biology, chemistry, physics, and mathematics. Several of its graduates are now working in newly established local biotechnology industries or in local ministries concerned with biotechnology. Promising research is under way at Tel Aviv as well as in biotechnology departments that have opened up in other institutes of higher learning.

After persuading the Prime Minister, as well as the Ministers of Commerce and Industry, Science and Technology, of the importance of setting up a biotechnology industry in this country, I was invited to chair a Biotechnology Committee to advise the government on the steps to be taken in this direction. We recommended that generous financial backing be provided for interdisciplinary research and development at the levels of the technical college, the university, and industry in both public and private sectors. The acceptance and application of our recommendations have led to the remarkably successful growth and development of biotechnology in Israel. This, and my unofficial designation as the "father of biotechnology" here, give me an enormous sense of satisfaction.

Research after Retirement

I have now returned at last to the Weizmann Institute where, as an Institute Professor, I may continue to reside within the Institute's campus and carry out my own research. At present I am particularly interested in protein-protein interactions and phage display techniques.

Prediction of the Structure of Protein-Protein Complexes—Almost every process in the living cell is dependent on molecular recognition and the formation of complexes. The latter can be transient or stable assemblies of two or more molecules, with one molecule acting on the other or promoting intra- and intercellular communication, or they can be permanent oligomeric ensembles.

The rapid accumulation of data on protein sequences and protein-protein structures calls for the development of computational methods to process and combine the information. Especially important are the methods designed to predict the structures of molecular complexes and ensembles that cannot be studied by current experimental methods. Transient complexes, for example, are too short-lived for crystallization or NMR spectroscopy.

In the theoretical approach that I developed with my colleges, we employed various grid representations of the complex component molecules and thereafter applied correlation functions to search the solution space and evaluate the putative complex. Our algorithms treat the molecules as rigid bodies, reducing the docking problem to a six-dimensional search through the rotation-translation space. Grid representation of molecules are digitized onto three-dimensional grids, and the surface and interior of the molecules are distinguished from each other by a digital process. For each orientation the correlation functions are calculated via fast Fourier transformations (FFT), thereby allowing all the relative translations to be searched. This simple and straightforward method has appealed to many research groups who adopted and modified this approach. The first era of FFT docking (the bound docking) and the second era of unbound protein-protein docking are described in detail in our recent review article (9).

Further development of the geometric docking procedure has enabled us to incorporate electrostatic complementarity, hydrophobic complementarity, and binding site information in our calculation. The method known as "MolFit," which we developed to predict the conformation of the complexes formed, proved unequivocally that geometric complementarity appears to be an essential feature for complex formation, even in unbound docking.

Use of Phage Display Peptide Libraries—Combinatorial phage display peptide libraries are useful tools for the production of peptide library repertoires from which users can readily select a single peptide that binds specifically with a well chosen desired protein. I chose α-bungarotoxin (α-BTX), the highly toxic component of the venom of the snake *Bungarus multicinctus*, as the first protein to be used for testing this technique. I chose this protein because of its relatively low molecular weight, its known three-dimensional structure, and its interesting and important biological characteristics. α-BTX binds specifically to the nicotinic acetylcholine receptor (AchR) present at the postsynaptic membrane of the neuromuscular junction and serves as a potent antagonist of this receptor. The peptide selected by the phage display peptide for its significant binding with α-BTX was MRYYESSLKSYPD. We therefore used this "lead peptide" in a novel chemical attempt to prepare peptides with the highest possible binding constant. We achieved this after elucidating the amino acid residues of the lead peptide, which are in close contact with α-BTX by NMR techniques and then systematically replacing the other free amino acid residues of the peptide by a set of well chosen amino acids. Using this synthetic technique, which we called "systematic residue replacement" (SRR), we obtained a set of peptides that inhibit the binding of α-BTX at nanomolar concentrations to AchR. X-ray and NMR spectroscopy showed that the high affinity peptides fold into an anti-parallel β-hairpin structure. The homologous loop of acetylcholine binding protein, a soluble analogue of the AchR, showed remarkable similarity. The superposition of the above described complexes indicated that the toxin wraps itself around the binding site loop blocking access of acetylcholine to its binding site. All of the available information led us to conclude that the peptides which bind α-BTX with high affinity mimic the three-dimensional structure of the binding site of the AchR (10).

In my recent research work, done in collaboration with Fortune Kohen, Roni Kasher, and other colleagues, the phage display technique enabled us to synthesize peptides that showed some estrogen-like activity when tested under appropriate conditions. The experimental approach adopted in this case is based on the ability to identify, by the use of the phage display peptide library, a peptide that binds specifically to a monoclonal antibody recognizing estrogen (11).

Looking Ahead

I have always thought of Israel as a pilot plant state in which dedicated people can explore all kinds of imaginative and creative possibilities aimed at improving society and the state. I feel certain that in the years to come we will continue to operate as a testing ground, drawing on the fruits of science and technology to determine the best and most satisfying ways of living in a country geared to the future. The highest standards of health care, educational practice, and cultural and recreational facilities will flow from research and development in the natural sciences, as well as in automation, computer science, information technology, communication, transportation, and biotechnology. I believe it is possible to create such a pilot plant state by encouraging the development of science-based high technology industry and agriculture. Once it gains momentum, this core of activity will contribute significantly to the economic growth and prosperity of the country. In this pilot plant state, I would like to see a free, pluralistic society, a democracy whose citizens live by the rule of law, and a welfare state in which public services are efficiently handled. Great emphasis will be laid on excellence in science and research, literature, and the arts, thus enriching the intellectual and cultural life of every citizen.

We Jews are eternal optimists. We have always believed, even in the depths of our despair, that the Messiah will come, even if he tarries a little. I am sure that ultimately we will create our model society geared for life in the twenty-first century and founded on the great moral and ethical tenets that we have held sacred since ancient times.

Address correspondence to: ephraim.katzir@weizmann.ac.il.

REFERENCES

1. Woodward, R. B., and Schramm, C. H. (1947) Synthesis of protein analogs. *J. Am. Chem. Soc.* **69,** 551–552
2. Stahmann, M. A. (ed) (1962) *Polyamino Acids, Polypeptides and Proteins*, p. 347, University of Wisconsin Press, Madison, WI
3. Katchalski, E., Sela, M., Silman, H. I., and Berger, A. (1964) Polyamino acids as protein models. In: *The Proteins* (Neurath, H., ed) Vol. 2, pp. 405–581, Academic Press, New York
4. Katchalski-Katzir, E. (1993) Immobilized enzymes—learning from past successes and failures. *Trends Biotechnol.* **11,** 471–478
5. Green, H., and Wang, N. (1994) Codon reiteration and the evolution of proteins. *Proc. Natl. Acad. Sci. U. S. A.* **91,** 4298–4302
6. Bar-Eli, A., and Katchalski-Katzir, E. (1960) A water-insoluble trypsin derivative and its use as a trypsin column. *Nature* **188,** 856–857
7. Katchalski-Katzir, E., and Sela, M. (1958) Biological properties of poly-α-amino acids. *Adv. Protein Chem.* **13,** 243–475
8. Goldstein, L., and Katchalski-Katzir, E. (1976) Immobilized enzymes—a survey. In: *Immobilized Enzyme Principles. Series Applied Biochemistry and Bioengineering* (Wingard, L. B., Jr., Katchalski-Katzir, E., and Goldstein, L., eds) Vol. 1, pp. 1–22, Academic Press, New York
9. Eisenstein, M., and Katchalski-Katzir, E. (2004) On proteins, grids, correlations, and docking. *C. R. Biol.* **327,** 409–420
10. Scherf, T., Kasher, R., Balass, M., Fridkin, M., Fuchs, S., and Katchalski-Katzir, E. (2001) A β-hairpin structure in a 13 mer peptide that binds α-BTX with high affinity and neutralizes its toxicity. *Proc. Natl. Acad. Sci. U. S. A.* **98,** 6629–6634
11. Natarajan, V., Zaltsman, Y., Somjen, D., Gayer, B., Boopathi, E., Kasher, R., Kulik, T., Katchalski-Katzir, E., and Kohen, F. (2002) A synthetic peptide with estrogen-like activity derived from a phage display peptide library. *Peptides* **23,** 570–580

THE JOURNAL OF BIOLOGICAL CHEMISTRY

Vol. 280, No. 19, Issue of May 13, pp. 18553–18557, 2005
Printed in U.S.A.

Reflections

A PAPER IN A SERIES COMMISSIONED TO CELEBRATE THE CENTENARY OF THE JBC IN 2005

JBC Centennial
1905–2005
100 Years of Biochemistry and Molecular Biology

An NIH Career: from Bedside to Basic Research and Back

Published, JBC Papers in Press, March 28, 2005, DOI 10.1074/jbc.X500002200

Ira Pastan

From the Laboratory of Molecular Biology, Center for Cancer Research, NCI, National Institutes of Health, Bethesda, Maryland 20892-4264

I was trained as a physician at Tufts Medical School where I had the opportunity to work in the laboratory of Ted Astwood, a premier endocrine researcher. This was my first taste of research, and I found it so exciting that in the summer of 1956, I actually braved a hurricane in order to go to the laboratory to finish an experiment. After medical school, I spent 2 years at Yale as an intern and assistant resident in internal medicine and then came to NIH in 1959 as a clinical associate in the Clinical Endocrinology Branch (CEB). My plan was to have a career in clinical medicine or clinical research.

At CEB I cared for patients with endocrine disorders and carried out research in the thyroid area, beginning to study the mechanism of action of thyroid-stimulating hormone (TSH). I enjoyed this research so much that when the 2 years were over I decided to pursue a career in basic research instead of clinical medicine. To do this successfully, however, I needed more training in biochemistry. NIH was growing then and was full of bright, interesting young people, several of whom have become close lifelong friends. One of these friends, Roy Vagelos, was working with Earl Stadtman. He encouraged me to apply for a postdoctoral position in Earl's laboratory, which I did. I was accepted, and for the next 2 years I was immersed in microbial biochemistry. After this I returned to the Clinical Endocrinology Branch as an independent investigator and began my own studies.

I went back to working on the mechanism of TSH action and expanded my efforts into studies on other peptide hormones and on cyclic AMP, the second messenger, which had just been discovered by Earl Sutherland. I spent the next 10 years studying hormone action and how cyclic AMP works. I was interested in studying the early steps in hormone action, and working with Jesse Roth, we used several new approaches to show that TSH and ACTH specifically bound to receptors on the surface of cells (1–3). I had also started studying the mechanism of action of cyclic AMP using the thyroid gland, but I decided to switch to *Escherichia coli* because I thought it would be much easier to solve the problem by studying this simple model organism. In these studies I worked very closely with Bob Perlman; we found that cyclic AMP had a major role in controlling gene expression in *E. coli* and subsequently showed it did this by producing an allosteric change in a specific cyclic AMP-binding protein (CRP). This change increased the affinity of CRP for DNA sequences in the promoter of many genes (4–6). As a consequence, transcription was initiated and gene activity increased. This was the first example of positive control of gene expression. Before our studies, the major mechanism of gene regulation was thought to be repression, as exemplified by studies on the lac repressor. I had several talented fellows who contributed to this project, including Harold Varmus, who says he became seriously interested in research while working in my laboratory. He joined my laboratory to continue his training in endocrinology but got converted into a molecular biologist instead.

By then I had moved to the National Cancer Institute where I started the Laboratory of Molecular Biology. I wanted to work on cancer, and I started by studying some of the special properties of cancer cells, such as their abnormal adhesion and motility. This, in turn, led to early studies on fibronectin with Ken Yamada (7) and collagen with Benoit de Crombrugghe and to the isolation of the first cDNA clones encoding collagen and fibronectin, proteins involved in cell adhesion and thought to be altered in cancer (8, 9).

Returning to my interest in peptide hormones, I began to investigate how important growth and regulatory factors like EGF and insulin interacted with cells; to visualize this interaction Mark Willingham and I used fluorescently labeled growth factors. We were able to visualize these proteins binding to the cell surface (10) and then entering living cells in vesicular structures (11). Mark designed and built a large part of the equipment by himself. We called this method video intensification microscopy; improved forms of this type of microscope are now standard equipment in all cell biology laboratories.

Around 1990, I made a major decision to change the focus of my research from basic to clinical and to use the skills I had developed in molecular and cell biology to develop a new approach to cancer treatment. After many years of effort we have recently had remarkable success in bringing patients with one type of advanced leukemia into complete remission using one of the agents we designed and produced. This article briefly chronicles how this came about.

Developing new treatments for cancer is something that attracts many physician researchers trained in the biological sciences. It particularly interested me because I was working in the National Cancer Institute and surrounded by scientists interested in cancer. For a variety of reasons very few scientists are able to undertake this type of research although we all hope (and often state in our grant applications) that our basic research will have a useful medical application. In 1983–1985, while we were investigating how polypeptide hormones and viruses enter cells, we employed a powerful bacterial toxin, *Pseudomonas* exotoxin A (PE), to help us in our studies. This came about because a new postdoctoral fellow, David FitzGerald, had recently joined our laboratory, and his thesis project had involved extensive studies on this exotoxin. After we had carried out just a few experiments with PE, we became very impressed by its potent cell-killing activity. For example, if the toxin is injected directly into the cytosol of a cell, it only requires a few molecules to kill that cell. The toxin catalyzes the ADP-ribosylation of elongation factor 2, which leads, by a still obscure mechanism, to programmed cell death. This potent activity prompted us to try to use this toxin to kill cancer cells by attaching it to an antibody to make what is called an immunotoxin. These are molecules composed of an antibody or an antibody fragment attached to a protein toxin.

I wanted to do something new, and I believed I could be successful in the immunotoxin field because much of my research career had been devoted to research relevant to this goal. I had studied how protein hormones bound to receptors and how they were internalized by cells. I also had the skills in molecular biology needed to make recombinant proteins. At that time many investigators were making immunotoxins in an effort to kill cancer cells and were using a variety of different plant and bacterial toxins to do so. We thought PE would have advantages over other toxins being used to make immunotoxins. One advantage was that it was not glycosylated the way most of the plant toxins being studied were and did not stick nonspecifically to cells. It was also easy to produce in large amounts in *E. coli*. One of the missions of the intramural research program at NIH is to carry out important but high risk research. This project clearly fell into this category.

The discovery of monoclonal antibodies by Köhler and Milstein (12) immediately led to the expectation that such antibodies would be useful in the treatment of cancer. This expectation has been fulfilled in recent years as is exemplified by the approval by the FDA of several antibodies for the treatment of cancer. Some examples are Rituxan for the treatment of lymphomas, Herceptin for the treatment of breast cancer, and Avastin for treating many different cancers. Rituxan and Herceptin bind to an antigen (protein) on the surface of the cancer cells and mobilize the immune system to kill the cancer cell. Avastin inactivates VEGF, an important growth factor for new blood vessels required for tumors to grow. Unfortunately, many cancers do not respond to therapy with unmodified antibodies. Potential ways to achieve cancer cell killing is to attach radioisotopes, small molecular weight drugs, and protein toxins to the antibody.

Many bacteria make protein toxins; they use these toxins to destroy cells and to obtain nutrients from the cells they have killed to support their growth. This invasive process must have begun soon after eukaryotic organisms evolved (at least hundreds of millions of years ago), and evolution has resulted in very potent toxins that enter and kill target cells. Because the toxins enter cells utilizing pathways and proteins that are essential for cell survival, toxin-resistant cells occur infrequently, and we do not expect that cancer cells will become immunotoxin-resistant as frequently as they become resistant to standard chemotherapy.

Chemotherapeutic agents are effective in cancer treatment because cancer cells are more effectively killed by these agents than normal cells are. The biochemical basis for this response is not clearly understood although recent studies on pathways of apoptosis have helped clarify some aspects of this selective response. Immunotoxins selectively kill cells that express the target protein to which the immunotoxin binds. Cells that do not bind to the immunotoxin are not killed. An ideal target is a protein that is present on the surface of a cancer cell and not on a normal cell so that the normal cell is not affected. Because this rarely occurs, one must instead find a protein target that is expressed (and preferably highly expressed) on cancer cells and is not expressed on normal cells of essential organs like the liver, kidney, brain, etc. Expression on cells that are not essential for survival and that are rapidly renewed from antigen-negative stem cells is acceptable. One popular class of therapeutic targets is differentiation antigens that are expressed on non-essential cells and on cancers derived from these cells. Examples are CD20 and CD22 on B cells and B cell malignancies, CD25 on T cells and T cell malignancies, and CD33 on monocytes and myelocytic leukemias. The normal blood cells that are killed by therapy targeted to these antigens are soon replaced from antigen-negative precursor cells that are not killed by the treatment.

To produce a highly effective immunotoxin, we needed to know the structure of the toxin and the function of each of its domains. Fortunately McKay, Collier, and colleagues (13) had determined the crystallographic structure of PE and demonstrated that it had 3 major domains. My postdoctoral fellow Jaulang Hwang then cloned and expressed each of these domains in *E. coli* and determined their functions. He showed that domain Ia is the cell binding domain, domain II is required to translocate the toxin across a cellular membrane into the cytosol, and domain III contains the ADP-ribosylation activity that inactivates EF2 and induces programmed cell death (14).

Antibodies are large proteins with many different functions. Antigen binding is located in the Fv portion at the amino terminus of the antibody molecule. We decided to replace domain Ia of the toxin (the cell recognition domain) with the Fv portion of an antibody that could direct the toxin to an antigen on the surface of a cancer cell. We initially chose to target cells expressing CD25 and to employ an anti-CD25 antibody to do this. Tom Waldmann at NCI had isolated a hybridoma making this antibody (15). Using just the antigen-binding fragment of the antibody, my postdoctoral fellow Vijay Chaudhary employed a new method of producing a small antigen-binding fragment (single chain Fv) in which genetic engineering was used to connect the light and heavy chains of the Fv together using a small peptide linker. He then connected the single-chain Fv directly to a toxin fragment containing the translocating and ADP-ribosylation domains of PE. The new chimeric protein was produced in *E. coli* and shown to selectively kill CD25-expressing cells (16).

For us this experiment was a milestone in the development of recombinant immunotoxin therapy, because it clearly showed one could design and produce a powerful and specific cell-killing agent using a combination of protein design and genetic engineering. Subsequently we have produced a variety of other single-chain immunotoxins using Fvs reacting with different antigens and a 38-kDa fragment of PE, termed PE38. We were surprised to find that single-chain Fvs of many antibodies are not stable at 37 °C because of dissociation of the light and heavy chains. To overcome this instability, B. K. Lee designed, and we genetically engineered and produced, Fvs in which the two antibody chains are held together by a disulfide bond instead of by a peptide linker (17). The disulfide bond is located in the framework region of the Fv distant from the complementary determining regions (CDRs) and therefore does not interfere with antigen binding. It is strategically located so that the same positions in the Fvs can be used for almost all antibodies. These disulfide-linked Fvs are used for all our current immunotoxins.

CD22 is a differentiation antigen found on B cells and most B cell malignancies. Using a monoclonal antibody reacting with CD22, David FitzGerald, Robert Kreitman, and I made a disulfide-linked immunotoxin (BL22) and showed that it was very active in killing malignant human cells growing in cell culture that expressed CD22. We also showed that BL22 produced complete remissions of B cell tumors growing in mice and that BL22 was well tolerated when given to various types of animals. With this safety and efficacy data and the help of a special recombinant protein production unit in the National Cancer Institute, we had sufficient amounts of BL22 produced to carry out a phase 1 clinical trial in humans.

The purpose of a phase 1 trial is to establish the safe dose of a drug. To do this, patients are treated at a very low dose, and the dose is gradually increased to one at which no serious side effects occur. In cancer treatment it is usually necessary to use a near toxic dose of drug to kill the cancer cells, so it is essential to determine the maximum amount of drug that can be given safely. This is different from the therapy of infections with antibiotics, where the effective dose is usually well below that causing serious side effects. To carry out these trials the NCI gave us resources to set up our own clinical team to treat patients. This team is led by Robert Kreitman, a physician scientist who had joined my group because he, like us, believed immunotoxins could be developed as a new cancer treatment. Because BL22 had never been given to patients, we began at a very low dose (about 200 μg per dose given every other day for 3 doses) and gradually increased this dose. The immunotoxin is given intravenously so that it can reach almost all cells in the body: normal cells and cancer cells. And because this agent is designed to kill cells expressing CD22, we were only allowed to evaluate the drug in patients with cancers expressing CD22 on their surface. These include many lymphomas, chronic lymphocytic leukemia, and a less common disease called hairy cell leukemia (HCL).

Patients with leukemia die because they have low numbers of normal cells in their blood. Low neutrophil counts lead to infections, low platelets to uncontrolled bleeding, and low red cells to severe fatigue. This occurs because the cancer cells occupy the bone marrow and produce substances that prevent the production of normal blood cells. We knew from laboratory studies that cells from patients with HCL have larger numbers of CD22 molecules on their surface than other malignancies, and we therefore expected these patients would have a strong response to BL22. Even though we started at very low dose level, we were amazed to see responses in patients with HCL at low doses, and as we raised the dose the responses were more frequent and more dramatic (18). The most obvious response was a fall in the leukemic cells in the blood; usually these completely disappeared. This fall in leukemic cells in the blood was accompanied by clearing of cancer cells from the bone marrow and spleen, sites at which the leukemic cells reside. Not only did the cancer cells disappear, but the levels of normal cells in the blood (neutrophils, platelets, and red cells) returned to normal levels.

This clinical experiment, in which more than half of the patients with an advanced malignancy were able to resume a normal life, was certainly the most rewarding experiment in my research career. Our goal now is to expand this therapeutic approach to other malignancies. There are several obstacles to overcome. These include finding appropriate target antigens on other cancers and preventing the formation of antibodies to the bacterial toxin that limit the number of cycles of therapy that can be given. Fortunately, patients with B cell malignancies such as HCL and CLL and some lymphomas have an impaired immune system and do not often make neutralizing antibodies to the immunotoxin. Therefore, these patients can receive many treatment cycles if necessary. However, patients with other types of cancer have normal immune systems and do make neutralizing antibodies after one, or at the most two, treatment cycles, and they cannot be re-treated. We are working now on how to solve this problem.

I have spent my entire research career at NIH. I do not believe this immunotoxin program would have been possible at any other institution, because it would have been regarded as too high risk to justify the funding needed to make it work.

Address correspondence to: pastani@mail.nih.gov.

REFERENCES

1. Pastan, I., Roth, J., and Macchia, V. (1966) *Proc. Natl. Acad. Sci. U. S. A.* **56,** 1802–1809
2. Lefkowitz, R., Roth, J., Pricer, W., and Pastan, I. (1970) *Proc. Natl. Acad. Sci. U. S. A.* **65,** 745–752
3. Lefkowitz, R., Roth, J., and Pastan, I. (1970) *Science* **170,** 633–635
4. Pastan, I., and Perlman, R. (1970) *Science* **169,** 339–344
5. Varmus, H. E., Perlman, R. L., and Pastan, I. (1970) *J. Biol. Chem.* **245,** 6366–6372
6. de Crombrugghe, B., Chen, B., Anderson, W. B., Gottesman, M. E., Perlman, R. L., and Pastan, I. (1971) *J. Biol. Chem.* **246,** 7343–7348
7. Yamada, K., Yamada, S., and Pastan, I. (1976) *Proc. Natl. Acad. Sci. U. S. A.* **73,** 1217–1221
8. Fagan, J. B., Pastan, I., and de Crombrugghe, B. (1980) *Nucleic Acids Res.* **8,** 3055–3064
9. Sobel, M. E., Yamamoto, T., Adams, S. L., DiLauro, R., Avvedimento, V. E., de Crombrugghe, B., and Pastan, I. (1978) *Proc. Natl. Acad. Sci. U. S. A.* **75,** 5846–5850
10. Willingham, M. C., and Pastan, I. (1978) *Cell* **13,** 501–507
11. Schlessinger, J., Shechter, Y., Cuatrecasas, P., Willingham, M., and Pastan, I. (1978) *Proc. Natl. Acad. Sci.*

U. S. A. **75,** 5353–5357

12. Köhler, G., and Milstein, C. (1975) *Nature* **256,** 495–497
13. Allured, V. S., Collier, R. J., Carroll, S. F., and McKay, D. B. (1986) *Proc. Natl. Acad. Sci. U. S. A.* **83,** 1320–1324
14. Hwang, J., FitzGerald, D. J. P., Adhya, S., and Pastan, I. (1987) *Cell* **48,** 129–136
15. Uchiyama, T., Broder, S., and Waldmann, T. A. (1981) *J. Immunol.* **126,** 1393–1397
16. Chaudhary, V. K., Queen, C., Junghans, R. P., Waldmann, T. A., FitzGerald, D. J., and Pastan, I. (1989) *Nature* **339,** 394–397
17. Brinkmann, U., Reiter, Y., Jung, S.-H., Lee, B., and Pastan, I. (1993) *Proc. Natl. Acad. Sci. U. S. A.* **90,** 7538–7542
18. Kreitman, R. J., Wilson, W. H., Bergeron, K., Raggio, M., Stetler-Stevenson, M., FitzGerald, D. J., and Pastan, I. (2001) *N. Engl. J. Med.* **345,** 241–247

THE JOURNAL OF BIOLOGICAL CHEMISTRY
© 2005 by The American Society for Biochemistry and Molecular Biology, Inc.

Vol. 280, No. 24, Issue of June 17, pp. 22557–22559, 2005
Printed in U.S.A.

Reflections

A PAPER IN A SERIES COMMISSIONED TO CELEBRATE THE CENTENARY OF THE JBC IN 2005

JBC Centennial
1905–2005
100 Years of Biochemistry and Molecular Biology

Origins

Published, JBC Papers in Press, April 19, 2005, DOI 10.1074/jbc.X500003200

Boris Magasanik

From the Department of Biochemistry, Massachusetts Institute of Technology, Cambridge, Massachusetts 02139-4307

Reflecting on my scientific career, I discovered that one of my papers published in 1952 (1) described the incidental observations that were the origin of the major portion of my subsequent scientific work.

I had started my independent research career in 1949 at the Department of Bacteriology and Immunology of Harvard Medical School, having obtained my Ph.D. in biochemistry at Columbia University in 1948. My thesis, carried out under the supervision of Erwin Chargaff, dealt with the stereochemistry of an enzymatic reaction, the oxidation of isomers of inositol to mono- or diketones by *Acetobacter suboxydans* (2). I therefore chose for my independent research the investigation of the pathway of *myo*-inositol degradation that enables *Klebsiella aerogenes* (then called *Aerobacter aerogenes*) to use this cyclitol as the sole source of carbon and energy. These studies led many years later to the identification of a series of enzymatic reactions responsible for the degradation of *myo*-inositol to CO_2 and the glycolytic intermediates dihydroxyacetone phosphate and acetyl-CoA (3). I was intrigued by the observation that the ability to degrade inositol was not constitutive but adaptive in that the cells acquired it after exposure to inositol (4). I therefore decided, in collaboration with a visitor from Japan, Dr. Daizo Ushiba, to use amino acid- and purine-requiring mutants to investigate whether this adaptation required the synthesis of proteins and nucleic acids (1). Our results supported the view that protein synthesis played a role in this adaptation; however, at about the same time Jacques Monod at the Pasteur Institute similarly found that the induced synthesis of β-galactosidase by *Escherichia coli* did not occur in the absence of a required amino acid (5) and subsequently proved that induction resulted in the synthesis *de novo* of this enzyme (6). Our results, particularly since the enzymes responsible for the degradation of *myo*-inositol had not yet been discovered, did not significantly contribute to the elucidation of the problem of induced enzyme synthesis.

However, the mutants we had isolated for this investigation proved to have unexpected properties. One mutant had a specific requirement for guanine and was found to excrete xanthosine (7), suggesting that xanthosine-5-P was an intermediate in the conversion of IMP to GMP. Further study of the interconversions of purine nucleotides resulted in the discovery of the enzymes responsible for this conversion (8, 9) as well as of GMP reductase, which catalyzes the NADPH-dependent reduction of GMP to IMP (10). In addition, our studies revealed that the nitrogen 1-carbon 2 portion of the purine ring was the precursor of the nitrogen 1-carbon 2 portion of the imidazole ring of histidine and demonstrated that the synthesis of the histidine precursor imidazoleglycerol phosphate from ATP, phosphoribosyl pyrophosphate, and glutamine resulted in the formation of the nucleotide of aminoimidazole carboxamide, which could be converted to IMP (the precursor of AMP and GMP (11)). The resulting cyclic network responsible for the synthesis of histidine and the interconversion of purine nucleotides was shown to be regulated by feedback inhibition of the critical enzymes by AMP, GMP, and histidine (12).

The properties of another mutant that had been isolated for our study of adaptation to inositol were also very interesting. This mutant required 30 times as much histidine for full growth when inositol rather than glucose served as the major source of carbon (1). We discovered that *K. aerogenes* has the ability to produce a series of four enzymes capable of converting histidine to glutamate, ammonia, and formamide. These enzymes allow histidine to serve as the source of carbon and nitrogen for the growth of this organism. We found that the presence of glucose, but not of inositol, in the growth medium prevents the synthesis of these enzymes (13, 14). In this manner glucose allows histidine, and in the case of *E. coli*, tryptophan, to fulfill its specific role in the synthesis of protein rather than to serve as a source of energy and carbon, which are more effectively produced by the degradation of glucose. This consideration led me to propose the name "catabolite repression" for this effect of glucose (15). According to this view, the high intracellular concentration of catabolites derived from glucose prevents the synthesis of enzymes whose activities would result in the formation of the same catabolites at a rate lower than that from other sources of carbon and energy.

We were subsequently able to identify a site closely linked to the promoter of the *lac* operon as the site responsible for the susceptibility of β-galactosidase to catabolite repression and to show that mutations in the promoter could make *lac* expression resistant to catabolite repression (16, 17). The site closely linked to the promoter was later identified as the binding site for CAP-cyclic AMP, which is required for the transcription of this operon.

Our studies on the genetics of the *hut* (histidine utilization) system in *Salmonella enterica* (serovar typhimurium) and in *K. aerogenes* showed that the genes for the four enzymes required for histidine degradation and a gene coding for a repressor capable of blocking the transcription of these genes are organized as two linked operons. The repressor is inactivated by urocanate, the product of histidase, the enzyme catalyzing the first step of the pathway. The observation that the gene coding for the repressor is a member of one of these operons was the first example of autogenous regulation of gene expression (these studies are reviewed in Ref. 18).

Even more important for the later work of my laboratory was the observation that the ability of glucose to prevent the synthesis of the enzymes required by *K. aerogenes* to degrade histidine could apparently be overcome by growing the cells in a medium containing glucose as the source of carbon and histidine as the sole source of nitrogen (19). This observation resulted in the discovery of a previously unknown global regulatory system responding to the availability of ammonia, the preferred nitrogen source of bacteria and fungi. We made this discovery when we examined the ability of a mutant of *K. aerogenes* requiring cyclic AMP to grow in media in which histidine either served as the sole source of carbon or served as the sole source of nitrogen with glucose as the source of carbon (20). We found that cyclic AMP, known to be essential for the synthesis of enzymes subject to catabolite repression, was required when histidine served as the source of carbon but not when it served as the source of nitrogen. Apparently in the latter condition an activator other than CAP-cyclic AMP was able to activate the expression of the *hut* operons. We also found that not only the expression of the *hut* genes but also the expression of the *put* genes coding for the enzyme and permease required for the utilization of proline (20) and the expression of *glnA*, the structural gene for glutamine synthetase, could be activated by substituting a non-preferred source of nitrogen for ammonia (20, 21).

All cellular nitrogen is derived either from the amino nitrogen of glutamate or the amide nitrogen of glutamine. Our discovery showed that the presence of ammonia, the preferred source of nitrogen, prevents the expression of genes coding for the enzymes able to produce the nitrogen required for the synthesis of glutamate and glutamine from other, non-preferred sources of nitrogen. The exploration of this nitrogen regulation has been the major subject of the studies of my laboratory for the last 30 years.

Our studies of this problem in enteric bacteria led to the discovery of the previously unknown σ factor, σ^{54}, the discovery that promoters using σ^{54}-RNA polymerase require activation by an activator binding to sites far from the promoter, an interaction that requires bending of the intervening DNA, and the discovery of two-component signal transduction. These studies are reviewed in Refs. 22 and 23.

We also began to study the problem of nitrogen regulation in *Saccharomyces cerevisiae* (24). We found that the activation of the expression of nitrogen-regulated genes requires one of two activators that recognize the nucleotide sequence 5′-GATAAG-3′ of an enhancer located upstream of the genes subject to this regulation. The activator Gln3p in the presence of glutamine binds to the product of the *URE2* gene and is thereby prevented from entering the nucleus to bind to the enhancer. These studies are reviewed in Ref. 25.

My scientific career reflects an aspect of the progress of microbial biochemistry in the last 50 years. From the study of glycolysis to the identification of the metabolic pathways responsible for the synthesis of the building blocks of proteins and nucleic acids to the elucidation of the genetics and molecular biology of the regulation of gene expression.

Acknowledgment—I thank Hilda Harris-Ransom for the preparation of the manuscript.

Address correspondence to: bmag@mit.edu.

REFERENCES

1. Ushiba, D., and Magasanik, B. (1952) Effects of auxotrophic mutations on the adaptation to inositol degradation in *Aerobacter aerogenes. Proc. Soc. Exp. Biol. Med.* **80,** 626–632
2. Magasanik, B. (1994) A charmed life. *Annu. Rev. Microbiol.* **48,** 1–24
3. Anderson, W. A., and Magasanik, B. (1971) The pathway of *myo*-inositol degradation in *Aerobacter aerogenes.* Conversion of 2-deoxy-5-keto-D-gluconic acid to glycolytic intermediates. *J. Biol. Chem.* **246,** 5662–5675
4. Magasanik, B. (1953) Enzymatic adaptation in the metabolism of cyclitols in *Aerobacter aerogenes. J. Biol. Chem.* **205,** 1007–1018
5. Monod, J., Pappenheimer, A. M., Jr., and Cohen-Bazire, G. (1952) The kinetics of the biosynthesis of β-glactosidase in *Escherichia coli* as a function of growth. *Biochim. Biophys. Acta* **9,** 648–660
6. Hogness, D. S., Cohn, M., and Monod, J. (1955) Studies on the induced synthesis of beta-galactosidase in *Escherichia coli*: the kinetics and mechanism of sulfur incorporation. *Biochim. Biophys. Acta* **16,** 99–116
7. Magasanik, B., and Brooke, M. S. (1953) The accumulation of xanthosine by a guanineless mutant of *Aerobacter aerogenes. J. Biol. Chem.* **206,** 83–87
8. Magasanik, B., Moyed, H. S., and Gehring, L. B. (1957) Enzymes essential for the biosynthesis of nucleic acid guanine:inosine 5′-phosphate dehydrogenase of *Aerobacter aerogenes. J. Biol. Chem.* **226,** 339–350
9. Moyed, H. S., and Magasanik, B. (1957) Enzymes essential for the biosynthesis of nucleic acid guanine:xanthosine 5′-phosphate aminase of *Aerobacter aerogenes. J. Biol. Chem.* **226,** 351–363
10. Mager, J., and Magasanik, B. (1960) Guanosine 5′-phosphate reductase and its role in the interconversion of purine nucleotides. *J. Biol. Chem.* **235,** 1474–1478
11. Moyed, H. S., and Magasanik, B. (1960) The biosynthesis of the imidazole ring of histidine. *J. Biol. Chem.* **235,** 149–153
12. Magasanik, B., and Karibian, D. (1960) Purine nucleotide cycles and their metabolic role. *J. Biol. Chem.* **235,** 2672–2681
13. Magasanik, B. (1955) The metabolic control of histidine assimilation and dissimilation in *Aerobacter aerogenes. J. Biol. Chem.* **213,** 557–569
14. Magasanik, B., and Bowser, H. R. (1955) The degradation of histidine by *Aerobacter aerogenes. J. Biol. Chem.* **213,** 571–580
15. Magasanik, B. (1961) Catabolite repression. *Cold Spring Harbor Symp. Quant. Biol.* **26,** 249–256
16. Silverstone, A. E., Magasanik, B., Reznikoff, W. S., Miller, J. H., and Beckwith, J. R. (1969) Catabolite sensitive site of the *lac* operon. *Nature* **221,** 1012–1014
17. Silverstone, A. E., Arditti, R. R., and Magasanik, B. (1970) Catabolite-insensitive revertants of *lac* promoter mutants. *Proc. Natl. Acad. Sci. U. S. A.* **66,** 773–779
18. Magasanik, B. (1978) Regulation in the *hut* system. In: *The Operon* (Miller, J. H., and Reznikoff, W. S., eds) pp. 373–387, Cold Spring Harbor Laboratory, Cold Spring Harbor, NY
19. Neidhardt, F. C., and Magasanik, B. (1957) Reversal of the glucose inhibition of histidase biosynthesis in *Aerobacter aerogenes. J. Bacteriol.* **73,** 253–259
20. Prival, M. J., and Magasanik, B. (1971) Resistance to catabolite repression of histidase and proline oxidase during nitrogen-limited growth of *Klebsiella aerogenes. J. Biol. Chem.* **246,** 6288–6296
21. Prival, M. J., Brenchley, J. E., and Magasanik, B. (1973) Glutamine synthetase and the regulation of histidase formation in *Klebsiella aerogenes. J. Biol. Chem.* **248,** 4334–4344
22. Magasanik, B. (1996) Historical perspective. In: *Two-component Signal Transduction* (Hoch, J. A., and Silhavy, A. J., eds) pp. 1–5, ASM Press, Washington, D. C.
23. Magasanik, B. (1996) Regulation of nitrogen utilization. In: *Escherichia coli and Salmonella typhimurium*: *Cellular and Molecular Biology* (Neidhardt, F. C., ed) Vol. 1, pp. 1344–1356, ASM Press, Washington, D. C.
24. Mitchell, A. P., and Magasanik, B. (1984) Regulation of glutamine-repressible gene products by the *GLN3* function in *Saccharomyces cerevisiae. Mol. Cell. Biol.* **4,** 2758–2766
25. Magasanik, B., and Kaiser, C. A. (2002) Nitrogen regulation in *Saccharomyces cerevisiae. Gene (Amst.)* **290,** 1–18

THE JOURNAL OF BIOLOGICAL CHEMISTRY
© 2005 by The American Society for Biochemistry and Molecular Biology, Inc.

Vol. 280, No. 32, Issue of August 12, pp. 28829–28847, 2005
Printed in U.S.A.

Reflections

A PAPER IN A SERIES COMMISSIONED TO CELEBRATE THE CENTENARY OF THE JBC IN 2005

JBC Centennial
1905–2005
100 Years of Biochemistry and Molecular Biology

A Fascination with Enzymes:
The Journey Not the Arrival Matters

Published, JBC Papers in Press, June 7, 2005, DOI 10.1074/jbc.X500004200

Paul Talalay

From the Lewis B. and Dorothy Cullman Cancer Chemoprotection Center, Department of Pharmacology and Molecular Sciences, The Johns Hopkins University School of Medicine, Baltimore, Maryland 21205

My journey of medical discovery spans more than 50 years: first at the University of Chicago (1944–1948 and 1950–1963) and then at Johns Hopkins (since 1963). Although enzymes have been the central theme in all our studies and the thread that has connected them, the control of cancer has always been the ultimate goal.

Coming to America: Massachusetts Institute of Technology

I arrived in New York from war-torn England on July 8, 1940, soon after the evacuation of the Allied Expeditionary Force from Dunkirk and after a harrowing 10-day voyage across the U-boat-infested Atlantic. It was a beautiful sunny morning and my first view of the crystal clear Manhattan skyline that dwarfed the Statue of Liberty still remains, 65 years later, an indelible memory symbolic of peace, freedom, and a better future. It was the second major disruption in the life of our family. On March 31, 1933, my 10th birthday, soon after Hitler came to power, my Russian father made the courageous and visionary decision that we should immediately leave Germany where we were living and where I was born. On the next day, the "Boykott" of the Jewish department stores on the Kuhrfürstendamm in Berlin led to their looting and burning. After further wanderings, we found our way to England where we received a warm welcome. I learned English and went to school regularly for the first time. I was fortunate to go to Bedford School where the excellent teaching in science, and especially biology, directed my interests toward a career in medicine.

In the fall of 1940, I entered MIT as an undergraduate majoring in biology. A remarkable lecture and laboratory course in enzymology taught by Irwin W. Sizer sparked a passion for enzymes that has never left me. It was one of the first courses in enzymology taught anywhere. My laboratory project required the purification of liver catalase according to the method of Sumner and Dounce (1). It is staggering now to look back on the primitive state of protein purification in those days.

Much of my four undergraduate years at MIT was spent in an electron microscopy laboratory studying biological ultrastructure under the direction of Francis O. Schmitt. I started out as a dishwasher in the laboratory but before long was analyzing the electron micrographs and became involved in a war-time project on the ultrastructure of natural and synthetic rubber fibers, described in the first paper in which I was an author (2). When I was leaving MIT for the medical school of the University of Chicago, Schmitt suggested that I might explore opportunities for research with the urologist Charles Huggins. I recall Schmitt's prophetic but seemingly casual remark: "You might do much worse than work with Huggins." I could not have known then that Charles Huggins would become the dominant force that molded my professional career and indeed much of my life. Huggins, whose laboratory motto was *"Discovery is our Business"* (which I have adopted), introduced me to the joys of scientific discovery and nurtured my belief that I too would be able to make contributions to our joint "business."

FIG. 1. **Charles Huggins (*left*) and the author in the Ben May Laboratories for Cancer Research at the University of Chicago in 1964.** The Chinese inscription in the panel (*left*) may be translated: "To make discoveries is man's calling," or as Huggins put it succinctly in his laboratory motto: "Discovery is our Business."

I learned an unforgettable lesson: encouragement not intimidation is the tool for identifying and developing scientific talent and potential in the young (Fig. 1).

The First Chicago Period: "Chromogenic Substrates"

In 1944 I started medical school at the University of Chicago and began working in the laboratory of Charles Huggins in the Department of Surgery. He asked me to develop simpler methods than those that were then available for measuring serum acid and alkaline phosphatases. Huggins was the Professor and Chief of Urology. There was an atmosphere of intense excitement in his laboratory. With R. E. Stevens and Clarence V. Hodges, Huggins had recently published two classic papers (3, 4): "Studies on Prostatic Cancer I and II," which demonstrated the effects of castration, of estrogens, and of androgens on serum phosphatase levels in patients with extensive metastatic carcinoma of the prostate. They reported large clinical improvements in a significant number of these patients after orchiectomy and estrogen treatment. As a freshman medical student I was profoundly moved when I saw the remissions of the disease in some of these desperately ill patients. It was the first time that cancer had been shown not to be a wholly "autonomous disease" but sustained, as Huggins put it, "by hormones of the body that were normal in amounts and kind" (5). These discoveries were a major scientific breakthrough. I was inspired by the revelation that even advanced and disseminated cancer could be controlled, and from that time on my research interests never strayed far from the cancer problem. Charles Huggins' contributions were finally recognized by award of the Nobel Prize in Physiology or Medicine in 1966 "for his discoveries concerning hormonal treatment of prostatic cancer."

Huggins was convinced that assays of serum phosphatase activities had made his discoveries possible, and he continually advocated the use of highly quantitative methods for assessing disease status in clinical research. The phosphatases were "biomarkers" for the status of prostate cancer. Simpler methods were needed to measure their activities, and he suggested that the phosphate ester of phenolphthalein might be a suitable new colorless substrate that upon hydrolysis by phosphatases would give rise to colored phenolphthalein. The synthesis was relatively simple, and when Huggins first saw the red color resulting from hydrolysis of phenolphthalein phosphate by alkaline phosphatase, he immediately offered me a job in his laboratory at $50 per month, provided I quit working in the Admitting Office where I received $8 each Sunday for a 15-hour day. It was an easy decision. Our method was published in the *Journal of Biological Chemistry* in 1945 (6).

The phenolphthalein ester presented one technical problem: it was a diphosphate and hydrolysis led to two products with different spectral characteristics, thus complicating the

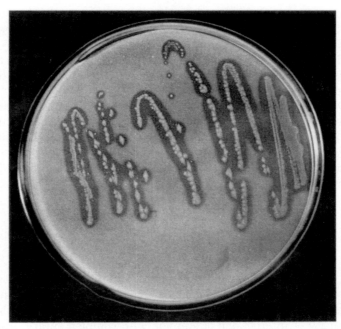

FIG. 2. **P. testosteroni growing on testosterone.** Fine particles of the steroid cause the opalescence of the agar, and the clearing around the bacterial colonies is due to solubilization and oxidation of testosterone (8).

kinetic behavior. Shortly thereafter, Oliver Lowry introduced *p*-nitrophenyl phosphate as a phosphatase substrate; its kinetics of hydrolysis was simple, and it became and remains the universally used substrate for measuring phosphatase activities.

Huggins was fascinated by the enzymatic conversions of colorless substrates to colored products and coined the term "chromogenic substrates," which was first used in our second paper describing the assay of β-glucuronidase (7). For this study, I isolated phenolphthalein monoglucuronide from the urine of rabbits dosed with phenolphthalein. This glucuronide was rapidly hydrolyzed by β-glucuronidase, its kinetic behavior was simple, and it has become the standard substrate for measuring β-glucuronidase activity. Chromogenic substrates have achieved widespread acceptance and now comprise countless examples.

The Second Chicago Period: Pseudomonas testosteroni and Enzymatic Transformations of Steroids

I transferred from Chicago to the Yale Medical School in 1946 so that I could spend more time with my family in New Haven where my father had been diagnosed with serious cardiovascular disease. After receiving the M.D. degree from Yale in 1948, I spent two very exciting years as a surgical House Officer at the Massachusetts General Hospital (1948–1950), a training period that played a major role in molding my scientific style. I returned to the University of Chicago on July 1, 1950 as an American Cancer Society-Damon Runyon Fund Postdoctoral Fellow and later that year was promoted to Assistant Professor in Charles Huggins' research group, which in 1951 became the Ben May Laboratory for Cancer Research. I wanted to work on steroid hormones to understand their mode of action and especially how androgens sustained and estrogens inhibited cancers of the prostate. At that time knowledge of the chemistry and stereochemistry of steroids was quite advanced, and there was a wealth of information on the structures of the many steroid metabolites found in the urine, but surprisingly not a single enzymatic transformation of steroids had been described.

The microbiologist Edward Adelberg suggested the possibility of advancing understanding of steroid enzymology by isolating bacterial auxotrophs that could grow on steroids as their sole source of carbon and energy. Thus I spent a most pleasant August 1951 at the Department of Microbiology of the University of California in Berkeley. From soil beneath a rosebush on the Berkeley campus I isolated a motile *Pseudomonas* that could grow on testosterone-containing medium as its only source of carbon and energy (8). It was named *P. testosteroni*. Manometric determinations of oxygen consumption revealed that under conditions in which carbon assimilation was blocked, *P. testosteroni* completely oxidized all 19 carbon atoms of testosterone to CO_2 by enzymes that were induced by steroids (Fig. 2).

In our initial 1952 paper (8) in *Nature* describing *P. testosteroni,* we noted that centrifuged cell-free extracts of the steroid-induced organism catalyzed the NADH-dependent (then known as DPNH, reduced diphosphopyridine nucleotide) reduction of the 17-ketone function of 4-androstene-3,17-dione to the 17β-hydroxyl group of testosterone. We even envisaged the analytical value of using this enzyme to estimate steroids by monitoring the oxidoreduction of NAD/NADH spectroscopically.

Hydroxysteroid Dehydrogenases (HSD)—P. testosteroni contained a family of enzymes catalyzing the nicotinamide nucleotide-dependent, reversible, and stereospecific interconversions of specific hydroxyl and carbonyl groups on the steroid skeleton and side chain. These enzymes were designated *hydroxysteroid dehydrogenases* (HSDs), with the appropriate positional and steric prefixes to specify the positions of the carbon atoms that were oxidized and the steric configurations of the reactive hydroxyl groups (Reaction 1).

$$\text{H} - \underset{|}{\overset{|}{\text{C}}} - \text{OH} \;+\; \text{NAD}^+ \;\rightleftharpoons\; \underset{/}{\overset{\backslash}{\text{C}}} = \text{O} \;+\; \text{NADH} \;+\; \text{H}^+$$

REACTION 1

The first two HSDs that were purified and characterized were a 3β-, 17β-, and 3α-hydroxysteroid dehydrogenase (9–12). Metabolic transformations of steroids could now be understood in enzymatic terms, and the specificity of interactions of steroids with complementary proteins could be elucidated. We believed then (erroneously) that detailed studies on the affinities and kinetics of the interactions of these enzymes or their mammalian counterparts with steroids might shed light on the biological specificity of steroids, their interactions with complementary intracellular proteins, and possibly their mode of action. In these early experiments on HSDs I was fortunate to have the highly skilled technical assistance of Marie M. Dobson and Philip I. Marcus. Philip went on to complete a Ph.D. and is now an internationally recognized virologist.

The important discovery of the estrogen receptor by my colleague Elwood Jensen diverted attention from our notion that steroid-transforming enzymes would provide insight into the mechanism of action of steroid hormones. Nevertheless, the availability of highly purified HSDs led to a number of new developments as discussed in the following paragraphs.

*Stereospecificity of Hydrogen Transfer from Nicotinamide Nucleotides—*Isolation of the first HSDs coincided with the classic demonstration by B. Vennesland and F. H. Westheimer and their colleagues at the University of Chicago that nicotinamide nucleotide-linked dehydrogenases promoted the direct and stereospecific transfer of a presumed hydride group between the 4-position of the dihydronicotinamide and the substrate. Birgit Vennesland, Frank Loewus, and H. Richard Levy determined the stereospecificity of hydrogen transfer catalyzed by our 17β-HSD (13). It was known then that alcohol, malic, and lactate dehydrogenases from a variety of sources all utilized the same diastereomeric hydrogen at position 4 of the dihydronicotinamide ring of NADH (later identified as having the 4S configuration by J. W. Cornforth). When 4-androstene-3,17-dione was converted to testosterone by 17β-HSD in the presence of deuterium-labeled NADD (prepared enzymatically from 2-deuteroethanol), surprisingly no deuterium was found in the testosterone. Although several possible explanations were considered, we established that 17β-HSD utilized the hydrogen on the opposite side (4R) from the previously studied dehydrogenases. This finding led to the realization that NAD(P)-linked dehydrogenases belong to two large classes that transfer, respectively, the 4S- or the 4R-hydrogen to and from NAD(P)H (13); 17β-HSD was the first representative of the family of enzymes that transferred the 4R-hydrogen.

*Equilibria of Oxidoreductions: Axial and Equatorial Conformations—*Direct measurements of the equilibria of the interconversions of hydroxy- and ketosteroids in relation to the configuration and conformation of their hydroxyl groups were made with purified HSDs. These reactions were easily reversible, and the equilibria could be shifted completely in the direction of oxidation or reduction. Accurate determination of the equilibrium constants of the oxidations of a variety of equatorial and axial hydroxyl substituents in solution provided the free energy differences between axial and equatorial conformations (14) and were in full agreement with the predictions of conformation theory.

*Analytical Applications of Hydroxysteroid Dehydrogenases—*The availability of purified HSDs of known positional and steric specificities led logically to their use for identification and quantification of steroids and groups of steroids on the basis of the stereospecific oxidoreduction of specific hydroxyl groups on the steroid skeleton and side chain and spectroscopic or fluorimetric determination of the accompanying changes in reduced nicotinamide nucleotides. This work continued for many years, beginning with the studies by Barbara Hurlock in the 1950s and subsequently by Donna Payne and Mikio Shikita. We attained sufficient analytic sensitivity to quantify steroids not only in urine but also in plasma. Ultimately, by use of the enzymatic cycling methods for nicotinamide nucleotides developed by Oliver Lowry, low picomole levels of steroids were estimated reliably (15). In the most recent contribution, a single step enzymatic assay was developed for 17-oxo- and 17-hydroxysteroids, based on their catalytic participation in the transfer of hydrogen from NADH to thionicotinamide-NAD by the transhydrogenase function of HSDs (see below) (16).

Although the principal value of these enzymatic methods was for the quantitative microanalyses of steroids, this was by no means their only usefulness. The HSDs were shown to be very valuable reagents for determining the steric configuration, the chemical and stereochemical purity of steroids, and for the resolution of synthetic ($\pm$)racemic steroids, as well as for the small scale stereospecific synthesis of steroids for chromatographic reference purposes.

Transhydrogenase Functions of Hydroxysteroid Dehydrogenases—One of the interesting (and enigmatic) properties of HSDs from animal tissues is their almost universal dual nucleotide specificity in contrast to the microbial enzymes, which were mostly NAD-dependent. I was aware of this but did not then (nor do I now) know how to assess its significance. One scientific excursion provided a scientific rationale although its ultimate importance remains in doubt.

In the mid-1950s, Claude A. Villee of Harvard reported that in the presence of isocitrate the reduction of NAD (but not of NADP) catalyzed by crude extracts of human placenta was accelerated by low concentrations of certain steroids, especially estradiol. At that time almost no credible effects of physiological concentrations of steroids on cell-free systems *in vitro* had been reported. The observed phenomenon was attributed to the presence of a steroid-stimulated NAD-dependent isocitrate dehydrogenase (ICD), which differed in this respect from the analogous and very much more active NADP-dependent ICD present in the same preparations. My colleague and dear friend H. Guy Williams-Ashman was intrigued by these findings. One day in the Fall of 1957, we were having lunch at the Quadrangle Club at the University of Chicago, and Guy scribbled on a paper napkin an imaginative explanation based on our knowledge that placental supernatant fractions also contained a 17β-HSD (studied by Lewis Engel) that interconverted estradiol and estrone and could utilize both nicotinamide nucleotides. That afternoon, we obtained a placenta from the Chicago Lying-in-Hospital (there were no concerns in those days about IRB approval or the hazards of human tissues) and showed that the stimulatory effect of estradiol on the NAD-linked ICD reaction was lost upon fractionation of placental supernatant fractions but could be restored by adding catalytic quantities of NADP. The apparent stimulation of the NAD-dependent ICD could be accounted for by the coupling of a "normal" steroid-insensitive NADP-specific ICD with the action of a soluble transhydrogenase which alone was steroid-dependent, as shown in Reaction 2.

$$\text{Isocitrate} + \text{NADP}^+ \longrightarrow \alpha\text{-ketoglutarate} + CO_2 + \text{NADPH} + H^+$$
$$\text{NADPH} + \text{NAD}^+ \longleftrightarrow \text{NADP}^+ + \text{NADH}$$
$$\overline{\text{Isocitrate} + \text{NAD}^+ \longrightarrow \alpha\text{-ketoglutarate} + CO_2 + \text{NADH} + H^+}$$

REACTION 2

We confirmed our suspicion that the steroid-dependent nicotinamide nucleotide transhydrogenase was indeed the 17β-HSD. The stimulatory effect of estradiol was unrelated to isocitrate and could be demonstrated equally well with any NADPH-generating system. We then established that the nicotinamide nucleotide transhydrogenase activity was promoted by the HSD, as shown in Scheme 1. These studies were published in two papers in *Proceedings of the National Academy of Sciences of the U. S. A.* in 1958 (17, 18). Our demonstration that oxidoreductions of steroid hormones by HSDs could promote reversible transfer of hydride groups between NAD(H) and NADP(H) was slowly accepted by others. Williams-Ashman and I hypothesized that these reactions could exercise cellular regulatory roles in adjusting the balance between NADH-dependent energy-generating oxidative reactions and NADPH-requiring cellular synthetic processes. There seemed to us to be a certain simple elegance to this proposal, but it received a less than enthusiastic reception by the scientific community. We envisaged a type of coenzymatic function of steroids that regulated the flow of reducing

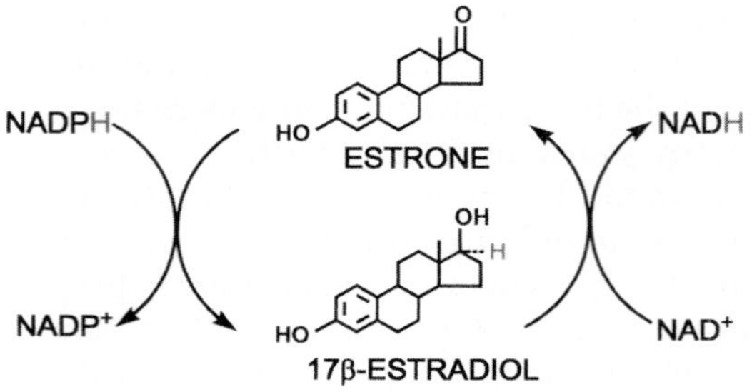

SCHEME 1

equivalents between the two large intracellular nicotinamide nucleotide pools. However, difficulties in obtaining experimental support for the importance of this process *in vivo* weakened our suggestion for its potential regulatory significance.

Other Microbiological Transformations of Steroids—H. Richard Levy (postdoctoral fellow) and S. J. Davidson (graduate student) identified three flavoproteins involved in the introduction of the Δ^1-, Δ^4-5α-, and Δ^4-5β-olefins into steroid Ring A (19–21). In another study, Richard Prairie, a graduate student, showed that the mechanism of lactonization of Ring D of testosterone to form testololactone involved oxidation of the 17β-hydroxyl group by an NAD-dependent 17β-HSD followed by action of an NADPH- and oxygen-requiring lactonase. Isotope incorporation and exchange experiments with $^{18}O_2$ and $H_2^{18}O$ established that the oxygen atom linking C-13 and C-17 in the six-membered D ring of the steroid lactone was derived from molecular oxygen. The lactonase mechanism was therefore formally similar to the Baeyer-Villiger oxidation of cyclic ketones to lactones by peracids (22).

At about this time, I left the University of Chicago and became the Director of the Department of Pharmacology and Experimental Therapeutics at the Medical School of Johns Hopkins University.

Studies on S-Adenosylmethionine

How the Microbial Degradation of Steroid Hormones Led to Inhibitors of the Synthesis of S-Adenosyl-L-methionine—Although we were intrigued by the undoubtedly intricate enzymatic pathways by which *P. testosteroni* could functionalize and completely oxidize all of the carbon atoms of testosterone ($C_{19}H_{28}O_2$) to carbon dioxide and water, we decided not to pursue this issue because it appeared to be only remotely relevant to the problems of medicine. Our limited studies focused on the enzymatic cleavage of steroid Ring A. Soluble extracts of steroid-induced *P. testosteroni* converted the A ring of 4-[^{14}C]androstene-3,17-dione to an unusual 6-carbon keto acid, 2-oxo-*cis*-4-hexenoic acid, which was rapidly aminated to 2-amino-*cis*-4-hexenoic acid (23, 24). (Fig. 3). Interestingly, much earlier, William Shive of the University of Texas (25) had observed that these conformationally restricted amino acids antagonized methionine-dependent bacterial growth, presumably because –CH=CH– and –S– groups are isosteric.

Therefore, we synthesized both the *cis* and *trans* isomers of the 6-carbon crotylglycines as well as their precursor oxo-acids. The potential of developing antitumor agents prompted us to undertake an extensive series of studies on conformationally restricted analogues of methionine as inhibitors of the methionine adenosyltransferase reaction. We selected adenosyltransferase preparations obtained from mammalian liver, bakers' yeast, and *Escherichia coli* as target enzymes. Postdoctoral fellows J. B. Lombardini, A. W. Coulter, Janice R. Sufrin, and T.-C. (David) Chou were my principal collaborators in this problem (26, 27). A large number of conformationally rigidified unsaturated and cyclic analogues were synthesized (*e.g.* 2-amino-4-hexynoic acid and 1-amino-3-methylcyclopentanecarboxylic acid). Unfortunately, several years of work did not uncover potent or species-selective enzyme inhibitors. The results were not promising, and we abandoned work on this project. Nevertheless, it was shown that inhibitors could depress levels of adenosylmethionine in tissues, and it provided an opportunity to undertake detailed kinetic studies of the enzymes synthesizing *S*-adenosyl-L-methionine (SAM).

In the course of these studies, we needed to quantify the combined effects of two or more inhibitors and to determine whether the effects were additive, synergistic, or antagonistic. David Chou undertook a formal analysis of these questions, and they developed into a major theme of his subsequent scientific life. Chou showed that the inhibition kinetics of two or more

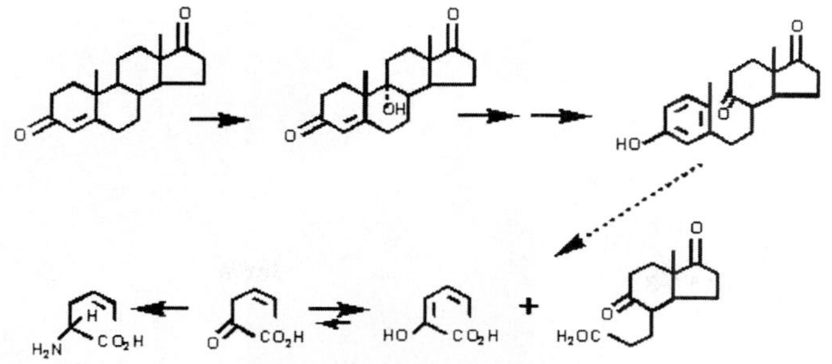

FIG. 3. **Microbial degradation of a steroid (Δ^4-androstene-3,17-dione) to a 2-ring carboxylic acid and 2-oxo-4-*cis*-hexenoic acid, which is aminated to *cis*-crotylglycine.**

reversible (but mutually exclusive) inhibitors (competitive, noncompetitive, or uncompetitive) could be described, irrespective of mechanism (sequential or ping-pong), by exceptionally simple equations that provided a rigorous definition for the summation, synergism, or antagonism of two or more inhibitors. Moreover, knowledge of the kinetic constants (K_m and V_{max}) for substrates and inhibitors was not required for this analysis (28). Chou then generalized these considerations to analyze the quantitative effects of a wide variety of inhibitors in cell, animal, and human systems. He developed a simple generalized relation, which he designated the *Median Effect Equation,* and computerized its use. This equation has become the standard tool for quantifying the effects of multiple drugs in systems varying in complexity from isolated enzymes to human diseases; it has been used to analyze thousands of chemotherapy studies worldwide (29, 30).

Absolute Configuration of the Sulfonium Center of S-Adenosylmethionine—By 1973, I had devoted 10 years to directing the Department of Pharmacology and Experimental Therapeutics at Johns Hopkins. It had been a satisfying but challenging experience. A number of outstanding faculty members had been appointed, including among others: Donald S. Coffey, Pedro Cuatrecasas, Cecil H. Robinson, and Solomon H. Snyder. Mackenzie Walser, a distinguished renal physiologist, was already a member of the faculty when I arrived. These individuals enjoyed international scientific reputations. A Ph.D. program in pharmacology was in place for the first time, the scope of our teaching had been expanded, and a mass spectrometry center had been established under the direction of Catherine C. Fenselau. However, my own research lagged. I was 50 years old, and the departmental and institutional demands of the directorship had left their mark on my science.

With support from a Guggenheim Fellowship, I took sabbatical leave to work with Professor John Warcup (Kappa) Cornforth, who was then head of the Milstead Laboratory for Chemical Enzymology at Shell Research in Sittingbourne, Kent. Australian by birth and trained under Robert Robinson at Oxford, Cornforth had spent the war as part of the British team that elucidated the structure of penicillin. A series of subsequent classical and very elegant studies on the stereochemistry of the biosynthesis of cholesterol and fatty acids (with George Popjak) were recognized by award of the Nobel Prize in Chemistry in 1975 for "work on the stereochemistry of enzyme-catalyzed reactions."

We spent a very happy year living in a tiny village in Kent (Bredgar) where my English wife Pamela enjoyed being "home" again, and my three daughters benefited from very successful exposures to British education. Kappa and his wife Rita (also a chemist) were most gracious hosts. It all seemed an idyllic time for us, but I could not have predicted at the outset that the sabbatical year would change the course of my professional career.

Cornforth suggested that I determine the absolute configuration of the sulfonium center of *S*-adenosyl-L-methionine (SAM). This compound was isolated and its structure was elucidated by Giulio Cantoni, who began his work on transmethylation mechanisms at Case Western Reserve University in Cleveland and has spent all of his subsequent scientific career at the NIH. Cantoni showed that the (−)-diastereomer participated preferentially in nearly all of its donor reactions. The molecule had defied numerous efforts at crystallization, and Cornforth suggested that the problem be solved by chemical degradation. He proposed a degradation scheme comprising the cleavage of the labile adenosylribose linkage by base, followed by periodate oxidation of the ribose moiety to provide (it was hoped) only one of the diastereomers of *S*-carboxymethyl-L-methionine (Fig. 4). The project was risky and technically demanding, because it was uncertain whether chirality would be preserved during the degradation and

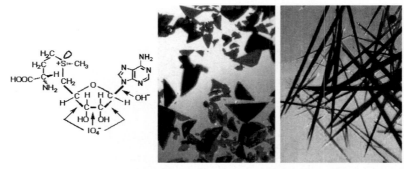

FIG. 4. *Left*, structure of *S*-adenosyl-L-methionine. The bonds cleaved by base and by periodate are indicated. The crystals of the diastereomeric polyiodides of carboxymethyl-L-methionine are shown: isomer A (*R*) (*center*), isomer B (*S*) (*right*).

whether the diastereomeric products could be obtained in adequate quantities for crystallization and establishment of configuration by x-ray crystallography. Fortunately, my professional future did not depend on the success of the outcome since grant-giving bodies were not exactly rushing to support an esoteric project of this type. Moreover, it was anticipated that the results could be summarized completely by a single letter: *S* or *R*. Earlier, W. H. Stein and S. Moore had separated the two diastereomers of *S*-carboxymethyl-L-methionine on an analytical scale by ion exchange chromatography, but we were not able to obtain adequate quantities for crystallization and chemical work by these methods. Cornforth recommended a more classical approach: separation by fractional crystallization. The polyiodide salts crystallized beautifully. The black crystals of the diastereomers had distinctive morphologies, and the shiny pyramids of the less soluble diastereomer could be separated mechanically from the long needles of the more soluble diastereomer (Fig. 4). Even my wife Pamela (a Ph.D. in Biochemistry from Cambridge) honed her experimental skills by sorting the crystals when I was away. As it turned out, the more soluble and more difficult to prepare diastereomer had the structure corresponding to the natural SAM. On hearing this, Cornforth remarked: "the desired isomer is always in the mother liquor."

The x-ray crystal structure was elucidated by Jenny P. Glusker and H. L. Carrell at Fox-Chase in Philadelphia on a more stable crystalline (2,4,6-trinitrobenzenesulfonate) derivative, which I prepared from one of the diastereomeric polyiodides. It took more than 3 years (long after I returned to Baltimore) to complete this project with the technical help of Scott Reichard, who subsequently went to medical school. The complete story was published in a single paper (31). It was the first report of the steric configuration of a naturally occurring sulfonium center: **S**.

On completion of the project, Cornforth observed: "You see, Paul, the classical methods are always more fun." He also offered an unsolicited assessment of my performance in his laboratory. In a Festschrift on the occasion of his 75th birthday, Cornforth wrote: "I think (Paul Talalay) enjoyed the bench work at Milstead like a boy on holiday, even the laborious initial separation of the A and B polyiodides, by picking out individual crystals." It was true. I had not realized how very much I enjoyed working at the bench. Just before Christmas 1973, I flew to Baltimore to inform Dr. Russell H. Morgan, the Dean of the Medical Faculty at Johns Hopkins, that I wished to relinquish the directorship of pharmacology to devote myself more fully to research. Morgan responded perceptively, graciously, and correctly: "You don't want me to talk you out of this decision, do you?" He created the Laboratory of Molecular Pharmacology for me, provided a budget, and recommended that I be named the first John Jacob Abel Distinguished Service Professor, a title that I continue to hold today. These generous administrative arrangements made it possible for me to remain in the same department that I had directed and to devote the last 25 years to devising strategies for chemoprotection against the risk of cancer.

Δ^5-3-Ketosteroid Isomerase (KSI): Diffusion-controlled Carbon-Hydrogen Bond Cleavage and Intramolecular Proton Transfer

Undoubtedly my longest and my most passionate enzymological love affair has been with Δ^5-3-ketosteroid isomerase (KSI). In the 50 years between its discovery (16) and the recent description of its intimate catalytic mechanism, we published more than 35 papers on this

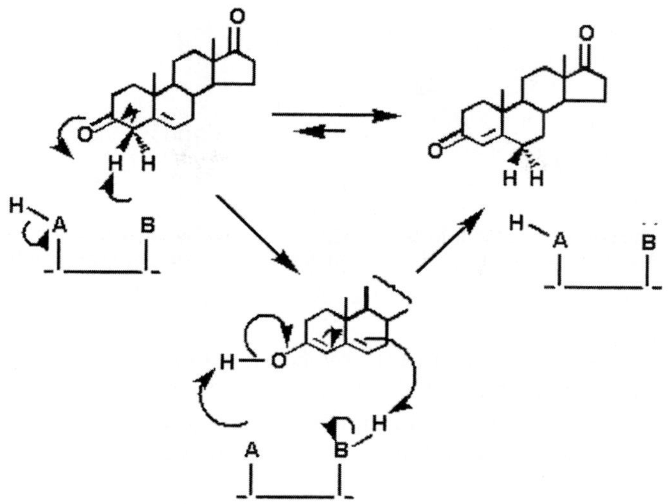

FIG. 5. **Schematic mechanism of the Δ^5-3-ketosteroid isomerase reaction showing the acid (HA) and the basic (B:) catalytic groups and the *enol* intermediate.**

steroid-induced enzyme from *P. testosteroni*. It provided a wonderful education for me and a satisfying exercise in mechanistic enzymology.

Many natural 3β-hydroxysteroids are also Δ^5-olefins (*e.g.* cholesterol, dehydroepiandrosterone). Nicotinamide nucleotide-dependent oxidations of these steroids to the 3-ketosteroid invariably give rise to Δ^4-3-ketosteroids. Although the double bond migration into conjugation occurs spontaneously and is acid- and base-catalyzed, we reported in a brief Communication (32): "We wish to present evidence for the existence of a widely distributed steroid isomerase, an enzyme which is distinct from the oxidizing enzyme, and which catalyzes the migration of the double bond from Δ^5 to the Δ^4 position of 3-ketosteroids," and suggested the name ketosteroid isomerase (KSI) (Fig. 5).

Frank Kawahara (a graduate student) developed an unorthodox method for the purification and crystallization of KSI. "Crystalline Δ^5-3-Ketosteroid Isomerase" was published as the first Preliminary Communication in this *Journal* (33). KSI enhanced the catalytic rate about 10^{11}-fold, approaching the diffusion-controlled maximum. The isomerization occurred at comparable rates in H_2O and D_2O and when conducted in media enriched with ^3H_2O or D_2O, resulted in little incorporation of the label into the product, unlike acid- or base-catalyzed isomerizations. We concluded that: "the enzymic mechanism suggests that there is a direct transfer of a proton from position 4 to 6 on the enzyme surface without exchange with the medium." With the use of appropriately deuterium-labeled steroids, Howard Ringold (34) established unequivocally that the isomerase reaction involved the direct intramolecular (suprafacial, diaxial) transfer of the 4β-proton to the 6β-position and observed a large primary kinetic isotope effect in the C-4β-D cleavage.

By good fortune, the 125-amino acid peptide chain of KSI contained neither cysteine nor tryptophan, and the 3 tyrosine and 8 phenylalanine residues provided a unique UV spectrum in which the absorbance bands of these residues were easily identifiable (35, 36). Considerable insight into the mechanism of KSI was therefore obtainable from absorption and fluorescence spectra of enzyme-steroid complexes, as well as from hydrogen isotope exchange between steroids and the medium (36). Although the catalytic mechanism of isomerization did not involve participation of protons of the medium, high concentrations of KSI catalyzed the exchange of protons of the medium with the hydrogen atoms of the steroid reaction products. The finding that the incorporated isotope could be removed completely under enolizing conditions suggested that the reaction involved an enolic intermediate. More direct evidence for this view was provided by spectroscopy. For instance, on binding to KSI, the typical absorption of Δ^4-3-ketosteroids was displaced to longer wavelengths, and binding of phenolic steroid competitive inhibitors (17β-estradiol and 17β-dihydroequilenin) produced large UV spectral (and for the equilenin also fluorescent) changes compatible with the formation of phenolate anions. The logical inference was that the KSI reaction involved *enol* or enolate intermediates.

Crystalline KSI of *P. testosteroni* was completely sequenced by Ann M. Benson, a postdoctoral colleague, by classical methods involving isolation of tryptic and chymotryptic peptides

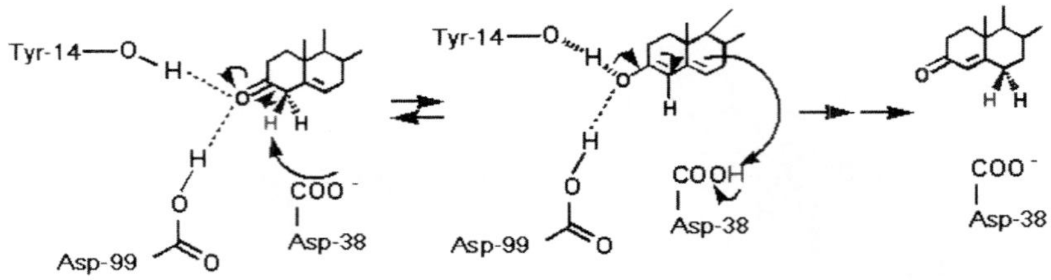

FIG. 6. **Catalytic mechanism of the Δ^5-3-ketosteroid isomerase reaction.** Tyr-14 protonates the 3-carbonyl group of the steroid, and Asp-38 accepts the 4β-H and transfers it to the 6β-position. Asp-99 assists in polarizing the steroid carbonyl group.

and their sequencing from the N terminus by Edman degradation and the C terminus by hydrazinolysis and carboxypeptidases (37). This task, which required more than 2 years, can now be accomplished in a few days. Ann Benson was my long time colleague. She brought protein sequencing expertise to our laboratory and went on to make many other important contributions.

Research on KSI remained somewhat dormant until 1987 when a highly successful collaboration was initiated with my colleague Albert S. Mildvan, Professor of Biological Chemistry at Hopkins, who had a lifelong dedication to mechanistic enzymology and wanted to apply NMR techniques to KSI. We were fortunate to interest a number of colleagues, students, and postdoctoral fellows (including Athan Kuliopulos, Liang Xue, Qinjian Zhao, and Yaw-kuen Li) in this project.

The KSI gene of *P. testosteroni* was isolated, sequenced, and overexpressed (38). Mutations of Tyr-14 to phenylalanine (Y14F) reduced k_{cat} by $10^{4.7}$, whereas replacement of Asp-38 by asparagines (D38N) reduced k_{cat} by $10^{5.6}$. In contrast, substitution of Tyr-55 by phenylalanine (Y55F) reduced k_{cat} by only a factor of 4. Thus, the two former mutations abolished the catalytic activity of KSI whereas mutation of Tyr-55 had only a minor effect (39, 40).

Extensive studies on the combined kinetic deuterium substrate and solvent isotope effects suggested that the reaction involved acid-base catalysis and led to the formulation of the following mechanistic model. The isomerase reaction occurs in two steps (not in a concerted manner) via a dienolic intermediate(s). In the rate-limiting first step, Tyr-14 acts as a general acid that protonates (by creating a low barrier hydrogen bond) (41) the carbonyl group of the steroid substrate, whereas Asp-38 is the base that accepts the 4β-proton from the steroid, resulting in the formation of a dienol. In the second step, the roles of the active site residues are reversed. Asp-38 transfers its acquired proton suprafacially and without exchange with the medium to the 6β-position, and the phenolic hydroxyl group of Tyr-14 undergoes reprotonation. Another residue (Asp-99) important for catalysis was identified by M. Summers at the University of Maryland (42). The final detailed mechanism based on NMR solution structures elucidated by Mildvan (43) and by Summers (42), and the x-ray crystal structure by Oh (44) suggests that Asp-99 assists in the polarization of the steroid carbonyl group (Fig. 6).

Inactivation of Δ^5-3-Ketosteroid Isomerase by Mechanism-based (Suicide) Inhibitors—During studies on the biosynthesis of long chain, unsaturated fatty acids in *E. coli*, Konrad Bloch uncovered a new principle in the design of highly selective enzyme inhibitors, which he summarized as follows: "By catalyzing the transformation of a relatively unreactive substrate analogue to an extremely reactive active-site-directed reagent, the enzyme causes its own destruction." The specificity of inhibition depends on the presence in the substrate analogue of latent functional groups that are specifically unmasked by the enzyme, thereby generating an affinity label at the desired site. Such reagents are also known as suicide substrates and mechanism-based or enzyme-activated inhibitors.

My colleague and friend Cecil H. Robinson recognized the basic similarities (of proton transfer) between the reaction promoted by the fatty acid synthetase and KSI, and made the very imaginative suggestion that A:B-*seco*-3-ketosteroids in which an acetylenic function replaced the C-5 to C-6 bond might be converted by the normal C-4β-proton-abstracting function of the enzyme to highly reactive α,β-unsaturated allenes susceptible to attack by nucleophilic residues of the enzyme. These predictions were fully borne out when Robinson, with his associates F. H. Batzold and D. F. Covey, synthesized a series of acetylenic *seco*-steroids and showed that they were rapidly converted by KSI to the conjugated allenic ketones, which inactivated the enzyme rapidly and irreversibly (45–48).

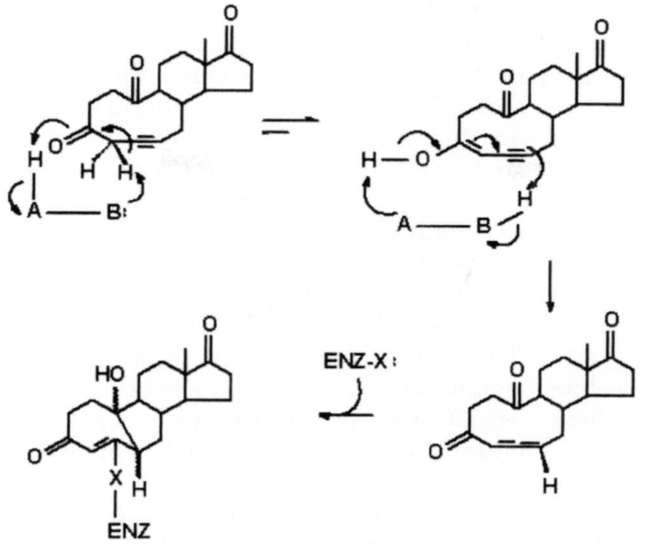

FIG. 7. **Inhibition of the Δ^5-3-ketosteroid isomerase by acetylenic 5,10-*seco*-3-ketosteroids.** The inhibitor is converted by the normal acid-base mechanism of the enzyme to the corresponding allenic ketone(s), which alkylates a nucleophilic group (Asn-57) and inactivates the enzyme.

Identification of the site, chemical nature, and location of attachment of these suicide *seco*-steroid substrates to KSI turned out to be a complex problem, which was finally solved by the enormously dedicated efforts of Trevor M. Penning, then a postdoctoral fellow and now Professor of Pharmacology at the University of Pennsylvania. Penning found that the linkage was labile to both mild acids and bases and that when the steroid was released, both the steroid and the protein underwent subtle chemical modifications. I cannot here describe the findings in detail and the way in which they were uncovered. It will suffice to say that the linkage was shown to be an *enol* ester linked to the amide group of Asn-57, which in the inactivated enzyme formed an *enol*-imidate with the enzymatically generated steroid allene (49) as shown in Fig. 7. Unfortunately, Asn-57 does not appear to play a significant role in the catalytic process.

Much of our work on KSI was continuously supported by a single NIH Grant (AM07422), which survived reviews for 33 years, more than half the life of the NIH granting system.

Mammalian Δ^5-3-Ketosteroid Isomerases—In a brief scientific diversion, Ann Benson searched for KSI activity in animal tissues. Supernatant fractions of beef liver displayed modest KSI activity, which was easily lost but could be restored by addition of glutathione. Purification disclosed that this KSI activity was very abundant and was promoted by glutathione *S*-transferases (GSTs). This identity was corroborated by chromatography and immunoprecipitation in collaboration with James H. Keen and William B. Jakoby of the NIH, who were then studying the multiplicity of GSTs (50). Δ^5-Androstene-3,17-dione became another useful substrate for characterizing GSTs. My good friend Professor Bengt Mannervik in Uppsala clarified the detailed mechanism of the GST-dependent KSI reaction and even identified GSTs for which Δ^5-androstene-3,17-dione was the preferred substrate (51). Through this scientific excursion we gained familiarity with GSTs, which proved invaluable in our later studies on chemoprotection against cancer.

Chemoprotection against Cancer: How Do Edible Plants Reduce the Risk?

For the last 25 years our laboratory has focused on developing strategies for reducing the risk of cancer. This interdisciplinary research program spans chemistry, growing of plants, molecular biology, animal disease models, and human studies. Our studies started with little hope or promise and were shunned as risky, if not foolhardy, by many members of the scientific community. Although this program consumes nearly all our current energies, it is summarized here only briefly because this work is very much in progress and has been recently reviewed comprehensively (52–55).

BHA and Glutathione Transferases—In 1978 my colleague and friend, the late Ernest Bueding, a biochemical parasitologist, was concerned with the question of how to avert the mutagenicity and carcinogenicity of his newly discovered agents that cured schistosomiasis. We were familiar with the then recent observations by Lee Wattenberg at the University of

Minnesota, who had shown that BHA (*tert*-butyl-4-hydroxyanisole) and other phenolic anti-oxidants that are widely used as preservative food additives could substantially reduce the tumorigenicity of several types of carcinogens in various animal organs. In one of our first experiments we showed that feeding BHA dramatically reduced the mutagenic activity in the urine of mice that received benzo[*a*]pyrene, strongly suggesting that the protective mechanism involved major alterations in carcinogen metabolism. Fortuitously, as indicated above, assays for GSTs were then routine in our laboratory, and we found marked elevations of the specific activities of GSTs and of GSH levels in the livers and other organs of the BHA-fed animals (56–58). These findings led us to propose that these phase 2 elevations were responsible for protection against carcinogens. In 1978 we wrote: "The most plausible mechanism for protective effects of antioxidants invokes alterations of the balance between metabolic activation and inactivation of carcinogens." The concept that induction of phase 2 genes is an effective and sufficient strategy for achieving protection against carcinogenesis is now widely accepted. The observations of Wattenberg were of profound importance because they showed for the first time that widely consumed dietary components, presumed to be of low toxicity, were able to block carcinogenesis.

Cloning of an abundant GST (mu class) in collaboration with John Morrow and his associates (59) demonstrated that BHA treatment raised the level of the mRNA transcripts for this enzyme substantially and increased its rate of synthesis in liver slices. The conclusion that induction resulted from enhanced gene transcription has been confirmed for many other phase 2 enzymes.

NADPH:Quinone Acceptor Oxidoreductase (Quinone Reductase; NQO1)—A very useful advance was the observation made with Ann Benson (60) that an enzyme discovered by Lars Ernster in Stockholm and that became known by a bewildering number of synonyms (*e.g.* DT diaphorase, NA(P)H:quinone reductase, quinone reductase, menadione reductase) and is now commonly called nicotinamide quinone oxidoreductase 1 (NQO1) was also induced by BHA in mouse organs, especially in the epithelia of the gastrointestinal and urinary tracts, where potential exposure to dietary carcinogens and mutagens is likely to be most intense. This FAD-dependent enzyme, which utilizes NADH and NADPH with comparable efficiencies and catalyzes the obligatory two-electron reduction of quinones to hydroquinones, has emerged as a fundamental prototype of the phase 2 response. NQO1 is of central importance in protecting cells against oxidative cycling (and the generation of reactive oxygen species) and GSH depletion by quinones (61) and has provided a highly useful index for phase 2 gene status of cells (62).

Mary De Long (a Research Associate), Hans Prochaska (an M.D.-Ph.D. student), and Annette Santamaria (a technical assistant) were the first to demonstrate phase 2 gene induction in cultured cells by a wide variety of chemical types of inducers (63–65). The very useful and widely adopted microtiter plate system that they developed involved quantifying the elevation of the specific activity of NQO1 in murine hepatoma 1c1c7 cells. This enzyme was relatively easy to measure and showed a large and highly reproducible response range, and the cells were robust and easy to manage. Moreover, mutants of Hepa1c1c7 were available that were deficient in expression or function of certain cytochromes P450. This made it possible to distinguish two classes of inducers of the phase 2 response, those that were dependent on and also induced cytochrome P450 function (mostly large planar aromatics), which we designated as *bifunctional* inducers, and those that can induce in the absence of cytochrome P450 function, as *monofunctional* inducers (66). A major implication of this distinction is that monofunctional inducers are more desirable as chemoprotectors since cytochromes P450 may be involved in carcinogen activation, whereas phase 2 enzymes only very rarely activate procarcinogens to carcinogens.

At the same time, we undertook structural and kinetic studies on NQO1. Hans Prochaska showed his scientific versatility by developing a highly efficient single step affinity chromatography for purifying NQO1 from rat liver and crystallized this enzyme for the first time (67). He also was the first to purify and crystallize two closely related NQO1 isoforms from mouse liver. We introduced our colleague L. Mario Amzel, a crystallographer and Professor of Biophysics and Biophysical Chemistry, to the world of quinone reductases. Rongbao Li (a graduate student) with Amzel and Mario Bianchett solved the structure of rat NQO1 (68). Qinjiang Zhao (postdoctoral fellow and an important contributor to the KSI problem) and my long time associate David Holtzclaw isolated, cloned, and overexpressed the closely related

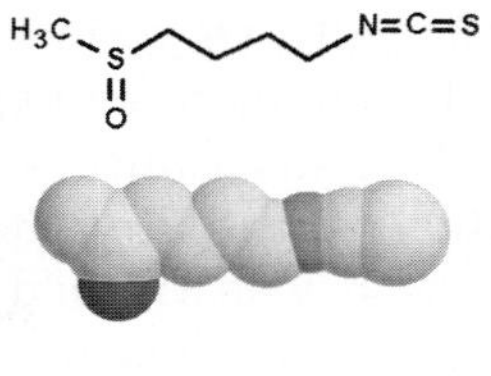

Sulforaphane

FIG. 8. **Structure and space-filling model of sulforaphane, the principal phase 2 gene inducer in broccoli.**

NQO2. The crystal structure of NQO2, an FAD-containing metalloflavoprotein, was elucidated by Christine Foster working jointly in Amzel and our laboratories (69). Amzel and Bianchett have since made important contributions to the structure of human NQO1 and especially how it is adapted to the unmasking of quinone groups of chemotherapeutic alkylating agents such as mitomycins, anthracyclines, and aziridylbenzoquinones (70).

Phase 2 Inducer Potency of Plant Extracts: Isolation of Sulforaphane—With the availability of a relatively simple microtiter plate method for quantifying inducer activity, we asked whether the widely recognized lower incidence of malignancies in high fruit and vegetable consumers might be attributable, even in part, to the presence of protective phase 2 enzyme inducers in these plants. Hans Prochaska attacked this problem with enthusiasm. Organic solvent extracts of a broad selection of fruits and vegetables from local markets disclosed not only that inducer activity was present but also that it varied enormously among plant families (65). The *Cruciferae*, and especially those belonging to the *Brassica* genus (*e.g.* cauliflower, kale, broccoli, cabbage) were the richest sources of inducer activity. Yuesheng Zhang, who obtained his Ph.D. degree in our department, isolated the active inducer principle from broccoli. Extensive studies with organically grown vegetables reassured us that the inducer activity was not due to contamination by pesticides or insecticides. We found a reliable source of SAGA broccoli, grown in Caribou, Maine, and shipped to us frozen. Repeated chromatographies monitored by NQO1 activity assays revealed that the inducer activity was attributable to a single compound and finally led Zhang to isolate a few milligrams of a liquid from 1 pound of broccoli. We had no preconceived notions as to its identity. Professor Gary H. Posner of the Department of Chemistry of Johns Hopkins University rapidly showed that it was an isothiocyanate (mustard oil), 1-isothiocyanato-4-(methylsulfinyl)butane (Fig. 8) (71). Sulforaphane had already been isolated many years earlier by Czech workers, based on its rather weak antibiotic activity, from a widely distributed cruciferous weed known as hoary cress and from savoy and red cabbage. Posner synthesized gram quantities of sulforaphane and also a number of its analogues, varying in the length of the methylene chain and the state of oxidation of the sulfur of the methylthio group. Bioassays revealed that sulforaphane was the most potent naturally occurring phase 2 inducer known.

Availability of gram quantities of sulforaphane made it possible to evaluate (in collaboration with my long time colleague Thomas W. Kensler) the ability of this compound to suppress tumor formation in the Huggins single-dose DMBA rat mammary cancer model. It was extremely gratifying that sulforaphane inhibited the incidence and multiplicity of mammary tumors and also delayed their development (72). This observation provided strong confirmation for the principle that phase 2 gene induction resulted in protection against carcinogenesis.

Gary Posner undertook a methodical analysis of the structure-inducer activity relation among a large series of isothiocyanate analogues that he synthesized. He designed a series of conformationally restricted (norbornyl) isothiocyanates and provided guidelines for predicting their inducer potencies. The most potent of the analogues were also inhibitors of tumor formation in the mammary tumor model (73).

The finding that broccoli contained a very potent cancer chemoprotective agent generated considerable and unanticipated media attention, including a story on the front page of *The New York Times*, inclusion among *Historic Documents of 1992* (Congressional Record), and selection as one of the 100 major discoveries of the last century by *Popular Mechanics*. This hyperbole was undoubtedly fueled by George H. W. Bush, then President of the United States, who had publicly declared his dislike for broccoli, claiming that his mother had made him eat broccoli but that now that he was President of the United States he was no longer obliged to do so.

We realized that plants were potentially very rich sources of anticarcinogenic phase 2 inducers and that we did not have the facilities or expertise to undertake their study. To remedy this deficiency we founded the Brassica Cancer Chemoprotection Laboratory in old but serviceable space in the Blalock Building of the Johns Hopkins Hospital. By very good fortune, Jed W. Fahey, a Hopkins graduate who was trained as a plant physiologist, joined our laboratory in 1994. His knowledge and contributions have been an essential part of developing plants to combat cancer. Fahey soon showed that sulforaphane was actually an artifact of isolation; the intact plants contain almost exclusively the glucosinolate precursor of sulforaphane, known as glucoraphanin. Upon plant injury, food preparation, or eating, the intracellularly segregated enzyme myrosinase is released and hydrolyzes the water-soluble and stable glucoraphanin to the highly reactive sulforaphane, which is the ultimate inducer (74).

Analysis of a selection of randomly selected broccoli heads from supermarkets disclosed huge variations in inducer potential that were unrelated to their appearance. Jed Fahey (74) then grew broccoli sprouts from seeds. Nearly 100 varieties of broccoli seeds are commercially available, and whereas they also vary greatly in their glucoraphanin content, the concentration of this glucosinolate in seeds and 3-day-old sprouts grown from them was always much higher than that in market stage broccoli heads. Indeed it became possible to grow sprouts that contained 20 times higher concentrations of glucoraphanin than many commercial broccolis. Three-day-old broccoli sprouts are well tolerated by humans. The repeated administration of calibrated doses of glucoraphanin or sulforaphane in the form of broccoli sprout extracts produced no significant toxicity in Phase 1 safety and tolerance tests in volunteers. Broccoli sprouts are a food and therefore an ideal vehicle for administration of glucoraphanin or sulforaphane (after myrosinase hydrolysis) to humans without elaborate regulatory requirements. A number of clinical trials of broccoli sprouts in high risk cancer-prone populations are in progress.

One serendipitous finding made by Fahey and his collaborators (75) is that sulforaphane is bactericidal for *Helicobacter pylori*, an infection that causes peptic ulcers and is associated with great increases in the risk for gastric cancer. The value of broccoli sprouts for treatment of *Helicobacter* infections is also being evaluated.

Chemistry of Inducers—Elucidation of the structural requirements for inducer activity led to two important advances: (i) it identified inducers of dietary origin that were suitable for chemoprotective studies in humans and (ii) it played a major role in providing insight into the mechanism whereby inducers signal the transcription of phase 2 genes.

Mechanistic understanding of the up-regulation of the phase 2 response required better information on the relation of structure to inducer potency. The first step was the finding that inducer potency of various BHA analogues was not highly dependent on structure (76, 77). Thus a number of synthetic dialkyl ethers of *tert*-butylhydroquinone were weaker phase 2 inducers than BHA itself. Indeed, the unsubstituted *tert*-butylhydroquinone and even hydroquinone itself were the most potent inducers. We concluded that BHA was metabolized to more potent intermediates and that involvement of a structurally complementary "receptor" in the signaling process was unlikely. Although this finding provided only a modest advance in our understanding of how structure affected inducer activity, Hans Prochaska, who had synthesized and tested all of the alkyl analogues of BHA, was not discouraged. He argued that all the compounds tested up to this time were substituted 1,4-diphenols and suggested that 1,2-diphenol (catechols) and 1,3-diphenol (resorcinol) derivatives should be tested to determine whether oxidative lability (to which hydroquinones and catechols but not resorcinol derivatives were susceptible) controlled inducer potency. Evaluation of a substantial number of analogues led to the conclusion that only oxidizable diphenols (and also the corresponding phenylenediamines) were inducers, whereas resorcinols were invariably inactive. These findings showed that oxidative lability was critical for inducer activity (78) but did not answer the question of whether the oxidizable diphenols themselves or their quinone oxidation products were the ultimate inducer species. Insight into this question was obtained unexpectedly by dissection of the structure of a series of coumarins. We concluded that inducers of this chemical family contained previously unrecognized structural features. They were Michael reaction acceptors (79), and their inducer potencies were closely correlated with their Michael reactivities. Quinones are potent Michael acceptors, and we inferred that the above mentioned oxidizable diphenols exerted their inducer activities through conversion to quinones. This permitted prediction of which structures were likely to be inducers, and many new synthetic and naturally occurring inducers have since been identified on this basis (80–82).

More than 10 different chemical classes of inducers have now been recognized including isothiocyanates and their thiol addition products, dithiocarbamates, as well as 1,2-dithiole-3-thiones, trivalent arsenic derivatives (*e.g.* phenyl arsenoxide), heavy metals, certain conjugated cyclic and acyclic polyenes (including porphyrins, chlorophyllins, and chlorophyll), and vicinal dimercaptans. Notably, these inducers have few structural similarities. They are mostly electrophiles, and all can react chemically with thiol groups by alkylation, oxidation, or reduction, suggesting to us that the intracellular sensor for inducers is likely to contain very highly reactive (cysteine) thiols. This suggestion was bolstered by the following: (*a*) the potencies of inducers paralleled their reactivity with thiols (the inducer potencies of Michael reaction acceptors are related to their reaction rates as electrophiles); (*b*) the very high inducer potency of trivalent arsenicals (*e.g.* phenyl arsenoxide) suggested the involvement of two vicinal thiols, possibly resulting in the formation of relatively stable cyclic thioarsenites; and (*c*) the potency order of divalent cations ($Hg^{2+} > Cd^{2+} > Zn^{2+}$) corresponded exactly to their thiol reactivity (83). Interestingly, inducers can modify thiol groups by a variety of mechanisms including: (i) alkylation (Michael reaction acceptors, isothiocyanates, quinones); (ii) oxidation (*e.g.* peroxides and hydroperoxides); and (iii) direct reaction with thiol/disulfide linkages (*e.g.* vicinal dithiols such as 1,2-dimercaptopropanol, lipoic acid). These rather promiscuous response mechanisms provide plasticity for cellular responses to a variety of electrophilic and oxidant stressors.

The molecular mechanisms by which a large number of inducers of different chemical types up-regulate the phase 2 response were analyzed by Tory Prestera (an M.D.-Ph.D. student). He transiently transfected hepatoma cells with a construct containing the promoter region of the mouse glutathione transferase Ya gene linked to a growth hormone promoter gene. In this system there was a very close correlation between the potencies of inducers in elevating growth hormone expression and in inducing the phase 2 response over a range of 4 orders of magnitude of concentration (84, 85). These experiments provided strong evidence that all classes of inducers stimulate the same regulatory element (the antioxidant response element (ARE) described below). We proposed that this cellular response to electrophile and oxidative stress be designated the "electrophile counterattack response." What, then, is the identity of the sensor for inducers?

The Quest for the Elusive Sensor for Phase 2 Inducers and the Molecular Mechanisms of Induction—Our initial efforts to identify the sensor containing highly reactive thiol groups that recognize and react with inducers involved use of tritiated dexamethasone mesylate, an alkylating agent that had been synthesized as a ligand for the corticosteroid receptor. This steroid mesylate was a moderately potent inducer, but we were unable to identify the sensor, although we isolated a number of more abundant proteins endowed with highly reactive cysteine residues (55). Identification of the sensor finally became possible with the discovery of Keap1 by Yamamoto and colleagues (86). Murine Keap1 is a multidomain 624-amino acid protein that includes 25 cysteine residues, many of which are intrinsically highly reactive because they are flanked by basic residues which results in substantial lowering of their pK_a values.

Three cellular components are centrally involved in phase 2 gene regulation: (i) antioxidant response elements (AREs), cis-acting promoters of transcription that are present in the upstream regions of many phase 2 genes and have the consensus sequence: TGA(G/C)NNNGC, first described by Cecil B. Pickett; (ii) Nrf2 (nuclear factor-erythroid 2-related factor 2), a basic leucine zipper transcription factor that is itself inducible, binds in heterodimeric combination with other transcription factors to the ARE promoters, and signals enhanced transcription of phase 2 genes; and (iii) Keap1, a Kelch family multidomain repressor protein that is normally localized in the cytoplasm where it is tethered to the actin cytoskeleton. Keap1 binds to Nrf2 very tightly and is thereby largely retained in the cytoplasm so that its activity is repressed. Inducers disrupt the Keap1-Nrf2 complex, thereby releasing Nrf2 for translocation to the nucleus and activation of the transcription of phase 2 genes (Fig. 9).

Cloned and overexpressed mouse Keap1 was purified by Albena Dinkova-Kostova (research associate) and David Holtzclaw. When pure Keap1 was exposed for a limited time to [^{3}H]dexamethasone mesylate, 4 of its 25 cysteine residues became labeled and were identified as Cys-257, Cys-273, Cys-288, and Cys-297 by MALDI-TOF mass spectrometry. All of these

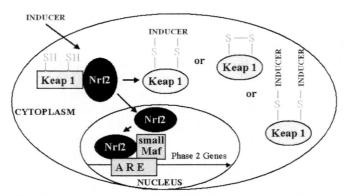

Fɪɢ. 9. **Regulation of the phase 2 response by the Nrf2-Keap1 complex.** Inducers disrupt the actin-bound Nrf2-Keap1 complex and liberate Nrf2 to migrate to the nucleus and activate transcription of phase 2 genes.

cysteine residues are located in the cysteine-rich intervening region (IVR) of Keap1 that links the BTB (broad complex) dimerization domain with the double glycine (DGR) or Kelch domain, which is involved in binding actin and Nrf2. Albena Dinkova-Kostova and David Holtzclaw also showed that complexes of pure Keap1 with the critical Neh2 segment of Nrf2 were disrupted by addition of inducers and that covalent interaction of Keap1 with various inducers could be demonstrated directly by ultraviolet spectroscopy. These findings finally provided very strong and direct evidence that certain cysteine residues of Keap1 were indeed the intracellular sensors for phase 2 inducers (87). With the knowledge that the highly reactive cysteines were located in the IVR of Keap1, mutation experiments were carried out by Nobunao Wakabayashi, a visiting scientist from Tsukuba University in collaboration with Dinkova-Kostova and Holtzclaw (88). Single and multiple mutations of the four aforementioned cysteine residues established that substitution of either Cys-273 or Cys-288 but not of any other cysteine residues abrogated the capacity of Keap1 to repress the activity of Nrf2 (88).

The question of what is responsible for the especially high reactivity of the cysteine residues that function as sensor for inducers has now turned in a new direction. My colleagues have established that Keap1 is a zinc-containing metalloprotein and that upon binding of inducers, the tightly bound zinc is displaced from the protein. It thus appears that Keap1 is regulated by inducers through the participation of a zinc-sulfhydryl switching mechanism (89). Work on the fascinating mechanism of Keap1 and its implications for chemoprotection against cancer is in full swing.

Some Final Thoughts

Any merit to which these discoveries might be entitled is due entirely to a remarkable group of students, postdoctoral fellows, and other collaborators who have been my laboratory family for more than 50 years and who have enriched my life immensely. Many have become lifelong friends. It has been a joy to witness their scientific development and to draw pleasure from their accomplishments. Unfortunately, it has not been possible to acknowledge explicitly all who have played a part in our scientific journey. In writing these Reflections, I was forced to consider whether they might provide any personal enlightenment about the nature of the process that Peyton Rous called "finding out." Since I have always considered science to be an artistic endeavor, it seemed highly unlikely that there are any rules for success. There is perhaps one conclusion to which my experiences lead. Good fortune plays a major role in discovery. Much as we might try, there is no "road map" to discovery. All "road maps" are based on mistaken notions and generally lead to failure. They cannot anticipate serendipity.

I am deeply honored to have been asked to write these "Reflections" as we celebrate the 100th birthday of *The Journal of Biological Chemistry*. It seems especially appropriate that this essay originates from the Department of Pharmacology at Johns Hopkins where the *Journal* was founded in 1905 and edited by John Jacob Abel, the first professor and acknowledged "father" of American pharmacology, and by Christian A. Herter.

I was privileged to serve as an Associate Editor of the Journal for 5 years (1962–1966) under John T. Edsall at a time when the Editorial Board consisted of only 22 members. Our annual board meetings were held each Spring during the Federation (FASEB) meetings in Atlantic City. Edsall read all the manuscripts, annotated them with his thick black pencil, and always signed the decision letters. A man of great dignity, Edsall was one of the most beloved Editors and taught all of us so much about the scholarship and ethics of scientific communication.

We regularly pay homage to the *JBC* in our department by asking our graduate students who was the author of the first paper in the *Journal*. If the reader needs a little help, the answer may be found in the list of references (90).

Acknowledgments

No Reflections would be complete without mention of the constant struggle to generate funds to support scientific research. We have been very fortunate to receive institutional support from: Johns Hopkins University, the National Institutes of Health, the American Cancer Society (including a Professorship), the American Institute for Cancer Research, the Cancer Research and Prevention Foundation, and the Ross Foundation (The Grateful Dead). I can mention only a few of the numerous individuals who have made substantial philanthropic contributions to our research. They include Barbara L. Goldsmith, W. Patrick McMullan III, and Robert K. Shaye.

Special acknowledgment is made for the more than 10 years of continuous and extremely generous unrestricted support from the Lewis B. and Dorothy Cullman Foundation, which made possible the creation of the Brassica Cancer Chemoprotection Laboratory and its incorporation into the Lewis B. and Dorothy Cullman Cancer Chemoprotection Center, which is a formally recognized organizational component of this University. This dedicated support for our research has made it possible to follow the path of serendipity on which science thrives. I am deeply grateful.

I cannot end without acknowledging that my scientific efforts would not have been possible without the love and support of my wife (and friend) Pamela and our four children. "Acknowledgment" is hardly the appropriate word to describe their role in my life.

Address correspondence to: ptalalay@jhmi.edu.

REFERENCES

1. Sumner, J. B., and Dounce, A. L. (1937) Crystalline catalase. *J. Biol. Chem.* **121,** 417–424
2. Hall, C. E., Hauser, E. A., LeBeau, D. S., Schmitt, F. O., and Talalay, P. (1944) Natural and synthetic rubber fibers. Electron microscope studies. *Ind. Eng. Chem.* **36,** 634–640
3. Huggins, C., and Hodges, C. V. (1941) Studies on prostatic cancer. I. Effects of castration, of estrogen and of androgen injection on serum phosphatases in metastatic carcinoma of the prostate. *Cancer Res.* **1,** 293–297
4. Huggins, C., Stevens, R. E., and Hodges, C. V. (1941) Studies on prostatic cancer. II. Effects of castration on advanced carcinoma of the prostate gland. *Arch. Surg.* **43,** 209–223
5. Huggins, C. B. (1979) *Experimental Leukemia and Mammary Cancer. Induction, Prevention, Cure.* The University of Chicago Press, Chicago
6. Huggins, C., and Talalay, P. (1945) Sodium phenolphthalein phosphate as a substrate for phosphatase tests. *J. Biol. Chem.* **159,** 399–410
7. Talalay, P., Fishman, W. H., and Huggins, C. (1946) Chromogenic substrates. II. Phenophthalein glucuronic acid as substrate for the assay of glucuronidase activity. *J. Biol. Chem.* **166,** 757–772
8. Talalay, P., Dobson, M. M., and Tapley, D. F. (1952) Oxidative degradation of testosterone by adaptive enzymes. *Nature* **170,** 620–621
9. Talalay, P., and Dobson, M. M. (1953) Purification and properties of β-hydroxysteroid dehydrogenase. *J. Biol. Chem.* **205,** 823–837
10. Talalay, P., and Marcus, P. I. (1954) Enzymatic formation of 3α-hydroxysteroids. *Nature* **173,** 1189–1192
11. Marcus, P. I., and Talalay, P. (1955) On the molecular specificity of steroid-enzyme combinations. The kinetics of β-hydroxysteroid dehydrogenase. *Proc. Roy. Soc. Biol. B.* **144,** 116–132
12. Talalay, P., and Marcus, P. I. (1956) Specificity, kinetics and inhibition of α- and β-hydroxysteroid dehydrogenases. *J. Biol. Chem.* **218,** 675–691
13. Talalay, P., Loewus, F. A., and Vennesland, B. (1955) The enzymatic transfer of hydrogen. IV. The reaction catalyzed by a β-hydroxysteroid dehydrogenase. *J. Biol. Chem.* **212,** 801–809
14. Talalay, P. (1962) Hydroxysteroid dehydrogenases. *Methods Enzymol.* **5,** 512–526
15. Payne, D. W., Shikita, M., and Talalay, P. (1982) Enzymatic estimation of steroids in subpicomole quantities by hydroxysteroid dehydrogenases and nicotinamide nucleotide cycling. *J. Biol. Chem.* **257,** 633–642
16. Payne, D. W., and Talalay, P. (1986) A one-step enzymatic assay for the measurement of 17β-hydroxy- and 17-oxo-steroid profiles in biological samples. *J. Steroid Biochem.* **25,** 403–410
17. Talalay, P., and Williams-Ashman, H. G. (1958) Activation of hydrogen transfer between pyridine nucleotides by steroid hormones. *Proc. Natl. Acad. Sci. U. S. A.* **44,** 15–26
18. Talalay, P., Hurlock, B., and Williams-Ashman, H. G. (1958) On a coenzymatic function of estradiol-17β. *Proc. Natl. Acad. Sci. U. S. A.* **44,** 862–884
19. Levy, H. R., and Talalay, P. (1959) Bacterial oxidation of steroids. I. Ring A dehydrogenations by intact cells. *J. Biol. Chem.* **234,** 2009–2013
20. Levy, H. R., and Talalay, P. (1959) Bacterial oxidation of steroids. II. Studies on the enzymatic mechanism of Ring A dehydrogenation. *J. Biol. Chem.* **234,** 2014–2021
21. Davidson, S. J., and Talalay, P. (1966) Purification and mechanism of action of a steroid Δ^4-5β-dehydrogenase. *J. Biol. Chem.* **241,** 906–915
22. Prairie, R. L., and Talalay, P. (1963) Enzymatic formation of testololactone. *Biochemistry* **2,** 203–208
23. Coulter, A. W., and Talalay, P. (1968) Studies on the microbiological degradation of steroid Ring A. *J. Biol. Chem.*

243, 3238–3247

24. Shaw, D. A., Borkenhagen, L. F., and Talalay, P. (1965) Enzymatic oxidation of steroids by cell-free extracts of *Pseudomonas testosteroni:* Isolation of cleavage products of Ring A. *Proc. Natl. Acad. Sci. U. S. A.* **54,** 837–844

25. Skinner, C. G., Edelson, J., and Shive, W. (1961) A conformation of methionine essential for its biological utilization. *J. Am. Chem. Soc.* **83,** 2281–2286

26. Lombardini, J. B., Coulter, A. W., and Talalay, P. (1970) Analogues of methionine as substrates and inhibitors of the methionine adenosyltransferase reaction. *Mol. Pharmacol.* **6,** 481–499

27. Lombardini, J. B., and Talalay, P. (1971) Formation, functions and regulatory importance of *S*-adenosyl-L-methionine. Deductions concerning the conformation of methionine. *Adv. Enzyme Regul.* **9,** 349–384

28. Chou, T.-C., and Talalay, P. (1977) A simple generalized equation for the analysis of multiple inhibitions of Michaelis-Menten kinetic systems. *J. Biol. Chem.* **252,** 6438–6442

29. Chou, T.-C., and Talalay, P. (1981) Generalized equations for the analysis of inhibitions of Michaelis-Menten and higher-order kinetic systems with two or more mutually exclusive and nonexclusive inhibitors. *Eur. J. Biochem.* **115,** 207–216

30. Chou, T.-C., and Talalay, P. (1984) Quantitative analysis of dose-effect relationships: the combined effects of multiple drugs or enzyme inhibitors. *Adv. Enzyme Regul.* **22,** 27–55

31. Cornforth, J. W., Reichard, S. A., Talalay, P., Carrell, H. L., and Glusker, J. P. (1977) Determination of the absolute configuration at the sulfonium center of *S*-adenosyl-methionine. Correlation with the absolute configuration of the diastereomeric *S*-carboxy-methyl-(*S*)-methionine salts. *J. Am. Chem. Soc.* **99,** 7292–7300

32. Talalay, P., and Wang, V. S. (1955) Enzymic isomerization of Δ^5-3-ketosteroids. *Biochim. Biophys. Acta* **18,** 300–301

33. Kawahara, F. S., and Talalay, P. (1960) Crystalline Δ^5-3-ketosteroid isomerase. *J. Biol. Chem.* **235,** PC1–2

34. Malhotra, S. K., and Ringold, H. J. (1965) Chemistry of conjugate anions and enols. V. Stereochemistry, kinetics, and mechanism of the acid- and enzymatic-catalyzed isomerization of Δ^5-3-ketosteroids. *J. Am. Chem. Soc.* **87,** 3228–3236

35. Kawahara, F. S., Wang, S.-F., and Talalay, P. (1962) The preparation and properties of crystalline Δ^5-3-ketosteroid isomerase. *J. Biol. Chem.* **237,** 1500–1506

36. Wang, S.-F., Kawahara, F. S., and Talalay, P. (1963) The mechanism of the Δ^5-3-ketosteroid isomerase reaction: absorption and fluorescence spectra of enzyme-steroid complexes. *J. Biol. Chem.* **238,** 576–585

37. Benson, A. M., Jarabak, R., and Talalay, P. (1971) The amino acid sequence of Δ^5-3-ketosteroid isomerase of *Pseudomonas testosteroni. J. Biol. Chem.* **246,** 7514–7525

38. Kuliopulos, A., Shortle, D., and Talalay, P. (1987) Isolation and sequencing of the gene encoding Δ^5-3-ketosteroid isomerase of *Pseudomonas testosteroni:* overexpression of the protein. *Proc. Natl. Acad. Sci. U. S. A.* **84,** 8893–8897

39. Kuliopulos, A., Mildvan, A. S., Shortle, D., and Talalay, P. (1989) Kinetic and ultraviolet spectroscopic studies of active-site mutants of Δ^5-3-ketosteroid isomerase. *Biochemistry* **28,** 149–159

40. Xue, L., Kuliopulos, A., Mildvan, A. S., and Talalay, P. (1991) Catalytic mechanism of an active-site mutant (D38N) of Δ^5-3-ketosteroid isomerase. Direct spectroscopic evidence for dienol intermediates. *Biochemistry* **30,** 4991–4997

41. Zhao, Q., Abeygunawardana, C., Talalay, P., and Mildvan, A. S. (1996) NMR evidence for the participation of a low-barrier hydrogen bond in the mechanism of Δ^5-3-ketosteroid isomerase. *Proc. Natl. Acad. Sci. U. S. A.* **93,** 8220–8224

42. Wu, Z. R., Ebrahimian, S., Zawrotny, M. E., Thornburg, L. D., Perez-Alvarado, G. C., Brothers, P., Pollack, R. M., and Summers, M. F. (1997) Solution structure of 3-oxo-Δ^5-steroid isomerase. *Science* **276,** 415–418

43. Massiah, M. A., Abeygunawardana, C., Gittis, A. G., and Mildvan, A. S. (1998) Solution structure of Δ^5-3-ketosteroid isomerase complexed with the steroid 19-nortestosterone hemisuccinate. *Biochemistry* **42,** 14701–14712

44. Cho, H.-S., Ha, N.-C., Choi, G., Kim, H.-J., Lee, D., Oh, K. S., Kim, K. S., Lee, W. Choi, K. Y., and Oh, B.-H. (1999) Crystal structure of Δ^5-3-ketosteroid isomerase from *Pseudomonas testosteroni* in complex with equilenin settles the correct hydrogen bonding scheme for transition state stabilization. *J. Biol. Chem.* **274,** 32863–32868

45. Batzold, F. H., Benson, A. M., Covey, D. F., Robinson, C. H., and Talalay, P. (1976) The Δ^5-3-ketosteroid isomerase reaction: catalytic mechanism, specificity, and inhibition. *Adv. Enzyme Regul.* **14,** 243–267

46. Penning, T. M., Covey, D. F., and Talalay, P. (1981) Inactivation of Δ^5-3-oxosteroid isomerase with active-site-directed acetylenic steroids. *Biochem. J.* **193,** 217–227

47. Penning, T. M., Covey, D. F., and Talalay, P. (1981) Irreversible inactivation of Δ^5-3-ketosteroid isomerase of *Pseudomonas testosteroni* by acetylenic suicide substrates: mechanism of formation and properties of the steroid-enzyme adduct. *J. Biol. Chem.* **256,** 6842–6850

48. Penning, T. M., and Talalay, P. (1981) Linkage of an acetylenic secosteroid suicide substrate to the active site of Δ^5-3-ketosteroid isomerase: isolation and characterization of a tetrapeptide. *J. Biol. Chem.* **256,** 6851–6858

49. Penning, T. M., Heller, D. N., Balasubramanian, T. M., Fenselau, C. C., and Talalay, P. (1982) Mass spectrometric studies of a modified active-site tetrapeptide from Δ^5-3-ketosteroid isomerase of *Pseudomonas testosteroni. J. Biol. Chem.* **257,** 12589–12593

50. Benson, A. M., Talalay, P., Keen, J. H., and Jakoby, W. B. (1977) Relationship between the soluble glutathione-dependent Δ^5-3-ketosteroid isomerase and the glutathione *S*-transferases of the liver. *Proc. Natl. Acad. Sci. U. S. A.* **74,** 158–162

51. Johansson A.-S., and Mannervik, B. (2002) Active-site residues governing high steroid isomerase activity in human glutathione transferases A3-3. *J. Biol. Chem.* **277,** 16648–16654

52. Talalay, P. (1999) The war against cancer: new hope. *Proc. Am. Philos. Soc.* **143,** 52–72

53. Talalay, P. (2000) Chemoprotection against cancer by induction of phase 2 enzymes. *BioFactors* **12,** 5–11

54. Talalay, P., Dinkova-Kostova, A. T., and Holtzclaw, W. D. (2003) Importance of phase 2 gene regulation in protection against electrophile and reactive oxygen toxicity and carcinogenesis. *Adv. Enzyme Regul.* **43,** 121–134

55. Holtzclaw, W. D., Dinkova-Kostova, A. T., and Talalay, P. (2004) Protection against electrophile and oxidative stress by induction of phase 2 genes: the quest for the elusive sensor that responds to inducers. *Adv. Enzyme Regul.* **44,** 335–367

56. Benson, A. M., Batzinger, R. P., Ou, S.-Y. L., Bueding, E., Cha, Y.-N., and Talalay, P. (1978) Elevation of hepatic glutathione *S*-transferase activities and protection against mutagenic metabolites of benzo(a)pyrene by dietary antioxidants. *Cancer Res.* **38,** 4486–4495

57. Talalay, P., Batzinger, R. P., Benson, A. M., Bueding, E., and Cha, Y.-N. (1979) Biochemical studies on the mechanisms by which dietary antioxidants suppress mutagenic activity. *Adv. Enzyme Regul.* **17,** 23–36

58. Benson, A. M., Cha, Y.-N., Bueding, E., Heine, H. S., and Talalay, P. (1979) Elevation of extrahepatic glutathione *S*-transferase and epoxide hydratase activities by 2(3)-*tert*-butyl-4-hydroxyanisole. *Cancer Res.* **39,** 2971–2977

59. Pearson, W. R., Windle, J. J., Morrow, J. F., Benson, A. M., and Talalay, P. (1983) Increased synthesis of glutathione *S*-transferases in response to anticarcinogenic antioxidants. Cloning and measurement of messenger RNA. *J. Biol. Chem.* **258**, 2052–2062

60. Benson, A. M., Hunkeler, M. J., and Talalay, P. (1980) Increase of NAD(P)H:quinone reductase by dietary antioxidants: possible role in protection against carcinogenesis and toxicity. *Proc. Natl. Acad. Sci. U. S. A.* **77**, 5216–5220

61. Prochaska, H. J., Talalay, P., and Sies, H. (1987) Direct protective effect of NAD(P)H:quinone reductase against menadione-induced chemiluminescence of postmitochondrial fractions of mouse liver. *J. Biol. Chem.* **262**, 1931–1934

62. Dinkova-Kostova, A. T., and Talalay, P. (2000) Persuasive evidence that quinone reductase type 1 (DT diaphorase) protects cells against the toxicity of electrophiles and reactive forms of oxygen. *Free Radic. Biol. Med.* **29**, 231–240

63. Prochaska, H. P., and Santamaria, A. B. (1988) Direct measurement of NAD(P)H:quinone reductase from cells cultured in microtiter wells: a screening assay for anticarcinogenic enzyme inducers. *Anal. Biochem.* **169**, 328–336

64. De Long, M. J., Prochaska, H. J., and Talalay, P. (1986) Induction of NAD(P)H:quinone reductase in murine hepatoma cells by phenolic antioxidants, azo dyes and other chemoprotectors: a model system for the study of anticarcinogens. *Proc. Natl. Acad. Sci. U. S. A.* **83**, 787–791

65. Prochaska, H. J., Santamaria, A. B., and Talalay, P. (1992) Rapid detection of inducers of enzymes that protect against carcinogens. *Proc. Natl. Acad. Sci. U. S. A.* **89**, 2394–2398

66. Prochaska, H. J., and Talalay, P. (1988) Regulatory mechanisms of monofunctional and bifunctional anticarcinogenic enzyme inducers in murine liver. *Cancer Res.* **48**, 4776–4782

67. Prochaska, H. J. (1988) Purification and crystallization of rat liver NAD(P)H:(quinone acceptor) oxidoreductase by Cibacron Blue affinity chromatography: identification of a new and potent inhibitor. *Arch. Biochem. Biophys.* **267**, 529–538

68. Li, R., Bianchett, M. A., Talalay, P., and Amzel, L. M. (1995) The three-dimensional structure of NAD(P)H: quinone reductase, a flavoprotein involved in cancer chemoprotection and chemotherapy. *Proc. Natl. Acad. Sci. U. S. A.* **92**, 8846–8850

69. Foster, C. E., Bianchett, M. A., Talalay, P., Zhao, Q., and Amzel, L. M. (1999) Crystal structure of human quinone reductase type 2, a metalloflavoprotein. *Biochemistry* **38**, 9881–9886

70. Bianchett, M. A., Faig, M., and Amzel, L. M. (2004) Structure and mechanism of NAD(P)H:quinone acceptor oxidoreductases (NQO). *Methods Enzymol.* **382**, 144–174

71. Zhang, Y., Talalay, P., Cho, C.-G., and Posner, G. H. (1992) A major inducer of anti-carcinogenic protective enzymes from broccoli: isolation and elucidation of structure. *Proc. Natl. Acad. Sci. U. S. A.* **89**, 2399–2403

72. Zhang, Y., Kensler, T. W., Cho, C.-G., Posner, G. H., and Talalay, P. (1994) Anticarcinogenic activities of sulforaphane and structurally related synthetic norbornyl isothiocyanates. *Proc. Natl. Acad. Sci. U. S. A.* **91**, 3147–3150

73. Posner, G. H., Cho, C.-G., Green, J. V., Zhang, Y., and Talalay, P. (1994) Design and synthesis of bifunctional isothiocyanate analogs of sulforaphane: correlation between structure and potency as inducers of anticarcinogenic detoxication enzymes. *J. Med. Chem.* **37**, 170–176

74. Fahey, J. W., Zhang, Y., and Talalay, P. (1997) Broccoli sprouts: an exceptionally rich source of inducers of enzymes that protect against chemical carcinogens. *Proc. Natl. Acad. Sci. U. S. A.* **94**, 10367–10372

75. Fahey, J. W., Haristoy, X., Dolan, P. M., Kensler, T. W., Scholtus, I., Stephenson, K. K., Talalay, P., and Lozniewski, A. (2002) Sulforaphane inhibits extracellular, intracellular and antibiotic-resistant strains of *Helicobacter pylori* and prevents benzo[*a*]pyrene-induced stomach tumors. *Proc. Natl. Acad. Sci. U. S. A.* **99**, 7610–7615

76. De Long, M. J., Prochaska, H. P., and Talalay, P. (1985) Tissue-specific induction patterns of cancer-protective enzymes in mice by *tert*-butyl-4-hydroxyanisole and related substituted phenols. *Cancer Res.* **45**, 546–551

77. Prochaska, H. J., Bregman, H. S., De Long, M. J., and Talalay, P. (1985) Specificity of induction of cancer protective enzymes by analogues of *tert*-butyl-4-hydroxyanisole (BHA). *Biochem. Pharmacol.* **34**, 3909–3914

78. Prochaska, H. J., De Long, M. J., and Talalay, P. (1985) On the mechanisms of induction of cancer-protective enzymes: a unifying proposal. *Proc. Natl. Acad. Sci. U. S. A.* **82**, 8232–8236

79. Talalay, P., De Long, M. J., and Prochaska, H. J. (1988) Identification of a common chemical signal regulating the induction of enzymes that protect against chemical carcinogenesis. *Proc. Natl. Acad. Sci. U. S. A.* **85**, 8261–8265

80. Fahey, J. W., Dinkova-Kostova, A. T., Stephenson, K. K., and Talalay, P. (2004) The "Prochaska" microtiter plate bioassay for inducers of NQO1. *Methods Enzymol.* **382**, 243–258

81. Kang, Y.-H., and Pezzuto, J. H. (2004) Induction of quinone reductase as a primary screen for natural product anticarcinogens. *Methods Enzymol.* **382**, 380–423

82. Dinkova-Kostova, A. T., Fahey, J. W., and Talalay, P. (2004) Chemical structures of inducers of nicotinamide quinone oxidoreductase 1 (NQO1). *Methods Enzymol.* **382**, 423–448

83. Dinkova-Kostova, A. T., Massiah, M. A., Bozak, R. E., Hicks, R. J., and Talalay, P. (2001) Potency of Michael reaction acceptors as inducers of enzymes that protect against carcinogenesis depends on their reactivity with sulfhydryl groups. *Proc. Natl. Acad. Sci. U. S. A.* **98**, 3404–3409

84. Prestera, T., Holtzclaw, W. D., Zhang, Y., and Talalay, P. (1993) Chemical and molecular regulation of enzymes that detoxify carcinogens. *Proc. Natl. Acad. Sci. U. S. A.* **90**, 2965–2969

85. Prestera T., Zhang, Y., Spencer, S. R., Wilczak, C. A., and Talalay, P. (1993) The electrophile counterattack response: protection against neoplasia and toxicity. *Adv. Enzyme Regul.* **33**, 281–296

86. Itoh, K., Wakabayashi, N., Katoh, Y., Ishii, T., Igarashi, K., Engel, J. D., and Yamamoto, M. (1999) Keap1 represses nuclear activation of antioxidant responsive elements by Nrf2 through binding to the amino-terminal Neh2 domain. *Genes Dev.* **13**, 76–86

87. Dinkova-Kostova, A. T., Holtzclaw, W. D., Cole, R. N., Itoh, K., Wakabayashi, N., Katoh, Y., Yamamoto, M., and Talalay, P. (2002) Direct evidence that sulfhydryl groups of Keap1 are the sensors regulating induction of phase 2 enzymes that protect against carcinogens and oxidants. *Proc. Natl. Acad. Sci. U. S. A.* **99**, 11908–11913

88. Wakabayashi, N., Dinkova-Kostova, A. T., Holtzclaw, W. D., Kang, M.-I., Kobayashi, A., Yamamoto, M., Kensler, T. W., and Talalay, P. (2004) Protection against electrophile and oxidant stress by induction of the phase 2 response: fate of cysteines of the Keap1 sensor modified by inducers. *Proc. Natl. Acad. Sci. U. S. A.* **101**, 2040–2045

89. Dinkova-Kostova, A. T., Holtzclaw, W. D., and Wakabayashi, N. (2005) Keap1, the sensor for electrophiles and oxidants that regulates the phase 2 response, is a zinc metalloprotein. *Biochemistry* **44**, 6889–6899

90. Abel, J. J., and Taveau, R. deM. (1905) On the decomposition products of epinephrine hydrate. *J. Biol. Chem.* **1**, 1–32

This paper is available online at www.jbc.org

THE JOURNAL OF BIOLOGICAL CHEMISTRY VOL. 280, NO. 47, pp. 38889–38897, November 25, 2005
© 2005 by The American Society for Biochemistry and Molecular Biology, Inc.   Printed in the U.S.A.

A PAPER IN A SERIES COMMISSIONED TO CELEBRATE THE CENTENARY OF THE JBC in 2005

JBC Centennial
1905–2005
100 Years of Biochemistry and Molecular Biology

From Polynucleotide Phosphorylase to Neurobiology

PUBLISHED, JBC PAPERS IN PRESS, SEPTEMBER 28, 2005, DOI 10.1074/JBC.X500007200

Uriel Z. Littauer

From the Department of Neurobiology, Weizmann Institute of Science, Rehovot 76100, Israel

In the fall of 1944, I enrolled at the Hebrew University of Jerusalem. The student body numbered about 700 and the choice of faculties was somewhat limited. My hope was to study medicine, but the plans to open a medical school were still at the drawing board stage. I therefore chose to study chemistry with biochemistry and bacteriology as minor subjects, which I thought I would need later if I went into medicine. As employment opportunities were limited in British Mandatory Palestine, it was hoped that university training would help me get a job in the food technology industry or at the Dead Sea potash industry.

When I started as a student, the structure and function of DNA and RNA were not known. Thymonucleic acid (DNA) had been isolated from thymus and pus, and zymonucleic acid (RNA) was found in yeast. The tetranucleotide hypothesis for DNA suggested by Phoebus Aaron Theodor Levene still prevailed, and there were speculations about branched chain as distinct from linear structures for RNA. Nucleic acids were also considered as nothing more than a storehouse of phosphorus for the varying requirements of the cell. However, the role of DNA in bacterial transformation, demonstrated by Oswald Theodore Avery, Colin MacLeod, and Maclyn McCarty in 1944, was discussed extensively during our bacteriology courses. Within a few years, I had the good fortune to enter the nucleic acid field where progress had evolved dramatically.

In June 1949, upon the completion of my studies at the Hebrew University of Jerusalem, Professor Ernst David Bergmann, the Scientific Director of the Weizmann Institute of Science, invited me to join him as his Ph.D. student. I gladly accepted and moved to Rehovot, which was then a small village with about 7000 inhabitants. Ernst Bergmann was an organic chemist, a former student of the noted German chemist, Wilhelm Schlenk, and co-worker of Professor Chaim Weizmann, the first President of the State of Israel. Bergmann had a dynamic and brilliant personality with an encyclopedic knowledge of chemistry and a broad interest in science (1). For my doctoral dissertation, Bergmann recommended I choose a subject close to Chaim Weizmann's scientific interests, namely the mechanism of pentose fermentation in bacteria. While I was in the advanced stages of my doctoral work, Sol Spiegelman from the Department of Microbiology of the University of Illinois, Urbana came to Rehovot to consider an offer that had been made to him to join the Weizmann Institute. Spiegelman suggested that for my postdoctoral studies I contact Arthur Kornberg, Head of the Department of Microbiology of the Washington University School of Medicine in St. Louis, Missouri. Kornberg had just moved from the National Institutes of Health (NIH) and was recruiting people for his new department. I was greatly impressed by Arthur Kornberg's early publications on coenzyme and nucleotide synthesis and decided to write and ask if he would accept me as a postdoctoral fellow. Spiegelman offered to talk to Kornberg on my behalf, and on the strength of his recommendation, I had the good fortune to be accepted and to receive a fellowship from the Dazian Foundation.

In March 1955, I arrived in St. Louis to join Arthur Kornberg's laboratory. He proposed that I try to construct a cell-free system that would catalyze the synthesis of RNA. As substrate, I used ^{14}C-labeled ATP, which I had to synthesize myself from ^{14}C-labeled adenine by a series of enzymatic reactions because commercially labeled nucleotides were not available then. Within a short time, I was able to construct a cell-free system from *Escherichia coli* cells that converted ^{14}C-labeled ATP to an acid-insoluble polyribonucleotide. Moreover, the addition of adenylate kinase (myokinase) to the system increased the rate of the reaction. Although the activity was barely detectable, Kornberg thought that I should attempt to characterize the polynucleotide-synthesizing system. While making rapid progress in purifying the *E. coli* enzyme, we learned from Herman Kalckar, an eminent Danish biochemist who came for a visit, that Marianne Grunberg-Manago and Severo Ochoa at New York University had independently discovered an activity, similar to ours, in extracts of *Azotobacter vinelandii* (*A. agilis*). The enzyme was named polynucleotide phosphorylase (PNPase) and was shown to convert nucleoside diphosphates into polynucleotides. Although we were disappointed by the news of their findings, we decided to continue our studies with the purified *E. coli* enzyme. Acting on this new information, we shifted to using ADP rather than ATP and found it to be the preferred substrate in our system (2, 3).

PNPase was the first enzyme to be discovered that catalyzes the *de novo* synthesis of polyribonucleotides with a 3′,5′-phosphodiester bond, and its discovery stimulated a considerable number of investigations. The cumulative studies have established that in the forward reaction long polyribonucleotides $(pN)_n$ are synthesized in a processive fashion from various ribonucleoside diphosphates (ppN) with concomitant release of inorganic phosphate (P_i). Each of the four common ribonucleoside diphosphates can serve separately as a substrate for the polymerization reaction, leading to formation of homopolymers. Polymerization of a mixture of ribonucleoside diphosphates that contains different bases results in a random copolymer. The enzyme does not require a template and cannot copy one. In the reverse reaction, PNPase is a processive 3′ to 5′ exoribonuclease that catalyzes the stepwise phosphorolysis of single-stranded polyribonucleotides, liberating ribonucleoside diphosphates.

$$n \cdot ppN \rightleftarrows (pN)_n + n \cdot P_i$$

In the processive phosphorolysis of long chain polyribonucleotides, the enzyme tends to degrade a single chain to completion, releasing ribonucleoside diphosphates plus a resistant short oligoribonucleotide before commencing phosphorolysis of another chain. In contrast, short oligoribonucleotides are degraded by a random nonprocessive mechanism in which the enzyme dissociates from the substrate after the phosphorolysis of each nucleotide (reviewed in Refs. 4 and 5). PNPase was also found to catalyze an exchange reaction between free in organic phosphate and the β-phosphate of several ribonucleoside diphosphates. This reaction is apparently a result of combined polymerization and phosphorolytic reactions that occur under equilibrium conditions (2–4, 6). Under suitable conditions, the enzyme also catalyzes the elongation of a primer oligoribonucleotide with a free 3′-terminal hydroxyl group (7, 8). At that early stage, we pointed out that it is not apparent how an enzyme that appears to polymerize the available ribonucleoside diphosphates in a random fashion produces the specific nucleotide composition of the RNA of a given species (3). Subsequent research in other laboratories showed that the cellular function of the enzyme is to degrade RNA and that RNA synthesis is catalyzed by DNA-directed RNA polymerase.

In the spring of 1956, the enzyme was already purified about 300-fold when Arthur informed me that Leon Heppel, then Head of the Section for Metabolic and Arthritis Diseases at the NIH, was interested in the enzyme. Leon then came for a visit of a few days to get acquainted with our purification procedure and assay systems. Leon, devoted to his scientific work, did not waste a minute and spent long hours into the night working in our laboratory. Prior to his return to Bethesda, I gave him some of our purified PNPase and an "activator" fraction. Toward the end of my stay in St.Louis, Alex Rich and Leon Heppel invited me to the NIH to acquaint them with my PNPase purification procedure and the synthesis of long polynucleotides. While there I also examined the phosphorolysis of several RNA preparations, and together with Gary Felsenfeld and Alex Rich we analyzed the various synthetic polyribonucleotides in the ultracentrifuge. The sedimentation data indicated molecular weights of about 400,000. They later obtained some excellent x-ray diffraction pictures from the polynucleotides. Heppel was very generous in providing me with samples of his RNA and enzyme collection, which I intended to use upon my return to the Weizmann Institute. In our experiments PNPase was found to readily catalyze the phosphorolysis of synthetic polyribonucleotides as well as high molecular weight RNA preparations, whereas commercial and low molecular weight RNA samples were not attacked to a significant extent (3). I suspected that the RNA samples were degraded products that were resistant to phosphorolysis by the enzyme.

Later, in Rehovot, these observations led me to develop a method for isolating intact bacterial and mammalian RNA. Analysis in the ultracentrifuge of the *E. coli* preparations revealed the existence of several types of RNA with sedimentation constants of 4.1, 16.5, and 23.7S. The two high molecular weight RNA components were separated from the low molecular weight fraction by ammonium sulfate precipitation and turned out to be derived from ribosomes. These were not trivial findings because a number of investigators considered ribosomal RNA (rRNA) as an aggregate of short polynucleotides and did not realize the inherent instability of RNA compared with DNA. As expected the high molecular weight rRNA components were efficiently phosphorolyzed by PNPase. On the other hand, transfer RNA (tRNA) preparations were attacked more slowly and to a limited extent (20–30%). Urea was found to increase the degree of breakdown of tRNA, indicating that the secondary structure of tRNA hinders the enzymatic attack (9, 10).

Having at hand intact rRNA preparations, I suggested to my good friend and colleague, Heini Eisenberg, that we collaborate in an attempt to determine their physical properties. At that time the structure of RNA, unlike that of double-stranded DNA, was unknown mainly because of the lack of undegraded RNA preparations and because the existence of several types of RNA was not yet realized. Early attempts to secure clear diffraction patterns of RNA had failed (11). We soon discovered the single-stranded nature of rRNA and the ways in which it differs from double-stranded DNA. Thus, viscosity and birefringence of flow measurements showed that rRNA is quite sensitive to increasing the ionic strength of the solution in contrast with double-stranded DNA, which shows a much smaller dependence on ionic strength concentrations. We proposed, therefore, that rRNA behaves as a flexible, contractile single-stranded coil and that each ribosomal subunit contains a single continuous uninterrupted RNA chain (reviewed in Ref. 10). Further experiments on rRNA were performed in collaboration with Robert Cox (a visiting scientist now at the National Institute for Medical Research, Mill Hill). Our studies showed a close correlation of the ionic strength dependence of optical rotation, optical density, and hydrodynamic properties. These early results indicated that rRNA possessed a significant secondary structure, a rather novel observation for its time. Several years later we demonstrated together with my

graduate student, Inder M. Verma (now a Professor and leading molecular biologist at the Salk Institute), and Marvin Edelman (then a visiting scientist from Harvard Medical School) the presence of rRNA in mitochondria from several fungal species. We also showed that the mitochondrial rRNA possesses a unique ordered structure that differs from that of the homologous cytoplasmic rRNA (reviewed in Refs. 10 and 12). By this time, we had become interested in understanding the mechanisms that govern the regulation of tRNA and mRNA activity. We devised methods for the purification of specific tRNA species and studied the post-transcriptional modification of tRNA chains. In particular we were intrigued by the high content of modified bases in tRNA. We showed that methylated bases in tRNA are not likely to be essential for cell viability but depending on the type of base modification and position along the tRNA chain they may play a role in the fine tuning of tRNA activity (12).

The late Violet Daniel, my first graduate student (who later became a Weizmann Institute Professor of Biochemistry), joined my laboratory in 1957. She purified and characterized tRNA nucleotidyltransferase from rat liver. The enzyme was found to have an important role in the proofreading and repair of the universal 3'-CCA end of tRNA. Further experiments by the late Jacov Tal (until recently Professor and Head of the Virology Department at Ben-Gurion University) showed that the enzyme adds CMP to tRNA . . . N by a nonprocessive mechanism. Moreover, together with Violet and colleagues we developed a novel method that allowed monitoring the hybridization of individually labeled aminoacylated tRNA species with DNA. Using that method, we were able to reveal the presence of several unique T4 phage-coded tRNA species (13). Our discovery was well received during an EMBO workshop on tRNA that was organized by Sydney Brenner in Cambridge, UK, in March 1969. In another project that involved Violet Daniel, Jacques S. Beckmann, Sara Sarid, Jacob I. Grimberg, and Max Herzberg we were the first to isolate a tRNA gene (14).

Simultaneously, our studies with PNPase have continued. Together with Yosef Kimhi, another graduate student (who became later Vice President of Scientific Affairs, Yeda Co.), we purified further the *E. coli* enzyme. Evidence was obtained to support our hypothesis that the same enzyme catalyzes the nucleotide polymerization and the ADP-P_i exchange reaction (6). In addition, the intracellular distribution of PNPase was examined in *E. coli* cells. We showed that the major part of the enzyme activity (80%) is present in the soluble fraction; 10% of the total activity is bound to the cell membrane; and about 10% remains bound to washed ribosomes (15). Several years later Hermona (Mona) Soreq, a graduate student (now Professor and Head of the Institute of Life Sciences at the Hebrew University of Jerusalem), succeeded in purifying *E. coli* PNPase to homogeneity (16). The purified enzyme was virtually free of contaminating nucleases, which allowed us to use its 3′-exonucleolytic activity to determine the size and composition of the 3′-terminal sequences of RNA molecules and their function. Thus, with a molar excess of PNPase over the substrate a synchronous mode of phosphorolysis is established in which NDP molecules are sequentially released from the 3′ terminus of the RNA chains (4, 17). Moreover, we observed that at 0 °C, the poly(A) tails of mRNA molecules are readily phosphorolyzed, whereas the deadenylated mRNA chains remain intact. Together with Uri Nudel, Raphael Salomon, and Michel Revel we found that globin poly(A)-free mRNA could still be translated in a Krebs ascites tumor cell-free extract (the nuclease-treated reticulocyte lysate cell-free system had not yet been developed). We also observed that at long periods of incubation, the rate of globin synthesis appeared to level off more sharply with deadenylated mRNA than with native mRNA (17). The *in vitro* systems survive no longer than 2 h and are inadequate for detection of long term effects of the poly(A) tail on mRNA stability. We, therefore, turned our attention to the use of *Xenopus laevis* oocytes and were fortunate to collaborate with Georges Huez and Gérard Marbaix from the Free University of Brussels, who were experts in the use of this relatively new system. To examine the functional stability (*i.e.* ability to be translated) of the mRNA, deadenylated mRNA samples were microinjected into the oocytes. The results showed that the rate of globin synthesis with poly(A)-free mRNA is considerably lower than with native mRNA, and this difference became more pronounced at longer periods of incubation (18). In subsequent experiments we were able to show that readenylation of poly(A)-free globin mRNA restores its functional stability. In retrospect, we were more than fortunate in choosing globin mRNA for our studies, as there are examples where the removal of poly(A) tracts from some other mRNA species does not affect their stability (reviewed in Ref. 19).

Rabbit globin mRNA species containing poly(A) segments of different lengths were prepared by Uri Nudel and Hermona Soreq. This was accomplished by partial phosphorolysis of mRNA with the purified *E. coli* PNPase. By varying the salt concentration and the time of incubation of the phosphorolysis reaction mixture, as well as per-

forming oligo(dT)-cellulose chromatography at different temperatures, globin mRNA preparations with poly(A) tails of varying size were obtained. In collaboration with our Belgian colleagues, Gérard Marbaix, Georges Huez, Madeleine Leclercq, Evelyne Hubert, and Hubert Chantrenne, the functional stability of these molecules was examined in *Xenopus* oocytes. Globin mRNA molecules with a segment of 32 or more adenylate residues had equivalent functional stability, whereas those with less than 32 adenylate residues were 10-fold less stable. We suggested that a minimal size of the poly(A) segment is essential for attaching to poly(A)-binding proteins (PABP), thereby protecting the mRNA from nucleolytic degradation (20). This suggestion correlates well with the observation of Bradford Baer and Roger Kornberg that the minimal length of the poly(A) tail necessary for PABP binding is 27 residues (21). To account for the great variability among mRNA species, it was proposed that the 3′-untranslated region (3′-UTR) can modulate the affinity of PABP for the poly(A) segment, thus permitting control of the poly(A) stability in individual mRNA species (22). It is also apparent that the interaction between the poly(A) tail-PABP complex and cap-associated translation initiation factors may be important in maintaining the physical integrity of mRNA (23). Thus, there is a multitude of systems that use the poly(A) tract to control the expressions of specific mRNA species. The number of *cis*-acting elements and *trans*-acting factors regulating turnover of mRNA is increasing rapidly, and the complexity of these processes grows in parallel.

We also used the 3′-exonucleolytic activity of PNPase to determine the size of the poly(A) tails from various mRNA species (17, 20, 24). In other studies, Raphael Salomon and colleagues were able to examine the regulatory function of the 3′-region of tobacco mosaic virus (TMV) RNA. This was accomplished by subjecting TMV RNA molecules to limited phosphorolysis by PNPase (25). Additional applications of the 3′-exonucleolytic activity of the enzyme were developed for sequence analysis of short oligoribonucleotides (26). Finally, Gabriel Kaufmann (now Professor and Head of the Department of Biochemistry at Tel Aviv University) determined the substrate specificity of PNPase. The enzyme was found to direct the reversible addition of a single deoxynucleotidyl residue to ribooligonucleotide primers, whereas further addition of deoxynucleotidyl residues to the resulting product continued at a very slow rate (27). The enzyme was also found to phosphorolyze aminoacyl-tRNAs, thereby yielding aminoacyl-ADP and nucleoside diphosphates (28). These observations prompted us to investigate the properties of ribonucleoside diphosphate analogs modified in their sugar moiety as substrates for the enzyme. We suggested that blocking of NDPs at their 3'-hydroxyl function would yield "monofunctional" substrates to which only one residue may be added to an oligonucleotide primer, thus serving as chain terminators. The blocking group can be subsequently removed chemically from the oligonucleotide products, permitting a succession of single addition reactions. This procedure was employed for the stepwise synthesis of polyribonucleotides of defined sequence (26, 29). Combinations of these reactions and using T4 RNA ligase to ligate the synthesized oligonucleotides allowed the synthesis of appreciable long oligonucleotides. Kaufmann further adapted the use of this ligase for unique sequence insertions and alterations in tRNA anticodon loops (30).

PNPase has been the subject of numerous studies. It was employed as a tool for producing model nucleic acids and solving many important biological problems. Thus, establishing the genetic code was facilitated by the ability of PNPase to synthesize heteropolymers and triplet nucleotides. The advances made in the understanding of the physicochemical properties of polyribonucleotide chains and their hybridization reactions, as well as the synthesis of polynucleotide inducers of interferon, are further examples of the role played by the enzyme. I was glad to have had the opportunity to write a review, together with Marianne Grunberg-Manago, summarizing the voluminous studies on this enzyme that have accumulated over the years (5). More recent studies in several laboratories have revealed that the PNPase gene sequence is evolutionary conserved. It is widely distributed among a variety of aerobic, anaerobic, halophilic, and thermophilic bacteria. However, it is absent in all *Archaea*-sequenced genomes examined to date. It is also missing in some single-celled eukaryotes such as yeast but is present in animal eukaryotes. Thus, functional human PNPase was identified in an overlapping pathway screen to discover nuclear genes that displayed coordinated expression as a consequence of terminal differentiation and cellular senescence of human melanoma cells (31–33). The human PNPase is localized in the mitochondria (34) and in comparison with bacterial PNPase contains an extended N-terminal sequence that might serve as a mitochondrial import signal (35). Plants were shown to contain two PNPase species (36, 37). Although genes in the nucleus encode both PNPase species, their presence in plants is very likely the result of two separate horizontal transfer events. One PNPase functions in the chloroplasts while the second is found in the mitochondria.

The *E. coli* enzyme is a homotrimer (16, 38) and all three enzyme subunits participate in the phosphorolysis of each RNA chain. Thus, only one polyribonucleotide can be processed per trimer (16). In addition, Portier and colleagues showed that the *E. coli* PNPase subunit contains 711 amino acids and is coexpressed with the gene for ribosomal protein S15 as part of the *rpsO-pnp* operon. Two promoters have been identified in the operon: P1, situated upstream of *rpsO*, and P2, located in the intergenic region between *rpsO* and *pnp* (39, 40). It was also demonstrated that in *E. coli* cells, PNPase autoregulates its own synthesis post-transcriptionally in an RNase III-dependent manner (41). In addition, it was found that the steady-state levels of the enzyme increase at relatively low temperatures and are linked to the efficiency of the autocontrol mechanism (40). The deduced amino acid sequences of PNPase from different bacteria, as well as that from the nuclear genomes of plants and mammals, have been compared. They display similar structures composed of five distinguishable domains, each of them highly conserved. The protein consists of two core domains having different degrees of identity to *E. coli* RNase PH and an α-helical domain located between the two core domains. In addition, there are two adjacent C-terminal RNA-binding domains, KH and S1 (35, 42–44). Like PNPase, RNase PH is a 3' to 5' exonuclease that catalyzes phosphate-dependent degradation of RNA. The degradation targets of these enzymes *in vivo*, however, are different. While PNPase is mainly involved in the degradation of mRNA decay intermediates (45, 46) and is stalled by RNA tertiary structure (5), the primary function of RNase PH is thought to be the processing of 3'-ends of precursor tRNA molecules (47, 48). The trimeric structure of PNPase is also suggested from electron microscopic studies in which the enzyme appears as a triangular complex with a visible central hole (49). Moreover, the crystal structure PNPase from *Streptomyces antibioticus* was recently determined by x-ray crystallography. The enzyme is arranged in a homotrimeric multidomain complex with a central channel that could accommodate a single-stranded RNA chain. It was also observed that each PNPase subunit is composed of a duplicated structural core. In addition, the tungstate derivative structure reveals the PNPse active site in the second of these core domains (42, 43). Analysis of the biochemical properties of each domain of spinach chloroplast PNPase revealed unique features that may be related to the general function of RNA degradation (37). A distinctive feature of the *S. antibioticus* PNPase is that it can carry out pyrophosphate transfer from ATP to the 3'-OH of GTP to produce guanosine 3'-diphosphate 5'-triphosphate. Thus, *S. antibioticus* PNPase appears to be a bifunctional enzyme that possesses not only PNPase activity but also a guanosine pentaphosphate synthase activity that is not found for the *E. coli* PNPase (50, 51).

The decay mechanism of mRNA in *E. coli* cells has been extensively studied in many laboratories and involves a series of endo- and exolytic events. Several parallel pathways appear to exist that can partially substitute for each other. It was suggested that the decay of many mRNA species is initiated by the endonuclease, RNase E. The mRNA fragments resulting from RNase E cleavage are believed to be further degraded endonucleolytically and then cleaved by the 3′ to 5′ exonucleases, PNPase and RNase II (reviewed in Ref. 52). In *E. coli* cells, PNPase is mostly present in the cytoplasm (15), and about 10–20% of the enzyme population is associated with other proteins in a high molecular weight complex called the "RNA degradosome" (reviewed in Ref. 53). The major protein components identified in the complex include: PNPase, the DEAD-box RhlB RNA helicase, and the glycolytic enzyme enolase assembled on the C-terminal region of the endoribonuclease, RNase E. It was suggested that the components of the degradosome along with poly(A) polymerase may cooperate in the processing of mRNA (for recent references see Refs. 54 and 55). However, questions remain about whether the degradosome assembly is essential for bacterial mRNA decay *in vivo* (52, 56). It was also reported that chloroplast PNPase is not associated with other proteins to form a degradosome-like complex and appears to be a homomultimer complex of 600 kDa (36). Recent studies have indicated that polyadenylation is required for initiating exonucleolytic RNA degradation. It was shown that PNPase may function as an alternative poly(A) polymerase in *E. coli* cells where under appropriate conditions it can either degrade RNA or synthesize poly(A) tails, also incorporating C and U residues at low frequency in wild-type cells (57).

In 1968, I proposed to the management of the Weizmann Institute that they should initiate research in neurobiology and open a department devoted to this field. My interest in neuroscience developed slowly coinciding with the successful advances made in molecular biology and genetics. It became obvious that the time was ripe to apply similar interdisciplinary approaches to neurobiology. In October 1969, the NIH invited me to be their first Fogarty Scholar in Residence. This was an opportunity to learn more about neurobiology. I chose to join Marshall Nirenberg, Chief of the Laboratory of Biochemical Genetics at NHLBI, as his interests had also shifted from molecular biology to neurobiology. Together with Marshall, we organized a Fogarty Conference on Neuronal Plasticity. About a dozen leading molecular biologists participated in the lively discussions. I learned a great deal during my stay in Marshall's laboratory, and out of that I established, upon my return to Israel, the Department of Neurobiology at the Weizmann Institute and served as its Chairman until 1988. Marshall very generously allowed us to use in Rehovot the cloned cell lines he had isolated from a spontaneous mouse neuroblastoma tumor, C-1300 (58). Already during my stay in his laboratory, I devised methods for separating neurites from cell bodies that we later used in collaboration with Mary Catherine Glick (Children's Hospital of Philadelphia) to investigate their glycoprotein composition (59). At the start, I asked whether it would be possible to induce these cells to differentiate. Together with Yosef Kimhi, Clive Palfrey, and Ilan Spector it was found that dimethyl sulfoxide (Me$_2$SO) is a potent inducer of differentiation of several of the mouse cell lines. Our results also suggested that the development of the excitable membrane could have taken place independently of the induction of neurospecific enzyme and did not require a sustained elevation of cyclic AMP levels (60). As with mouse neuroblastoma, we have found that several human cell lines could be induced to differentiate with different external biological response modifiers. In collaboration with Paul Marks (then at Columbia University) and colleagues, we demonstrated that hexamethylene bisacetamide (HMBA) is effective in inducing differentiation of mouse and human neuroblastoma cells at concentrations 50-fold lower than that of Me$_2$SO, an observation that has clinical implications. The ability of some human cell lines to differentiate *in vitro* provides a model system to study the molecular events regulating cell growth and maturation of these neural crest derivatives and may provide insight into the mechanisms contributing to their tumorigenic conversion. Thus, with Mary Catherine Glick, we detected a 200-kDa glycoprotein that was associated with the surface membranes of mouse and human neuroblastoma cells displaying active Na$^+$ channels (59). In other studies, Mona Soreq, Aliza Zutra, and Ruth Miskin observed significant levels of intracellular and secreted tissue-type plasminogen activator (tPA) activities in cultured mouse neuroblastoma cells, and upon differentiation with dibutyryl cyclic AMP the level of tPA increased about 20-fold (61). The high level of secreted tPA in neuroblastoma cells may perhaps be linked to recent results suggesting the involvement of plasmin in the processing of human amyloid precursor protein (reviewed in Ref. 62).

Because of the universal occurrence and importance of microtubules for neurite outgrowth, synapse formation, and axoplasmic transport, we decided to investigate the *in vitro* synthesis of tubulin, the major structural subunit protein of microtubules. The regulation of tubulin synthesis at both the transcriptional and translational levels was followed in these studies by Henri Schmitt (a visiting scientist from the Free University of Brussels) and Illana Gozes (then a graduate student and currently a Professor and Head of the Department of Clinical Biochemistry at Tel Aviv University). Subsequent studies by Illana led to the exciting discovery that brain α-tubulin and β-tubulin display extensive microheterogeneity that was developmentally determined, increasing in the mature brain (63). In subsequent studies Irith Ginzburg (now a Professor at the Department of Neurobiology of the Weizmann Institute) and her colleagues isolated several cDNA clones bearing sequences coding for rat brain tubulin and actin (64). We used the tubulin and actin cDNA clones to study the control of mRNA expression in a number of cell systems. Irith also was a pioneer in the use of tubulin antisense oligodeoxyribonucleotides to prevent neurite extension in nerve growth factor-induced PC12 cells. The results showed that at least two tubulin isoforms are involved in neurite outgrowth (65, 66). In further studies we focused our efforts on the expression of microtubule-associated proteins (MAPs). Thus, I developed a specific binding assay that monitors the interaction of MAPs with tubulin cleavage peptides fixed to nitrocellulose membranes. To identify the tubulin-binding domains for MAPs we examined, in collaboration with Professor Herwig Ponstingl (from the German Cancer Research Center, Heidelberg) the binding of labeled rat brain MAP2 and tau factors to 60 cleavage peptides derived from pig α- and β-tubulin. Both MAP2 and tau factors were found to specifically interact with peptides derived from the C-terminal region of β-tubulin. The binding studies suggested that amino acid residues 434–440 of β-tubulin are essential for the interaction of MAP2 and tau factors (67). It is interesting to note that the main amino acid sequence divergence of the various isotubulins and most of the post-translational modifications take place within their C-terminal regions. This led to the hypothesis that the variability in the C-terminal region will determine the strength and specificity of interaction of isotubulins with the various MAPs, thus generating functionally different microtubules. About that time, studies by Joachim Kirsch (a visiting scientist and currently Professor at the University of Heidelberg) revealed that neurite outgrowth is accompanied by reorganization of the microtubular cytoskeleton. Thus, upon neurite extension in neuroblastoma cells, microtubule bundles are formed in which MAP2 is found in the proximal part and in branching points. By contrast, MAP1B is distributed along the entire length of the neurite. The differences in spatial distribution between MAP1B and MAP2 along the neurites illustrate the heterogeneity in microtubule composition in various parts of the cell process and may suggest a different function for MAP1B (68).

We have also shown that differentiation of cultured human neuroblastoma cells requires priming with an inducer and subsequent interaction with components of the extracellular matrix (in particular, adhesion to laminin). The major binding site in laminin (mediating cell attachment) was then identified as containing the YIGSR peptide sequence. Affinity chromatography revealed one major YIGSR-binding protein with an apparent molecular mass of 67 kDa. The 67-kDa laminin-binding protein (LBP) appeared to be down-regulated upon differentiation of human neuroblastoma cells (69). Cross-linking experiments indicated that in neuroblastoma cells the 67-kDa LBP binds to the YIGSR sequence in a cooperative manner through an association with another protein. About that time, Joachim Kirsch identified a new 250-kDa MAP2 isoform (designated MAP2d) in cultured human neuroblastoma cells. MAP2d was also observed in fetal human brain but was not found in adult human cerebellum (68). Analysis of human nerve cell-derived tumors showed that MAP2d is present in specimens from solid tumors diagnosed as neuroblastoma but hardly in ganglioneuroma tumors. In contrast both neuroblastoma and ganglioneuroma tumors contain significant levels of MAP1B. These studies indicated that MAP2d is associated with human embryonic nerve cells, as well as immature undifferentiated neuroblastoma tumors, and together with the 67-kDa LBP may lead to new prognostic tools for neuroblastoma tumors.

Other studies by Joachim Kirsch in collaboration with Professor Heinrich Betz and his colleagues at the Max-Planck-Institute for Brain Research, Frankfurt, have demonstrated that a 93-kDa glycine receptor-associated protein binds to tubulin. This 93-kDa protein (termed Gephyrin) appears to anchor the glycine receptor at post-synaptic sites via binding to subsynaptic tubulin and thus serves an important role in the topological organization of the post-synaptic membrane (70).

Address correspondence to: uri.littauer@weizmann.ac.il.

REFERENCES

1. Ginsburg, D. (1963) Ernst David Bergmann, an appreciation on the occasion of his sixtieth birthday. *Isr. J. Chem.* **1**, 323–350
2. Grunberg-Manago, M., Ortiz, P. J., and Ochoa, S. (1956) Enzymic synthesis of polynucleotides. I. Polynucleotide phosphorylase of *Azotobacter vinelandii*. *Biochim. Biophys. Acta* **20**, 269–285
3. Littauer, U. Z., and Kornberg, A. (1957) Reversible synthesis of polyribonucleotides with an enzyme from *Escherichia coli*. *J. Biol. Chem.* **226**, 1077–1092
4. Littauer, U. Z., and Soreq, H. 1982. Polynucleotide phosphorylase. In *The En-*

zyme (Boyer, P. D., ed) Vol. 15, pp. 517–553, Academic Press, New York

5. Littauer, U. Z., and Grunberg-Manago, M. (1999) Polynucleotide phosphorylase. In *Encyclopedia of Molecular Biology* (Creighton, T. E., ed) Vol. 3, pp. 1911–1918, John Wiley and Sons, New York

6. Kimhi, Y., and Littauer, U. Z. (1968) Purification and properties of polynucleotide phosphorylase from *Escherichia coli. J. Biol. Chem.* **243**, 231–240

7. Leder, P., Singer, M. F., and Brimacombe, R. L. (1965) Synthesis of trinucleoside diphosphates with polynucleotide phosphorylase. *Biochemistry* **4**, 1561–1567

8. Moses, R. E., and Singer, M. F. (1970) Polynucleotide phosphorylase of *Micrococcus luteus*. Studies on the polymerization reaction catalyzed by primer-dependent and primer-independent enzymes. *J. Biol. Chem.* **245**, 2414–2422

9. Littauer, U. Z., and Eisenberg, H. (1959) Ribonucleic acid from *Escherichia coli* preparation, characterization and physical properties. *Biochim. Biophys. Acta* **32**, 320–337

10. Littauer, U. Z. (2000) The unfolding of our understanding of RNA structure: a personal reflection. *Biophys. Chem.* **86**, 259–266

11. Rich, A., and Watson, J. D. (1954) Physical studies on ribonucleic acid. *Nature* **173**, 995–996

12. Littauer, U. Z. (2003) RNA enzymology and beyond. In *Comprehensive Biochemistry* (Semenza, G., and Turner, A. J., eds) Vol. 42, pp. 221–284, Elsevier Science Publishers B.V., Amsterdam

13. Daniel, V., Sarid, S., and Littauer, U. Z. (1970) Bacteriophage induced transfer RNA in *Escherichia coli*. New transfer RNA molecules are synthesized on the bacteriophage genome. *Science* **167**, 1682–1688

14. Daniel, V., Beckmann, J. S., Sarid, S., Grimberg, J. I., Herzberg, M., and Littauer, U. Z. (1971) Purification and *in vitro* transcription of a transfer RNA gene. *Proc. Natl. Acad. Sci. U. S. A.* **68**, 2268–2272

15. Kimhi, Y., and Littauer, U. Z. (1967) The intracellular distribution of polynucleotide phosphorylase in *Escherichia coli* cells. *Biochemistry* **6**, 2066–2073

16. Soreq, H., and Littauer, U. Z. (1977) Purification and characterization of polynucleotide phosphorylase from *Escherichia coli*. Probe for the analysis of 3′ sequences of RNA. *J. Biol. Chem.* **252**, 6885–6888

17. Soreq, H., Nudel, U., Salomon, R., Revel, M., and Littauer, U. Z. (1974) *In vitro* translation of polyadenylic acid-free rabbit globin messenger RNA. *J. Mol. Biol.* **88**, 233–245

18. Huez, G., Marbaix, G., Hubert, E., Leclercq, M., Nudel, U., Soreq, H., Salomom, R., Lebleu, B., Revel, M., and Littauer, U. Z. (1974) Role of the polyadenylate segment in the translation of globin messenger RNA in *Xenopus* oocytes. *Proc. Natl. Acad. Sci. U. S. A.* **71**, 3143–3146

19. Littauer, U. Z., and Soreq, H. (1982) The regulatory function of poly(A) and adjacent 3′ sequences in translated RNA. *Prog. Nucleic Acids Res. Mol. Biol.* **27**, 53–83

20. Nudel, U., Soreq, H., Littauer, U. Z., Marbaix, G., Huez, G., Leclercq, M., Hubert, E., and Chantrenne, H. (1976) Globin mRNA species containing poly(A) segments of different lengths. Their functional stability in *Xenopus* oocytes. *Eur. J. Biochem.* **64**, 115–121

21. Baer, B. W., and Kornberg, R. D. (1983) The protein responsible for the repeating structure of cytoplasmic poly(A)-ribonucleoprotein. *J. Cell Biol.* **96**, 717–721

22. Littauer, U. Z. (1993) Co-chairman's remarks: reflections on RNA. *Gene* (*Amst.*) **135**, 209–214

23. Deo, R. C., Bonanno, J. B., Sonenberg, N., and Burley, S. K. (1999) Recognition of polyadenylate RNA by the poly(A)-binding protein. *Cell* **98**, 835–845

24. Grosfeld, H., Soreq, H., and Littauer, U. Z. (1977) Membrane associated cytoplasmic mRNA in Artemia salina; functional and physical changes during development. *Nucleic Acids Res.* **4**, 2109–2121

25. Salomon, R., Sela, I., Soreq, H., Giveon, D., and Littauer, U. Z. (1976) Enzymatic acylation of histidine to tobacco mosaic virus RNA. *Virology* **71**, 74–84

26. Kaufmann, G., Grosfeld, H., and Littauer, U. Z. (1973) Stepwise phosphorolysis with polynucleotide phosphorylse: a novel method for sequence analysis of oligoribonucleotides. *FEBS Lett.* **31**, 47–52

27. Kaufmann, G., and Littauer, U. Z. (1969) Deoxyadenosine diphosphate as substrate for polynucleotide phosphorylase from *Escherichia coli. FEBS Lett.* **4**, 79–83

28. Kaufmann, G., and Littauer, U. Z. (1970) Phosphorolysis of aminoacyl-tRNA by polynucleotide phosphorylase from *Escherichia coli. Eur. J. Biochem.* **12**, 85–92

29. Kaufmann, G., Fridkin, M., Zutra, A., and Littauer, U. Z. (1971) Monofunctional substrates of polynucleotide phosphorylase. The monoaddition of 2′(3′)-isovaleryl-nucleoside diphosphate to an initiator oligonucleotide. *Eur. J. Biochem.* **24**, 4–11

30. Kaufmann, G., and Littauer, U. Z. (1974) Covalent joining of phenylalanine transfer ribonucleic acid half-molecules by T4 RNA ligase. *Proc. Natl. Acad. Sci.*

U. S. A. **71**, 3741–3745

31. Leszczyniecka, M., Kang, D. C., Sarkar, D., Su, Z. Z., Holmes, M., Valerie, K., and Fisher, P. B. (2002) Identification and cloning of human polynucleotide phosphorylase, *hPNPase^{old−35}*, in the context of terminal differentiation and cellular senescence. *Proc. Natl. Acad. Sci. U. S. A.* **99**, 16636–16641

32. Leszczyniecka, M., DeSalle, R., Kang, D. C., and Fisher, P. B. (2004) The origin of polynucleotide phosphorylase domains. *Mol. Phylogenet. Evol.* **31**, 123–130

33. Sarkar, D., Lebedeva, I. V., Emdad, L., Kang, D. C., Baldwin, A. S., Jr., and Fisher, P. B. (2004) Human polynucleotide phosphorylase (*hPNPase^{old−35}*): a potential link between aging and inflammation. *Cancer Res.* **64**, 7473–7478

34. Piwowarski, J., Grzechnik, P., Dziembowski, A., Dmochowska, A., Minczuk, M., and Stepien, P. P. (2003) Human polynucleotide phosphorylase, hPNPase, is localized in mitochondria. *J. Mol. Biol.* **329**, 853–857

35. Raijmakers, R., Egberts, W. V., van Venrooij, W. J., and Pruijn, G. J. (2002) Protein-protein interactions between human exosome components support the assembly of RNase PH-type subunits into a six-membered PNPase-like ring. *J. Mol. Biol.* **323**, 653–663

36. Baginsky, S., Shteiman-Kotler, A., Liveanu, V., Yehudai-Resheff, S., Bellaoui, M., Settlage, R. E., Shabanowitz, J., Hunt, D. F., Schuster, G., and Gruissem, W. (2001) Chloroplast PNPase exists as a homo-multimer enzyme complex that is distinct from the *Escherichia coli* degradosome. *RNA* **7**, 1464–1475

37. Yehudai-Resheff, S., Portnoy, V., Yogev, S., Adir, N., and Schuster, G. (2003) Domain analysis of the chloroplast polynucleotide phosphorylase reveals discrete functions in RNA degradation, polyadenylation, and sequence homology with exosome proteins. *Plant Cell* **15**, 2003–2019

38. Portier, C. (1975) Quaternary structure of polynucleotide phosphorylase from *Escherichia coli*: evidence of a complex between two types of polypeptide chains. *Eur. J. Biochem.* **55**, 573–582

39. Régnier, P., Grunberg-Manago, M., and Portier, C. (1987) Nucleotide sequence of the pnp gene of *Escherichia coli* encoding polynucleotide phosphorylase. Homology of the primary structure of the protein with the RNA-binding domain of ribosomal protein S1. *J. Biol. Chem.* **262**, 63–68

40. Mathy, N., Jarrige, A. C., Robert-Le Meur, M., and Portier, C. (2001) Increased expression of *Escherichia coli* polynucleotide phosphorylase at low temperatures is linked to a decrease in the efficiency of autocontrol. *J. Bacteriol.* **183**, 3848–3854

41. Jarrige, A. C., Mathy, N., and Portier, C. (2001) PNPase autocontrols its expression by degrading a double-stranded structure in the *pnp* mRNA leader. *EMBO J.* **20**, 6845–6855

42. Symmons, M. F., Jones, G. H., and Luisi, B. F. (2000) A duplicated fold is the structural basis for polynucleotide phosphorylase catalytic activity, processivity, and regulation. *Structure* **8**, 1215–1226

43. Symmons, M. F., Williams, M. G., Luisi, B. F., Jones, G. H., and Carpousis, A. J. (2002) Running rings around RNA: a superfamily of phosphate-dependent RNases. *Trends Biochem. Sci.* **27**, 11–18

44. Zuo, Y., and Deutscher, M. P. (2001) Exoribonuclease superfamilies: structural analysis and phylogenetic distribution. *Nucleic Acids Res.* **29**, 1017–1026

45. Donovan, W. P., and Kushner, S. R. (1986) Polynucleotide phosphorylase and ribonuclease II are required for cell viability and mRNA turnover in *Escherichia coli* K-12. *Proc. Natl. Acad. Sci. U. S. A.* **83**, 120–124

46. Li, Z., Reimers, S., Pandit, S., and Deutscher, M. P. (2002) RNA quality control: degradation of defective transfer RNA. *EMBO J.* **21**, 1132–1138

47. Kelly, K. O., and Deutscher, M. P. (1992) Characterization of *Escherichia coli* RNase PH. *J. Biol. Chem.* **267**, 17153–17158

48. Harlow, L. S., Kadziola, A., Jensen, K. F., and Larsen, S. (2004) Crystal structure of the phosphorolytic exoribonuclease RNase PH from *Bacillus subtilis* and implications for its quaternary structure and tRNA binding. *Protein Sci.* **13**, 668–677

49. Valentine, R. C., Thang, M. N., and Grunberg-Manago, M. (1969) Electron microscopy of *Escherichia coli* polynucleotide phosphorylase molecules and polyribonucleotide formation. *J. Mol. Biol.* **39**, 389–391

50. Jones, G. H., and Bibb, M. J. (1996) Guanosine pentaphosphate synthetase from *Streptomyces antibioticus* is also a polynucleotide phosphorylase. *J. Bacteriol.* **178**, 4281–4288

51. Bralley, P., and Jones, G. H. (2004) Organization and expression of the polynucleotide phosphorylase gene (*pnp*) of *Streptomyces*: processing of *pnp* transcripts in *Streptomyces antibioticus. J. Bacteriol.* **186**, 3160–3172

52. Kushner, S. R. (2002) mRNA decay in *Escherichia coli* comes of age. *J. Bacteriol.* **184**, 4658–4665

53. Carpousis, A. J., Vanzo, N. F., and Raynal, L. C. (1999) mRNA degradation. A tale of poly(A) and multiprotein machines. *Trends Genet.* **15**, 24–28

54. Khemici, V., and Carpousis, A. J. (2004) The RNA degradosome and poly(A) polymerase of *Escherichia coli* are required *in vivo* for the degradation of small

mRNA decay intermediates containing REP-stabilizers. *Mol. Microbiol.* **51,** 777–790

55. Bernstein, J. A., Lin, P. H., Cohen, S. N., and Lin-Chao, S. (2004) Global analysis of *Escherichia coli* RNA degradosome function using DNA microarrays. *Proc. Natl. Acad. Sci. U. S. A.* **101,** 2758–2763

56. Ow, M. C., Liu, Q., and Kushner, S. R. (2000) Analysis of mRNA decay and rRNA processing in *Escherichia coli* in the absence of RNase E-based degradosome assembly. *Mol. Microbiol.* **38,** 854–866

57. Mohanty, B. K., and Kushner, S. R. (2000) Polynucleotide phosphorylase functions both as a 3'–5' exonuclease and a poly(A) polymerase in *Escherichia coli*. *Proc. Natl. Acad. Sci. U. S. A.* **97,** 11966–11971

58. Schrier, B. K., Wilson, S. H., and Nirenberg, M. (1974) Cultured cell systems and methods for neurobiology. *Methods Enzymol.* **32,** 765–788

59. Littauer, U. Z., Giovanni, M., and Glick, M. C. (1980) Glycoprotein from neurite of differentiated neuroblastoma cells. *J. Biol. Chem.* **255,** 5448–5453

60. Kimhi, Y., Palfrey, C., Spector, I., Barak, Y., and Littauer, U. Z. (1976) Maturation of neuroblastoma cells in the presence of dimethylsulfoxide. *Proc. Natl. Acad. Sci. U. S. A.* **73,** 462–466

61. Soreq, H., Miskin, R., Zutra, A., and Littauer, U. Z. (1983) Modulation in the levels and localization of plasminogen activator in differentiating neuroblastoma cells. *Dev. Brain Res.* **7,** 257–269

62. Periz, G., and Fortini, M. E. (2000) Proteolysis in Alzheimer's disease. Can plasmin tip the balance? *EMBO Rep.* **1,** 477–478

63. Gozes, I., and Littauer, U. Z. (1978) Tubulin microheterogeneity increases with rat brain maturation. *Nature* **278,** 411–413

64. Ginzburg, I., Behar, L., Givol, D., and Littauer, U. Z. (1981) The nucleotide sequence of rat α-tubulin: 3'-end characteristics, and evolutionary conservation. *Nucleic Acids Res.* **9,** 2691–2697

65. Ginzburg, I., Scherson, T., Rybak, S., Kimhi, Y., Neuman, D., Schwartz, M., and Littauer, U. Z. (1983) Expression of mRNA for microtubule proteins in the developing nervous system. *Cold Spring Harbor Symp. Quant. Biol.* **48,** 783–790

66. Teichman-Weinberg, A., Littauer, U. Z., and Ginzburg, I. (1988) The inhibition of neurite outgrwth in PC12 cells by tubulin antisense oligodeoyribonucleotides. *Gene (Amst.)* **72,** 297–307

67. Littauer, U. Z., Giveon, D., Thierauf, M., Ginzburg, I., and Ponstingl, H. (1986) Common and distinct tubulin binding sites for microtubule-associated proteins. *Proc. Natl. Acad. Sci. U. S. A.* **83,** 7162–7166

68. Kirsch, J., Zutra, A., and Littauer, U. Z. (1990) Characterization and intracellular distribution of microtubule-associated protein 2 in differentiating human neuroblastoma cells. *J. Neurochem.* **55,** 1031–1041

69. Bushkin-Harav, I., Garty, N., and Littauer, U. Z. (1995) Down-regulation of a 67-kDa YIGSR-binding protein upon differentiation of human neuroblastoma cells. *J. Biol. Chem.* **270,** 13422–13428

70. Kirsch, J., Langosch, D., Prior, P., Littauer, U. Z., Schmitt, B., and Betz, H. (1991) The 93-kDa glycine receptor-asociated protein binds to tubulin. *J. Biol. Chem.* **266,** 22242–22245

This paper is available online at www.jbc.org

THE JOURNAL OF BIOLOGICAL CHEMISTRY VOL. 280, NO. 49, pp. 40385–40397, December 9, 2005
© 2005 by The American Society for Biochemistry and Molecular Biology, Inc.   Printed in the U.S.A.

A PAPER IN A SERIES COMMISSIONED TO CELEBRATE THE CENTENARY OF THE JBC in 2005

JBC Centennial
1905–2005
100 Years of Biochemistry and Molecular Biology

Adventures of a Biochemist in Virology

PUBLISHED, JBC PAPERS IN PRESS, OCTOBER 7, 2005, DOI 10.1074/JBC.X500005200

Wolfgang Karl (Bill) Joklik

From the Department of Molecular Genetics and Microbiology, Duke University Medical Center,
Durham, North Carolina 27710

I was born on November 16, 1926 in Vienna, Austria, where I had my first 5 years of schooling. When I was 11 years old my family moved to Sydney, Australia, where my father had a business appointment as manager of the Australian branch of an Austrian company that marketed fine steels. I went to school in Sydney and then, from 1944 to 1947, to Sydney University where I majored in biochemistry (First Class Honors B.Sc.) and then did an M.Sc. in biochemistry in 1948. Both my thesis work and my M.Sc. work were carried out with Prof. Jack Still. I purified the hydrogenase and the nitrate reductase of *Escherichia coli* and using then relevant Warburg manometry techniques carried out detailed enzymological studies involving the identification of activators and inhibitors of both enzymes with a view to identifying their prosthetic groups, and constructed a hydrogenase-nitrate reductase system involving either dyes or flavoprotein as carrier between the two enzymes. This work provided excellent rigorous training in biochemistry and more specifically in enzymology/enzyme chemistry that I always viewed as my fundamental base for further studies.

The Introduction to Virology: Doctor of Philosophy Thesis Research, Sir William Dunn School of Pathology, Oxford

During this time I became very interested in and did a lot of reading on yeast genetics. This was the golden period of yeast genetics with Lindegren and Winge laying the groundwork. I also became very interested in the work on the T bacteriophages of *E. coli* being done at Cold Spring Harbor by the group headed by Delbruck, Hershey, Luria, and Cohen; so much so, that for my Doctor of Philosophy I went, in December of 1949, to the Sir William Dunn School of Pathology in Oxford, which was headed by Nobel Prize winner Sir Howard Florey, to work with Sir Paul Fildes on the biochemistry of bacteriophage T1 (and to a lesser extent, T2) multiplication. The William Dunn School was an impressive place; the Nobel Prize for Medicine had, after all, been awarded in December of 1946 to Howard Florey and Boris Chain, both of the Dunn School, and to Alexander Fleming. Three years later, the School still basked in its glory (1). Florey, born in Adelaide, was an Australian who had been in Oxford for 2 years as a Rhodes Scholar and who was appointed to the Chair of Pathology and Head of the Sir William Dunn School of Pathology in 1935 at the extraordinarily young age of 37. By the time I arrived in Oxford as an Australian National University Scholar, Chain had left, but several key members of the team that isolated and characterized penicillin were still there. There was Edward Abraham who had (working next door with the famous chemist Sir Robert Robinson) crystallized lysozyme in 1937 and in 1943 been a key member of the team that elucidated the β-lactam structure of penicillin. There was also Norman

Heatley, an extremely ingenious microbiologist and biochemist who developed and supervised the production of penicillin as well as its extraction from culture fluids by countercurrent distribution and who also developed the cylinder plate method of assaying penicillin; Gordon Sanders, a pathologist who was often Florey's right-hand man; Margaret Jennings, who, together with Florey, conducted the biological tests; Lady Ethel Florey (who was also an M.D.), who organized the clinical trials; and Jim Kent, Florey's highly skilled and valued technician.

Sir Paul Fildes, a most delightful crusty old gentleman, was generally regarded as the father of British microbiology. Although a medical graduate, he had never practiced medicine but found his niche in the laboratory. He had been in on the discovery of bacteriophages with Twort in Bullock's laboratory. He had an outstanding career in bacterial physiology, formulated the Woods-Fildes theory of inhibition that explained the role of sulfonamide as an antagonist of *p*-aminobenzoic acid, and at the time I joined his laboratory, was characterizing *Bacterium typhosum* bacteriophages. My work, on *E. coli* bacteriophages T1 and T2, fell into two areas. First, I measured adsorption kinetics as a function of the concentration of monovalent and divalent ions and one-step growth curves as a function of the multiplicity of infection. Second, I became interested in an aspect of virus multiplication that had as yet received scant attention, namely the nature of the changes in host metabolism induced by infection. I measured oxygen uptake using a wide variety of substrates 1 h after infection and found that oxidation of certain substrates was not affected whereas that of others was greatly inhibited; when the ability to use a specific substrate was adaptive, adaptation was inhibited (2). This was one of the first demonstrations that host-specified synthetic reactions are rapidly inhibited following virus infection. I obtained my Doctor of Philosophy in 1952.

Interlude

For my postdoctoral work I continued my biochemical training. At the beginning of 1953 I went to Copenhagen to the Laboratory of Cytophysiology headed by Herman Kalckar where I teamed with Paul Berg, and together we isolated and characterized nucleoside diphosphokinase, the enzyme that exchanges the gamma P between nucleoside triphosphates and is now implicated as functioning in signal transduction pathways (3).

At the end of 1953 I returned to Australia to join the Department of Microbiology in the John Curtin School for Medical Research of the newly created Australian National University in Canberra where I remained for 9 years until 1962. It was, in the '50s and '60s, one of the most outstanding Departments of Microbiology in the world (4). Its Head was Frank Fenner who joined McFarlane Burnet (Nobel Prize in Medicine, 1960) at the Walter & Eliza Hall Institute for Medical Research in Melbourne in 1946 and embarked on a study of the pathogenesis of ectromelia virus in mice (in which it causes fatal hepatitis), which became a classic and has served as a model for such studies ever since. Fenner came to Canberra in 1949 and turned his attention to myxoma virus, a virus highly lethal for rabbits, which had been introduced into the wild rabbit population with the idea of decimating it; it was so large that it was a significant negative factor in Australia's rural economy. After carrying out model epidemiological studies Fenner turned his attention to genetic studies on orthopoxviruses and played a major role in the smallpox eradication program in the '70s. He remains an influential spokesman in this area to this day. He celebrated his 91st birthday in 2005.

Several other faculty members were also outstanding. One was Stephen Fazekas de St. Groth, who pioneered quantitative studies on aspects of influenza virus replication with particular relevance to interference by noninfectious virus particles; studies on what are now known as defective interfering virus particles; and studies of the immune response to influenza virus, including exploration of the concept of "original antigenic sin." Another was John Cairns who came to the Department in 1954; during the next 10 years he worked on the effect of multiplicity on asynchrony of infection and the initiation of vaccinia virus infection by autoradiography, studies that revealed that infecting virus particles set up foci of replication that he termed "factories," a designation that was then applied to several other virus infections. He also pioneered the use of autoradiography to visualize DNA, in particular that of bacteriophage T4, for which he for the first time deduced an accurate estimate of its size. This work created a great deal of interest. In 1965 John became Director of the Cold Spring Harbor Laboratory for Quantitative Biology, preceding Jim Watson. A third outstanding faculty member was Graham Laver who joined the Department in 1957 and initiated a series of biochemical and molecular studies of the two glycoprotein components of influenza virus, namely the hemagglutinin and the neuraminidase. He started this work even before the advent of polyacrylamide gel electrophoresis; he employed electrophoresis on cellulose acetate strips. Using peptide mapping and immunologic assays with carefully prepared antisera, Laver, in collaboration with Robert Webster who obtained his Ph.D. in the Department in 1963 (see below), formulated the concepts of antigenic drift and antigenic shift as well as theories of the origin of influenza virus strains responsible for pandemics that postulated the introduction of genome segments from influenza virus strains circulating in pelagic birds, horses, pigs, and chickens into influenza strains circulating in human populations. Laver has been elected to the Royal Society of London and Webster to the National Academy of Sciences. Finally, there was Cedric Mims, who joined the Department in 1956. Mims was/is an experimental pathologist interested in the pathogenesis of viral infections who pioneered many aspects of this field, focusing on the effect of viral infections on lymphoid tissue, the role of immune lymphocytes in arresting viral infections, and the nature of immunosuppression caused by viral infections using as his model systems mice infected with LCM, poxviruses, Sendai virus, and Ross River virus. Mims is the long term Head of the Department of Microbiology at Guy's Hospital Medical School in London.

This outstanding faculty trained graduate students, many of whom attained positions of eminence. Thus David White was the long term Chairman of the Department of Microbiology at the University of Melbourne; Kevin Lafferty became Director of the John Curtin School of Medical Research after 10 years as Research Director of the Barbara Davis Center at the University of Colorado; Robert Webster (see above) is the long term Chairman of the Department of Virology at the St. Jude Children's Research Hospital in Memphis; and Joe Sambrook, Ian Holmes, and Ken Easterbrook also became leaders in their fields and acquired international reputations.

This then was the Department that I joined in 1953 as a Research Fellow, and then as a Fellow, and in which I remained for 9 years until 1962. When I came Fenner asked me to work on the biochemistry of myxoma virus replication, but that proved impossible with the techniques available at that time because the titers of myxoma virus turned out to be extremely low, even in the rabbits that it kills. So I spent some time following up loose ends of my earlier work on transphosphorylation and identifying two interesting hitherto unidentified ultraviolet light-absorbing substances in mammalian livers that turned out to be adenine and adenyl succinic acid. The function of these two substances that occur in surprisingly high concentrations at one time considered to be possible intermediates in the transformation of IMP-5' to AMP-5' was a matter of considerable debate and conjecture.

The Beginning of Work on Mammalian Molecular Virology, Canberra, 1957

It was around the middle of 1957 that I actually decided to shift my attention seriously to molecular animal virol-ogy. It was certainly a good time for a biochemist to begin working in animal virology. Techniques for culturing homogeneous populations of mammalian cells had been developed by Enders in the late '40s, and in the early '50s Renato Dulbecco adapted the techniques for working with bacterial viruses to mammalian viruses. The stage was thus set for applying Ellis and Delbruck's single-step growth cycle procedures to mammalian viruses.

Before I recall and discuss the issues in molecular virology that claimed my attention most intensely over the years, let me provide an outline of where I was located during the next four or five decades.

I remained in Canberra for another 5 years, from 1957 to 1962, interrupted by a fascinating sabbatical year at the NIH in 1959–1960. In 1962 I moved to the Albert Einstein College of Medicine in New York, where I stayed for 6 years until 1968 when I moved to Duke University Medical Center in Durham, North Carolina, where I have been ever since.

My first major interest was poxviruses, from the late '50s to the late '80s; then reoviruses, from the mid-'60s into the new millennium; and in the '70s just after I moved to Duke, I also worked with retroviruses for a decade or so.

My overarching interest has always been molecular virology. I worked on the nature of the genetic material of these viruses, on its replication, on the nature of the mechanisms that express the information that it encodes, and on the nature of this information. I isolated many virus-encoded proteins and characterized their enzymic functions, if any, and how they interact with each other and with their genomes in studies of viral morphogenesis. I was always looking for reactions involved in virus replication that could be inhibited in order to prevent/abort viral infection. Among the agents capable of inhibiting virus multiplication on which I worked were: interferon, for which I established its primary antiviral mode of action; IBT, a methylated derivative of which was an important factor in eliminating smallpox virus from human populations in the late '70s; and ribavirin, which is now used as an antiviral agent to control respiratory syncytial virus infections in children. Thus my central theme was to find out as much as possible about how viruses replicate and to use the knowledge gained to inhibit/abort viral infections.

Research on Poxviruses

In starting work on poxviruses I proceeded along two lines. The first was to study the incorporation of adenine into normal and vaccinia virus-infected HeLa cell monolayers. The rate of incorporation was increased relative to that of uninfected cells; the peak rate was reached when the first progeny virus particles were observed. Interestingly, although vaccinia virus contains DNA, all incorporated adenine was located in RNA. This was not without significance; this was in the days preceding knowledge of messenger RNA.

My second interest was elucidation of the mechanisms involved in the fibroma-myxoma Berry-Dedrick transformation. It was in 1936 that Berry and Dedrick reported that active myxoma virus could be recovered from rabbits injected with mixtures of heat-inactivated myxoma virus and active fibroma virus. The term "transformation" was suggested by Griffith's studies on the transformation of pneumococcal pseudotypes. However, Berry soon recognized that reactivation of the heat-inactivated myxoma virus by the presence of the active fibroma virus was a possible alternative explanation. The study of this phenomenon was taken up by several of us in the Department in Canberra in 1959, and we soon showed that it could be reproduced with other poxviruses like heated rabbitpox virus being reactivated by active vaccinia virus. Further, we were soon able to show that the reactivation phenomenon involves a non-genetic mechanism because virus, the DNA of which had been inactivated by nitrogen mustard, was still able to "reactivate" heat-inactivated virus.

I became very interested in this phenomenon and worked out techniques for assaying the phenomenon, demonstrated that the ability to reactivate resides in the central portion, namely the core, of the poxvirus particle, and studied the fate of reactivable poxvirus particles within the cell prior to reactivation (5). I concluded that the most likely mechanism of the Berry-Dedrick reactivation is that denaturation inactivates a protein that is essential for the viral genome to express itself within host cells. This protein can, however, be introduced into the cell by any other poxvirus particle, which may itself be damaged in the genome (6).

Although we were unable to identify specifically the protein that is inactivated in reactivable virus particles and that is supplied by reactivating virus particles, these studies taught us a great deal about the early stages of poxvirus infection and helped me focus my developing interests in animal virology. Before starting seriously, however, I had a sabbatical coming up in 1959, and the nature of that sabbatical greatly influenced my subsequent career.

Sabbatical in the Laboratory of Cell Biology, NIAID, 1959–1960

I spent the second half of 1959 and the first half of 1960 in the Laboratory of Dr. Harry Eagle at the National Institutes of Health. Eagle was at that time in the process of putting the finishing touches to his monumental studies defining the nutritional requirements of cultured mammalian cells; his was the top laboratory in the world for tissue culture (4). My reason for joining his laboratory was that availability of reasonably large amounts of log phase suspension and monolayer mammalian cells of various types was a prerequisite for the sort of biochemical and molecular virology that I was hoping to get into.

Eagle was one of the most respected scientists of his generation. He was highly articulate and wrote extremely well; and he knew more people than any scientist I ever knew. At the NIH he had been the first Scientific Director of the NCI; at the time I joined his laboratory he was Chief of the Laboratory of Cell Biology in NIAID. The staff consisted of Leon Levintow, Bob Krooth, Norman Salzman, Jim Darnell, Ed Cohen, and Jake Maizel. I made the fifth virologist. Jim Darnell and I teamed up in a project to unravel the earliest stages of poliovirus infection. We adsorbed highly purified poliovirus labeled in either protein or RNA to suspension culture cells and followed changes in the disposition of the label (7). The results were clear: some virus was uncoated, and some was eluted. It was the success of this approach that encouraged me to carry out similar studies with the structurally much more complex poxviruses when I returned to Australia. As for the sabbatical, I enjoyed it enormously. All members of the Department of Cell Biology and many others I met for the first time became lifelong friends; and we (my wife and two children, aged 3 and 1) did a lot of traveling on the East Coast at what was a fascinating time.

The End of My Australian Career: Canberra 1960–1962

Once back in Canberra I worked out techniques for the purification/isolation of poxviruses, the last step being sucrose density gradient centrifugation (8), and applied the technique to poxviruses labeled in the DNA or in the protein coat. I then isolated poxvirus DNA and characterized it chemically and with respect to size by measuring its sedimentation coefficient. This work indicated that half-length molecules (molecular weight, 80 million) of poxvirus DNA could be isolated readily.

Moving to the United States: The Albert Einstein College of Medicine, 1962–1968

Dr. Eagle left the NIH at the end of 1960 to take the Chair of Cell Biology at the Albert Einstein College of Medicine in New York; when he did so, he asked me to join him as an Associate Professor in his Department. I did, for although the Department of Microbiology in Canberra was outstanding with a variety of faculty members with worldwide reputations, scientific opportunities were clearly much greater in an arena 10–20 times larger. Thus in 1962 my family (my wife Judith, my son Richard aged 5, and my daughter Vivien aged 3) and I moved to New York to the Albert Einstein College of Medicine. This caused us no culture shock. Not only had we all been in the United States in 1959–1960, but there are surely no two countries that are more similar than Australia and the United States; both are young, huge, with booming economies, ample amounts of entrepreneurship, and loads of welcome for immigrants. The move was, therefore, for us no different from moving from one city to another in Australia. I received a good size laboratory next to Jake Maizel, who had also just moved to the Albert Einstein and started work.

The work I carried out at the Albert Einstein followed half a dozen or more avenues all focused on critical events during the rabbitpox/vaccinia virus infection cycle. They can be summarized in the following paragraphs.

Studies on the Uncoating of Rabbitpox Virus—First, I continued the work I had just started in Canberra, namely observing the fate of poxvirus following infection, that is its intracellular uncoating, using for this purpose highly radioactively labeled rabbitpox virus (8). The results were far more complex than what Jim Darnell and I had observed for the simple poliovirus. It turns out that the uncoating of poxvirus DNA is a two-step process. The first is effected by enzymes present in uninfected cells. Its products are viral cores and the viral inducer protein. The second, namely the breakdown of cores to liberate the viral genome, requires *de novo* synthesis of the uncoating protein induced by the inducer protein (9). The relevance to the studies of the mechanisms operative during Berry-Dedrick reactivation is obvious. We also carried out a series of studies of the intracellular fate of rabbitpox virus rendered noninfectious by a variety of reagents and treatments.

Studies on the Genesis of Rabbitpox Virus-specific Polyribosomes—Yechiel Becker and I characterized both viral and host cell mRNAs in infected cells. Viral mRNA transcription, which occurs in the cytoplasm, is easily detectable by 30 min after infection and decreases rapidly at about 7 h after infection. Host cell mRNA tends, on the average, to be larger than poxvirus mRNA. Viral and host mRNA can be distinguished by their quite different base ratios: A+T/G+C for cellular mRNA is 1.24 and 1.75 for rabbitpox mRNA. Hybridization to host and viral DNA was also demonstrated and used. The genesis of polyribosomes was then investigated. Messenger RNAs combine first with 40 S subribosomal particles (the free half-life of mRNA being about 30 s)and then with 60 S subribosomal particles to form polyribosomes. 40 S and 60 S subriboso-

mal particles are always present in strictly equivalent numbers; they are made in the nucleus and enter the cytoplasm as individual entities (10).

Studies on the Replication and Coating of the Vaccinia Genome—Yechiel studied the formation and coating of the vaccinia virus genome by examining the size and nature of the structures, complexes, or aggregates (factories?) in which the newly formed DNA is located. During the early stages of infection newly replicated viral DNA is associated with large structures; later on it is released from them and becomes coated with protein. The final stage of maturation occurs at 5–6 h and results in the incorporation of the viral DNA into immature and mature virus particles.

Studies on "Early" Enzymes in HeLa Cells Infected with Vaccinia Virus—Chris Jungwirth and I found that DNA polymerase activity in the cytoplasm begins to increase at about 1.5 h after infection. The host cell and viral enzymes differ in several properties like saturating concentrations of DNA primer, pH activity curves, etc. The kinetics of formation of virus-specific DNase and thymidine kinase were also studied. The mRNAs encoding "early" viral enzymes are remarkably long lived (11).

Inhibition of Vaccinia Virus by Isatin-β-thiosemicarbazone(IBT)—IBT and *N*-Me-IBT were used during the smallpox eradication program in the '70s. Bruce Woodson and I were able to show that IBT affects the ability of late vaccinia virus mRNA to express itself normally. Late vaccinia virus mRNA is formed normally and forms polyribosomes, but within less than 5 min the size of these polyribosomes decreases, thus greatly reducing the functional half-life of late viral mRNA and therefore the amount of protein that is formed. The functional half-life of early viral mRNA is not affected (12).

Studies on the Mechanism of Action of Interferon—Tom Merigan and I were able to show that in interferon-treated cells viral mRNA and ribosomes do not combine to form polyribosomes. Infected interferon-treated cells tend to disintegrate at 3–4 h after infection, whereas untreated infected cells are still in reasonable shape at 21 h after infection (13).

Hybridization and Sedimentation Studies on "Early" and "Late" Vaccinia Virus mRNA—Kin Oda carried out a superb analysis of early and late vaccinia mRNAs, using hybridization and density gradient sedimentation. He found the following. 1) Early mRNAs are smaller than late mRNAs. 2) Early mRNAs are also transcribed late. 3) The pattern of transcription of early and late viral mRNAs in HeLa and L cells is quite different. In HeLa cells much more late mRNA is made than early mRNA; in L cells the reverse is true. 4) At 5 h after infection the mRNA molecules in polyribosomes contain all sequences characteristic of early mRNA; by 8 h after infection mRNA in polyribosomes is very significantly depleted with respect to early mRNA. 5) The large mRNA molecules transcribed late contain sequences also present in small early mRNA. Some small mRNA molecules are also transcribed late; they contain at least some sequences characteristic of late mRNA. 6) Early mRNA is very stable in HeLa cells. Late mRNA is significantly less stable, but late mRNA that contains some early sequences is as stable as early mRNA itself (14).

Structural Proteins of Vaccinia Virions and Cores—John Holowczak undertook the first detailed analysis of the structural proteins of vaccinia virus particles and cores. He calculated their molecular weights from the amount of radioactive label in each. The principal component (VSP4) accounts for about 28% of the total viral particle mass. Nonidet P-40 liberates the second most abundant protein component (VSP6), which accounts for about 19% of the total viral particle mass. John followed up this work by measuring the kinetics of synthesis of groups of viral structural proteins by pulse-labeling infected cells at intervals throughout the multiplication cycle. This provided a highly valuable and fascinating picture of the functional relationships between the various vaccinia structural proteins (15).

This work was continued by Izzy Sarov, who showed that 5 proteins are located near the virus particle surface; that 17 proteins are present in cores; that 2 proteins contain glucosamine and are therefore glycopolypeptides; and that 6 proteins are phosphoproteins, the major phosphoprotein being VP11b, a major virus particle component.

Izzy also characterized intermediates in the uncoating of vaccinia virus DNA and intermediates of vaccinia virus morphogenesis. He found complexes that contain newly replicated DNA, spherical particles about 280 nm in diameter that exhibit a highly characteristic layer of capsomers about 5 nm in diameter at their surface (immature particles), and two types of particles that contain DNA and resemble virus morphologically but sediment at only 0.6 and 0.8 times their rate in sucrose density gradients.

Vaccinia Virus Poly(A) and RNA Polymerases—Joe Nevins, who actually joined my laboratory when I was already at Duke, examined the nature, mode of addition, and function during translation of the poly(A) sequences of vaccinia virus mRNA and also isolated and characterized three poly(A) polymerases from HeLa cells infected with vaccinia virus (16). Two were cellular enzymes, whereas the third was present only in infected cells. The latter is a heterodimer composed of two subunits (57,000 and 37,000) and is able to use both RNA and oligo(A) as primer. It is identical with the poly(A) polymerase present in vaccinia virus cores except for somewhat different chromatographic properties caused, possibly, by a charge difference. Its two subunits differ from those of the two host poly(A) polymerases as well as from those of the vaccinia virus-specified DNA-dependent RNA polymerase that Joe also isolated and characterized. This enzyme is different from all other known DNA-dependent RNA polymerases including the two HeLa cell polymerases that Joe also characterized. It is composed of 7 subunits ranging in size from 13,500 to 135,000. The three largest subunits migrate in gels at the same rate as core proteins VP1c, VP1d, and VP2c. The enzyme may therefore be the same as the vaccinia virus core-associated RNA polymerase.

Nature of Terminal Loops of Vaccinia Virus DNA—David Pickup, who also joined me at Duke, carried out a detailed analysis of the nature of the terminal loop of poxvirus genomes. First, he identified the arrangement of repeated and unique sequence elements in the terminal regions of cowpox virus DNA; second, he cloned an EcoRI fragment of vaccinia virus strain WR that contained the terminal "flip-flop" sequence into pBR322; and third, he found that the genomes of 9 out of 10 white-pock variants of cowpox virus DNA possess spontaneous deletions and duplications in their terminal regions; they had lost regions from their right-hand ends that had been replaced (presumably by nonhomologous recombination or by random nonreciprocal sequence transfer) by inverted copies of regions from the left-hand end of their genomes (17).

Dhaval Patel isolated cowpox virus A-type inclusions (ATIs) and characterized their major protein component.

One aspect of the pathogenesis of the Brighton Red strain of cowpox virus is its production of hemorrhagic lesions. David Pickup established that the hemorrhage is caused by a viral protein that is related to plasma protein inhibitors of serine proteases (18).

Studies of Vaccinia ts Mutants—Claudio Basilico isolated several vaccinia virus ts mutants and characterized one that is an early mutant. It exhibits decreased mRNA transcription and delayed and decreased DNA replication at nonpermissive temperatures. This mutant has only one-half the normal amount of RNA polymerase associated with it, and the DNA polymerase encoded by this mutant is twice as heat-labile as normal vaccinia virus DNA polymerase. Virus particles formed by this mutant at 39 °C are normal in appearance and possess the normal capsid protein complement and normal amounts of DNA but are only 3% as infectious as wild-type virus particles.

Research on Retroviruses

In the '70s shortly after I moved to Duke, there were several postdoctoral fellows in the laboratory who were interested in retroviruses. They carried out some cutting edge research, the highlights of which are described in the following paragraphs.

Ken Stone and Ralph Smith investigated the nature of changes in the protein complement of plasma membranes of avian (chick embryo fibroblasts (CEF)) and mammalian (normal rabbit kidney (NRK)) cells following infection with avian sarcoma viruses RSV and B77. Infection of CEF led to morphologic transformation and simultaneous changes in the rates of formation of several proteins. Infection with ts mutants at the nonpermissive temperature caused only one of the observed changes. Identical membrane protein changes were observed in NRK cells at permissive, but not at nonpermissive, temperatures.

Amnon Hizi isolated and characterized the α, β_2, and $\alpha\beta$ forms of the RNA-dependent DNA polymerase of avian sarcoma virus B77 from duck embryo fibroblasts. The α and $\alpha\beta$ forms were already known; the β_2 form was a new form that could be isolated from duck embryo (but not chick embryo) fibroblasts because the former contain very little retrovirus genetic information (less than one genome) so that certain precursor cleavages proceed more slowly in them than in other cells like CEF. Amnon compared the three forms of the enzyme with respect to a variety of parameters, including catalytic properties. He also showed that the β subunit is a phosphoprotein (19).

Amnon also isolated and characterized a protein kinase from the Prague-C strain of RSV.

Michael Perdue isolated and characterized a large hairpin segment from avian retrovirus RNA. When subjected to limited digestion with pancreatic RNase, it was an almost perfectly double-stranded hairpin about 350 bp long. It was located in the region between 5,000 and 6,000 residues from the 3' terminus of viral RNA, close to the junction of the *pol* and *env* genes. The RNA of the helper-free Bryan high titer strain of RSV lacks most of the *env* gene; it also failed to yield the above hairpin segment.

The Move to Duke, 1968

In the summer of 1968 I moved to Duke University Medical Center in Durham, NC, as Chairman of the Department of Microbiology and Immunology. The Department at that time was small, with only 6 faculty members, but I was given the opportunity to enlarge it; when I retired in 1993 we had 33 faculty members and the Department was then split into a Department of Microbiology and a Department of Immunology.

Research into the Molecular Biology of Reovirus Replication

I started work on reovirus in 1966 while I was still at the Albert Einstein College of Medicine. Gomatos and Tamm had just reported that the genome of reovirus comprises a new form of RNA that could be interpreted as being dsRNA, which caused considerable excitement; furthermore, the laboratories of Kleinschmidt and of Shatkin had presented results that suggested that the reovirus genome is either extremely fragile or comprises several genome segments arranged in three size classes.

This was the situation when we decided to characterize more closely reovirus genome RNA (20). We found no evidence of complete large molecules and concluded that it was segmented. We found the segments to be dsRNA by all available criteria. We then showed that reovirus mRNAs are transcribed in the form of three size classes that are the same size as denatured genome segment strands (21). We also found that reovirions contain about 3,000 molecules (15–20% of total RNA) of short (3–20 nucleotides) ssRNA molecules that are very rich in A (more than 85%). The significance of these molecules, which are not free in the cytoplasm but are present only in virions, was subsequently elucidated by Jack Nichols, who showed (by sequencing them) that they are the products of abortive transcription within virions from which they fail to escape (22).

Following careful definition of the nature of the protein components of reovirions, top component and cores, we devised the assignment of λ, μ, and σ for the members of the three protein size class groups, an assignment that has stuck. The sizes of all capsid proteins were measured, as was the number of each of the proteins in each of the particle classes. It was noted that the sizes of the λ, μ, and σ size class proteins were very close to the proteins that could be encoded by the l, m, and s size class mRNAs.

Studies on the intracellular synthesis of reovirus proteins followed. Core proteins tend to be formed early; outer shell components tend to be formed later. Host protein synthesis does not decrease until late during the infection cycle. At the same time we developed an *in vitro* protein-synthesizing system derived from mouse L fibroblasts that is capable of translating either mRNA or denatured dsRNA that performs very efficiently and that we have used extensively (23). In particular, we have used it to identify definitively the protein encoded by each of the 10 dsRNA genome segments, measured the relative translation efficiencies of the 10 species of reovirus mRNA (24), and demonstrated that regions upstream of initiation codons control reovirus mRNA translation efficiency.

Reovirus mRNA is transcribed in cores; and we were interested to determine whether cores were capable of transcribing mRNA *in vitro* also. John Skehel found that they do so very efficiently for long periods of time (25). There is an absolute requirement for magnesium. The products of the reaction are intact single-stranded copies of all 10 genome segments; the number of copies of each segment made is inversely proportional to its size.

While these studies were ongoing, a variety of careful morphological studies were carried out (26). One concerned virions and cores, the emphasis being on discerning capsomer interactions and the geometry and morphology of the 12 core projections or spikes (27). Another study focused on the effect of chymotrypsin on reovirions (28). At low enzyme concentrations virions are converted to cores via several stages, individual components of the outer capsid shell being removed one by one. At high enzyme concentrations a variety of particles are formed that possess full infectivity and no transcriptase activity and lack about one-third of their capsid protein complement.

Over the years a considerable amount of effort was devoted to characterizing a series of reovirus ts mutants that had been isolated by Bernie Fields using nitrous acid, nitrosoguanidine, and proflavine as mutagens (29). He studied 35 mutants, identified 5 recombination groups, and classified them according to their ability to induce the formation of virus-specific RNA at nonpermissive temperatures. Others then characterized these mutants further. For example, Ito determined the patterns of gene expression of mutants of recombination groups C, D, and E and then identified group D ("RNA-negative") mutants as being $\mu 2$ mutants; and Tadao Matsuhisa identified the mutated protein of the group C mutant ts447, a mutant that we often used in a variety of studies (30).

As an aside and because I have long been interested in interferon, we tested a variety of forms of reovirions for their ability to induce interferon, examined mechanisms of interferon induction by UV-irradiated reovirus, and studied the mechanism of inhibition of reovirus replication by interferon. Wild-type reovirus, cores, top component, and various ts mutants were tested for their ability to induce interferon. Top component and cores did not, and most ts mutants induced significantly less interferon at nonpermissive temperatures than wild-type virus. UV irradiation not only did not inhibit the ability to induce interferon but often greatly increased it (31): 200-fold for wild-type virus and 10^4-fold for ts 447 at 38 °C! The reason is that UV irradiation labilizes the inner capsid shell and causes some dsRNA to be liberated into the interior of the

cell. As for the reason why reovirus replication is inhibited in cells treated with interferon, the explanation is that in such cells the translation of early reovirus mRNA, particularly that of the mRNA that encodes protein $\lambda 1$, is suppressed (32).

Some time later we examined the mechanism of the antiviral activity of ribavirin, a broad spectrum antiviral agent active against 12 DNA- and 40 RNA-containing viruses, against reovirus (33). Ribavirin inhibits ssRNA and dsRNA formation, protein synthesis, and viral multiplication, the prime target being ssRNA formation. When the effect of ribavirin triphosphate was tested on core-catalyzed transcription, elongation was inhibited to the greatest extent; initiation was 2.5 times less sensitive and cap formation/methylation were unaffected. Remarkably, the transcription of plus strands into minus strands by immature virus particles, the replicase reaction, was unaffected. We proposed that ribavirin triphosphate binds to a site close to the catalytic site of the transcriptase, thereby inhibiting its helicase function (which is not necessary for the transcription of plus strands into minus strands) and lowering its affinity for template RNA, thereby greatly increasing premature replication.

The next stage in our elucidation of the nature of reovirus was the crucial one of sequencing the genome segments and characterizing the proteins that they encode. The work was started by cloning all 10 genome segments into pBR322 (34). The first genome segment to be sequenced was the ST3 S2 genome segment (35), which encodes the 331-codon long protein $\sigma 2$, and for which we also sequenced the corresponding genome segment of ts447, the ts lesion of which is in this protein. The two sequences differ in three locations. The mutation at position 581 (Ala to Val) causes significant reduction of the size of an α-helix and may be that which is responsible for its phenotype. This was followed by the sequencing of the three serotypes of genome segment S1 (36), the three serotypes of S3 (37), the three serotypes of M2 (38), the ST3 L3 genome segment (39), the ST3 M1 and M3 genome segments (40), and the three serotypes of the L1 genome segment (41). We thus sequenced 8 of the 10 reovirus genome segments. In all cases where all three serotype genome segments were sequenced, a detailed analysis was carried out concerning their genetic relatedness. Particular attention was paid to nucleotide changes in first or second as opposed to third base codon positions, few of which entail amino acid changes. For genome segment S3, the figures for the first, second, and third base codon mismatch comparisons for the ST 1:3, ST 1:2, and ST 2:3 pairs are 10, 23, and 24; 4, 7, and 7; and 86, 71, and 69. Thus most mismatches are in third base codon positions. For all genome segments STs 1 and 3 are the most closely related as judged by nucleotide homology (more than 85%), whereas serotypes 1 and 2 and 2 and 3 are somewhat less closely related (about 75%). The only exception is genome segment S1; here ST1 and ST2 exhibit 28% nucleotide base homology, whereas STs 1 and 3 and STs 2 and 3 exhibit 5 and 9% homology, respectively. As for changes in terminal sequences, many of which had been known for some time from sequencing of terminal regions prior to complete genome segment sequencing, it was noted that they tend to be conserved, even in the case of genome segment S1. Terminal regions may include recognition signals for ribosomes, RNA polymerase, and encapsidation (42). As for the antigenic relationships of the proteins encoded by the three serotypes, Gaillard had shown some time before that these are highly conserved, even those encoded by ST2. The only exception is provided by the three $\sigma 1$ proteins which display type specificity (43).

There remained the problem of identifying the functions of the proteins encoded by the reovirus genome. These proteins were expressed in large amounts by cloning the relevant genome segments into the thymidine kinase gene of vaccinia virus strain WR, which was then grown in HeLa cells or in strain 143 osteosarcoma cells. Each protein was then isolated and characterized. The following results were obtained. 1) Protein $\lambda 2$, the major component of the 12 icosahedrally located core projections/spikes, is the reovirus guanylyl transferase, that is it is the reovirus capping enzyme that forms the GpppG caps at the 5′ termini of reovirus mRNAs (44). It possesses no methyl transferase activities. 2) Protein $\lambda 3$ is a poly(C)-dependent poly(G) polymerase, that is it transcribes poly(C) into poly(G). It is thus the reovirus RNA polymerase. Neither protein $\lambda 1$ nor protein $\lambda 2$ enable it to transcribe RNA; the ability to exercise this function is presumably provided by a host protein (45). 3) Protein $\sigma 1$ is the cell attachment protein (46). It modulates tissue tropism and the nature of the antiviral response. It is present in reovirus particles in the form of 12 trimers anchored to the projections/spikes. It is formed in very small amounts only in infected cells, but Akhil Banerjea devised a mammalian expression vector system that produces large amounts of it (47). 4) Protein $\sigma 2A$ is a nonstructural protein that exists in the cytoplasm of infected cells in significant amounts in the form of large complexes that contain both it and ssRNA, including l, m, and s reovirus ssRNA species. The complexes can be dissociated with salt. Protein $\sigma 2A$ forms complexes with poly(A), poly(C), poly(G), and poly(U). Neither its function nor that of its complexes with ssRNA are known

(48). 5) Protein $\sigma 3$ is one of the two major components of the reovirus outer capsid shell (900 molecules/particle, 28% of the reovirus particle's protein complement). It possesses high affinity for dsRNA. It binds to poly(AU) and poly(IC) (48).

Before going on to the last chapter of this account of almost four decades of work on the nature of reovirus, I would like to describe two rather interesting techniques: one for dealing with the functions of reovirus proteins during the actual reovirus multiplication cycle and the other with reovirus genome segment reassortment into progeny genomes.

The first of these techniques operates as follows. When cultured cells are injected with mixtures of cores of two different reovirus serotypes, a high proportion of the resulting assortants are monoreassortants, that is virus particles that contain one genome segment of one parent and nine from the other parent. We isolated complete sets of these monoreassortant viruses. These viruses can then be used to determine which protein controls replication cycle parameters. Applying this analysis, we established that proteins $\lambda 2$, $\mu 1/\mu 1C$, and $\sigma 3$ control yield size and extent of RNA and protein synthesis; proteins $\mu 2$ and $\sigma 1$ control severity of pathogenic effects; and proteins $\sigma 1$, $\mu 1/\mu 1C$, and $\mu 2$ control plaque size. Identification of monoreassortant phenotypes is very useful for identifying which viral proteins are functionally involved at the various stages of the reovirus multiplication cycle (49).

The second technique involves the use of monoclonal antibodies against reovirus proteins. We isolated a complete set of such antibodies against all reovirus proteins (50) and used it, for example, to demonstrate that protein $\lambda 2$ is exposed on the virus particle surface. We then used this antibody set in a major study to identify proteins that associate with reovirus mRNA prior to the generation of progeny dsRNA genome segments and proteins that are components of the structures within which progeny double-stranded genome segments are generated. Three proteins rapidly become associated with mRNA molecules to form ssRNA-containing complexes: μNS, σNS, and $\sigma 3$. Some complexes contain only μNS, others μNS and σNS or $\sigma 3$, and others all three proteins. Each complex contains one mRNA molecule and, depending on the size of the RNA, 10–30 protein molecules. Complexes that contain dsRNA, which become detectable as early as 4 h after infection, contain not only the above three proteins but also $\lambda 2$. The relative proportions of the 10 genome segments in the total number of complexes is equimolar. This suggests that genome segment assortment into progeny genomes is linked to the transcription of plus strands into minus strands (51).

Two other interesting studies were the demonstration that reovirus subviral particles of any type are formed in cells infected with various combinations of hybrid vaccinia viruses that express various reovirus genome segments. Thus particles that are very similar to reovirus core shells are formed in cells infected with vaccinia virus expressing genome segments L1 and S2; if also infected with vaccinia virus expressing L2, the particles formed also possess the characteristic projections/spikes; and if also infected with vaccinia virus expressing L3, the particles formed are morphologically identical to those formed in its absence but also contain the reovirus RNA polymerase (52).

The other study is simply the observation that reovirus exists in the form of 13 particle species that differ in their content of protein $\sigma 1$: from 0 to 12 trimers of this protein at the ends of the projections/spikes (53).

The final, and potentially most interesting study on reovirus with which I have been associated, is the demonstration by Roner that reovirus RNA is infectious (54). In brief, single-stranded or double-stranded ST3 RNA is lipofected into L929 mouse fibroblasts together with a rabbit reticulocyte lysate in which ssRNA or melted dsRNA has been translated. After 8 h the cells are then infected with a helper virus, say ST2 virus, and virus yields are harvested 24 or 48 h later. Under these conditions virus that forms plaques by 5 days is produced, all of which is ST3 virus. dsRNA is 20 times as infectious as ssRNA. The primed rabbit reticulocyte lysate is not essential but increases viral yields by 100-fold. Translation of all species of RNA is essential. Whereas no reassortants are formed when ss- and dsRNA of different genotypes are lipofected together, mixtures of dsRNAs of different genotypes do yield reassortants. The same is true for mixtures of ssRNA.

These findings permit the introduction of new or altered genome segments into the reovirus genome. They open the way to the identification of encapsidation and assortment signals on reovirus genome segments, the characterization of functional domains in reovirus proteins, the construction of highly efficient vaccine strains (for pathogenic dsRNA-containing viruses like rotaviruses), and the development of reovirus, a virus nonpathogenic for humans, as an expression vector. Identification of signals required for the insertion of heterologous genome segments into the reovirus genome is already under way (55); and the feasibility of constructing novel reovirus strains has been demonstrated by the successful introduction of a functional CAT gene into the reovirus genome (56) and by the construction of a double ts mutant of reovirus (57).

Comments, Extracurricular Activities, and Background

I have been very fortunate in always having been well funded and having had bright and enthusiastic young collaborators. I had close to 100 graduate students and post-doctoral fellows. Many among them have done extremely well, like Bernie Fields, who died tragically of pancreatic cancer in 1995 and who was Chairman of the Department of Microbiology and Molecular Genetics at Harvard and a member of the National Academy of Sciences, and John Skehel, who has now been Director of the MRC Institute for Medical Research at Mill Hill for more than 10 years, is a Fellow of the Royal Society, and 5 years ago was knighted by the Queen.

My laboratory has never been large, generally 10–12, because I have always had many responsibilities besides research. For 25 years, from 1968 to 1993, I was Chairman of the Department of Microbiology and Immunology at Duke University Medical Center, which I built up from 6 faculty members to 33 and which in the mid-'80s was ranked as one of the top three microbiology/immunology departments in the country. Not only was it outstanding in research but also in teaching. Our teaching load was large: bacteriology, virology, mycology, parasitology, and immunology, all from both the biological and the molecular point of view. Not only did faculty members lecture to medical students, but they also contributed to writing Zinsser Microbiology, the major, premier microbiology/immunology textbook, which the Department had inherited from Hans Zinsser of Harvard, who initiated it in 1910. We wrote the 15th, 16th, 17th, 18th, 19th, and 20th editions spanning the period from 1972 to 1990. The book, new editions of which appeared every 4 years, was very successful. It generally comprised about 1,260 pages. I acted as Editor-in-Chief and wrote the basic virology chapters, which generally amounted to about 180 pages. Compiling each new edition always involved 18 months of intensive literature research, writing, and coordinating contributions. Each edition comprised about 100 chapters from about 25 authors, about one-half of whom were members of the Department, and 90% were faculty members of Duke University Medical Center.

In addition to my administrative, teaching, and research activities at DUMC I served for many years on review committees. I was Chairman of the Virology Study Section of NIH in the early '70s; served as President of the Microbiology Chairmen's Association in 1979; Editor-in-Chief of *Virology* for 24 years; Editor-in-Chief of *Microbiological*

Reviews for 5 years; one of the eight Associate Editors of the *Journal of Biological Chemistry* for 10 years; and a member of several other Editorial Boards.

I was fortunate to have had my efforts and work well recognized. I was elected to the National Academy of Sciences in 1981 and to the Institute of Medicine of the National Academy of Sciences in 1982 and was awarded the $50,000 ICN International Prize in Virology in 1991.

Let me review briefly several issues/activities with which I was associated or that I initiated and that afforded me great satisfaction. The first was within Duke and that was my role in founding the Duke Comprehensive Cancer Center. The late '60s and early '70s were a unique time in biomedical research. Spectacular advances in molecular biology, genetics, and virology were beginning to permit definition of cancer in far more concrete terms than had hitherto been possible. In particular, recent discoveries had shown that certain viruses were capable of transforming normal cells into tumor cells, which permitted detailed examination of the transformation process in molecular terms. The resulting intellectual ferment generated a strong feeling that here was a golden opportunity for implementing an all-out assault on cancer, and in January 1971 President Nixon, in his State of the Union message, declared a "war on cancer," a key ingredient of which was the creation of a series of Comprehensive Cancer Centers.

This was the situation shortly after I came to Duke in 1968 as Chairman of one of the five basic science departments. I became interested in the new horizons for cancer research for two reasons: Judith, my first wife, had breast cancer (she had had a mastectomy the year before when we were still in New York), and as a molecular virologist building up a department, it appeared to me that Duke was the perfect place for one of the regional Comprehensive Cancer Centers. I prepared a rationale for such a Center and what would be required in terms of staff and facilities and circulated this material in January 1971 among key Department Chairmen. As a result of the keen interest and support that it received I discussed it in detail with Dr. Anlyan and in February 1971 he and I went to brief President Sanford. He also was enthusiastic and fully supportive. As a result I formally proposed to MedSac in April 1971 that DUMC apply for one of the regional Comprehensive Cancer Centers, and MedSac approved. Dr. Anlyan set up a Cancer Planning Committee with me as Chairman and Bill Shingleton as Vice-Chairman. Intensive planning for a couple of years culminated in a successful application to the NCI for a Comprehensive Cancer Center, followed by two applications for facilities, the first for the Jones Building for Basic Cancer Research and the second for the Morris Building for Clinical Cancer Research. As for the Directorship of the new Comprehensive Cancer, we decided that the Director of the CCC should not also be a departmental chairman; and Dr. Anlyan, Wayne Rundles, and I decided that the Director of the CCC should be Bill Shingleton, which turned out to be an excellent choice. The DCCC is now in its 34th year and very successful; its five yearly core support grant applications are always approved with high priority.

The second such activity was my founding of the American Society for Virology. Viruses were discovered in the 1890s; and it was not long before the unique advantages as model systems of these extraordinarily simple self-replicating biological units capable of inducing most profound changes in the cells that they infect began to attract attention. Molecular studies of bacterial viruses provided the basis for the generation of molecular biology and molecular genetics; Nobel Prizes began to be awarded to virologists; yet by the mid-1960s no Society for Virology existed anywhere in the world, virology being subsumed under the heading of microbiology, which included bacteriology, mycology, parasitology, and virology. The problem was that bacteria, fungi/yeasts, and many parasites are unicellular organisms, whereas the dominant branch of virology by the mid-1960s was concerned with viruses that infect humans and other vertebrates. As a result, virologists no longer felt at home with the American Society for Microbiology (ASM), the annual meetings of which were the only annual get togethers for virologists. Hence discussions began in the '70s and gathered momentum as to what should be done to remedy this situation.

In December 1980 I sent a letter to a dozen friends who were leading virologists, suggesting that we might form an American Society for Virology (ASV) and suggested meeting at a central location to discuss such an initiative. Because the response was overwhelmingly positive, we sent the same letter to 180 virologists; of 140 replies, 138 were positive. As a result 40 leading virologists met at O'Hare International Airport on June 9, 1981, where we discussed specifics and finally passed unanimously a resolution to found an ASV. I was elected Interim President. The first annual meeting of the new society, attended by about 900 virologists, was held August 1–5, 1982 on the campus of Cornell University in Ithaca, NY, where the new society was officially promulgated and I was elected first President. This was the first society for virology anywhere in the world; now there are more than a dozen. The ASV now has almost 3,500 members, 600 of whom are citizens from 44 countries outside the United States. This year we will have our 24th 4-day long annual meeting; about 1,500 virologist will be present.

The third such activity devolved from my research on vaccinia virus. WHO had mounted a worldwide smallpox eradication campaign in the 1970s and had set up a committee, the Smallpox Eradication Committee, to keep track of it and coordinate it with related activities. I was one of the two United States representatives on it. The campaign terminated when smallpox was officially declared eradicated in 1980. Although eradicated in humans, there was still a great deal of smallpox virus around in the form of samples, isolates, and specimens in many laboratories; and efforts were made to track these down and destroy them. When this goal was within reach, the leadership of the Smallpox Eradication Campaign recommended that all smallpox samples/stocks everywhere be destroyed, so that smallpox could officially be declared to be totally eradicated from the planet. This proposal was brought before the Smallpox Eradication Committee where the United States had no objection, but the Soviet Union objected. We then decided that all smallpox virus stocks worldwide should be destroyed except stocks in two institutes: the CDC in Atlanta and the Institute of Viral Preparations in Moscow, which was later changed to the NPO "Vector" Institute of Molecular Biology in Koltsovo, Novosibirsk region, Russia.

This was fine until, in the late '80s, the Eradication Campaign leadership renewed their efforts to destroy these stocks also. This did not seem smart to me for several reasons. First, one could not possibly be certain that no smallpox virus whatsoever escaped destruction either by chance (in an unmarked tube or in an overlooked location) or by design. Second, one of the major concerns of the Smallpox Eradication Committee was to follow infections caused by monkeypox virus in Africa. Monkeypox virus, a close relative of smallpox virus, causes a smallpox-like disease in humans but is much less readily transmitted among humans than smallpox virus. The problem is that mutation could at any time increase the rate of transmission of monkeypox virus among humans by several orders of magnitude. Third, there is always the possibility that smallpox virus might be surviving in smallpox patients buried in permafrost; smallpox antigens have, in fact, been recovered from such accidentally exposed patients. Finally, if smallpox virus does appear again for any of these or other reasons and no smallpox virus is available for measuring the potency of old or newly prepared stocks of smallpox vaccine, huge epidemics could result with no way of arresting them. Therefore, at the 9th International Congress of Virology in Glasgow in August 1993 I pointed out, in the course of opening a Round Table Conference entitled "Smallpox: the final steps toward eradication," how shortsighted and self-destructive destruction of the officially sanctioned stocks of smallpox virus would be. I followed up this talk with three articles entitled "Why the smallpox virus stocks should not be destroyed" (in *Science*, 1993), "The destruction of smallpox virus stocks in national repositories: a grave mistake and a bad precedent" (in *Infectious Agents and Disease*, 1994), and "The remaining smallpox virus stocks are too valuable to be destroyed" (in *The Scientist*, 1996) that elicited a great deal of interest and a deluge of comments. The official United States position vacillated for several years until in the late '90s the United States officially decided (after urging by Britain) not to destroy its smallpox virus stocks. The wisdom of this decision became apparent during the smallpox virus scare several years ago when the efficacy of smallpox vaccine stocks could be accurately determined.

As for my interests outside the laboratory and the office, I might mention the following. First, because I am equally at home in two cultures (the Austrian/German and the British/American) I am greatly interested in international affairs and love to travel; I have traveled widely. I love classical music and opera, the theater, and reading. I play tennis and golf when time permits. I have devoted a considerable amount of time and effort to two causes in Durham: Caring House, a home-away-from-home residential facility for out-of-town patients of the Duke Comprehensive Cancer Center who are undergoing intensive chemotherapy or radiotherapy, for which I was President of the Board of Directors and directed a successful $2.25 million Endowment Raising Campaign; and the Durham County Public Library, of whose Foundation I am a member, the current objective of which is, once again, to raise an endowment.

My first wife, Judith, an Australian who was the mother of my son Richard and my daughter Vivien, died in 1975. Two years later I married my present wife, Pat, born in Columbus, OH, whose first husband Chuck had died 4 months before Judith. Together we have 6 children and 17 grandchildren (including two sets of twin girls) who range in age from 23 years to 1. What could be better!!!

Address correspondence to: finch012@mc.duke.edu

REFERENCES

1. Joklik, W. K. (1996) The story of penicillin: the view from Oxford in the early 1950s. *FASEB J.* **10**, 525–528
2. Joklik, W. K. (1952) The effect of phage infection on the metabolic activity of the host cell. *Br. J. Exp. Pathol.* **33**, 368–379
3. Berg, P., and Joklik, W. K. (1954) Enzymatic phosphorylation of nucleoside diphosphates. *J. Biol. Chem.* **210**, 657–672
4. Joklik, W. K. (1996) Famous institutions in virology: The Department of Mi-

crobiology, Australian National University and the Laboratory of Cell Biology, National Institute of Allergy and Infectious Diseases. *Arch. Virol.* **141,** 969–982

5. Joklik, W. K., Holmes, I. H., and Briggs, M. J. (1960) The reactivation of poxviruses. III. Properties of reactivable particles. *Virology* **11,** 202–208

6. Joklik, W. K., Abel, P., and Holmes, I. H. (1960) Reactivation of poxviruses by a non-genetic mechanism. *Nature* **196,** 992–993

7. Joklik, W. K., and Darnell, J. E., Jr. (1961) The adsorption and early fate of purified poliovirus in HeLa cells. *Virology* **13,** 439–447

8. Joklik, W. K. (1962) The preparation and characteristics of highly purified radioactively labeled poxvirus. *Biochim. Biophys. Acta* **61,** 290–301

9. Joklik, W. K. (1964) The intracellular uncoating of poxvirus DNA. II. The molecular basis of the uncoating process. *J. Mol. Biol.* **8,** 277–288

10. Becker, Y., and Joklik, W. K. (1964) Messenger RNA in cells infected with vaccinia virus. *Proc. Natl. Acad. Sci. U. S. A.* **51,** 577–585

11. Jungwirth, C., and Joklik, W. K. (1965) Studies on "early" enzymes in HeLa cells infected with vaccinia virus. *Virology* **27,** 80–93

12. Woodson, B., and Joklik, W. K. (1965) The inhibition of vaccinia virus multiplication by isatin-β-thiosemicarbazone. *Proc. Natl. Acad. Sci. U. S. A.* **54,** 946–953

13. Joklik, W. K., and Merigan, T. C. (1966) Concerning the mechanism of action of interferon. *Proc. Natl. Acad. Sci. U. S. A.* **56,** 558–565

14. Oda, K., and Joklik, W. K. (1967) Hybridization and sedimentation studies on "early" and "late" vaccinia messenger RNA. *J. Mol. Biol.* **27,** 395–419

15. Holowczak, J. A., and Joklik, W. K. (1967) Studies on the structural proteins of vaccinia virus. II. Kinetics of synthesis of individual groups of structural proteins. *Virology* **33,** 726–739

16. Nevins, J. R., and Joklik, W. K. (1975). Poly(A) sequences of vaccinia virus messenger RNA: nature, mode of addition and function during translation *in vitro* and *in vivo. Virology* **63,** 1–14

17. Pickup, D. J., Bastia, D., and Joklik, W. K. (1983) Cloning of the terminal loop of vaccinia virus DNA. *Virology* **108,** 215–217

18. Pickup, D. J., Ink, B. S., Hu, W., Ray, C. A., and Joklik, W. K. (1986) Hemorrhage in lesions caused by cowpox virus is induced by a viral protein that is related to plasma protein inhibitors of serine proteases. *Proc. Natl. Acad. Sci. U. S. A.* **83,** 7698–7702

19. Hizi, A., and Joklik, W. K. (1977) RNA-dependent DNA polymerase of avian sarcoma virus B77. I. Isolation and partial characterization of the α, β₂ and αβ forms of the enzyme. *J. Biol. Chem.* **252,** 2281–2289

20. Bellamy, A. R., Shapiro, L., August, J. T., and Joklik, W. K. (1967) Studies on reovirus RNA. I. Characterization of reovirus genome RNA. *J. Mol. Biol.* **29,** 1–17

21. Bellamy, A. R., and Joklik, W. K. (1967) Studies on reovirus RNA. II. Characterization of reovirus messenger RNA and of the genome RNA segments from which it is transcribed. *J. Mol. Biol.* **29,** 19–26

22. Nichols, J. L., Bellamy, A. R., and Joklik, W. K. (1972) Identification of the nucleotide sequences of the oligonucleotides present in reovirions. *Virology* **49,** 562–572

23. McDowell, M. J., Joklik, W. K., Villa-Komaroff, L., and Lodish, H. E. (1972) Translation of reovirus messenger RNAs synthesized *in vitro* into reovirus polypeptides by several mammalian cell-free extracts. *Proc. Natl. Acad. Sci. U. S. A.* **69,** 2649–2653

24. Gaillard, R. K., Jr., and Joklik, W. K. (1985) The relative translation efficiencies of reovirus messenger RNAs. *Virology* **147,** 336–348

25. Skehel, J. J., and Joklik, W. K. (1969) Studies on the *in vitro* transcription of reovirus RNA catalyzed by reovirus cores. *Virology* **39,** 822–831

26. Smith, R. E., Zweerink, H. J., and Joklik, W. K. (1969) Polypeptide components of virions, top component and cores of reovirus type 3. *Virology* **39,** 791–810

27. Luftig, R. B., Kilham, S. S., Hay, A. J., Zweerink, H. J., and Joklik, W. K. (1972) An ultrastructural study of virions and cores of reovirus type 3. *Virology* **48,** 170–181

28. Joklik, W. K. (1972) Studies on the effect of chymotrypsin in reovirions. *Virology* **49,** 700–715

29. Fields, B. N., and Joklik, W. K. (1969) Isolation and preliminary genetic and biochemical characterization of temperature-sensitive mutants of reovirus. *Virology* **37,** 335–342

30. Matsuhisa, T., and Joklik, W. K. (1974) Temperature-sensitive mutants of reovirus. V. Studies on the nature of the temperature-sensitive lesion of the Group C mutant ts447. *Virology* **60,** 380–389

31. Lai, M.-H. T., and Joklik, W. K. (1973) The induction of interferon by temperature-sensitive mutants of reovirus, UV-irradiated reovirus and subviral reovirus particles. *Virology* **51,** 191–204

32. Wiebe, M., and Joklik, W. K. (1975) The mechanism of inhibition of reovirus replication by interferon. *Virology* **66,** 229–240

33. Rankin, J. T., Jr., Eppes, S. B., Antczak, J. B., and Joklik, W. K. (1989) Studies on the mechanism of the antiviral activity of ribavirin against reovirus. *Virology* **168,** 147–158

34. Cashdollar, L. W., Chmelo, R., Esparza, J., Hudson, G. R., and Joklik, W. K. (1984) Molecular cloning of the complete genome of reovirus serotype 3. *Virology* **133,** 191–196

35. Cashdollar, L. W., Esparza, J., Hudson, G.R., Chmelo, R., Lee, P. W. K., and Joklik, W. K. (1982) Cloning the double-stranded RNA genes of reovirus: sequence of the cloned S2 gene. *Proc. Natl. Acad. Sci. U. S. A.* **79,** 7644–7648

36. Cashdollar, L. W., Chmelo, R., Wiener, J. R., and Joklik, W. K. (1985) The sequences of the S1 genes of the three serotypes of reovirus. *Proc. Natl. Acad. Sci. U. S. A.* **82,** 24–28

37. Wiener, J. R., and Joklik, W. K. (1987) Comparison of the reovirus serotype 1, 2 and 3 S3 genome segments encoding the nonstructural protein σNS. *Virology* **161,** 332–339

38. Wiener, J. R., and Joklik, W. K. (1988) Evolution of reovirus genes: a comparison of serotype 1, 2 and 3 M2 genome segments, which encode the major structural capsid protein m1C. *Virology* **163,** 603–613

39. Bartlett, J. A., and Joklik, W. K. (1988) The sequence of the reovirus serotype 3 L3 genome segment which encodes the major core protein λ1. *Virology* **167,** 31–37

40. Wiener, J. R., Bartlett, J. A., and Joklik, W. K. (1989) The sequences of reovirus serotype 3 genome segments M1 and M3 encoding the minor protein μ2 and the major nonstructural protein μNS, respectively. *Virology* **169,** 293–304

41. Wiener, J. R., and Joklik, W. K. (1989) The sequences of the reovirus serotype 1, 2 and 3 L1 genome segments and analysis of the mode of divergence of the reovirus serotypes. *Virology* **169,** 194–203

42. Antczak, J. B., Chmelo, R., Pickup, D. J., and Joklik, W. K. (1982) The sequences at both termini of the 10 genes of reovirus serotype 3 (strain Dearing). *Virology* **121,** 307–319

43. Gaillard, R. K., Jr., and Joklik, W. K. (1980) The antigenic determinants of most of the proteins coded by the three serotypes of reovirus are highly conserved during evolution. *Virology* **107,** 533–536

44. Mao, Z., and Joklik, W. K. (1991) Isolation and enzymatic characterization of protein λ2, the reovirus guanylyltransferase. *Virology* **185,** 377–386

45. Starnes, M. C., and Joklik, W. K. (1993) Reovirus protein λ3 is a poly(C)-dependent poly(G) polymerase. *Virology* **193,** 356–366

46. Lee, P. W. K., Hayes, E. C., and Joklik, W. K. (1981) Protein σ1 is the reovirus cell attachment protein. *Virology* **108,** 156–163

47. Banerjea, A. C., Brechling, K. A., Ray, C. A., Erikson, H., Pickup, D. J., and Joklik, W. K. (1988) High-level synthesis of biologically active reovirus protein σ1 in a mammalian expression vector system. *Virology* **167,** 601–612

48. Huismans, H., and Joklik, W. K. (1976) Reovirus-coded polypeptides in infected cells: isolation of two native monomeric polypeptides with affinity for single-stranded and double-stranded RNA, respectively. *Virology* **70,** 411–424

49. Moody, M. D., and Joklik, W. K. (1989) The function of reovirus proteins during the reovirus multiplication cycle: analysis using monoreassortants. *Virology* **173,** 437–446

50. Lee, P. W. K., Hayes, E. C., and Joklik, W. K. (1981) Characterization of antireovirus immunoglobulins secreted by clonal hybridoma cell lines. *Virology* **108,** 134–146

51. Antczak, J. B., and Joklik, W. K. (1992) Reovirs genome segment assortment into progeny genomes studied by the use of monoclonal antibodies directed against reovirus proteins. *Virology* **187,** 760–776

52. Xu, P., Miller, S. E., and Joklik, W. K. (1993) Generation of reovirus core-like particles in cells infected with hybrid vaccinia viruses that express genome segments L1, L2, L3 and S2. *Virology* **197,** 726–731

53. Larson, S. M., Antczak, J. B., and Joklik, W. K. (1994) Reovirus exists in the form of thirteen particle species that differ in their content of protein σ1. *Virology* **201,** 303–311

54. Roner, M. R., Sutphin, L. A., and Joklik, W. K. (1990) Reovirus RNA is infectious. *Virology* **179,** 845–852

55. Roner, M. R., Lin, P.-N., Nepluev, I., Kong, L.-J., and Joklik, W. K. (1995) Identification of signals required for the insertion of heterologous genome segments into the reovirus genome. *Proc. Natl. Acad. Sci. U. S. A.* **92,** 12362–12366

56. Roner, M. R., and Joklik, W. K. (2001) Reovirus reverse genetics: incorporation of the CAT gene into the reovirus genome. *Proc. Natl. Acad. Sci. U. S. A.* **98,** 8036–8041

57. Roner, M. R., and Joklik, W. K. (2001) Construction and characterization of a reovirus double temperature-sensitive mutant. *Proc. Natl. Acad. Sci. U. S. A.* **94,** 6826–6830

REFLECTIONS

This paper is available online at www.jbc.org

THE JOURNAL OF BIOLOGICAL CHEMISTRY VOL. 280, NO. 52, pp. 42477–42485, December 30, 2005
© 2005 by The American Society for Biochemistry and Molecular Biology, Inc. Printed in the U.S.A.

A PAPER IN A SERIES COMMISSIONED TO CELEBRATE THE CENTENARY OF THE JBC IN 2005

JBC Centennial
1905–2005
100 Years of Biochemistry and Molecular Biology

The Discovery of RNA Polymerase

PUBLISHED, JBC PAPERS IN PRESS, OCTOBER 17, 2005, DOI 10.1074/JBC.X500006200

Jerard Hurwitz

From the Program of Molecular Biology, Sloan-Kettering Institute, Memorial Sloan-Kettering
Cancer Center, New York, New York 10021

In all organisms, genes coding for proteins are transcribed by the multisubunit complex, DNA-dependent RNA polymerase. In prokaryotes, this is accomplished by the core RNA polymerase linked to a number of sigma factors that specify its binding to different promoter elements. In eukaryotes, this process is more complex because of the presence of three distinct RNA polymerases, each responsible for the transcription of a different class of RNA. During the past few years, structural and biochemical studies have provided enormous insight into how these macromolecular machines interact with DNA and carry out many of the detailed steps in the initiation and elongation of RNA chains (1, 2). Today, DNA microarray experiments permit the simultaneous analysis of the transcription of thousands of genes in a single experiment under a variety of conditions. Because of the availability of data banks containing sequences of many genomes, we can change or delete promoter sites selectively to alter transcription. More than 50 years ago such techniques and knowledge were unimaginable. However, it was during the period spanning 1955–1961 that discoveries were made which resulted in the isolation of polynucleotides phosphorylase, *Escherichia coli* DNA polymerase I, and DNA-dependent RNA polymerase and the solution of the genetic code, all of which contributed importantly to the future of research. Recollections concerning the discovery of polynucleotide phosphorylase (3), DNA polymerase I (4), and a historical review of the deciphering of the genetic code (5) have appeared. The purpose of this article is to describe the discovery of DNA-dependent RNA polymerase. Because it is included among articles entitled "Reflections," I have taken the liberty to describe this discovery as a personal journey and how I and others contributed to this important finding.

Early Training in Biochemistry

My early training was carried out in the Department of Biochemistry at Western Reserve University where I received my Ph.D. in 1953. The biochemistry department at that time was chaired by Harland G. Wood. The focus of the research effort of the department was primarily intermediary metabolism. Though all graduate students were required to take advanced chemistry, biochemistry, and microbiology courses, my exposure to what could be described as the beginnings of molecular biology was minimal and my appreciation of genetics was rudimentary at best. These deficiencies were personally troubling because my sister Zella was married to Salvador Luria. Dating back to 1945 and my first visit to the Cold Spring Harbor Biological laboratories where the Lurias were spending a sabbatical year, I had listened with little comprehension to Salva, Max Delbrück, Al Hershey, Renato Dulbecco, and other luminaries of the phage field discuss their research. During my early graduate training I noticed their disdain for biochemistry, and years later, I was more than pleased when they contacted me for biochemical advice. In 1951, hoping to overcome this lack of knowledge, I took the phage course at Cold Spring Harbor. I recall being excited about the course and the phage field, but this enthusiasm was dissipated quickly on my return to Cleveland. My fellow students, who at that time included Sasha Englard, Paul Berg, and Harry Rudney, among others, were too engrossed in their own research efforts to listen to my description of the newly discovered area of lysogeny or my appreciation of the Luria-Delbrück fluctuation experiment. I recall Luria telling me during a visit to Urbana in the summer of 1952 that Jim Watson (who had been a graduate student in his laboratory at Indiana University) was carrying out important work on the structure of DNA. It made little impression on me since by that time I was immersed in studying the enzymatic phosphorylation of vitamin B_6 derivatives and their function as coenzymes. The excellent training we graduate students received in biochemistry at Western Reserve was influenced by Harland Wood's work ethic and devotion to science. His extraordinary research accomplishments and role in training young scientists have been chronicled in wonderful articles by David Goldthwait and Richard Hanson (6) and Paul Berg (7). Wood invited many distinguished scientists of the period who presented exciting seminars that kept us up to date with their new discoveries. These included Hans Krebs, Fritz Lipmann, Ephraim Racker, Severo Ochoa, Fred Sanger, Arthur Kornberg, Seymour Cohen, Melvin Calvin, and Bernard Horecker. Because a substantial focus of the department was on CO_2 fixation, I became interested in photosynthesis. I was particularly excited by the seminars given by Calvin and Horecker. Between 1950 and 1952, Calvin's group carried out *in vivo* studies on CO_2 fixation in photosynthetic organisms while Horecker's laboratory examined the enzymes involved in the oxidation of 6-phosphogluconate (Warburg-Dickens-Lipmann pathway) in animal tissues and yeast. Independently, they both identified a number of key common phosphorylated sugar derivatives (ribulose phosphate in particular), suggesting that the pathway by which CO_2 fixation occurred in photosynthesis was biochemically tractable. I thought that the purification and isolation of the enzymes involved in photosynthetic CO_2 fixation was the best way to define this pathway. Because this was the approach Horecker's group used to elucidate the oxidation of 6-phosphogluconate, which then led to the discovery of the transketolase and transaldolase, I decided to apply for postdoctoral training in his laboratory at the National Institutes of Health. Horecker graciously accepted me as a postdoctoral fellow. In the interim period, Wood convinced me that I needed additional training in chemistry. For that reason, immediately after receiving my Ph.D. degree, I spent 1953–1954 working in Albert Neuberger's laboratory at the Institute for Medical Research at Mill Hill in London, England, where I carried out stereochemical organic syntheses. I was given the problem of synthesizing hydroxyornithine in order to evaluate whether it rather than hydroxyproline was a constituent of collagen. Though I never accomplished this feat, I did synthesize both D- and L-carnitine primarily because they could be readily made from D- and L-isoserine, well defined stereochemical intermediates I had prepared for the production of hydroxyornithine. I never published this work because I naively considered these compounds biologically uninteresting at the time. Shortly thereafter, carnitine was shown to function as a carrier of acetyl groups through the mitochondrial membrane (8, 9). However, this period did give me the opportunity to learn some organic chemistry, how to use the many volumes of Beilstein, and travel.

Postdoctoral Training at the NIH

Between 1954 and 1956, I was a postdoctoral fellow at the National Institutes of Health in Horecker's laboratory. During this period, in collaboration with Bernie, Pauline (Polly) Smyrniotis, and Arthur Weissbach, we isolated and characterized a number of enzymes and substrates that firmly established the photosynthetic CO_2 fixation cycle proposed by Calvin, which Horecker has summarized in a "Reflections" article (10). Horecker, Ed Heath, and I also solved a vexing biochemical puzzle at that time, which involved the fermentation of pentoses by several *Lactobacillus* species whereby the methyl and carboxyl residues of acetate arise from the carbon atoms 1 and 2 of pentose, respectively, whereas lactate is derived from carbon atoms 3, 4, and 5. We demonstrated that xylulose 5-phosphate was cleaved phosphorolytically to acetyl phosphate and triose phosphate by a thiamine pyrophosphate-dependent enzyme that we called phosphoketolase (11). This highly productive period was due largely to Horecker's impressive expertise in carbohydrate metabolism, enthusiasm for research, and general positive personality. Harry Eagle, also cognizant of this buoyant demeanor, aptly described Bernie as a reincarnated Dr. Pangloss. The exploits of the Enzyme Section, first organized by Arthur Kornberg and headed by Horecker during the mid-1950s, included a daily luncheon seminar on literature (and any new exciting findings) with Herbert Tabor, Celia Tabor, Alan Mehler, Leon Heppel, Herman Kalckar, Jesse Rabinowitz, Bruce Ames, and anyone else willing to squeeze into the small library of Building 3 or later on the 9th floor of the Clinical

Center and have been described in a number of "Reflections" articles (10, 12). During this period, I recall Severo Ochoa's visit at which time he was scheduled to present a seminar on aspects of oxidative phosphorylation in *Azotobacter vinelandii*. Though he initiated his seminar discussing β-hydroxybutyrate oxidation, I recall being tremendously excited when he described the experiments that he and Marianne Grunberg-Manago had carried out, which led to the discovery of polynucleotide phosphorylase (PNPase). At that time, Ochoa elicited Leon Heppel's expertise to help characterize the polymer products. Leon, in collaboration with Roy Markham's group at the Molteno Institute in Cambridge, England, pioneered many of the chemical and enzymological techniques that established the 5'-3' internucleotidic phosphodiester linkage in RNA. During his studies with the *A. vinelandii* PNPase, Heppel noted that the preparations were contaminated with an activity that converted ADP to ribose phosphate and adenine, which severely limited the synthesis of poly(A). He proposed that Horecker, he, and I jointly investigate this problem. We quickly showed that it was due to an enzyme that cleaved AMP to adenine and ribose 5-phosphate. The PNPase preparations also contained a myokinase activity that converted ADP to AMP and ATP. Surprisingly, the cleavage of AMP required ATP only as an effector (13). During these studies, I delighted in my interactions with Leon. These included his many handwritten notes (sometime 5–10 pages), which often included totally "off the wall" quotes from newspapers, information about various classical symphonies, and quizzes. During our work on the AMP-cleaving activity, he once appeared in the doorway of my laboratory in Building 10 asking what he should do next. When I responded that I thought that he should think more about what we were doing, he quickly stated "I don't have the time. Just tell me what to do." I suspect that these pranks provided Heppel periods of respite from his focused and dedicated research efforts that resulted in his many important contributions to RNA biochemistry, already described by Maxine Singer (12).

Early Years in St. Louis and Studies in Nucleic Acid Biochemistry

Though I thoroughly enjoyed my postdoctoral period at the NIH, in 1956 I joined the Microbiology Department of Washington University in St. Louis, MO, which was chaired by Arthur Kornberg. My decision to leave the NIH was influenced in part by my strong aversion to the loyalty oath required at government institutions and more so by my desire to return to a more academic environment and interests in studying nucleic acid biochemistry. Kornberg's research accomplishments were already legendary,

and the department he had assembled in St. Louis was first rate and included Paul Berg, Melvin Cohn, David Hogness, and Dale Kaiser. At that time, I. R. (Bob) Lehman was a postdoctoral fellow in Kornberg's laboratory and was appointed to the faculty soon after. The group was highly congenial, mutually supportive, and intensely research oriented. The department was housed on the fourth floor of an ancient clinic building that bustled with the influx and efflux of many patients. A rickety old caged elevator carried us to our laboratories on the fourth floor. As the elevator ascended the patients milling about in the waiting rooms became more visible because of the high ceilings of the large waiting rooms. On one occasion while riding in the elevator with Kornberg, he told me that he felt exhilarated by the clinic because it kept him in touch with reality. Years later, I told him that I was impressed by his positive attitude about the old clinic building at Washington University. He looked at me with horror and said, "I thought it was terrible."

During my postdoctoral period at the NIH and our interests in pentose metabolism, Horecker and I wondered how deoxyribose was formed but made no effort to investigate this problem. Earlier studies by Ephraim Racker (14) demonstrated that deoxyribose 5-phosphate could be formed by an aldol condensation of glyceraldehyde 3-phosphate and acetaldehyde, a reaction catalyzed by the enzyme deoxyribose-phosphate aldolase. This enzyme was found widely distributed in microorganisms and animal tissues. However, its physiological role as the source of deoxyribose in DNA was questioned by the findings of I. A. Rose and B. S. Schweigert (15), who demonstrated that uniformly labeled ribonucleosides (isolated from *Euglena* grown on $^{14}CO_2$) were converted into deoxynucleotides of DNA *in vivo* with no change in the ratio of the radioactivity found in the base and sugar. Impressively, these results were obtained with cytidine in *E. coli* and the rat as well was with GMP and CMP in *Lactobacillus leichmanii*. I decided to study whether ribonucleotides were reduced directly to deoxynucleotides when I got to St. Louis.

However, soon after I arrived in St. Louis, Harland Wood contacted me and wanted to know whether the glucose fermentation pathway used by *Leuconostoc mesenteroides* included the phosphorolytic cleavage of pentose that Horecker, Heath, and I had discovered. His laboratory had successfully used the pattern of C^{14} in the glucose of liver glycogen as an indicator of carbohydrate metabolic pathways (16). They showed that glucose fermentation by *L. mesenteroides* produced equimolar quantities of CO_2, ethanol, and lactate from the carbon atoms 1,

2 and 3 and 4–6 of glucose, respectively. Because the reagents required to detect phosphoketolase were readily available (albeit in Horecker's freezers at the NIH), I had little difficulty in showing that xylulose 5-phosphate was phosphorolyzed by extracts of *L. mesenteroides* to acetate and triose phosphate (17), verifying the fermentation pathway which made the organism such a useful means for the isolation of each glucose carbon atom. Upon completion of this diversion, I began studies on the reduction of ribonucleotides to deoxynucleotides. At this time, a highly sensitive colorimetric assay for deoxyribose appeared (16). It depended on the periodate oxidation of the sugar to malondialdehyde, which on interaction with thiobarbituric acid yielded a chromogen with an absorption maximum at 532 mμ. Incubation of AMP or ribose 5-phosphate with extracts of *E. coli* resulted in substantial levels of the chromogen. However, the spectrum of the product formed in the periodate-thiobarbituric acid test differed from that found with deoxyribose. Arthur Weissbach, who was then working at the NIH, made similar observations, and we combined our efforts to identify the product. In a short time, using chemical and enzymatic approaches, we showed the product was 2-keto-3-deoxyheptonic acid, an intermediate in shikimic acid formation, which was formed by the enzymatic interaction between erythrose 4-phosphate and phosphoenolpyruvate, products readily produced from ribose 5-phosphate (19, 20).

I then used labeled nucleotides to explore the conversion of ribonucleotides to deoxynucleotides. Because labeled ribonucleotides of high specific activity were not commercially available at the time, I isolated this material initially by growing *E. coli* in the presence of large amounts of ^{32}P in low phosphate media and then degrading the ^{32}P-labeled RNA with venom phosphodiesterase to 5'-mononucleotides, which were then chromatographically separated on Dowex 1-Cl columns. Contaminating deoxynucleotides were removed by paper chromatography in borate-containing solvents. I replaced this laborious procedure with one suggested by Gobind Khorana. At that time, Khorana was at the University of British Columbia in Canada and visited St. Louis to complete studies that he and Kornberg were carrying out on the structure of phosphorylribose pyrophosphate (PRPP), the active ribose phosphate derivative involved in the synthesis of pyrimidine and purine nucleotides (21). While in St. Louis, Gobind worked in my laboratory during which time we became good friends. He suggested a simple chemical procedure that his group had developed. For this purpose, ^{32}P$_i$ was converted to polyphosphoric acid at 250 °C, neutralized, and then incubated with cytidine at 60 °C for 3–4 h.

This resulted in the formation of a mixture of labeled 2'-, 3'-, and 5'-CMP from which 5'-CMP could be isolated. I then found that the incubation of ^{32}P-labeled 5'-CMP with crude extracts of *E. coli* resulted in the production of low levels of ^{32}P-labeled 5'-dCMP, which were resolved from ^{32}P-labeled 5'-CMP by borate-paper chromatography. I noted that the reaction required ATP and that treatment of reaction mixtures with potato apyrase (which cleaved the β and γ phosphate residues of NTPs) increased the yield of [^{32}P]dCMP. My next task was to purify the system and identify the reducing agent. At this point, I made a fateful decision to change the paper chromatographic assay for a more rapid one. Kornberg's laboratory (which at that time included Maurice Bessman, Bob Lehman, and Ernie Simms) was examining the action of *E. coli* DNA polymerase I, first discovered by Arthur's group in 1955. Their exquisite work had shown that purified enzyme fractions incorporated all 4 dNTPs into DNA and (most critical for the assay I planned to use) worked specifically with dNTPs and not rNTPs. I decided to couple the [^{32}P]CMP conversion to [^{32}P]dCMP reaction with the DNA polymerase I system and measure the incorporation of dCMP into DNA. Acid precipitation was a more rapid means to measure this reaction. For this purpose, I incubated [^{32}P]CMP with crude extracts of *E. coli* (which contained kinases capable of forming the nucleoside di- and triphosphate derivatives) and then added dATP, dGTP, dTTP, and purified DNA polymerase I. Indeed labeled DNA accumulated. The reaction required crude extracts, the dNTPs, and DNA and was blocked by the addition of pancreatic DNase. Initial attempts to further purify the components necessary to support the incorporation of 5'-^{32}P-labeled CMP into DNA resulted in considerable loss of activity. Searching for factors that increased the yield, I discovered that a mixture of Mn^{2+} + Mg^{2+} was considerably more effective than Mg^{2+} alone. Much to my surprise, when I isolated the labeled DNA products formed in the reaction and degraded this material with pancreatic DNase I plus venom phosphodiesterase, conditions that I expected would yield ^{32}P-labeled 5'-dCMP, I observed that the labeled CMP had been incorporated directly into DNA with no detectable labeled dCMP present in DNA. The ^{32}P-labeled polynucleotide product was rendered partially acid-soluble after either RNase or NaOH hydrolysis but completely acid-soluble by DNase I digestion. These properties suggested that rCMP had been incorporated distributively throughout the polynucleotide chain synthesized. Reactions that were carried out with [α-^{32}P]CTP + UTP + GTP +ATP (no dNTPs) yielded low levels of labeled acid-insoluble material, which were reduced upon omission of a single rNTP. I published this work in a paper entitled "The Enzymatic Incorporation of Ribonucleotides in Polydeoxynucleotide Material" in which I indicated that the biological significance of this enzymatic reaction was unclear (22). Nearly 5 years later, it was shown that the presence of Mn^{2+} altered the nucleotide specificity of DNA polymerase I, leading to the incorporation of both rNTPs and dNTPs into DNA (23). In retrospect, it is likely that my findings were due to multiple activities including DNA polymerase I and possibly low levels of DNA-dependent RNA polymerase. How I missed discovering RNA polymerase during these studies in 1958 mystifies me to this day. Though my initial goal was to discover how deoxynucleotides were formed from ribonucleotides, I never returned to this problem. In 1961, Peter Reichard's laboratory demonstrated that rCDP was converted to dCDP by extracts of *E. coli* (24) and later showed that the reducing agent was a pair of intrinsic sulf-hydryl groups on the enzyme (ribonucleotide reductase) that was regenerated after catalyzing the reduction by thioredoxin, which acts as a protein disulfide reductase (25).

The Discovery of DNA-dependent RNA Polymerase

In 1958, I moved to New York and joined the Microbiology Department at New York University, School of Medicine. Bernie Horecker was appointed chairman of the department. At that time, influenced by the work I carried out in St. Louis, I decided to focus on RNA synthesis. During this period, our thinking about the biosynthesis of RNA was dominated by the action of PNPase first discovered by Grunberg-Manago and Ochoa (3) and independently somewhat later by Uriel Littauer when he was a postdoctoral fellow in Arthur Kornberg's laboratory (26). The role of PNPase in synthesizing biologically relevant RNA, however, was questioned by its mode of action. The enzyme required high levels of ribonucleoside diphosphates as substrate and produced P_i and high molecular weight RNA polymers whose composition depended on the level and particular nucleoside diphosphates added to the reaction. The reaction was freely reversible, and RNA polymers were readily phosphorolyzed to the corresponding ribonucleoside diphosphates. There was no evidence of a template-directed synthesis of RNA, though at the time of its discovery the possibility was raised that the aberrant products formed resulted from the loss of factors during its purification that were required to form more physiological RNA products. Though further studies validated these concerns and PNPase was found to be a variable component of the prokaryotic degradosome, which regulates RNA hydrolysis, the enzyme proved to be of enormous importance. It provided the means for the synthesis of many different RNAs that helped to define the genetic code and the first hybridization experiments between poly(A) and poly(U), carried out by the laboratories of Alex Rich and Robert Warner (27, 28) and between RNA and DNA (poly(A) and a synthetic poly(dT) oligomer chemically synthesized by Khorana) by Alex Rich (29). Marmur, Doty, and their colleagues also showed that complementary single-stranded DNAs formed by heat denaturation of duplex DNA could be reannealed to duplex DNA by slow cooling (30). These discoveries eventually led to the demonstration that all RNA species were formed from DNA and later contributed to the discovery of RNA splicing.

During the period between 1953 and 1958, a number of reports described the existence of enzyme activities that utilized rNTPs rather than rNDPs and extended RNA chains by only a few nucleotides (specifically C and/or A residues). They were defined eventually by the tRNA terminal -CCA adding enzyme, an activity dedicated solely to the addition of C and A residues to the 3'-ends of tRNAs (31, 32). Subsequently, it was shown that DNA sequences encoding tRNAs do not include the 3'-terminal -CCA sequence, which is essential for amino acid acylation. Uniquely, in 1960, Edmonds and Abrams reported the synthesis of poly(A) chains from ATP (33), the first indication of poly(A) polymerase. At this time, it was evident that none of the aforementioned enzyme activities explained how RNA was synthesized. In contrast to the biosynthesis of DNA, which simplistically could be considered a single entity, the biosynthesis of RNA appeared to be more complicated because of its heterogeneity. Furthermore, there was evidence that the function of these distinct RNA species differed. It was evident that a number of specific small molecular weight RNAs (tRNAs) were carriers for individual amino acids in protein synthesis (34, 35) whereas the multiple larger RNA species (ribosomal RNAs), constituting the bulk of cellular RNA, existed as a ribonucleoprotein complex where amino acids appeared to be incorporated into proteins (36). By the late 1950s, it was generally accepted though not proven that the genetic information coded in the sequence of DNA contributed to the amino acid sequence of proteins and RNA acted as an intermediate in this process. In support of this notion, the pioneering phage work done by Seymour Cohen showed that infection of *E. coli* by virulent phages such as T2 caused bacterial DNA degradation that blocked bacterial protein and DNA synthesis and diverted the host to synthesis phage DNA and phage proteins (37). Similar phage experiments by Al Hershey noted that a minor RNA species was rapidly synthesized and degraded (38). By far the most compelling evidence for an important role for DNA in RNA synthesis came from the experiments of Volkin and Astrachan in which T2 infection of *E. coli* in the presence of $^{32}P_i$ resulted in the rapid formation and degradation of RNA containing the same base ratio of the T2 DNA (39). Though I was fully aware of these results and had thought about the role of DNA in RNA synthesis in St. Louis, my efforts to screen for DNA-dependent RNA synthesis started in 1959 and were carried out with *E. coli* extracts. In light of my earlier confusing work that detected the incorporation of ribonucleotides into DNA, I decided it was essential to uncover an enzymatic activity that required DNA and all four rNTPs. Influenced by the findings of the Kornberg laboratory that a single enzyme carried out DNA synthesis in the presence of a DNA template and all four dNTPs, I thought it likely that a single enzyme dedicated to the synthesis of RNA existed. To avoid complications from the tRNA -CCA terminal adding enzyme, I used $[\alpha\text{-}^{32}P]UTP$ and carried out experiments with *E. coli* DNA to circumvent the possibility that there might be species specificity.

Results from our initial experiments were encouraging, but crude extracts from *E. coli* were variable, especially in their dependence on exogenously added DNA. Attempts to remove DNA resulted in considerable loss or inactivation of the activity. After much effort, I found that protamine sulfate co-precipitated the ribonucleotide incorporating activity, which could be extracted preferentially at low salt concentrations. Subsequent purification steps yielded preparations that supported *E. coli* DNA-dependent ribonucleotide incorporation. The possibility that this activity was because of PNPase I thought remote but necessary to rule out because Littauer and Kornberg (26) had shown that *E. coli* was a rich source of this enzyme. Much to my discomfort, we readily detected its presence in our preparations. I was encouraged to think that the DNA-dependent reaction was not catalyzed by PNPase because the concentration of rNTPs required to support robust DNA-dependent RNA synthesis was in the range of 10^{-5} M whereas 10^{-3} M quantities of rNDPs were required for PNPase activity. Furthermore, RNA could not replace DNA under the conditions used, and the presence of P_i did not block the DNA-dependent synthesis of RNA but markedly inhibited the PNPase activity.

In 1959, Samuel B. Weiss' laboratory reported that rat liver nuclei supported RNA synthesis in reaction mixtures containing all four rNTPs (40). Importantly, the omission of a single rNTP markedly reduced RNA synthesis. They also showed that the synthesis of RNA was sensitive to RNase and that alkaline hydrolysis of the labeled RNA product led to the recovery of radioactivity in all four 2′ (3′)-mononucleotides. However, the addition of DNase reduced the incorporation of ribonucleotides into RNA only slightly. Clearly, Weiss' group had detected an RNA-synthesizing system that differed from the tRNA -CCA terminal adding enzyme, but at that time it was not clear whether they were examining a DNA-dependent reaction. By the late spring of 1960, we had reproducibly demonstrated a marked stimulation of RNA synthesis by externally added DNA with our *E. coli* preparations. The synthesis of RNA was completely blocked by low levels of DNase or RNase and required all four rNTPs. Importantly, a wide variety of heterologous DNAs supported RNA synthesis. We published a note describing these findings (41). Much to my surprise, in the same issue of the journal containing our results, Audrey Stevens, who was then working as a postdoctoral fellow in Leon Heppel's laboratory at the NIH, reported that extracts of *E. coli* incorporated labeled ATP into RNA in a reaction requiring all four rNTPs (42). Her paper indicated that the reaction was RNase-sensitive but did not evaluate the role of DNA in the reaction (42). In a later issue of the same volume of this Journal, James Bonner's group at the California Institute of Technology reported similar findings with extracts of peas (43). Thus, RNA synthesis was clearly becoming a highly competitive race.

Though we had used only partially purified fractions in our experiments, I noticed that the incorporations of ribonucleotides mirrored the base composition of the DNA template used. To study this in more detail, we compared DNAs that had high and low AT contents (varying as much as 4-fold) as templates in the reaction and showed that the pattern of ribonucleotide incorporation reflected these biases. During this period, I contacted Erwin Chargaff at Columbia University hoping to obtain a small amount of mycobacterial DNA (high GC content). Chargaff required that I inform him in person rather than by telephone how I planned to use his DNA. Shortly thereafter, I went to his laboratory and summarized the experiments I planned to carry out with his DNA. I began by telling him that I was studying a system in which DNA appeared to act as a template for RNA synthesis. He required that I define what I meant by DNA and what I meant by RNA. After much effort on my part, he appeared impressed by my results and agreed to give me the DNA. I followed him into his laboratory where he presented me with a few milligrams of the DNA from a bottle stored on a chemical shelf at room temperature. Somewhat surprised at seeing DNA stored at room temperature, I apologetically asked whether he had any material stored at a lower temperature. He did not. Because the assay used to measure DNA-dependent RNA synthesis was rapid, within a short time after returning to my laboratory I realized that this DNA preparation was inactive because it was quantitatively acid-soluble. I thought little about this experiment, but I was amused years later when I read a short article written by Maurice Wilkens in which he described his early experiments on the structure of DNA. At that time he wanted to determine whether the x-ray diffraction pattern of DNA was influenced by its base composition and carried out such studies with mycobacterial DNA obtained from Erwin Chargaff. To his disappointment, he found no diffraction with this preparation. I suspect that Wilkens and I did experiments with the same material.

By the Spring of 1961, in collaboration with John J. Furth who as a fellow in the Pathology Department joined my laboratory as a postdoctoral fellow, we had accumulated data to conclude that the RNA synthesized by DNA-dependent RNA polymerase reflected both the base composition as well as the sequence of the DNA template used in the reaction. RNA synthesis carried out in the presence of two special DNA templates supported this conclusion. They included the use of a short poly(dT) oligomer chemically synthesized by Gobind Khorana's group (and generously supplied by him), which resulted in the synthesis of poly(A) without the incorporation of any other rNTP and the demonstration that a poly[d(A-T)] copolymer containing the alternating ATAT . . . sequence directed RNA synthesis only with ATP and UTP in the presence or absence of GTP and CTP. More importantly, the AU ribopolymer synthesized contained the alternating AUAU . . . sequence (32). Poly[d(A-T)] was first discovered in Arthur Kornberg's laboratory and occurred in an apparently unprimed reaction catalyzed by DNA polymerase I. It was discovered in 1957 by Howard Schachman (during a sabbatical in Arthur's laboratory) and Bob Lehman. The discovery of this polymer has been described by Lehman (4). We obtained poly[d(A-T)] from Arthur Kornberg. When I called Arthur to request this material, he informed me that Michael Chamberlin, then a graduate student in Paul Berg's laboratory, was also working on *E. coli* RNA polymerase (unknown to me) and planned to do the same experiment with this DNA and felt obliged to give it to him first. Arthur proposed that after Mike did the experiment, he would consider sending the material to me. Begrudgingly, I understood this collegial requirement. Shortly thereafter, Arthur informed me that Chamberlin found that the poly[d(A-T)] copolymer did not support

RNA synthesis and if I still wanted the material he would send it to me. Because Mike's experiment yielded a negative result, I said that I would still like to try the experiment. I recall that we later exchanged enzymes and discovered that the early preparations he made were contaminated with more nuclease activity than ours, possibly explaining why his experiment failed. Among his many important contributions to the function of DNA-dependent RNA polymerase, in 1970 Chamberlin discovered that infection of *E. coli* by phage T7 induced the formation of a single polypeptide RNA polymerase (44). I was surprised by this finding because we had carried out similar experiments but failed to detect this activity. When I told him of our failure, he commented wryly that you win some and you lose some.

At this time, Weiss and Nakamoto reported the isolation of DNA-dependent RNA polymerase from *Micrococcus lysodeikticus* (45). In contrast to their earlier studies with rat liver nuclei, RNA synthesis with the purified *M. lysodeikticus* enzyme was completely dependent on DNA and carried out extensive RNA synthesis that possessed the same frequency of dinucleotide pairs (nearest neighbor analysis) as that found in DNA templates (46). Subsequent experiments from the laboratories of Stevens (47) and Chamberlin and Berg (48) showed that the molar amount of nucleotides incorporated into RNA by RNA polymerase reactions exceeded the molar level of nucleotides added as DNA, indicating that the DNA template acted catalytically. Experiments carried out by Geidushek, Nakamoto, and Weiss (49) and later by Chamberlin, Baldwin, and Berg (50) demonstrated that RNA products generated *in vitro* with purified RNA polymerase from duplex DNA were not associated with template DNA and formed DNA-RNA hybrids specifically with the DNA used in the reaction after heating and cooling. Importantly, both laboratories showed that the template duplex remained intact after supporting extensive RNA synthesis. These findings established that RNA polymerase copied duplex DNA in a fully conservative manner.

1961 Cold Spring Harbor Symposia on Quantitative Biology

In my opinion, this early phase (1959–1961) concerned with the discovery of DNA-dependent RNA polymerase culminated with the 1961 Cold Spring Harbor Symposia on Quantitative Biology, which was entitled "Cellular Regulatory Mechanisms." The highlight of the meeting was the paper of François Jacob and Jacques Monod on the "Regulation of Gene Activity" in which they proposed the "messenger" RNA hypothesis to explain the role of unstable RNA synthesized after phage infection with the wealth of information they and their co-workers had gathered on the kinetics of β-galactosidase induction and repression in bacteria (51). Their paper masterfully defined and predicted transcriptional regulation. It included schemes for the control of protein synthesis through the negative action of trans-acting regulatory proteins (repressors, later shown to be positive as well), target sites at which repressors act (called operators), and the critical need for rapidly turning over "messenger" RNAs arising as intermediates from DNA that program the protein-synthesizing machinery located in ribosomes. Other exciting papers presented at the meeting by Sol Spiegelman (52) and François Gros *et al.* (53) contributed importantly to the "messenger" RNA hypothesis. Their data extended the Volkin-Astrachan findings and included the isolation of phage T2 RNA as a physical entity, the demonstration that it possessed the same base ratio as T2 phage DNA, hybridized specifically to T2 DNA, and was ribosome-bound with a linkage more sensitive to disruption than normal ribosomal RNA. In keeping with the universality of the "messenger" RNA model, they also detected the synthesis of metabolically unstable RNA complementary to DNA in a variety of microorganisms. I presented a summary of our studies with the *E. coli* RNA polymerase, which provided an enzymatic mechanism by which DNA supported RNA synthesis (54). Sidney Brenner summarized the data that laid to rest the notion that ribosomal RNA present in ribosomes carried information for the synthesis of proteins and showed that T4 phage messenger RNA interacted with ribosomes and acted as the template for the synthesis of protein (55).

During the meeting, papers from the laboratories of Charles Yanofsky, George Streisinger, and Cyrus Levinthal focused on the gene-protein colinearity problem. Though I do not recall specific discussions about the genetic code, it was obvious that they planned to use a variety of lengthy strategies aimed at this solution. It was during this period, but unknown to me and most of us at the meeting, that Marshall Nirenberg and Heinrich Matthei at the National Institutes of Health carried out their dramatic experiments that would lead to the solution of the genetic code. In the early summer of 1961 I first heard of their work from Max Delbrück, who was at Cold Spring Harbor Laboratories. He called to find out whether I knew of the work carried out by Nirenberg and Matthei. Matthei was a student in the bacteriophage course at that time and like all students who participated in the course (as I had done in 1951) presented a short summary of his research efforts carried out at his home institution. Max summarized their results and asked if I believed them. My first response was no but I told him that I could check it out. I immediately telephoned Gordon Tompkins who I knew well and who was in the same group at the NIH as Nirenberg, and he told me that it was true. A historical review of the period describing this discovery has been presented by Nirenberg (5).

Epilogue

The important discoveries made between 1955 and 1961, like all important findings, raised many more questions than answers. They ushered in the fields of replication, transcription, and translation, their interdependence, and the complicated controls that govern cell cycle events. These early discoveries wedded biochemistry and genetics giving rise to molecular biology. The discovery of DNA-dependent RNA polymerase, simultaneously made by Sam Weiss, Audrey Stevens, and my own laboratory, was an exciting and stimulating period. It convinced me that I could do important work even if it required fierce competition. However, it also made me realize that if we had not made these discoveries, others would have soon after.

Address correspondence to: j-hurwitz@ski.mskcc.org

REFERENCES

1. Murakami, K. S., and Darst, S. A. (2003) *Curr. Opin. Struct. Biol.* **13,** 31–39
2. Boeger, H., Burshnell, Davis, R., Griesenbeck, J., Lorch, Y., Strattin, J. S., Westover, K. D., and Kornberg, R. D. (2005) *FEBS Lett.* **579,** 899–903
3. Grunberg-Manago, M. (1989) *Biochim. Biophys. Acta* **1000,** 59–64
4. Lehman, I. R. (2003) *J. Biol. Chem.* **278,** 34733–34738
5. Nirenberg, M. (2004) *Trends Biochem. Sci.* **29,** 46–54
6. Goldthwait, D. A., and Hanson, R. W. (1996) *Biogr. Mem. Natl. Acad. Sci.* **69,** 3–36
7. Berg, P. (2003) *J. Biol. Chem.* **278,** 40417–40424
8. Friedman, S., and Fraenkel, G. (1955) *Arch. Biochem. Biophys.* **59,** 491–501
9. Bremer, J. (1962) *J. Biol. Chem.* **237,** 3628–3632
10. Horecker, B. L. (2002) *J. Biol. Chem.* **237,** 47965–47971
11. Heath, E. C., Hurwitz, J., and Horecker, B. L. (1956) *J. Am. Chem. Soc.* **78,** 5494
12. Singer, M. (2003) *J. Biol. Chem.* **278,** 47351–47356
13. Hurwitz, J., Heppel, L. A., and Horecker, B. L. (1957) *J. Biol. Chem.* **226,** 525–540
14. Racker, E. (1952) *J. Biol. Chem.* **196,** 347–365
15. Rose, I. A., and Schweigert, B. S. (1953) *J. Biol. Chem.* **202,** 635–645
16. Bernstein, I. A., Lentz, K., Malm, M., Schambye, P., and Wood, H. G. (1955) *J. Biol. Chem.* **215,** 137–152
17. Hurwitz, J. (1958) *Biochim. Biophys. Acta* **28,** 599–602
18. Waravdekar, V. S., and Saslaw, L. D. (1957) *Biochim. Biophys, Acta* **24,** 439
19. Weissbach, A., and Hurwitz, J. (1959) *J. Biol. Chem.* **234,** 705–709
20. Hurwitz, J., and Weissbach, A. (1959) *J. Biol. Chem.* **234,** 710–712
21. Khorana, H. G., Fernandez, J. F., and Kornberg, A. (1958) *J. Biol. Chem.* **230,** 941–948
22. Hurwitz, J. (1959) *J. Biol. Chem.* **234,** 2351–2358
23. Berg, P., Fancher, H., and Chamberlin, M. (1963) in *Informational Macromolecules* (Vogel, H., Bryson, B., and Lampen, J. O., eds) p. 469, Academic Press, New York
24. Reichard, P., Baldesten, A., and Rutberg, L. (1961) *J. Biol. Chem.* **236,** 1150–1157
25. Reichard, P. (1967) *The Biosynthesis of Deoxyribose Ciba Lectures in Biochemistry*, John Wiley & Sons, Inc., New York
26. Littauer, U. Z., and Kornberg, A. (1957) *J. Biol. Chem.* **226,** 1077–1092
27. Rich, A., and Davies, D. R. (1956) *J. Am. Chem. Soc.* **78,** 3548

28. Warner, R. C. (1957) *J. Biol. Chem.* **229,** 711–724

29. Rich, A. (1960) *Proc. Natl. Acad. Sci. U. S. A.* **46,** 1044–1053

30. Doty, P., Marmur, J., Eigner, J., and Schildkraut, C. (1960) *Proc. Natl. Acad. Sci. U. S. A.* **46,** 461–476

31. Preiss, J., Dieckmann, M., and Berg, P. (1961) *J. Biol. Chem.* **236,** 1748–1752

32. Furth, J. J., Hurwitz, J., Krug, M., and Alexander, M. (1961) *J. Biol. Chem.* **236,** 3317–3322

33. Edmonds, M., and Abrams, R. (1960) *J. Biol. Chem.* **235,** 1142–1149

34. Hoagland, M. B., Zamecnik, P. C., and Stephenson, M. L. (1957) *Biochim. Biophys. Acta* **24,** 215–216

35. Berg, P., and Ofengand, E. J. (1958) *Proc. Natl. Acad. Sci. U. S. A.* **44,** 78–86

36. Lamberg, J. R., and Zamecnik, P. C. (1960) *Biochim. Biophys. Acta* **42,** 206–211

37. Cohen, S. S. (1949) *Bacteriol. Rev.* **13,** 1–24

38. Hershey, A. D. (1953) *J. Gen. Physiol.* **36,** 777–789

39. Volkin, E., and Astrachan, L. (1956) *Virology* **3,** 149–161

40. Weiss, S. B., and Gladstone, L. (1959) *J. Am. Chem. Soc.* **81,** 4118

41. Hurwitz, J., Bresler, A., and Diringer, R. (1960) *Biochem. Biophys. Res. Commun.* **3,** 15–18

42. Stevens, A. (1960) *Biochem. Biophys. Res. Commun.* **3,** 92–96

43. Huang, R. C., Maheshwari, N., and Bonner, J. (1960) *Biochem. Biophys. Res. Commun.* **3,** 689–694

44. Chamberlin, M., McGrath, J., and Waskell, L. (1970) *Nature* **228,** 227–231

45. Weiss, S. B., and Nakamoto, T. (1961) *J. Biol. Chem.* **236,** PC18-PC20

46. Weiss, S. B., and Nakamoto, T. (1961) *Proc. Natl. Acad. Sci. U. S. A.* **47,** 604–607

47. Stevens, A. (1961) *J. Biol. Chem.* **236,** PC43-PC45

48. Chamberlin, M., and Berg, P. (1962) *Proc. Natl. Acad. Sci. U. S. A.* **48,** 81–94

49. Geidushek, E. P., Nakamoto, T., and Weiss, S. B. (1961) *Proc. Natl. Acad. Sci. U. S. A.* **47,** 1405–1415

50. Chamberlin, M., Baldwin, R. L., and Berg, P. (1963) *J. Mol. Biol.* **20,** 334–349

51. Jacob, F., and Monod, J. (1961) *Cold Spring Harbor Symp. Quant. Biol.* **26,** 193–209

52. Spiegelman, S. (1961) *Cold Spring Harbor Symp. Quant. Biol.* **26,** 75–90

53. Gros, F., Gilbert, W., Hiatt, H. H., Attardi, G., Spahr, P. F., and Watson, J. D. (1961) *Cold Spring Harbor Symp. Quant. Biol.* **26,** 111–132

54. Hurwitz, J., Furth, J. J., Anders, M., Ortiz, P. J., and August, J. T. (1961) *Cold Spring Harbor Symp. Quant. Biol.* **26,** 91–100

55. Brenner, S. (1961) *Cold Spring Harbor Symp. Quant. Biol.* **26,** 101–109

This paper is available online at www.jbc.org

THE JOURNAL OF BIOLOGICAL CHEMISTRY VOL. 281, NO. 10, pp. 6117–6119, March 10, 2006
© 2006 by The American Society for Biochemistry and Molecular Biology, Inc.   Printed in the U.S.A.

A PAPER IN A SERIES COMMISSIONED TO CELEBRATE THE CENTENARY OF THE JBC in 2005

JBC Centennial
1905–2005
100 Years of Biochemistry and Molecular Biology

Mechanistic Inferences from Stereochemistry

PUBLISHED, JBC PAPERS IN PRESS, FEBRUARY 1, 2006, DOI 10.1074/JBC.X600001200

I. A. Rose

From the Department of Physiology and Biophysics, University of California School of Medicine, Irvine, California 92717

I am still impressed that the textbook language of organic chemistry is so successful in explaining the reactions that we find in nature. This might not have been anticipated because we find that biological reactions are invariably stereospecific whereas nonbiological reactions are invariably not. This realization came to light about 150 years ago when Pasteur found that only half of chemically prepared tartarate was fermentable contrary to chemically identical tartarate from grapes. Only the natural product rotated the plane of polarized light (1). A new geometry had to be found for carbon to explain this. It could not be planar. As understood by Ogston in 1948 (2) the stereospecificity of biological reactions derives from the chiral properties of the active sites of the enzymes that catalyze them. (Pasteur realized that only a chiral reagent would be able to distinguish between substrates that were not superimposable on their mirror images. He spent much effort searching for a natural force that might have caused chirality in the first place. It remains an unsolved problem.)

When I began studying simple enzymatic reactions at carbon centers in 1955, I was not at all sure what I might run into. Organic chemists were acquiring evidence for stable ion pair intermediates in carbonium and carbanion rearrangements in solution that were completely stereospecific. Would the stereospecificity of enzymatic reactions turn out to be explained in terms of a physical or chemical role of the enzyme? If this seems like an overstatement it may be recalled that in 1955 there were no examples to cite in which an enzyme could be analyzed to be acting as a base to abstract a proton from $-CH \alpha$ to a carbonyl. However, there were well known enzymes available such as the aldolases and aldose-ketose isomerases, the mechanisms of which had not been analyzed. My hope then was to use a stereochemical approach to the study of enzyme reaction chemistry as my first research problem.

Fortunately scintillation counters were becoming available in 1955. I was somewhat ahead of the game because of the hobby of Seymour Lipsky, an M.D. in the Department of Medicine who consulted for the New Haven-based Technical Measurement Co. and had one of their first commercial counters. Tritium, especially T-water, was also becoming available, making it unnecessary for me to repair the Rittenberg model mass spectrometer that Henry Hoberman had left to the Yale Department of Biochemistry.

The first demonstration of an enzyme acting as a base was probably our observation in 1955 that muscle aldolase catalyzed the stereospecific exchange of one of the C-1 hydroxymethyl protons of dihydroxyacetone-P with TOH in the absence of an aldehyde partner (3). From the stereochemistry of the T-exchanged product (4) compared with that of C-4 of the condensation products one could conclude that the aldehyde and the proton must approach the stable intermediate from the same direction. Evidence that "proton abstraction" is the result of transfer to a stable position on the enzyme and not to an anionic group on substrates comes from a number of examples in which intermolecular proton transfer could be shown. For example, with fumarase the reacting tritium derived from malate can be rescued from exchange with solvent by carrying out the reaction in the presence of fluorofumarate. In fact the loss of the proton from free enzyme is the slowest step of the reaction cycle.

In 1957 the conversion of fructose-6-P to glucose-6-P in D_2O had been reported to occur with little or no transfer of the substrate hydrogen to the neighboring carbon of the product by phosphoglucose isomerase (PGI) (5). The absence of transfer might indicate that the enzyme did not act as a base or that different bases were used for C-1 and C-2. We inadvertently discovered that the PGI result was misleading, caused by inadequate trapping of the product that led to its redundant exchange with the medium. In the Glc-6-P to Fru-6-P direction in D_2O we found a surprising overshoot of the equilibrium that was seen when the Fru-6-P was determined by a color test but not when determined by an enzymatic assay that went to completion (6). The colorimetric assay typically does not go to completion and therefore is sensitive to a kinetic deuterium isotope effect. The first Fru-6-P to be formed had derived some of its proton from the substrate as hydrogen. At later times this Fru-6-P acquired deuterium by back exchange with the solvent giving a lower color equivalent with time although the reaction was already close to equilibrium. Hence the apparent overshoot (6). Both T-transfer and T-exchange were found to occur in a single turnover when the reaction was run in the opposite direction with a good trap for the product: $1T$-Fru-6-P $\rightarrow$ Glc-6-P $\rightarrow$ 6-P-gluconate. Thus was established the formation of an exchange-sensitive E-T enediol intermediate. Transfer was shown to be intramolecular (7). The stereochemistry of C-1 of $1T$-Fru-6-P and the intramolecular nature of the transfer establish that the enediol was of the *cis* configuration (8). The same stereochemistry was found for all seven isomerases that we examined (9). Only xylose isomerase showed no exchange and is believed to be a hydride transfer reaction.

The generally observed *cis*-enediol mechanism allows a unique acid group to polarize either the C-1 or the C-2 carbonyl of the substrates. Because nucleophilic attack by epoxides is acid-catalyzed we anticipated their value in the active site labeling of isomerases (10). Subsequent structural studies of triose-P isomerase have confirmed our

general picture and extended it in great detail (11). The simple single acid/single base mechanism may have provided the evolutionary pressure that seems to favor this mechanism.

Because pentoses and hexoses must be acted upon in their far more abundant cyclic forms it was of interest to ask if the anomeric specificity of each isomerase could be predicted from the topology of its E-H *cis*-enediol intermediate (9, 12). When C-2 becomes tetrahedral by proton transfer from one face of the enediol, the ring-closing OH of C-4 (for a pentose) or of C-5 (for a hexose) would only be able to reach C-1 from the opposite face. The predictions made on this basis proved to be correct in all five cases that have been examined (8).

Absolute stereochemistry often obscures the details of an enzyme's reaction mechanism. In the classic experiments of Bender (13, 14) the tetrahedral gem-diol intermediate formed in the base-catalyzed hydrolysis of esters was readily detected by back exchange of ^{18}O between water and the recovered ester. However, an enzymatic reaction with a comparable mechanism would not be expected to show exchange because the reversal of the hydration step would remove the same oxygen that was introduced in forming the intermediate. Only if the intermediate was able to interchange the identical groups (positional exchange, not possible for C in this case) could one expect otherwise.

Middlefort and Rose (15) used positional isotope exchange to establish the formation of glutamyl-P as an intermediate in the glutamine synthetase reaction: glutamate + ATP + NH_3 $\rightarrow$ glutamine + ADP + P_i. A two-step mechanism, E + glutamate + ATP $\leftrightarrow$ E-ADP-glutamyl-P $\leftrightarrow$ E + glutamine + P_i, was contraindicated by failure to observe ATP:ADP exchange unless NH_3 was also present. However, this could have been due to tightly bound ADP. We realized that even tightly bound ADP might be able to achieve torsional equilibration of its phosphoryl oxygens, in which case the β-γ bridge O of ATP would scramble into non-bridge positions of reisolated ATP if ATP:ADP exchange proved to be the case. Indeed, positional isotope exchange was found in the absence of NH_3 at a rate greater than required from the maximum rates of the forward and reverse net reactions (16).

Such is my confidence that all enzymatic reactions are stereospecific that finding one otherwise suggests that a nonenzymatic step must be part of the reaction sequence. As an example, the enzyme called methylglyoxal (MG) synthase actually produces enol-pyruvaldehyde (ePy), not MG, from dihydroxyacetone-P. The MG arises from ketonization of the product ePy in solution. This was anticipated when the –CH$_3$ group of the MG was found to have been made nonstereospecifically (17). The ketonization of ePy is a slow step for which no enzyme has been found. Instead, glutathione adds spontaneously to the carbonyl of the ePy, and the rapidly ketonized adduct becomes the substrate for reaction with glyoxalase I (18). Why the synthase did not evolve to carry out the ketonization step is a puzzle because there is a very active enzyme, glyoxalase III, that would utilize MG directly. Perhaps it has something to do with the fact that methylglyoxal is fairly toxic, forming stable complexes with proteins.

For an excellent presentation see *Stereochemistry and Its Application to Biochemistry* by William L. Alworth, John Wiley & Sons, Inc., New York (1972). Autobiographical presentations relating to subjects discussed in this paper can be found in *Protein Science* (1995), pp. 1430–1433 and in "Les Prix Nobel, 2004," pp. 203–217.

Acknowledgments—*I have been very fortunate in collaborations with many skilled colleagues. Some of the more significant of these have been: Kenneth Hanson, whose scholarship provided the idea for doing the chiral specificity of citric acid; Lindo A. Patterson, for the idea and guidance in doing the absolute structure of chiral 2-deutero-glycolate by neutron diffraction crystallography, allowing us to confirm chirality of many reactions; Mildred Cohn, for the NMR determination of specific 3-deutero-PEP that allowed us to study the chirality of reactions with PEP and enolpyruvate; Jacob bar Tana for help in developing the pulse-chase method for determining the functionality of enzyme-substrate complexes; C. F. Middlefort for creative work in analyzing the distribution of ^{18}O in ATP in the PIX study of glutamine synthetase; John Richard who alerted me to the inherent instability of 1,2-propenediol-3-P, which I had tried to generate for mechanism studies; and Avram Hershko for many years of fruitful collaboration in the area of ubiquitin-dependent protein breakdown. Thanks are also due to Edward O'Connell and Jessie Warms for excellent technical assistance.*

Address correspondence to: aagsalog@uci.edu

REFERENCES

1. Mason, S. F. (1991) *Chemical Evolution*, pp. 260–284, Clarendon Press, Oxford
2. Ogston, A. G. (1948) *Nature* **162,** 963
3. Rose, I. A., and Rieder, S. V. (1955) *J. Am. Chem. Soc.* **77,** 5764–5765
4. Rose, I. A. (1958) *J. Am. Chem. Soc.* **80,** 5835–5836
5. Topper, Y. J. (1957) *J. Biol. Chem.* **225,** 419–426
6. Rose, I. A. (1962) *Brookhaven Symp. Biol.* **15,** 293–309
7. Rose, I. A., and O'Connell, E. L. (1961) *J. Biol. Chem.* **236,** 3086–3092
8. Rose, I. A., and O'Connell, E. L. (1960) *Biochim. Biophys. Acta* **42,** 159–160
9. Rose, I. A. (1975) *Adv. Enzymol.* **43,** 491–517
10. O'Connell, E. L., and Rose, I. A. (1977) *Methods Enzymol.* **46,** 381–388
11. Davenport, R. C., Bash, P. A., Seaton, P. A., Karplus, M., Petsko, G. A., and Ringe, D. (1991) *Biochemistry* **30,** 5821–5826
12. Schray, K. J., Benkovic, S. J., Benkovic, P. A., and Rose, I. A. (1973) *J. Biol. Chem.* **248,** 2219–2224
13. Bender, M. L. (1951) *J. Am. Chem. Soc.* **73,** 1626–1629
14. Bender, M. L., and Heck, H. (1967) *J. Am. Chem. Soc.* **89,** 1211–1220
15. Middlefort, C. F., and Rose, I. A. (1976) *J. Biol. Chem.* **251,** 5881–5887
16. Rose, I. A. (1978) *Fed. Proc.* **37,** 2775–2782
17. Summers, M. C., and Rose, I. A. (1977) *J. Am. Chem. Soc.* **99,** 4475–4478
18. Rose, I. A., and Nowick, J. S. (2002) *J. Am. Chem. Soc.* **124,** 13047–13052

This paper is available online at www.jbc.org

THE JOURNAL OF BIOLOGICAL CHEMISTRY VOL. 281, NO. 11, pp. 6889–6903, March 17, 2006
© 2006 by The American Society for Biochemistry and Molecular Biology, Inc.   Printed in the U.S.A.

A PAPER IN A SERIES COMMISSIONED TO CELEBRATE THE CENTENARY OF THE JBC in 2005

JBC Centennial
1905–2005
100 Years of Biochemistry and Molecular Biology

From "Publish or Perish" to "Patent and Prosper"

PUBLISHED, JBC PAPERS IN PRESS, FEBRUARY 2, 2006, DOI 10.1074/JBC.X600002200

Howard K. Schachman

From the Department of Molecular and Cell Biology, University of California,
Berkeley, California 94720-3206

After spending more than 55 years doing research and 45 years teaching a graduate course in physical biochemistry with the last 5 years spent attempting to teach ethics in a required course on Responsible Conduct of Research, I had wondered about what to write in response to Herb Tabor's kind invitation and urging to submit an article on "Reflections." Tempting as it is to write about my love affairs with the ultracentrifuge, tobacco mosaic virus, nucleic acids, ribosomes, and a host of proteins including aspartate transcarbamoylase in particular (1), I decided instead to look back at the way science was done at the start of my career and how our research environment and academia, in particular, have changed in the past half-century. In doing so, I offer apologies at the outset. This account cannot be construed as "history." Instead it offers personal recollections, biases, impressions, and evaluations, frequently without documentation. Indeed many of the papers and historical records that I would cite are not readily available. Regrettably from my point of view, Stanley Hall, my home on the Berkeley Campus for 50 years, was demolished several years ago to be replaced by a much larger laboratory, and this Reflections is being written in a temporary office.

The following pages present my views on various topics such as how careers in science have changed, how federal funding of research in universities was initiated, and how politics interfered with the funding process. In addition, the peer review system is discussed along with the plight of dissatisfied applicants. Finally, I present my impression of the impact of federal funding on universities, the controversy over indirect costs, the burden of government regulations, the enduring struggle over fraud in science, and the major changes in the culture of academia and the commercialization of universities stemming from the Bayh-Dole Act. On many of these controversial issues I was personally involved both in advocating and opposing policies under consideration by government agencies. As President of the American Society of Biological Chemists (ASBC), now the American Society for Biochemistry and Molecular Biology (ASBMB), and later as President of the Federation of American Societies for Experimental Biology (FASEB) and Chair of the Public Affairs Committee of ASBMB, I traveled extensively to Bethesda and, in concert with other concerned biomedical researchers, helped to formulate positions that we hoped represented the working scientist's point of view. Moreover, I had the privilege of serving for 6 years as an advisor to the Director of the National Institutes of Health (NIH), Harold Varmus, and as its Ombudsman in the Basic Sciences. This part-time activity involved extensive visits to more than 45 universities and medical schools where I learned a great deal about the conduct of biomedical research and the problems encountered by investigators. To some extent, therefore, this Reflections, although not about my research, is indeed a personal memoir.

Although a significant amount of material presented below is critical of government agencies and policies, university administrators, and actions of fellow scientists, I wish to emphasize that the triumphs of biochemistry in the past 60 years are almost impossible to encompass. Although biochemistry formerly was concentrated in medical schools and a few schools of agriculture, now university campuses throughout the country have thriving departments. Moreover biochemistry is "invading" chemistry and physics departments as well as engineering schools. Leadership in research is now in the hands of innumerable creative young people who have fallen in love with biochemistry and are largely responsible for the startling discoveries of the past half-century. The training of these scientists and the support of their research resulted from the magnificent contributions of those great institutions, NIH and the National Science Foundation (NSF). Conducting scientific research today is dramatically different from what I and others of my age experienced, and the pace of discovery is much more rapid. Superb commercial instruments for numerous techniques are now available. In addition, innumerable reagents biochemists formerly prepared in their laboratories can now be purchased, thereby freeing investigators to perform imaginative experiments. New journals, numbering in the thousands, are available for publication of the findings. Who could have imagined that the *Journal of Biological Chemistry* (*JBC*), which in 1945 had an Editorial Board of 12 members and published 365 articles comprising about 3600 pages, would 60 years later have 650 biochemists on the Editorial Board leading to the publication of about 5000 articles comprising 43,000 pages? And today's *JBC* pages are much larger than those in the 1950s. How did this come about? What factors led to such dramatic growth? How did little Biochemistry morph into Molecular Biology and Cell Biology, Big Science, and Big Business? How did academia change from "Publish or Perish" to "Patent and Prosper?" What may we expect for the next 60 years?

Independence in Research Comes Later in Careers

As a newly minted Instructor in Biochemistry at Berkeley in 1948 just after receiving my Ph.D., I was acutely aware of the unpredictability and hazards of an academic career. My training as an undergraduate in chemical engineering at MIT followed by graduate school in physical chemistry at Princeton provided me with little knowledge of biochemistry, and there I was, by good luck, on the faculty of a biochemistry department. Accordingly, by auditing various courses, I slowly became familiar with metabolic pathways leading me to describe the auspicious position of Instructor as a "Hypothetical Unstable Intermediate." Today, virtually no one is appointed as an Instructor. On the contrary, most individuals enter academia in science as Assistant Professors or even Associate Professors. Such appointments are made after they have spent several years, and often too many years, as postdoctoral fellows. It is now commonplace for young investigators to have two, or even three, different postdoctoral stints. As a consequence, researchers in the biomedical sciences do not become independent investigators until a significantly older age than was the case 40–60 years ago. Appointments to faculty positions at an older age coupled with the termination of mandatory retirement have resulted in numerous reports bemoaning the aging of the research community.

I can recall joking 30 years ago that consideration of promotion of a biochemistry faculty member to tenure no longer involved reading their papers. The inability to comprehend the contents of the burgeoning literature resulted, according to folklore, in the practice of "weighing" the papers and, at a later time, of "counting" them. Finally, a rebellion occurred over the "quickies," and academic departments began considering content again. However in the past 10 years, it appears that more consideration is focused on *where* an article was published rather than on *what* was published. Fortunately, leading academics responsible for this "need" to publish in *Cell*, *Nature*, *Science*, or the *Proceedings of the National Academy of Sciences* (*PNAS*) are now realizing that they have become captives of their own creation; papers in those journals are essential for winning prizes and for promotion of younger faculty members to tenure. Although there is still considerable "hype" by Editors of these prestigious journals in order to attract papers, resentment is now growing in the academic community about this emphasis on where to publish. Whether this change in the culture of academia will have an impact on young investigators and their decisions as to where to send their "hot" papers remains to be seen. In that regard, it is relevant to ask whether the almost limitless proliferation of journals will ever end. Professional societies justify publishing new specialized journals based on the growth of science, and private companies have found science reporting a profitable venture.

Federal Support of Science

From the perspective of today it is difficult for those whose careers began in the 1940s to recall how research was done before federal funds became commonplace. The birth of the NSF in 1950 was the outcome of the remarkable report (2) by Vannevar Bush to the President of the United States on July 5, 1945. That insightful and visionary report, entitled "Science—The Endless Frontier," should be required reading today for Members of the United States House of Representatives and the Senate as they are perilously close to reducing the budget of NIH for next year. The report of only 40 pages, plus the more detailed appendices by various subcommittees, has only 6 parts (or chapters). Individual sections are devoted to research aimed at understanding and eliminating disease, the benefits to public welfare from scientific research, the need for training future generations of scientists, the importance of openness in science and the "freedom of inquiry," and finally the establishment of a government agency to foster and fund scientific research in universities. Basic scientific research and training in this country today stem directly from the Bush report, an outgrowth of his experience as head of the Office of Scientific Research and Development (OSRD) in supervising civilian scientific activities during World War II. The recognition of the invaluable contributions to the war effort made by the scientific community led to extensive deliberation of the potential role of government in the support of science in peacetime.

Not only is the NSF the direct beneficiary as spelled out magnificently in the section termed "The Means to the End" but also, to a substantial extent, that "great invention," NIH, from which most biochemists receive research support, owes its largesse to the spirit of the Bush Report in the part entitled "The War Against Disease." However it should be noted that 5 years elapsed between the submission of the Bush Report and the establishment of the NSF. During that interval of debate and political bickering over the governance of the proposed agency (3), the medical community, many of whose members were not enthusiastic about biomedical research being centered in the new foundation, devoted efforts to steer more government funds to the Public Health Service and thereby to NIH. That activity led to the astonishing increase in NIH funding for extramural research from less than 1 million dollars in 1946 to about 4 million in 1947 (4). Ever since, NIH has become the sponsor of most biomedical research and training. The role of NSF in supporting basic biological research is meager by comparison. Whereas there was substantial support for doubling the NIH budget recently, a similar effort to double the NSF budget has not been successful. Indeed Congress and the public have been extremely enthusiastic about increasing funding for research aimed at improving the health of the citizenry. Almost invariably over the past 60 years, the annual increases in NIH funding approved by Congress exceeded those proposed by the President. Some have attributed that to the personal interests of members of Congress in their own health. Whatever the motivation, funding of NIH has increased phenomenally, reaching the present staggering level of about $29 billion. But it should not come as a surprise that the "doubling" policy of funding from 1999 to 2003 was bound to end. The scientific community was hoping for "a soft landing" with increases of 7–9% annually as contrasted to the 15% increase during the doubling period. That soft landing has not materialized, and complaints are now widespread about the inadequacy of annual increases that do not even account for inflation.

As can be readily gleaned from this brief history of federal funding, scientists of my generation did not spend much time writing grant applications as they launched their careers. In my first few years as a faculty member, I received funds kindly provided by Wendell Stanley who, as a Nobel Laureate, had grants from various private foundations. The first graduate student in my laboratory was supported by university funds. Several years after initiating my research in Berkeley, I received my first grant. Actually it was a contract, of about $7,000, from the Office of Naval Research (ONR) for research on tobacco mosaic virus and the ultracentrifuge. Administrators at ONR were enthusiastic about basic science and provided enormous freedom to investigators. After a few years, many of the staff at ONR moved to NSF, and I began receiving funding from NSF. That support continued for many years, culminating years later in an annual budget of about $70,000. In the early days of federal support, I had the narrow view that my laboratory was not doing biomedical research, and I didn't apply to NIH even though larger grants were readily available. My NSF grant was adequate for many years. Graduate students in the early 1950s were supported as teaching assistants or research assistants funded by small grants to faculty members or departmental funds. A typical laboratory would have one or two graduate students, a technician, and perhaps one postdoc, a far cry from the research group of today.

Intrusion of Politics in Federal Support of Research

Although most scientists were ecstatic about the Bush report and the concept of federal funding of research at universities, some expressed reservations; there was considerable apprehension about the possibility of political interference and curtailment of free inquiry. Indeed over the years, there have been periods, such as the 1950s, when NIH grants to individuals were terminated because of their presumed political activities. In 1953, while McCarthyism was rampant, the Federal Bureau of Investigation (FBI) began screening grantees. Based on FBI reports, Oveta Culp Hobby, as Secretary of Health, Education and Welfare (HEW) in the Eisenhower administration, interceded and ordered the cancellation of grants to Linus Pauling and other prominent scientists. Protests were mounted both within NIH and in the extramural community. Some leading administrators at NIH were so appalled about the policy dictated by the Secretary that they suggested to some of the "debarred" investigators that they substitute a colleague's name as the Principal Investigator, in which case the grant would still be funded to the institution. About 4 years elapsed before the policy of screening grantees under the policy initiated by Secretary Hobby was essentially abandoned. During that period, William Consolazio, who headed the section on Molecular Biology at NSF and was one of the pioneers at both ONR and NSF, sent me an urgent request for a prompt review of an application from Pauling for funding his research previously supported by NIH. According to my recollection, I sent Consolazio two responses. One was a detailed review of the proposal along with a summary indicating that the proposed research was ground-breaking and would have a great impact on our understanding of protein structure. In addition, my formal evaluation included, "The principal investigator is a giant in the field of science and is eminently and uniquely qualified to perform the research that is outlined." That was for the record. The second response was much more personal because I knew Consolazio well and served on his panel. It asked rhetorically, "Who am I to evaluate a research grant application from God?" For anyone interested in physical chemistry and its application to biological problems, Linus Pauling was God! Not only did NSF, through Consolazio's intervention, fund Pauling's grant application, but others who were cut off by NIH also received funds from NSF.

There have been other episodes of political interference in the operation of the granting agencies, with the most serious threats occurring during the Nixon administration. Beginning in 1971, for example, the training grant function at NIH was taken away from the Institutes, the number of review committees was reduced drastically, appropriated funds were impounded, and plans to separate the National Cancer Institute from NIH were initiated. Finally, Robert Q. Marston, Director of NIH for 5 years, was summarily fired in 1973 for refusing to cooperate with the Office of Management and Budget (OMB) in cutting basic research programs. At that time the entire peer review process was in jeopardy. Other less serious assaults on the grant systems at NSF and NIH dealt mainly with appointments to high level positions, such as the Director of the NSF or advisory councils at NIH. Some grant applications have also been rejected because a political official thought that government should not support the type of research described in the proposal. One prominent former senator, William Proxmire, who crusaded against waste in government, periodically ridiculed granting agencies over grants whose *titles* he didn't like by publishing his list of "Golden Fleece Awards." His complaints were often unwarranted. These interferences with peer review arose primarily in areas of social or political controversy such as sexual behavior, AIDS, reproduction science, or climate control. However by and large, granting agencies have managed to resist external political pressure, with the exception of the response to priorities in the appropriation process during times of budgetary constraints. Apprehensions expressed in the 1940s that funding of research by government would be swayed or dominated by politics have not materialized. Although actions in the past few years have caused concern about political interference jeopardizing the peer review process and interfering with the freedom of inquiry, the granting agencies have functioned magnificently.

Unhappy and Dissatisfied Applicants—Peer Review

The success of the grant programs does not mean that applicants for grants were not complaining. On the contrary, over the past 40 years there have been many periods when the scientific community has been up in arms about the shortage of funds. Young investigators of today almost certainly will conclude that my description of experience on study sections of NSF and NIH in the 1950s and 1960s is apocryphal.

As members of an NSF panel, we were obligated to read all of the applications being considered at a specific meeting even though some of them were outside our area of expertise. The reviews at home, in preparation for the meeting in Washington, required several weeks of intense study. Applications receiving ratings in the highest two grades (out of five) were generally funded. Many of the applications did not receive sufficiently high scores to warrant funding, and a significant number were actually *disapproved*. For me, as a young Assistant Professor, it was a humbling experience, reading superb applications and attending meetings with older panel members who were my heroes in science. I can recall being pleased to see that senior members on the panel were thorough in their review of the proposals as well as generous and fair in their criticisms. After about 4 years my term ended, and I was appointed to an NIH Study Section where I experienced a culture shock. When we were about to record our vote on a particularly bad proposal, one of the more experienced panel members sitting next to me asked how I was going to rate it. My response was, "Disapprove; it is terrible; the investigator will not learn anything interesting, and the research is not worth doing." To which he responded, "On NIH panels we hardly ever disapprove grant applications." At that time NIH was growing rapidly with budgets increasing substantially every year, and "disapproval" was devastating to young investigators. NIH staff justified requests for additional funds on the grounds that so many *approved* applications were unfunded because of insufficient funds. Quickly recognizing the differences in culture and funding between NSF and NIH, I indicated that I would rate the proposal so low (about 3.0) that the research would not be funded. But my colleague at the table quickly informed me that applications with a rating of 3.0 would be funded. Even many of those with a score of 4.0 were funded. In that one meeting, I learned how much easier it was to receive support from NIH than from NSF. That is still true today, but now applicants to NIH are experiencing major difficulties and even first class proposals receiving ratings of 1.5 or better are not being funded.

Grievances about poor ratings are many, diverse and contradictory. They include "those young guys on the panel don't even know about my classical work"; "starting scientists don't have a chance because of the prejudiced senior members on the study sections"; or "the reviewers succumb to fashions and you can't get funds for research on prokaryotic enzymes." During my tenure in the 1990s as NIH Ombudsman in the Basic Sciences, I had the dubious pleasure of sitting in at many sessions of different Study Sections. Like those scientists whose applications did not lead to funding, I can cite shortcomings in the system. There is much too much nitpicking by members of the panels, such as "the magnesium ion concentration is too low." Also, the summary statement on the "Pink Sheet" is not consistent with the score. Old timers still refer to Pink Summary Sheets; they haven't been pink for some years and are now replaced by electronic messages. Reviewers, in trying to be kind in their write-ups, frequently offer complimentary comments thereby giving applicants an erroneous impression about the *real* evaluation of the proposal. Scores often are not consistent with the commentary. As a result, applicants submit a slightly revised request that again receives a poor rating. Hence there are too many amended applications. Panels often have too many "ad hoc" members. Some of them, flattered by the opportunity to evaluate the research of others, go to

great lengths to demonstrate their erudition by essentially rewriting the proposals. Applications are too long; experimental minutiae are included thereby becoming the focus of nitpicking. Despite these criticisms, I find the Peer Review System remarkable.

One of the most common and often repeated complaints is that panel members don't support highly original proposals. Innovative proposals, according to the complainants, are dismissed with the remark: "it won't work." Based on my experience as an observer at Study Section meetings as Ombudsman, I have no doubt that panel members prematurely and inappropriately conclude that very original proposals won't work. Despite their favorable comments about the excellent "track record" of the investigators, they give low ratings to such applications. But this criticism of the peer review system is not new. About 50 years ago in a talk on a fictitious enzyme "Money Transferase" at the Gordon Conference on Proteins, I showed the enclosed plot of the probability of obtaining a grant *versus* the originality of the grant request (Fig. 1). Unfortunately, it still has some validity.

Many of the complaints about the peer review system are legitimate, but it is astonishing to hear scientists, whose grant applications were not funded, criticize NIH or NSF when the decisions were rendered largely by panels of outside reviewers. My rejoinder to the critics is that the

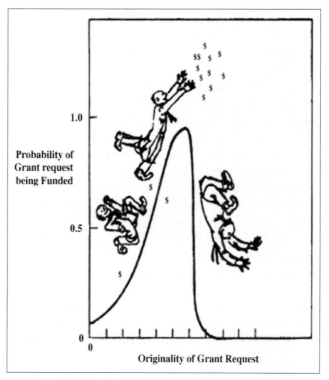

Fig. 1. Prospect of grant request being funded in relation to the originality of the research proposal.

ratings are attributable to the judgments of the panel members on the review committees and "the enemy is us."

Numerous committees have studied the peer review process (5), and their recommendations invariably have led to improvements in the system. The Division of Research Grants (DRG), established in 1946, initiated many reforms over the years in response to suggestions from the extramural community, and an important change occurred when that division was converted in 1997 to the Center for Scientific Review (CSR). A major reclassification of Study Sections is now being implemented. Although individual scientists have expressed concern about which Study Section will review their application, this reorganization was necessary because developments in biomedical science over the past 50 years have resulted in radical changes in the way research is conducted. Whether this new classification will reduce the number of times that important areas of scientific research fall between the cracks remains to be seen. Much will depend on the conduct of reviewers, and attempts by NIH staff to overcome bias in rating approaches to science. It should not be a surprise, for example, that a panel comprising many NMR spectroscopists and crystallographers would give high scores to proposals using these techniques. However in the process, scientists using other physical-chemical tools found themselves disadvantaged, and the ratings of their proposals were poor. In my judgment, this type of bias has occurred in the area of biophysical chemistry and in other areas of scientific research. This deficiency is likely to be mitigated as a result of the reorganization.

Doubtless complaints about peer review will continue and probably even increase because the demand for more R01s from the growing scientific community far exceeds the available source of funds. That government has delegated to the scientific community the right to design and operate the peer review system is a remarkable achievement and criticism is invaluable.

Impact of Federal Funding on Universities

During the 1950s and 1960s, the number of graduate students interested in biochemistry and molecular biology increased tremendously, appointments to the faculty grew rapidly, and new departments were established in many institutions. At Berkeley in the 1960s, we had both a biochemistry department and a virology department that was later converted into a Department of Molecular Biology. Both thrived despite occasional competition for space, faculty positions, graduate students, and university funds. Growth was rampant, influenced in large measure by the increased federal funding for biomedical research. My own laboratory group, including students from both Bio-

chemistry and Molecular Biology, had grown to about 5 graduate students, several undergraduates, 2 postdocs, and 2 technicians. Despite the large increase in the number of postdoctoral fellowships and the establishment of NIH Training Grants, there was a need for additional funding to individual faculty members. Accordingly in 1964, I applied to NIH for funds and received my first, and still continuing, NIH grant entitled "Structure-Interactions of Biological Macromolecules," which was significantly larger than the existing NSF grant. Other faculty members experienced similar growth, and not surprisingly, space problems became acute. New buildings became the issue in nearly every research-oriented university. Amalgamation of departments ensued shortly thereafter. Here at Berkeley about 15 years ago there was a major reorganization. The Biochemistry and Molecular Biology group of about 25 faculty members was restructured as 1 of 5 divisions in the mega-Department of Molecular and Cell Biology (MCB) comprising about 90 faculty. This reorganization clearly has been advantageous in recruiting faculty and graduate students, and the resulting clout on campus coupled with the size of MCB has led to occasional calls for even more independence and authority. Why not establish a College of Biology? Whether this growth has resulted in a loss of community and collegiality is for others to judge. Moreover, it will be of interest to observe the interactions of the diverse groups in the new, greatly expanded Stanley Hall. Will there be extensive collaboration leading to Big Science, or will there be just more scientists in the enlarged building not talking to one another?

University administrators reacted to the growth of federal funds and desires for additional faculty by encouraging, and even requiring, full time faculty to raise substantial parts of their salaries through grant funds. The practice began when faculty members on 9-month appointments used some of their grant funds to pay summer salaries for 2 or sometimes 3 months. Soon using grant funds to supplement faculty salaries became widespread. That step led to the policy of establishing "soft money" faculty positions. This practice is particularly prevalent in medical schools. In one state institution I visited, a large department had state funds for 30 FTEs (full time equivalents) with about 300 faculty members occupying those slots. Each faculty member had to raise about 90% of the salary from federal funds. Clearly NIH was subsidizing universities to an extent not anticipated. This increase in the number of faculty positions led, of course, to greater demands for research grants and for additional laboratory space. In turn lobbying was initiated for government funds to build new buildings on university campuses. This effort was partially successful but for only a limited period. Some agencies participated in matching fund programs with universities, and there have been repeated periods of earmarking, or "pork," when individual members of Congress without debate inserted into appropriation bills funds for their favorite institution. Not surprisingly there were all too few protests from university administrators over this abandonment of the concept of peer review.

Struggles over "Indirect Costs"

Almost from the beginning of government funding of research there has been acrimony among government officials, university administrators, and research scientists over the issue of "indirect costs" or "overhead." Members of Congress maintained that federal appropriations were to support research not to sustain universities. Administrators of educational institutions claimed that there were substantial, indirect costs incurred in supporting federally funded research of faculty, and universities needed "full cost recovery." Researchers complained that too much NIH and NSF money allocated to institutions was *not* used to support research. Research scientists, faced with stringent budgets and with ratings on their grants below the funding level, argued strenuously that indirect costs, amounting to billions of dollars annually, should be reduced markedly. In their view, the money saved could then be used to support more research.

Administrators at universities, in focusing on the total cost of the research activity, demanded compensation for many general facilities, indirectly related to the research, such as the purchasing department, the libraries, and the additional administrative staff involved in dealing with government offices. Universities also made claims for depreciation and use allowances, such as operation and maintenance of physical facilities including heat, light, and custodial services, monitoring health and safety regulations, and waste disposal. Most research scientists viewed these charges legitimate although the amounts were questioned. In contrast, many of the other claims were considered not justifiable. These included charges for those administrators who spent a small portion of their time on matters only peripherally related to the research itself, such as university presidents, vice-presidents, deans, and others who work on management issues. The most serious complaint of scientists was that the funds requested by university administrators as "indirect costs" were not being used to "aid and abet" the research itself. Instead the money was being treated and used as income for general university support.

Saving and accumulating indirect costs by institutions for future expansion was another source of difficulty. In California a major brouhaha occurred at the first meeting of the Board of Regents attended by the newly elected Governor, Ronald Reagan. At that meeting the issue of indirect costs arose, and in response to the Governor's inquiry, the President of the University of California explained the concept and indicated that they had accumulated about 20 million dollars, money being saved for a "rainy day." It required essentially no time for the Governor to proclaim: the rainy day had arrived, the state budget to the University for that year would be reduced by the amount accumulated, and the income from indirect costs would henceforth be returned to the State. That draconian action lasted for a few years, and gradually control of most of the indirect costs did return to the individual campuses.

How federally funded money for research was used by universities had been of interest to members of Congress for many years. In 1991, that issue became the focus of Congressional hearings (6) especially in the light of audits by the General Accounting Office and the Inspector General of the Department of Health and Human Services (HHS). Representative John Dingell, as Chairman of the Subcommittee on Oversight and Investigations, was particularly incensed about some of the overhead costs submitted by major universities like Stanford. His investigations led to the recovery of large sums of money from various, private institutions where "indirect costs" rates were generally greater than 60%. During this period of intense acrimony over indirect costs, ASBMB became a major "spokesman" for the scientific community. As Chair of the Public Affairs Committee of ASBMB, I testified before the Subcommittee on Science of the Committee on Science, Space and Technology of the U. S. House of Representatives. It was a particularly pleasant experience because members of Congress present at the hearings were sympathetic to our position and decidedly opposed to the arguments of the university representatives testifying at the same session. We argued that "indirect costs" should be "limited to those expenditures that were clearly related to and provided support for the research being conducted." Funds for maintaining and repairing laboratories or for their depreciation, in our view, were justifiable charges as indirect costs. However we opposed the proposed timetable of 20 years for the depreciation of a laboratory building. In our view, the lifetime of laboratories was much longer, and the 50-year schedule was much more appropriate. The practice of accumulating funds, essentially placing them "in escrow," for expansion through the construction of new buildings, we considered an illegitimate practice. Similarly, we viewed as indefensible the request of university administrators for "full cost recovery." The policy whereby universities collected indirect costs of about 60% on top of the salaries of tenured faculty members paid from grants we considered intolerable. This pattern of enlarging the faculty by charging for salaries, needing more laboratory space, and accumulating indirect costs for construction of new buildings and expansion of universities amounts to Ponzi economics. For research scientists the Herblock cartoon from the Washington Post in 1991 was a picturesque and relevant portrayal of the "indirect cost" or "overhead" issue (Fig. 2).

Burdensome Regulations and Unfunded Mandates

A corollary of the social contract between government and institutions over federal funding of research has been the imposition of regulations stemming from public pressure and the political response. Because the three constituencies, government, universities, and the scientific community, have different obligations, responsibilities, and

Fig. 2. Trickle Down, Winsocki, Trickle Down. © 1991 by Herblock in *The Washington Post.*

cultures, friction among them is almost inevitable. Scientists, for the most part, are temperamentally and culturally skeptical about proscriptive policies. They tend to doubt the legitimacy of policies restricting scientific activities, and they are concerned when these policies are transformed into rules and regulations followed by laws. Nonetheless, most scientists acknowledge, respect, and support regulations promulgated with the goal of protecting human subjects, animals, and the environment. Regardless of the inconvenience, cost, and burden they abide by those regulations widely recognized as furthering the interests of society. They tend to oppose regulations that in their view provide very little benefit, appear ill-advised or poorly crafted, or are costly and impede scientific research. Doubtless there are legitimate differences of opinion as to whether a given regulation is poorly conceived, inappropriately interpreted, or incorrectly enforced. Because of the different orientations of government officials and research scientists, there have been repeated incidents of irritation and controversy over many regulations imposed as a result of political pressures. Invariably regulations require enforcement procedures that are extremely costly, and universities join the fray by complaining about the fact that no funds were provided by the government. Hence "unfunded mandates" have become a major battleground.

Until only a few years ago, researchers had few complaints about regulations dealing with humane care and treatment of laboratory animals. Although some scientists have been cavalier in their laboratory practices leading to abuse of animals, most have been ardent advocates for responsible care and use of animals in research. As members of professional societies like FASEB, they have supported policies regarding care of animals despite the burden of regulations and the not inconsiderable administrative costs. However, complaints from those in society who oppose all use of animals in biomedical research appear repeatedly (7). In turn, government responses aimed at ameliorating this pressure lead to additional regulations. For example in 2000, the excellent working relationships between those concerned with the proper implementation of the Animal Welfare Act and researchers who use animals in biomedical research were disrupted over action proposed by the Animal and Plant Health Inspection Service (APHIS) of the United States Department of Agriculture (USDA). In considering animal welfare and the problem of pain and distress, APHIS proposed a definition of distress referring to "a state in which an animal cannot escape from, or adapt to, the internal or external stressors or conditions it experiences, resulting in negative effects on its well being." Just reading the proposed definition causes distress. Action or regulations, based on such vague and uninterpretable language, are not likely to contribute to animal welfare.

About 5 years ago the USDA, in response to a complaint that laboratory rats allegedly were receiving "inadequate housing, water, food, and veterinary care," proposed amending the regulation that excluded rats, mice, and birds from coverage under the Animal Welfare Act. This act was designed for large animals and was concerned with the protection of family pets. Other policies covering the humane care and use of laboratory animals already existed, and research institutions were required to file assurances committing them to responsible animal care. Standards and regulations established for cats and dogs were not appropriate for mice and rats bred for research purposes. Their imposition, as proposed by the USDA, would have constituted a major impediment to biomedical research (8). Fortunately, as result of extensive lobbying by the scientific community, this proposed change in implementation of the Animal Welfare Act has been thwarted, at least temporarily.

Other conflicts have arisen as a result of proposed government action aimed at regulating research activities of scientists. In response to what he and others considered unreasonable withholding of data from a federally funded investigation at the Harvard University School of Public Health, Senator Shelby introduced an amendment to the FY 1999 Omnibus Spending Bill (Public Law 105-277) designed to correct what was perceived to be a serious transgression. This action required OMB to revise Circular A-110 so that all data produced through federal funding must be made available under the Freedom of Information Act (FOIA). Scientists in general support the concept of the public's access to raw data and the aims of FOIA, but they recognize that unintended consequences frequently result from well meaning proposals. Harassment of investigators through the use of FOIA is not rare (9). Fortunately, in revising Circular 110-A, the OMB recognized the threat to scientific investigations and responded by formulating a reasonable modification to an unreasonable mandate.

Struggles over regulations will almost certainly continue to persist with researchers maintaining that they impede scientific investigations, with university administrators maintaining that they are too costly and funds are needed for implementation, and with government officials reacting to the numerous and diverse complaints of their constituencies. The vulnerability of the scientific community to regulations is greatest, as it should be, in the treatment and research affecting human subjects. Every inci-

dent of harm or death, whether inadvertent or through negligence, is bound to bring forth new calls for regulations. This occurred as a result of the tragic death of a young man, Jesse Gelsinger, who was suffering from a genetic disease and being treated at the University of Pennsylvania. As described by Koski (10), the former Director of the Office for Human Research Protection, Gelsinger "entered a trial in 1999 without full knowledge of what was going to be involved. He was not presented with information that might have been invaluable in making a decision in concert with his family about whether or not to participate in the trial. There were gross deficiencies in the conduct of the trial, gross deficiencies in documentation of the data, and gross deficiencies in reporting requirements." Clearly instances like that, though few in number, are intolerable. They immediately provoke a major outcry for new regulations. However it should be noted that it is the enforcement of existing regulations and compliance by investigators that are needed rather than the crafting of additional ones.

For the foreseeable future, we can expect a storm of proposals and counterproposals over the issue of human embryonic stem cells, and biomedical scientists will have to deal with complaints from various constituencies in society.

War on "Fraud in Science"

Biomedical research hit the headlines in the 1980s. It started with the congressional hearings on "Fraud in Biomedical Research" (11) conducted by the Subcommittee on Investigations and Oversight of the Committee of Science and Technology under the Chairmanship of Albert Gore, Jr. In those hearings and others that followed, individual scientists testified about their own unethical behavior. One witness described how he falsified results of experiments that he had not conducted. Another researcher, according to the Chairman, "became entangled in a network of fraud and plagiarism, and a possible cover-up." Subsequent congressional hearings were entitled, "Scientific Fraud and Misconduct and the Federal Response" and "Fraud in NIH Grant Programs." The press was merciless. One had the impression that fraud was rampant and that a substantial fraction of scientific findings was fabricated or falsified. Books describing notorious cases of fraud soon appeared with titles like "Betrayers of the Truth" (12) and "False Prophets" (13). The March 19, 1989 issue of the Chicago Tribune had a long article entitled "Cheating in the Lab" with the subheading "Under pressure some researchers break the law." Various cases were described with the author drawing conclusions even though the allegations had not yet been investigated. The cover of Time on August 26, 1991 had a mocking caricature of a miniaturized scientist under a microscope with the blaring headline "Science Under Siege" along with a remark about "scandal plaguing America's researchers." In the principal article of that issue, the accused scientists were judged "guilty" by the author when the trial had not yet been conducted.

The word "fraud" was predominant in all the early discussions because many of the cases dealt with falsifying data, making up data, and reporting results of experiments that had not been performed. During that period, Congress directed the Secretary of HHS to "require institutional applicants for NIH funds to review reports of *fraud* and report to the Secretary any investigation of suspected *fraud* which appears substantial." To implement this directive, numerous groups both within and outside of government began meeting frequently to discuss policies and potential regulations. Unfortunately, the lawyers took over. To them, the burden of establishing "fraud" in accordance with U. S. law seemed insuperable because of the requirement to prove both intent to deceive and injury or damage to persons relying on the scientific research. As a consequence, the word fraud previously used to describe many of the intolerable breaches of ethics by scientists disappeared from the dialog. In its place was "misconduct in science." Although there was little confusion in the scientific community over the meaning of fraud, it was immediately recognized that the phrase, misconduct in science, would be interpreted differently by different people.

At that time I happened to be President of ASBC and began flying across the country to attend innumerable meetings aimed at defining misconduct in science. In a session at NIH, the Director, James B. Wyngaarden, and I were the only scientists in a room with about 30 lawyers representing different agencies of government and many universities. The various attorneys, especially those representing government agencies, wanted a broad definition including words like "deception" and "misrepresentation." In contrast, scientists argued for a narrow definition. We stressed the uncertainties in research and the need for scientists to be free to use their judgment and intuition in selecting data based on their experience. To lawyers, selection of data constituted misrepresentation or deception. Scientists maintained that the definition should be restricted to acts such as making up data, changing data, and stealing data or ideas without attribution; *i.e.* "fabrication," "falsification," and "plagiarism." Despite numerous arguments from the attorneys, the two of us prevailed at that meeting. Unfortunately, our victory was short-lived.

As they say at NIH, the issue was moved downtown, meaning to higher authority at the Public Health Service (PHS) or the Secretary of HHS. All of our objections were ignored. The rule proposed several years later by the PHS entitled "Responsibilities of PHS Awardees and Applicant Institutions for Dealing with Reporting Possible Misconduct in Science" included in the definition, "fabrication, falsification, plagiarism, deception or other practices that seriously deviate from those that are commonly accepted within the scientific community for proposing, conducting or reporting research . . . " For more than a decade, that definition formed the basis of investigations and adjudication by different government agencies such as NSF, the Office of Scientific Integrity (OSI), and its successor, the Office of Research Integrity (ORI).

Many scientists found the language about "other practices that seriously deviate" vague and open ended, inviting overexpansive interpretation. In arguing against that definition in an article (14) entitled "What Is Misconduct in Science?" I noted that "brilliant, creative, pioneering research often deviates from that commonly accepted within the scientific community." The absurdity of the government definition became evident with a ruling of the Office of Inspector General (OIG) of NSF in a case of a researcher "involved in 16 incidents of sexual misfeasance with female graduate and undergraduate students at the research site; on the way to the site; and in his home, car, and office." According to the OIG, "Many of these incidents were classifiable as sexual assaults." OIG concluded with " . . . these incidents were an integral part of this researcher's performance as a researcher and research mentor and represented a serious deviation from accepted practice. Therefore, they amounted to research misconduct under NSF regulations." Whether this preposterous and appalling application of the definition of "misconduct in science" was a significant factor in the ultimate removal of the "serious deviate" clause is not clear. But after about 15 years of struggle, innumerable committees, and reports, that clause is gone. Now the accepted government-wide definition of misconduct in research focuses on "fabrication," "falsification," and "plagiarism," now known as FFP. In recalling my repeated trips across the country over this single issue, I refer to FFP as Frequent Flyer Program.

In the 25 years since fraud in science became front-page news, many instances of misconduct have been unveiled. However it is important to note that the major instances of FFP described in the congressional hearings and in books (12, 13) were uncovered by the traditional methods of science; *i.e.* inability to replicate and extend findings, competition among researchers, and complaints by co-workers and whistleblowers. It has been said repeatedly that science; i.e. is self-correcting and that, therefore, fraudulent or mistaken research is detected in the normal course of extending the work. That is true, but the correction of scientific reports applies to research that is ground-breaking and has a significant impact. Both fraud and errors in such research are generally discovered relatively soon because attempts to replicate or extend the findings are not successful. However, a great deal of research does not attract the attention of other researchers; fraud and mistakes in such research frequently go undetected for long periods of time. Hence, increasing the awareness of these potential problems by offices like OSI and ORI has been valuable. Unfortunately, in a few celebrated cases involving investigations and adjudication of alleged "misconduct in research," there were serious abuses committed by officials in those agencies. Investigations were seriously flawed; convictions were not warranted by the evidence; leaks of confidential information occurred; and reputations of scientists were seriously damaged. Substantial periods of time elapsed before the convictions were overturned and the accused scientists were cleared through appropriate appellate machinery. Procedures providing "due process" have now been installed, and it is likely that they will preclude overzealous investigators causing such incidents in the future.

Officials at ORI repeatedly emphasize their goal "to prevent misconduct in research." In my view, they will not succeed. Misconduct like that described recently by ORI (15) cannot be prevented. Similarly, the fraud in the research on stem cells by the group in South Korea could not have been prevented (16–19). In such cases individuals should be charged, investigations should be conducted, verdicts should be reached, and punishment should be meted out, and there should be disclosure thereby diminishing the chances of repetition by the same individual. In the past, disclosure was rare because of the fear of litigation but institutions slowly have begun releasing information about the results of investigations. ORI is now providing material to individuals in universities responsible for teaching courses on "Responsible Conduct of Research." Such courses are now required for all graduate students supported by NIH Institutional Training Grants. Postdoctoral recipients of Ruth L. Kirschstein National Research Service Awards (NRSA) are also required to take such courses. Teaching such courses on "ethics" has become a significant new activity for academic departments, and ORI is expending considerable effort to broaden that mandate so as to require ethical training for *all* people implicated in biomedical research. As one involved in such

teaching activity for the past 5 years and as one generally opposed to "required courses," I am somewhat skeptical about their value. Many of the 120 or so students enrolled in our department course would not take the course if it were voluntary. Their cynicism is illustrated in the accompanying cartoon, kindly furnished by the artist (Fig. 3) (©2001 Ed Himelblau).

Any discussion of "responsible conduct of research" must, in my view, include all the participants in the research enterprise. There should be a focus on the scientists engaged in research, the universities and academic centers where research is conducted, the professional societies responsible for developing standards, the journals in which scientific findings are published, the industrialists who contribute funds and collaborate with academicians, and government agencies fostering, sponsoring, and regulating research. Although their obligations vary, all of them have a role in achieving and maintaining an ethical climate of responsible conduct of research. Transgressions of scientists have justifiably been the subject of most courses on scientific integrity, but there has been scant attention paid to the roles of others in contributing to the loss of the public's confidence in the ethical behavior of scientists. It is useful to describe some of the notorious cases that have attracted widespread attention in the popular press and have become the focus of government agencies. Describing the actions of Summerlin, Darsee, Soman, Spector, Bruening, Bates, Slutsky, and Poehlman, for example, have educational value. It is useful to show how

I *have* to fake my data...with all these ethics seminars I don't have time to do experiments!

Fig. 3.

their "misconduct in research" was discovered, the extent of recidivism, and the sanctions imposed by government. But in discussing government activity in the investigation of FFP, it is important also to describe those instances of over-reaching, unproven allegations, and unjustifiable "leaks" of confidential, derogatory information that have damaged reputations of scientists. Only after appeals providing "due process" were they finally judged not guilty of misconduct. The Popovic and Imanishi-Kari cases demonstrate the serious defects in the earlier, informal procedures for investigating allegations and the impediments arising from political interference. It is indeed unfortunate that quasi-legal procedures need to be invoked, but the consequences stemming from allegations that prove to be unfounded demand this protection for the accused. These formal procedures also protect whistleblowers.

Almost daily over the past few weeks, headlines in the public press and scientific journals have described the apparently fraudulent research on embryonic stem cells in Hwang's laboratory in South Korea. Articles such as "Global Trend: More Science, More Fraud" (16), "Baffling, Infuriating, and Sad" (17), "Verdict: Hwang's Human Stem Cells Were All Fakes" (18), and "Cloning: South Korean Team's Remaining Human Stem Cell Claim Demolished" (19) dominate the news. This sad episode is particularly tragic because the claimed success in the South Korean laboratory was so sensational that many researchers, who hoped for such developments, accepted the results instead of being skeptical. Uncovering the fraud involved a complex investigation over (*a*) the donors of eggs, (*b*) charges raised by whistleblowers, and (*c*) the role of a senior author in the United States. Doubtless, further scientific research would have unveiled its flaws. It is important to recognize that research on human embryonic stem cells is now a political issue in the United States. Therefore this fraudulent activity has attracted much more attention in the press and in daily discourse than equally reprehensible, unethical behavior in research such as the alleged discovery of new isotopes and organic semiconductors (20–22). These latter fabrications occurred in world-class laboratories in the United States.

Authorship practices occasionally are a source of irritation. There is a tendency among some to try codifying policies without recognizing the uncertainties and ambiguities in assigning credit. This issue is now the focus of attention because of questions raised about Gerald P. Schatten's role as the senior author on a paper from South Korea on human embryonic stem cells (23). Sharing data and citing previous work pose ongoing ethical problems. Plagiarism represents the most frequent abuse of ethical practices in research, and little can be done about it other than education and imposition of sanctions upon those proven guilty. However the issue of "conflict of interest" is looming as one of the major ethical problems facing the scientific community. Courses on Responsible Conduct of Research can treat this subject in terms of the research and reporting of findings by investigators, the activities and responsibilities of university administrators, and the roles of the directors of companies and government officials. Editors of scientific journals have been derelict in fostering good publication practices aimed at maintaining integrity of science. When they are so interested in attracting papers that authors are not required to release all the relevant data, the scientific literature is compromised. For years *Science*, *Nature*, and *Cell*, along with other journals, published papers describing crystal structures of proteins with the editors knowing that authors were not depositing the coordinates in the appropriate data banks. After considerable protest within the scientific community and through the intervention of NIH, this practice was rectified. Announcing that grants would not be funded to those who did not deposit coordinates in a data bank constituted an effective remedy. Both authors and editors responded to this use of money to solve an ethical problem. Despite this contention over making coordinates available at the time of publication, the editor of *Science* somewhat later authorized the publication of the sequence of the human genome even though the company did not release to the scientific community all the details. Much larger ethical burdens are now confronting editors of medical journals as described below.

Commercialization of Biomedical Research in Universities

Almost 40 years ago Garrett Hardin wrote a remarkable paper entitled "The Tragedy of the Commons" (24), which in the past decade has influenced scholars in diverse fields such as economics, political science, law, sociology, psychology, agricultural science, and environmentalism, as well as biology, Hardin's own field. In that seminal paper, Hardin refers to an even earlier commentary (25) by Lloyd in his Oxford Lectures of 1833. Lloyd, in considering "what happens to pasturelands left open to many herds of cattle," noted that a time would come when "the unmanaged commons would be ruined by overgrazing." Using that model, Hardin pointed out that when a resource is open to all it becomes available to no one; *i.e.* the "Tragedy of Freedom in a Commons." This concept is readily adapted to the quandary that the great discoveries in biomedical research in the 1960s and 1970s did not benefit the public. The exciting results of research in universities funded by NIH and NSF were described in the scientific literature, but they were not exploited by companies because of the lack of exclusive rights to manufacture drugs. "What was available to all was available to no one." Recognition of this dilemma led to the Bayh-Dole Act of 1980 permitting universities to obtain patents on the results of federally funded research. Passage of this act has had almost as profound an effect on the culture of biomedical research in universities as the start of federal funding in the 1940s.

The triumphs of commercialization of this research in academia are legendary. A multibillion dollar biotech industry was spawned by academic research sponsored by the federal government and turned loose under the auspices of the Bayh-Dole Act. New drugs of enormous benefit to suffering people became available. However, as pointed out in a recent article in *Fortune* (26), there were "unintended consequences." In accepting this new freedom to patent discoveries made by researchers funded by government, university administrators decided to share any potential income from the patents with the inventors. This has enriched many researchers leading to their active participation in this cultural change in academia from publishing to patenting. Accompanying the modified attitudes were major institutional changes. Licensing discoveries by institutions became a major preoccupation requiring the formation of Technology Transfer Offices that now have morphed into new Industry Alliance Offices. Along with considerations of technology transfer and intellectual property came Material Transfer Agreements. Whereas 20 years ago a simple request from a researcher at one institution to a scientist at another university was handled promptly by the furnishing of the strain, clone, or plasmid, now the response not infrequently is different. "Have your Technology Transfer Office contact our office and they will work out an appropriate Material Transfer Agreement." Derek Bok, in his book "Universities in the Marketplace" (27), wrote "Unfortunately, in their zeal to bring more revenue to their universities, technology transfer officers have occasionally acted, especially in situations involving fundamental early-stage discoveries in ways that threaten to slow progress rather than promote it." Many investigators are now finding that Technology Transfer Offices are impeding the exchanges of scientific materials and knowledge that have been the cornerstone of biomedical research in academic institutions.

For the past half-dozen years innumerable articles have deplored the conflicts of interest that have arisen in medical schools involving investigators and their collaborations with industry. Some of the stories that surfaced over

financial ties and their influence on biomedical research led to editorials like that in the *New England Journal of Medicine* (*NEJM*) on May 18, 2000 with the title "Is Academic Medicine for Sale?" Both *NEJM* and the *Journal of the American Medical Association* (*JAMA*) have repeatedly stressed the need for disclosure about sponsorship and financial interests, but scandals persist. This is not too surprising because the journals themselves have neglected enforcing policies about disclosure that they espouse for medical schools that are involved in clinical trials with drug companies. Allegations about abuses by investigators in academic medical centers during the conduct of clinical trials are now front-page news in the popular press. The problems have risen to such proportions that a recent article (28) by a distinguished group of authors begins with "The current influence of market incentives in the United States is posing extraordinary challenges to the principles of medical professionalism. Physicians' commitment to altruism, putting the interests of the patients first, scientific integrity, and an absence of bias in medical decision making now regularly come up against financial conflicts of interest." In formulating a policy proposal for academic medical centers, the authors call for more stringent regulation. One of the authors, Jerome P. Kassirer, who had been a former editor of *NEJM*, had previously written an article (29) with the amusing title "Financial Indigestion" in which he described turning down a meal hosted by a company at an institution where he was a Visiting Professor. After the company representatives had left the room, Kassirer asked a resident at that lunch to read a paragraph written by Rothman (30) which stated "Medical schools should adopt formal rules that prohibit all gifts from drug companies to students, whether books, stethoscopes, or meals. Medical training should not include acquiring a sense of entitlement to the largesse of drug companies. Finally teaching hospitals should enforce these same restrictions, proscribing drug-company sponsorships of lunches, conferences, and travel for home staff, and should make it clear that accepting birthday presents, Christmas gifts, or food and drink off the premises from drug-company representatives violates the ethical norms of the profession."

Just as medical schools have not solved the problem of conflict of interest, so university campuses are facing similar problems. By fostering the formation of industrial connections, patents, and complex licensing procedures, universities and researchers increasingly are encountering conflicts of interest. As pointed out by Bok (27) in commenting about the tragic death of Jesse Gelsinger in a gene therapy trial at the University of Pennsylvania, "As it happened, the director of the institute directing the research was the founder and major stockholder of the company that funded the research. The university, too, was a stockholder, having been given an equity share by the company. Although the director did not participate personally in the trials, both he and the university stood to gain financially if the therapy being tested proved to be successful." There have been numerous charges in the popular press about conflicts of interest. Doubtless some of them may prove not to be *actual* conflicts of interest; but the *perception* is real and the reports clearly undermine the public's view of the integrity of science.

Patent and Prosper

Prior to the 1970s, patenting was alien to most scientists involved in biological research. This attitude changed abruptly as a result of two independent discoveries. The first patent on a living organism was awarded to Chakrabarty at the General Electric Company who "invented" a bacterium capable of consuming oil slicks. It is of interest that the original application was denied by the United States Patent Office (PTO). Living organisms had been considered non-patentable. The patent was granted only after a ruling by the Supreme Court to the effect that the particular organism did not exist naturally and was indeed an invention. Somewhat earlier, Stanford University had filed an application to patent the recombinant DNA technique developed by Cohen and Boyer. Much discussion among the inventors, others in the scientific community, officials at NIH, and members of Congress ensued before patents on the gene-splicing technique were granted, and licensing agreements were signed in the 1980s. This particular patent and the licensing agreements have been extremely profitable for Stanford University, the University of California at San Francisco, and the two inventors of the elegant technique. In a very important respect the non-exclusive licensing agreements put in place were contrary to what was anticipated by the Bayh-Dole Act. It had been assumed that exclusivity would be a necessary inducement for the commercial development of the results of academic research, and many of the subsequent agreements did involve exclusive licenses. In the 25 years following the awarding of the gene-splicing patent, technology transfer officers in concert with the heads of universities have stimulated activity on campuses aimed at converting the research of their faculties into financial benefits. A flurry of patents has resulted, but it should be emphasized that many have yielded virtually no income. Nonetheless, that activity persists, and the culture in basic science departments involved in biomedical research has changed.

In fiscal year 2004, there were 425 new "start-up" companies fueled by discoveries of professors on university campuses and a record number of patents and licenses. Legal fees incurred in the commercialization of this research in academic institutions amounted to more than $189 million. Barton (31), in an article entitled "Reforming the Patent System," pointed out "The number of intellectual property lawyers in the United States is growing faster than the amount of research." Among his suggested reforms was tightening the standards of "novelty" and "non-obviousness" used in judging patentability. Also Barton, like Eisenberg (32) who has written extensively on the subject of patents and their use in actually barring or impeding research, criticized the patenting of research tools dealing with fundamental research processes. The patenting of expressed sequence tags (ESTs) is one such example. It is difficult to understand how the PTO approved the widespread patenting of ESTs under the "utility" standard when not only was the gene downstream unknown but also the encoded protein and its role were not known. Certainly no drug or diagnostic treatment could be visualized from the EST. Recently there has been a court decision contesting the patentability of ESTs, but appeals are likely. Other research tools like the "oncomouse," the world's first animal patented by Harvard Medical School and licensed exclusively to DuPont (33), have been viewed as impeding downstream product development.

In raising the question whether patents can deter innovation, Heller and Eisenberg (34) refer to the "Tragedy of the Anticommons" when "a proliferation of intellectual property rights upstream may be stifling life-saving innovations downstream in the course of research and product development." A subsequent article (35) by Rai and Eisenberg entitled "Bayh-Dole Reform and the Progress of Biomedicine" raises the very important question whether "allowing universities to patent the results of government-sponsored research sometimes works against the public interest."

With passage of the Bayh-Dole Act 25 years ago, basic biomedical discoveries are now reaching the public in the form of effective drugs and treatments at a greatly increased pace. However, we will have to determine whether the pendulum has swung too far and whether basic research and the openness of universities will be curtailed in the long run. The President of Amherst College, Anthony W. Marx, in his review of Bok's book (27), indicated his concerns over the purpose of universities (36). In that review entitled "Academia for Sale (Standards Included)," Marx wrote "Universities cannot effectively teach ethics if they are themselves unethical; nor can they hope to teach that there is more to life than making money if they are unconstrained in their search for revenue."

Although major issues such as reform of the Bayh-Dole Act and policies over patenting remain unresolved, it seems clear that the culture of "patent and prosper" is now entrenched in academia. It will be interesting to witness whether these relatively new practices jeopardize the openness of universities and how they can be accommodated with the much older, traditional roles in creating and dispensing knowledge.

Address correspondence to: howardschachman@berkeley.edu

REFERENCES

1. Schachman, H. K. (2000) Still looking for the ivory tower. *Annu. Rev. Biochem.* **69,** 1–29
2. Bush, V. (1945) Science—the endless frontier. *A Report to the President on a Program for Postwar Scientific Research,* U. S. Government Printing Office, Washington, D. C.
3. Lomask, M. (1975) *A Minor Miracle: an Informal History of the National Science Foundation,* National Science Foundation, Washington, D. C.
4. Allen, E. M. (1980) Early years of research grants. *NIH Alumni Association Newsletter* **2,** 6–8
5. Mandel, R. (1996) *The Division of Research Grants: a Half Century of Peer Review from 1946 to 1996,* National Institutes of Health, Bethesda, MD
6. Hamilton, D. P. (1991) Indirect costs: round II. *Science* **254,** 788–790
7. Haywood, J. R., and Greene, M. (2001) In the battle over animal welfare, truth is not always what it seems. *FASEB News* 18–19
8. Fishbein, E. A. (2001) What price mice? *J. Am. Med. Assoc.* **285,** 939–940
9. Deyo, R. A., Psaty, B. M., Simon, G., Wagner, E. H., and Omenn, G. S. (1997) The messenger under attack—intimidation of researchers by special interest groups. *N. Engl. J. Med.* **336,** 1176–1180
10. Koski, G. (2002) Protection of human research subjects: from compliance to conscience. *AAAS Science and Technology Policy Yearbook,* pp. 193–197, American Association for the Advancement of Science, Washington, D. C.
11. Fraud in Biomedical Research: Hearings before the Subcommittee on Investigations and Oversight of the Committee on Science and Technology. U. S. House of Representatives, 97th Congress (1981)
12. Broad, W., and Wade, N. (1982) *Betrayers of the Truth: Fraud and Deceit in the Halls of Science,* Simon and Schuster, Inc., New York
13. Kohn, A. (1986) *False Prophets: Fraud and Error in Science and Medicine,* Basil Blackwell, New York
14. Schachman, H. K. (1993) What is misconduct in science? *Science* **261,** 148–149
15. Office of Research Integrity Press Release. (2005) Dr. Eric T. Poehlman. *Science* **307,** 1851
16. Altman, L. K., and Broad, W. J. (2005) Global Trend: More Science, More Fraud, New York Times, Dec. 20
17. Baum, R. M. (2006) Baffling, infuriating, and sad. *Chem. Eng. News* **84,** 3
18. Cyranoski, D. (2006) Verdict: Hwang's human stem cells were all fake. *Nature* **439,** 122–123
19. Normile, D., Vogel, G., and Couzin, J. (2006) Cloning: South Korean team's remaining human stem cell claim demolished. *Science* **311,** 156–157
20. Jacoby, M. (2002) Fraud in the physical sciences. *Chem.Eng. News* **80,** 31–33
21. Johnson, G. (2002) At Lawrence Berkeley, physicists say a colleague took them for a ride, New York Times, Oct. 15
22. Chang, K. (2002). On scientific fakery and the systems to catch it, New York Times, Oct. 15
23. Guterman L. (2006). Silent scientist under fire: the American collaborator of a disgraced South Korean is keeping mum, Chronicle of Higher Education, Jan. 27
24. Hardin, Garrett. (1968) The tragedy of the commons. *Science* **162,** 1243–1258
25. Lloyd, W. F. (1833) *Two Lectures on the Checks to Population,* Oxford University Press, Oxford, England
26. Leaf, C. (2005) The law of unintended consequences. *Fortune* Sept. 19, 250–268
27. Bok, D. (2003) *Universities in the Marketplace—the Commercialization of Higher Education,* Princeton University Press, Princeton, NJ
28. Brennan, T. A., Rothman, D. J., Blank, L., Blumenthal, D., Chimonas, S. C., Cohen, J. J., Goldman, J., Kassirer, J. P., Kimball, H., Naughton, J., and Smelser, N. (2006) Health industry practices that create conflicts of interest—a policy proposal for academic medical centers. *J. Am. Med. Assoc.* **295,** 429–433
29. Kassirer, J. P., (2000) Financial indigestion. *J. Am. Med. Assoc.* **284,** 2156–2157
30. Rothman, D. J. (2000) Medical professionalism—focusing on the real issues. *N. Engl. J. Med.* **342,** 1284–1286
31. Barton, J. H. (2000) Reforming the patent system. *Science* **287,** 1933–1934
32. Eisenberg, R. S. (1997) *Patenting Research Tools and the Law, in Summary of a Workshop on Intellectual Property Rights and Research Tools in Molecular Biology, February 15–16, 1996,* National Academy of Sciences, National Academy Press, Washington, D. C.
33. Kevles, D. J. (2002) Of mice and money: the story of the world's first animal patent. *Daedalus,* Spring 2002, 78–88
34. Heller, M. A., and Eisenberg, R. S. (1998) Can patents deter innovation? The anticommons in biomedical research. *Science* **280,** 698–701
35. Rai, A. K., and Eisenberg, R. S. (2003) Bayh-Dole reform and the progress of biomedicine. *Am. Sci.* **91,** 52–59
36. Marx, A. W. (2003) Academia for sale (standards included), review of "Universities in the Marketplace" by Derek Bok, New York Times, May 17

This paper is available online at www.jbc.org

THE JOURNAL OF BIOLOGICAL CHEMISTRY VOL. 281, NO. 12, pp. 7693–7696, March 24, 2006
© 2006 by The American Society for Biochemistry and Molecular Biology, Inc.   Printed in the U.S.A.

A PAPER IN A SERIES COMMISSIONED TO CELEBRATE THE CENTENARY OF THE JBC in 2005

JBC Centennial
1905–2005
100 Years of Biochemistry and Molecular Biology

Discovery of the Hybrid Helix and the First DNA-RNA Hybridization

PUBLISHED, JBC PAPERS IN PRESS, FEBRUARY 7, 2006, DOI 10.1074/JBC.X600003200

Alexander Rich

From the Biology Department, Massachusetts Institute of Technology,
Cambridge, Massachusetts 02139

Here I describe early research on RNA structure and the discovery of the DNA-RNA hybrid helix, a key component of information transfer. More than 50 years ago it was realized that the interaction between DNA and RNA was at the core of molecular biology. The problem was chemical in nature: could two different types of molecules interact and serve in the transmission of biological information?

In the 1950s it was widely assumed that "DNA makes RNA, RNA makes protein." This was not based on experimental evidence that DNA and RNA could combine but was more in the nature of an intuitive belief. However, by early 1960 I was finally able to carry out a direct experiment, the first DNA-RNA hybridization. In 1960, messenger RNA was still 1 year in the future, and there was not a great deal of understanding of the major components of information transfer. The DNA double helix proposed by Watson and Crick in 1953 (1) clearly suggested that information was contained in the order of nucleotides, but during the 1950s our understanding of RNA was fragmentary.

The origins of the 1960 experiment go back to the mid-1950s. In 1954, while at Caltech, Jim Watson and I had been trying to find out if RNA by itself could form a double helix, but the fiber diffraction studies of RNA gave inconclusive results (2, 3). The fuzzy diffraction patterns all looked alike, but unlike DNA, the RNA base ratios were all different in the samples we examined. It was clear that RNA was more complex than DNA, and its structure was unknown. In their 1953 paper Watson and Crick (1) pointed out that it was probably impossible to form their double helix with ribose due to van der Waals interference of the 2′-OH with the structure. Thus, it was likely to be different.

A New Type of Polymer Chemistry

The research changed dramatically at the National Institutes of Health (NIH) in 1956 when David Davies and I began working with synthetic polyribonucleotides made using the polynucleotide phosphorylase enzyme discovered by Grunberg-Manago and Ochoa (4). When we mixed together polyriboadenylic acid (poly(rA)) and polyribouridylic acid (poly(rU)) and pulled fibers, they yielded a clear diffraction pattern of a double helix (5). The two molecules had combined to make an RNA double helix! This was a new type of chemical reaction, one that involved thousands of units binding specifically to each other in an extended array. Furthermore, no polymer reaction had ever been seen in which the monomers from two polymers bound together with great specificity. Two weeks after sending off the 1956 *Journal of the American Chemical Society* note, I wrote a letter to my postdoctoral mentor, Linus Pauling, describing these results. The letter reveals a sense of incredulity on my part that this reaction could happen and that it was "completely reproducible." The experimental demonstration that these molecules could form a double helix seems obvious today. However, it was a considerable surprise at that time and was often greeted with skepticism. Most biochemists felt that a double helix could only be made by an enzyme, such as the one discovered by Arthur Kornberg and associates, which appeared to replicate the DNA double helix (6). Polymer chemists felt that very long molecules involving thousands of nucleotides would probably become entangled and could not sort themselves out to form a regular double helix. Still other researchers, on theoretical grounds, felt that two highly negatively charged polymers were unlikely to combine to make a single structure.

However many scientists were receptive. In the early fall of 1956, a McCollum Pratt meeting was organized at Johns Hopkins University in Baltimore around the subject of the "Chemical Basis of Heredity." It was an excellent meeting with all of the major research workers in the field. In my talk (7) I included a discussion of the specificity of the interaction and the fact that these long molecules seek each other out in solution and adopt this elongated helical form. Julian Huxley, a prominent scientist and writer, came up to me after my talk and warmly congratulated me for having discovered "molecular sex."

Gradually, the idea became fixed in the thinking of biologists and biochemists that these long nucleic acid molecules had considerable flexibility and could be made to form helical structures in solution. Although no one used the phrase at the time, this was the first hybridization reaction, and it represented a paradigm shift in the way chemists and biochemists thought about macromolecular nucleic acids.

Two Different Structures

Watson and Crick (1) pointed out that RNA would not form the DNA structure. This was confirmed as the RNA x-ray diffraction pattern revealed significant differences from the DNA double helix pattern. The diameter of the RNA double helix was 6 Å larger than the DNA double helix (7, 8). Analysis of the diffraction pattern revealed that the first layer line of the RNA-RNA duplex was stronger than the second—a reversal from that seen in the diffraction pattern of the DNA-DNA duplex (7, 8). Another significant difference was that alterations in relative humidity changed the DNA double helix, producing both the A and

B forms, whereas the RNA double helix seemed invariant to changes in relative humidity.

The reaction between poly(rA) and poly(rU) was associated with a drop in optical density in the ultraviolet (9), a property that could be used to identify the 1:1 stoichiometry and analyze the reaction quantitatively (10). Only much later was it realized that the RNA duplex structure was close to the dehydrated A conformation of DNA duplex. However, by 1960, it was clear that DNA and RNA duplexes were significantly different.

In 1957, together with Felsenfeld, we discovered that the poly(rA)·poly(rU) duplex could take on a third strand of poly(rU) to form a triple helix (11). We pointed out that this could be associated with forming two hydrogen bonds between the incoming uracil O4 and N3 and adenine N6 and N7, an interaction of bases that was confirmed 2 years later by Hoogsteen in a single crystal x-ray analysis (12). Between 1956 and 1960 a number of experiments were carried out with polyribonucleotides of different composition (13–15), and their interactions could generally be explained in terms of the ability of the bases to form at least two hydrogen bonds in the center of the molecule.

Could DNA and RNA interact? Polymers of ribonucleotides were available because of the discovery of polynucleotide phosphorylase (4). This made it possible to produce polyribonucleotides with a variety of compositions, but there was no analogous method of producing DNA polymers. The question "How does DNA make RNA?" remained an open issue. Several biochemists were trying to isolate the enzyme known as RNA polymerase which is dependent upon a DNA template. Experiments by Stevens, Hurwitz, and Weiss developed preparations that had some activity, but they were not purified enough to show what was actually happening. In a reflective article published in 1959 called "An Analysis of the Relation between DNA and RNA," I surveyed the various possibilities for DNA-RNA interactions (16). In particular, I asked whether RNA synthesis could be based on a double-stranded primer or a single-stranded primer of DNA. The discovery of several triple helical complexes of RNA molecules made it reasonable to consider a model in which RNA nucleotides were assembled by binding in a sequence-specific manner to double-stranded DNA. The analysis showed that such a model was unlikely because there were not enough stereospecific interactions to specify an RNA molecule. I concluded that it was likely to be based on forming an RNA strand on a single-stranded primer (16). These conclusions were fortified by the recent discoveries that denatured DNA could provide a primer for Kornberg's DNA polymerase enzyme (17), and furthermore, Sinsheimer had discovered that the virus φX174 had a single-stranded genome (18) and it was a primer for the DNA polymerase. This reinforced the idea that single strands were adequate templates. In the same article (16), I speculated that RNA was likely to be the first polynucleotide molecule in the origin and early evolution of life and also pointed out the possibility of an enzyme that used a single-stranded RNA primer to make a DNA strand; it was called reverse transcriptase when it was discovered 10 years later.

Formation of a Hybrid Helix

Could a DNA-RNA hybrid helix form and have the stability needed so that it could be used for information transfer in view of the different physical properties and geometries of the RNA and the DNA duplex? I was finally able to address this problem with the chemical synthesis of oligodeoxythymidylic acid by Khorana and colleagues (19). Khorana kindly gave me a reaction mixture, which I fractionated and took the longer molecules to see if they would react with polyriboadenylic acid. The experiment worked (20)! The discovery in 1960 that these could form a double helix represented the first experimental demonstration that a hybrid helix could be a method for the transfer of information from DNA to RNA. The evidence was based on measurements of the hypochromism, which occurs when helical molecules are formed, and the changes in sedimentation rate associated with complex formation. These results indicated that DNA could make RNA by using a single-stranded template to make a complementary RNA strand, and it was a model for RNA polymerase activity. However, the discovery of messenger RNA was still 1 year in the future.

It is interesting that 1 year later in 1961, with a more highly purified preparation of RNA polymerase and using as a template the same oligodeoxythymidylate synthesized by Khorana, Hurwitz was able to synthesize polyriboadenylic acid using his enzyme preparation (21). This proved that a single-stranded template was adequate for RNA polymerase.

The publication in the summer of 1960 (20) was the first demonstration of DNA-RNA hybridization although that term had not yet been invented. That particular hybridization is still widely used today in that immobilized oligo(dT) molecules are used to isolate eukaryotic messenger RNA through their poly(rA) tails. At the same time in 1960, Marmur, Doty, and colleagues found they could take denatured DNA molecules and hold them for a prolonged period at an intermediate temperature, called an annealing temperature, thereby allowing the DNA molecules to find each other and re-form a double helix (22, 23). After pre-

senting my work on DNA-RNA interactions at the Gordon Conference in 1960, Sol Spiegelman and Ben Hall came up to me and said they were inspired to try that reaction with a viral system. One year later they combined my work with the annealing work of Marmur and Doty and found that a newly synthesized RNA strand from T2 virus infection could be similarly annealed with DNA from the virus to make a hybrid helix (24). Thus, by 1961 both DNA-DNA and RNA-DNA hybridizations were available for a variety of biological studies.

The significance of the discovery of the DNA-RNA hybrid helix is relevant not only to understanding the activity of RNA polymerase, but it also explains how reverse transcriptase works, as well as telomerase, retrotransposons, and a variety of other interactions in which DNA and RNA strands combine. Today, fluorescence *in situ* hybridization is used in which DNA-RNA hybrids are formed to identify specific areas of the genome. Similarly, microarray gene expression profiling studies use DNA-RNA hybrid formation and are dependent on this 1960 discovery.

The full structural analysis of how these RNA and DNA chains accommodated each other was not revealed until much later. In 1982 the first DNA-RNA single-crystal hybrid molecule was solved in my laboratory (25). It showed that a DNA decamer containing four ribonucleotides formed a hybrid segment that stabilized the entire molecule in the A conformation. In 1992, we carried out a single-crystal x-ray analysis of an Okazaki fragment in which the nucleating ribonucleotides that initiate DNA synthesis in DNA replication were crystallized on DNA (26). Again, the presence of a few ribonucleotides was sufficient to convert the entire fragment into the A conformation.

The central role of the ribose ring puckers that differ in DNA and RNA is widely understood today. The van der Waals crowding of the ribose C2′ oxygen determines the RNA pucker in the RNA double helical A conformation. This interaction provides a sufficient energy barrier to prevent a change in pucker in double helical RNA, in contrast to the facile manner with which the deoxyribose in DNA changes its ring pucker on lowering the water content to form A-DNA or to accommodate the presence of RNA in a hybrid double helix.

The hybrid DNA-RNA helix remains the bedrock of information transfer in biological systems. Indeed, the existence of a hybrid helix seems so obvious today that young research workers simply take it for granted. There is little realization of the extent to which, almost a half-century ago, scientists wrestled with problems of understanding how different polymers can react together to make a stable structure. The roots of our understanding of hybrid helix formation go back to 1960 and even further to the mid-1950s.

Address correspondence to: cbeckman@mit.edu.

REFERENCES

1. Watson, J. D., and Crick, F. H. C. (1953) A structure for deoxyribose nucleic acid. *Nature* **171,** 738–740
2. Rich, A., and Watson, J. D. (1954) Physical studies on ribonucleic acid. *Nature* **173,** 995–996
3. Rich, A., and Watson, J. D. (1954) Some relations between DNA and RNA. *Proc. Natl. Acad. Sci. U. S. A.* **40,** 759–764
4. Grunberg-Manago, M., Ortiz, P. J., and Ochoa, S. (1955) Enzymatic synthesis of nucleic acidlike polynucleotides. *Science* **122,** 907–910
5. Rich, A., and Davies, D. R. (1956) A new two-stranded helical structure: polyadenylic acid and polyuridylic acid. *J. Am. Chem. Soc.* **78,** 3548
6. Kornberg, A., Lehman, I. R., Bessman, M. J., and Simms, E. S. (1956) Enzymic synthesis of deoxyribonucleic acid. *Biochim. Biophys. Acta* **21,** 197–198
7. Rich, A. (1957) The structure of synthetic polyribonucleotides and the spontaneous formation of a new two-stranded helical molecule. In *The Chemical Basis of Heredity* (McElroy, W. D., and Glass, B., eds) pp. 557–562, The Johns Hopkins University Press, Baltimore
8. Rich, A. (1957) The structure of the nucleic acids and related substances. *Special Publication, N. Y. Acad. Sci.* **5,** 186–190
9. Warner, R. C. (1956) Ultraviolet spectra of enzymatically synthesized polynucleotides. *Fed. Proc.* **15,** 379
10. Felsenfeld, G., and Rich, A. (1957) Studies on the formation of two- and three-stranded polyribonucleotides. *Biochim. Biophys. Acta* **26,** 457–468
11. Felsenfeld, G., Davies, D. R., and Rich, A. (1957) Formation of a three-stranded polynucleotide molecule. *J. Am. Chem. Soc.* **79,** 2023–2024
12. Hoogsteen, K. (1959) The crystal and molecular structure of a hydrogen-bonded complex between 1-methylthymine and 9-methyladenine. *Acta Crystallogr.* **12,** 822–823
13. Rich, A. (1958) Formation of two- and three-stranded helical molecules by polyinosinic acid and polyadenylic acid. *Nature* **181,** 521–525
14. Davies, D. R., and Rich, A. (1958) The formation of a helical complex between polyinosinic acid and polycytidylic acid. *J. Am. Chem. Soc.* **80,** 1003
15. Rich, A. (1959) Polynucleotide interactions and the nucleic acids. *Brookhaven Symp. Biol.* **12,** 17–26
16. Rich, A. (1959) An analysis of the relation between DNA and RNA. *Ann. N. Y. Acad. Sci.* **81,** 709–722
17. Lehman, I. R., Zimmerman, S. B., Adler, J., Bessman, M. J., Sims, E. S., and Kornberg, A. (1958) Enzymatic synthesis of deoxyribonucleic acid. V. Chemical composition of enzymatically synthesized deoxyribonucleic acid. *Proc. Natl. Acad. Sci. U. S. A.* **44,** 1191–1196
18. Sinsheimer, R. L. (1959) A single-stranded deoxyribonucleic acid from bacteriophage ϕX174. *J. Mol. Biol.* **1,** 43–53
19. Tener, G. M., Khorana, H. G., Markham, R., and Pol, E. H. (1958) Studies on polynucleotides. II. The synthesis and characterization of linear and cyclic thymidine oligonucleotides. *J. Am. Chem. Soc.* **80,** 6223–6230
20. Rich, A. (1960) A hybrid helix containing both deoxyribose and ribose polynucleotides and its relation to the transfer of information between the nucleic acids. *Proc. Natl. Acad. Sci. U. S. A.* **46,** 1044–1053
21. Furth, J. J., Hurvitz, J., and Goldmann, M. (1961) The directing role of DNA in RNA synthesis. *Biochem. Biophys. Res. Commun.* **4,** 362–367
22. Marmur, J., and Lane, D. (1960) Strand separation and specific recombination in deoxyribonucleic acids: biological studies. *Proc. Natl. Acad. Sci. U. S. A.* **46,** 453–461
23. Doty, P., Marmur, J., Eigner, J., and Schildkraut, C. (1960) Strand separation and specific recombination in deoxyribonucleic acids: physical chemical studies. *Proc. Natl. Acad. Sci. U. S. A.* **46,** 461–476
24. Hall, B. D., and Speigelman, S. (1961) Sequence complementarity of T2-DNA and T2-specific RNA. *Proc. Natl. Acad. Sci. U. S. A.* **47,** 137–146
25. Wang, A. H.-J., Fujii, S., van Boom, J. H., van der Marel, G.A., van Boeckel, S. A. A., and Rich, A. (1982) Molecular structure of r(GCG)d(TATACGC): a DNA-RNA hybrid helix joined to double helical DNA. *Nature* **299,** 601–604
26. Egli, M., Usman, N., Zhang, S., and Rich, A. (1992) Crystal structure of an Okazaki fragment at 2-Å resolution. *Proc. Natl. Acad. Sci. U. S. A.* **89,** 534–538

Classics

The Journal of Biological Chemistry
TABLE OF CONTENTS

CLASSICS

THE JOURNAL OF BIOLOGICAL CHEMISTRY
© 2002 by The American Society for Biochemistry and Molecular Biology, Inc.

Vol. 277, No. 12, Issue of March 22, p. e1, 2002
Printed in U.S.A.

Classics

A PAPER IN A SERIES REPRINTED TO CELEBRATE THE CENTENARY OF THE JBC IN 2005

JBC Centennial
1905–2005
100 Years of Biochemistry and Molecular Biology

The First Paper Published in the JBC: John Jacob Abel, Co-founder of the Journal of Biological Chemistry and the American Society of Biological Chemists

On the Decomposition Products of Epinephrine Hydrate
(Abel, J. J., and Taveau, R. DeM. (1905) *J. Biol. Chem.* 1, 1–32)

This is the first paper published in the *Journal of Biological Chemistry* (JBC). The title page and the table of contents of the issue in which it appeared are also reprinted to provide a glimpse into the field of biochemistry at that time. Similar ancillary information will be published periodically with Classic papers to record changes in the Journal and the field during the past century.

The contributions of John Jacob Abel, Professor of Pharmacology at Johns Hopkins University Medical School, to the Journal and the Society deserve special note. He was not only a distinguished scientist, but also one of the founders of both the Journal and the American Society of Biological Chemists (ASBC). Abel convinced Christian A. Herter, then Professor of Pharmacology and Therapeutics at Columbia University, to finance and start the Journal. In 1905, Abel wrote to 21 other American biochemists (1, 2).

"Dr. Herter and I have decided that the time has arrived for the establishment in this country of a *Journal of Biological Chemistry*. The scope of the Journal is to be a wide one. We hope to publish articles on bacteriological chemistry, plant chemistry and the better sort of clinical chemistry. Then pharmacological work which is of a chemical character will also be welcomed. The pharmacological papers of a more physiological character should be published elsewhere." Later in the same letter to emphasize the broad scope of the Journal "we are willing to publish anything of a chemical nature in the whole field of biology whether this touches the plant or animal kingdom." (1) (This statement of Journal scope and mission is as useful today as it was in 1905.)

Before the first issue of JBC appeared in October 1905, an announcement of the intended scope was issued.

"Without rigidly defining the scope of the Journal, it may be stated that its pages will be open

First. To workers in Zoology and Botany and the branches of knowledge in which these sciences are applied, for such of their researches as are of a chemical or physicochemical nature.

Second. To workers on the chemical side of the experimental medical sciences, as Physiology, Pathology, Pharmacology, Hygiene, Physiological Chemistry, and Bacteriology.

Third. To those who are engaged in any branch of Clinical Medicine when their researches are of a chemical nature.

Fourth. To the specialist in organic chemistry, who will find here a fitting place for publication of researches which have biological or medical interest.

The growing importance of chemical research in the elucidation of general biological and medical problems and also the increasing activity of American investigators in this field, point to the need of a journal of the character here outlined. At present there is no periodical in the English language that meets the requirements of the biological chemist" (1).

John Jacob Abel. Photo courtesy of the National Library of Medicine.

As seen on the title page, Abel and Herter served as the first Editors, and Abel continued as the Managing Editor for several years. (Herter's important contributions will be addressed in a subsequent issue.)

Abel also acted as the founder of the ASBC. He made the initial proposal, convened a meeting of well known biological chemists that led to its formation, and later he became the second President of the Society. Interest in the formation of the new society came primarily from members of the American Physiological Society, which had been formed in 1887, who felt that the chemical side of physiology had attracted a significant and growing number of scientists and a separate society would be desirable. The American Chemical Society had started a biochemical section in 1905 and an increasing number of chemical papers were presented at the American Physiological Society meetings. The success of the JBC in its first year also suggested that a new society would be welcome.

Abel circulated the following letter dated October 16, 1906 to the 24 scientists whose names appear on the title page of the Journal.

"The enclosed circular is being sent to the gentlemen whose names appear on the title page of the Journal of Biological Chemistry for the purpose of obtaining their signatures, should the project therein outlined meet with their approval. These gentlemen are also requested to name other prominent workers in biological chemistry whose signatures should be secured.

When the circular has received the signatures of a sufficient number of representative men, it will be sent to a selected list of chemists in various branches of biology and medicine as an invitation to membership in the new society.

The responsibility of selecting this list should fall on the signers of the proposal. Will you not cooperate in this matter? Have you any suggestions to offer in respect to the method of selection? It is of course assumed that only those who are worthy of membership by virtue of acquirements and work accomplished will be nominated.

The proposal has followed as the result of conversations with biological chemists in different parts of the country, and it would seem that the time has come for bringing the project to the attention of those most capable of launching it.

Details, such as the form of constitution to be adopted, the question of affiliation with other scientific bodies, annual time and place of meeting, etc. will naturally be subjects for consideration at the meeting for organization" (2).

At a meeting on December 26, 1906, the ASBC was officially formed with 29 charter members. Shortly thereafter, the Council of the Society elected 52 additional members bringing the total membership in the first year to 81. (ASBMB membership in 2001 is about 10,000.)

Abel was a great scientist with many major accomplishments during an active 50-year career. Overall, his research can be characterized as primarily directed toward the isolation and characterization of hormones. He and his collaborators worked for over 10 years to describe the active secretion of the suprarenal gland that raised blood pressure, epinephrine. He also isolated and crystallized insulin (3).[1]

During his long and productive research career, Abel also provided a training ground for many scientists. Notable among them was Vincent Du Vigneaud who was a postdoctoral fellow with Abel and in 1955 received the Nobel Prize in Chemistry for his work on the chemical synthesis of oxytocin and vasopressin.

In addition to his scientific accomplishments, Abel was notable as an organization builder. Before his critical efforts in founding the JBC and the ASBC, he had founded the *Journal of Experimental Medicine* in 1895 and later, in 1909, he was influential in founding the American Society of Pharmacology and Experimental Therapeutics. He was instrumental in founding the *Journal of Pharmacology and Experimental Therapeutics* and served as its Editor for 23 years.

A remarkable career and a fitting way to begin the series of JBC Classics reprinted.

Robert D. Simoni, Robert L. Hill, and Martha Vaughan

REFERENCES

1. Edsall, J. (1980) The Journal of Biological Chemistry after seventy five years. *J. Biol. Chem.* **255,** 8939–8951 (A wonderful history of the JBC)
2. Chittenden, R. H. (1945) *The First Twenty-five Years of the American Society of Biological Chemists*, Williams & Wilkins, Baltimore, MD
3. Abel, J. J. (1926) *Proc. Natl. Acad. Sci. U. S. A.* **12,** 132–136

---

[1] For a detailed biography of J. J. Abel see MacNider, W. DeB. (1947) *Biographical Memoir of John Jacob Abel*, Vol. 24, Sixth Memoir, National Academy of Sciences, Washington, D. C.

THE JOURNAL OF BIOLOGICAL CHEMISTRY
© 2002 by The American Society for Biochemistry and Molecular Biology, Inc.

Vol. 277, No. 13, Issue of March 29, p. e2, 2002
Printed in U.S.A.

Classics

A PAPER IN A SERIES REPRINTED TO CELEBRATE THE CENTENARY OF THE JBC IN 2005

JBC Centennial
1905–2005
100 Years of Biochemistry and Molecular Biology

Founding of the American Society of Biological Chemists (ASBC), Now American Society for Biochemistry and Molecular Biology (ASBMB). The Proceedings of the First Annual Meeting in 1907

Proceedings of The First Annual Meeting of the American Society of Biological Chemists (American Society of Biological Chemists (1907) *J. Biol. Chem.* **3, vii)***

The American Society of Biological Chemists (ASBC) was organized in December 1906 by a group of members of the American Physiological Society (APS) with research interests in the chemical side of physiology. This research area was attracting increasing attention and interest, and many APS members felt that a new society was needed. The organization of the new society was initiated by John J. Abel, Professor of Pharmacology at Johns Hopkins University (see introduction to Abel, J. J., and Taveau, R. DeM. (1905) *J. Biol. Chem.* **1**, 1–32 for more information on Abel's contributions to the Society and the *Journal of Biological Chemistry* (JBC)).

The organizational meeting was held on December 26, 1906, and Articles of Agreement for the ASBC were approved by the 29 attendees. In his address to the group, Abel defined the scope of the Society, "We wish to draw into our Society the biological chemists of all departments of biology, including those organic and physical chemists who take a lively interest in our subject . . . Our common meeting ground should be chemistry as applied to animal or vegetable structures, living or dead, throwing light on life processes and functions of living structures."

The members of the new Society elected the following officers: President, Russell H. Chittenden; Vice-President, John J. Abel; Secretary, William J Gies; Treasurer, Layfayette B. Mendel. Members of the Council were: Otto Folin, Walter Jones, Waldemar Koch, John Marshall, and Thomas B. Osborne. Within the first year, membership had grown from the 29 charter members to a total of 81.

After the organizational meeting, the first meeting of the Society was held in Washington, D. C., May 8–9, 1907, in conjunction with meetings of the American Physiological Society and the Washington section of the American Chemical Society, in order to hold joint sessions. (Meeting with the APS may have been important in alleviating concerns of APS members who did not join the ASBC.)

No record of the Society finances could be found in the report of the first meeting. At the second annual meeting it was mentioned in the Treasurer's report that total Society expenses for the period 1906–1908 were $223.55, mostly for printing and postage by the Secretary's office. It was also noted that the annual dues of $2.00 were more than adequate to cover these expenses. (ASBMB membership dues for 2001 are $110, a very modest 55-fold increase in 94 years.)

A more complete Society budget was presented in the report of the Eighth Annual Meeting of ASBC as follows (Table I). The budget for the ASBMB for 2001 is over $1 million exclusive of the Journal operations. Quite a contrast!

---

* All of the information for this Introduction was taken from: Chittenden, R. H. (1945) *The First Twenty-five Years of the American Society of Biological Chemists*, Williams & Wilkins, Baltimore, MD.

This paper is available on line at http://www.jbc.org

TABLE I

In the treasury, January 1, 1913	$22.17
Dues collected during 1913	$285.25
Total receipts	$307.41
Expenditures during 1913	$180.42
In the treasury January 1, 1914	$127.00
Unpaid dues	$40.00

At the 1907 meeting, 43 papers were presented. Publication of the Proceedings in JBC was financed by Christian A. Herter. The Proceedings that are reprinted in this issue provide a good sense of the field of biological chemistry in this early period. Of the 43 papers, the great majority are analytical methods, compositional analysis of biological materials, or metabolic studies. In addition, the Proceedings provide an introduction to many leading biological chemists, some of whom later wrote Classic papers that will be reprinted in future issues.

Robert D. Simoni, Robert L. Hill, and Martha Vaughan

THE JOURNAL OF BIOLOGICAL CHEMISTRY
© 2002 by The American Society for Biochemistry and Molecular Biology, Inc.

Vol. 277, No. 14, Issue of April 5, p. e3, 2002
Printed in U.S.A.

Classics

A PAPER IN A SERIES REPRINTED TO CELEBRATE THE CENTENARY OF THE JBC IN 2005

JBC Centennial
1905–2005
100 Years of Biochemistry and Molecular Biology

Is Nerve Conduction a Physical or Chemical Process? The Temperature Dependence of Nerve Impulses. S. S. Maxwell

Is the Conduction of the Nerve Impulse a Chemical or a Physical Process? (Maxwell, S. S. (1907) *J. Biol. Chem.* 7, 359–385)

The study reprinted in this issue of JBC Classics represents a period when attempts to define physiological processes in chemical or physical terms were at the interface between physiology and biochemistry. In the introduction to the paper, the author, S. S. Maxwell, pointed out that the fundamental question posed had been experimentally addressed without clear resolution but had led to a "mountain of physical hypotheses as to the nature of the nerve impulse." Maxwell summarized the four general types of experiments that had been intended to provide positive evidence that nerve impulses are chemical in nature: 1) attempts to prove fatigue of the stimulated nerve; 2) attempts to demonstrate the presence of the products of chemical change in stimulated nerve; 3) attempts to demonstrate a change in temperature of stimulated nerve; and 4) attempts to prove a requirement for oxygen in nerve conduction. He concluded that the experiments were either negative or flawed so that the question remained open.

Professor Jacques Loeb is credited in the paper for suggesting to Maxwell, who was a faculty member at Berkeley but had been Loeb's student at the University of Chicago, that he try to answer this question by measuring the temperature dependence of the rate of the nerve impulse. Loeb was a Herzstein Professor at University of California, Berkeley and a distinguished physiologist, once called "the strongest physiologist in the world" (1). He had already demonstrated, using the temperature dependence of rates, that maturation of fertilized eggs of *Lottia*, a limpet, is a chemical process. Loeb was probably best known for his studies on artificial parthenogenesis, "sea urchins without fathers," but also worked on problems in colloid chemistry, tropisms, and many other areas of science during a remarkable career.[1]

The principle of using temperature dependence to characterize a chemical process had been established by van't Hoff (1884) and Arrhenius (1899). It had been shown that a 10-degree rise in temperature would increase the rate of a chemical reaction or process by about 2–3-fold but would increase the rate of a purely physical process by only 10–15%. This has come to be known as the Q_{10} effect. It is generally stated that for every 10-degree increase in temperature, the reaction rate increases by a factor of 2.

The experimental system, the pedal nerve of the slug, *Ariolimax columbianus*, was chosen with great care, recognizing the technical challenge of accurately measuring the rate of a nerve impulse. Descriptions of the nerve preparation, generation and measurement of the impulses, regulation of the temperature, and analysis of the data were precisely detailed. One might

---

[1] Loeb held the Herzstein Chair, which was established by Morris Herzstein, a physician and real estate speculator, as part of the effort to recruit Loeb from the University of Chicago to Berkeley. (Later Herzstein Chairs, all in the Department of Biological Sciences at Stanford, were held by C. B. Van Neil, Charles Yanofsky, and Bruce Baker, current Chair holder.) Loeb's salary was paid by Phoebe Apperson Hearst, the mother of William Randolph Hearst. Loeb's move from Chicago to Berkeley had repercussions. Russell Chittenden, then President of the American Physiological Society (APS) and Professor of Physiological Chemistry at Yale, removed Loeb from the Editorial Board of the *American Journal of Physiology* because "he no longer represented a major institution." Loeb responded by refusing to publish in that *Journal*, and the controversy that arose within the APS forced Chittenden out of office. Christian Herter invited Loeb to join the Editorial Board of the JBC. Chittenden was a leader in the formation of the ASBC and was its first President (1).

repeat these experiments today with little other guidance. (A desirable goal of every JBC author.)

Although the voluminous experimental data were quite variable, Maxwell determined that, on average, there was a 1.78-fold increase in the rate of the nerve impulse for every 10-degree increase in temperature. He confidently concluded that "the temperature coefficient of the velocity of the nerve impulse indicates definitely that the conduction is a chemical process, but probably not an oxidation."

With 94 years of hindsight, we can see that Maxwell, although correct, probably should not have been quite so confident in his conclusion. His experiment involved stimulating the nerve electrically and measuring the time elapsed until a twitch was recorded from the associated muscle. Thus, he timed a series of complex reactions that included the nerve impulse and also the muscle contraction. Because muscle contraction is a chemical process, even if the nerve impulse were a physical process he would have obtained the same result. Maxwell reported that it had been shown in 1906 by one of his colleagues that the temperature coefficient for the contraction of striated muscle was high, thus establishing muscle contraction as a chemical process. Should we conclude that the JBC editorial review process has improved?

Acknowledgment—We thank Professor David Epel, Loeb Building, The Hopkins Marine Station, Stanford University, for providing information on Jacques Loeb and S. S. Maxwell.

Robert D. Simoni, Robert L. Hill, and Martha Vaughan

REFERENCES

1. Pauly, P. J. (1987) *Controlling Life: Jacques Loeb and the Engineering Ideal in Biology*, Oxford University Press, New York

THE JOURNAL OF BIOLOGICAL CHEMISTRY
© 2002 by The American Society for Biochemistry and Molecular Biology, Inc.

Vol. 277, No. 15, Issue of April 12, p. e4, 2002
Printed in U.S.A.

Classics

A PAPER IN A SERIES REPRINTED TO CELEBRATE THE CENTENARY OF THE JBC IN 2005

JBC Centennial
1905–2005
100 Years of Biochemistry and Molecular Biology

The Metabolism of Fatty Acids as Measured with Phenyl Derivative "Tracers": the Work of Henry Drysdale Dakin

Comparative Studies of the Mode of Oxidation of Phenyl Derivatives of Fatty Acids by the Animal Organism and by Hydrogen Peroxide
(Dakin, H. D. (1908) *J. Biol. Chem.* 4, 419–435)

This *Journal of Biological Chemistry* (JBC) Classic is an instructive example of the early application of organic chemistry to questions of biochemical interest. The author, Henry Drysdale Dakin, was trained as an organic chemist in England. From 1905 to 1914, he worked in the private laboratory of Christian A. Herter in New York City. After Herter's untimely death in 1910 at the age of 45, Dakin continued directing Herter's laboratory at Mrs. Herter's request . . . (There will be more about Herter's role as a scientist and founder of the JBC in a future installment of JBC Classics.)

In 1914, Dakin returned to Europe to help in the war effort. He worked in a French military hospital on the development of antiseptics. "Dakin's Solution," a buffered hypochlorite solution, was an important antiseptic for treating wounds. He was also responsible for the use of *N*-chloro-*p*-toluenesulfonamide sodium salt (chloramine-T) for the sterilization of drinking water (2).

In 1916, Dakin married Mrs. Susan Dows Herter, and they moved to a house overlooking the Hudson River at Scarborough. He constructed his own private laboratory in an annex and worked alone, except for the help of an "elderly technician," for the rest of his career (2). Dakin is best known for his studies on the oxidations and reductions that take place in the "animal organism." He discovered the enzymes arginase and glyoxidase. He synthesized the hormone adrenalin. Dakin also developed a method using "wet" butanol for extraction of amino acids from a neutralized protein hydrolysate. This method allowed a relatively complete amino acid analysis of two proteins zein and gelatin (1, 2).

Dakin was one of the first 81 members of the American Society of Biological Chemists (ASBC) and one of the early members of the JBC Editorial Board on which he served from 1911 to 1930. Among his many papers this one was selected for the JBC Classics series because it introduces a novel and very important approach to studying metabolism. In the introduction, Dakin pointed out that studying the metabolism of fatty acids in animals is difficult because the intermediate oxidation products are rapidly oxidized further making them difficult to isolate and to thereby define individual steps in the process. He decided to "tag" the fatty acids with a phenyl group as a "difficultyly (*sic*) oxidizable aromatic nucleus" so that the phenyl derivatives of fatty acid oxidation intermediates could be isolated and their structures determined. He argued that even though the phenyl derivatives were unnatural and metabolically inert, studying the metabolism of the fatty acid side chain would "undoubtedly throw light upon the mode of oxidation of the purely fatty acid of related structure."

The experiments were classic in design. Test compounds were synthesized. Dogs were injected subcutaneously with a dilute aqueous solution containing 4–8 g of a compound, and urine was collected for 3 days. (One might wonder what the total volume of the dilute aqueous solution containing 8 g of phenylpropionic acid might have been and whether such a protocol would be approved by the committees of today that review animal studies.) The urine was fractionated in several steps, and finally, individual compounds were crystallized, re-crystallized, and characterized by derivatization and comparison to reference compounds.

This paper is available on line at http://www.jbc.org

This work, introducing the application of phenyl-tagged molecules in metabolic studies, predates the use of stable isotopes by nearly 20 years and of radioactive isotopes by more than 30 years, yet uses, for the first time, the same logic to trace biologically active molecules through complex metabolic reactions.

Robert D. Simoni, Robert L. Hill, and Martha Vaughan

REFERENCES

1. Chittenden, R. H. (1945) *The First Twenty-five Years of the American Society of Biological Chemistry*, Williams & Wilkins, Baltimore, MD
2. Clarke, H. T. (1952) *J. Biol. Chem.* **198,** 491

THE JOURNAL OF BIOLOGICAL CHEMISTRY
© 2002 by The American Society for Biochemistry and Molecular Biology, Inc.

Vol. 277, No. 16, Issue of April 19, p. e5, 2002
Printed in U.S.A.

Classics

A PAPER IN A SERIES REPRINTED TO CELEBRATE THE CENTENARY OF THE JBC IN 2005

JBC Centennial
1905–2005
100 Years of Biochemistry and Molecular Biology

Benedict's Solution, a Reagent for Measuring Reducing Sugars: the Clinical Chemistry of Stanley R. Benedict

A Reagent For the Detection of Reducing Sugars
(Benedict, S. R. (1908) *J. Biol. Chem.* 5, 485–487)

Stanley Rossiter Benedict was born in Cincinnati in 1884. While a student at the University of Cincinnati he worked with J. F. Snell, and together they published nine papers describing new analytical methods in inorganic chemistry. This research experience as a college student provided the intellectual foundation for his career. After a mistaken year in medical school at Cincinnati, he went to Yale, to the Department of Physiological Chemistry, to study with Russell Chittenden and Lafayette Mendel where he received training in metabolism and physiology. He received his Ph.D. in 1908, 2 years after entering graduate school. (Current students take note.) In 1910, he became Professor of Chemistry at Cornell University Medical College, the position he held until his death in 1936 at the age of 52 (1).

In a biographical review of Benedict's career, E. V. McCollum wrote, "It is not possible to give an accurate account of the scientific work of Stanley Benedict without at the same time discussing the parallel researches of Otto Folin . . . they succeeded, through many years of intensive investigations, in devising and refining analytical procedures for determination of minute amounts of the principal non-protein constituents of blood and urine so that, for the first time, chemical analysis became a highly useful technic (*sic*) for the discovery of the chemical processes in the normal functioning of the body" (1).

Of Benedict's relationship with Folin, Shaffer wrote, "Both excelled in designing very clever analytical methods of the widest usefulness, and in using these tools with rare success for the discovery of new facts about metabolism. In spite of seventeen years difference in their age (Folin was the older), of the rivalry and controversy sometimes evident in their papers, there early developed between them a warm friendship which reveals the fine character of both. They were kindred spirits" (2). (We will present a classic paper by Otto Folin in a subsequent installment of JBC Classics, stay tuned.)

As McCollum and Shaffer described, Benedict's major contributions to biochemistry were in devising analytical methods. Although he published many papers in the *Journal of Biological Chemistry* (JBC), the paper reprinted here seemed appropriate to characterize a distinguished career. It had been known for many years that the common sugars had carbonyl groups and were therefore, "reducing sugars." That is, they were oxidized by a variety of metal ions, Ag^+, Fe^{3+}, and Cu^{2+}. Treatment with hot alkali fragments the sugars, and the resulting products reduce Cu^{2+} to Cu^+ with the formation of a precipitate of Cu_2O. As noted in the paper, Benedict's goal was to improve this general method to make the reagent less corrosive and more stable. He accomplished this by substituting carbonate for hydroxide as the alkali component, to reduce the corrosiveness, and by substituting citrate for tartrate as the agent to chelate the Cu^{2+}, to make the reagent more stable.

Benedict's Solution, or one of the many variants that evolved over the years, was used as the reagent of choice for measuring sugar content for more than 50 years. It was the most common test for diabetes and was the standard procedure for virtually all clinical laboratories. Saul Roseman remembers that all inductees into the army during World War II had their urine

This paper is available on line at http://www.jbc.org

Stanley R. Benedict. Photo courtesy of the National Library of Medicine.

tested for sugar with Benedict's Solution.[1] Although Benedict's assay was the method of choice for more than 50 years, it suffered from lack of sugar specificity and was eventually supplanted by the use of enzymatic methods such as glucose oxidase.

Benedict's work on analytical methods was particularly important for clinical applications. There was, for many years, a very close relationship between basic biochemistry research and biochemical clinical applications. Many biochemists were employed as clinical chemists because academic jobs as biochemists were difficult to find. Many of the methods that have been taken for granted for many years find their origins with biochemists working in clinical laboratories.

Benedict was active in the Society and the JBC. He served as Secretary of the Society and, in 1919, served as President. It was during his tenure as President that the JBC was transferred to the Society for management. (Officially the financial relationship between the Society and the Journal Corporation was not finalized until 1942.) Benedict became a member of the JBC Editorial Board and in 1926 became Managing Editor, a position he held until his death in 1936. An interesting characterization of Benedict's service as JBC Managing Editor is made in the obituary of Benedict written by Philip A. Shaffer (2), "With many other contributor (*sic*), the present writer has occasionally smarted under sometimes sharp criticism of the editor; but rarely if ever were the criticisms unjustified. His standards were high, he expected clarity, logic, and brevity in exposition, his opinions were definite and outspoken his judgements were based on essential facts and were impartial as to individuals." (During this period of the Journal, and later as well, all communication between authors and the Journal was conducted personally by the Managing Editor.)

Robert D. Simoni, Robert L. Hill, and Martha Vaughan

REFERENCES

1. McCollum, E. V. (1974) *Memoir of Stanley Rossiter Benedict*, Vol. 27, National Academy of Sciences, Washington, D. C.
2. Shaffer, P. A. (1937) Obituary for Stanley Rossiter Benedict. *J. Biol. Chem.* **117,** 428

---

[1] Much of the background information for sugar chemistry and clinical usage of Benedict's Reagent was kindly provided by Professor Saul Roseman, Professor of Biology, Johns Hopkins University. Professor Roseman knew Stanley R. Benedict personally.

THE JOURNAL OF BIOLOGICAL CHEMISTRY
© 2002 by The American Society for Biochemistry and Molecular Biology, Inc.

Vol. 277, No. 17, Issue of April 26, p. e6, 2002
Printed in U.S.A.

Classics

A PAPER IN A SERIES REPRINTED TO CELEBRATE THE CENTENARY OF THE JBC IN 2005

JBC Centennial
1905–2005
100 Years of Biochemistry and Molecular Biology

Christian A. Herter: Co-founder of the Journal of Biological Chemistry and Benefactor of Biochemistry. Obituary

Obituary for Christian A. Herter, M.D.
((1910) *J. Biol. Chem.* 8, 437–439)

Christian Archibald Herter, with John J. Abel, founded the *Journal of Biological Chemistry* (JBC) in 1905. This JBC Classic has two parts, the obituary for Herter, which was published in the JBC, and the announcement of the establishment of the Herter Memorial Fund. (Abel's roles in founding the Journal and the Society were presented as an earlier JBC Classic (1).)

Christian A. Herter was born in 1865. His father, Christian Herter, was an artist and a very successful interior decorator/architect. He was educated privately under his father's direction, and it was his father who chose a medical career for his son. He enrolled in The College of Physicians and Surgeons of Columbia University at the age of 15 and received his M.D. degree 3 years later. He then studied with pathologist William H. Welch at Johns Hopkins University and with August Forel in Zurich. As a result of this additional training, Herter became interested in scientific laboratory medicine. He started a medical practice in New York City and also established a private laboratory in his home to conduct medical research, particularly related to the diseases of his patients. His laboratory became a center for biochemical research related to disease, and it supported the research of many scientists including H. D. Dakin. (Dakin's work was presented in an earlier installment of JBC Classics (2).) Herter became Professor of the Department of Pharmacology and Therapeutics at his alma mater, a position he held until his death in 1910 at the age of 45. (Herter's father died at the age of 44 (3).) He died of a wasting neurological disease, possibly myasthenia gravis.

The founding of the JBC was initiated with an exchange of letters between Abel and Herter in 1903. The letter from Abel has not been found that prompted Herter to reply as follows, "I am a good deal interested in your letter suggesting the propriety of a new medium for the publication of biochemical writings in this country. A similar idea has often been in my mind although I never had any clear views to the best way of reaching the desired end. It is inevitable that much good material for a journal devoted to chemical problems in physiology and pathology should be forthcoming in this country and I cannot see where it is to be printed unless there is some new publication for this purpose . . . To restate my position then, I would say that I favor the establishment of a journal such as you have in mind and will gladly help along in any way I can."

By 1905, support had grown for a new journal, and the first issue of JBC was published in December 1905. Fittingly, Herter and Abel were the first Editors. Herter was true to his commitment to "help along in any way I can." He financed the start of the Journal and continued to subsidize its operation until his death 5 years later. To guarantee its permanence, he established the Journal as a non-profit corporation with Herter, Abel, Edward K. Dunham, Reid Hunt, and A. N. Richards each holding one share of stock. They agreed that no share could be sold or transferred without the consent of the other shareholders. JBC Inc. continued until its transfer to the American Society of Biological Chemists (ASBC) in 1942 (4).

Herter's personal fortune allowed him to establish and run his private laboratory, including as many as six independent scientists, and to support the Journal, as well as many other

Christian A. Herter. Photo courtesy of the National Library of Medicine.

worthy causes. He had significant Herter family wealth, and his wife, Susan Dows Herter, was the daughter of the nation's largest grain merchant (3). Herter's nephew and namesake, Christian Archibald Herter, was Governor of Massachusetts and later Secretary of State in the Eisenhower administration.

Herter's contributions go well beyond his own research and the JBC. He was a close friend of John D. Rockefeller and was probably the person most influential in assembling the Board of Directors of the Rockefeller Institute for Medical Research, now Rockefeller University. He became a charter member of the Board, serving as treasurer in administering research grants, and he also arranged for the establishment of the associated research and teaching hospital (3).

After Herter's death, friends and colleagues established the Christian A. Herter Memorial Fund, the announcement of which is reprinted here. The fund amounted to $40,000 and was intended to honor Herter by ensuring the Journal a solid and independent financial footing. John Edsall reported that in 1980 the fund totaled $184,000 (5). In 2001, the Herter Fund totals $960,000 and continues to provide the Journal with a significant and stabilizing income.

Christian A. Herter left many important legacies but none more significant than the JBC.

Robert D. Simoni, Robert L. Hill, and Martha Vaughan

REFERENCES

1. JBC Classics: Abel, J. J., and Taveau, R. DeM. (1905) *J. Biol. Chem.* **1,** 1–32 (http://www.jbc.org/cgi/content/full/277/12/e1)
2. JBC Classics: Dakin, H. D. (1908) *J. Biol. Chem.* **4,** 419–435 (http://www.jbc.org/cgi/content/full/277/15/e4)
3. Garraty, J. A., and Carnes, M. C. (1999) *American National Biography*, Vol. 10, p. 685, American Council of Learned Societies General Editors, Oxford University Press, New York
4. Richards, A. N. (1956) Journal of Biological Chemistry: recollections of its early years and of its founders. *Fed. Proc.* **15,** 803–806 (Richards was Herter's assistant at Columbia and was Assistant Editor of the Journal when it was founded.)
5. Chittenden, R. H. (1945) *The First Twenty-five Years of the American Society of Biological Chemists*, Williams & Wilkins, Baltimore, MD

THE JOURNAL OF BIOLOGICAL CHEMISTRY
© 2002 by The American Society for Biochemistry and Molecular Biology, Inc.

Vol. 277, No. 18, Issue of May 3, p. e7, 2002
Printed in U.S.A.

Classics

A PAPER IN A SERIES REPRINTED TO CELEBRATE THE CENTENARY OF THE JBC IN 2005

JBC Centennial
1905–2005
100 Years of Biochemistry and Molecular Biology

Nutritional Biochemistry and the Amino Acid Composition of Proteins: the Early Years of Protein Chemistry. The Work of Thomas B. Osborne and Lafayette B. Mendel

The Amino-Acid Minimum for Maintenance and Growth, as Exemplified by Further Experiments with Lysine and Tryptophane
(Osborne, T. B., and Mendel, L. B. (1916) *J. Biol. Chem.* 25, 1–12)

The Role of Vitamines in the Diet
(Osborne, T. B., and Mendel, L. B. (1917) *J. Biol. Chem.* 31, 149–163)

The research described in the two papers in this installment of JBC Classics represents the beginning of nutritional studies as a major focus of biochemistry for many years.

Lafayette Benedict Mendel was Professor of Physiological Chemistry at the Sheffield Scientific School at Yale, his alma mater. From 1921 to 1935, the year he died, he was the Sterling Professor of Physiological Chemistry. Although Mendel's accomplishments were many and varied, he received major recognition for his work in nutrition. Mendel was one of the first 81 members of the American Society of Biological Chemists (ASBC) and continued to be very active in the Society, serving as both Vice President and President. He was also a member of the first Editorial Board of the *Journal of Biological Chemistry* (JBC) (1). In addition Mendel was regarded as a gifted teacher. His students referred to him as "The Professor." On his 60th birthday, Graham Lusk said of him, "He has been the guide, philosopher, and friend to many young men and women; he has guided them to walk by themselves when they were able to stand alone; and he has given them wise council in times of difficulty. Herein he has shown himself as one of the great teachers of his time" (2).

Thomas Burr Osborne was a long time collaborator with Mendel at Yale. Like Mendel, he received his Ph.D. from Yale. He was primarily a chemist, and his interests were in the amino acid composition of proteins, particularly plant proteins. He was Research Chemist at Yale and subsequently Research Chemist at the Connecticut Agricultural Experiment Station at New Haven, Research Associate at the Carnegie Institution, and Research Associate in Biochemistry at Yale. Osborne was quite active in the Society serving as both Vice President and President and was, like Mendel, a member of the first JBC Editorial Board (1).

Osborne's work focused on determining the exact composition of many plant proteins and showing that the amino acid composition varied enormously among different proteins, even those from the same plant seed. Zein, for example, had 1.5% arginine whereas edestin contained 14.4%. With this kind of compositional data, he was able to suggest that, given such varied composition, different proteins would have different nutritive value.

Osborne's work fit nicely with Mendel's interests in determining the relative values of various isolated proteins in both the maintenance of adult animals and growth of young animals. They had determined that zein, the major protein of maize, lacks tryptophane (*sic*) and lysine. As described in the first of the two JBC Classics reprinted here, they demonstrated that maintenance of adult rats required the addition of tryptophane (*sic*) to the diet. Rats would not grow, however, unless lysine was also added.

This work led to other nutritional insights including the description of "fat soluble" and "water soluble" vitamins, the subject of the second Classic in this set. The introduction to this paper offers interesting insight into the controversy of the "vitamine (*sic*) hypothesis." Osborne

This paper is available on line at http://www.jbc.org

Thomas B. Osborne. Photo courtesy of the National
Library of Medicine.

Lafayette B. Mendel. Photo courtesy of the National
Library of Medicine.

and Mendel write that Rohmann, an opponent of the vitamin hypothesis, said, "The assumption that some unknown substances are indispensable for growth is a convenient device for explaining experiments that result in failure — a device that becomes superfluous as soon as the experiment succeeds." One detects that Mendel, Osborne, and no doubt their contemporary nutritionists took some delight in proving Rohmann wrong.

This work by Mendel and Osborne serves as an introduction to other nutritional biochemistry papers that follow in later installments of JBC Classics, particularly those by E. V. McCollum and E. A. Doisy.

Robert D. Simoni, Robert L. Hill, and Martha Vaughan

REFERENCES

1. Chittenden, R. (1945) *The First Twenty-five Years of the American Society of Biological Chemists*, Williams & Wilkins, Baltimore, MD
2. Obituary for Lafayette Benedict Mendel (1936) *J. Biol. Chem.* **112**, 431–432

THE JOURNAL OF BIOLOGICAL CHEMISTRY
© 2002 by The American Society for Biochemistry and Molecular Biology, Inc.

Vol. 277, No. 19, Issue of May 10, p. e8, 2002
Printed in U.S.A.

Classics

A PAPER IN A SERIES REPRINTED TO CELEBRATE THE CENTENARY OF THE JBC IN 2005

JBC Centennial
1905–2005
100 Years of Biochemistry and Molecular Biology

Nutritional Biochemistry and the Discovery of Vitamins: the Work of Elmer Verner McCollum

The "Vitamine" Hypothesis and Deficiency Diseases
(McCollum, E. V., and Pitz, W. (1917) *J. Biol. Chem.* **31, 229–253)**

Studies on Experimental Rickets. XXI. An Experimental Demonstration of the Existence of a Vitamin Which Promotes Calcium Deposition
(McCollum, E. V., Simmonds, N., Becker, J. E., and Shipley, P. G. (1922) *J. Biol. Chem.* **53, 293–312)**

The Effect of Additions of Fluorine to the Diet of the Rat on the Quality of the Teeth
(McCollum, E. V., Simmonds, N., Becker, J. E., and Bunting, R. W. (1925) *J. Biol. Chem.* **63, 553–562)**

Elmer Verner McCollum was one of the giants of nutritional biochemistry. He was born and raised in Kansas and attended the University of Kansas. His studies were initially directed toward medicine, but he eventually decided that chemistry better captured his interests, and he completed his work for a Masters degree in chemistry at Kansas. He was accepted into the Ph.D. program at the Sheffield Scientific School at Yale. One of his classmates at Yale was Stanley R. Benedict, the subject of a previous JBC Classic (1).

McCollum completed his Ph.D. work in 2 years and, given the lack of university positions, stayed at Yale for another year working with T. B. Osborne and Lafayette B. Mendel on problems of plant protein composition and diet. This work was influential to McCollum's career, and Mendel helped McCollum secure a faculty position at the University of Wisconsin. (The work of Osborne and Mendel was the subject of a previous installment of JBC Classics (2).)

On arrival at Wisconsin, McCollum was assigned to the famous heifer project. Three groups of heifers were fed restricted diets from single plant sources: wheat, corn, and oat. A fourth group of animals was fed all three plants. The animals fed all three plants did remarkably better, but there was no satisfactory explanation for the difference. McCollum decided that "the most important problem in nutrition was to discover what was lacking in such diets" (3).

He decided that nutritional studies would benefit from using small animals with short lifespans. He started with a colony of wild rats he had captured himself, but these quickly proved unsatisfactory, and he persuaded his Dean to allow him to purchase 12 albino rats even though the purchase was with his own funds. This colony of rats was the first established in the United States for nutritional studies (3).

McCollum first proposed that the nutritive failure of certain diets was due to a lack of "palatability." He proposed that if a diet could be made to taste good with flavor additives and the animals induced to eat larger quantities, the diets would be adequate. This hypothesis, and the supporting data, were criticized by Osborne and Mendel who demonstrated that plant protein diets were not adequate unless protein-free milk was added as a supplement. In some of their papers, Mendel and Osborne suggested that McCollum had been careless in some of his experiments (3). This criticism was no doubt painful especially coming form his mentors at Yale. McCollum acknowledged this error and rededicated himself to more careful analyses including an analysis of the growth-promoting factor(s) in protein-free milk, which then led to the isolation of the first known fat-soluble vitamin, later to be called vitamin A.

16

Elmer V. McCollum. Photo courtesy of the National Library of Medicine.

In 1916 McCollum and C. Kennedy, concerned with the growing confusion about nomenclature for dietary factors, proposed an alphabetical designation preceded by a notation of the solubility of the factor, thus fat-soluble A and water-soluble B. This was the beginning of the common nomenclature for vitamins.

In 1917, McCollum accepted the position of professor and head of the Department of Chemical Hygiene, later Biochemistry, in the newly formed School of Hygiene and Public Health at Johns Hopkins University. He had a distinguished research career supplemented by great public service including service on many government boards and panels and international nutrition organizations. Through his research and public service, McCollum, probably more than anyone, influenced human dietary policy and practices. In a commentary on his life, Time magazine stated, " He has done more than any other man to put vitamins back in the nation's bread and milk, to put fruit on American breakfast tables, fresh vegetables and salad greens in the daily diet" (3).

McCollum was involved in many policy debates including one over the best strategy to fortify bread. He had shown, and publicized, that white bread was nutritionally deficient. With the development of synthetic vitamins, it was proposed that bread and flour be enriched with thiamin, niacin, and iron. This effort was lead by the Food and Nutrition Board of the National Research Council. McCollum was a member of the Board but disagreed and was strongly critical of the recommendation because supplementation with such nutrients failed to make up for all the losses suffered during milling wheat. As a result of his disagreement with the other members of the Board, his Board colleagues changed his status from Board member to panel member. As a panel member he was not invited to any of the Board meetings (3).

The McCollum papers reprinted in this installment of JBC Classics are intended to represent a career. The first paper describes the controversy of the time about the "vitamine hypothesis" and also presents the kind of data characteristic of nutritional studies for many years. The second paper details the discovery of a growth substance distinct from vitamin A, later known as vitamin D, and necessary for bone formation. The third paper describes the role of fluoride in preventing tooth decay and eventually led to the widespread addition of fluoride to water supplies and toothpaste and a dramatic reduction in the frequency of dental caries in the United States.[1]

---

[1] Harry G. Day was a student in McCollum's department at Johns Hopkins. He, along with his students and colleagues at the University of Indiana and collaborators at Procter and Gamble, developed stannous fluoride as the first fluoride supplement for toothpaste, *i.e.* Crest.

McCollum was a member of the *Journal of Biological Chemistry* (JBC) Editorial Board and, in 1927 and 1928, President of the American Society of Biological Chemists (ASBC).

Robert D. Simoni, Robert L. Hill, and Martha Vaughan

REFERENCES

1. JBC Classics: Benedict, S. R. (1908) *J. Biol. Chem.* **5,** 485–487 (http://www.jbc.org/cgi/content/full/277/16/e5)
2. JBC Classics: Osborne, T. B., and Mendel, L. B. (1916) *J. Biol. Chem.* **25,** 1–12; (1917) *J. Biol. Chem.* **31,** 149–163 (http://www.jbc.org/cgi/content/full/277/18/e7)
3. Day, H. G. (1974) *Biographical Memoir of Elmer Verner McCollum*, Vol. 45, pp. 263–335, National Academy of Sciences, Washington, D. C.

THE JOURNAL OF BIOLOGICAL CHEMISTRY
© 2002 by The American Society for Biochemistry and Molecular Biology, Inc.

Vol. 277, No. 20, Issue of May 17, p. e9, 2002
Printed in U.S.A.

Classics

A PAPER IN A SERIES REPRINTED TO CELEBRATE THE CENTENARY OF THE JBC IN 2005

JBC Centennial
1905–2005
100 Years of Biochemistry and Molecular Biology

Analytical Biochemistry: the Work of Otto Knuf Olof Folin on Blood Analysis

A System of Blood Analysis
(Folin, O., and Wu, H. (1919) *J. Biol. Chem.* 38, 81–110)

Otto Knut Olof Folin was born in Sweden, but at age 15 he was sent by his parents to Minnesota to join two brothers and an aunt. He attended the University of Minnesota and subsequently received a Ph.D. degree from the University of Chicago (1). After a time in Europe learning physiological chemistry, he was employed as a research biochemist at McLean Hospital (for the Insane) in Waverly, Massachusetts. He was charged with comparing the composition of urine from normal and insane people. He realized that to do this in a meaningful way required new analytical approaches to urinalysis. In 1905, Folin published three papers in the *American Journal of Physiology* (2–4) which, according to E. V. McCollum, "marked a turning point in the history of biochemistry" and "immediately brought him distinction" (1). These papers reported methods for analysis of urine for urea, ammonia, creatine, creatinine, and uric acid, the major non-protein nitrogen-containing compounds in urine. Unlike previous analytical methods for these compounds, Folin's methods were relatively specific and sensitive so that small sample volumes were adequate. His research was very highly regarded, and in 1907, a professorship in biochemistry was created at Harvard Medical School where he served until his death in 1934 (5).

Folin's work stimulated laboratories around the world to approach the study of urine samples as a way to understand normal and pathological physiological processes. The work also stimulated experiments on animals treated in ways to mimic disease states.

Folin turned his attention to applying his analytical methods, developed for urinalysis, to the analysis of blood. He was probably the first, as McCollum states, "to realize that it is much more important to know what the kidneys have failed to excrete, among the products of metabolic activity of the body, and which products accordingly, accumulate to harmful concentrations in the blood, than it is to know what and how much of these have cleared the kidneys" (1).

Folin's work, including the paper reprinted in this installment of the *Journal of Biological Chemistry* (JBC) Classics, represents several "firsts" in biochemistry: the systematic development of "micromethods"; the use of colorimetry in biochemistry, the Duboscq colorimeter; and the use of an enzyme for analytical purposes, urease to measure urea. This paper is a model of the Folin approach to biochemistry with very careful detail and accuracy.

Among many lasting contributions, Folin, with Vintila Ciocalteu, developed the "Phenol Reagent" for use in protein determinations (6). This reagent is the basis of the Lowry method for protein determination, which is the most highly cited paper in science (7). The Folin-Ciocalteu paper will be reprinted with the Lowry paper in a future installment of JBC Classics and is itself a "Classic." The same can be said for an advertisement for the Duboscq colorimeter, which we are also reprinting here.

As described by McCollum in his obituary for Stanley R. Benedict (1), Benedict and Folin had parallel careers and common interests in analytical biochemistry/clinical chemistry and disagreed on many scientific issues. On this point, Benedict wrote of Folin soon after his death. "One of the qualities which so impressed me of Folin, so rare among scientific workers, was the fact that he was able to drop out personalities when it came to a matter of difference of

Otto Folin

scientific opinion. I have known no one with whom it was possible to have such a strenuous difference of opinion or viewpoint in scientific work and have this not interfere one iota in the close personal relationship which lasted for more than twenty-five years."

In 1919, Folin was the third President of the American Society of Biological Chemists (ASBC) and was a member of the JBC Editorial Board for more than 25 years starting with the first issue in 1905 (5).

Robert D. Simoni, Robert L. Hill, and Martha Vaughan

REFERENCES

1. Shaffer, P. A. (1937) Obituary of Stanley Rossiter Benedict. *J. Biol. Chem.* **117,** 428
2. Folin, O. (1905) Approximately complete analysis of thirty "normal" urines. *Am. J. Physiol.* **13,** 45–65
3. Folin, O. (1905) Laws governing the chemical composition of urine. *Am. J. Physiol.* **13,** 66–115
4. Folin, O. (1905) A theory of protein metabolism. *J. Am. Physiol.* **13,** 117–138
5. Chittenden, R. H. (1945) *The First Twenty-five Years of the American Society of Biological Chemists*, Williams & Wilkins, Baltimore, MD
6. Folin, O., and Ciocalteu, V. (1927) On tyrosine and tryptophane determinations in proteins. *J. Biol. Chem.* **73,** 627
7. Lowry, O. H., Rosebrough, N. J., Farr, A. L., and Randall, R. J. (1951) Protein measurement with the Folin Phenol Reagent. *J. Biol. Chem.* **193,** 265–275
8. Shaffer, P. A. (1927) *Biographical Memoir of Otto Folin. National Academy of Sciences Biographical Memoirs*, Vol. 27, pp. 47–82, National Academy of Sciences, Washington, D. C.

THE JOURNAL OF BIOLOGICAL CHEMISTRY
© 2002 by The American Society for Biochemistry and Molecular Biology, Inc.

Vol. 277, No. 21, Issue of May 24, p. e10, 2002
Printed in U.S.A.

Classics

A PAPER IN A SERIES REPRINTED TO CELEBRATE THE CENTENARY OF THE JBC IN 2005

JBC Centennial
1905–2005
100 Years of Biochemistry and Molecular Biology

The Isolation of Thyroxine and Cortisone: the Work of Edward C. Kendall

Isolation of the Iodine Compound Which Occurs in the Thyroid
(Kendall, E. C. (1919) *J. Biol. Chem.* 39, 125–147)

Edward C. Kendall isolated thyroxine from the thyroid gland, he crystallized glutathione and determined its structure, and he isolated and characterized several steroid hormones from the adrenal cortex, including cortisone. He was awarded the Nobel Prize, with P. S. Hench and T. Reichstein, in 1950 (1).[1]

After receiving his Bachelor, Master, and Ph.D. degrees from Columbia University, Kendall started his research career at St. Luke's Hospital in New York City. His work focused on the hormones of the thyroid, following an earlier report from Professor Eugen Baumann that extracts of thyroid gland were effective in treating human hypothyroidism. By 1913 Kendall had purified the thyroid factor using a bioassay that measured changes in the urinary nitrogen of dogs. In a biography of Kendall (1), Dwight J. Ingle relates that at about this time, the hospital administrator at St. Luke's sent Kendall a box of breakfast cereal with a letter directing him to analyze the cereal. "The letter and cereal were summarily thrown into the wastebasket," and Kendall quit.

In 1914 Kendall was invited to join the staff of the Mayo Clinic where there was special interest in diseases of the thyroid. The work reported in this *Journal of Biological Chemistry* (JBC) Classic paper describes the isolation and crystallization of thyroxine from 6500 pounds of hog thyroid glands.

Kendall and his associates spent the next 10 years trying to determine the structure of thyroxine but failed. Kendall incorrectly concluded that the structure was triiodohexahydroxy-indole propionic acid (2). In 1926, Dr. C. R. Harrington of University College London showed that thyroxine is the tetraiodo derivative of thyronine, and he was able to synthesize the active compound. Despite the error in determining the structure, Kendall's feat of isolation was impressive.

Kendall initiated his study of adrenal glands in the early 1930s when it became clear that gland extracts would prolong the lives of adrenalectomized animals. This work occupied him and his associates for more than 20 years. The search for the active factor of the adrenal gland was an internationally competitive effort. It eventually became clear that the gland extracts contained several factors, which were given letter names by different groups leading to much confusion. Once the compounds were recognized as steroids and the structures were established, it became possible to name them properly. Kendall's Compound A was 11-dehydrocorticosterone; Compound B, corticosterone; Compound E, 17-hydroxy-11-dehydrocorticosterone (cortisone); Compound F, 17-hydroxycorticosterone (cortisol or hydrocortisone).

As World War II began in Europe, research efforts in the United States were focused on supporting the war effort. In 1941, a group of leading chemists, including Kendall, was charged with an effort to synthesize adrenal steroid hormones. According to Ingle, it was rumored "that Germany was buying beef adrenal glands in South America for the purpose of making adrenal cortical extract." It was said that the extract was being used by the Germans to counteract hypoxia of Luftwaffe pilots to permit them to fly at higher altitudes (1).

---

[1] All of the information for this Classic Introduction was taken from this biography.

Edward Kendall. Photo courtesy of the National Library of Medicine.

After several years, the efforts to synthesize these compounds waned as their effectiveness for various war-related uses became doubtful. Eventually, only Kendall's group at Mayo and a collaborative effort at Merck continued. The first large scale synthesis of cortisone was completed in 1948. At the Mayo Clinic, Dr. Philip S. Hench convinced Kendall to do a small clinical trial of cortisone on a patient suffering from rheumatoid arthritis. It was a dramatic success, and subsequent tests on several patients were equally successful in reducing inflammation. Kendall's conviction that the steroid hormones of the adrenal gland would be therapeutically useful was borne out.

It is now known that treatment of arthritis patients with steroid anti-inflammatory drugs is fraught with deleterious side effects, but at the time, this was a major discovery and probably the one for which Kendall is most recognized.

Robert D. Simoni, Robert L. Hill, and Martha Vaughan

REFERENCES

1. Ingle, D. J. (1975) *Biographical Memoir of Edward C. Kendall*, Vol. 47, National Academy of Sciences, Washington, D. C.
2. Kendall, E. C., and Osterberg, A. E. (1919) The chemical identification of thyroxin. *J. Biol. Chem.* **40,** 265–334

THE JOURNAL OF BIOLOGICAL CHEMISTRY
© 2002 by The American Society for Biochemistry and Molecular Biology, Inc.

Vol. 277, No. 22, Issue of May 31, p. e11, 2002
Printed in U.S.A.

Classics

A PAPER IN A SERIES REPRINTED TO CELEBRATE THE CENTENARY OF THE JBC IN 2005

JBC Centennial
1905–2005
100 Years of Biochemistry and Molecular Biology

The Structure of Nucleic Acids and Many Other Natural Products: Phoebus Aaron Levene

The Structure of Yeast Nucleic Acid. IV. Ammonia Hydrolysis
(Levene, P. A. (1919) *J. Biol. Chem.* 40, 415–424)

Phoebus Aaron Theodor Levene was born in Russia and attended school in St. Petersburg completing work for a medical degree from the Imperial Military Medical Academy in 1892. He was one of very few Jewish students admitted for medical studies, and with growing anti-Semitism in Russia and a desire for greater opportunities, Levene moved with his family to New York City. During the period from 1892 to 1905, he practiced medicine, recovered from tuberculosis, studied in Europe, and served as physiological chemist at the Pathological Institute of the New York State Hospitals. In 1905, he was appointed to a position as laboratory assistant with Dr. Simon Flexner at the Rockefeller Institute for Medical Research, later Rockefeller University. His talent in physiological chemistry was quickly recognized, and in 1907 he was made a Member of the Institute in charge of its Division of Chemistry. He served in this capacity until his death in 1940 (1).

Levene might best be described as a natural product chemist. He published over 700 papers covering a wide range of biological molecules including the chemistry of nucleic acids, proteins and amino acids, lipids and carbohydrates, glycoproteins, and amino sugars. He was an enormously important figure at the dawn of biochemistry and contributed greatly to the emergence of biochemistry in the United States.

The paper reprinted in this installment of *Journal of Biological Chemistry* (JBC) Classics represents a typical Levene paper with purification and chemical characterization of the nucleotides of yeast nucleic acids. His study, and others, used alkali to hydrolyze nucleic acid, and as a result, the study really focuses on RNA composition and structure because DNA is alkali-resistant. For these reasons, the nucleosides isolated from alkaline hydrolysis were AMP, CMP, GMP, and UMP. There was no TMP. (In the paper, these compounds are referred to as guanosinphosphoric acid, adenosinphosphoric acid, etc.)

Levene reviews the proposals that others, the groups of Thannhauser and of Jones, had made for the structure of nucleic acids and proceeds to discredit them. He then concludes, incorrectly, that the linkage between the bases is a phosphomonoester linkage between the ribose residues (see page 420). He adds confidently that now, "there is no doubt as to the polynucleotide structure of the yeast nucleic acid." We know, of course, that the correct linkage is a phosphodiester. It is also interesting that he notes that earlier results published in 1917 by Thannhauser in Germany did not reach the United States until 1919, the end of World War I.

Among many awards, in 1931 Levene received the Willard Gibbs Medal of the American Chemical Society. In his acceptance address, "The Revolt of the Biochemist" he described his view of the future of biochemistry. "Thus step by step, one mystery of life after another is being revealed. Whether the human mind will ever attain complete and absolute knowledge of and complete mastery of life is not essential. It is certain, however, that the revolt of the biochemist against the idea of a restriction to human curiosity will continue. Biochemistry will continue to function as if all knowledge, even that of life, were accessible to human understanding. The past has taught that the solution of some problem always opens up a new one. New discoveries in physics, in mathematics, in theoretical chemistry, furnish new tools to biochemistry, new

Phoebus A. Levene. Photo courtesy of the National Library of Medicine.

tools for the solution of old problems and the creation of new ones. So long as Life continues, the human mind will create mysteries and biochemistry will play a part in their solution" (1).

In addition to wide ranging and important research contributions, Levene was a great teacher (1). Of particular note, one of his collaborators on earlier nucleic acid papers was W. A. Jacobs who later became a distinguished alkaloid chemist at the Rockefeller University. Jacobs, in turn, was the research advisor of Lyman C. Craig, a distinguished biochemist, also at The Rockefeller University. A JBC Classic by Lyman C. Craig, the development of countercurrent distribution methods, will be published in a future installment.

Levene was a member of the JBC Editorial Board for the first issue in 1905 and served for over 15 years. He was also a charter member of The American Society of Biological Chemists (ASBC).

Robert D. Simoni, Robert L. Hill, and Martha Vaughan

REFERENCES

1. Van Slyke, D. D., and Jacobs, W. (1945) *Biographical Memoir of Phoebus Aaron Theodor Levene*, Vol. 23, pp. 75–86, National Academy of Sciences, Washington, D. C.

THE JOURNAL OF BIOLOGICAL CHEMISTRY
© 2002 by The American Society for Biochemistry and Molecular Biology, Inc.

Vol. 277, No. 23, Issue of June 7, p. e12, 2002
Printed in U.S.A.

Classics

A PAPER IN A SERIES REPRINTED TO CELEBRATE THE CENTENARY OF THE JBC IN 2005

JBC Centennial
1905–2005
100 Years of Biochemistry and Molecular Biology

Light Is Essential for Bone Deposition. Sunlight Prevents Rickets in Rats. The Work of A. M. Pappenheimer

Experimental Rickets in Rats. III. The Prevention of Rickets in Rats by Exposure to Sunlight
(Hess, A. F., Unger, L. J., and Pappenheimer, A. M. (1922) *J. Biol. Chem.* 50, 77–81)

A. M. Pappenheimer was a distinguished pathologist at Columbia University College of Physicians and Surgeons. As described in the introduction to this *Journal of Biological Chemistry* (JBC) Classic, it had been shown that exposure of infants to sunlight eliminated the symptoms of rickets. Rickets was a very common disease in the 17th century, particularly in countries like England where the climate often provided several months without sunlight. Rickets is characterized by deficiencies in calcification of bone and cartilage in children, which results in abnormalities of skeletal development. The adult form of the disease is called osteomalacia.

Earlier, Pappenheimer had discovered that a diet high in calcium and low in phosphorus could cause rickets in rats (1). The study reprinted here exploits this animal model for a controlled examination of the effects of diet and sunlight on bone development in rats. It was shown that rats fed exclusively a diet of flour, calcium lactate, sodium chloride, and ferric citrate developed bone lesions characteristic of rickets in human infants. However, if the rats were exposed to sunlight for 15 or 30 min each day, there were no symptoms of rickets like those in the control rats housed entirely in the dark. It was also shown that supplementation of the diet with potassium phosphate could, in part, overcome the effects of the "richitic" diet. This study illustrated the necessity to treat light as an experimental variable. As the authors point out, "It seems probable that some of the irregularities and lack of conformity observed by investigators in this field may be attributed to keeping the experimental animals under dissimilar intensities of light."

It is now also known that the effect of sunlight, UV light specifically, is to catalyze the non-enzymatic conversion of 7-dehydrocholesterol, an intermediate in cholesterol biosynthesis, to "provitamin D_3" which spontaneously isomerizes to vitamin D_3, cholecalciferol. Cholecalciferol is subsequently hydroxylated to form calcitriol, the active form of the hormone. So, vitamin D is not really a vitamin at all, because there is no dietary requirement as long exposure to sunlight is sufficient to initiate the conversion of 7-dehydrocholesterol to vitamin D_3. The active form of the hormone regulates transcription with products necessary for calcium absorption by intestinal cells and calcium uptake by bone-forming osteoclasts.

Because of the seriousness of rickets and because of seasonally inadequate sunlight in many geographical regions, most individuals obtain vitamin D from food or supplements like the children's favorite, cod liver oil. Today, most vitamin D in the Western diet comes from fortified foods such as milk.

In experiments that paralleled those of Pappenheimer and his colleagues, E. V. McCollum discovered vitamin D (2) as reported in the paper featured in a previous installment of JBC Classics (3).

Classics

Alwin M. Pappenheimer. Photo courtesy of the National Library of Medicine.

The biochemical relationships between vitamin D, the effects of sunlight, and bone metabolism were not made until many years later. It was shown in a series of papers that sunlight caused the conversion of 7-dehydrocholesterol to provitamin D_3 (4–8).[1]

Robert D. Simoni, Robert L. Hill, and Martha Vaughan

REFERENCES

1. Sherman, H. C., and Pappenheimer, A. M. (1921) *J. Exp. Med.* **xxxiv,** 189
2. McCollum, E. V., Simmonds, N., Becker, J. E., and Shipley, P. G. (1922) Studies on experimental rickets. XXI. An experimental demonstration of the existence of a vitamin which promotes calcium deposition. *J. Biol. Chem.* **53,** 293–312
3. JBC Classics: McCollum, E. V. *et al.* (1917) *J. Biol. Chem.* **31,** 229–253; (1922) *J. Biol. Chem.* **53,** 293–312; (1925) *J. Biol. Chem.* **63,** 553–562 (http://www.jbc.org/cgi/content/full/277/19/e8)
4. Velluz, L., and Amiard, G. (1949) Chemie organique-equilibre de reaction entre precalciferol et calciferol. *Compt. Rend.* **228,** 853–855
5. Velluz, L., and Amirad, G., (1949) Chimie organique-le precalciferol. *Compt. Rend.* **228,** 692–694
6. Velluz, L., Amiard, G., and Petit, A. (1949) Le precalciferol: ses relations d'equilibre avec le calciferol. *Bull. Soc. Chim. France* **16,** 501–507
7. Velluz, L., and Amiard, G. (1949) Chimie organique-nouveau precursor de la vitamine D3. *Compt. Rend.* **228,** 1037–1038
8. Verloop, A., Koevoet, A. L., and Havinga, E. (1955) Studies on vitamin D and related compounds III. *Recl. Trav. Chim. Psys-Bas.* **74,** 1125–1130

---

[1] Hector F. Deluca, Professor and Chairman of the Biochemistry Dept. at the University of Wisconsin, kindly provided the references for the UV-catalyzed conversion of 7-dehydrocholesterol to vitamin D_3.

THE JOURNAL OF BIOLOGICAL CHEMISTRY
© 2002 by The American Society for Biochemistry and Molecular Biology, Inc.

Vol. 277, No. 24, Issue of June 14, p. e13, 2002
Printed in U.S.A.

Classics

A PAPER IN A SERIES REPRINTED TO CELEBRATE THE CENTENARY OF THE JBC IN 2005

JBC Centennial
1905–2005
100 Years of Biochemistry and Molecular Biology

The Discovery of Glutathione by F. Gowland Hopkins and the Beginning of Biochemistry at Cambridge University

On Glutathione. II. A Thermostable Oxidation-Reduction System
(Hopkins, F. G., and Dixon, M. (1922) *J. Biol. Chem.* 54, 527–563)

Sir Frederick Gowland Hopkins (1861–1947) was born in East Sussex, Great Britain. He founded the Department of Biochemistry at the University of Cambridge in 1914. In 1920, the estate of Sir William Dunn provided funds for the establishment of a School of Biochemistry, a Chair of Biochemistry, and a new building for the Department at Cambridge. The Sir William Dunn Institute of Biochemistry was opened in 1924, and Hopkins was the first Sir William Dunn Chair (subsequent occupants of the Dunn Chair at Cambridge were A. C. Chibnall, Sir Frank Young, Sir Hans Kornberg, and, at present, Tom L. Blundell). Hopkins focused his own research on "accessory food factors," later termed vitamins, and his interests shaped the directions of research in this distinguished department.

Among the many contributions Hopkins made is the discovery and characterization of glutathione that is described in this *Journal of Biological Chemistry* (JBC) Classic Paper. It had been recognized that glutathione underwent reversible oxidation-reduction, which involved a disulfide linkage between two molecules of GSH in GSSG. In this paper, Hopkins cites the discovery of "coferment" of alcoholic fermentation by Harden, Young, and Meyerhof for his discovery of the factors necessary for respiratory oxidations as well as for the method of simple extraction of tissues with water to identify the factors necessary for a biochemical process. After studying chopped muscle tissue extracted with water, Hopkins concluded that "When a tissue is washed until it has lost its power to reduce methylene blue, the subsequent addition of glutathione to a buffer solution in which the tissue residue is suspended restores reducing power." By using boiled tissue, he demonstrated that the system was heat-stable and is non-enzymatic.

Although the discovery of glutathione certainly ranks among the major discoveries in biochemistry, Hopkins is unfortunately remembered for his error regarding the structure of glutathione, which he had concluded was a dipeptide of glutamic acid and cysteine. The structure of glutathione was controversial for several years. In 1927, Hunter and Eagles described a product, isolated using the same procedure employed by Hopkins, that had significantly less sulfur per mass than Hopkins had reported and was possibly a tripeptide (1). After seeing a preprint version of the Hunter and Eagles paper provided by the Editors of JBC with permission of the authors, Hopkins responded that their preparation of glutathione was impure and reasserted that glutathione was a dipeptide (2). In 1929, after developing a new procedure for preparing crystalline glutathione, Hopkins recognized that "Hunter and Eagles were right in doubting that the substance is a simple dipeptide of glutamic acid and cysteine. . . . " (3). He then showed that glutathione is indeed a tripeptide of glutamic acid, glycine, and cysteine. Although he did not determine the precise structure, he suggested it was Glu-Cys-Gly. (The structure of glutathione is, in fact, γ-L-glutamyl-L-cysteinylglycine). In reference to the mistake, Hopkins wrote that "The grave discomfort involved in making an admission of previous error is mitigated by the circumstances that I am now able to describe a method, not without special interest in itself, which with ease and rapidity separates from yeast and red blood cells a pure crystalline thiol compound with a. . . . tripeptide structure" (3).

Frederick G. Hopkins. Photo courtesy of the National Library of Medicine.

His error on the structure of glutathione has not been forgotten many decades later. Hopkins is more appropriately remembered, however, as a giant of biochemistry. He was knighted in 1925 and received the Nobel Prize in Physiology or Medicine in 1929. In 1936, a young undergraduate student, Max Perutz, left his native Vienna, with the rise in anti-Semitism, and moved to Cambridge. He was attracted to Hopkins's department and Hopkins's work on vitamins and enzymes. Perutz worked with John Desmond Bernal in the Cavendish Laboratory and began his historic crystallographic analysis of the structure of hemoglobin.

Robert D. Simoni, Robert L. Hill, and Martha Vaughan

REFERENCES

1. Hunter, G., and Eagles, B. A. (1927) *J. Biol. Chem.* **72,** 133
2. Hopkins, F. G. (1927) *J. Biol. Chem.* **72,** 185
3. Hopkins, F. G. (1929) *J. Biol. Chem.* **84,** 269

THE JOURNAL OF BIOLOGICAL CHEMISTRY
Vol. 277, No. 25, Issue of June 21, p. e14, 2002

Classics

A PAPER IN A SERIES REPRINTED TO CELEBRATE THE CENTENARY OF THE JBC IN 2005

JBC Centennial
1905–2005
100 Years of Biochemistry and Molecular Biology

Nutritional Bacteriology and the Discovery of Methionine by John Howard Mueller

A New Sulfur-containing Amino-Acid Isolated from the Hydrolytic Products of Protein (Mueller, J. H. (1923) *J. Biol. Chem.* 56, 157–169)

John Howard Mueller (1891–1954) was born in Sheffield, MA. He received a Bachelors degree in biology at Illinois Wesleyan University and a Masters degree in 1914 from the University of Louisville where he first became interested in bacteriology and pathology. He attended graduate school at Columbia University and received a Ph.D. in 1916. In 1917, he enlisted in the army war effort and was stationed with a hospital unit in France becoming part of the group who demonstrated that trench fever, now known to be a rickettsial disease, was transmitted by lice (1). After the war, he was appointed an Instructor in Bacteriology at the Columbia University College of Physicians and Surgeons in the department chaired by Hans Zinsser. He later moved with Zinsser to the Department of Bacteriology and Immunology at Harvard Medical School where he started as an Assistant Professor and remained for the rest of his career.

It was at Columbia that Mueller initiated his studies on cultural requirements of pathogenic bacteria. As an introduction to his initial publications on this subject in 1922 he wrote prophetically as follows: "Perhaps the most important results to which success in such a piece of work might lead are the applications of the findings to problems of more general biological importance, particularly those of animal metabolism. For whatever may prove to be the nature of these substances which cause growth of bacteria, they are largely or entirely components of animal tissue and it is probably that they are either needed also by the animal body and supplied by plant or other sources or else are synthesized by the animal itself to fill some metabolic requirement. When it is possible to catalogue the substances required by pathogenic bacteria for growth, it will probably be found that most of them are either required by, or important in, animal metabolism and while many of them will surely be compounds at present familiar to the physiological chemist, it is equally probable that some will be new, or at least of hitherto unrecognized importance" (1).

Mueller's prediction of generally important discoveries to come from his bacterial nutrition studies was borne out almost immediately. His 1923 paper selected as this *Journal of Biological Chemistry* (JBC) Classic describes the discovery of the amino acid methionine. Mueller was able to show that *Streptococcus hemolyticus* could use an acid hydrolysate of animal protein supplemented with tryptophan to replace the poorly characterized "peptone" to support growth. He also showed that the hydrolysate could not be replaced by a mixture of amino acids then known. He fractionated casein hydrolysate and discovered a new sulfur-containing amino acid, which when added to the medium supported bacterial growth. He also demonstrated that the same amino acid could be isolated from hydrolysates of other proteins. The purification and characterization of the newly identified amino acid were meticulous, including the correct empirical formula of $C_5H_{11}NO_2S$. It had properties quite distinctive from those of cysteine, the already known sulfur-containing amino acid. Mueller was not able to determine the structure of the new amino acid although he did show that it was not the ethyl thioether of cysteine, as had been suggested by a colleague. The correct structure and synthesis were contributed by Barger and Coyne in 1928 (2). They also apparently were the first to name Mueller's amino acid methionine and cite consultation with Mueller about selection of the name (2).

In a footnote in this JBC Classic, Mueller acknowledges, with gratitude, that he spent the summer of 1922 in the laboratory of F. Gowland Hopkins at the University of Cambridge where some of the purification of methionine was done. The report by Hopkins and Dixon of the isolation of glutathione was the preceding JBC Classic (3).

Mueller discovered several more of what he called "accessory factors" using his basic bacterial nutritional approach. Nicotinic acid was isolated from liver, and it or nicotinamide was required to support the growth of diphtheria bacteria. β-Alanine was also shown to be essential and could be replaced by pantothenic acid. Pimelic acid, another accessory factor that he isolated from cow urine, undoubtedly produced by the bacterial flora in the cow's gut, was later shown by Vincent du Vigneaud to be an intermediate in the synthesis of biotin (1).

In 1940, after the death of Hans Zinsser, Mueller became Chairman of the Department of Bacteriology and Immunology at Harvard Medical School where he worked until his death in 1954 (1).

Robert D. Simoni, Robert L. Hill, and Martha Vaughan

REFERENCES

1. Pappenheimer, A. M., Jr. (1987) *Biographical Memoir of John Howard Mueller*, Vol. 57, pp. 307–321, National Academy of Sciences, Washington D. C.
2. Barger, G., and Coyne, F. P. (1928) The amino-acid methionine: constitution and synthesis. *Biochem. J.* **176,** 1417
3. JBC Classics: Hopkins, F. G., and Dixon, M. (1922) *J. Biol. Chem.* **54,** 527–563 (http://www.jbc.org/cgi/content/full/277/24/e13)

THE JOURNAL OF BIOLOGICAL CHEMISTRY
© 2002 by The American Society for Biochemistry and Molecular Biology, Inc.

Vol. 277, No. 26, Issue of June 28, p. e15, 2002
Printed in U.S.A.

Classics

A PAPER IN A SERIES REPRINTED TO CELEBRATE THE CENTENARY OF THE JBC IN 2005

JBC Centennial
1905–2005
100 Years of Biochemistry and Molecular Biology

The Discovery of Insulin: the Work of Frederick Banting and Charles Best

The Preparation of Insulin
(Best, C. H., and Scott, D. A. (1923) *J. Biol. Chem.* 57, 709–723)

The story of the discovery of insulin has been well chronicled beginning with a young physician, Frederick Banting, in London, Ontario, imagining that it might be possible to isolate the internal secretions of the pancreas by ligating the pancreatic ducts to induce atrophy of the acinar cells and thereby minimize contamination of the tissue extract with digestive enzymes. Banting presented his suggestion to J. J. R. Macleod, a distinguished physiologist at the University of Toronto who provided Banting with a laboratory for the summer and some dogs for the experiments. Macleod also assigned Charles Best, a young student, to work as Banting's assistant for the summer. During the summer of 1921, Banting and Best made remarkable progress, and by fall they had isolated material from pancreas extracts that dramatically prolonged the lives of dogs made diabetic by removal of the pancreas. In the winter of 1922, Banting and Best treated their first human patient, a young boy, who's life was saved by the treatment. This was a stunning accomplishment. Consider that from the start of the research in the summer of 1921 to treating a human patient successfully in the winter of 1922, the pace, especially by current standards for clinical treatments, was remarkable.

With that achievement, Macleod, who had been initially unenthusiastic about the work, assigned his entire laboratory to the insulin project. He also enlisted the Eli Lilly Company to aid in the large scale, commercial preparation of insulin although the University of Toronto received the patent for insulin production. By 1923, insulin was available in quantities adequate for relatively widespread treatment of diabetes. Although the success of the insulin project was remarkable, the rewards for the research workers were, it seems, quite controversial. The 1923 Noble Prize in Physiology or Medicine was awarded to Banting and Macleod. Apparently, Banting was annoyed at the omission of Best and gave him half of his share of the prize. There was also, perhaps, the feeling that Macleod had done little in the initial stages of the work and was an undeserving recipient. Macleod split his share of the Prize with J. B. Collip who had made contributions to the later stages of the work on insulin purification.

After the spectacular events of 1921–1923, the University of Toronto established the Banting and Best Department of Medical Research separate from the University. Banting accomplished little during the rest of his career and died in a plane crash in 1940. Best, however, had a long successful tenure at the University of Toronto working on insulin and subsequently other important topics including the importance of dietary choline and the development of heparin as an anticoagulant.

The paper selected as this *Journal of Biological Chemistry* Classic is not itself "classic" in the usual sense. It reviews very well, however, a remarkable body of classic work. The information regarding various procedures that had been developed quickly and compared in attempts to improve the yield and purity of insulin also contains clues to some special properties of the protein, although so little was known at that time about the structure of insulin (or any protein) that there seemed little rationale for its purification. Insulin was crystallized in 1926 by John J. Abel (1). Virtually all of the information in this Introduction is from Ref. 2.

Robert D. Simoni, Robert L. Hill, and Martha Vaughan

Frederick G. Banting. Photo courtesy of the National
Library of Medicine.

Charles H. Best. Photo courtesy of the National Library
of Medicine.

REFERENCES

1. Abel, J. J. (1926) Crystalline insulin. *Proc. Natl. Acad. Sci. U. S. A.* **12,** 132–136
2. Bliss, M. (1982) *The Discovery of Insulin*, The University of Chicago Press, Chicago, IL

THE JOURNAL OF BIOLOGICAL CHEMISTRY
© 2002 by The American Society for Biochemistry and Molecular Biology, Inc.

Vol. 277, No. 27, Issue of July 5, p. e16, 2002
Printed in U.S.A.

Classics

A PAPER IN A SERIES REPRINTED TO CELEBRATE THE CENTENARY OF THE JBC IN 2005

JBC Centennial
1905–2005
100 Years of Biochemistry and Molecular Biology

The Measurement of Blood Gases and the Manometric Techniques Developed by Donald Dexter Van Slyke

The Determination of Gases in Blood and Other Solutions by Vacuum Extraction and Manometric Measurement. I.
(Van Slyke, D. D., and Neill, J. M. (1924) *J. Biol. Chem.* **61, 523–543)**

Donald Dexter Van Slyke (1883–1971) was born in Pike, New York and attended high school in Geneva, New York. In biochemical circles, he was known universally as Van with no last name required. He received a Bachelors degree in Chemistry and a Ph.D. degree in Organic Chemistry (1907) from the University of Michigan. He had intended to become an agricultural chemist like his father, but after his father met P. A. Levene at the Rockefeller Institute for Medical Research (later Rockefeller University) he convinced his son to work with Levene. (Levene was the author of an earlier *Journal of Biological Chemistry* (JBC) Classic (1).) Van Slyke's biochemical career thus began at Rockefeller in 1907 and would continue until 1949. His first independent report described the quantification of aliphatic amino acids by using nitrous acid to measure α-amino acid nitrogen (2). This was a gasometric method, an approach that characterized his research career. It has been said that if a biochemical process involved a gas, Van Slyke could measure it.

In 1914, Van Slyke was appointed chemist at the newly opened Rockefeller Hospital, although he was not trained in medical chemistry. He noted that patients dying from diabetes experienced an acidotic coma, but there was no way to assess accurately the onset of acidosis or to measure the effects of alkali therapy. To this end, he devised a simple gasometric method for measuring accurately the concentration of sodium bicarbonate in a milliliter of blood. For this assay he invented the Van Slyke volumetric gas apparatus, which was soon found to be so useful that it was found in virtually all clinical laboratories and many biochemistry laboratories as well. The culmination of his work on blood acid-base balance was published between 1921 and 1924 (3, 4) and established the basic parameters that are used even today for diagnosis of acid-base abnormalities and includes the paper selected as this JBC Classic. This paper describes the construction and use of the manometric system and the methodology for measuring and calculating the CO_2, O_2, and HCO_3^- concentrations in blood. (An advertisement for the Van Slyke manometric apparatus is presented along with the Classic paper.) The new method improved both the accuracy and sensitivity of his original volumetric apparatus, and with it he published a particularly important series of papers on the complete gas and electrolyte equilibria in blood and their variation as a function of respiration. These studies focused on the role of hemoglobin as an O_2 and CO_2 carrier, and Van Slyke was able to account quantitatively for the effect of pH changes on O_2 and CO_2 transport and for the distribution of water and diffusable ions, HCO_3^-, Cl^-, and H^+ between blood plasma and red cells (4).

Among his other scientific contributions, he developed approaches with a sound biochemical basis to study clinical problems such as acidosis and kidney disease. He showed that the liver played an important role in amino acid metabolism and that the kidney produces ammonia. He also discovered a new amino acid, hydroxylysine, which is a prominent constituent of collagen (5).

The majority of Van Slyke's 317 publications are in the JBC. At the age of 31, he was asked to become the Managing Editor of the JBC and served in that capacity until 1925. He was involved in the review of every paper and took personal responsibility for maintaining the high

Donald D. Van Slyke. Photo courtesy of the National Library of Medicine.

standards of the Journal. It is reported that he occasionally rewrote papers for authors, if he felt the science was worth reporting. After resigning as Managing Editor, he continued to serve as a member of the Editorial Board until 1950. In 1949, he became professor emeritus at Rockefeller, and although he could have continued his research there, he decided to accept the position of Assistant Director for Biology and Medicine at the newly formed Brookhaven National Laboratory. He continued his research at Brookhaven until a few months before his death at the age of 88.[1]

Robert D. Simoni, Robert L. Hill, and Martha Vaughan

REFERENCES

1. JBC Classics: Levene, P. A. (1919) *J. Biol. Chem.* **40,** 415–424 (http://www.jbc.org/cgi/content/full/277/22/e11)
2. Van Slyke, D. D. (1911) A method for quantitative determination of aliphatic amino acids. Applications to the study of proteolysis and proteolytic products. *J. Biol. Chem.* **9,** 185
3. Van Slyke, D. D. (1921) Studies on acidosis. XVII. The normal and abnormal variations in the acid-base balance of the blood. *J. Biol. Chem.* **48,** 153
4. Van Slyke, D. D., Wu, H., and McLean, F. C. (1923) Studies of gas and electrolyte equilibria in the blood. V. Factors controlling the electrolyte and water distribution in the blood. *J. Biol. Chem.* **56,** 765
5. Van Slyke, D. D., Hiller, A., Dillon, R. T., and MacFadyen, D. (1938) The unidentified base in gelatin. *Proc. Soc. Exp. Biol. Med.* **38,** 548
6. Hastings, A. B. (1972) Obituary of Donald Dexter Van Slyke. *J. Biol. Chem.* **247,** 1635–1640
7. Hastings, A. B. (1976) *Biographical Memoir of Donald Dexter Van Slyke*, Vol. 48, pp. 309–360, National Academy of Sciences, Washington, D. C.

---

[1] The biographical information for this Classic Introduction was taken from two articles (6, 7).

THE JOURNAL OF BIOLOGICAL CHEMISTRY
© 2002 by The American Society for Biochemistry and Molecular Biology, Inc.

Vol. 277, No. 28, Issue of July 12, p. e17, 2002
Printed in U.S.A.

Classics

A PAPER IN A SERIES REPRINTED TO CELEBRATE THE CENTENARY OF THE JBC IN 2005

JBC Centennial
1905–2005
100 Years of Biochemistry and Molecular Biology

The Discovery of Estrone, Estriol, and Estradiol and the Biochemical Study of Reproduction. The Work of Edward Adelbert Doisy

The Preparation of the Crystalline Follicular Ovarian Hormone: Theelin
(Veler, C. D., Thayer, S., and Doisy, E. A. (1930) *J. Biol. Chem.* 87, 357–371)

Characterization of Theelol
(Thayer, S. A., Levin, L., and Doisy, E. A. (1931) *J. Biol. Chem.* 91, 655–665)

The Constitution and Synthesis of Vitamin K₁
(MacCorquodale, D. W., Cheney, L. C., Binkley, S. B., Holcomb, W. F., McKee, R. W., Thayer, S. A., and Doisy, E. A. (1939) *J. Biol. Chem.* 131, 357–370)

Edward Adelbert Doisy (1893–1986) was born in Hume, Illinois. He received a Bachelors degree (1914) and Masters degree (1916) in Chemistry from the University of Illinois. He then continued his graduate studies at Harvard Medical School with Otto Folin. Together they developed many analytical techniques used to measure important substances in urine and blood including creatine, creatinine, and uric acid. (Folin was the subject of an earlier *Journal of Biological Chemistry* (JBC) Classic (1).) Doisy was drafted into the army in 1917 for service during World War I, and from 1917 to 1919 he worked first with D. D. Van Slyke at the Rockefeller Institute for Medical Research and subsequently at the Walter Reed Research Institute in Washington D. C. (D. D. Van Slyke was also the subject of an earlier JBC Classic (2).) After completing his army service, Doisy received his Ph.D. in 1920 for the work done with Folin.

In 1919, Doisy became Instructor and later Associate Professor of Biochemistry at Washington University in St. Louis. In 1923, he moved across town to St. Louis University Medical School to become Professor and Chairman of a new biochemistry department, the positions he held until his retirement in 1965.

His work at St. Louis University began with the study of the estrous cycle in mice. He determined that ovarian follicles precede the appearance of cornified cells in the vagina. He showed that extracts from sow ovaries, when injected into ovarectomized mice, resulted in the production of cornified cells in the vagina. Using this as an assay, Doisy isolated the female sex hormones, estrone (Theelin) and estriol (Theelol), from hundreds of gallons of human pregnancy urine. The first two JBC Classics in this set represent this work. Doisy told the following story about collecting the urine.

One driver, while making collections of urine, committed a traffic violation, and the policeman who glanced in the back of the car and saw the bottles with amber fluid thought he had caught a bootlegger. He would not believe the driver so he was invited to get in to sample the amber fluid. After pulling the cork (summertime and the preservative had evaporated) and sniffing, the cop said, "My God it is urine! Your job is bad enough without getting pinched for it—drive on."

Doisy later isolated a third estrogen, estradiol from pig follicular fluid. This work opened fertility research to biochemical analysis and had lasting consequences for the development of reproductive biology and birth control.

In 1929, Hendrik Dam discovered vitamin K as a new fat-soluble vitamin that promoted blood coagulation in chicks and rats (3). In 1936, Doisy started to isolate this vitamin, and in

Edward A. Doisy. Photo courtesy of the National Library of Medicine.

1939 he succeeded in crystallizing vitamin K_1 from alfalfa. This work is represented by the third paper in this set of JBC Classics. For his work on vitamin K, Doisy, along with Hendrik Dam, received the Nobel Prize in Physiology or Medicine in 1943. Many felt that the Nobel Prize was also warranted for his work on estrogens.

Doisy received many honors for his pioneering research. According to Robert Olson, Doisy's successor as Chairman of Biochemistry at St. Louis University, Doisy did not receive any research support from the National Institutes of Health or other government agency. He supported his work entirely from patent income from his research discoveries (4). Doisy served as President of the American Society of Biological Chemists (ASBC) in 1945.[1,2]

Robert D. Simoni, Robert L. Hill, and Martha Vaughan

REFERENCES

1. JBC Classics: Folin, O., and Wu, H. (1919) *J. Biol. Chem.* **38,** 81–110 (http://www.jbc.org/cgi/content/full/277/20/e9)
2. JBC Classics: Van Slyke, D. D., and Neill, J. M. (1924) *J. Biol. Chem.* **61,** 523–543 (http://www.jbc.org/cgi/content/full/277/27/e16)
3. Dam, H. (1929) *Biochem. Z.* **215,** 475
4. Olson, R. E. (1990) *Nobel Laureates in Medicine or Physiology* (Fox, D. M., Meldrum, M., and Rezak, I., eds) Garland Publishing, Inc., New York
5. Doisy, E. A. (1976) *Annu. Rev. Biochem.* **45,** 1–9

---

[1] Much of the background material for this Classic Introduction was taken from an autobiographical prefatory chapter in Ref. 5.

[2] Special thanks to William S. Sly, Professor and Chairman of the Edward A. Doisy Department of Biochemistry and Molecular Biology at St. Louis University, for providing biographical material for this Introduction.

THE JOURNAL OF BIOLOGICAL CHEMISTRY
© 2002 by The American Society for Biochemistry and Molecular Biology, Inc.

Vol. 277, No. 29, Issue of July 19, p. e18, 2002
Printed in U.S.A.

Classics

A PAPER IN A SERIES REPRINTED TO CELEBRATE THE CENTENARY OF THE JBC IN 2005

JBC Centennial
1905–2005
100 Years of Biochemistry and Molecular Biology

Carbohydrate Metabolism: Glycogen Phosphorylase and the Work of Carl F. and Gerty T. Cori

The Mechanism of Epinephrine Action. II. The Influence of Epinephrine and Insulin on the Carbohydrate Metabolism of Rats in the Postabsorptive State
(Cori, C. F., and Cori, G. T. (1928) *J. Biol. Chem.* **79,** 321–341)

The Enzymatic Conversion of Glucose-1-phosphoric Ester to 6-Ester in Tissue Extracts
(Cori, G. T., Colowick, S. P., and Cori, C. F. (1938) *J. Biol. Chem.* **124,** 543–555)

The Activity of the Phosphorylating Enzyme in Muscle Extracts
(Cori, G. T., Colowick, S. P., and Cori, C. F. (1939) *J. Biol. Chem.* **127,** 771–782)

Crystalline Muscle Phosphorylase. I. Preparation, Properties, and Molecular Weight
(Green, A. A., and Cori, G. T. (1943) *J. Biol. Chem.* **151,** 21–29)

Crystalline Muscle Phosphorylase. II. Prosthetic Group
(Cori, G. T., and Green, A. A. (1943) *J. Biol. Chem.* **151,** 31–38)

Carl F. Cori (1896–1984) and Gerty T. Radnitz (1896–1957) received M. D. degrees from the German University in Prague in 1920 and later that year moved to Vienna where they were married. This was the beginning of a lifelong personal and professional collaboration. Life in Vienna was very difficult after World War I, with near starvation conditions, yet the Coris found work in clinical laboratories and even found some time for research. Carl Cori quoted one of his physician supervisors in the clinical laboratories who had criticized the thoroughness of his work, "Why make duplicate determinations, they don't agree anyway?" Carl seemed destined for a research career perhaps because both his parents were university professors. Gerty, on the other hand, seemed determined to be a pediatrician, following the path of a favorite uncle. Although most aspects of life in Vienna were hard, the Coris found enjoyment in the many free museums and art galleries. They did not, however, have means sufficient to enjoy the opera and symphony for which Vienna was famous. Carl cited a common Viennese saying that characterized the times: "The situation was hopeless, but not serious."

As the atmosphere in Austria became more disturbing, Carl was required to prove Aryan descent to be employed at the University of Graz, to which he had moved in 1921. The Coris were so discouraged about the future in Europe that they applied to the Dutch government to serve for 5 years as physicians to the natives of Java. Before receiving a decision on their application, they had an opportunity to move to the State Institute for the Study of Malignant Disease, later Roswell Park Memorial Institute, in Buffalo, NY. Carl was to run the clinical laboratories associated with the hospital but was also allowed to use any free time for research. He wrote that he was entirely "self propelled," because no one cared what he was doing. His only contact with the hospital administration was a monthly meeting at which the Director would announce to the staff "Gentlemen, it behooves us to find the cause or cure of cancer, and it's got to be intravenous" after which he would disappear for another month leaving Carl to do whatever he pleased. Gerty arrived in Buffalo 6 months after Carl and obtained a position in the pathology laboratory, where she primarily made diagnoses based on microscopic evaluation of specimens submitted by physicians from the surrounding area.

Carl Cori. Photo courtesy of the National Library of Medicine.

Gerty Cori. Photo courtesy of the National Library of Medicine.

After nine generally happy and productive years in Buffalo, the Coris began to feel uncomfortable that their growing interest in carbohydrate metabolism did not fit the cancer research mission of the Institute. By 1931, they had developed a scientific reputation through their publications, and after exploring several job opportunities, they received offers to move to Washington University School of Medicine in St. Louis, Carl as Chairman of the pharmacology department and Gerty as Research Associate. Clearly equal opportunity was yet to come. In addition, many institutions had nepotism rules forbidding the employment of members of the same family. In 1946, Carl moved to the biochemistry department as Chairman where he served until his retirement in 1966.

The move to St. Louis marked a transition for the Coris from physiology to biochemistry. These *Journal of Biological Chemistry* (JBC) Classics were selected in an attempt to represent the breadth of their work. The first reports the late stages of the physiological work done in Buffalo and is prophetic in its examination of the role of epinephrine in glycogen metabolism. In the second Classic, the investigation of glycogen breakdown in minced frog muscle had become biochemical. Using this approach, they had already described the "Cori ester," glucose 1-phosphate, as a breakdown product of glycogen. In this paper, they described phosphoglucomutase, the enzyme that converts glucose 1-phosphate to glucose 6-phosphate, which is necessary for subsequent metabolism. The third Classic paper describes and characterizes glycogen phosphorylase, the enzyme responsible for breakdown of glycogen to glucose 1-phosphate. This is a novel biochemical reaction, preserving in the glucose phosphoester the energy of the glycosidic linkage in glycogen. In this paper it was suggested that glycogen phosphorylase is able to synthesize glycogen which, although enzymatically true, was later shown not to be the physiological pathway of glycogen synthesis. Sydney Colowick, co-author of these papers, who became a distinguished biochemist and the author of a future JBC Classic, was the first graduate student to work with the Coris.

Arda Green, already an outstanding protein chemist, joined the Coris in 1942 as they began to purify and crystallize some of the enzymes that they had earlier described. Glycogen phosphorylase, most notably, had many secrets to reveal. The final Classic in this group reports that glycogen phosphorylase from muscle exists in two forms, phosphorylase *a*, which was easily crystallized and was active without the addition of AMP, and phosphorylase *b*, a more soluble protein, which was inactive without AMP. This represents the discovery of the first allosteric effector, AMP. An enzyme that converts phosphorylase *a* to phosphorylase *b* by removal of a "prosthetic group," was named PR for "prosthetic group-removing" enzyme. The enzyme was later shown to be a protein phosphatase that functions in the interconversion of glycogen phosphorylases *a* and *b* by phosphorylation/dephosphorylation. This work led eventually to a Nobel Prize for Edwin G. Krebs and Edmond H. Fischer, the authors of future JBC Classics.

The Cori laboratory was for many years a world center for enzymology with numerous visitors, graduate students, and postdoctoral fellows. In recognition of their remarkable work, Carl and Gerty Cori received the Nobel Prize in Medicine or Physiology in 1947. It is notable that Nobel Prizes were later awarded to six scientists who had trained with the Coris, Arthur Kornberg and Severo Ochoa in 1959, Luis Leloir in 1970, Earl Sutherland in 1971, Christian de Duve in 1974, and Edwin G. Krebs in 1991.

The year that brought the Nobel Prize to the Coris also brought the news that Gerty Cori had a fatal anemia. She lived, however, for another 10 very active and productive years during which she described the enzymatic defects for several diseases of glycogen metabolism. She died in 1957. In 1966, Carl retired as Chairman of the Department of Biological Chemistry at Washington University. He died in 1984.[1,2,3]

Robert D. Simoni, Robert L. Hill, and Martha Vaughan

REFERENCES

1. Cori, C. F. (1969) The call of science. *Annu. Rev. Biochem.* **38**, 1
2. Kornberg, A. (2001) Remembering our teachers. *J. Biol. Chem.* **276**, 3–11

[1] Much of the material for this Classic Introduction came from the autobiographical prefatory chapter written by Carl Cori for the *Annual Review of Biochemistry* (1).
[2] A wonderful description of the personal and professional lives of the Coris and some of their co-workers was written by Arthur Kornberg as a JBC Reflections (2).
[3] We thank Edwin G. Krebs, Emeritus Professor, Department of Pharmacology, University of Washington for help in selecting these JBC Classics to represent the work of Carl and Gerty Cori from among the many papers that were candidates.

THE JOURNAL OF BIOLOGICAL CHEMISTRY
© 2002 by The American Society for Biochemistry and Molecular Biology, Inc.

Vol. 277, No. 30, Issue of July 26, p. e19, 2002
Printed in U.S.A.

Classics

A PAPER IN A SERIES REPRINTED TO CELEBRATE THE CENTENARY OF THE JBC IN 2005

JBC Centennial
1905–2005
100 Years of Biochemistry and Molecular Biology

The Beginning of Protein Physical Chemistry. Determinations of Protein Molecular Weights. The Work of Edwin Joseph Cohn

Studies in the Physical Chemistry of the Proteins. V. Molecular Weights of the Proteins (Cohn, E. J., Hendry, J. L., and Prentiss, A. M. (1925) *J. Biol. Chem.* **63, 721–766)**

Edwin Joseph Cohn (1892–1953) began his college education at Amherst College as a humanities student but developed an interest in science and, with the encouragement of Jacques Loeb, transferred to the University of Chicago where he received both his Bachelors (1914) and Ph.D. degrees in Chemistry. During his Ph.D. work he had been strongly influenced by Lawrence J. Henderson of Harvard who was the first Chairman of the Department of Physical Chemistry at Harvard Medical School. Cohn had done some of his thesis work with Henderson, and from that experience he decided that proteins would be his life's work. After his Ph.D., he worked with Thomas D. Osborne in New Haven who had been studying plant proteins for many years and was one of the few protein chemists in the United States.

With the beginning of World War I, Cohn moved to Harvard to again work with Henderson on a war project studying the physical chemistry of bread making. The shortage of wheat made this an important project. After the war, he studied in Copenhagen with S. P. L. Sorensen who had shown that egg albumin, although a large molecule of approximately 40,000 daltons, formed solutions that obey the classical laws of physical chemistry. In 1920, he returned to the United States and was invited by Henderson to play a leading role in the Department of Physical Chemistry. Henderson's research interests were taking him away from the department, and Cohn was put in charge. His research initially was an extension of studies done with Osborne and Sorensen and focused on solubility and acid-base properties of casein, zein, and serum globulins. It was an interesting time in the study of proteins because there was not complete agreement that proteins were actually discrete molecules. Among colloid chemists, it was thought that proteins were not true molecules but aggregates of small peptides held together by noncovalent interactions. One of the most prominent of the colloid school was The Svedberg in Uppsala, who would later develop the ultracentrifuge and also eventually recognize that proteins were indeed discrete molecules. It would, however, take another decade to finally bury the colloid view although Cohn never considered their views seriously (1).

The Cohn paper selected as this *Journal of Biological Chemistry* (JBC) Classic represents a very thorough examination and comparison of the molecular weights of several proteins as determined by various methods. The methods include molecular weight determination by osmotic pressure and by composition. The compositional studies used various reference components, iron for hemoglobin, copper for hemocyanin, sulfur for many proteins, and low frequency amino acids. The compositional analysis would provide a minimal molecular weight and other information from dialysis, and ultrafiltration, reported in a subsequent paper, would allow a calculation of the even multiple of the minimal molecular weight for the intact protein. Drawing on data from many sources, he concludes this paper with the estimated minimal molecular weights of 14 proteins. Although all of the estimates are wrong, the important conclusion is that proteins are large, discrete molecules, which at the time was an important conclusion.

Cohn continued his studies of protein solubility and increasingly focused on amino acids and peptides and eventually on serum proteins. In the course of these latter studies he developed

This paper is available on line at http://www.jbc.org

Edwin J. Cohn. Photo courtesy of the National Library of Medicine.

sound physical-chemical approaches to fractionation of serum proteins, including salting in/salting out, alcohol precipitation, etc. that would be of enormous practical importance as the United States prepared for World War II. In 1940, the National Research Council recognized the need for providing material for blood transfusions for the war effort. It was the hope initially that bovine albumin could be used as a "plasma expander" for the prevention of shock. In 1941 Cohn published a review, "The Properties and Functions of Plasma Proteins with consideration of the Methods for their Separation and Purification" (3). With his vast experience with serum proteins, he was enlisted to direct an effort for large scale purification of bovine albumin. He wisely also worked on the isolation of human albumin as well because bovine albumin was never proven safe for humans. In the course of this work, Cohn insisted that the full complexity of plasma be appreciated, and fractionation was designed to produce particular components for specific purposes: albumin for transfusion and shock treatment, fibrinogen and prothrombin for clotting problems, and γ-globulins for certain diseases. The scale of the national effort was enormous, and with the support of the Office of Scientific Research and Development and blood from the Red Cross, over a half-million transfusions of albumin were prepared in the United States between 1942 and 1945. Cohn was the driving force behind this effort. Driven by the war effort, the understanding of plasma proteins was advanced enormously.

Cohn provided a very fruitful training ground for many of the most important protein chemists of a generation. John Edsall, Jeffries Wyman, and Alex von Muralt were all in the Cohn laboratory at the same time. He was a demanding mentor and supervisor. He is described by John Edsall, "In applying pressure to get things done he was often imperious and demanding, sometimes rude to the point of insult. Certainly he made many enemies by his extreme forcefulness and sometimes by an aggressiveness which went beyond obvious necessity" (1).

Among many honors, Cohn was the first Harvard professor of the life sciences to be named University Professor, and he received the Medal of Merit from the U.S. Government for his war efforts (1).

Robert D. Simoni, Robert L. Hill, and Martha Vaughan

REFERENCES

1. Edsall, J. T. (1961) *Biographical Memoir for Edwin Joseph Cohn*, Vol. 20, pp. 47–72, National Academy of Sciences, Washington, D. C.
2. Edsall, J. T. (1992) Memories of the early days of protein science. *Protein Sci.* **1,** 1526–1530
3. Cohn, E. J. (1941) The properties and functions of the plasma proteins with a consideration of the methods for their separation and purification. *Chem. Rev.* **28,** 395

THE JOURNAL OF BIOLOGICAL CHEMISTRY
© 2002 by The American Society for Biochemistry and Molecular Biology, Inc.

Vol. 277, No. 31, Issue of August 2, p. e20, 2002
Printed in U.S.A.

Classics

A PAPER IN A SERIES REPRINTED TO CELEBRATE THE CENTENARY OF THE JBC IN 2005

JBC Centennial
1905–2005
100 Years of Biochemistry and Molecular Biology

The Structure and Function of Hemoglobin: Gilbert Smithson Adair and the Adair Equations

The Hemoglobin System. VI. The Oxygen Dissociation Curve of Hemoglobin
(Adair, G. S. (1925) *J. Biol. Chem.* 63, 529–545)

Gilbert Smithson Adair (1896–1979) was a pioneer in the application of physical chemistry to the study of proteins. He was born in Whitehaven, England and received much of his early schooling at home. He entered King's College, Cambridge, in 1915 and received a first class degree in natural sciences in 1917. After graduation he joined the Food Investigation Board, which was considering ways to prevent the spoilage of food sent on cargo ships. He returned to King's College in 1920 as a research student, and in 1928 he was made an official Fellow of the College, which allowed him to devote five years to research. In 1931 he became assistant director of the Physiological Laboratory at Cambridge, and in 1945 he was named Reader in Biophysics, the post he held until retiring in 1963.

John Edsall described Adair as the person most influential in shaping his career as a young protein chemist (1). Edsall spent two years in the laboratory of F. Gowland Hopkins at Cambridge, the author of a previous *Journal of Biological Chemistry* (JBC) Classic (2), between his second and third years as a medical student at Harvard. During the time at Cambridge, Edsall met and interacted with Adair. Early in his career, Adair resolved a long standing controversy about the molecular weight of hemoglobin. It was widely agreed, primarily from measurements of iron content, that the minimum molecular weight of hemoglobin was about 16,000, but there was little agreement about what multiple of 16,000 was correct. Using osmotic pressure measurements, which he had pioneered, and five years of work, Adair was able to demonstrate that the molecular weight of hemoglobin was $4 \times 16,000$. This conclusion was controversial, because most still thought that the true molecular weight was 16,000. Several months later, and not knowing of Adair's work, The Svedberg in Uppsala, using his newly developed analytical ultracentrifuge, demonstrated that Adair's molecular weight for hemoglobin was correct.

The work reported in this JBC Classic describes the oxygen-binding properties of pure hemoglobin under various conditions. This study is one of the first on ligand binding by hemoglobin in a pure system, as blood had been used in most previous studies. Adair concluded that $Hb(O_2)_4$ dissociates in stages to $Hb + 4 (O_2)$. It was clear that oxygen binding by hemoglobin could not be explained by the well known law of mass action, which gives rise to a hyperbolic binding curve, and thus contradicted the proposals of A. V. Hill and J. B. S. Haldane, themselves giants in physical chemistry. The binding curves that Adair obtained are clearly sigmoidal, defining a much more complex binding mechanism, *i.e.* cooperativity. The data presented in Fig. 1 of this JBC Classic are stunning for their precision and show clearly both the cooperativity and the pH dependence of oxygen binding, two hallmarks of the physiological function of hemoglobin. Adair had established the analytical basis and theoretical framework for describing the phenomenon of cooperative oxygen binding by hemoglobin although it was only many years later that the mechanism was understood. The Adair equations that describe oxygen binding are still used today.

It is interesting that Adair provided the first crystals of horse hemoglobin to Max Perutz, as Perutz began his historic work on hemoglobin structure. By 1968, with elucidation of the structure of hemoglobin at atomic resolution, the mechanism of the cooperative binding of

This paper is available on line at http://www.jbc.org

oxygen by hemoglobin that Adair had reported 43 years earlier was understood in structural terms. Adair was elected a Fellow of the Royal Society in 1939.

Robert D. Simoni, Robert L. Hill, and Martha Vaughan

REFERENCES

1. Edsall, J. T. (1992) Memories of early days in protein science. *Protein Sci.* **1,** 1526–1530
2. JBC Classics: Hopkins, F. G., and Dixon, M. (1922) *J. Biol. Chem.* **54,** 527–563 (http://www.jbc.org/cgi/content/full/277/24/e13)

THE JOURNAL OF BIOLOGICAL CHEMISTRY
© 2002 by The American Society for Biochemistry and Molecular Biology, Inc.

Vol. 277, No. 32, Issue of August 9, p. e21, 2002
Printed in U.S.A.

Classics

A PAPER IN A SERIES REPRINTED TO CELEBRATE THE CENTENARY OF THE JBC IN 2005

JBC Centennial
1905–2005
100 Years of Biochemistry and Molecular Biology

The Determination of Phosphorus and the Discovery of Phosphocreatine and ATP: the Work of Fiske and SubbaRow

The Colorimetric Determination of Phosphorus
(Fiske, C. H., and SubbaRow, Y. (1925) *J. Biol. Chem.* 66, 375–400)

Phosphocreatine
(Fiske, C. H., and SubbaRow, Y. (1929) *J. Biol. Chem.* 81, 629–679)

Cyrus Hartwell Fiske (1890–1978) received an A.B. degree from the University of Minnesota in 1910 and an M.D. degree from Harvard in 1914. From 1914–1917 he spent two years of study in biochemistry at Harvard Medical School followed by two years at Western Reserve School of Medicine. He then joined the faculty at Harvard as an Assistant Professor and rose through the ranks to Professor in 1937 before retiring in 1957.

Yellagaprada SubbaRow (1896–1948) came to Harvard in 1923 to study tropical medicine after completing his medical training in India. After receiving a diploma from the Harvard School of Tropical Medicine, he became interested in biochemistry and started working with Fiske. He received his Ph.D. in 1930 in part for the work described in these Classic papers. With the support of Otto Folin, Chairman of Biological Chemistry and the author of a previous *Journal of Biological Chemistry* (JBC) Classic (1), he was appointed to a junior faculty position. In 1940, he moved to Lederle Laboratories where he worked until his death in 1948.

Fiske and SubbaRow, the two names are nearly inseparable, made many discoveries together, but the most notable and lasting resulted from their work on the metabolism of muscle tissue leading to the discovery of both phosphocreatine and ATP (2–4). Neither discovery, however, would have been possible without the simple, accurate phosphate determination method they developed.

The colorimetric determination of phosphorus described in the first paper of this JBC Classic set is one of the most highly cited papers in the history of biochemistry and certainly the one for which Fiske and SubbaRow are most remembered. Citation information from ISI indicates that this paper is the fourth most highly cited JBC paper of all time with over 19,000 citations as of March 2001. This a large underestimate because ISI only started to monitor citations in 1945, and this paper was published in 1925 so there are 20 years of uncaptured citations. (For reference, the most highly cited JBC paper is the method for protein determination developed by Oliver Lowry and co-workers, which was published in 1951, after ISI started collecting citation data, with about 250,000 citations. The Lowry paper and the Folin-Ciocalteu paper, which was the basis of the Lowry method, will be reprinted in a future installment of JBC Classics.) As with many methodological studies, this one built on earlier work, particularly the work by Doisy, the author of previous JBC Classics (5). It attempted to resolve shortcomings in three areas, stability of the color reaction, sensitivity, and interfering substances. The original assays for phosphorus relied on the reduction of phosphomolybdic acid by hydroquinone to form a blue color. This reduction was slow and influenced by various interfering substances. Somewhat by chance, they tried 1-amino-2-naphthol-6-sulfonic acid as the reducing agent with great improvement in results. Although the assay was developed initially for use with urine and blood samples, it was quickly adapted for many other kinds of samples and for use in measuring, not only inorganic phosphorus but organic phosphorus as well.

44

The inquiry into phosphate compounds of muscle filtrates may well have been initiated because of the work of Otto Folin, chairman of their department, on nitrogenous compounds in blood and urine including creatine. Fiske and SubbaRow were able to demonstrate that much of the phosphate in muscle filtrates was not inorganic phosphate, as had been believed, but a compound that was equimolar creatine and phosphate. They also were able to show that phosphocreatine was hydrolyzed during muscle contraction and resynthesized during the recovery period (2, 3). This JBC Classic, although not their first report of phosphocreatine, presents the most thorough characterization of both its chemical and physiological properties. This paper also provides an interesting glimpse into the competition involved in the discovery of both phosphocreatine and ATP between Fiske and SubbaRow and Karl Lohmann, a member of Meyerhof's group in Germany. On page 630 of the phosphocreatine JBC Classic reprinted here, there is the following passage related to the method for determining phosphorous: "Lohmann and Jendrassik, in Meyerhof's laboratory, finding also that color develops slowly in the case of muscle filtrates, and assuming the presence of some interfering substance to be responsible, adopted the use of heat (as suggested by us earlier) under the guise of a new modification of the method. Since Lohmann and Jendrassik's interpretation of the delayed reaction is not correct, their criticisms of our technique are altogether pointless."

The competition between the two groups continued over the discovery of ATP. Fiske and SubbaRow published their isolation and characterization of "adenosinetriphosphate" in 1929 (4). Also in 1929, Lohmann published his identification of "adenylpyrophosphate" (6).

Fiske provided a supportive research/training environment. One of his Ph.D. students, George H. Hitchings, had come to Harvard Medical School as a Teaching Fellow in Biological Chemistry intending to work with Otto Folin. Folin sent him to Fiske for the first year, as was his practice, and Hitchings was caught up in the work of Fiske and SubbaRow and decided to complete his thesis work in this laboratory. His project was to develop analytic methods for the determination of purine bases for physiological studies. This work provided the foundation for a career developing cancer chemotherapies based on purine and pyrimidine analogs. Hitchings received the Nobel Prize in Physiology or Medicine, along with James W. Black and Gertrude B. Elion in 1988.[1]

Robert D. Simoni, Robert L. Hill, and Martha Vaughan

REFERENCES

1. JBC Classics: Folin, O., and Wu, H. (1919) *J. Biol. Chem.* **38,** 81–110 (http://www.jbc.org/cgi/content/full/277/20/e9)
2. Fiske, C. H., and SubbaRow, Y. (1927) *Science* **65,** 401
3. Fiske, C. H., and SubbaRow, Y. (1927) *J. Biol. Chem.* **74,** 22
4. Fiske, C. H., and SubbaRow, Y. (1929) *Science* **70,** 381–382
5. JBC Classics: Veler, C. D., Thayer, S., and Doisy, E. A. (1930) *J. Biol. Chem.* **87,** 357–371; Thayer, S. A., Levin, L., and Doisy, E. A. (1931) *J. Biol. Chem.* **91,** 655–665; MacCorquodale, D. W., Cheney, L. C., Binkley, S. B., Holcomb, W. F., McKee, R. W., Thayer, S. A., and Doisy, E. A. (1939) *J. Biol. Chem.* **131,** 357–370 (http://www.jbc.org/cgi/content/full/277/28/e17)
6. Lohmann, K. (1929) *Naturwissenschaften* **17,** 624–625

[1] We thank Eugene Kennedy, Professor Emeritus of Biological Chemistry at Harvard Medical School, for providing much of the biographical information for Cyrus H. Fiske. Professor Kennedy was Chairman of the Department of Biological Chemistry during the later stages of Professor Fiske's career.

THE JOURNAL OF BIOLOGICAL CHEMISTRY
© 2002 by The American Society for Biochemistry and Molecular Biology, Inc.

Vol. 277, No. 33, Issue of August 16, pp. 29351–29353, 2002
Printed in U.S.A.

Classics

A PAPER IN A SERIES REPRINTED TO CELEBRATE THE CENTENARY OF THE JBC IN 2005

JBC Centennial
1905–2005
100 Years of Biochemistry and Molecular Biology

John T. Edsall: Biochemist, Teacher, *Journal of Biological Chemistry* Editor, and Responsible Scientist

Studies in the Physical Chemistry of Muscle Globulin. II. On Some Physicochemical Properties of Muscle Globulin (Myosin)
(Edsall, J. T. (1930) *J. Biol. Chem.* 89, 289–313)

Studies in the Physical Chemistry of the Proteins. XI. The Amphoteric Properties of Zein
(Cohn, E. J., Edsall, J. T., and Blanchard, M. H. (1933) *J. Biol. Chem.* 105, 319–326)

John Tileston Edsall (1902–2002) was born in Philadelphia to families that had emigrated to the United States in the 17th century. His mother, Margaret Tileston, was a teacher, and his father, David Linn Edsall, was a Professor of Medicine at the University of Pennsylvania Medical School. In 1918, David Linn Edsall became the Dean of Harvard Medical School, a position he held for 17 years. The move from Philadelphia to Boston and Harvard marked, for John, the beginning of a lifelong association with Harvard. At the age of 13, he was fascinated by a science class at Milton Academy which, along with being raised in a medical family, helped to guide him toward medical school and a career in science. John enrolled in Harvard College to study chemistry at age 16 and he was, by his own admission, an average student. In his last two years, however, he was inspired by two teachers/scientists, the organic chemist E. P. Kohler, and the biochemist Lawrence J. Henderson, who was the Chairman of the Department of Physical Chemistry at Harvard Medical School (1).

After completing his undergraduate studies in 1923, Edsall entered Harvard Medical School, where his interest in science and research was further stimulated by Otto Folin's biochemistry course. (Folin is the author of an earlier *Journal of Biological Chemistry* (JBC) Classic (2).) Most important during his first year of medical school was the opportunity to do research with Alfred C. Redfield, Director of the Woods Hole Oceanographic Institute, on the physiology of heart muscle function. This work initiated a career-long interest in the structure and function of muscle proteins. In 1924, Edsall, along with Jeffries Wyman his college friend and colleague (and author of a future JBC Classic), began two years of study at Cambridge University in the Department of Biochemistry chaired by F. Gowland Hopkins (author of a previous JBC Classic (3)). He took biochemistry courses and did some research but, more importantly, came under the influence of G. S. Adair who, Edsall wrote, was his "most important contact" at Cambridge (4). Adair was in the process of determining the molecular weight of hemoglobin, describing hemoglobin oxygen dissociation curves, and applying physicochemical principles to the study of proteins. Adair's work was reported in a previous JBC Classic (5).

Edsall returned to Harvard in 1926 as a third year medical student to begin his clinical training, much of which he felt was "trivial and stupid" (1). In spite of this view, however, he decided to complete his medical degree and in free time from his clinical studies began to work with Edwin J. Cohn in the Department of Physical Chemistry in Harvard Medical School and the author of a previous JBC Classic (6). Cohn was interested in protein physical chemistry and guided Edsall to examine the globulins of muscle. During his early experiments with myosin, in fact actomyosin, it was observed by refractive index measurements that myosin solutions forced to flow through a capillary exhibited streaming birefringence (7, 8). This ordering, induced by capillary flow, was compared to the ordered morphology observed in

John T. Edsall. Photo courtesy of the National Library of Medicine.

intact muscle cells by his colleague Alexander von Muralt suggesting that the extracted protein(s) represented a basic unit of muscle structure. At that time, there was no good theory that related flow birefringence to the size and shape of the molecules producing it, but Edsall determined from hydrodynamic considerations that the dimensions of the myosin molecules must be long and thin in order to explain the ordering induced by capillary flow.

In addition to work on muscle proteins, Edsall and his colleagues in the Department of Physical Chemistry, including Jeffries Wyman, began systematically to study the physical and solution properties of amino acids and small peptides. One of Edsall's contributions was the description of an amino acid as a dipolar ion or, as he preferred, ionic dipole (4). Using Raman spectroscopy, he showed that both the amino and carboxyl groups of amino acids were charged at isoelectric pH (9), which supported evidence obtained with other methods.

The two papers reprinted in this installment of JBC Classics are intended to represent a body of work focused on the physical chemistry of proteins. As was common in Edsall's time, much of his work was published in the chemical literature. The first paper examines primarily the solubility properties of myosin as a function of ionic strength and pH. Further it is reported that the viscosity of a myosin solution was much greater than that of plasma proteins such as albumin. The second paper presents titration data for the protein zein and reports the pK values for the titratable groups, primarily the carboxyl groups and the imidazole of histidine. The titrations were carried out only to pH 8 so the ionization of the lysine and arginine residues were not observed as Edsall pointed out.

Edsall was a devoted teacher and because the Department of Physical Chemistry in the Medical School had few formal teaching responsibilities, he volunteered to be a tutor at Harvard College, a position he held from 1928 to 1968. This program was an integral part of the Harvard biochemical sciences teaching program and covered all aspects of biochemistry. He met with small groups of undergraduates and advised seniors on their honors research projects. Edsall served as Chairman of the Board of Tutors from 1931 to 1968, a few years before his retirement. Among the students in Edsall's groups were R. Gordon Gould, I. Herbert Scheinberg, Alton Meister, Alexander Rich, Gary Felsenfeld, Jared Diamond, W. French Anderson, Eliot Elson, Michael Chamberlain, David Eisenberg, Robert Eisenberg, and Joel Huberman. All were to have successful careers in science and medicine (1). He also taught a formal course in the Biology Department of Harvard College on biophysical chemistry.

With the beginning of World War II, work in the Department of Physical Chemistry was redirected to support the war effort. Led by Edwin J. Cohn, this group spearheaded the national plasma fractionation program. The large scale fractionation procedures they developed provided many protein products to meet the needs of the war including clotting factors and human albumin as a "plasma extender" for transfusions (6). This applied research also produced valuable fundamental knowledge of protein solubility properties and techniques for fractionation.

After Cohn's death in 1953, Edsall moved to Harvard College where he continued both his research and teaching without the necessity of the four-mile trips between the Medical School and College. For much of the remainder of Edsall's career, his research was focused on carbonic anhydrase. In 1954, he was invited to become a member of the Editorial Board of the JBC, and in 1958 he was asked to succeed Rudolph J. Anderson as Editor. He accepted and served as Editor until 1967. The editorial office of the Journal was set up at Harvard, and the basic structure of the JBC manuscript review process as it exists today was established. In 1958, the Journal page was enlarged to enable presentation of 2.4 times the content of the previous, smaller format. The result was a thinner Journal but only for a short time. Edsall was responsible for the first appointments of women to the Editorial Board, Mildred Cohn, Sarah Ratner, and Sofia Simmonds.

During Edsall's 10-year term, the size of the Editorial Board doubled from 26 to 54 members. (In 2002, there are about 500 members of the editorial board.) The number of pages published annually by the Journal had also doubled reaching 5800 during his tenure. He believed that some sort of limit made it likely that the JBC would become divided into subspecialty journals. It survived that period of growth without fission, however, and remains a general journal of biochemistry and molecular biology. (In 2002 the Journal will publish over 50,000 pages.) During Edsall's last year as Editor, page charges of $35 were instituted and were then, as they are now, somewhat controversial albeit essential to the financial health of the Journal. (Page charges in 2002 are $65.) Edsall was succeeded as Editor by William H. Stein, who was stricken by a crippling paralytic illness and served only a short term. Herbert Tabor became Acting Editor, and in 1971 with Stein's resignation was appointed Editor, a position he occupies in 2002 (1, 10).

Among Edsall's many roles was that of a vigorous advocate for freedom of scientific inquiry as well as the responsible conduct of research and usage of applied science. At the Annual Meeting of the American Society of Biological Chemists (ASBC) in 1954, it was reported that the United States Public Health Service (USPHS) was withholding research support from some investigators because their security files contained unevaluated, adverse information. The investigators were not made aware of this information nor were they given any opportunity to respond to the allegations, which were irrelevant in any case, Edsall felt, because none of the research was classified. With a general sense of outrage, Edsall, along with Philip Handler, Wendell Stanley, and a few others (1), prepared a resolution to send to the National Academy of Sciences asking for an investigation of this action by the USPHS. At the general business meeting of the ASBC, the resolution was passed unanimously.

The National Academy, after a thorough investigation, recommended to President Dwight D. Eisenhower that grants for unclassified research should be awarded solely on the basis of scientific merit. The Eisenhower administration made this policy effective in all federal granting agencies. During the months of preparation of the National Academy report, Edsall undertook a personal protest. He wrote an article that was published in *Science* (11), condemning the actions of the USPHS and declaring his refusal to accept support from the USPHS for his research as long as their practices continued (1). Not until two years later, with assurance that they had stopped, did he apply for and accept research support from the USPHS. Edsall played an important role also in the establishment of the Committee on Scientific Freedom and Responsibility (CSFR) of the American Association for Advancement of Science (AAAS). His article published in *Science* in 1975 "Scientific Freedom and Responsibility" (12) is a seminal statement of issues confronting scientists and citizens that is still relevant.

Throughout his long career, Edsall continued to be an informed, articulate, and effective voice of concern regarding nuclear, biological, and chemical agents for war, environmental degradation, and the relationship of technology to society. He died on June 12, 2002, five months before his 100th birthday.

Robert D. Simoni, Robert L. Hill, and Martha Vaughan

REFERENCES

1. Edsall, J. T. (1971) Some personal history and reflections from the life of a biochemist. *Annu. Rev. Biochem.* **20,** 1–28
2. JBC Classics: Folin, O., and Wu, H. (1919) *J. Biol. Chem.* **38,** 81–110 (http://www.jbc.org/cgi/content/full/277/20/e9)
3. JBC Classics: Hopkins, F. G., and Dixon, M. (1922) *J. Biol. Chem.* **54,** 527–563 (http://www.jbc.org/cgi/content/full/277/24/e13)
4. Edsall, J. T. (1992) Memories of early days of protein science, 1926–1940. *Protein Sci.* **1,** 1526–1530
5. JBC Classics: Adair, G. S. (1925) *J. Biol. Chem.* **63,** 529–545 (http://www.jbc.org/cgi/content/full/277/31/e20)

6. JBC Classics: Cohn, E. J., Hendry, J. L., and Prentiss, A. M. (1925) *J. Biol. Chem.* **63,** 721–766 (http://www.jbc.org/cgi/content/full/277/30/e19)

7. Von Muralt, A. L., and Edsall, J. T. (1930) *J. Biol. Chem.* **89,** 315–350

8. Von Muralt, A. L., and Edsall, J. T. (1930) *J. Biol. Chem.* **89,** 351–386

9. Edsall, J. T. (1936) *J. Phys. Chem.* **4,** 1–8; (1937) **41,** 133–141; (1937) **5,** 225–237, 508–517

10. Edsall, J. T. (1980) The Journal of Biological Chemistry after seventy-five years. *J. Biol. Chem.* **255,** 8939–8948

11. Edsall, J. T. (1955) *Science* **121,** 615–619

12. Edsall, J. T. (1975) *Science* **188,** 687

THE JOURNAL OF BIOLOGICAL CHEMISTRY
© 2002 by The American Society for Biochemistry and Molecular Biology, Inc.

Vol. 277, No. 34, Issue of August 23, p. e22, 2002
Printed in U.S.A.

Classics

A PAPER IN A SERIES REPRINTED TO CELEBRATE THE CENTENARY OF THE JBC IN 2005

JBC Centennial
1905–2005
100 Years of Biochemistry and Molecular Biology

Copper as an Essential Nutrient and Nicotinic Acid as the Anti-black Tongue (Pelagra) Factor: the Work of Conrad Arnold Elvehjem

Iron in Nutrition. VII. Copper as a Supplement to Iron for Hemoglobin Building in the Rat
(Hart, E. B., Steenbock, H., Waddell, J., and Elvehjem, C. A. (1930) *J. Biol. Chem.* **77,** 797–812)

The Isolation and Identification of the Anti-black Tongue Factor
(Elvehjem, C. A., Madden, R. J., Strong, F. M., and Woolley, D. W. (1938) *J. Biol. Chem.* **123,** 137–149)

Conrad Arnold Elvehjem (1901–1962) was born and raised on a farm in the Norwegian community of McFarland, WI. The state capitol building in Madison could be seen from the farm, and Elvehjem would spend his entire career, from undergraduate student to University President, at the University of Wisconsin at Madison. In 1919, when he started his college education, the University of Wisconsin was a center of nutritional biochemistry with Babcock, Steenbock, McCollum (see previous *Journal of Biological Chemistry* (JBC) Classic (1)) and Peterson. He chose agricultural chemistry as his major and did his senior thesis research with both Harry Steenbock and W. P. Elmsley. In 1923 he started his Ph.D. research with E. B. Hart and received his degree in 1927. The work described in the first of the JBC Classics reprinted here is from this period. Elvehjem and Hart would be close collaborators for over 20 years. (2).

The first of the two Elvehjem papers reprinted in this installment of JBC Classics describes work done primarily during his graduate years. He had shown in an earlier paper (3) that rats fed a cow's milk diet developed a progressive anemia that could not be prevented or reversed with high amounts of relatively pure iron salts. However, ashed material from lettuce, corn, or liver, containing equal amounts of iron, were quite effective in raising hemoglobin levels (3). This paper reports the fractionation and identification of the material in the ash as copper and supplementation of the milk diet with both iron and copper reversed the anemia. This was an interesting result because hemoglobin contains no copper, and it became clear to Elvehjem that copper must act by providing other material necessary for synthesis of hemoglobin. Demonstration of the nutritional requirement for copper was met with great excitement. E. B. Hart, Elvehjem's thesis advisor, presented their results at the annual Federation meeting held in Ann Arbor in 1928. Midway through his presentation, the audience gave him a standing ovation. Henry Lardy, in an article marking the 50th anniversary of this work (4), quotes Edward Doisy, the author of earlier JBC Classics (5), who was in attendance at this Federation meeting: "I have never seen that done before nor since at a Federation meeting."

The only significant time Elvehjem was away from Madison was two years spent in Cambridge working with David Keilin. During this time E. B. Hart offered him a faculty position, at the annual salary of $3000, and he returned to Madison for the remainder of his career.

On returning to Madison, he worked on many aspects of nutritional biochemistry including trace metal requirements and also the study of respiratory complexes, which he had started with Keilin in Cambridge. It was the latter work that prompted the development of the

This paper is available on line at http://www.jbc.org

Conrad A. Elvehjem. Photo courtesy of the National Library of Medicine.

Potter-Elvehjem tissue homogenizer, for which most biochemists would recognize him. Of far greater importance, however, was a large program on the B vitamin complex. The second paper in this set of JBC Classics describes Elvehjem's effort to identify the "anti-black tongue factor" in liver extracts. He had implicated "Factor W" as an unidentified growth factor in liver extracts, which was required for growth in addition to the known B vitamins. Omission of the liver extract from a deficient diet resulted in black tongue in dogs as well as severe weight loss and poor health generally. In a highly collaborative effort, Elvehjem and his colleagues isolated the critical factor from liver extracts, determined that the structure was nicotinic acid, and showed that pure nicotinic acid, as well as nicotinic acid amide, would completely substitute for the liver extract. Important to this work was the collaboration of two of the co-authors of this paper. Frank M. Strong was able to isolate the nicotinic acid by sublimation, and Dilworth Wayne Woolley, using the sublimate, obtained the crystals. Both co-authors had notable careers in biochemistry. Strong was a long time member of the faculty in the Biochemistry Department at Madison, and Woolley was to spend his career in nutritional related research at the Rockefeller Institute. It was a short time after their discovery that nicotinic acid was shown to be effective in preventing pellagra in humans (2).

In addition to being a great scientist, Elvehjem was active in public service as a member of many nutritional boards. He was also a very effective University administrator. He served as Chairman of the Department of Biochemistry succeeding E. B. Hart who had served as chairman for 38 years. Elvehjem became Dean of the Graduate School during which time he established the Institute for Enzyme Research at the University and hired the co-directors David Green and Henry Lardy. In 1958 he became President of the University, but his service as President was short because in 1962, at the age of 61, he died of a heart attack while sitting at this desk (2).[1]

Robert D. Simoni, Robert L. Hill, and Martha Vaughan

REFERENCES

1. JBC Classics: McCollum, E. V., and Pitz, W. (1917) *J. Biol. Chem.* **31,** 229–253; McCollum, E. V., Simmonds, N., Becker, J. E., and Shipley, P. G. (1922) *J. Biol. Chem.* **53,** 293–312; McCollum, E. V., Simmonds, N., Becker, J. E., and Bunting, R. W. (1925) *J. Biol. Chem.* **63,** 553–562 (http://www.jbc.org/cgi/content/full/277/19/e8)
2. Burris, R. H., Bauuman, C. A., and Potter, V. R. (1990) *Biographical Memoir for Conrad Arnold Elvehjem,* Vol. 59, pp. 135–167, National Academy of Sciences, Washington, D.C.
3. Hart, E. B., Steenbock, H., Elvehjem, C. A., and Waddell, J. (1925) *J. Biol. Chem.* **65,** 67–80
4. Lardy, H. (1978) *Trends Biochem. Sci.* **3,** 93–94
5. JBC Classics: Veler, C. D., Thayer, S., and Doisy, E. A. (1930) *J. Biol. Chem.* **87,** 357–371; Thayer, S. A., Levin, L., and Doisy, E. A. (1931) *J. Biol. Chem.* **91,** 655–665; MacCorquodale, D. W., Cheney, L. C., Binkley, S. B., Holcomb, W. F., McKee, R. W., Thayer, S. A., and Doisy, E. A. (1939) *J. Biol. Chem.* **131,** 357–370 (http://www.jbc.org/cgi/content/full/277/28/e17)

[1] We thank Henry A. Lardy, Vilas Professor Emeritus, Institute for Enzyme Research, University of Wisconsin, for helpful biographical information and for reading this introduction.

THE JOURNAL OF BIOLOGICAL CHEMISTRY
© 2002 by The American Society for Biochemistry and Molecular Biology, Inc.

Vol. 277, No. 35, Issue of August 30, p. e23, 2002
Printed in U.S.A.

Classics

A PAPER IN A SERIES REPRINTED TO CELEBRATE THE CENTENARY OF THE JBC IN 2005

JBC Centennial
1905–2005
100 Years of Biochemistry and Molecular Biology

Urease, the First Crystalline Enzyme and the Proof That Enzymes Are Proteins: the Work of James B. Sumner

The Isolation and Crystallization of the Enzyme Urease. Preliminary Paper
(Sumner, J. B. (1926) *J. Biol. Chem.* 69, 435–441)

The Digestion and Inactivation of Crystalline Urease by Pepsin and by Papain
(Sumner, J. B., Kirk, J. S., and Howell, S. F. (1932) *J. Biol. Chem.* 98, 543–552)

James Batcheller Sumner (1887–1955) was born in Canton, MA, near Boston. As a boy, he had many interests including hunting. During an afternoon of hunting with a friend, the friend accidentally shot Sumner in the arm requiring that it be amputated above the elbow. He worked his entire life to be sure that this handicap did not interfere with his goals and aspirations. He enrolled in Harvard College in 1906 planning to study electrical engineering but lacked the necessary mathematics training so he changed his field to chemistry and graduated in 1910. After a year teaching chemistry at Worcester Polytechnic Institute, he returned to Harvard to study for his Ph.D. It had been suggested that he work with Otto Folin, Chairman of the biochemistry department at Harvard Medical School and author of a previous *Journal of Biological Chemistry* (JBC) Classic (1). Folin told him during the interview that he should consider law school because "a one armed man could never make it in chemistry." Sumner, challenged by this remark, did his thesis work with Folin. He graduated in 1914 with his thesis on "The Formation of Urea in the Animal Body" and with Folin's admiration.

During the summer of 1914, Sumner accepted an offer as Assistant Professor in the Department of Physiology and Biochemistry in the Ithaca Division of Cornell University Medical College. He would serve his entire career at Cornell in Ithaca in various departments and schools as the University reorganized itself. Sumner was the pioneer in biochemistry in Ithaca and remained a leader for over 40 years.

In spite of a very heavy teaching responsibility and little technical support, Sumner chose isolation of an enzyme in pure form for his research program. During his Nobel Laureate lecture in 1948, he offered an explanation: "I wish to tell next why I decided in 1917 to attempt to isolate an enzyme. At that time I had little time for research, not much apparatus, research money or assistance. I desired to accomplish something of real importance. In other words, I decided to take a long shot. A number of persons advised me that my attempt to isolate an enzyme was foolish, but this advice made me feel all the more certain that if successful the quest would be worthwhile."

It would take 9 years before his goal was reached and many more years before his work was generally accepted. (How many Assistant Professors would survive today with this record?). In the first paper of this set of JBC Classics, Sumner reports crystallization of a new globulin isolated from jack bean meal and presents evidence that the globulin was identical with the enzyme urease. The crystallization is from a water/acetone extract of jack bean meal allowed to stand in the cold overnight. Sumner presents extensive experimental evidence that the crystalline material is the enzyme urease including the observation that the most active preparations of urease they had prepared had a specific activity of 30,000 units/g of enzyme whereas the dissolved crystals had a specific activity of 100,000.

The publication of this Classic paper and the evidence that an enzyme, urease, was a protein was met with skepticism by most and disbelief by others. Most critical were Willstater and his students in Germany who had tried for many years to isolate a pure enzyme and, having failed, concluded that pure enzymes contained no protein. They dismissed Sumner's work concluding that the protein that had been crystallized was the carrier for the enzyme that had been adsorbed to it.

Sumner followed the initial report with ten papers reporting additional evidence that the globulin he had crystallized was the enzyme urease. One of these supporting papers is the second in this set of JBC Classics. Using proteolytic enzymes, papain and pepsin, Sumner and his colleagues show that proteolysis of urease results in loss of enzymatic activity. The case that enzymes were proteins was given a boost in 1930 when J. H. Northrup at Rockefeller Institute reported the crystallization of pepsin and later trypsin and chymotrypsin.

Only in 1946, with the award of the Nobel Prize, was Sumner's work fully accepted. He received the award "for his discovery that enzymes can be crystallized." The other half of the award went to J. H. Northrup and Wendell Stanley "for their preparation of enzymes and virus proteins in pure form." Sumner retired in July 1955 and died of cancer a month later.[1]

Robert D. Simoni, Robert L. Hill, and Martha Vaughan

REFERENCES

1. JBC Classics: Folin, O., and Wu, H. (1919) *J. Biol. Chem.* **38,** 81–110 (http://www.jbc.org/cgi/content/full/277/20/e9)
2. Maynard, L. A. (1958) *Biographical Memoir of James Batcheller Sumner*, Vol. 31, pp. 376–386, National Academy of Sciences, Washington, D. C.

[1] All the biographical information for the Classic Introduction was taken from Ref. 2.

THE JOURNAL OF BIOLOGICAL CHEMISTRY
© 2002 by The American Society for Biochemistry and Molecular Biology, Inc.

Vol. 277, No. 36, Issue of September 6, p. e24, 2002
Printed in U.S.A.

Classics

A PAPER IN A SERIES REPRINTED TO CELEBRATE THE CENTENARY OF THE JBC IN 2005

JBC Centennial
1905–2005
100 Years of Biochemistry and Molecular Biology

Michael Heidelberger and the Beginning of Immunochemistry

The Soluble Specific Substance of Pneumococcus. IV. On the Nature of the Specific Polysaccharide of Type III Pneumococcus
(Heidelberger, M., and Goebel, W. F. (1926) *J. Biol. Chem.* **70,** 613–624)

Michael Heidelberger (1888–1991) was a founder of immunochemistry. He was born in New York City and was educated in his early years by his mother. She was able to cover the basic subjects in an hour or two each day leaving time for the classics and music and to wander the city visiting museums and going to the opera (1). He decided to become a chemist at the age of 8. He attended Columbia University receiving his B.S. (1908), A.M. (1909), and Ph.D. (1911) degrees, all in organic chemistry. After a postdoctoral year in Zurich working with Richard Willstater, he returned to New York and was appointed a Fellow of the Rockefeller Institute by Simon Flexner where he would stay until 1927 rising to Associate Member. For the first nine years at Rockefeller, Heidelberger worked with Walter A. Jacobs in a close and productive collaboration synthesizing potential chemotherapeutic drugs. (Walter A. Jacobs was an outstanding natural products alkaloid chemist and the author of a future *Journal of Biological Chemistry* (JBC) Classic). One great success of the Jacobs-Heidelberger collaboration was the synthesis of tryparsamide, sodium para-phenylglycinamide arsonate, which was effective against African sleeping sickness, *i.e.* trypanosomiasis. The Belgian government awarded Heidelberger, Jacobs, and their collaborators the Order of Leopold II for this accomplishment (3).

The work featured in this JBC Classic was done in Heidelberger's last few years at the Rockefeller. He was enlisted by Oswald T. Avery to help identify the "specific soluble substance" of pneumococci. It had been shown by Dochez and Avery (4) that the culture fluids of pneumococci contained a substance that precipitates specifically with anti-pneumococci serum. The "soluble specific substance" was also found in the body fluids of infected organisms including humans. Using the laborious purification techniques required before the advent of chromatography, Heidelberger eventually purified the material from Types I, II, and III pneumococci. It was surprising that the material was not protein and contained no nitrogen and was shown to be a polysaccharide. The lack of nitrogen in the antigen made it possible in later work to use the polysaccharide antigen to quantitate the amount of protein, antibody, present in an immunoprecipitate. This work launched Heidelberger's scientific career in immunology, and he, along with Forrest E. Kendall, worked for many years to quantitatively define the precipitin reaction of polysaccharides and eventually the much more difficult problem of defining the antibody reaction with protein antigens.

On advice of colleagues at the Rockefeller, Heidelberger sought an independent position. After a year of reorganizing the chemistry laboratories at Mt. Sinai Hospital, which allowed little time for research, he took a position as Associate Professor in the Department of Medicine at Columbia University College of Physicians and Surgeons where he would serve until the age of 67 and mandatory retirement. During the period at Physicians and Surgeons, Heidelberger and colleagues, including Elvin Kabat, a gifted graduate student and later distinguished immunologist, proved that antibodies were globulins and that specific precipitation, agglutination, and complement fixation were different manifestations of a single

This paper is available on line at http://www.jbc.org

Michael Heidelberger. Photo courtesy of the National Library of Medicine.

antibody. Heidelberger's quantitative work resulted in the preparation of more effective anti-influenza sera that saved the lives of many infants with influenzal meningitis (2, 3).

After leaving Physicians and Surgeons, Heidelberger accepted Selman Wazman's offer of a position at the Institute of Microbiology at Rutgers University and continued his research for another 10 years after which he moved to the Department of Pathology at New York University and continued his research until his death in 1991. His career was devoted to the development of rigorous quantitative methods for the measurement of antibodies and the purification of antibody molecules. It was a career of nearly 80 years!

Heidelberger received many awards during his career, including the National Medal of Science and two Lasker Awards (1953 and 1978). In addition to science, Heidelberger was a talented musician and composer. He was also a citizen of the world, a strong spokesman for world peace, supporter of the mission of the United Nations, and a participant in the World Health Organization. He had a particular concern about nuclear proliferation and had a lecture entitled "The Scientist and Survival in an Atomic Era."

Robert D. Simoni, Robert L. Hill, and Martha Vaughan

REFERENCES

1. Heidelberger, M. (1977) A "pure" organic chemist's downward path. *Annu. Rev. Microbiol.* **31**, 1–12
2. Heidelberger, M. (1979) A pure organic chemist's downward path: chapter 2—The Years at P. and S. *Annu. Rev. Biochem.* **48**, 1–21
3. Cruse, J. (1988) A centenary tribute. Michael Heidelberger and the metamorphosis of immunologic science. *J. Immunol.* **140**, 2861–2863
4. Dochez, A. R., and Avery, O. T. (1917) *J. Exp. Med.* **26**, 447

THE JOURNAL OF BIOLOGICAL CHEMISTRY
© 2002 by The American Society for Biochemistry and Molecular Biology, Inc.

Vol. 277, No. 37, Issue of September 13, p. e25, 2002
Printed in U.S.A.

Classics

A PAPER IN A SERIES REPRINTED TO CELEBRATE THE CENTENARY OF THE JBC IN 2005

JBC Centennial
1905–2005
100 Years of Biochemistry and Molecular Biology

The Discovery of the Amino Acid Threonine: the Work of William C. Rose

Feeding Experiments with Mixtures of Highly Purified Amino Acids. I. The Inadequacy of Diets Containing Nineteen Amino Acids
(Rose, W. C. (1931) *J. Biol. Chem.* **94,** 155–165)

Feeding Experiments with Mixtures of Highly Purified Amino Acids. VIII. Isolation and Identification of a New Essential Amino Acid
(McCoy, R. H., Meyer, C. E., and Rose, W. C. (1935) *J. Biol. Chem.* **112,** 283–302)

William Cumming Rose (1887–1985) discovered threonine, the last of the 20 amino acids universally present in proteins to be identified. He was born in Greenfield, South Carolina, and at age 16, after schooling at home, entered Davidson College where he majored in chemistry. When Rose started graduate school at Yale, Russell Chittenden was Director of the Sheffield School of Science, which was at that time one of the centers of biochemistry in the United States. During his interview with Chittenden, Rose mentioned nutritional chemistry as an interest and was directed to meet Lafayette B. Mendel, who, with Thomas B. Osborne, was studying the nutritional value of proteins. (Osborne and Mendel are the authors of a previous JBC Classic (1).) Rose's work with Mendel, although not on proteins and amino acids, guided his research throughout his career.

After completing his doctoral studies at Yale, Rose moved to a position as Instructor of Physiological Chemistry at the University of Pennsylvania. During a brief leave in Germany to work with Franz Knoop, he was offered the opportunity to organize a department of biochemistry at the University of Texas College of Medicine in Galveston. There he became professor and head of the department but was persuaded in 1922 to move to the University of Illinois to head the Division of Physiological Chemistry, later Biochemistry, within the Chemistry Department. Until his retirement in 1955, Rose spent the remaining 33 years of his scientific career at Illinois (3).

While interested in many aspects of metabolism, Rose focused his research work on amino acid metabolism and nutrition after arriving at Illinois. Osborne and Mendel had demonstrated nutritional requirements for the individual amino acids (1). The corn protein zein was not adequate as a sole source of nitrogen; tryptophan and lysine were also needed. Rose showed that casein hydrolysate was likewise inadequate as a sole dietary protein; additional histidine was required. It was important that arginine would not replace histidine, which proved incorrect a proposal that histidine and arginine were interchangeable (2). These observations led to efforts to use mixtures of pure, individual amino acids as substitutes for proteins or protein hydrolysates in nutritional studies. The first of this pair of *Journal of Biological Chemistry* (JBC) Classics reports that 19 pure amino acids did support the growth of rats. Rose and his colleagues had purified 13 of the known amino acids from natural sources, synthesized 6 others, and established the purity of each. Rats lost weight when fed the 19 amino acids as their sole source of dietary nitrogen. Rose concluded that growth-supporting proteins contained at least one additional component that was lacking in the synthetic mixture, or that the proteins provided one or more of the known amino acids in significantly larger quantities. He favored the first explanation.

The second of these JBC Classics identifies the component essential for growth that was missing from the mixture of 19 amino acids. With growth stimulation as an assay, Rose and

This paper is available on line at http://www.jbc.org

William C. Rose. Photo courtesy of the National Library of Medicine.

his colleagues used the laborious techniques available before the development of chromatography to purify the new amino acid. It was crystallized, and the structure was determined to be α-amino-β-hydroxy-n-butyric acid, later named threonine. With the addition of threonine to the other 19 amino acids, rats were, for the first time, successfully reared on a diet in which pure amino acids were the sole source of nitrogen.

Over the next 20 years, Rose extended his studies to quantify the dietary requirements for individual amino acids. This quantitative work distinguished the amino acids that are absolutely essential from those that are necessary only for optimal growth. For rats, the omission of histidine, isoleucine, leucine, threonine, lysine, methionine, phenylalanine, tryptophan, or valine resulted in eventual death, whereas omission of arginine resulted in suboptimal growth. Rose went on to determine for each amino acid the minimum daily requirements for optimal growth.

In 1942, Rose and associates turned their attention to the amino acid requirements for humans using basically the same methodology he had with rats except that healthy, male graduate students were the experimental animals. "Subjects" were fed a diet consisting of corn starch, sucrose, butter fat without protein, corn oil, inorganic salts, the known vitamins, and mixtures of highly purified amino acids. The diet included also a large brown "candy," which contained a concentrated liver extract to supply unknown vitamins, sugar, and peppermint oil to provide a "never-to-be-forgotten taste" (3). The adequacy of the diet was assessed, not by survival of the subjects, but by measuring total nitrogen excretion in urine and feces to determine the nitrogen equilibrium. The results proved that only eight amino acids, isoleucine, leucine, tryptophan, lysine, methionine, phenylalanine, threonine, and valine, are required in the human diet. Rose used University of Illinois graduate students for many other studies, and "they were grateful in those days for the free rations, the dollar a day they were paid and the prospect of getting their initials in print in Rose's widely read publications" (3).

As an authority on protein nutrition, Rose was appointed to many panels and boards, including the Food and Nutrition Board of the National Research Council, and was instrumental in advising government agencies on dietary recommendations. He was a dedicated teacher and mentor who inspired many students to follow careers in biochemistry and received many honors for both his research and teaching. Rose served as President of the American Society of Biological Chemists from 1939 to 1941.

On his 90th birthday, former students, colleagues, and friends honored him by establishing the William C. Rose Lectureship in Biochemistry and Nutrition to recognize annually a biochemist who exemplifies Rose's dedication to research training and teaching. The award and lecture were originally given at the University of Illinois to enable Rose to attend. The William C. Rose Award in Biochemistry, as it was later named, is administered by the

American Society for Biochemistry and Molecular Biology. The award and lecture are presented each year at the national meeting of the Society.[1,2]

Robert D. Simoni, Robert L. Hill, and Martha Vaughan

REFERENCES

1. JBC Classics: Osborne, T. B., and Mendel, L. B. (1916) *J. Biol. Chem.* **25,** 1–12; (1917) *J. Biol. Chem.* **31,** 149–163 (http://www.jbc.org/cgi/content/full/277/18/e7)
2. Rose, W. C., and Cox, G. J. (1926) *J. Biol. Chem.* **68,** 217–223
3. Carter, H. E., and Coon, M. J. (1995) *Biographical Memoir for William Cumming Rose*, Vol. 68, pp. 253–271, National Academy of Sciences, Washington, D. C.
4. Coon, M. J. (2002) JBC Reflection: Enzyme ingenuity in biological oxidations: a trail leading to cytochrome P-450. *J. Biol. Chem.* **277,** 28351–28363

---

[1] Virtually all of the biographical information was taken from Ref. 3.

[2] We thank Minor J. Coon, Emeritus Professor of Biological Chemistry at the University of Michigan, for reading this Introduction to the Rose Classic papers and helpful comments. Professor Coon was a student with Rose. Additional information about Rose can be found in the JBC Reflection by Professor Coon (4).

THE JOURNAL OF BIOLOGICAL CHEMISTRY
© 2002 by The American Society for Biochemistry and Molecular Biology, Inc.

Vol. 277, No. 38, Issue of September 20, p. e26, 2002
Printed in U.S.A.

Classics

A PAPER IN A SERIES REPRINTED TO CELEBRATE THE CENTENARY OF THE JBC IN 2005

JBC Centennial
1905–2005
100 Years of Biochemistry and Molecular Biology

Alkaloid Chemistry: the Work of Walter A. Jacobs

The Ergot Alkaloids. II. The Degradation of Ergotinine with Alkali. Lysergic Acid (Jacobs, W. A., and Craig, L. C. (1934) *J. Biol. Chem.* 104, 547–551)

Walter Abraham Jacobs (1883–1967) was born in New York City and after a public school education, attended Columbia University from which he received both A. B. (1904) and A. M. (1905) degrees in chemistry. He enrolled in the University of Berlin and received the Ph.D. degree in 1907 for work done with Emil Fischer. He returned to New York and a position as a fellow in chemistry with Phoebus A. Levene, the author of a previous *Journal of Biological Chemistry* (JBC) Classic (1), at the newly founded Rockefeller Institute for Medical Research, later Rockefeller University. Levene was a preeminent natural product chemist, and Jacobs worked with him for several years particularly on the chemistry of nucleic acids (2). In 1912, Jacobs was promoted to Associate Member of the Institute and given independent status. The Institute Director, Simon B. Flexner, felt that chemotherapy deserved a division of its own, and Jacobs was made the head.

He was joined by Michael Heidelberger, author of another JBC Classic (3), in a remarkably productive collaboration. Their first project, the synthesis of drugs to treat poliomyelitis, failed. When they turned their attention to drugs to treat African sleeping sickness, trypanosomiasis, however, the effort was successful. With the synthesis of Tryparsimide, para-phenylglycine amide arsonate, they created a drug for the disease, more effective than anything then available. Their work was widely recognized, and some years later, in 1953, Jacobs and Heidelberger and their collaborators were made Officers of the Order of Leopold II by the Belgian government. The Jacobs-Heidelberger team later worked on other problems including attempts to synthesize anti-pneumococcal and -streptococcal drugs albeit with only modest sucesss. After nine years with Jacobs, Heidelberger went to work with Donald D. Van Slyke at the Rockefeller, also the author of a JBC Classic (4), to learn biochemistry. Heidelberger began his independent career at Columbia University where he became a pioneer and later legendary immunochemist (3). Jacobs was appointed a Full Member at the Rockefeller Institute and began to investigate the structures of physiologically active natural products, especially alkaloids.

He first explored the structures of several cardiac glycosides from digitalis and strophanthidin and ultimately determined many complex structures. In 1932, Jacobs began a period of intense study of the ergot alkaloids with Lyman C. Craig, the author of a future JBC Classic and co-author of the JBC Classic reprinted here. (Jacobs and Craig published more than 50 papers together during the period of a decade.) Ergot is the product of a fungus that grows on rye plants. Its effects on pregnancy have been known for more than 2000 years, and it was used by physicians to induce abortion 400 years ago. In addition, the consumption of contaminated grain had resulted in many epidemics the cause of which was not recognized until 1670 (2). The chemistry of the ergot alkaloids was very poorly understood in 1932 when Jacobs and Craig started their work. By 1934, as reported in this JBC Classic, they had identified lysergic acid in an alkali digest of ergotinine. Subsequently they demonstrated that lysergic acid is the structural core of the ergot alkaloids. LSD, the diethyl amide of lysergic acid, was synthesized a few years later by other workers (2). Jacobs continued to investigate alkaloid structures, among them the aconite alkaloids, which include some of the most poisonous substances known such as the toxic heteratisine, hetisine, and benzoylheteratisine from monkshood (2).

Walter A. Jacobs. Photo courtesy of the National Library of Medicine.

The last alkaloids that he studied were the complex group of veratrum alkaloids also known as the steroid bases.

Jacobs was a very distinguished chemist and a highly respected member of the Rockefeller Institute for more than 50 years. He received many honors including election to the National Academy of Sciences in 1932. He was granted emeritus status in 1949 and retired in 1957.

Robert D. Simoni, Robert L. Hill, and Martha Vaughan

REFERENCES

1. JBC Classics: Levene, P. A. (1919) *J. Biol. Chem.* **40,** 415–424 (http://www.jbc.org/cgi/content/full/277/22/e11)
2. Elderfield, R. C. (1980) *Biographical Memoir for Walter Abraham Jacobs*, Vol. 51, pp. 247–278, National Academy of Sciences, Washington, D. C.
3. JBC Classics: Heidelberger, M., and Goebel, W. F. (1926) *J. Biol. Chem.* **70,** 613–624 (http://www.jbc.org/cgi/content/full/277/36/e24)
4. JBC Classics: Van Slyke, D. D., and Neill, J. M. (1924) *J. Biol. Chem.* **61,** 523–543 (http://www.jbc.org/cgi/content/full/277/27/e16)

THE JOURNAL OF BIOLOGICAL CHEMISTRY
© 2002 by The American Society for Biochemistry and Molecular Biology, Inc.

Vol. 277, No. 39, Issue of September 27, p. e27, 2002
Printed in U.S.A.

Classics

A PAPER IN A SERIES REPRINTED TO CELEBRATE THE CENTENARY OF THE JBC IN 2005

JBC Centennial
1905–2005
100 Years of Biochemistry and Molecular Biology

The Discovery of Hyaluronan by Karl Meyer

The Polysaccharide of the Vitreous Humor
(Meyer, K., and Palmer, J. W. (1934) *J. Biol. Chem.* 107, 629–634)

Karl Meyer (1899–1990) was born in the village of Karpen, Germany, near Cologne. In 1917, he was drafted into the German army and served in the last year of World War I. After the war, he entered medical school at the University of Cologne and received the M.D. degree in 1924. He then went to Berlin for a year of study in medical chemistry and met several promising young biochemists including Fritz Lippman, Hans Krebs, and Ernst Chain. To gain more training in chemistry, he enrolled as a graduate student with Otto Meyerhof. For his Ph.D. thesis work, he investigated lactic acid formation in yeast and muscle demonstrating the requirement for a "co-enzyme" later identified as ADP. His research career was launched. After three years as a Rockefeller Fellow in Zurich studying heme-catalyzed oxidation of unsaturated compounds with Professor Kuhn, he was offered a position as Assistant Professor at the University of California at Berkeley with Herbert Evans.

In 1932, while at Berkeley, he attended a conference in Europe. During the conference, he received notice that Evans had terminated his position with the suggestion that he stay in Germany. He decided, no doubt in part because of the rising anti-Semitism in Europe and the increasing probability of war, to go back to the United States. His return was facilitated by Hans T. Clarke at Columbia University who provided interim fellowship support until 1933 when he received a position as Assistant Professor in the Department of Ophthalmology at the College of Physicians and Surgeons. In part because of the mission of his department, Meyer began to study the lysozyme present in tears and undertook to identify a physiological substrate for the enzyme. Examination of the viscous vitreous humor of the eye as a plausible source of substrate quickly led to the discovery of hyaluronan, which is reported in this *Journal of Biological Chemistry* (JBC) Classic.

Meyer and his assistant John Palmer isolated a novel, high molecular weight polysaccharide and reported that it was composed of "a uronic acid, an amino sugar, and possibly a pentose." (The last is incorrect.) They proposed "for convenience, the name hyaluronic acid, from hyaloid (vitreous) + uronic acid." Nearly 25 years of work were required to establish the structure of the repeating disaccharide that is the basic unit of the hyaluranan polymer, namely glucuronate-β-1,3-N-acetylglucosamine-β1,4-.

Hyaluronan is one member of a family of glycosaminoglycans that includes chondroitin/dermatan sulfate, keratan sulfate, and heparin/heparan sulfate, each with a characteristic disaccharide-repeat structure of an amino sugar, either glucosamine or galactosamine, plus a negatively charged sugar, a carboxylate and/or a sulfate. The polymers are found as cell surface molecules and in the extracellular matrix. Glycosaminoglycans, with the exception of hyaluronan, are covalently bound to proteins to form proteoglycans. These ubiquitous and structurally diverse macromolecules are found as cell surface molecules and in the extracellular matrix. The multiplicity of their functions that is now recognized was not always appreciated. In a symposium at the 1958 annual meeting of the American Society of Biological Chemists entitled "Acid Mucopolysaccharides of Animal Origin," which was chaired by Meyer, he states in an opening remark, "It is my opinion that the mucopolysaccharides will never be a highly popular field in biochemistry, but they will probably not be relegated again to the insignificance and disregard in which they were held not so long ago."

Karl Meyer. Photo courtesy of the National Library of Medicine.

Meyer's scientific contributions were not limited to the discovery of hyaluronan. He is considered the father of glycosaminoglycan chemistry and received many honors including election to the National Academy of Sciences in 1967. On the occasion of his induction he commented as follows: "Looking back on my scientific career, I have often wondered whether it was worthwhile to stick so tenaciously to a technically difficult and conceptually apparently unexciting field, while my colleagues and friends shifted over to more fashionable and rewarding areas. The reasons for my persistence are manifold, among them a distaste for jumping in on ground broken by others. Besides, I felt committed to problems such as the biological functions of the mucopolysaccharides of connective tissues to their role in differentiation, in cell membranes and in inherited diseases."

His persistence was biochemistry's gain.[1]

Robert D. Simoni, Robert L. Hill, Martha Vaughan, and Vincent Hascall

REFERENCES

1. McDonald, J., and Hascall, V. C. (2002) *J. Biol. Chem.* **277**, 4575–4579

---

[1] A recent overview of glycosaminoglycan biochemistry and additional information about Karl Meyer are included in the JBC Hyaluronan Minireview Series edited by John McDonald and Vincent Hascall (1).

THE JOURNAL OF BIOLOGICAL CHEMISTRY
© 2002 by The American Society for Biochemistry and Molecular Biology, Inc.

Vol. 277, No. 40, Issue of October 4, p. e28, 2002
Printed in U.S.A.

Classics

A PAPER IN A SERIES REPRINTED TO CELEBRATE THE CENTENARY OF THE JBC IN 2005

JBC Centennial
1905–2005
100 Years of Biochemistry and Molecular Biology

The Use of Chromatography in Biochemistry

Carotene. VIII. Separation of Carotenes by Adsorption
(Strain, H. H. (1934) *J. Biol. Chem.* 105, 523–535)

Harold H. Strain received his Ph.D. from Stanford University and worked most of his career at the Carnegie Institution of Washington, Plant Biology Division, located on the Stanford campus. He was hired as an organic chemist specifically to aid in the characterization of pigments from photosynthetic organisms. In the course of this work, he developed a procedure for the separation, isolation, and characterization of carotenes by adsorption chromatography. Adsorption chromatography was first described in 1906 by the Russian botanist Michael Tswett (1) who successfully fractionated petroleum ether extracts of chlorophyll and other plant pigments on narrow glass columns packed with dry calcium carbonate. Many of the leading chemists at the time did not value Tswett's chromatographic method and made little use of it. However, several chemists gradually appreciated its value, and by the 1930s adsorption chromatography was widely used. Strain's *Journal of Biological Chemistry* (JBC) Classic is an excellent example of how organic chemists applied the principles of adsorption chromatography first enunciated by Tswett for the separation of complex mixtures. The power of adsorption chromatography must have been recognized by those who subsequently went on to develop different kinds of chromatographic methods that depend on other principles for separation including partition chromatography, ion exchange chromatography, gas chromatography, and gel filtration. These methods provided the tools needed by biochemists in the last half of the twentieth century to separate and characterize the complex mixtures of compounds in living things that were present in very small amounts, had very similar properties, were often extremely labile, and were not amenable to separation by the conventional methods of the organic chemist.

In this JBC Classic, Strain explores the use of various adsorbents for the purification of individual carotenes from mixtures. There was motivation for a new approach because many of the traditional chemical methods for carotene purification altered them irreversibly, calling into question the structures of the natural material. Strain tested various adsorbents including metallic oxides, charcoal, and fuller's earth. After preliminary testing, he concluded that magnesium oxide had the most desirable properties for separation of α- and β-carotenes and that the adsorbent did not chemically alter the carotenes being separated. The experimental description is as useful today as it was in 1934. He reports that using a glass column to hold the adsorbent was more effective than batch adsorption. He describes packing the columns and the use of siliceous earth mixed with the adsorbent to increase the flow rate. He also describes differential elution with solvents of different polarity. Ultimately, he proves that the carotenes purified by these methods were pure and unaltered by the purification technique.[1]

Robert D. Simoni, Robert L. Hill, and Martha Vaughan

REFERENCES

1. Tswett, M. S. (1906) Physikalisch-chemische studien uber das chlorophyll. Die adsorptionen. *Ber. Bot. Ges.* **24,** 316–332

[1] We thank Dr. Arthur Grossman, Carnegie Institute for Plant Biology at Stanford University, where Strain did his work, and Pat Craig for providing biographical information and correspondence that she has collected about Strain for a history of the Carnegie Institution that she has written.

THE JOURNAL OF BIOLOGICAL CHEMISTRY
© 2002 by The American Society for Biochemistry and Molecular Biology, Inc.

Vol. 277, No. 41, Issue of October 11, p. e29, 2002
Printed in U.S.A.

Classics

A PAPER IN A SERIES REPRINTED TO CELEBRATE THE CENTENARY OF THE JBC IN 2005

JBC Centennial
1905–2005
100 Years of Biochemistry and Molecular Biology

The Synthesis and Structure of Threonine: Herbert E. Carter

Synthesis of α-Amino-β-hydroxy-*n*-butyric Acids
(Carter, H. E. (1935) *J. Biol. Chem.* 112, 769–773)

As reported in a previous *Journal of Biological Chemistry* (JBC) Classic (1), William C. Rose and his colleagues at the University of Illinois discovered the amino acid threonine as the twentieth of the amino acids that are universal components of proteins. As also reported by Rose (1), they did not determine which isomer of threonine is the naturally occurring amino acid. Considering that threonine, α-amino-β-hydroxy-*n*-butyric acid, has two asymmetric carbons and thus four possible optical isomers, it was possible that one or more isomers might have satisfied the dietary requirement for threonine in the rats that Rose used as an assay.

Herbert E. Carter, the author of this JBC Classic, was born in 1910. He received the A.B. degree from DePauw University in 1930 and M.S. and Ph.D. degrees in organic chemistry from the University of Illinois in 1931 and 1934, respectively. Although working for his Ph.D. with Professor C. S. Marvel in the chemistry department, Carter was prevailed upon by Rose to define the structure of the naturally occurring threonine that he had isolated. In 1934, Carter was appointed Assistant Professor of Biochemistry, a division within the chemistry department that Rose chaired, and was assigned to identify the isomeric form of this newest constituent of proteins. The results of Carter's first research project after his Ph.D. thesis work are reported in this JBC Classic, the first of a series of seven papers that ultimately demonstrate the structure of threonine as it occurs in nature. The experimental plan was to synthesize relevant model molecules and to determine and/or deduce the isomeric structures that had been produced. The mixtures of synthetic products were tested in the rat nutrition assay to determine whether or not they could replace the natural, isolated amino acid. Using the method of Abderhalden and Heyns (2), Carter prepared α-amino-β-hydroxy-*n*-butyric acid and found that it did not support the growth of rats. Reasoning that this method yielded only one possible isomer, he converted the inactive form into the two possible epimers that did support growth. This work by Carter and his co-workers exemplifies an important general approach to the elucidation of structures of naturally occurring compounds that was widely used, *i.e.* the synthesis and evaluation of biological functions of candidate molecules.

Following his appointment as Assistant Professor of Biochemistry in 1934, Carter had a long and distinguished career at the University of Illinois in Urbana. He rose through the academic ranks to Professor by 1945 and was Head of the Department of Chemistry and Chemical Engineering from 1954 to 1967. He also served as Vice Chancellor for Academic Affairs. In 1971, he moved to the University of Arizona as Coordinator of Interdisciplinary Programs where he continues to be active. Carter has made many important contributions, particularly in antibiotic chemistry and the biochemistry of complex lipids. In the latter area, he determined the structure of sphingosine and cerebrosides and identified novel lipids in plants including phytosphingosine, phytoglycolipids, and galactosylglycerides.

Carter received many honors for his research, including election to the National Academy of Sciences in 1953. He was a member, and then chairman, of the National Science Board, and in recognition of his chairmanship, a mountain ridge in Antarctica, "Carter Ridge," has been

64

Herbert E. Carter

named. He served also as Chairman of the President's Committee on the National Medal of Science. He is a past President of the American Society of Biological Chemists.[1]

Robert D. Simoni, Robert L. Hill, and Martha Vaughan

REFERENCES

1. JBC Classics: Rose, W. C. (1931) *J. Biol. Chem.* **94,** 155–165; McCoy, R. H., Meyer, C. E., and Rose, W. C. (1935) *J. Biol. Chem.* **112,** 283–302 (http://www.jbc.org/cgi/content/full/277/37/e25)
2. Abderhalden, E., and Heyns, K. (1934) *Ber. Chem. Ges.* **67,** 530

[1] We thank Professor Carter for providing biographical information for this introduction to his Classic paper.

THE JOURNAL OF BIOLOGICAL CHEMISTRY
© 2002 by The American Society for Biochemistry and Molecular Biology, Inc.

Vol. 277, No. 42, Issue of October 18, p. e30, 2002
Printed in U.S.A.

Classics

A PAPER IN A SERIES REPRINTED TO CELEBRATE THE CENTENARY OF THE JBC IN 2005

JBC Centennial
1905–2005
100 Years of Biochemistry and Molecular Biology

Purification of Progestin(s): Oskar Wintersteiner

Crystalline Progestin
(Wintersteiner, O., and Allen, W. M. (1934) *J. Biol. Chem.* **107, 321–336)**

Oskar Paul Wintersteiner (1898–1971) was born in Bruck, Austria. He received his Ph.D. degree from the University of Graz in microchemistry working with Pregl. He continued at the University of Graz as an assistant instructor until 1926 when he moved to Johns Hopkins University to work with John J. Abel, the author of a previous *Journal of Biological Chemistry* (JBC) Classic (1). At the time, Abel was trying to find the active principle in crystalline preparations of insulin thinking that it could be some low molecular weight organic compound. In spite of considerable effort, Wintersteiner and his laboratory colleague, Vincent Du Vigneaud, the author of a future JBC Classic, demonstrated that the hormonally active insulin preparations contained nothing but amino acids.

After his postdoctoral training with Abel, Wintersteiner spent a year working with P. A. Levene, also the author of a previous JBC Classic (2), at the Rockefeller Institute and in 1929 was appointed Assistant Professor of Chemistry at Columbia University. By 1940, he had achieved the rank of Associate Professor, and in 1941 he moved to Squibb Institute for Medical Research where he spent the years during World War II working on various projects related to national needs and the war effort. He purified penicillin and through microanalysis was the first to show that it contained sulfur.

The JBC Classic reprinted here demonstrates a classic approach to the isolation and characterization of important natural products that was standard prior to the general use of chromatography. As described in the introduction, there had been several reports of the isolation of progestin but no evidence that the preparations were pure. Wintersteiner and his collaborator Allen, an academic obstetrician/gynecologist at the University of Rochester, fractionated extracts prepared from rabbit corpus luteum and eventually succeeded in

Oskar Wintersteiner. Photo courtesy of the National Library of Medicine.

separating several compounds by fractional crystallization. The major component, compound A, had no hormonal activity as measured by the capacity to induce endometrial proliferation when injected into castrated rabbits. The remaining material was further fractionated to yield two different crystalline products, Compounds B and C, both of which had hormonal activity. Characterization of Compound B indicated that it was what now is known as progesterone. Compound C was either a different progestin or an alternative crystal form of progesterone. It was not realized at the time that progestin is a mixture of hormones among which progesterone constitutes the largest fraction.

Wintersteiner received widespread recognition for his work, particularly on the isolation and synthesis of adrenocorticosteroids, and was elected to the National Academy of Sciences in 1950.[1]

Robert D. Simoni, Robert L. Hill, and Martha Vaughan

REFERENCES

1. JBC Classics: Abel, J. J., and Taveau, R. DeM. (1905) *J. Biol. Chem.* **1,** 1–32 (http://www.jbc.org/cgi/content/full/277/12/e1)
2. JBC Classics: Levene, P. A. (1919) *J. Biol. Chem.* **40,** 415–424 (http://www.jbc.org/cgi/content/full/277/22/e11)

---

[1] We thank Emil L. Smith, Emeritus Professor of Biological Chemistry at the University of California at Los Angeles for providing the biographical information about Wintersteiner for this JBC Classic Introduction.

THE JOURNAL OF BIOLOGICAL CHEMISTRY
© 2002 by The American Society for Biochemistry and Molecular Biology, Inc.

Vol. 277, No. 43, Issue of October 25, p. e31, 2002
Printed in U.S.A.

Classics

A PAPER IN A SERIES REPRINTED TO CELEBRATE THE CENTENARY OF THE JBC IN 2005

JBC Centennial
1905–2005
100 Years of Biochemistry and Molecular Biology

The Use of Isotope Tracers to Study Intermediary Metabolism: Rudolf Schoenheimer

Deuterium as an Indicator in the Study of Intermediary Metabolism. I.
(Schoenheimer, R., and Rittenberg, D. (1935) *J. Biol. Chem.* **111, 163–168)**

Deuterium as an Indicator in the Study of Intermediary Metabolism. XI. Further Studies on the Biological Uptake of Deuterium into Organic Substances, with Special Reference to Fat and Cholesterol Formation
(Rittenberg, D., and Schoenheimer, R. (1937) *J. Biol. Chem.* **121, 235–253)**

Rudolf Schoenheimer (1898–1941) pioneered the use of isotopes for the study of metabolism and transformed biochemistry. He was born and educated in Berlin, receiving his M.D. degree in 1922. He worked with Karl Thomas in Leipzig for three years to extend his education and experiences with synthetic chemistry of biological molecules. In 1926, he moved to the University of Freiburg to work with Ludwig Aschoff to study the role of dietary cholesterol in the development of atherosclerosis in rabbits. This experience shaped his research interests for the rest of his career. By 1933, the racial policies of the Nazi government in Germany forced Schoenheimer, and many other European Jews, to leave Europe. Hans T. Clarke, Chairman of the Department of Biological Chemistry at Columbia University, provided Schoenheimer a faculty position with salary and research support from the Josiah Macy Foundation. It is remarkable that, in addition to Schoenheimer and Karl Meyer, the author of a previous *Journal of Biological Chemistry* (JBC) Classic (1), many other European biochemists including Erwin Chargaff, Zacharias Dische, Heinrich Waelsch, and Erwin Brand also benefited from positions and research support provided by Clarke. He not only offered sanctuary to these talented refugees but also created one of the premier biochemistry departments in the country (2, 3). As Eugene Kennedy rightly reminded us (3) in describing Clarke's account of the recruitment of these scientists to Columbia, "Clarke modestly omitted to mention that his own vision and humane instincts in welcoming these gifted refugees were by no means to be found in every American academic institution."

In 1932, the year before Schoenheimer's arrival at Columbia, Harold Urey, who was working in the chemistry department at Columbia, discovered deuterium, a heavy isotope of hydrogen. Urey was awarded the 1934 Nobel Prize in Chemistry for this notable achievement. The successful preparation of D_2O, "heavy water," began immediately in Urey's laboratory as well as in many others. With Urey's interest and assistance, David Rittenberg, the recent recipient of a Ph.D. in Physical Chemistry in Urey's department, was recruited to work with Schoenheimer to explore the biological applications of the deuterium isotope (2, 3). According to Clarke, Rittenberg's arrival in Schoenheimer's laboratory led to the "idea of employing a stable isotope as a label in organic compounds, destined for experiments in intermediary metabolism, which should be biochemically indistinguishable from their natural analogs" (2). The concept of "tagged" molecules had been applied earlier when metabolically inert phenyl groups were attached to long chain fatty acids to permit identification of the products of fatty acid metabolism in animals. One example of this approach is described by H. D. Dakin in an earlier JBC Classic (4). Schoenheimer points out in the first paper selected as a Classic that the physical properties of phenyl derivatives are so different for the natural molecules that the results are suspect.

It was difficult to select the JBC Classic papers to be representative of Schoenheimer's work because so many qualify. Of the two that were chosen, the first introduces the rationale and methodology for the use of deuterium to study metabolism. The second applies that approach to the study of cholesterol metabolism, a problem Schoenheimer had first considered while in Freiburg in 1926. In the introduction of the first Classic, Schoenheimer and Rittenberg summarize nicely the technical obstacles that had limited the study and understanding of metabolism. "If substances such as natural fatty acids, amino acids etc. are administered to animals, we lose track of them the moment they enter the body, since they are mixed with the same substances already present. Furthermore, if a substance A is given to an animal and a substance B is afterwards discovered in the body or in the excretions, we can never be sure that the substance A has been converted into B . . . " Clearly, the administration of specific deuterium-tagged molecules overcame these obstacles. For studies reported in the second JBC Classic reprinted here, rather than administer a specific deuterium-tagged molecule and follow its fate in the body, Rittenberg and Schoenheimer used a more sophisticated design. They administered D_2O to animals and measured the rate of incorporation of deuterium into fatty acids and cholesterol. These experiments are meticulous in their reasoning, technique, and rationale. Their description is preceded by a careful consideration of the kinds of chemical reactions that would introduce a stable, non-exchangeable deuterium from D_2O into organic molecules by the body. Both paradigms, administration of specifically tagged molecules to determine their fate and administration of precursors such as D_2O to determine rates of synthesis, continue to be the design for metabolic studies. Many studies followed from these initial efforts. Urey succeeded in accomplishing the enrichment of nitrogen for ^{15}N, which provided a "tag" for amino acids and the study of protein synthesis. Schoenheimer, Ratner, and Rittenberg reported that after the administration of ^{15}N-labeled tyrosine to rats, only about half of the ^{15}N was excreted, and the rest was retained in the body proteins (5). This finding was a blow to the prevalent notion that ingested foods were metabolized and the products were excreted. The conclusions of this and subsequent experiments made clear that body constituents were not stable or static but in a dynamic state of turnover. Schoenheimer was invited to present his important studies in the prestigious Edward K. Dunham Lecture at Harvard University entitled "The Dynamic State of Body Constituents." His lecture notes were edited by Hans Clarke, David Rittenberg, and Sarah Ratner and published posthumously in 1942 (6). They had an immeasurable influence on a generation of biochemists.

In the course of establishing his research program, Schoenheimer attracted an interdisciplinary group of notable scientists including physicists, chemists, and biologists. He provided outstanding leadership during a short life troubled by bouts of depression, leading to suicide at the age of 43, at the height of his career (3). His young colleagues were encouraged by Hans Clarke to continue their work (3). David Rittenberg continued to study protein synthesis and, with Konrad Bloch, fat metabolism, particularly cholesterol. David Shemin continued to study amino acid metabolism and later described the pathway for heme biosynthesis (7). Sarah Ratner continued to work on the metabolism of nitrogen-containing compounds. DeWitt Stetten Jr. studied fatty acid metabolism. All would have distinguished careers in biochemistry. Two of Schoenheimer's young colleagues later received Nobel Prizes, Konrad Bloch for the elucidation of the biosynthetic pathway for cholesterol and Rosalyn Yalow for development of the radioimmunoassay with Solomon Berson. Yalow had been interested in science from an early age but the barriers to careers for women in science had caused her to take a position as part-time secretary to Schoenheimer, which provided "back door" access to graduate courses as long as she also took stenography (8).[1]

Although radioactive isotopes were beginning to replace stable isotopes by the early 1940s, the paradigm established by Schoenheimer for the use of isotopes for metabolic studies is as important today as it was in 1935.

Robert D. Simoni, Robert L. Hill, and Martha Vaughan

REFERENCES

1. JBC Classics: Meyer, K., and Palmer, J. W. (1934) *J. Biol. Chem.* **107,** 629–634 (http://www.jbc.org/cgi/content/full/277/39/e27)

---

[1] Much of the biographical material about Schoenheimer was taken from Ref. 3, which provides a wonderfully rich account of the careers of Fritz Lippman, Konrad Bloch, and Rudolf Schoenheimer as they fled Nazi Europe to start careers in the United States.

2. Clarke, H. T. (1958) *Annu. Rev. Biochem.* **27,** 1–14
3. Kennedy, E. P. (2001) JBC Reflections: Hitler's gift and the era of biosynthesis. *J. Biol. Chem.* **276,** 42619–42631
4. JBC Classics: Dakin, H. D. (1908) *J. Biol. Chem.* **4,** 419–435 (http://www.jbc.org/cgi/content/full/277/15/e4)
5. Schoenheimer, R., Ratner, S., and Rittenberg, D. (1939) *J. Biol. Chem.* **127,** 333–344
6. Schoenheimer, R. (1942) *The Dynamic State of Body Constituents*, Harvard University Press, Cambridge, MA
7. Bloch, K. (1987) *Annu. Rev. Biochem.* **56,** 1–19
8. Yalow, R. (1977) *Autobiography for the Nobel Foundation* (www.nobel.se/medicine/laureates/1977/yalow-auto-bio.html)

THE JOURNAL OF BIOLOGICAL CHEMISTRY
© 2002 by The American Society for Biochemistry and Molecular Biology, Inc.

Vol. 277, No. 44, Issue of November 1, p. e32, 2002
Printed in U.S.A.

Classics

A PAPER IN A SERIES REPRINTED TO CELEBRATE THE CENTENARY OF THE JBC IN 2005

JBC Centennial
1905–2005
100 Years of Biochemistry and Molecular Biology

Viral Proteins by X-ray Diffraction: Ralph Wyckoff and Robert Corey

X-ray Diffraction Patterns of Crystalline Tobacco Mosaic Proteins
(Wyckoff, R. W. G., and Corey, R. B. (1936) *J. Biol. Chem.* 116, 51–55)

The *Journal of Biological Chemistry* (JBC) Classic paper reprinted here represents one of the first published in the Journal on the use of x-ray diffraction to study protein structure. The paper is interesting albeit predicated on the misconception that tobacco mosaic virus is a pure protein and nothing else. Such a misconception no doubt resulted from and contributed to the prevailing view of the time that genes were proteins.

Ralph W. G. Wyckoff (1897–1994) received his B.S. degree in chemistry from Hobart College in his hometown of Geneva, New York. He entered Cornell University in Ithaca to study astronomy but became interested in x-ray crystallography thanks to S. Nishikawa who was on leave in the physics department. With Nishikawa as his thesis advisor, Wyckoff determined the structures $NaNO_3$ and $CsICl_2$. He received the Ph.D. degree in 1919 at the age of 21. After completing his thesis work, Wyckoff worked at the Geophysical Laboratory in Washington D. C. continuing to apply x-ray analysis to the study of minerals. His approach, like that of Nishikawa, was to collect x-ray diffraction data from multiwavelength Laue patterns and powder patterns. This analysis relied on space group theory and not on diffraction intensities in marked contrast to the British crystallographers who, using monochromatic radiation, regarded quantitative intensity measurements as essential. These issues were controversial until the study of more complicated structures like proteins required knowledge of both space groups and quantitative intensities. Wyckoff published several books including the *The Structure of Crystals* in 1924, a compilation of structural data available at the time. This book was last updated in 1971 (1).

Wyckoff moved to the Rockefeller Institute for Medical Research in 1927 with the intention of applying x-ray analysis to organic molecules. He completed the structure of urea and had started on the amino acid glycine with the intention of studying proteins. Robert B. Corey joined Wyckoff in this work, and the two worked together for 10 years, publishing 18 papers. Unfortunately, the Rockefeller Institute lost interest in x-ray crystallography. In 1937 Wyckoff's laboratory was closed, and he was dismissed. During the next 15 years he held several positions including those in industrial laboratories, the University of Michigan, and the National Institutes of Health. He became an electron microscopist and continued his study of proteins and viruses. He was involved also in the founding of the International Union of Crystallographers serving as Vice President and President from 1951 to 1957. He completed his scientific career at the University of Arizona as Professor of Physics and Microbiology, from which he retired at the age of 80.

Robert B. Corey (1897–1971) received his B.S. degree in Chemistry from the University of Pittsburgh in 1919. About that time, he contracted polio, which left him with a paralyzed left arm, a limp, and a "frail constitution" (2). He attended Cornell University and received the Ph.D. degree in inorganic chemistry in 1924. After completing his thesis research, Corey stayed at Cornell as Instructor of Analytical Chemistry and became fascinated with one of the first GE x-ray spectrometers, which Ralph Wyckoff had used a few years earlier. Corey decided to join Wyckoff at the Rockefeller Institute, and the two began a systematic analysis of C–C and C–N bonds as prelude to the study of proteins.

Ralph W. G. Wyckoff photographed by Vernon E. Taylor, National Institutes of Health, courtesy of AIP Emilio Segrè Visual Archives.

Robert B. Corey. Photo courtesy of the Archives, California Institute of Technology.

When Wyckoff was dismissed by the Rockefeller Institute, Corey was given a one-year fellowship "to be used in any institution where I could profitably continue my crystal structure studies" (2). Corey wrote to Linus Pauling at the California Institute of Technology who was becoming interested in the structure of biological macromolecules. Pauling replied to Corey's letter, "I would be very glad indeed to have you spend the year in Pasadena" offering an appointment as a research fellow without stipend. Pauling added "so far as I can tell, there would be no possibility for you to be added to the staff at the end of the year." Pauling may have been as interested in Corey's equipment as he was in Corey and wrote "Apparatus which we do not have and which you might well need for your work would include a Weissenberg camera, a simple spectrometer for rapid measurement of intensities, a special apparatus for taking powder photographs etc." (2). (Apparently the Weissenberg camera was used at Caltech for over 40 years after Corey's arrival (2).) In spite of Pauling's caveat about future employment, Corey had, by 1949, risen through the ranks to become Professor of Structural Chemistry at Caltech. He and Pauling collaborated until 1964, when Pauling left Caltech. Corey became professor emeritus in 1968 and died in 1971.

Corey's work at Caltech began with determining the structures of three small molecules, glycine, alanine, and diketopiperazine (the cyclic anhydride of the dipeptide glycylglycine). These three molecules were among the first organic molecules to have their structures determined. Glycine and alanine were the first amino acids and diketopiperazine the first peptide. The measurements, and especially the calculations of diffraction intensities, for these studies, about 300 for alanine, were a prodigious undertaking considering that the computing aids were a slide rule and an adding machine. From the analysis of diketopiperazine came the critically important data demonstrating that the peptide bond is planar.

During World War II, Pauling was asked to lead a project to evaluate the stability and explosive characteristics of various forms of gunpowder. Pauling put Corey in charge of administration of the projects and dealing with the bureaucracy of the War Department. Only after the war was Corey able to return to research.

By the late 1940s, Pauling had developed the notion that polypeptide chains in proteins, particularly fibrous proteins like those in hair, muscle, and tendons, which gave good diffraction patterns suggesting extended chains, might form helical structures. With the experimental work as background, Corey and Pauling constructed helical models and demonstrated that one, the α-helix, was compatible with the diffraction data. In addition, they were able to demonstrate the existence of both parallel and anti-parallel β-sheet structures. This work was published in a set of papers in the *Proceedings of the National Academy of Sciences* (3–5) and was a landmark of the beginning of molecular biology!

Corey's work relied on model building and required that atomic models be constructed in the Caltech shop to precise dimensions of bond angles and distances and atomic radii. Eventually, these evolved into accurate space-filling models that were relied upon by a generation of chemists and biologists. These CPK models were named for Corey, Pauling, and Walter Koltun, who oversaw their construction.

In the final years of his career, Corey worked on the structure of lysozyme and had collected a great deal of data from various crystal forms with heavy atom replacements when the structure was published by D. C. Philips (6). This was an enormous disappointment to Corey and signaled the end of his research career. He retired in poor health in 1968 and died in 1971 (2).

Robert D. Simoni, Robert L. Hill, and Martha Vaughan

REFERENCES

1. Drenth, J. (1995) *Obituary of Ralph W. G. Wyckoff (1897–1994). Acta Crystallogr.* **51,** 649–650
2. Marsh, R. E. (1997) *Biographical Memoir of Robert Brainard Corey.* Vol. 72, p. 51, National Academy of Sciences, Washington D. C.
3. Corey, R. B., Branson, H. R., and Pauling, L. (1951) The structure of proteins: two hydrogen-bonded helical configurations of the polypeptide chain. *Proc. Natl. Acad. Sci. U. S. A.* **37,** 205–211
4. Corey, R. B., and Pauling, L. (1951) The pleated sheet, a new layer configuration of polypeptide chains. *Proc. Natl. Acad. Sci. U. S. A.* **37,** 251–256
5. Corey, R. B., and Pauling, L. (1951) Configurations of polypeptide chains favored orientation around single bonds: two new pleated sheets. *Proc. Natl. Acad. Sci. U. S. A.* **37,** 729–740
6. Philips, D. C. (1967) The hen egg-white lysozyme molecule. *Proc. Natl. Acad. Sci. U. S. A.* **57,** 484–495

THE JOURNAL OF BIOLOGICAL CHEMISTRY

Vol. 277, No. 45, Issue of November 8, p. e33, 2002
Printed in U.S.A.

Classics

A PAPER IN A SERIES REPRINTED TO CELEBRATE THE CENTENARY OF THE JBC IN 2005

JBC Centennial
1905–2005
100 Years of Biochemistry and Molecular Biology

The Early Use of Artificial Radioactive Isotopes: Waldo E. Cohn

Studies in Mineral Metabolism with the Aid of Artificial Radioactive Isotopes. I. Absorption, Distribution, and Excretion of Phosphorus
(Cohn, W. E., and Greenberg, D. M. (1938) *J. Biol. Chem.* **123,** 185–198)

The employment of radioactive isotopes in biology probably began in 1923 at the University of Freiburg with the work of Georg Hevesy who was measuring the uptake and distribution of radioactive lead in plants (1). The application of isotopes in biochemistry became much more sophisticated with the landmark experiments of Rudolf Schoenheimer using deuterium to investigate fat and cholesterol formation as described in an earlier *Journal of Biological Chemistry* (JBC) Classic (2) and later ^{15}N to study protein synthesis. By the mid-1930s, the cyclotron had been invented and developed at the University of California at Berkeley by Ernest O. Lawrence (3, 4). With it the came the capability of creating artificial radioactive isotopes. One of the first radioactive isotopes produced was ^{32}P, which was immediately put to use in seeking solutions to biological problems.

Waldo E. Cohn was a graduate student at Berkeley when the work reported in this JBC Classic was performed. His collaborator and thesis advisor, David M. Greenberg, was Professor of Biochemistry at the University of California Medical School, then at Berkeley. Greenberg also edited of one of the first textbooks on proteins, *Amino Acids and Proteins*, published in 1951 (7). The book reviewed specific aspects of proteins, from purification, criteria for homogeneity, and metabolism to functional properties, such as proteins as hormones, proteins as antibodies, and structural proteins.

This Cohn and Greenberg work represents one of the early applications of radioactive isotopes in metabolic studies, several years before ^{14}C and ^{3}H were produced and available to biochemistry. The ^{32}P was prepared in the cyclotron of the Radiation Laboratory at Berkeley by bombardment of red phosphorus with deuterons. After purification and oxidation to H_3PO_4, the radioactive material was administered to rats, and the distribution of radioactivity in various tissues was followed with time. Although the results are not especially revealing, they do establish an approach to the estimation of uptake and distribution of minerals by different tissues.

Cohn's experiences with radioactive isotopes as a graduate student shaped his career. After receiving his Ph.D. degree in Biochemistry from Berkeley in 1938, Cohn went to Harvard where he spent four years as a postdoctoral fellow. In 1942, he was recruited to the Metallurgical Laboratory of the University of Chicago as a member of the Manhattan Project, which produced plutonium for the first atomic bomb (5). His role was to study the biological effects of fission products on biological systems. After one year, Cohn moved to the Oak Ridge National Laboratory where he came Senior Chemist and Group Leader of the Oak Ridge Biology Division, a position that he held until his retirement in 1975.

Cohn was involved in the formation of the Isotope Distribution Committee, which was assigned the responsibility of making isotopes available to qualified researchers. In 1946, Cohn and Paul Aebersold published a paper in *Science* that established the administration of isotope distribution and preparation of the catalog of isotopes that were available for research (6). It was one of the first post-war efforts toward the "peaceful use" of atomic energy. Cohn became well known for his efforts to establish and enforce standardized biochemical nomen-

This paper is available on line at http://www.jbc.org

Waldo Cohn. Photo courtesy of Oak Ridge National Laboratory.

clature. From 1965 to 1976, he was Director of the Office of Biochemical Nomenclature of the National Academy of Sciences (5).

Robert D. Simoni, Robert L. Hill, and Martha Vaughan

REFERENCES

1. Hevesy, G. (1923) *Biochem. J.* **17,** 439–445
2. JBC Classics: Schoenheimer, R., and Rittenberg, D. (1935) *J. Biol. Chem.* **111,** 163–168; Rittenberg, D., and Schoenheimer, R. (1937) *J. Biol. Chem.* **121,** 235–253 (http://www.jbc.org/cgi/content/full/277/43/e31)
3. Lawrence, E. O., and Livingston, M. S. (1932) *Physic. Rev.* **40,** 19
4. Lawrence, E. O., and Cooksey, D. (1936) *Physic. Rev.* **50,** 1131
5. Oral History of Biochemist Waldo E. Cohn. *Human Radiation Studies: Remembering the Early Years* (http://tis.eh.doe.gov/ohre/roadmap/histories/0464/0464toc.html)
6. Availability of Radioactive Isotopes (1946) *Science* **103,** 697–705
7. Greenberg, D. M., ed (1951) *Amino Acids and Proteins*, Charles C. Thomas, Springfield, IL

THE JOURNAL OF BIOLOGICAL CHEMISTRY
© 2002 by The American Society for Biochemistry and Molecular Biology, Inc.

Vol. 277, No. 46, Issue of November 15, p. e34, 2002
Printed in U.S.A.

Classics

A PAPER IN A SERIES REPRINTED TO CELEBRATE THE CENTENARY OF THE JBC IN 2005

JBC Centennial
1905–2005
100 Years of Biochemistry and Molecular Biology

Protein Chemistry and the Development of Allosterism: Jeffries Wyman

An Analysis of the Titration Data of Oxyhemoglobin of the Horse by a Thermal Method
(Wyman, J., Jr. (1939) *J. Biol. Chem.* **127**, 1–13)

Jeffries Wyman (1901–1995) was born in West Newton, Massachusetts into a prominent Boston family. After receiving a classical education at Noble and Greenogh's School, a preparatory school in Boston, he entered Harvard College. A great uncle, C. C. Felton, had been President of Harvard, and his grandfather, Jeffries Wyman, had been a distinguished Harvard Professor of Natural History and Comparative Anatomy and founder of the Peabody Museum as well as a founding member of the National Academy of Sciences. During Wyman's undergraduate years at Harvard, he studied philosophy and became interested in biology only toward the end of his undergraduate years. After receiving his degree, he stayed at Harvard for another year taking additional courses in thermodynamics and physical chemistry, both of which would significantly contribute to his career preparation. During his undergraduate years, he also developed what became a lifelong friendship with John T. Edsall, the author of a previous *Journal of Biological Chemistry* (JBC) Classic (1).

Wyman and Edsall left Harvard for Cambridge University together to study biochemistry. The biochemistry department at Cambridge was chaired by F. Gowland Hopkins, author of another JBC Classic (2), and provided excellent opportunities for students to conduct research and take courses in biochemistry. While Edsall remained at Cambridge for a year before returning to Harvard to complete the M. D. degree, Wyman transferred to University College, London to work with Archibald Vivian Hill, the preeminent physiologist. Hill was working on a variety of biological problems including a description of oxygen binding by hemoglobin. It was Hill's work on hemoglobin that led to his description of the Hill coefficient to describe the oxygen binding to hemoglobin and that has subsequently been used as a measure of cooperativity. Hill showed that for hemoglobin the coefficient, n, = 2.8 whereas for myoglobin, $n = 1$. His assumption in the interpretation was that hemoglobin was a monomeric protein and that a value of $n > 1$ indicated that the protein was aggregated. (It was G. S. Adair, also the author of a previous JBC Classic (9), who correctly measured the molecular weight of hemoglobin, recognized it was a tetramer, and correctly interpreted the oxygen binding by hemoglobin as a cooperative process.) Although much of Wyman's later work was focused on hemoglobin and cooperative oxygen binding, he worked with Hill on the thermodynamics of muscle action, not hemoglobin.

After completing his research in London, Wyman returned to Harvard as an Instructor in Zoology. Edsall too returned to Harvard. The two friends were rejoined. Even though Wyman was in the biology department in the College, he and Edsall both worked together with Edwin J. Cohn, Chairman of the Department of Physical Chemistry at Harvard Medical School. With Cohn, author of another JBC Classic (3), whose major interest was the physical chemistry of proteins, Wyman worked on a variety of problems including dielectric measurements of amino acids, peptides, and proteins. The paper reprinted here as a JBC Classic describes the titration of oxyhemoglobin and identification of the ionizable groups. Wyman argued that titrations of the different ionizable groups in proteins could be characterized by their different heats of dissociation. Titrations were conducted at different temperatures between pH 4 and pH 10. He

This paper is available on line at http://www.jbc.org

Jeffries Wyman. Photo courtesy of the National Library of Medicine.

concluded that groups that ionize up to pH 5.5 are carboxyl groups, those between pH 5.5 and pH 8.5 are the imidazole groups of histidine, and those ionizing above pH 8.5 are either the amino or the guanidino groups of lysine or arginine, respectively. Wyman also concluded that a change in pK of the imidazole groups of a few histidine residues occurs on oxygenation of hemoglobin and accounts for the well known Bohr effect. These assignments are in agreement with determinations by other methods, so the conclusions of the work are not in themselves particularly insightful. The approach, however, reflects a notable understanding of basic thermodynamics and its application to complex problems of protein chemistry. Wyman began to teach his own course in biophysical chemistry at Harvard. He was later joined by Edsall, and together they published their classic textbook, *Biophysical Chemistry*, Volume 1 (7). They had planned a second volume, but it was never published.

Wyman's work, like that of most American scientists, was interrupted by World War II as attention turned to the war effort. Wyman joined the Woods Hole Oceanographic Institution, which was a major contractor for the Navy. He worked on submarine detection by echo ranging and the tactical use of smoke screens, which required considerable understanding of meteorology and atmospheric conditions.

After the war, Wyman published a review of hemeproteins that is one of his classic papers (4). He had by then begun to formulate ideas about how conformational changes in proteins could lead to changes in functional properties. His first report on this subject, which was later called allosterism, was published in 1951 (5). About that time, Wyman decided not to continue his career as a university professor and accepted the newly created position as science attaché at the United States Embassy in Paris. He was to be responsible for the development of scientific activities in France, Italy, and Belgium. While he was in Paris, Wyman continued to extend his thoughts about cooperativity in molecular interactions, which led to the classic paper published with Jacques Monod and Jean-Pierre Changeux, for which he is probably best known, the model for allosteric transitions (6). The "plausible model" came to be known as the "concerted" or the "MWC" model, for **M**onod, **W**yman, and **C**hangeux. It was proposed that proteins that exhibit cooperativity can exist in only two conformational states, and the equilibrium between these two states is modified by binding of a ligand, oxygen in the case of hemoglobin. The model, which has stood the test of time, can explain quantitatively the behavior of many allosteric proteins.

After spending four years in Paris, Wyman held a series of positions elsewhere in Europe and the Middle East including several years in Cairo as Director of the Middle East Science Cooperation Office of UNESCO. He worked in Rome for 25 years at the Institute Regina Elena where he continued to develop his ideas on protein conformational states until his death in 1995.[1]

Robert D. Simoni, Robert L. Hill, and Martha Vaughan

REFERENCES

1. JBC Classics: Edsall, J. T. (1930) *J. Biol. Chem.* **89,** 289–313; Cohn, E. J., Edsall, J. T., and Blanchard, M. H. (1933) *J. Biol. Chem.* **105,** 319–326 (http://www.jbc.org/cgi/content/full/277/33/29351–29353)
2. JBC Classics: Hopkins, F. G., and Dixon, M. (1922) *J. Biol. Chem.* **54,** 527–563 (http://www.jbc.org/cgi/content/full/277/24/e13)
3. JBC Classics: Cohn, E. J., Hendry, J. L., and Prentiss, A. M. (1925) *J. Biol. Chem.* **63,** 721–766 (http://www.jbc.org/cgi/content/full/277/30/e19)
4. Wyman, J. (1948) Heme proteins. *Adv. Protein Chem.* **4,** 407–531
5. Wyman, J., and Allen, D. W. (1951) The problem of the heme interactions in hemoglobin and the Bohr effect. *J. Polymer Sci.* **7,** 499–518
6. Monod, J., Wyman, J., and Changeux, J. P. (1965) On the nature of the allosteric transition: a plausible model. *J. Mol. Biol.* **12,** 88–118
7. Edsall, J. T., and Wyman, J. (1958) *Biophysical Chemistry*, Vol. 1, Academic Press, New York
8. Gill, S. J. (1987) Conversations with Jeffries Wyman. *Annu. Rev. Biophys. Biophys.* Chem. **16,** 1–23
9. JBC Classics: Adair, G. S. (1925) *J. Biol. Chem.* **63,** 529–545 (http://www.jbc.org/cgi/content/full/277/31/e20)

---

[1] Virtually all the biographical information for this Classic introduction was taken from Ref. 8.

THE JOURNAL OF BIOLOGICAL CHEMISTRY
Vol. 278, No. 49, Issue of December 5, p. e1, 2003
© 2003 by The American Society for Biochemistry and Molecular Biology, Inc.
Printed in U.S.A.

Classics

A PAPER IN A SERIES REPRINTED TO CELEBRATE THE CENTENARY OF THE JBC IN 2005

JBC Centennial
1905–2005
100 Years of Biochemistry and Molecular Biology

A Classic Instrument: The Beckman DU Spectrophotometer and Its Inventor, Arnold O. Beckman

Although this is a departure from the series of JBC Classics reprinted thus far, we believe it is interesting and appropriate to feature the Beckman DU spectrophotometer, an instrument that for at least three decades contributed greatly to the development of biochemistry.

Beginning in 1940, the first in what became a series of Beckman spectrophotometers was developed at the National Technical Laboratories Company headed by Arnold O. Beckman. This later became the Beckman Instrument Company. Initially, the sole product of the company was the world's first pH meter, which Beckman had invented, and from which the Beckman empire was launched. Commercial spectrophotometers had been developed some years before, but the two most popular instruments, the Cenco "Spectrophotelometer" and the Coleman Model DM Spectrophotometer, did not have the capabilities to enable work at wavelengths in the ultraviolet.[1]

In 1940, using the amplifier from their pH meter, a glass prism, and a vacuum tube photocell, Beckman and colleagues at National Technologies Laboratories made their first spectrophotometer. (The project was led by Howard H. Cary who later headed the Cary Instrument Company and the development of many very high quality Cary spectrophotometers.) The performance of the first spectrophotometer was not satisfactory, but the design was quickly modified in the Model B version with the replacement of the glass prism with a quartz prism resulting in improved UV capabilities. It was followed with a Model C with improved wavelength resolution in the UV. Three Model C instruments were produced.

The Model D, to now be known as the Model DU, instrument incorporated all of the electronics within the instrument case and featured a new hydrogen lamp with ultraviolet continuum as well as a better monochromator. A diagram of the DU taken from the original instruction manual is shown on the following page. This instrument retained essentially the same design from 1941 until it was discontinued in 1976, a commercial lifetime of 35 years. In 1941, the Model DU had higher resolution and less stray light than other commercial spectrophotometers and was an immediate success. By the end of 1941, 18 Model DU instruments had been sold and by the middle of 1942 another 54. By the time production stopped in 1976, over 30,000 DU and DU-2 (a minor modification of the original DU) spectrophotometers had been sold. They were used in chemistry, biochemistry, and clinical and industrial laboratories. In 1941, the DU cost $723. An advertisement for the Beckman DU Photoelectric Quartz Spectrophotometer from the Arthur H. Thomas Company was published in a 1941 issue of the JBC. The Beckman Model DU Spectrophotometer was considered the Model T of laboratory instruments. It was referred to by Nobel laureate and author of an upcoming JBC Classic, Bruce Merrifield, as "probably the most important instrument ever developed towards the advancement of bioscience."

Arnold O. Beckman was born in Cullom, Illinois in 1900. He received a B. S. degree in Chemical Engineering from the University of Illinois in 1923 and entered the California Institute of Technology to pursue a Ph.D in chemistry. His work at Cal Tech was interrupted

---

[1] Information about the history of the Beckman DU Spectrophotometer from unpublished documents kindly provided by the Beckman-Coulter Instrument Company archives. Biographical information for Arnold O. Beckman is from an article published by the Chemical Heritage Foundation entitled "Arnold O. Beckman: The Man and His Instruments" (www.chemheritage.org/explore/Beckman/all.htm).

Arnold O. Beckman. Photograph by Inbert Gruttner, courtesy of AIP Emilio Segrè Visual Archives, Physics Today Collection.

by a move to New York to be nearer his fiancé, Mabel Meinzer. While in New York, he worked for 2 years at the Bell Laboratories. In 1925, Arnold and Mabel were married and returned to Pasadena where he resumed his Ph.D. studies. After receiving his Ph.D degree in 1928, Beckman became a member of the Cal Tech chemistry faculty. While at Cal Tech, Beckman was a dedicated and popular teacher of freshman chemistry, but his interests were increasingly directed toward applied work and commercial ventures. In 1935, he founded National Technologies Laboratories, where he developed the pH meter as his first successful commercial venture. He was named president of the company in 1939. The company's greatest success came with the production of the DU spectrophotometer in 1940.

The Beckman Instrument Company grew to become one of the most important producers of a wide range of research and medical instruments. Nearly every biochemistry and clinical laboratory in the world had, or had access to, a Beckman pH meter, a Beckman DU spectrophotometer, a Beckman analytical ultracentrifuge, and other Beckman instruments.

Arnold Beckman amassed a fortune in the scientific instrument business and, through the Arnold and Mabel Beckman Foundation, has been an enormously generous philanthropist. He established five important Beckman Institutes within universities: University of Illinois, California Institute of Technology, City of Hope, University of California at Irvine, and Stanford University. These Institutes are considered the five jewels of Beckman's philanthropy. Beckman received many honors and awards as an inventor and business and civic leader. He was a recipient of both the National Medal of Technology and the National Medal of Science. He was also awarded the Public Welfare Medal by the National Academy of Sciences in recognition of distinguished contributions in the application of science to the public welfare.

Robert D. Simoni, Robert L. Hill, Martha Vaughan, and Herbert Tabor

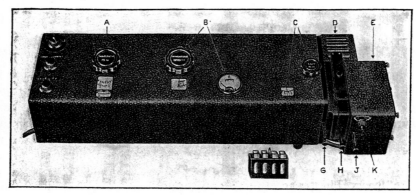

THE JOURNAL OF BIOLOGICAL CHEMISTRY
© 2003 by The American Society for Biochemistry and Molecular Biology, Inc.

Vol. 278, No. 50, Issue of December 12, p. e2, 2003
Printed in U.S.A.

Classics

A PAPER IN A SERIES REPRINTED TO CELEBRATE THE CENTENARY OF THE JBC IN 2005

JBC Centennial
1905–2005
100 Years of Biochemistry and Molecular Biology

The Metabolism of Steroid Hormones: Ralph I. Dorfman

Conversion by the Human of the Testis Hormone, Testosterone, into the Urinary Androgen, Androsterone
(Dorfman, R. I., Cook, J. W., and Hamilton, J. B. (1939) *J. Biol. Chem.* 130, 285–295)

Ralph I. Dorfman (1911–1985), who was a native of Chicago, received his bachelor's degree from the University of Illinois and his Ph.D. degree in physiological chemistry from the University of Chicago. He taught at Louisiana State University, Yale University, and Western Reserve University before joining the Worcester Foundation for Experimental Biology in 1951 as Associate Director and later became Co-director. During his 13 years at the Worcester Foundation, it became an international center for bioassays and the study of the chemistry, biochemistry, and biology of steroid hormones, which were Dorfman's research interests.[1]

In 1950, Dorfman was made a consultant to the Syntex Corporation and in 1964 joined the company full time becoming president of Syntex Research. At Syntex, he led the growth of steroid hormone research and was a pioneer in the development of the first oral contraceptive. He served also as Consulting Professor of Pharmacology at Stanford University, and after his death in 1985, the pharmacology department established the Ralph I. Dorfman Memorial Lectureship in his honor. During his research career, Dorfman focused on the metabolism and mechanism of action of the steroid hormones and their role in reproductive physiology, cancer, and rheumatoid arthritis. He introduced the concept of anti-estrogens and anti-androgens to the field of reproductive biology.

The paper selected as a JBC Classic is Dorfman's analysis of the metabolism of testosterone in humans. Although testosterone was recognized as a product of the testis, there were other compounds in urine that had androgenic activity and were structurally related to testosterone but of unknown origin. The work reported in this JBC Classic is classic in design. Testosterone was administered to males who had been diagnosed with insufficient testicular secretion. Urine was collected, analyzed for products of testosterone metabolism, and tested for androgenic activity using effects on the comb of day-old chickens as a bioassay. Compounds in the urine were fractioned by standard chemical techniques, crystallized, and characterized structurally. Androsterone was identified as the major metabolite of testosterone in human urine.

Dorfman received many honors for his research, including election to the National Academy of Sciences in 1978. His younger brother, Albert Dorfman, who studied the biosynthesis of bacterial and connective tissue polysaccharides, was also a member of the National Academy of Sciences and is the author of an upcoming JBC Classic.

Robert D. Simoni, Robert L. Hill, Martha Vaughan, and Herbert Tabor

---

[1] All of the biographical information for this Introduction was kindly provided by Prof. Daria Mochly Rosen, Dept. of Molecular Pharmacology, Stanford University.

This paper is available on line at http://www.jbc.org

THE JOURNAL OF BIOLOGICAL CHEMISTRY
© 2003 by The American Society for Biochemistry and Molecular Biology, Inc.

Vol. 278, No. 51, Issue of December 19, p. e3, 2003
Printed in U.S.A.

Classics

A PAPER IN A SERIES REPRINTED TO CELEBRATE THE CENTENARY OF THE JBC IN 2005

JBC Centennial
1905–2005
100 Years of Biochemistry and Molecular Biology

Linus Pauling: Scientist and Social Activist

A Structural Interpretation of the Acidity of Groups Associated with the Hemes of Hemoglobin and Hemoglobin Derivatives
(Coryell, C. D., and Pauling, L. (1940) *J. Biol. Chem.* 132, 769–779)

Linus Carl Pauling (1901–1994) was born in Portland, Oregon. His father, Herman Pauling, a pharmacist, died when Linus was 9, and by the age of 12, Linus was working to support his mother and two sisters. In spite of his family responsibilities, he excelled in high school and began to develop an interest in science with support and encouragement from his high school teachers. Although his mother wanted him to become a machinist, Linus was determined to become a research scientist and entered the Oregon Agricultural College (now Oregon State University) to study chemistry. Because he was a very successful student, he was often asked to teach courses he had just taken. While teaching chemistry to home economics majors, he met his future wife, Ava Helen Miller.[1]

In 1922, Pauling enrolled in the Ph.D. program in chemistry at California Institute of Technology and received his degree in 1927. After a year in Europe, he returned to Cal Tech as an Assistant Professor of Theoretical Chemistry to begin his pioneering work on the nature of chemical bonds. His work followed on the fundamental changes in physical science from the mathematical approaches of Bohr, Heisenberg, and Schrodinger. Pauling developed approximate methods for using empirically the mathematical treatments of quantum theory. The values that he calculated for orientation and bond strength of atoms in molecules matched closely the results from x-ray diffraction studies. His marriage of quantum theory and experimental work contributed concepts such as "hydrogen bonding," "resonance," "hybrid bond," and "valence bond" to the chemist's vocabulary. In 1939, Pauling published his famous book, *The Nature of the Chemical Bond*. The paper selected as a JBC Classic represents Pauling's exploration of protein structure at an early stage. In 1904 Bohr had discovered that pH affected the oxygen binding equilibrium of hemoglobin. This work stimulated many investigators to examine the relationship of the acid groups of amino acid side chains to the heme moieties in hemoglobin. The worked described in this JBC Classic defined the pK value of the critical histidine imidazole ring as the acid group that coordinated with the heme iron. Pauling's work predicted the structural change that occurs as the iron moves into the plane of the heme upon oxygenation. The prediction was confirmed many years later when Perutz determined the three-dimensional structure of different forms of hemoglobin.

Pauling's major contributions to biochemistry came with the application of his structural approaches and insights to the study of peptides and proteins. In 1937, Robert Corey, the author of a previous JBC Classic (3), joined Pauling as a research fellow, and together they developed the application of x-ray diffraction analysis to the structures of amino acids and small peptides. The resulting description of protein secondary structures, the α-helix and the β-pleated sheet, was published in three classic papers (4–6). Here again, these forms were confirmed to exist in proteins only many years later by x-ray crystallographic analysis.

Like many other scientists during World War II, Pauling devoted himself and his laboratory to the war effort. He devised explosives and missile propellants for the Navy, invented an oxygen meter for submarines, and, together with others, developed a synthetic blood plasma

---

[1] Much of the information for this JBC Classic introduction is from a biography provided by the Linus Pauling Institute at Oregon State University (1) and one in the Dictionary of Unitarian and Universalists Biography (2).

Linus C. Pauling. Photo courtesy of the National Library of Medicine.

substitute to be used for emergency transfusions on the battlefield. He also served as a member of a Presidential Commission on the direction of government science policy. For his efforts, Pauling was awarded the Presidential Medal of Merit by President Harry S. Truman. This award later seemed ironic when Pauling's antinuclear efforts were met with government persecution, questions about patriotism, and some public disapproval.

After the war, Pauling returned to his research on protein structure but was increasingly concerned about the dangers he saw in the dawning nuclear age. He became a very active and outspoken opponent of further development, testing, and abuse of nuclear weapons. As a result, he was treated almost as a traitor by the government during the McCarthy/loyalty oath era and for several years was denied a passport to travel to scientific meetings. His unrestricted passport was restored in 1954 to enable him to travel to Stockholm to receive the Nobel Prize in Chemistry. On October 10, 1963, the day that the limited nuclear test ban treaty, signed by the United States, Great Britain, and the USSR, became effective, Pauling's efforts as an opponent of nuclear proliferation and a social activist were recognized by the Nobel Prize for Peace for 1962. Pauling is the only person to have received two unshared Nobel Prizes.

After 42 years, Pauling left Cal Tech under pressure from the University administration and some of the trustees because of his persistent and very public antinuclear and international peace efforts. Subsequently, he held professorships at the University of California at Santa Barbara, the University of California at San Diego, and Stanford University from which he retired in 1973. After retiring, Pauling founded the Linus Pauling Institute of Science and Medicine to explore and promote his growing interest in the role of nutrition in health. From this base, he became best known for championing the use of vitamin C to combat a range of illnesses including the common cold. It is unfortunate that one of the greatest scientists of the twentieth century is probably best known today for his efforts to promote vitamin C as an unproven cure for many illnesses.

Robert D. Simoni, Robert L. Hill, Martha Vaughan, and Herbert Tabor

REFERENCES

1. Biography of Linus Pauling provided by the Linus Pauling Institute at Oregon State University (lpi.oregonstate. edu/lpbio2.html)
2. Biography of Linus Pauling in the Dictionary of Unitarian and Universalists (www.uua.org/uuhs/duub/articles/ linuspauling.html). Pauling, who did not believe in God or the mystical aspects of religion, was a member of the Los Angeles Unitarian Church, which often provided venues or platforms for his social activism.
3. JBC Classics: Wycoff, R. W. G., and Corey, R. B. (1936) *J. Biol. Chem.* **116,** 51–55 (http://www.jbc.org/cgi/content/ full/277/44/e32)
4. Corey, R. B., Branson, H. R., and Pauling L. (1951) The structure of proteins: two hydrogen-bonded helical configurations of the polypeptide chain. *Proc. Natl. Acad. Sci. U. S. A.* **37,** 205–211
5. Corey, R. B. and Pauling, L. (1951). The pleated sheet, a new layer configuration of polypeptide chains. *Proc. Natl. Acad. Sci. U. S. A.* **37,** 251–256
6. Corey, R. B., and Pauling, L. (1951) Configurations of polypeptide chains favored orientation around single bonds: two new pleated sheets. *Proc. Natl. Acad. Sci. U. S. A.* **37,** 729–740

THE JOURNAL OF BIOLOGICAL CHEMISTRY
© 2003 by The American Society for Biochemistry and Molecular Biology, Inc.

Vol. 278, No. 52, Issue of December 26, p. e4, 2003
Printed in U.S.A.

Classics

A PAPER IN A SERIES REPRINTED TO CELEBRATE THE CENTENARY OF THE JBC IN 2005

JBC Centennial
1905–2005
100 Years of Biochemistry and Molecular Biology

Contributions of Organic Chemists to Biochemistry: Louis F. Fieser, Mary Fieser, and Max Tishler

Vitamin K Activity and Structure
(Fieser, L. F., Tishler, M., and Sampson, W. L. (1941) *J. Biol. Chem.* 137, 659–692)

This paper was selected as a JBC Classic because it represents the research and teaching accomplishments of giants of organic chemistry and the application of synthetic organic chemistry to biochemistry. The work is a classic structure-function analysis of a class of compounds for biological activity. Using a bioassay for the antihemorrhagic activity of vitamin K, the authors screened 79 naphthoquinones either synthesized for this purpose or previously studied to determine which structural elements are essential for activity.

Louis Frederick Fieser (1899–1977) was born in Columbus, Ohio. After completing high school in Columbus, he attended Williams College graduating in 1920 with a degree in chemistry. He attended graduate school at Harvard and completed his thesis on the oxidation-reduction potentials of quinones with James Bryant Conant, who later became President of Harvard. After a fellowship year in Europe, he assumed his first teaching position at Bryn Mawr College. He served there until 1930 when he returned to Harvard as an assistant professor and remained until he became emeritus in 1968 (1).[1]

While at Bryn Mawr, Fieser met Mary Peters (1909–1997), who was a member of his second class. After graduating in 1930, she entered Radcliffe College for graduate study in chemistry with Fieser who had moved to Harvard the same year. Her enrollment at Radcliffe was necessary in order for her to take chemistry classes at Harvard because Harvard did not accept women. Although she took the same classes from Harvard faculty as Harvard men, women were not allowed to take the classes at the same time or in the same building as the men. Therefore the Harvard faculty would give one lecture to men and the same lecture to women in a different building (2).

Mary and Louis Fieser were married in 1932 and began a remarkable research, teaching, and literary collaboration which lasted until Louis' death in 1977. Together they published 35 research papers, 8 books, and the important series *Reagents for Organic Synthesis*. Their textbooks *Organic Chemistry*, *Textbook of Organic Chemistry*, *Introduction to Organic Chemistry*, *Basic Organic Chemistry*, *Advanced Organic Chemistry*, *Topics in Organic Chemistry*, and *Current Topics in Organic Chemistry* introduced generations of students to the study of organic chemistry. The first volume of their series, *Reagents for Organic Synthesis*, was published in 1967, and Volume 15 was published in 1990. Seven volumes were published before Louis' death in 1977; the remainder were prepared by Mary often with a collaborator. This series is the most important of the Fiesers' publications and has been indispensable for all practicing organic chemists. In 1936, Mary received her masters degree from Radcliffe and decided not to pursue doctoral studies. She never was granted a salary by Harvard University but was given the title, Research Fellow of Chemistry, 29 years after she had begun her work there. In 1996, Mary dedicated the Louis and Mary Fieser Laboratory for Undergraduate Organic Chemistry at Harvard.

Louis' research was varied. His interest in quinones, exhibited first in his thesis work, led to the studies and synthesis of vitamin K (3) plus numerous structural variants, the subject of

---

[1] The biographical information for Louis Fieser is from Ref. 1.

this JBC Classic. He was a virtuoso experimentalist, who took particular pride in devising simple, practical, and ingenious solutions to experimental problems. There was an annual contest between Fieser and students in his class based on the preparation of the yellow dye Martius Yellow from 1-naphthol. The criteria were judged on speed and purity of the product. Fieser always won but also was always disqualified on some technicality. During World War II, Fieser devoted much of his research effort to the synthesis and screening of quinones as antimalarial agents. More than 300 compounds were synthesized and tested, and although some appeared promising, none proved to be clinically effective.

Fieser was also well known as a dedicated and gifted teacher. For many years, he taught Chemistry 2, later Chemistry 20, the introductory course in organic chemistry at Harvard. His lab manuals were meticulous. He was also famous for dramatic lab demonstrations including a lesson on how not to do a recrystallization, which resulted in his being covered with decolorizing charcoal to the delight of his students. He used his classes also to test syntheses before publication and to engage his students in research. In one JBC paper (4), Fieser recorded that "all procedures were submitted for trial to a group of students in a course in elementary organic chemistry with fully successful results."

Fieser received many honors for his research and teaching including election to the National Academy of Sciences (1940) and an award from the American Chemical Society as a "Giant in Chemical Education" (1976). In his honor, the June 1965 issue of the *Journal of Organic Chemistry* published 112 papers by his former students and colleagues. He also received many honorary degrees.

Max Tishler (1906–1989), a co-author of this JBC Classic, was another legendary organic chemist, whose career path was rather different from Fieser's and took him to industry rather than industry. Born in Boston, he was the fifth of six children in a family that had been deserted by their father when Max was 5 years old. As he grew up, he shared the burden of supporting the family including working as a pharmacist's assistant. This experience sparked his interest in chemistry and desire to make a contribution to health care, which endured throughout his life. An outstanding high school record earned him a scholarship to Tufts College, now Tufts University, and he graduated *magna cum laude* with a B.S. in chemistry in 1928. He enrolled in graduate school at Harvard and received a Ph.D. degree in organic chemistry in 1934 for his thesis work with Elmer P. Kohler. He was also influenced by James Bryant Conant who, together with Kohler, helped him to get his first job at Merck in 1937, a time when academic positions were scarce (5).[2]

When Tishler joined Merck in 1937, it was a relatively small company making fine chemicals in Rahway, New Jersey. George W. Merck, son of the founder, wanted to use the firm's sales base in commodity chemicals to build a more innovative organization for the creation of therapeutic chemicals. He initiated an expansion of the laboratories and introduced basic research. He recruited Karl Folkers from Yale who had expertise in the isolation of natural products that were medically useful such as hormones and vitamins. They both recognized the importance of developing manufacturing techniques to expand the milligram quantities prepared in a research laboratory to the relatively massive amounts necessary for medicinal purposes. Max Tishler's first job at Merck was as a product development chemist. His first production-scale product was riboflavin, and Merck was able to produce quantities sufficient for enriching white bread.

His biggest challenge was the production of cortisone. During World War II there was enormous pressure from the medical community and from the government to produce cortisone on a large scale. Tishler eventually succeeded in establishing the most complex manufacturing process ever developed by the pharmaceutical industry and created a supply of cortisone sufficient for medical use. Many more successes followed, and Tishler rose through the ranks to become the first president of the Merck Sharp & Dohme Research Laboratory Division of Merck & Co. Inc. Among numerous products developed under Tishler's leadership were ascorbic acid, riboflavin, cortisone, thiamin, pyridoxine, pantothenic acid, nicotinamide, methionine, threonine, tryptophan, actinomycin D, vitamin B_{12}, streptomycin, and penicillin.

In 1969, Tishler was appointed Senior Vice-President for Science and Technology, a position that removed him from interactions with scientists, and in 1970, 18 months before his mandatory retirement at Merck, he accepted a position as Professor of Chemistry at Wesleyan

---

[2] The biographical information for Max Tishler is from Ref. 5.

University. To Wesleyan, Tishler brought the same energy and leadership that had characterized his tenure at Merck, and at the age of 64, he launched a new career. He helped lead the effort to establish a Ph.D. program in chemistry. He supervised graduate students and was a model mentor. He became University Professor of the Sciences and chairman of the chemistry department. He remained active in all phases of departmental life even after becoming emeritus in 1975 and continued to do so until a few weeks before his death.

Tishler received many honors during his career. He was elected to the National Academy of Sciences (1954) and received the National Medal of Science from Ronald Reagan (1987).

Robert D. Simoni, Robert L. Hill, Martha Vaughan, and Herbert Tabor

REFERENCES

1. Gates, M. (1994) Biographical memoir for Louis Frederick Fieser. *Biogr. Mem. Natl. Acad. Sci.* **65,** 161–175
2. Biographical Snapshots of Famous Women and Minority Chemists. *Journal of Chemical Education Online* (http://jchemed.chem.wisc.edu/JCEWWW/Features/eChemists/Bios/fieser.html)
3. Fieser, L. F. (1940) The synthesis of vitamin K. *Science* **91,** 31
4. Fieser, L. F. (1940) Convenient procedure for the preparation of antihemorrhagic compounds. *J. Biol. Chem.* **133,** 391–396
5. Sarett, L. H., and Roche, C. (1995) Biographical memoir for Max Tishler. *Biogr. Mem. Natl. Acad. Sci.* **66,** 353–369 (www.nap.edu/readingroom/books/biomems/mtishler.html)

THE JOURNAL OF BIOLOGICAL CHEMISTRY
© 2004 by The American Society for Biochemistry and Molecular Biology, Inc.

Vol. 279, No. 1, Issue of January 2, p. e1, 2004
Printed in U.S.A.

Classics

A PAPER IN A SERIES REPRINTED TO CELEBRATE THE CENTENARY OF THE JBC IN 2005

JBC Centennial
1905–2005
100 Years of Biochemistry and Molecular Biology

Transaminases: the Work of Philip P. Cohen

Transamination with Purified Enzyme Preparations (Transaminase)
(Cohen, P. P. (1940) *J. Biol. Chem.* 136, 565–584)

Philip Pacy Cohen (1908–1993), universally known as P. P. Cohen, was born in Derry, New Hampshire, attended high school in Boston, and graduated from Tufts College, now Tufts University, in 1930. He then enrolled in graduate school at the University of Wisconsin from which he received a Ph.D. degree in physiological chemistry in 1937 and an M.D. degree in 1938. Cohen was awarded a postdoctoral fellowship to work with Hans Krebs in Sheffield, England, and it was in Krebs' laboratory that Cohen's focus on nitrogen metabolism and transaminases started. Cohen completed his fellowship in the laboratory of Cyril N. H. Long at the Yale University School of Medicine with the work reported in this JBC Classic. After completion of his postdoctoral studies, Cohen returned to the University of Wisconsin as Research Associate in Physiological Chemistry and rose through the academic ranks to become Professor in 1947. In 1968, he succeeded Harold C. Bradley as Chairman of the Department of Physiological Chemistry, a post he held for 27 years. He was highly respected at the University and was asked to serve as Acting Dean of the Medical School during a turbulent 2-year period (1).[1]

The paper selected as a JBC Classic is impressive for its thoroughness and insight. In addition, it places transamination reactions and transaminases on a solid biochemical basis. Studies of transamination reactions were first reported by Braunstein and Kritzman (2), but as Cohen pointed out, they had considered the reaction to be a general one involving numerous α-amino acids and α-keto acids. Cohen reported in this JBC Classic that the extract preparations, of pigeon breast muscle and pig heart used in the study, were only highly active with three specific amino acids, alanine, glutamic acid, and aspartic acid, in the following reactions.

Glutamic acid + oxaloacetic acid ↔ α-ketoglutaric acid + aspartic acid

Glutamic acid + pyruvic acid ↔ α-ketoglutaric acid + alanine

Aspartic acid + pyruvic acid ↔ oxaloacetic acid + alanine

We now know, of course, that these are the major transamination reactions responsible for amino acid synthesis from Krebs cycle intermediates. It is notable that the α-keto acid substrates for these reactions, oxaloacetic acid and α-ketoglutaric acid, had to be synthesized whereas most of the amino acids tested were available commercially. Cohen acknowledged receiving glutamic acid from Joseph Fruton, alanine from Vincent Du Vigneaud, phosphoserine from Fritz Lipmann, and cysteine from Abraham White, all of whom became distinguished biochemists.

Cohen's interests extended to other aspects of nitrogen metabolism, and he is well known, in addition, for his studies of urea metabolism. In a particularly interesting set of studies, he investigated the developmental biochemistry of metamorphosis from the tadpole that excretes ammonia to the frog that excretes urea. Cohen and his collaborators demonstrated that the rate-limiting enzymes in urea synthesis, carbamyl phosphate synthetase and

---

[1] The biographical information for this JBC Classic introduction was entirely from Ref. 1.

This paper is available on line at http://www.jbc.org

Philip P. Cohen. Photo courtesy of the National Library of Medicine.

argininosuccinate synthetase, increased in the liver as metamorphosis progressed and urea excretion began (3).

Cohen received many honors for his work, including election to the National Academy of Sciences, and he served on many important national committees and commissions. He also was very supportive of biochemistry in Mexico, South America, and Japan through the numerous foreign visitors to his laboratory and his many trips abroad for teaching and lectures.

Robert D. Simoni, Robert L. Hill, Martha Vaughan, and Herbert Tabor

REFERENCES

1. Burris, R. H. (1999) Biographical memoir of Philip Pacy Cohen. *Biogr. Mem. Natl. Acad. Sci.* **77,** 3–17 (www.nap.edu/readingroom/books/biomems/pcohen.html)
2. Braunstein, A. E., and Kritzman, M. G. (1937) *Enzymologia* **2,** 129–146
3. Cohen, P. P. (1970) Biochemical differentiation during amphibian metamorphosis. *Science* **168,** 533–543

THE JOURNAL OF BIOLOGICAL CHEMISTRY
© 2004 by The American Society for Biochemistry and Molecular Biology, Inc.

Vol. 279, No. 2, Issue of January 9, p. e2, 2004
Printed in U.S.A.

Classics

A PAPER IN A SERIES REPRINTED TO CELEBRATE THE CENTENARY OF THE JBC IN 2005

JBC Centennial
1905–2005
100 Years of Biochemistry and Molecular Biology

Metabolic Studies with Radioactive Carbon, [11]C: A. Baird Hastings

**Metabolism of Lactic Acid Containing Radioactive Carboxyl Carbon
(Conant, J. B., Cramer, R. D., Hastings, A. B., Klemperer, F. W., Solomon, A. K.,
and Vennesland, B. (1941) *J. Biol. Chem.* 137, 557–566)**

**The Participation of Carbon Dioxide in the Carbohydrate Cycle
(Soloman, A. K., Vennesland, B., Klemperer, F. W., Buchanan, J. M.,
and Hastings, A. B. (1941) *J. Biol. Chem.* 140, 171–182)**

A. Baird Hastings (1895–1987) was born in Dayton, Kentucky but lived in Indianapolis until he went to college (1).[1] A high school teacher, Ella Marthens, was strongly influential and encouraged his interests in biology and in going to college. He chose the University of Michigan and decided to major in chemical engineering primarily because after graduation he would be able to get a job quickly and help support his family. After a time at Michigan, Hastings gravitated toward physical chemistry and was asked by Professor Floyd Bartell to serve as his course assistant. As graduation approached, Hastings was prepared to get a job but was encouraged by Bartell to consider graduate school. He entered the University of Michigan graduate school in 1916, but with the beginning of World War I his graduate training was interrupted and his advisor, Bartell, joined the Chemical Warfare Service. Hastings' persistent efforts to enlist in the military were rejected primarily because he was underweight. He took a job as a "sanitary chemist" with the Public Health Service to study fatigue, convinced that it would be a contribution to the war effort. It was a notable opportunity because it introduced Hastings to the study of physiology, which eventually became his life's work.

The Public Health Service officials had decided that fatigue in munitions factory workers was due to acidosis. Hastings' assignment was to measure the pH of the urine of workers at the Ford Motor Company in the morning as they arrived for work and again in the evening after they had completed their day's work. Hastings perceived immediately that this was an exceedingly complex problem and told the project leader, Frederic S. Lee, Head of the Department of Physiology at Columbia, that the project was hopeless and a waste of government money. Lee ordered him to come to Columbia to continue his studies on fatigue in the controlled experimental way that Hastings had argued was necessary. After the war, Hastings decided to complete his graduate education in physiology at Columbia studying acid-base balance as affected by exercise. For use in some of his studies, he adapted a hydrogen electrode for titrations and devised a procedure to measure the alkali reserve in blood. In his efforts to publish this work, it was submitted to Donald D. Van Slyke at the Rockefeller Institute, then Editor of the *Journal of Biological Chemistry* (JBC). His paper entitled "A Hydrogen Electrode Vessel Adapted for Titrations" was published in the JBC in 1921 (2). Even more important; Van Slyke invited Hastings to join his group at the Rockefeller Institute once he received his Ph.D. degree. (Van Slyke is the author of a previous JBC Classic (3).)

Hastings spent five years with Van Slyke during which time the group was describing electrolyte balance in blood (3). In 1926, Hastings accepted a professorship at the University of Chicago while continuing his studies on electrolyte balance and initiating experiments on bone deposition. In 1935, when Otto Folin, the author of a previous JBC Classic (4), died,

---

[1] All biographical information about A. Baird Hastings for this introduction to the JBC Classics is from Ref. 1.

A. Baird Hastings. Photo courtesy of the National Library of Medicine.

Harvard President James B. Conant asked Hastings to replace Folin as Head of the Department of Biological Chemistry at the Harvard Medical School. He accepted the position and remained for 25 years building a notably strong department. To return personally to laboratory research, he left Harvard for the Scripps Clinic and Research Foundation in 1959 where he remained active in research for another 20 years.

The papers selected as JBC Classics are noteworthy for several reasons, among them Hastings' distinguished co-authors. James B. Conant was President of Harvard, and Birgit Vennesland, then a postdoctoral fellow, had a distinguished career as a biochemist and is the author of an upcoming JBC Classic. John Buchanan likewise had a distinguished career in biochemistry and is also the author of an upcoming JBC Classic.

The work reported in these JBC Classics is noteworthy as an example of one of the early uses of radioactive carbon, ^{11}C, for metabolic studies. (The use of isotopes for metabolic studies was pioneered by Rudolf Schoenheimer (5) who employed the heavy isotopes, deuterium and ^{15}N.) ^{11}C was prepared in the Harvard cyclotron. Because it has a half-life of 20.6 min, these metabolic studies required rapid procedures for chemical synthesis of precursor molecules, administration to animals, and analysis of metabolic products. The experiments reported in these two JBC Classics were completed in about 6 h after removal of isotope from the cyclotron. Radioactive lactate with ^{11}C in the carboxyl group was prepared and administered to rats, which were sacrificed 2.5 h later, and the radioactivity was quantified in expired CO_2 and in purified liver glycogen. In an interesting note, the authors commented that the integrated dose of radioactivity was 65 microcurie hours, and no deleterious effects of this level of radiation on the health of the rats were noted. The metabolic information provided by the experiments described in the first paper is rather meager. About 20% of the administered ^{11}C was expired as CO_2, and only about 1.6% found its way into glycogen. The authors concluded that lactate was not the principle source of carbon for liver glycogen synthesized during the experiment. They also pointed out the many caveats that apply to the interpretation of the experiment, for example the unknown extent of isotope dilution-like dilution of isotope in pools of glycogen precursors.

The second paper is scientifically more interesting and showed that [^{11}C]bicarbonate was incorporated into glycogen. It follows up the classical work of Wood and Werkman who demonstrated the incorporation of CO_2 into organic matter by microorganisms (6). This is the subject of another upcoming JBC Classic. In addition, Evans and Slotin had reported in a JBC Letter to the Editor, CO_2 incorporation into α-ketoglutaric acid by pigeon liver (7). Thus the work of Hastings and his colleagues contributed to the growing recognition that CO_2 is metabolically active in many organisms as well as in plants. Moreover, the use of radioactive isotopes of carbon, later ^{14}C, had clearly transformed the conduct of metabolic and biochemical studies.

Hastings served on countless national and international advisory panels, commissions, and committees and received many honors for his research accomplishments during a distinguished career. As a member of the very influential Committee for Medical Research during World War II, he received the National Medal of Merit from President Harry S. Truman. He was elected to the National Academy of Sciences in 1937. He was especially devoted to students and colleagues and was very involved with as well as effective in finding them excellent positions.

Robert D. Simoni, Robert L. Hill, and Martha Vaughan

REFERENCES

1. Christiansen, H. N. (1994) Biographical memoir of Albert Baird Hastings. *Natl. Acad. Sci.* **63,** 172–216
2. Hastings, A. B. (1921) A hydrogen electrode vessel adapted for titrations. *J. Biol. Chem.* **46,** 463–466
3. JBC Classics: Van Slyke, D. D, and Neill, J. M. (1924) *J. Biol. Chem.* **61,** 523–543 (http://www.jbc.org/cgi/content/full/277/27/e16)
4. JBC Classics: Folin, O., and Wu, H. (1919) *J. Biol. Chem.* **38,** 81–110 (http://www.jbc.org/cgi/content/full/277/20/e9)
5. JBC Classics: Schoenheimer, R., and Rittenberg, D. (1935) *J. Biol. Chem.* **111,** 163–168; (1937) *J. Biol. Chem.* **121,** 235–253 (http://www.jbc.org/cgi/content/full/277/43/e31)
6. Wood, H. G., and Werkman, C. H. (1935) *J. Bacteriol.* **30,** 332–344
7. Evans, E. A., Jr., and Slotin, L. (1940) *J. Biol. Chem.* **136,** 301–302

THE JOURNAL OF BIOLOGICAL CHEMISTRY
© 2004 by The American Society for Biochemistry and Molecular Biology, Inc.

Vol. 279, No. 3, Issue of January 16, p. e3, 2004
Printed in U.S.A.

Classics

A PAPER IN A SERIES REPRINTED TO CELEBRATE THE CENTENARY OF THE JBC IN 2005

JBC Centennial
1905–2005
100 Years of Biochemistry and Molecular Biology

The Stereochemistry and Reaction Mechanism of Dehydrogenases and Their Coenzymes, DPN (NAD) and TPN (NADP): the Work of Birgit Vennesland

The Enzymatic Transfer of Hydrogen. I. The Reaction Catalyzed by Alcohol Dehydrogenase
(Fisher, H. F., Conn, E. E., Vennesland, B., and Westheimer, F. H. (1953) *J. Biol. Chem.* **202,** 687–697)

The Enzymatic Transfer of Hydrogen. II. The Reaction Catalyzed by Lactic Dehydrogenase
(Loewus, F. A., Ofner, P., Fisher, H. F., Westheimer, F. H., and Vennesland, B. (1953) *J. Biol. Chem.* **202,** 699–704)

Birgit Vennesland (1913–2001) and her twin sister, Kirsten, were born in Kristiansand, Norway. Their father had immigrated to the United States to study dentistry, and "tired of waiting for the end of World War I," in 1917 their mother sailed for the United States with her two daughters to rejoin her husband in Chicago (1).[1] After early schooling in Chicago, Vennesland entered the University of Chicago with a scholarship awarded on the basis of a competitive exam in physics. She settled on a biochemistry major and received her B.S. degree in 1934. After working for a year as a technician, she returned to the University of Chicago for graduate education in biochemistry and chose her own Ph.D. thesis project, the oxidation-reduction potential of a strict anaerobic bacteria, which was completed in 1938. During her thesis work, she discovered that bacteria require a small amount of CO_2 for growth, a discovery that influenced her later work (1).

In 1939, Vennesland received a fellowship from the International Federation of University Women to work with Otto Myerhoff who was then in Paris after fleeing Germany and the increase of anti-Semitism. As war in Europe intensified, however, she decided instead to join A. Baird Hastings in the Department of Biochemistry at Harvard Medical School. With Hastings, Vennesland was among the first to use radioactive carbon, ^{11}C, to investigate metabolism. Those were challenging studies because the 20.6-min half-life of ^{11}C meant that experiments had to be completed very quickly. Among the most notable of their findings was the demonstration that starved rats incorporated the isotope from $^{11}CO_2$ into liver glycogen. Vennesland's work with Hastings was reported in an earlier JBC Classic (2).

Vennesland returned to the University of Chicago in 1941 as Instructor of Biochemistry intending to work on CO_2 incorporation by non-photosynthetic plant tissues; however, she, like many scientists at the time, enlisted in the war effort and worked on a malaria research project until the end of the war. In 1946, she, along with an influx of post-war students and a newly available Beckman DU spectrophotometer, began to examine the enzymology of dehydrogenases that utilized DPN^+ and TPN^+, as NAD^+ and $NADP^+$ were then called. Upon reduction, these coenzyme molecules increase their absorbance at 340 nm thus providing a convenient spectrophotometric assay to quantify reaction progress. In 1950, after a great deal of experi-

[1] The biographical information for Birgit Vennesland was taken from Ref. 1. We thank Eric E. Conn, Professor Emeritus of Biochemistry and Biophysics at the University of California at Davis for sharing his recollections of the work reported in these JBC Classics which was going on while during he was a postdoctoral fellow in Vennesland's laboratory.

ence with these enzymes and their metabolic functions, Vennesland initiated a collaboration with Frank H. Westheimer, then in the chemistry department at the University of Chicago, that led to important mechanistic insight into the reactions of pyridine nucleotide-dependent dehydrogenases.

In the two JBC Classics reprinted here, Vennesland and co-workers describe experiments to show that the two hydrogen atoms at one of the carbons in the dihydropyridine ring of both DPNH and TPNH (NADH and NADPH) are enzymatically non-equivalent and that the dehyrogenases transfer hydrogen, as hydride ion, stereospecifically between substrate and coenzyme. Using alcohol dehydrogenase (ADH), they accomplished the first demonstration of the enzymatic discrimination between the two enantiotopic hydrogen atoms on the methylene carbon atom of ethanol. With dideuteroethanol as substrate, they established that the reaction products were monodeutero-reduced DPN and monodeuteroacetaldehyde

$$\text{CH}_3\text{CD}_2\text{OH} + \text{(oxidized) DPN}^+ \xrightarrow{\text{ADH}} \text{CH}_3\text{CDO} + \text{(reduced) monodeutero-DPN}$$

Subsequent analysis also demonstrated that incubation of the enzymatically prepared reduced monodeutero-DPN with ADH and acetaldehyde resulted in complete transfer of deuterium from reduced DPN to acetaldehyde to form monodeuteroethanol. If, on the other hand, chemically reduced deutero-DPN was subjected to the same reaction, about one-half of the deuterium remained in the oxidized DPN. Vennesland and colleagues concluded that: 1) with enzymatic oxidation-reduction reactions, hydrogen is transferred directly from the alcohol to the coenzyme, and 2) the enzymatic reduction is stereospecific with respect to the position of the electrons in the dihydropyridine ring that are to be removed or added. The work described in the second JBC Classic is an extension of the initial work on alcohol dehydrogenase to lactate dehydrogenase, leading to the same conclusions. It is of interest that in these two papers the authors incorrectly designated the 6-position of the pyridine ring as the site of oxidation-reduction. They pointed out in an addendum to the first paper that M. E. Pullman had just reported (3) that the site of reduction was the 4-position, which is correct, but the validity of their work is independent of the position reduced.

Vennesland made several extended visits to work with Otto Warburg at the Max Planck Institute for Cell Physiology in Berlin, and Warburg offered her a position as both Director and his successor. She left the University of Chicago for Berlin in 1968. Soon after arriving, however, the circumstances, both personal and scientific, proved unsatisfactory and she moved to a nearby Max Planck Institute designated by the Max Planck Gesellschaft as Forschungstelle Vennesland or literally Vennesland research place. Her studies during this period focused on nitrate assimilation by photosynthetic organisms and included numerous noteworthy accomplishments before her retirement in 1984. Vennesland received many honors for her research including the Stephen Hales Prize from the Society of Plant Physiologists (1950), an honorary degree from Mount Holyoke College (1960), and the Garvin Medal of the American Chemical Society. She was revered by her students and post docs and was an excellent role model, particularly for women in science.

In 1953, shortly after the work for these JBC Classics was completed, Vennesland's collaborator Frank H. Westheimer returned to Harvard where he had been a Ph.D. student with James B. Conant and E. P. Kohler. In his distinguished research career Westheimer was concerned with the mechanisms of both chemical and enzymatic reactions. He was an early pioneer in the field of molecular mechanics and invented photoaffinity labeling, as well as the application of pseudorotation to phosphate ester chemistry. As one of the most distinguished physical-organic chemists of his generation, he was the recipient of countless honors including election to the National Academy of Sciences (1954) and the National Medal of Science (1986).

Robert D. Simoni, Robert L. Hill, and Martha Vaughan

REFERENCES

1. Conn, E., and Solomonson, L. (1994) *Women Pioneers in Plant Biology: Birgit Vennesland*, Women in Plant Biology Committee of the American Society of Plant Biologists (http://www.aspb.org/committees_societies/women/pioneers.cfm)
2. JBC Classics: Conant, J. B., Cramer, R. D., Hastings, A. B., Klemperer, F. W., Solomon, A. K., and Vennesland, B. (1941) *J. Biol. Chem.* **137,** 557–566; Solomon, A. K., Vennesland, B., Klemperer, F. W., Buchanan, J. M., and Hastings, A. B. (1941) *J. Biol. Chem.* **140,** 171–182 (http://www.jbc.org/cgi/content/full/279/2/e2)
3. Pullman, M. E. (1953) *Fed. Proc.* **12,** 255

THE JOURNAL OF BIOLOGICAL CHEMISTRY
© 2004 by The American Society for Biochemistry and Molecular Biology, Inc.

Vol. 279, No. 4, Issue of January 23, p. e4, 2004
Printed in U.S.A.

Classics

A PAPER IN A SERIES REPRINTED TO CELEBRATE THE CENTENARY OF THE JBC IN 2005

JBC Centennial
1905–2005
100 Years of Biochemistry and Molecular Biology

The Purification of Diphtheria Toxin by Alwin M. Pappenheimer, Jr.

Diphtheria Toxin. I. Isolation and Characterization of a Toxic Protein from Cornynebacterium Diphtheriæ Filtrates
(Pappenheimer, A. M., Jr. (1937) *J. Biol. Chem.* 120, 543–553)

Alwin M. Pappenheimer Jr. (1908–1995) was born in Cedarhurst, New York. His father, Alwin M. Pappenheimer, was a distinguished pathologist at the College of Physicians and Surgeons at Columbia University. Among his father's many contributions was his discovery of the link between light and bone deposition, which was published in a previous JBC Classic (1). Pappenheimer grew up in an intellectual household and was interested in science from an early age. He entered Harvard in 1925 at the age of 17; he was among the first students to enroll in the new biochemical sciences tutorial. Appropriately, he later returned to Harvard and succeeded John T. Edsall, author of a previous JBC Classic (2), as Chairman of the Board of Tutors of the Biochemical Sciences Program. After choosing graduate school rather than medical school, Pappenheimer entered the graduate program in organic chemistry at Harvard with James B. Conant as his advisor even though he was determined already at the time to have a career in biological research. When he completed his Ph.D. work in 1932, in the midst of the Great Depression, although jobs were difficult to find he was able to spend 1 year as a postdoctoral fellow with Hans Zinsser at Harvard studying pneumococcal polysaccharides. This was followed by a 2-year National Research Council Fellowship with Sir Henry Dale at the National Institute of Medical Research in London working on the isolation of a bacterial growth factor called "sporogenes vitamin." This experience sparked his future interests in isolation of a bacterial toxin.

In 1935, Pappenheimer returned to Cambridge, Massachusetts without a job but with the plan in mind "to isolate a pure potent bacterial toxin and to find out what makes it so toxic" (3).[1] He discussed his ideas with J. Howard Mueller in the Department of Bacteriology at Harvard, another author of a previous JBC Classic (4). Mueller helped him to obtain a Bradford Fellowship at Harvard. He was provided space and some technical support at the Jamaica Plains antitoxin and vaccine laboratory where the work reported in this JBC Classic was done.

Attempts to purify diphtheria toxin had been frustrated because the bacterial culture medium from which the toxin was to be isolated contained a complex mixture of protein, and the purification of toxin free of contaminating culture components had been proven impossible. Pappenheimer set out to devise a better defined culture medium without high molecular weight ingredients to interfere with toxin purification. He was successful in optimizing growth conditions and succeeded in the complete purification of the toxin, as reported in this JBC Classic. The modification of the growth medium had ensured that it contained no ammonium sulfate-precipitable material permitting separation and purification of the toxin by differential ammonium sulfate fractionation. This was the first bacterial toxin purified in crystalline form and brought Pappenheimer great international recognition.

In 1939, Pappenheimer moved to the University of Pennsylvania as an Assistant Professor of Bacteriology but after only 2 years was recruited to the Department of Bacteriology at New

---

[1] All biographical material was taken from this source.

Alwin M. Pappenheimer, Jr. Photo courtesy of the National Library of Medicine.

York University (NYU) by the new chairman Colin E. MacLeod. MacLeod and Pappenheimer built a new Department of Microbiology while the latter continued his work on bacterial growth and toxin production. His research was interrupted by his service as an Army captain in World War II but resumed when he returned to NYU in 1945. After MacLeod left NYU for the University of Pennsylvania, Pappenheimer became chairman of the Department of Microbiology, but John T. Edsall soon recruited him to return to Harvard as Professor of Biology and Chairman of the Board of Tutors in Biochemical Sciences, the program in which he had been enrolled as an undergraduate.

After achieving his first goal with the purification of diphtheria toxin, Pappenheimer, his students, and others worked on discovering the mechanism of its toxicity. With R. John Collier, he showed that diphtheria toxin inhibited protein synthesis in HeLa cells and in HeLa cell extracts (5). Then Collier in 1966–1967 showed that elongation factor 2, EF-2, was inactivated by diphtheria toxin in the presence of NAD and in 1968–1969 D. Michael Gill described the ADP-ribosylation reaction catalyzed by diphtheria toxin, which results in the inactivation of EF-2.

Pappenheimer received many honors for his work including the Eli Lilly Award in 1942 and election to the National Academy of Sciences in 1973. Together with his former student R. John Collier, Pappenheimer was awarded the Paul Ehrlich Prize and Gold Medal.

Robert D. Simoni, Robert L. Hill, and Martha Vaughan

REFERENCES

1. JBC Classics: Hess, A. F., Unger, L. J., and Pappenheimer, A. M. (1922) *J. Biol. Chem.* **50,** 77–81 (http://www.jbc.org/cgi/content/full/277/23/e12)
2. JBC Classics: Edsall, J. T. (1930) *J. Biol. Chem.* **89,** 289–313; Cohn, E. J., Edsall, J. T., and Blanchard, M. H. (1933) *J. Biol. Chem.* **105,** 319–326 (http://www.jbc.org/cgi/content/full/277/33/29351)
3. Lawrence, H. S. (1999) Biographical memoir of Alwin Max Pappenheimer, Jr. *Natl. Acad. Sci.* **77,** 3–18
4. JBC Classics: Mueller, J. H. (1923) *J. Biol. Chem.* **56,** 157–169 (http://www.jbc.org/cgi/content/full/277/25/e14)
5. Collier, R. J., and Pappenheimer, A. M. (1964) *J. Exp. Med.* **120,** 1007–1018, 1019–1039

THE JOURNAL OF BIOLOGICAL CHEMISTRY
© 2004 by The American Society for Biochemistry and Molecular Biology, Inc.

Vol. 279, No. 41, Issue of October 8, p. e5, 2004
Printed in U.S.A.

Classics

A PAPER IN A SERIES REPRINTED TO CELEBRATE THE CENTENARY OF THE JBC IN 2005

JBC Centennial
1905–2005
100 Years of Biochemistry and Molecular Biology

The Discovery of Avidin by Esmond E. Snell

A Constituent of Raw Egg White Capable of Inactivating Biotin *in Vitro*
(Eakin, R. E., Snell, E. E., and Williams, R. J. (1940) *J. Biol. Chem.* **136,** 801–802)

The Concentration and Assay of Avidin, the Injury-producing Protein in Raw Egg White
(Eakin, R. E., Snell, E. E., and Williams, R. J. (1941) *J. Biol. Chem.* **140,** 535–543)

Esmond Emerson Snell (1914–2003) was born in Salt Lake City, Utah. After receiving his Bachelor's degree in biochemistry from Brigham Young University in 1935, Snell was awarded a $400 scholarship to attend the University of Wisconsin in Madison. There he worked with W. H. Peterson, a biochemist interested in microbial metabolism. Snell's thesis project involved identifying growth factors for lactic acid bacteria by starting with a simple medium and determining what supplements were necessary for growth. Along with Frank Strong, Snell published an assay for riboflavin, which was the first widely used microbiological assay method for a vitamin and served as a prototype for assays for each of the B vitamins (1). (Incidentally, this paper was originally submitted to the *Journal of Biological Chemistry* (JBC), but it was rejected on the grounds that it was not biochemical enough and was more suited to a bacteriology journal.)

Snell received his Ph.D. in 1938 and a year later joined Roger J. Williams at the University of Texas in Austin for a postdoctoral fellowship. His first project was to purify a new yeast growth factor that Williams and Robert E. Eakin discovered and named "biotic acid." Because Koegl and Toennis (2) had identified biotin 3 years before, Williams requested a few micrograms of biotin from Koegl to differentiate between the two growth factors. Within a month, Snell found that biotin and biotic acid were one and the same. Nonetheless, Snell continued to study biotin, and this work is the subject of the two JBC Classics reprinted here.

In the first paper of this set of JBC Classics, Snell reports on the finding that biotin can be inactivated *in vitro* by commercial egg albumin. Previous research had shown that chicks on a diet of raw egg whites were deficient in biotin despite an abundance of the vitamin in their diet, indicating that something in the egg whites was sequestering biotin (3). To see if this interaction could be replicated *in vitro*, Snell added egg albumin to a sterile biotin solution and tested it for biotin activity using a yeast assay that he developed (4). Snell also purified the raw egg white component responsible for binding biotin and found that it could be dissociated from biotin by heating but not by dialysis or a change in pH. Later, Snell collaborated with Paul Gyorgy and confirmed that this egg white protein produced "egg white injury" when administered to rats (5).

In the second paper reprinted here, Snell describes a concentration procedure and an assay method for the egg white protein. By this time, the protein had been named "avidin" because of its affinity for biotin (<u>avid</u> + bio<u>tin</u>). Snell determined that an acetone precipitation procedure with a salt extraction worked best for purification of avidin from egg whites. To develop this concentration procedure, Snell also had to come up with an avidin assay. The assay was a simple one in which avidin samples were added to two sterile aliquots of biotin, and one aliquot was heated to 100 °C for 15 min to denature the avidin. Snell then used his yeast assay for biotin to determine the difference in biotin content between the two aliquots and thereby establish how much avidin was present in the samples.

Because biotin was so rare at the time, Snell never imagined that the vitamin would become a reagent for biotinylation of other biofactors and that avidin would be so widely used in purification. However, he did speculate on a future use for avidin when he stated in the first Classic, "The ability of this substance to take up and release biotin specifically and quantitatively suggests its possible use as a tool in the purification of biotin."

Snell went on to make many more important contributions to the field of nutritional biochemistry, including the discovery of the B vitamins folic acid and pantothenic acid, and the coenzyme forms of vitamin B6, pyridoxal, and pyridoxamine. Some of this work on the B vitamins will be the subject of a future JBC Classic.

Snell's philosophy of science can be summarized by a message he once wrote for his students, "Hard work on interesting problems is enjoyable and preferable to aimless wasting of leisure time. It may also lead to unexpected findings that give insights into important related problems. Such unexpected findings—sometimes called "luck"—frequently happen to the active researcher, but only rarely to those who prefer talk to study and work. So one should study and work hard, on interesting problems of any nature, with the purpose of explaining nature and helping others."[1]

Nicole Kresge, Robert D. Simoni, and Robert L. Hill

REFERENCES

1. Snell, E. E., and Strong, F. M. (1939) A microbiological assay for riboflavin. *Ind. Eng. Chem. Anal. Ed.* **11**, 346–350
2. Koegl, F., and Toennis, B. (1936) *Z. Physiol. Chem.* **242**, 43–73
3. Eakin, R. E., McKinley, W. A., and Williams, R. J. (1940) Egg-white injury in chicks and its relationship to a deficiency of vitamin H (biotin). *Science* **92**, 224
4. Snell, E. E., Eakin, R. E., and Williams, R. J. (1940) A quantitative test for biotin and observations regarding its occurrence and properties. *J. Am. Chem. Soc.* **62**, 175–178
5. Gyorgy, P., Rose, C. S., Eakin, R. E., Snell, E. E., and Williams, R. J. (1941) Egg-white injury as the result of nonabsorption or inactivation of biotin. *Science* **93**, 477–478
6. Snell, E. E. (1993) From bacterial nutrition to enzyme structure: a personal odyssey. *Annu. Rev. Biochem.* **62**, 1–27

[1] Virtually all the biographical information for this Classic introduction was taken from Ref. 6 and a paper by Miles and Metzler (E. W. Miles and D. E. Metzler (2004) Esmond Emerson Snell (1914–2003), submitted for publication).

THE JOURNAL OF BIOLOGICAL CHEMISTRY
© 2004 by The American Society for Biochemistry and Molecular Biology, Inc.

Vol. 279, No. 47, Issue of November 19, p. e6, 2004
Printed in U.S.A.

Classics

A PAPER IN A SERIES REPRINTED TO CELEBRATE THE CENTENARY OF THE JBC IN 2005

JBC Centennial
1905–2005
100 Years of Biochemistry and Molecular Biology

The Characterization of Intestinal Peptidases by Emil L. Smith

The Peptidases of Intestinal Mucosa
(Smith, E. L., and Bergmann, M. (1944) *J. Biol. Chem.* 153, 627–651)

Emil L. Smith was born in New York City in 1911. Unlike many other prominent scientists, Smith was not especially interested in science as a child. Says Smith, "It has always intrigued me to learn that so many of my fellow scientists came to their interest in science early in life—because of a gift of a chemistry set or a telescope, or because they observed nature at first hand. I was a late starter and came to science largely by accident and by what, in retrospect, seems a process of drifting first to my interest in science and later to biochemistry" (1).[1]

At age 16, Smith enrolled as a premedical student at Columbia University, because "the required courses in the sciences could lead to another type of career." Fortunately, Smith's attitude changed during his sophomore year when two gifted teachers stimulated his interest in biology and organic chemistry. After graduating, Smith remained at Columbia to do a Ph.D. on photosynthesis in Selig Hecht's laboratory.

By the time he finished his graduate studies in 1936, Smith realized a revolution was happening in biochemistry as more and more physiological phenomena were being attributed to the activity of proteins. Although he had a teaching position as Instructor at Columbia, in 1938 he decided to go to Cambridge University on a Guggenheim Fellowship to work with David Keilin. There he studied the chlorophyll-protein complex until the war forced him to return to the U.S., where he finished his fellowship work with Hubert Bradford Vickery at the Connecticut Agricultural Experiment Station in New Haven.

In 1940, he joined Max Bergmann at the Rockefeller Institute. Bergmann had come to the U.S. from Germany because of the rise of Adolph Hitler and the National Socialist government. He had been the Director of the Institut für Lederforschung in Berlin and a student of the prominent German chemist Emil Fischer, who pioneered the study of protein and enzyme chemistry. His laboratory at the Rockefeller provided an opportunity to learn protein and enzyme chemistry without going to Europe, and notable biochemists who worked with Bergmann included Joseph S. Fruton (Yale), William H. Stein (Rockefeller), Stanford Moore (Rockefeller), Carl Nieman (Cal Tech), Klaus Hofmann (Pittsburgh), Heinz Fraenkel-Conrat (University of California, Berkeley), and Paul Zamecnik (Harvard). Bergmann's laboratory was devoted to developing methods of amino acid analysis and the synthesis of synthetic peptides to study proteolytic enzyme specificity. Bergmann suggested that Smith examine the specificity of intestinal erepsin, which is the subject of the *Journal of Biological Chemistry* (JBC) Classic reprinted here.

The motivation behind Bergmann's suggestion was his irritation with a report that the crude enzyme preparation hydrolyzed both L-leucylglycine and D-leucylglycine, which would contradict his "polyaffinity theory." By purifying what was known as "leucylpeptidase" from the crude intestinal extract, Smith was able to show that the activity toward D-leucylglycine was removed, proving that distinct enzymes cause the splitting of the two stereoisomeric peptides. Smith also found that leucylpeptidase became increasingly responsive to activation by Mn^{2+} and Mg^{2+} during the course of purification and that the enzyme displayed equal

---

[1] All of the biographical information for this Classic introduction was taken from Ref. 1.

Emil L. Smith. Photo courtesy of the National Library of Medicine.

ability to hydrolyze L-leucylglycine, L-leucylglycylglycine, and L-leucinamide. Because these results indicated that leucylpeptidase was neither a dipeptidase nor a carboxypeptidase but actually an aminoexopeptidase, he renamed it L-leucine-aminoexopeptidase. Smith purified and characterized a variety of other intestinal peptidases, many of which he found also required the addition of metal ions to maintain activity.

In 1942 Smith was offered a position at E. R. Squibb and Sons to aid in the development and production of purified human plasma proteins for use by the armed forces. After 4 years of being "knee-deep in blood and other large scale protein fractionations," Smith left Squibb to head up his own laboratory at the University of Utah, College of Medicine.

In 1958 Emanuel Margoliash joined Smith's laboratory and sequenced cytochrome c from several evolutionarily diverse species. Smith and Margoliash found that cytochromes from closely related species showed only a few differences in sequence whereas more distantly related species had a greater number of variant residues. Later Emile Zuckerkandl and Linus Pauling (2) proposed the idea of the molecular clock based on the sequences of hemoglobin published earlier by others. Smith and Margoliash's cytochrome c sequences (3) supported this idea. Zuckerkandl and Pauling's theory (2) also proposed that mutations accumulate at an approximately constant rate in DNA as long as the gene retains its original function. Thus, the difference between the DNA sequences of two species should be proportional to the time since the species diverged from a common ancestor.

Smith remained in Utah until 1963, when he accepted an appointment as Chairman of the Department of Biological Chemistry at the University of California, School of Medicine in Los Angeles. He eventually terminated his research activities in June 1979 when he was awarded the title of Emeritus.

In addition to the above mentioned work, Emil Smith has made numerous other valuable contributions to the field of biochemistry, including determining the sequences of the plant proteinase papain, the subtilisins, and several glutamate dehydrogenases. In 1969, Smith teamed up with James Bonner to sequence cow and pea histone H4. They determined that the two proteins were almost identical, which is the subject of a future JBC Classic. He also spearheaded, in 1954, the writing of the classic textbook *Principles of Biochemistry* with Abraham White, Philip Handler, and DeWitt Stetten. Smith was recognized for his many scientific achievements with his election to the National Academy of Sciences in 1962.

Nicole Kresge, Robert D. Simoni, and Robert L. Hill

REFERENCES

1. Smith, E. L. (1982) The evolution of a biochemist. *Of Oxygen, Fuels, and Living Matter, Part 2* (Semenza, G., ed) John Wiley & Sons, Ltd., New York
2. Zuckerkandl, E. and Pauling, L. (1965) Evolutionary divergence and convergence in proteins. *Evolving Genes and Proteins* (Bryson, V., and Vogel, H. J., eds) pp. 97–166, Academic Press, New York
3. Margoliash, E., and Smith. E. L. (1965) Structural and functional aspects of cytochrome c in relation to evolution. *Evolving Genes and Proteins* (Bryson, V., and Vogel, H. J., eds) pp. 221–242, Academic Press, New York

THE JOURNAL OF BIOLOGICAL CHEMISTRY
© 2004 by The American Society for Biochemistry and Molecular Biology, Inc.

Vol. 279, No. 48, Issue of November 26, p. e7, 2004
Printed in U.S.A.

Classics

A PAPER IN A SERIES REPRINTED TO CELEBRATE THE CENTENARY OF THE JBC IN 2005

JBC Centennial
1905–2005
100 Years of Biochemistry and Molecular Biology

Selman Waksman: the Father of Antibiotics

The Chemical Nature of Actinomycin, an Anti-microbial Substance Produced by Actinomyces Antibioticus
(Waksman, S. A., and Tishler, M. (1942) *J. Biol. Chem.* 142, 519–528)

Selman Abraham Waksman (1888–1973) was born in the rural Ukrainian town of Novaya Priluka. The town and its nearby villages were surrounded by a rich black soil that supported abundant agricultural life. Although Waksman did not do much farming as a child, the chemistry of the fertile soil incited a curiosity in him that would eventually influence the direction of his future endeavors.

In 1910, after completing his matriculation diploma, Waksman followed the example of several relatives and migrated to the United States. He worked for a few years on a family farm in New Jersey and then enrolled in Rutgers College. There he studied bacteria in culture samples from successive soil layers, which resulted in his introduction to the actinomycetes. These bacteria became an enduring interest that Waksman studied for both his Master's and Doctorate degrees and on which he would eventually become a major expert.

After receiving his doctorate from the University of California, Berkeley, in 1918, Waksman secured a position at the Rutgers Bacteriology Department where he continued his research on soil microflora. Several years later, a young French biologist named Rene Dubois joined his laboratory. By 1927, Dubois was studying the one-on-one effects of soil organisms in decomposing cellulose and was beginning an approach that would lead to modern antibiotics. In collaboration with Oswald Avery at the Rockefeller Institute Hospital, Dubois isolated a soil bacterium that could attack the capsular polysaccharide of *Streptococcus pneumoniae* (1). This discovery inspired Waksman to look for more pre-existing antibacterial organisms in soil samples.

By 1940, Waksman and H. Boyd Woodruff had devised a technique for identifying natural substances with antibacterial properties (2). The screening was done by looking for growth inhibition zones around single colonies of systematically isolated soil microbes, grown under a variety of culture conditions, and then testing the inhibition on specifically targeted pathogenic bacteria.

The first true antibiotic Waksman identified was from *Actinomyces antibioticus*, a member of the actinomycetes family (3). The microbe produced a substance, actinomycin, that had both bacteriostatic and bactericidal properties. Waksman and Woodruff determined that actinomycin could be separated with petroleum ether into two constituents, an orange-red colored actinomycin A and a colorless actinomycin B. Actinomycin A had strong bacteriostatic and bactericidal properties whereas actinomycin B displayed only bactericidal characteristics.

In the *Journal of Biological Chemistry* (JBC) Classic reprinted here, Waksman and Max Tishler, who was featured in a previous JBC Classic (4), describe the nature and properties of actinomycin A. The pair found that actinomycin is a quinine-like pigment with a molecular formula of either $C_{41}H_{56}N_8O_{11}$, $C_{37}H_{50}N_7O_{10}$, or $C_{36}H_{49}N_7O_9 \cdot \frac{1}{2}H_2O$. The compound is highly active against various gram-positive bacteria but less active against gram-negative organisms. Unfortunately, Waksman and Tishler also discovered that actinomycin is extremely toxic to experimental animals and thus of little therapeutic value.

Waksman followed this initial failure with a comprehensive program of screening actinomycetes for their ability to produce antibacterials. He identified more than 20 new natural

Selman Waksman. Photo courtesy of the National Library of Medicine.

inhibitory substances, including streptomycin and neomycin, and proposed the now standard term "antibiotics" for this class of natural growth inhibitors.

With his discovery of streptomycin in 1944, Waksman initiated a collaboration with Merck and Company. Tishler led the microbiological group that developed the fermentation process for producing bulk quantities of streptomycin. As a result of his success in developing manufacturing processes for products such as streptomycin, riboflavin, cortisone, vitamin B_{12}, and penicillin, Tisher eventually became the first president of the Merck Sharp & Dohme Research Laboratory Division of Merck & Co. Inc. and remained there until 1970, running the research programs.

Waksman patented and licensed his promising antibiotics, but rather than keeping the money for himself, he gave 80% of his patent earnings to Rutgers University. In 1951 he established an Institute of Microbiology in association with Rutgers, the construction of which was completed in 1954. The institute was endowed and supported by the generous assignment of 80% of Waksman's streptomycin patent royalties to Rutgers. Waksman's philanthropic nature was further evident when he established the Foundation for Microbiology in 1951 and assigned one-half of his 20% personal royalties for its support.

During his lifetime, Waksman received some 66 awards and 22 honorary degrees for his scientific work. He was elected to the National Academy of Sciences in 1942. However, Waksman's greatest honor came when he won the Nobel Prize in physiology or medicine in 1952 "for his discovery of streptomycin, the first antibiotic effective against tuberculosis." This distinction earned him the title of "Father of Antibiotics" and gained him well deserved recognition for his philanthropy and contributions to science and medicine.[1]

Nicole Kresge, Robert D. Simoni, and Robert L. Hill

REFERENCES

1. Dubois, R. J. (1939) Bactericidal effect of an extract of a soil bacillus on Gram-positive bacteria. *Proc. Soc. Exp. Biol. Med.* **70**, 1–17
2. Waksman, S. A., and Woodruff, H. B. (1940) The soil as a source of microorganisms antagonistic to disease-producing bacteria. *J. Bacteriol.* **40**, 581–600
3. Waksman, S. A., and Woodruff, H. B. (1941) *Actinomyces antibioticus*, a new soil organism antagonistic to pathogenic and non-pathogenic bacteria. *J. Bacteriol.* **42**, 231–249
4. JBC Classics: Fieser, L. F., Tishler, M., and Sampson, W. L. (1941) *J. Biol. Chem.* **137**, 659–692 (http://www.jbc.org/cgi/content/full/278/52/e4)
5. Hotchkiss, R. D. (2003) Biographical memoir of Selman Abraham Waksman, Vol. 83, pp. 320–343, National Academy of Sciences, Washington, D. C.

[1] All biographical information on Selman Waksman was taken from Ref. 5.

THE JOURNAL OF BIOLOGICAL CHEMISTRY
Vol. 279, No. 48, Issue of November 26, p. e8, 2004
Printed in U.S.A.

Classics

A PAPER IN A SERIES REPRINTED TO CELEBRATE THE CENTENARY OF THE JBC IN 2005

JBC Centennial
1905–2005
100 Years of Biochemistry and Molecular Biology

Blacktongue and Nicotinic Acid Metabolism: Philip Handler

The Biochemical Defect in Nicotinic Acid Deficiency
(Handler, P., and Dann, W. J. (1942) *J. Biol. Chem.* **145,** 145–153)

Synthesis of Nicotinamide Mononucleotide by Human Erythrocytes *in Vitro*
(Leder, I. G., and Handler, P. (1951) *J. Biol. Chem.* **189,** 889–899)

Philip Handler (1917–1981) was born in New York City. As a child, he spent many summers on his grandparents' farm, which aroused in him a curiosity about the nature of living things. As a result, when Handler entered the College of the City of New York in 1933, he majored in biology and chemistry in preparation for a career in medicine. However, a biochemistry course taught by Benjamin Harrow, a particularly vibrant and exciting lecturer, converted Handler, and instead of entering medical school he attended graduate school at the University of Illinois.

Despite the fact that the University of Illinois had a large number of prominent faculty members, Handler did his thesis research with the newly appointed Herbert E. Carter, who was the subject of a previous *Journal of Biological Chemistry* (JBC) Classic (1). Due to the lack of available scholarships, Handler also took a part-time job at the U.S. Department of Agriculture on the Illinois campus, working in a laboratory that studied soybeans and industrial byproducts. Although he had to divide his time between Carter's laboratory and the soybean laboratory, Handler managed to finish his doctorate in 3 years and graduate in 1939.

At Illinois, Handler developed an interest in nutritional research and thus chose to do his postdoctoral work at the Duke University School of Medicine with William J. Dann, a nutritionist who studied human pellagra and the related disease in dogs, blacktongue. At the time, pellagra, which resulted from a dietary deficiency of nicotinic acid, was prevalent in the southern United States. Handler and Dann developed a method to determine the levels of nicotinic acid and pyridine nucleotides in the tissues of normal and vitamin-deficient animals. These studies, which established a link between the disease and metabolism of nicotinic acid, were published by Handler and Dann between 1940 and 1942 in a series of nine papers (2–9). The first JBC Classic reprinted here is from this series.

In this paper, Handler and Dann present their finding that saline alleviates the symptoms of blacktongue in dogs. Noticing that blacktongue is often accompanied by severe diarrhea and the refusal of the dogs to eat or drink, Hander and Dann hypothesized that, "dehydration and electrolyte imbalance might be factors of primary importance in death due to nicotinic acid deficiency." To test this, they administered large volumes of 0.9% NaCl solution twice daily to dogs with blacktongue. The symptoms of blacktongue disappeared within about 2 weeks, and the dogs' lives were extended by as many as 180 days. When the animals finally did succumb to the disease, their nicotinic acid deficiencies were seldom as extreme as in classic cases of blacktongue.

Subsequently, Handler observed that blacktongue was not a disease resulting from a lack of dietary nicotinic acid but rather a product of eating corn. It was later shown that corn was deficient in tryptophan, which was a metabolic precursor of nicotinic acid, explaining Handler's observations. These studies prompted Handler to investigate the biosynthesis and degradation of nicotinic acid.

Philip Handler. Photo courtesy of the National Library of Medicine.

In the second JBC Classic reprinted here, Handler and Irwin G. Leder describe the synthesis of nicotinamide mononucleotide by erythrocytes in a solution of inorganic phosphate, glucose, and nicotinamide. Other laboratories had attempted to synthesize pyridine nucleotides from nicotinic acid but had only been able to produce small amounts of diphosphopyridine nucleotide. Using nicotinamide, rather than nicotinic acid, Handler and Leder were able to obtain 10 times the normal pyridine nucleotide concentration. They also found that synthesis could be optimized by washing the cells prior to incubation to remove "an inhibitor which was not associated with the plasma." Using an enzyme that forms diphosphopyridine nucleotide from ATP and nicotinamide mononucleotide to assay their product, Handler and Leder were able to demonstrate that 75–95% of the product was nicotinamide mononucleotide, and the remainder was diphosphopyridine nucleotide.

Handler, along with Jack Preiss, later determined the steps leading to NAD synthesis from nicotinic acid and ATP and showed that the degradation of NAD yields nicotinamide and adenosine diphosphoribose. These pathways, now called the Handler-Preiss cycle, helped elucidate one on the major principles of biochemistry: that major metabolic pathways are essentially irreversible and that the interconversion of two metabolites usually proceeds by different metabolic pathways.

Handler remained at Duke University for the duration of his research career. He was promoted to associate professor of biochemistry in 1945, chairman of the Department of Biochemistry in 1950, and James B. Duke professor in 1961. During his time at Duke, Handler transformed the biochemistry department from a small department with limited activities to one of the outstanding research departments in the country. His research activities at Duke encompassed a wide variety of subjects including coenzyme metabolism, renal hypertension, the mechanisms of hormone action, amino acid metabolism, biological oxidations, the mechanism of action of enzymes, and biochemical evolution. While at Duke, Handler also coauthored the "Principles of Biochemistry" with Abraham White, DeWitt Stetten, and Emil L. Smith.

Handler was also heavily involved in public service at a variety of academic institutions, societies, and government institutions. He served as president of the American Society of Biological Chemists (now the American Society for Biochemistry and Molecular Biology) and chairman of the board of the Federation of American Societies for Experimental Biology (FASEB). He was also appointed to the National Science Board and the President's Science Advisory Committee.

In 1969 Handler was elected president of the National Academy of Sciences and served two 6-year terms. During his 12 years in office he became a major spokesman for science in the U.S. and internationally. He always emphasized that the Academy was not a branch of government but an independent body with a mandate to advise the government on science policy. Handler's leadership as president was especially important during the Vietnam War, the arms race with the Soviet Union, and the violation of the human rights of scientists worldwide. In recognition of his great contributions to science, Handler was awarded the National Medal of Science by Ronald Reagan in 1981.[1]

Nicole Kresge, Robert D. Simoni, and Robert L. Hill

REFERENCES

1. JBC Classics: Carter, H. E. (1935) *J. Biol. Chem.* **112**, 769–773 (http://www.jbc.org/cgi/content/full/277/41/e29)
2. Dann, W. J., Kohn, H. I., and Handler, P. (1940) The effect of pyrazine acids and quinolinic acid on the V-factor content of human blood and upon canine blacktongue. *J. Nutr.* **20**, 477–490
3. Dann, W. J., and Handler, P. (1941) Inactivity of nicotinuric acid in canine blacktongue. *Proc. Soc. Exp. Biol. Med.* **48**, 355–356
4. Dann, W. J., and Handler, P. (1941) The quantitative estimation of nicotinic acid in animal tissues. *J. Biol. Chem.* **140**, 201–213
5. Dann, W. J., and Handler, P. (1941) Synthesis of nicotinic acid by the chick embryo *J. Biol. Chem.* **140**, 935–936
6. Handler, P. and Dann, W. J. (1941) The nicotinic acid and coenzyme content of animal tissues. *J. Biol. Chem.* **140**, 739–745
7. Dann, W. J., and Handler, P. (1941) The nicotinic acid and coenzyme content of the tissues of normal and blacktongue dogs. *J. Nutr.* **22**, 409–414
8. Dann, W. J., and Handler, P. (1942) The nicotonic acid content of meat. *J. Nutr.* **24**, 153–158
9. Handler, P., and Dann, W. J. (1942) The inhibition of rat growth by nicotinamide. *J. Biol. Chem.* **146**, 357–368
10. Smith, E. L., and Hill, R. L. (1985) Biographical memoir of Philip Handler, Vol. 55, pp. 305–353, National Academy of Sciences, Washington, D. C.

---

[1] All biographical information on Philip Handler was taken from Ref. 10.

THE JOURNAL OF BIOLOGICAL CHEMISTRY
© 2004 by The American Society for Biochemistry and Molecular Biology, Inc.

Vol. 279, No. 49, Issue of December 3, p. e9, 2004
Printed in U.S.A.

Classics

A PAPER IN A SERIES REPRINTED TO CELEBRATE THE CENTENARY OF THE JBC IN 2005

JBC Centennial
1905–2005
100 Years of Biochemistry and Molecular Biology

The Characterization of Ferritin and Apoferritin by Leonor Michaelis and Sam Granick

Ferritin. I. Physical and Chemical Properties of Horse Spleen Ferritin
(Granick, S. (1942) *J. Biol. Chem.* 146, 451–461)

Ferritin. II. Apoferritin of Horse Spleen
(Granick, S., and Michaelis, L. (1943) *J. Biol. Chem.* 147, 91–97)

Leonor Michaelis (1875–1949) was born in Berlin, Germany. He received his doctorate from Berlin University in 1897 and then became a private assistant to Paul Ehrlich in Berlin where he devised a method for *in vivo* mitochondrial staining with Janus green. After working for Moritz Litten and later Ernst Viktor von Leyden, Michaelis accepted a position at the Urban Hospital in Berlin. There he worked on a variety of bacteriology and physicochemical problems, including developing the hydrogen electrode to measure hydrogen ion concentration (pH).

In 1912, Maud Leonora Menten (1879–1960), one of the first Canadian women to become a doctor, came to Berlin to spend a year working with Michaelis. In Berlin, she studied the effects of substrate concentration on invertase enzyme activity and devised an equation with Michaelis to describe the relationship between reaction rate and substrate concentration (1). The Michaelis-Menten Equation has been called the foundation of modern enzymology and is now a standard for most enzyme-kinetic measurements. After her time in Berlin, Menten went to the University of Chicago and earned a Ph.D. in biochemistry. In 1918 she joined the Department of Pathology at the University of Pittsburgh medical school and published more than 70 papers during her time there. Despite her productivity, Menten was not promoted to full professor until 1948, one year before she retired from her position at the University of Pittsburgh.[1]

Michaelis left Berlin in 1922 when he was offered a professorship in biochemistry at the University of Nagoya in Japan. He remained in Japan until 1926 when he moved to America to be a resident lecturer at Johns Hopkins University. After three years at Johns Hopkins, Michaelis joined the Rockefeller Institute in New York. Michaelis' subsequent research in America focused mainly on oxidation-reduction processes, although he wasn't opposed to branching out into other areas as well.

In 1939, Sam Granick (1909–1977), who had just earned his Ph.D. from the University of Michigan, joined Michaelis' laboratory to study iron metabolism. Between 1942 and 1946, Granick and Michaelis published a series of papers on ferritin and ferric compounds in the *Journal of Biological Chemistry* (JBC). The series, which was done in collaboration with Alexandre Rothen, not only formed the basis of our current knowledge of ferritin but also presented convincing evidence which contradicted previous beliefs about the structure and composition of the protein. The first and second papers in this series are reprinted here as JBC Classics.

Prior to the publication of Granick and Michaelis' JBC series, Victor Laufberger had isolated a protein from horse spleen by crystallizing it as a cadmium salt (2). Because the protein contained over 20% iron by dry weight, he named it "ferritin" from the Latin "ferratus" or "bound with iron." Several years later, Kuhn, Sorensen, and Birkofer published a paper in

---

[1] All the biographical information on Maud Menten was taken from Ref. 11.

which they confirmed Laufberger's findings and concluded that ferritin consisted of 54.5% protein, 12.1% nucleic acid, and 35% $Fe^{3+}OH$ (3). Because it worked out that there was an iron atom for every almost every peptide group, Kuhn, Sorensen, and Birkofer proposed that iron was incorporated into ferritin via bonds between single iron atoms and CONH groups.

In the first paper in this set of JBC Classics, Granick describes the isolation of horse spleen ferritin by crystallization and reports on his characterization of the purified protein. Unlike Kuhn *et al.,* Granick did not find evidence of nucleic acid in ferritin. He did, however, deduce that purified ferritin was inhomogeneous, based on ultracentrifugation and solubility experiments, as well as the observation that different crystallized ferritin samples contained different amounts of iron and phosphorus. Granick concluded that ferritin is "made up of brown particles having a molecular weight in the neighborhood of several million and grading down to colorless particles the size of large globulin molecules."

In the second paper reprinted here, Granick and Michaelis describe how they removed iron from ferritin to produce apoferritin. They did this by reducing the iron from the ferric to the ferrous state "in a solution not acid enough to denature the protein yet acid enough to be compatible with the existence of ferrous ions in solution." Dialysis then produced a colorless protein which could be crystallized in the same conditions as ferritin.

Granick and Michaelis' subsequent analysis of apoferritin unearthed two results which helped explain Granick's previous observations. First, the scientists discovered that apoferritin, unlike ferritin, is homogeneous. Second, they found that the only way to reinsert iron into apoferritin was by adding what they called "non-crystallizable ferritin" to a solution of apoferritin. This "non-crystallizable ferritin" was the iron-rich brown mother liquor that remained after ferritin was crystallized with cadmium sulfate. Importantly, they also found that "non-crystallizable ferritin" could not produce ferritin from apoferritin crystals, suggesting the iron was in a colloidal state that was not able to spontaneously diffuse into the crystals. Granick and Michaelis concluded that ferritin's iron does not occur as individual atoms attached to individual peptide groups but is instead present as micelles of colloidal iron that fill the interstices of the protein. This also explained why ferritin was non-homogeneous, the micelles could contain different amounts of iron as well as small amounts of phosphorus and nitrogen.

In the remaining papers in the series (4–10), Granick, Michaelis, and others reported on subsequent discoveries such as the finding that ferritin occurs in a variety of organs in many animal species including humans and that it is used by the body to store iron in the Fe^{3+} state.

Building on the groundwork laid by Granick and Michaelis, enormous amounts of research have added to the initial portrait of ferritin. We now know that ferritin is a 480,000-Da protein with a large cavity that can hold as many as 4,000 iron atoms as a solid oxo-mineral. Studies have also revealed that iron enters ferritin through pores in the protein where it is immediately oxidized and released into the interior of the protein.

After publishing this series of JBC papers, Granick remained at Rockefeller where he worked on chloroplasts, chlorophyll biosynthesis, and iron metabolism until his death. In 1947, he and Keith R. Porter were the first to use an electron microscope to take pictures of chloroplasts, revealing dense grana and disk-like components. In recognition of his numerous contributions to science, Granick was elected to the National Academy of Sciences in 1965.[2]

Michaelis remained at Rockefeller as well and kept up active research until his death. He was elected to the National Academy of Sciences in 1943 and became a Fellow of the New York Academy of Sciences and the American Association for the Advancement of Science. He also received the honorary degree of LL.D. from the University of California, Los Angeles, in 1945.[3]

Nicole Kresge, Robert D. Simoni, and Robert L. Hill

REFERENCES

1. Michaelis, L, and Menten, M. L. (1913) Die Kinetik der Invertinwerkung. *Biochem. Z.* **49,** 333
2. Laufberger V. (1937) Sur la Cristallisation de la Ferritine. *Bull. Soc. Chim. Biol.* **19,** 1575–1582
3. Kuhn, R., Sorensen, N. A., and Birkofer, L. (1940) *Ber. Chem. Ges.* **73B,** 823
4. Michaelis, L., Coryell, C. D., and Granick, S. (1943) Ferritin. III. The magnetic properties of ferritin and some other colloidal ferric compounds. *J. Biol. Chem.* **148,** 463–480
5. Granick, S. (1943) Ferritin. IV. Occurrence and immunological properties of ferritin. *J. Biol. Chem.* **149,** 157–167
6. Fankuchen, I. (1943) Ferritin. V. X-ray diffraction data on ferritin and apoferritin. *J. Biol. Chem.* **150,** 57–59

---

[2] All the biographical information on Sam Granick was taken from Ref. 12.
[3] All the biographical information on Leonor Michaelis was taken from Ref. 13.

7. Hahn, P. F., Granick, S., Bale, W. F., and Michaelis, L. (1943) Ferritin. VI. Conversion of inorganic and hemoglobin iron into ferritin iron in the animal body. Storage function of ferritin iron as shown by radioactive and magnetic measurements. *J. Biol. Chem.* **150,** 407–412

8. Greenberg, D. M., Copp, D. H., and Cuthbertson, E. M. (1943) Studies in mineral metabolism with the aid of artificial radioactive isotopes. VII. The distribution and excretion, particularly by way of the bile, of iron, cobalt, and manganese. *J. Biol. Chem.* **147,** 749–756

9. Granick, S., and Hahn, P. F. (1944) Ferritin. VIII. Speed of uptake of iron by the liver and its conversion to ferritin iron. *J. Biol. Chem.* **155,** 661–669

10. Granick, S. (1946) Ferritin. IX. Increase of the protein apoferritin in the gastrointestinal mucosa as a direct response to iron feeding. The function of ferritin in the regulation of iron absorption. *J. Biol. Chem.* **164,** 737–746

11. Skloot, R. (2000) Some called her Miss Menten. *Pittmed Magazine* **2,** 18–21

12. Bamberger, W., Prof. Sam Granick, chlorophyll expert, found new protein. *The New York Times*, May 3, 1977, p. 44

13. Michaelis, L, Macinnes, D. A., and Granick, S. (1958) Biographical memoir of Leonor Michaelis. Vol. 31, p. 282, National Academy of Sciences, Washington D. C.

THE JOURNAL OF BIOLOGICAL CHEMISTRY
© 2004 by The American Society for Biochemistry and Molecular Biology, Inc.

Vol. 279, No. 50, Issue of December 10, p. e10, 2004
Printed in U.S.A.

Classics

A PAPER IN A SERIES REPRINTED TO CELEBRATE THE CENTENARY OF THE JBC IN 2005

JBC Centennial
1905–2005
100 Years of Biochemistry and Molecular Biology

Britton Chance: Olympian and Developer of Stop-Flow Methods

The Kinetics of the Enzyme-Substrate Compound of Peroxidase
(Chance, B. (1943) *J. Biol. Chem.* **151,** 553–577)

Britton Chance was born in Wilkes-Barre, Pennsylvania in 1913. He spent many summers during his youth sailing, and his love of the sea was the catalyst for his first significant contribution to science and technology. When he was just a teenager, Chance invented an autosteering device that detected deviations in a ship's course and generated a feedback signal to redirect the ship's steering mechanisms. Later in life, his love of sailing and intense competitive spirit landed him a spot on the U.S. yacht Olympic team where he won a gold medal in the 1952 Olympics.

Chance received his Bachelor's of Science degree from the University of Pennsylvania in 1935 and remained there for graduate school. Around this time, Glenn Millikan, at Cambridge University, had developed a novel stop-flow apparatus to measure the formation of oxymyoglobin resulting from the combination of oxygen with myoglobin (1). During his thesis research, Chance observed that "adding H_2O_2 to a crude preparation of peroxidase gave a colored compound that could go on to oxidize a variety of phenols" (2). He believed it might be possible to study the intermediates in the peroxide interaction if he could make a "micro" version of Millikan's apparatus. So, in 1937, under the supervision of Martin Kilpatrick, he started construction of a rapid-flow apparatus.

In 1938, while still a graduate student at the University of Pennsylvania, Chance was offered a contract by the British General Electric Company to test his autosteering device on a ship going from London to New Zealand and Australia. Shortly after his arrival in London, Chance visited with Millikan hoping to study under him. Millikan accepted him as his research student, and after Chance returned from his voyage he started constructing a second microflow apparatus. He completed the apparatus by 1939 and did some initial studies on luciferase O_2 reactions.

In 1940, Chance returned to Pennsylvania to visit his parents but was unable to return to Cambridge due to the onset of World War II. Fortunately, he was accepted back at the University of Pennsylvania and began construction of a third version of his rapid-flow instrument. Once it was completed, Chance used this new instrument to elucidate the peroxidase enzyme-substrate reactions, which is the subject of the *Journal of Biological Chemistry* (JBC) Classic reprinted here.

At this time, there were many theories about how enzymes worked. Leonor Michaelis, the subject of a previous JBC Classic (3), and Maud Menten had proposed their theory which stated that the relationship between enzymatic activity and enzyme and substrate concentration could be explained by the existence of an intermediate enzyme-substrate compound (4). Their theory was modified by Thaddeus Briggs and J. B. S. Haldane who pointed out that the rate of formation of the intermediate could be limited by the number of collisions between the enzyme and substrate (5). However, at the time, there were no experimental observations of the intermediates, and the reaction velocity constants were lumped into one term, the Michaelis-Menten constant, rather than determined separately.

In his paper, Chance used the reaction between horseradish peroxidase and hydrogen peroxide to prove the existence of the intermediate compound and to determine the rates of

Britton Chance. Photo courtesy of the National Library of Medicine.

$$\text{Peroxidase} + H_2O_2 \rightarrow \text{peroxidase-}H_2O_2 \rightarrow \text{peroxidase} + H_2O + O$$

REACTION 1

formation and breakdown of the enzyme-substrate compound. Chance detected the products of the reaction with ascorbic acid and leucomalachite green, which formed the colored malachite green when oxidized. In his experiments, he filled one syringe of his microflow apparatus with hydrogen peroxide, or a combination of hydrogen peroxide and leucomalachite green, and the other syringe with peroxidase. Pushing the syringe plungers simultaneously caused the reactants to be mixed and to flow down the observation tube. The solution eventually stopped at a photocell and light beam where the progress of the reaction was followed by measuring the concentrations of malachite green and enzyme-substrate compound. By varying substrate or acceptor concentration and measuring the resulting changes in the rate of formation and equilibrium concentration of the peroxidase-H_2O_2 compound, Chance was able to study the kinetics of the reaction intermediate.

Using his data, Chance solved the equations representing the Briggs and Haldane modifications to the Michaelis-Menten theory. He found that the activity of peroxidase could be described by a second-order reaction of the enzyme with H_2O_2, followed by a second-order irreversible reaction of the peroxidase-H_2O_2 intermediate with the hydrogen donor. By making a point by point comparison between experiment and theory, Chance was able to confirm the validity of the Michaelis-Menten theory and the Briggs and Haldane modifications. He later won the Paul Lewis award in enzyme chemistry for this work.

Chance ended up getting two Ph.D. degrees, one in physical chemistry from the University of Pennsylvania and one in biology and physiology from Cambridge University. After the war, he went to Stockholm on a 2-year Guggenheim Fellowship to work with Hugo Theorell. He and Theorell used another version of the stop-flow apparatus to study the kinetics of NAD in alcohol-aldehyde interconversion and found that product release was rate-determining (6). This is now called the Theorell-Chance (T-C) mechanism.

Chance returned to the University of Pennsylvania after his fellowship was over and became Professor of Biophysics and Physical Biochemistry and Director of the Johnson Foundation in

1949. In the early 1950s, he shifted his focus more toward biological phenomenon and studied the control of oxidative phosphorylation in mitochondria. Chance, along with Henry Lardy and later Ron Williams, worked out methods to separate mitochondria from cells and preserve their metabolic activity *in vitro* and invented the dual wavelength spectrophotometer to watch ATP synthesis in mitochondria. Spurred by this success, Chance later developed methods for using optical spectroscopy to study living tissues. In the late 1970s, he was the first to use magnetic resonance spectroscopy on a whole organ, the excised brain of a hedgehog.

Chance has received many honors in recognition of his contributions to science, including election to the National Academy of Science in 1954. He was presented the National Medal of Science in 1974 by President Ford, "For his contributions to our knowledge of cellular and subcellular physiology made through work on enzyme-substrate complexes, on the kinetics of enzyme action, and on the mechanism and control of membrane-bound electron transfer during cellular respiration." Today he remains at the University of Pennsylvania where he is still actively involved in research.[1]

Nicole Kresge, Robert D. Simoni, and Robert L. Hill

REFERENCES

1. Millikan, G. A. (1936) Muscle hemoglobin. *Proc. R. Soc. Lond. Ser. B Biol. Sci.* **120**, 366–388
2. Chance, B. (2004) The stopped-flow method and chemical intermediates in enzyme reactions—a personal essay. *Photosynth. Res.* **80**, 387–400
3. JBC Classics: Granick, S., and Michaelis, L. (1943) *J. Biol. Chem.* **147**, 91–97 (http://www.jbc.org/cgi/content/full/279/49/e9)
4. Michaelis, L, and Menten, M. L. (1913) Die Kinetik der Invertinwerkung. *Biochem. Z.* **49**, 333–369
5. Briggs, G. E., and Haldane, J. B. S. (1925) A note on the kinetics of enzyme action. *Biochem. J.* **19**, 339–339
6. Theorell, H., and Chance, B. (1951) Studies of liver alcohol dehydrogenase. II. The kinetics of the compound of horse liver alcohol dehydrogenase and reduced diphosphopyridine nucleotide. *Acta Chem. Scand.* **5**, 1127–1144
7. Yodh, A. G., and Tromberg, B. J. (2000) Celebrating Britton Chance. *J. Biomed. Optics* **5**, 115–118

---

[1] All biographical information on Britton Chance was taken from Refs. 2 and 7.

THE JOURNAL OF BIOLOGICAL CHEMISTRY
© 2004 by The American Society for Biochemistry and Molecular Biology, Inc.

Vol. 279, No. 51, Issue of December 17, p. e11, 2004
Printed in U.S.A.

Classics

A PAPER IN A SERIES REPRINTED TO CELEBRATE THE CENTENARY OF THE JBC IN 2005

JBC Centennial
1905–2005
100 Years of Biochemistry and Molecular Biology

A Trail of Research in Sulfur Chemistry and Metabolism: the Work of Vincent du Vigneaud

The Utilization of the Methyl Group of Methionine in the Biological Synthesis of Choline and Creatine
(du Vigneaud, V., Cohn, M., Chandler, J. P., Schenck, J. R., and Simmonds, S. (1941) *J. Biol. Chem.* 140, 625–641)

The Structure of Biotin: a Study of Desthiobiotin
(du Vigneaud, V., Melville, D. B., Folkers, K., Wolf, D. E., Mozingo, R., Keresztesy, J. C., and Harris, S. A. (1942) *J. Biol. Chem.* 146, 475–485)

The Sequence of Amino Acids in Oxytocin, with a Proposal for the Structure of Oxytocin
(du Vigneaud, V., Ressler, C., and Trippett, S. (1953) *J. Biol. Chem.* 205, 949–957)

Arginine-Vasotocin, a Synthetic Analogue of the Posterior Pituitary Hormones Containing the Ring of Oxytocin and the Side Chain of Vasopressin
(Katsoyannis, P. G., and du Vigneaud, V. (1958) *J. Biol. Chem.* 233, 1352–1354)

Vincent du Vigneaud (1901–1978) was born in Chicago in 1901. His first exposure to chemistry came in high school, when he and his friends would obtain chemicals from a pharmacist and conduct experiments involving the fabrication of sulfur-containing explosives. Although he did not know it at the time, sulfur would figure prominently later in his life.

When he finished high school, du Vigneaud went to the University of Illinois at Urbana-Champaign to study chemistry. While at Illinois, he was particularly impressed by a lecture given by W. C. Rose on the discovery of insulin by Frederick Banting and Charles Best. After earning his Masters degree in 1924, du Vigneaud received an invitation from John R. Murlin at the University of Rochester to do graduate work on the chemistry of insulin. "The chance to work on the chemistry of insulin transcended all other interests for me, and I accepted Professor Murlin's invitation," said du Vigneaud (1).[1] During his graduate studies, du Vigneaud became intrigued with the fact that insulin contained sulfur and spent the next 2 years studying this phenomenon, coming to the conclusion that sulfur was present in insulin as disulfide linkages.

He finished his degree in 1927 and then began postdoctoral studies on insulin at Johns Hopkins with J. J. Abel, who was a co-founder of the *Journal of Biological Chemistry* (JBC) and author of a previous JBC Classic (2). In Abel's laboratory he collaborated with Oskar Wintersteiner on work that allowed him to conclude that insulin was a protein rather than a small organic molecule bound to a protein carrier, thereby establishing that proteins could be hormones. He then carried out further postdoctoral studies with Max Bergmann (author of a previous JBC Classic (3)) in Germany, where his interest in peptide synthesis began.

In 1929, du Vigneaud was offered a position at the University of Illinois. He stayed there until 1932 when he became Professor and Chairman of Biochemistry at George Washington University Medical School. In 1938, he left George Washington to head the Department of Biochemistry at Cornell Medical College in New York City where he remained until 1967 when he joined the Chemistry Department at Cornell University in Ithaca. du Vigneaud's scientific

---

[1] All biographical information on Vincent du Vigneaud was taken from Refs. 1 and 11.

This paper is available on line at http://www.jbc.org

research encompassed a wide focus, from insulin to cysteine, methionine, biotin, oxytocin, and vasopressin, but it was united by what he called "a trail of research in sulfur chemistry and metabolism."

The first JBC Classic reprinted here is from du Vigneaud's metabolism research trail. Previously, he had discovered that homocystine could support rats on a methionine-free diet only if choline or a related substance was included in the diet (4). On the basis of these findings, he speculated that choline acted as a methyl donor for the conversion of homocysteine to methionine and that animals were incapable of generating methyl groups themselves. He also suspected that methionine could serve as a source of methyl for choline synthesis and set out to prove this by following the migration of deuterium-labeled methyl groups from methionine to choline and creatine. du Vigneaud synthesized deuteriomethionine and fed it to rats on a diet free of methionine and choline. He then analyzed the deuterium content of choline and creatine from the tissues of these animals and found that both compounds contained approximately the same amount of deuterium, proving his hypothesis.

Sometime later, Paul Gyorgy asked du Vigneaud to aid in establishing the chemical nature of a sulfur-containing compound: the anti-egg-white injury factor known as biotin. In the second JBC Classic reprinted here, du Vigneaud reports on his elucidation of the structure of biotin on the basis of several degradation reactions. In prior studies, he had come up with two possible structures for biotin (5).

STRUCTURES I and II

du Vigneaud hypothesized that if he performed a sulfide cleavage reaction on biotin and then hydrolyzed the product, he would obtain desthiodiaminocarboxylic acid with either one carbon methyl group, in the case of structure I, or two carbon methyl groups, in the case of structure II. He could then use a carbon-methyl group determination to differentiate between the two structures. Using these and other methods, du Vigneaud proved that structure I is the structure of biotin.

In 1932, du Vigneaud started working on the sulfur-containing posterior pituitary hormones, oxytocin and vasopressin, focusing on the metabolic aspects of the two peptides. His studies were briefly interrupted by World War II, when he was invited by the war time Committee on Medical Research to join the effort to work on the chemistry of another sulfur-containing compound, penicillin. After the war, du Vigneaud resumed his study of the peptides and determined the primary sequence of oxytocin, which is the subject of the third JBC Classic reprinted here.

Vincent du Vigneaud. Photo courtesy of the National Library of Medicine.

du Vigneaud knew from previous studies that oxytocin contained equal amounts of leucine, isoleucine, tyrosine, proline, glutamic acid, aspartic acid, glycine, and cystine (6, 7). In this paper, he uses partial hydrolysis of oxytocin, desulfurized oxytocin, and a heptapeptide fragment of oxytocin along with ion exchange and paper chromatography to determine the amino acid sequence of the peptide. He also proposed a tentative cyclic structure for oxytocin based on his data. However, displaying characteristic caution, du Vigneaud stated, "It is obvious that, in spite of the fact that this was the only structure we could arrive at through the realization of the results from our degradative work, synthetic proof of structure was mandatory." Following up on this statement, du Vigneaud published the first oxytocin synthesis in 1953, which was also the first synthesis of a polypeptide hormone (8).

du Vigneaud also determined the structure of vasopressin and realized that its structure was very similar to that of oxytocin (9). Vasopressin has the same ring structure as oxytocin but differs in two amino acids. However, the two compounds have different physiological activities, oxytocin stimulates uterine contractions and lactation while vasopressin regulates the function of the kidneys. These findings were of great importance because they demonstrated, for the first time, that replacing certain amino acids in a physiologically active peptide can cause significant changes in biological action.

The final JBC Classic reprinted here focuses on the synthesis of an oxytocin-vasopressin peptide. Over the years, du Vigneaud had synthesized several oxytocin and vasopressin analogues in hopes of understanding correlations between the structures and properties of the two compounds. One of the structures, oxypressin IV, had a cyclic pentapeptide amide portion identical to that found in vasopressin, linked to a tripeptide amide side chain from oxytocin (10). du Vigneaud found that oxypressin had very low pressor activity, even though it contained the ring structure present in the vasopressin, possibly due to the lack of a strongly basic amino acid in the oxytocin side chain. In order to test this hypothesis, du Vigneaud synthesized arginine-vasotocin, a "cyclic octapeptide amide that contains a cyclic pentapeptide amide portion identical with the one existing in oxytocin I, linked to the tripeptide amide side chain that is present in arginine-vasopressin II." When du Vigneaud assayed his peptide for activity, he found that it possessed high levels of oxytocic, avian depressor, and pressor activities, confirming his hypothesis.

du Vigneaud had a large number of students and postdoctoral fellows during his career and collaborated with many more senior biochemists. Among this group many went on to distinguished research careers of their own; 3 won Nobel prizes and 15 became members of the National Academy of Sciences, whereas many more held prominent academic and industrial positions in the U. S. Thus, he had a remarkable influence on biochemical research in the U. S. du Vigneaud received many awards and distinctions for his research, including the Nobel Prize in Chemistry in 1955, "for his work on biochemically important sulfur compounds, especially for the first synthesis of a polypeptide hormone." However, he had definite opinions about awarding prizes for scientific achievement and once said to a reporter, "I am expecting to stay in the research field, in the academic world, but I want to tell you I will never work for any prize. I refuse to let my rewards rest in the hands of any committee."

Nicole Kresge, Robert D. Simoni, and Robert L. Hill

REFERENCES

1. du Vigneaud, V. (1955) A trail of sulfa research: from insulin to oxytocin. Nobel Lecture, December 12, 1955.
2. JBC Classics: Abel, J. J., and Taveau, R. DeM. (1905) *J. Biol. Chem.* **1**, 1–32 (http://www.jbc.org/cgi/content/full/277/12/e1)
3. JBC Classics: Smith, E. L., and Bergmann, M. (1944) *J. Biol. Chem.* **153**, 627–651 (http://www.jbc.org/cgi/content/full/279/47/e6)
4. du Vigneaud, V., Chandler, J. P., Moyer, A. W., and Keppel, D. M. (1939) The effect of choline on the ability of homocystine to replace methionine in the diet. *J. Biol. Chem.* **131**, 57–76
5. Hofmann, K., Kilmer, G. W., Melville, D. B., du Vigneaud, V., and Darby, H. H. (1942) The condensation of phenanthrenequinone with the diaminocarboxylic acid derived from biotin. *J. Biol. Chem.* **145**, 503–509
6. Pierce, J. G., and du Vigneaud, V. (1950) Preliminary studies on the amino acid content of a high potency preparation of the oxytocic hormone of the posterior lobe of the pituitary gland. *J. Biol. Chem.* **182**, 359–366
7. Pierce, J. G., and du Vigneaud, V. (1950) Studies on high potency oxytocic material from beef posterior pituitary lobes. *J. Biol. Chem.* **186**, 77–84
8. du Vigneaud, V., Ressler, C., Swan, J. M., Roberts, C. W., Katsoyannis, P. G., and Gordon, S. (1953) The synthesis of an octapeptide amide with the hormonal activity of oxytocin. *J. Am. Chem. Soc.* **75,** 4879–4880
9. du Vigneaud, V., Gish, D. T., and Katsoyannis, P. G. (1954) A synthetic preparation possessing biological properties associated with arginine-vasopressin. *J. Am. Chem. Soc.* **76**, 4751–4752
10. Katsoyannis, P. G. (1957) Oxypressin, a synthetic octapeptide amide with hormonal properties. *J. Am. Chem. Soc.* **79**, 109–111
11. Hofmann, K. (1987) Biographical memoir of Vincent du Vigneaud. Vol. 56, pp. 542–595, National Academy of Sciences, Washington, D. C.

THE JOURNAL OF BIOLOGICAL CHEMISTRY
© 2004 by The American Society for Biochemistry and Molecular Biology, Inc.

Vol. 279, No. 53, Issue of December 31, p. e12, 2004
Printed in U.S.A.

Classics

A PAPER IN A SERIES REPRINTED TO CELEBRATE THE CENTENARY OF THE JBC IN 2005

JBC Centennial
1905–2005
100 Years of Biochemistry and Molecular Biology

Succeeding in Science Despite the Odds; Studying Metabolism with NMR by Mildred Cohn

A Study of Oxidative Phosphorylation with O^{18}-labeled Inorganic Phosphate (Cohn, M. (1953) *J. Biol. Chem.* **201,** 735–750)

Nuclear Magnetic Resonance Spectra of Adenosine Di- and Triphosphate. II. Effect of Complexing with Divalent Metal Ions (Cohn, M., and Hughes, T. R. (1962) *J. Biol. Chem.* **237,** 176–181)

Mildred Cohn was born in New York City in 1913. When she was young, her father told her she could achieve anything she chose to, but not without some difficulty because she was both female and Jewish. With her parents' encouragement, Cohn moved rapidly through the New York public school system and graduated from high school at age 14. She decided to go to Hunter College in Manhattan, then an all-girls college, and majored in chemistry and minored in physics. Hunter's attitude toward science education at that time can be summed up by the chairman of the chemistry department who declared that it was not ladylike for women to be chemists and that his sole purpose was to prepare his students to become chemistry teachers.

When Cohn graduated from Hunter College in 1931 she tried to get a scholarship for graduate studies in chemistry but was unsuccessful. She enrolled in Columbia University nonetheless and used her savings to pay for her education. At Columbia, she studied under Nobel laureate Harold Urey but had to drop out after a year because of lack of money. She then took a job with the National Advisory Committee of Aeronautics and after a few years was able to earn enough money to return to Columbia. Working with Urey, she used isotopic tracers to examine biochemical reactions in human and animal cells and received her Ph.D. in physical chemistry in 1938.

Unfortunately, jobs were scarce in 1938, during the years of the Great Depression, and academic positions for women were even more scarce. Industrial recruiters regularly posted notices announcing that, "Mr. X of Y Company will interview prospective doctorate recipients—Male, Christian"(1).[1] With Urey's help, Cohn was able to obtain a postdoctoral position at George Washington University with future Nobel prize winner Vincent du Vigneaud. In du Vigneaud's laboratory, Cohn pioneered the effort to use isotopic tracers to follow the metabolism of sulfur-containing compounds, the subject of a previous *Journal of Biological Chemistry* (JBC) Classic (2). Cohn worked with du Vigneaud for 9 years and moved with him to New York when he went to Cornell Medical College.

In 1946, Cohn went to Washington University in St. Louis to work with Carl and Gerty Cori, Nobel prize laureates and authors of a previous JBC Classic (3), who were studying biological catalysts. There, she did independent research, mainly focusing on using isotopes and NMR to study metabolic processes. Cohn was promoted to Associate Professor in Biochemistry in 1958 but left Washington University 2 years later to move to the University of Pennsylvania School of Medicine. She became a full Professor in 1961 and retired as Benjamin Rush Professor Emerita of Biochemistry and Biophysics in 1982.

Once, when asked what her most exciting scientific moments were (4), Cohn replied, "In 1958, using nuclear magnetic resonance, I saw the first three peaks of ATP (5). That was exciting. [I could] distinguish the three phosphorus atoms of ATP with a spectroscopic method,

---

[1] All biographical information on Mildred Cohn was taken from Refs. 1 and 4.

This paper is available on line at http://www.jbc.org

which had never been done before. Another paper, in 1962 (the second JBC Classic reprinted here), was about the effect of metal ions on the phosphorus spectrum of ATP. And earlier, I found that oxygen in inorganic phosphate exchanged with water through oxidative phosphorylation (the first JBC Classic reprinted here)."

Cohn's study of oxidative phosphorylation came at a time when it was known that phosphorylation occurred concomitantly with oxidation in the electron transport chain. However, no one had yet discovered the nature of the interaction of the electron transport system with phosphate or any part of the phosphorylating system. Cohn approached this problem by tracking the loss of O^{18} from inorganic phosphate during oxidative phosphorylation in rat liver mitochondria. In the first JBC Classic reprinted here, she describes her findings as, "a new reaction which occurs in oxidative phosphorylation associated with the electron transport system has been observed in the rat liver mitochondria with α-ketoglutarate, $\bar{a}$-hydroxybutyrate, and succinate as substrates. This reaction manifests itself by a replacement of O^{18} with normal O^{16} in inorganic phosphate labeled with O^{18} and parallels the phosphorylation which is associated with the oxidation." Cohn concluded that water must be involved in this reaction because there was no other source of oxygen large enough to account for the amounts she saw introduced into inorganic phosphate.

In the second JBC Classic Cohn describes her use of NMR to examine the structural changes in ADP and ATP caused by various divalent metal ions. Cohn knew that divalent ions were involved in enzymatic reactions of ADP and ATP but didn't know their functions. Using NMR, she measured the changes in the chemical shifts in the peaks of the ATP and ADP phosphorus nuclei in the presence of Mg^{2+}, Ca^{2+}, and Zn^{2+} as well as the paramagnetic ions Cu^{2+}, Mn^{2+}, and Co^{2+}. By analyzing the resultant spectra, she was able to determine which metals bound to which phosphate groups and thus gained insight into the nature of the metal complexes formed.

Cohn received many awards and honors for her contributions to science, including the National Medal of Science in 1982, "for pioneering the use of stable isotopic tracers and nuclear magnetic resonance spectroscopy in the study of the mechanisms of enzymatic catalysis," as well as election to the National Academies of Science in 1971. She also served the American Society of Biological Chemists (ASBC), now American Society for Biochemistry and Molecular Biology (ASBMB), in many ways. She was President of the Society in 1978 and was on the Federation of American Societies for Experimental Biology (FASEB) Board from 1978 to 1980 as ASBC representative. In addition, Cohn was one of the first women to be appointed to the JBC Editorial Board, along with Sarah Ratner and Sofia Simmonds.

Despite her success, Cohn's father was right about the difficulties she would encounter in her life. "My career has been affected at every stage by the fact that I am a woman, beginning with my undergraduate education, which was very inferior in chemistry, and physics was not even offered [as a major] at Hunter College, unlike the excellent science education that my male counterparts received at City College," she notes. "In my day, I experienced discrimination in academia, government, and industry."

Nicole Kresge, Robert D. Simoni, and Robert L. Hill

REFERENCES

1. Wasserman, E. (2000) *The Door in the Dream: Conversations with Eminent Women in Science*, pp. 43–46, Joseph Henry Press, Washington, D. C.
2. JBC Classics: Du Vigneaud, V., Cohn, M., Chandler, J. P., Schenck, J. R., and Simmonds, S. (1941) *J. Biol. Chem.* **140**, 625–641 (http://www.jbc.org/cgi/content/full/279/51/e11)
3. JBC Classics: Cori, C. F., and Cori, G. T. (1928) *J. Biol. Chem.* **79**, 321–341; Cori, G. T., Colowick, S. P., and Cori, C. F. (1938) *J. Biol. Chem.* **124**, 543–555; Cori, G. T., Colowick, S. P., and Cori, C. F. (1939) *J. Biol. Chem.* **127**, 771–782; Green, A. A., and Cori, G. T. (1943) *J. Biol. Chem.* **151**, 21–29; Cori, G. T., and Green, A. A. (1943) *J. Biol. Chem.* **151**, 31–38 (http://www.jbc.org/cgi/content/full/277/29/e18)
4. First Person: Mildred Cohn (2003) *The Scientist* **17**, 16
5. Cohn, M., and Hughes, T.R. (1960) Phosphorus magnetic resonance spectra of adenosine diphosphate and triphosphate. I. Effect of pH. *J. Biol. Chem.* **235**, 3250–3253

THE JOURNAL OF BIOLOGICAL CHEMISTRY
© 2005 by The American Society for Biochemistry and Molecular Biology, Inc.

Vol. 280, No. 2, Issue of January 14, p. e1, 2005
Printed in U.S.A.

Classics

A PAPER IN A SERIES REPRINTED TO CELEBRATE THE CENTENARY OF THE JBC IN 2005

JBC Centennial
1905–2005
100 Years of Biochemistry and Molecular Biology

Hans Neurath: the Difference between Proteins That Digest and Proteins That Are Digested

The Specific Esterase Activity of Trypsin
(Schwert, G. W., Neurath, H., Kaufman, S., and Snoke, J. E. (1948) *J. Biol. Chem.* **172**, 221–239

Identification of a Peptide Released during Autocatalytic Activation of Trypsinogen
(Davie, E. W., and Neurath, H. (1955) *J. Biol. Chem.* **212**, 515–530

Born in Vienna, Austria, Hans Neurath (1909–2002) was the youngest child of a pediatrician and a Red Cross volunteer. He studied at the University of Vienna under Wolfgang Paul Sr. and received his doctorate in chemistry in 1933. In 1934 he emigrated to England to do postdoctoral research at the University of London with N. K. Adams. The next year he went to the United States for a postdoctoral fellowship at the University of Minnesota where he studied the surface denaturation of proteins with Henry Bull. In 1936, Neurath was appointed George Fisher Baker Fellow and Instructor in the Department of Chemistry at Cornell University. During his 2 years at Cornell, he developed a method for the diffusion of proteins and applied it to determine the hydrodynamic properties of proteins of particular interest. In 1938 he moved again, this time to Duke University, where he was appointed Assistant Professor in the Department of Biochemistry.

At Duke, Neurath began what would be a lifelong study of proteolytic enzymes, starting with trypsin. Max Bergmann had already established, through the use of synthetic substrates, that trypsin contained amidase activity and could catalyze the hydrolysis of amides of lysine and arginine derivatives into ammonia and amino acid derivatives (1, 2). While investigating the inhibition of crystalline pancreatic proteolytic enzymes by low molecular weight compounds, Neurath discovered that trypsin could also hydrolyze certain amino acid esters. The first *Journal of Biological Chemistry* (JBC) Classic reprinted here reports Neurath's discovery as well as his subsequent kinetic studies comparing the amidase and esterase abilities of trypsin. Neurath concluded from his data that trypsin uses the same active surfaces to catalyze the hydrolysis of both esters and amides.

The second JBC Classic reprinted here focuses on more of Neurath's trypsin studies, this time the chemical changes accompanying the conversion of bovine trypsinogen to active trypsin. At the time, it was known that trypsinogen was activated proteolytically by trypsin and that the activation was accompanied by a change in the N-terminal residue from valine to isoleucine, but the identity of the peptide that was released during activation was unknown. Neurath and Earl Davie isolated the activation peptide by removing aliquots at various stages of the tryptic activation of trypsinogen. Using chromatography, they purified the peptide and determined that it had the structure Val-(Asp)$_4$-Lys. Neurath and Davie's description of the activation of trypsinogen eventually became a prototype for the biological mechanism of the activation of other proteolytic enzymes.

Neurath later elucidated the complete amino acid sequence of bovine trypsinogen with Kenneth Walsh and established its homology to chymotrypsinogen (3). This laid the foundation for the concept that proteolytic enzymes can be classified in terms of families of homologous structures and similar mechanisms of action.

In 1950, Neurath left Duke to establish the Biochemistry Department at the University of Washington School of Medicine in Seattle. When Neurath initially arrived, there were only five

This paper is available on line at http://www.jbc.org

Hans Neurath. Photo courtesy of the National Library of Medicine.

faculty members, a dozen graduate students, and two postdoctoral fellows. As the department's first chairman, he enlarged the faculty and space, established a graduate training program, and promoted the department's growth in size, stature, and reputation. He is credited for recruiting a strong faculty and fostering the atmosphere for academic research for which the medical school is well known. Three faculty members from Neurath's department went on to be awarded Nobel Prizes in physiology and medicine (Edwin Krebs, Edmond Fischer, and Martin Rodbell), and one dozen of the present and past faculty members of the department have been elected to the National Academy of Sciences.

The research Neurath did during his 50 years at Washington has led many to regard him as one of the founding fathers of modern protein science. He studied a wide variety of topics related to proteolytic enzymes including their structures, precursor activation, mechanisms of action, amino acid sequences, evolution, and phylogenetic variations and was adamant about using new experimental approaches such as x-ray crystallography and chemical synthesis in his research. Once, when asked why he chose to study proteolytic enzymes, Neurath replied, "My interests in proteases were solicited and stimulated by the simple question: What differentiates proteins that catalyze the digestion of other proteins from those that are being digested?"(4).[1] In addition to trypsin, Neurath is known for his studies on chymotrypsin, carboxypeptidase, mast cell proteases, and bacterial thermolysin.

Neurath retired in 1979 but continued his research and also worked as part-time scientific director at the Fred Hutchinson Cancer Research Center in Seattle. He also spent 2 years in Germany as the scientific director of the German Cancer Research Center in Heidelberg. Neurath was a member of the National Academy of Sciences, the Institute of Medicine, the American Academy of Arts and Sciences, and a foreign member of the Max-Planck Society.

In addition to his many scientific achievements in the field of protein chemistry, Neurath had a huge impact on scientific publishing. He assembled the first comprehensive treatise on proteins, *The Proteins: Chemistry, Biological Activity and Methods*, with Kenneth Bailey in 1953. The second edition, published in 1963, was edited by Neurath alone, and the third edition, between 1975 and 1979, was co-edited with Robert L. Hill.

In 1962, Neurath founded the American Chemical Society journal *Biochemistry*, because he "felt that there should be an alternative to the *Journal of Biological Chemistry* that would place greater emphasis on the chemical aspects of biochemistry, particularly in the areas of protein chemistry and enzymology." Neurath remained Editor-in-chief of *Biochemistry* until 1989. During that time, the journal grew from 1,200 to 12,000 pages. In 1991, at age 81, he founded the Protein Society journal *Protein Science*, which he edited until 1998. Publication of the journal increased the membership of the Protein Society from ~1800 to ~3000. In honor of his many contributions to science and the society, the Protein Society established the Hans Neurath Award in 1988.

Neurath was also an avid hiker, mountain climber and skier, and a first class pianist. He continued his outdoor activities throughout his life. His frequent ski trips with his wife Susi qualified them to join the "Ancient Skiers" ski club, of which they were the oldest members.

Nicole Kresge, Robert D. Simoni, and Robert L. Hill

---

[1] All biographical information on Hans Neurath was taken from Refs. 4 and 5.

REFERENCES

1. Bergmann, M., Fruton, J. S., and Pollok, H. (1939) The specificity of trypsin. I. *J. Biol. Chem.* **127,** 643–648
2. Hofmann, K., and Bergmann, M. (1939) The specificity of trypsin. II. *J. Biol. Chem.* **130**, 81–86
3. Neurath, H., and Walsh, K. A. (1964) Trypsinogen and chymotrypsinogen as homologous proteins. *Proc. Natl. Acad. Sci. U. S. A.* **52**, 884–889
4. Neurath, H. (2001) From proteases to proteomics. *Protein Sci.* **10**, 892–904
5. Travis, J. (2000) Hans Neurath. *Biochim. Biophys. Acta* **1477**, 3–6

THE JOURNAL OF BIOLOGICAL CHEMISTRY
© 2005 by The American Society for Biochemistry and Molecular Biology, Inc.

Vol. 280, No. 3, Issue of January 21, p. e2, 2005
Printed in U.S.A.

Classics

A PAPER IN A SERIES REPRINTED TO CELEBRATE THE CENTENARY OF THE JBC IN 2005

JBC Centennial
1905–2005
100 Years of Biochemistry and Molecular Biology

The Isolation of Adrenocorticotropic Hormone by Three Pioneers in Molecular Endocrinology: Choh Hao Li, Abraham White, and Cyril Norman Hugh Long

Adrenocorticotropic Hormone
(Li, C. H., Evans, H. M., and Simpson, M. E. (1943) *J. Biol. Chem.* **149, 413–424)**

Preparation and Properties of Pituitary Adrenotropic Hormone
(Sayers, G., White, A., and Long, C. N. H. (1943) *J. Biol. Chem.* **149, 425–436)**

In the 1930s and 1940s, Yale Medical School was a driving force for the beginnings of molecular endocrinology thanks to the pioneering research of scientists like Cyril Norman Hugh Long (1901–1970) and Abraham White (1908–1980). Together, in 1937, the two isolated bovine prolactin (1), the first of the protein pituitary hormones to be obtained in pure crystalline form. Then in 1943, Long and White along with George Sayers, who also did significant work in the beginnings of molecular endocrinology, isolated a highly purified preparation of porcine adrenocorticotropic hormone (ACTH) by isoelectric precipitation. However, at the same time, another scientist at Berkeley, Choh Hao Li (1913–1987), reported that he had purified ACTH from sheep by salt fractionation. Both groups published their results back-to-back in one issue of the *Journal of Biological Chemistry* (JBC). The papers, reprinted here as JBC Classics, show that both methods produced good yields of the same protein (as determined by similar isoelectric points, molecular weights, and carbon, hydrogen, nitrogen, and sulfur contents), and both were proven active by similar biological assays.

What is so interesting about Long, White, and Li is that not only did they isolate, characterize, and sequence most of the pituitary hormones as well as many other hormones, but they also each contributed enormously to the heritage of biochemistry.

At the time Choh Hao Li published his method for isolating ACTH, he was working with Herbert Evans at the University of California, Berkeley. Li, who grew up in Guangzhou, China, came to Berkeley in 1935 from the University of Nanking to earn a Ph.D. After finishing a Ph.D. in chemical kinetics in 1938, Evans offered him a job studying the endocrinology of the pituitary gland at the Berkeley Institute for Experimental Biology. This marked the beginning of the half-century that Li would spend studying peptide and protein hormones, making significant contributions to the field of endocrinology and eventually leading to his establishment of the Berkeley Hormone Research Laboratory in 1950.[1]

In addition to isolating ACTH, Li contributed to the identification, purification, and molecular structure determination of many of the other anterior pituitary hormones, including luteinizing hormone, follicle-stimulating hormone, growth hormone, lipotropin, melanotropin, and prolactin, as well as other hormones such as endorphin and insulin-like growth factor I. By doing some of the first detailed amino acid sequence studies on many of these hormones, Li was able to show that portions of their structures were homologous, explaining why many of them had overlapping biological functions. Li also pioneered the idea that hormones consist of biologically active fragments combined with regulatory regions, which he proved by synthesizing peptide fragments of the hormones in the early 1950s. Throughout the 1960s Li's team synthesized longer and longer peptides until they were able to synthesize the entire corticotrophin molecule in 1973 (2).

---

[1] All the biographical information on Choh Hao Li was taken from Ref. 4.

Cyril N. H. Long. Photo courtesy of the National Library of Medicine.

Choh H. Li. Photo courtesy of the National Library of Medicine.

Li also made several editorial contributions to biochemistry, including serving as editor of the series *Hormonal Proteins and Peptides* and *Archives of Biochemistry and Biophysics*, as well as serving as co-associate editor and then editor-in-chief of the *International Journal of Peptide and Protein Research*. He had a very generous spirit, and his collection of pure pituitary hormones, which he doled out to other investigators in microgram amounts, was legendary. In honor of Li, memorial lectureships were established at Berkeley, the Academia Sinica, and the National University of Taiwan. His family also endowed a professorship in his name at Berkeley.

Like Li, Cyril Norman Hugh Long was a chemist from abroad. He was born in Wiltshire, England and was educated as an organic chemist at Manchester University. Shortly after earning an M.D. from McGill University, Long became director of the newly formed George S. Cox Research Institute at the University of Pennsylvania. The purpose of the institute was to find a cure for diabetes, which as Long later recalled was, "a rather overwhelming assignment for a young man." Despite the daunting nature of this task, Long and Francis Lukens made a significant contribution to diabetes research by showing that diabetes could be ameliorated with the removal of the adrenal glands, causing the disease to be reconsidered in the light of knowledge of the parts played by the pituitary and other ductless glands. As a result of this research, in 1936, Long proposed what is still one of the most important ideas in endocrine research, that "the clinical condition that follows hypo- or hyper-function of an endocrine organ is not merely due to the loss or plethora of that particular internal secretion but is a result of the disturbance of the normal hormonal equilibrium of the body." [2]

In 1936, Long moved again, this time to Yale Medical School to become Chairman of the Department of Physiological Chemistry where he remained for the next 33 years. His department, renamed the Department of Biochemistry in 1952, was the first "Biochemistry" department to be created in the U.S. (by Russell Henry Chittenden in 1882) and to be distinguished from the parent discipline, Physiology. Later, Long became Chairman of the Department of Physiology and eventually Dean of the School of Medicine.

While at Yale Medical School, Long participated in the overall reorganization of the teaching of biology at the university. He strongly believed that the most important responsibility of the school to the community was to provide leadership in teaching and research. His own leadership was eventually recognized by the endowment of a chair in his name at Yale devoted to endocrinology and metabolism. Long was also a great supporter of women in science, encouraging and training a large number of women, starting with his first graduate student, Eleanor Venning, who worked for Long at a time when women were not accepted universally in the laboratory or as physicians. Long was also elected to the National Academy of Sciences in 1948 and was president of the Endocrine Society in 1947–1948.

Long's research at Yale centered around the effects of pituitary and adrenal extracts on the metabolism of carbohydrates, and he is recognized as one of the leading investigators of his generation in the field of endocrinology. On the basis of work carried out with Edith Fry and B. Katzin, Long was able to describe quantitatively for the first time the biological properties

---

[2] All the biographical information on Cyril Norman Hugh Long was taken from Ref. 5.

of the adrenal cortical hormones (3). This led to the eventual development of the adrenal ascorbic acid bioassay for the pituitary adrenocortical hormones in Long's laboratory.

While at Yale, Long met a young faculty member named Abraham White. White, whose postdoctoral research had focused on the metabolism of sulfur-containing compounds and the amino acid sequence of proteins, was newly appointed to the Medical School faculty in 1933. Long convinced White to use his knowledge and experience in protein chemistry in investigations of the protein hormones of the pituitary, starting a new and fruitful series of investigations into endocrinology to which White devoted much of his subsequent research efforts.[3]

White's initial work on ACTH led to his observation, with Thomas F. Dougherty, that the actions of ACTH on the adrenal glands produced an involution of all lymphoid tissues and a pronounced lymphocytopenia effected by the dissolution of lymphocytes. This and other studies by White and Dougherty provided the basis for the later clinical use of adrenal steroids in the treatment of lymphoid neoplasms as well as the use of steroids on patients prior to organ transplants to depress their immune systems. White followed these studies with investigations of the enzymes involved in the metabolism of adrenal steroids, on the role of lymphoid tissue in immunity, and on the nature of the pituitary control of the adrenal cortex. He also studied the thymus gland, establishing it as an endocrine gland, and purified thymosin from the thymus.

Like Long, White was interested in innovative medical education and eventually left Yale in 1948 to chair and found the Department of Physiological Chemistry at the UCLA School of Medicine. Later, he helped Carl Djerassi found Syntex Research based on isolation of steroid hormones from Mexican plants. He worked at Syntex for 2 years (1951–1953) and then returned to academia to become one of the major figures in the organization of the Albert Einstein College of Medicine in New York. After retiring in 1972, White moved to Palo Alto to work at Syntex and also enjoyed a teaching affiliation with the biochemistry department of Stanford Medical School. White's interest in education and recognition that there was no satisfactory modern textbook of biochemistry also led him to join Philip Handler, DeWitt Stetten, and Emil L. Smith in writing the classic textbook *Principles of Biochemistry* in 1954.

Nicole Kresge, Robert D. Simoni, and Robert L. Hill

REFERENCES

1. White, A., Catchpole, H. R., and Long, C. N. H. (1937) A crystalline protein with high lactogenic activity. *Science* **86**, 82–83
2. Yamashiro, D., and Li, C. H. (1973) Adrenocorticotropins. 44. Total synthesis of the human hormone by the solid-phase method. *J. Am. Chem. Soc.* **95**, 1310–1315
3. Long, C. N. H., Katzin, B., and Fry, E. G. (1950) The adrenal cortex and carbohydrate metabolism. *Endocrinology* **26**, 309–344
4. Cole, R. D. (1996) Biographical Memoir of Choh Hao Li, Vol. 70, pp. 220–239, National Academy of Sciences, Washington D. C.
5. Smith, O. L. K., and Hardy, J. D. (1975) Biographical Memoir of Cyril Norman Hugh Long, Vol. 46, pp. 264–309, National Academy of Sciences, Washington D. C.
6. Smith, E. L. (1985) Biographical Memoir of Abraham White, Vol. 55, pp. 506–536, National Academy of Sciences, Washington D. C.

---

[3] All the biographical information on Abraham White was taken from Ref. 6.

THE JOURNAL OF BIOLOGICAL CHEMISTRY
© 2005 by The American Society for Biochemistry and Molecular Biology, Inc.

Vol. 280, No. 4, Issue of January 28, p. e3, 2005
Printed in U.S.A.

Classics

A PAPER IN A SERIES REPRINTED TO CELEBRATE THE CENTENARY OF THE JBC IN 2005

JBC Centennial
1905–2005
100 Years of Biochemistry and Molecular Biology

Otto Fritz Meyerhof and the Elucidation of the Glycolytic Pathway

The Equilibria of Isomerase and Aldolase, and the Problem of the Phosphorylation of Glyceraldehyde Phosphate
(Meyerhof, O., and Junowicz-Kocholaty, R. (1943) *J. Biol. Chem.* 149, 71–92)

The Origin of the Reaction of Harden and Young in Cell-free Alcoholic Fermentation
(Meyerhof, O. (1945) *J. Biol. Chem.* 157, 105–120)

The Mechanism of the Oxidative Reaction in Fermentation
(Meyerhof, O. and Oesper, P. (1947) *J. Biol. Chem.* 170, 1–22)

The elucidation of the glycolytic pathway, the process whereby glucose is converted into pyruvate and ATP, began in 1860 when Louis Pasteur observed that microorganisms were responsible for fermentation. Several years later, in 1897, Eduard Buchner made the significant discovery that cell-free extracts could carry out fermentation. The next important contribution was from Arthur Harden and William Young in 1905. They realized that inorganic phosphate was necessary for glycolysis and that fermentation requires the presence of both a heat-labile component they called "zymase" and a low molecular weight, heat-stable fraction called "cozymase." (It was later shown that zymase contains a number of enzymes whereas cozymase consists of metal ions, ATP, ADP, and coenzymes such as NAD.) Building on these initial observations, the complete glycolytic pathway was elucidated by 1940 by the combined efforts of several scientists including Otto Fritz Meyerhof (1884–1951).

Meyerhof was born in Hanover, Germany and grew up in Berlin. In 1909, he graduated as a doctor of medicine from the University of Heidelberg. Around this time, Ludolf von Krehl was building a small research program on metabolism at the University of Heidelberg Medical Clinic, and he offered Meyerhof a position in his laboratory. There, Meyerhof met Otto Warburg whose innovative ideas and confident approach inspired him to focus his career on physiological chemistry.[1]

In 1912, Meyerhof took a position at the University of Kiel. A year later, he delivered a lecture on the energetics of living cells, one of the very first adaptations of the physical laws of thermodynamics to physiological chemistry. Meyerhof had recognized that after energy is input as food it is transformed through a series of intermediate steps and finally dissipated as heat. He soon began using muscle to look at energy transformations and chemical changes during cellular function. Meyerhof was also interested in analogies between oxygen respiration in muscle and alcoholic fermentation in yeast and proved, in 1918, that the coenzymes involved in lactic acid production were the same as the yeast coenzymes discovered by Harden and Young, revealing an underlying unity in biochemistry.

Soon after World War I, Meyerhof began collaborating with Archibald Vivian Hill who was investigating heat production in muscle. The pair worked to decipher metabolism in terms of heat development, mechanical work, and cellular chemical reactions. Meyerhof determined that glycogen is converted to lactic acid in the absence of oxygen and showed that in the presence of oxygen only a small portion of lactic acid is oxidized and the rest is converted back to glycogen. This discovery of the lactic acid cycle provided the first evidence of the cyclical

---

[1] All biographical information on Otto Fritz Meyerhof was taken from Ref. 6.

This paper is available on line at http://www.jbc.org

Otto F. Meyerhof. Photo courtesy of the National Library of Medicine.

nature of energy transformation in cells. These results also confirmed and extended Louis Pasteur's theory (now called the Pasteur-Meyerhof effect) that less glycogen is consumed in muscle metabolism in the presence of oxygen than in its absence. Meyerhof and Hill won the Nobel Prize in Physiology or Medicine in 1922 for their analysis of the lactic acid cycle and its relation to respiration.

Two years after wining the Nobel Prize, Meyerhof joined the Kaiser Wilhelm Institutes in Berlin-Dahlem. Then, in 1929, he took charge of the newly founded Kaiser Wilhelm Institute for Medical Research at Heidelberg.

By this time, it was clear that glycolysis was far more complicated than anyone had imagined. The sheer number of components and their short lived nature made the task of sorting out the pathway daunting. However, during his time at Heidelberg, Meyerhof's group was extremely successful at breaking down glycolysis into its many separate components. In 1932, Meyerhof made the first associations between the uptake of phosphate during the breakdown of carbohydrates to lactic acid and the splitting of ATP. By 1934, Kurt Lohmann in Meyerhof's laboratory provided direct evidence that ATP synthesis was the byproduct of utilization of glucose. Lohmann also established that creatine phosphate is an energy source for ATP phosphorylation, which led Meyerh of to the conclusion that the energy release from ATP hydrolysis was the primary event leading to muscle contraction.

By the 1930s Meyerhof had managed to isolate and purify the co-enzymes involved in the conversion of glycogen to lactic acid and had reconstructed the main steps of this set of reactions in cell-free solution. All in all, Meyerhof's group discovered more than one-third of the enzymes involved in glycolysis. In 1932, Gustav Embden constructed a detailed proposal for reaction sequences for almost the entire glycolytic pathway. Over the next 5 years, Meyerhof, along with Warburg, Jacob Parnas, Carl Neuberg, Gerti and Karl Cori, and Hans von Euler worked out the details of glycolysis, which is often referred to as the Embden-Meyerhof pathway.

With Adolf Hitler's rise to power, Meyerhof left Germany in 1938 and became director of the Institut de Biologie Physiochimique in Paris. In 1940, when the Nazis invaded France, Meyerhof fled to the United States where the post of Research Professor of Physiological Chemistry was created for him by the University of Pennsylvania and the Rockefeller Foundation. He remained at Pennsylvania where he continued to study metabolism until his death. The three *Journal of Biological Chemistry* (JBC) Classics reprinted here are from Meyerhof's time at Pennsylvania.

The first paper deals with one of the intermediate reactions that occurs in glycolysis: the splitting of hexose diphosphate (now known as fructose 1,6-bisphosphate) into two triose phosphate isomers, glyceraldehyde 3-phosphate and dihydroxyacetone phosphate, by zymohexase (fructose-1,6-bisphosphate aldolase). Triose-phosphate isomerase then converts dihydroxyacetone phosphate into glyceraldehyde 3-phosphate. In the next step of glycolysis, glyceraldehyde 3-phosphate is oxidized and phosphorylated to become 1,3-diphosphoglyceric acid. Warburg and Christian (1, 2) and Negelein and Brömel (3, 4) proposed that this step occurs through the intermediate 1,3-diphosphoglyceraldehyde with the aid of an oxidizing enzyme and cozymase. If this were true, then inorganic phosphate could be used to remove glyceraldehyde 3-phosphate from the hexose diphosphate reaction.

To investigate this matter further, Meyerhof and Renate Junowicz-Kocholaty redetermined the equilibrium constant for the isomerase and aldolase reactions in the presence and absence of inorganic phosphate, cozymase, and Warburg's oxidizing enzyme. They found that their values agreed with those previously determined and that equilibrium is not influenced by the presence of inorganic phosphate, cozymase, or Warburg's enzyme. They were also unable to detect the formation of any substance that would break down into glyceraldehyde phosphate and phosphate, prompting them to write that Warburg's claims of a diphosphoglyceraldehyde intermediate may have been "premature."

The second Classic deals with the next two steps of glycolysis shown as Reactions 1 and 2.

Glyceraldehyde 3-phosphate + phosphate + cozymase $\rightleftarrows$

1,3-diphosphoglyceric acid + dihydrocozymase

REACTION 1

1,3-Diphosphoglyceric acid + ADP $\rightleftarrows$ 3-phosphoglyceric acid + ATP

REACTION 2

Harden and Young stated that during fermentation, one sugar molecule is fermented to CO_2 and alcohol while a second is esterfied to hexose diphosphate (5). In a cell-free system, this reaction can be divided into two phases, a rapid "phosphate period" and a slower phase that depends on the rate of hexose diphosphate fermentation. Meyerhof proposed that the rate of the hexose diphosphate reaction was much slower in cell-free systems than in live yeast because the majority of the enzyme needed to split ATP, adenylpyrophosphatase (apyrase), was lost during the extraction process. He backed up his claim by studying the distribution of apyrase in the yeast cell and showing that it remains mainly with solid elements that are not used in cell-free systems. Meyerhof also purified apyrase from potatoes and added it to cell-free preparations to prove that it raises the rate of hexose diphosphate fermentation.

The final JBC Classic revisits the phosphorylation of glyceraldehyde 3-phosphate and its subsequent oxidation. In this paper, Meyerhof and Peter Oesper use a Beckman spectrophotometer to follow the reaction and provide further proof that a diphosphoglyceric aldehyde intermediate does not exist. They also alter the equation for this step of glycolysis to reflect the fact that the reduction of cozymase is accompanied by the formation of an H^+ ion.

Nicole Kresge, Robert D. Simoni, and Robert L. Hill

REFERENCES

1. Warburg, O., and Christian, W. (1939) *Biochem. Z.* **301**, 201
2. Warburg, O., and Christian, W. (1939) *Biochem. Z.* **303**, 40
3. Negelein, E., and Brömel, H. (1939) *Biochem. Z.* **301**, 135
4. Negelein, E., and Brömel, H. (1939) *Biochem. Z.* **303**, 132
5. Harden A., and Young, W. J. (1908) *Proc. R. Soc. Lond. Ser. B Biol. Sci.* **80**, 299
6. States, D. M. Otto Meyerhof and the Physiology Department: the Birth of Modern Biochemistry. *A History of the Max Planck Institute for Medical Research* (http://sun0.mpimf-heidelberg.mpg.de/History/Meyerhof.html)

THE JOURNAL OF BIOLOGICAL CHEMISTRY
© 2005 by The American Society for Biochemistry and Molecular Biology, Inc.

Vol. 280, No. 7, Issue of February 18, p. e4, 2005
Printed in U.S.A.

Classics

A PAPER IN A SERIES REPRINTED TO CELEBRATE THE CENTENARY OF THE JBC IN 2005

JBC Centennial
1905–2005
100 Years of Biochemistry and Molecular Biology

Lyman Creighton Craig: Developer of the Counter-current Distribution Method

Identification of Small Amounts of Organic Compounds by Distribution Studies. Application to Atabrine
(Craig, L. C. (1943) *J. Biol. Chem.* 150, 33–45)

Identification of Small Amounts of Organic Compounds by Distribution Studies. II. Separation By Counter-current Distribution
(Craig, L. C. (1944) *J. Biol. Chem.* 155, 519–534)

Lyman Creighton Craig (1906–1974) was born on a farm in Iowa. Influenced by his older brother's enthusiasm for chemistry, Craig graduated from Iowa State College in 1928 with a B.S. degree. He remained at Iowa State for graduate school where he majored in chemistry and minored in entomology, partly due to his appreciation for the role of insecticides in agriculture. After earning his Ph.D. in 1931, Craig went to Johns Hopkins University to study with E. Emmet Reid. During his three years at Iowa State and his two years at Johns Hopkins, Craig published twelve papers, mostly in the *Journal of the American Chemical Society*, on the chemistry of nicotine alkaloids and their insecticidal action.[1]

These accomplishments earned Craig an appointment in 1933 as a research assistant in chemical pharmacology at the Rockefeller Institute for Medical Research in New York. At Rockefeller, Craig worked on the ergot alkaloids with Walter A. Jacobs, the subject of a previous *Journal of Biological Chemistry* (JBC) Classic (1). Craig was a gifted experimentalist with skill in equipment design, and his first of many contributions to chemical instrumentation was in 1936 when he designed and built a microdistillation apparatus (2).

Craig was forced to shift his research focus during the war and applied his efforts to aspects of the wartime program on antimalarials. It was during the course of examining whether the antimalarial drug atabrine, or a product of its metabolism, was the active parasiticide in humans that Craig invented a laboratory apparatus for the separation of organic compounds by the technique of counter-current distribution (CCD).

Faced with having to identify small amounts of atabrine and its transformation products in urine and blood, Craig developed a method that could be used to accurately detect microgram amounts of compounds. This method is the subject of the first JBC Classic reprinted here. Milton T. Bush of Vanderbilt University School of Medicine suggested to Craig that the distribution coefficient might be a useful physical constant for the identification and purity determination of an organic compound that could be used along with the melting point and the boiling point. Craig enlarged upon this idea by measuring a series of distribution constants ("the ratio of the weight per cc. in ethylene dichloride solution to the apparent weight so derived for the aqueous layer") for atabrine while progressively diluting the solution with methyl alcohol. He repeated the experiment with several compounds closely related to atabrine. The resulting plots of distribution coefficients *versus* volume percentage of water in the aqueous phase gave characteristic curves for each compound. Craig then used these standard curves to analyze the blood and urine from patients and dogs receiving atabrine.

A. J. P. Martin and R. L. M. Synge at the Wool Research Laboratory in Leeds, England used CCD to separate different types of *N*-acetyl amino acids, which were prepared by acteylation

---

[1] All biographical information on Lyman C. Craig was taken from Ref. 7.

Lyman C. Craig. Photo courtesy of the National Library of Medicine.

of the amino acids in acid hydrolysates of wool. They did this manually in separatory funnels by transferring the dissolved *N*-acetyl amino acids partitioned between the upper and lower phases of two immiscible solvents from one funnel to another. This then led them to use the principle of CCD to develop partition chromatography in which one of the liquid phases was immobilized on a column of gel, and the other phase, the mobile phase, was passed down the column. Partition chromatography led then to the development of paper chromatography that opened new worlds to biochemists. Craig, however, decided to build an apparatus for the separation of mixtures of organic compounds by CCD. In the second JBC Classic reprinted here, Craig describes an apparatus that could accomplish, simultaneously, 20 quantitative extractions in a single step. The device, which was made of stainless steel, consisted of a series of 20 small separatory funnels (plates) with the capability, after each shaking and settling, of sliding the top phase from one funnel into the lower phase of the next. The distribution of the compounds being extracted was based on a Gaussian curve that could be calculated from the number of plates, the distribution constant, and the concentration. He tested his apparatus on β-naphthoic acid in an ethylene dichloride-water-methanol solvent system and showed that the actual performance of the machine was very close to theoretical predictions. The novelty and originality of this work is attested by the fact that Craig is the sole author and there are no references cited at the end of the paper.

Craig's first major application of this technique was with Vincent du Vigneaud, author of a previous JBC Classic (3), in characterizing penicillins and estimating the purity of benzylpenicillin, with an ether-aqueous buffer solvent system (4). In 1950 he built a 200-tube CCD apparatus made from glass and another in 1958 with 1000 tubes. He used his equipment to examine substances such as gramicidin, bacitracin, insulin, bile acids, tyrocidine, serum albumin, parathyroid hormone, ribonucleic acids, and ribonuclease.

CCD has also been used by other scientists to isolate hormones such as oxytocin, vasopressin, adrenocorticotrophic hormone (ACTH), growth hormone, lactogenic hormone, melanophore-stimulating hormone, and parathyroid hormone. It has also aided in studies on the structure of the tobacco mosaic virus protein, human hemoglobin α and β chains, angiotensin, and other biologically active peptides. Also, CCD was used by Robert Holley at Cornell University to fractionate crude RNA from liver to give a pure tRNA, which was then fully sequenced for the first time.

In addition to his CCD apparatus, Craig was involved in the design of several other instruments widely used in biochemistry. For example, his rotary evaporator for removal of solvents (5) increased the speed of the process and eliminated the problem of bumping of the solution often encountered in distillation. He also devised ways to use dialysis for the separation of compounds on the basis of size. He developed a dialysis cell in which the entering solution flows over a cellophane membrane, which is stretched or acetylated to vary the pore size (6). Because a molecule's ability to diffuse through a membrane depends on its conformation, Craig also used rotatory dispersion, nuclear magnetic resonance, tritium-hydrogen exchange, circular dichroism, and fluorescent probes to get additional information on the shapes of molecules in solution. This broad approach to studying polypeptide conformation was the principle theme of Craig's research at Rockefeller during the last decade of his life.

Lyman Craig received wide recognition and many honors for his scientific work. He was elected to the National Academy of Sciences in 1950 and received the Albert Lasker Award for Basic Medical Research in 1963. In 1966 he received the Fisher Award in Analytical Chemistry from the American Chemical Society and the Kolthoff Medal of the American Pharmaceutical Association in 1971.

Nicole Kresge, Robert D. Simoni, and Robert L. Hill

REFERENCES

1. JBC Classics: Jacobs, W. A., and Craig, L. C. (1934) *J. Biol. Chem.* **104, 547–551** (http://www.jbc.org/cgi/content/full/277/38/e26)
2. Craig, L. C. (1936) A microdistillation apparatus. *Ind. Eng. Chem. Anal. Ed.* **8**, 219–220
3. JBC Classics: du Vigneaud, V., Cohn, M., Chandler, J. P., Schenck, J. R., and Simmonds, S. (1941) *J. Biol. Chem.* **140**, 625–641; du Vigneaud, V., Melville, D. B., Folkers, K., Wolf, D. E., Mozingo, R., Keresztesy, J. C., and Harris, S. A. (1942) *J. Biol. Chem.* **146,** 475–485; du Vigneaud, V., Ressler, C., and Trippett, S. (1953) *J. Biol. Chem.* **205**, 949–957; Katsoyannis, P. G., and du Vigneaud, V. (1958) *J. Biol. Chem.* **233**, 1352–1354 (http://www.jbc.org/cgi/content/full/279/51/e11)
4. Craig, L. C., Hogeboom, G. H., Carpenter, F. H., and du Vigneaud, V. (1947) Separation and characterization of some penicillins by the method of counter-current distribution. *J. Biol. Chem.* **168**, 665–686
5. Craig, L. C., Gregory, J. D., and Hausmann, W. (1950) Versatile laboratory concentration device. *Anal. Chem.* **22**, 1462
6. Craig, L. C. and Stewart, K. (1965) Dialysis. X. On thin film counter-current dialysis. *Biochemistry* **4**, 2712–2719
7. Moore, S. (1978) *Biographical Memoir of Lyman Creighton Craig*, Vol. 49, pp. 49–77, National Academy of Sciences, Washington, D. C.

THE JOURNAL OF BIOLOGICAL CHEMISTRY
© 2005 by The American Society for Biochemistry and Molecular Biology, Inc.

Vol. 280, No. 8, Issue of February 25, p. e5, 2005
Printed in U.S.A.

Classics

A PAPER IN A SERIES REPRINTED TO CELEBRATE THE CENTENARY OF THE JBC IN 2005

JBC Centennial
1905–2005
100 Years of Biochemistry and Molecular Biology

Hemorrhagic Sweet Clover Disease, Dicumarol, and Warfarin: the Work of Karl Paul Link

Studies on the Hemorrhagic Sweet Clover Disease. IV. The Isolation and Crystallization of the Hemorrhagic Agent
(Campbell, H. A., and Link, K. P. (1941) *J. Biol. Chem.* 138, 21–33)

Studies on the Hemorrhagic Sweet Clover Disease. V. Identification and Synthesis of the Hemorrhagic Agent
(Stahmann, M. A., Huebner, C. F., and Link, K. P. (1941) *J. Biol. Chem.* 138, 513–527)

Studies on the Hemorrhagic Sweet Clover Disease. XIII. Anticoagulant Activity and Structure in the 4-Hydroxycoumarin Group
(Overman, R. S., Stahmann, M. A., Huebner, C. F., Sullivan, W. R., Spero, L., Doherty, D. G., Ikawa, M., Graf, L., Roseman, S., and Link, K. P. (1944) *J. Biol. Chem.* 153, 5–24)

Karl Paul Link (1901–1978) received his Ph.D. in 1925 from the University of Wisconsin, working with plant biochemist William E. Tottingham. He spent the next 2 years in Europe studying carbohydrate chemistry with Sir James Irvine in Scotland, microchemistry with Fritz Pregl in Austria, and organic chemistry with Paul Karrer in Switzerland. He returned to the University of Wisconsin as an assistant professor in agricultural chemistry (now biochemistry) in 1927 and was promoted to associate professor in 1928.

Initially when he set up his laboratory, Link concentrated on plant carbohydrates and soon established himself as one of the outstanding carbohydrate chemists of his day. Using the microchemical techniques he learned with Pregl, he and his students were able to characterize carbohydrate derivatives that they had isolated and synthesized.

However, the direction of Link's research changed drastically when he became involved in the isolation and characterization of the hemorrhagic factor produced in spoiled sweet clover hay. These experiments are the subject of the three *Journal of Biological Chemistry* (JBC) Classics reprinted here. Sweet clover was widely used as hay in the 1920s when a series of wet summers had led to an epidemic of "bleeding disease" in cattle. The cause of the disease was traced to sweet clover hay that had been improperly cured and infected with molds. There was also evidence that the defective coagulation in the cows was due to a deficiency in prothrombin.

Link became interested in the sweet clover problem in 1933 when a farmer came to his laboratory with about 100 lbs of spoiled sweet clover and blood from a cow that had died from hemorrhaging after eating the spoiled hay. Realizing that the farmer's dying cattle represented a huge loss in the depths of the great depression, Link and his students set out to isolate and characterize the hemorrhagic agent from the spoiled hay. It ended up taking 5 years for Link's student Harold A. Campbell to recover 6 mg of crystalline anticoagulant. In the first JBC Classic reprinted here Campbell presents his isolation and crystallization of the hemorrhagic agent. To follow the progression of the fractionation he developed an assay in which he fed his concentrates to rabbits and tested their blood for changes in prothrombin levels (1). From his experiments, Campbell concluded that the hemorrhagic agent had the formula $C_{19}H_{12}O_6$ and that it represented a product that had never before been found in nature.

Next, Link's student Mark A. Stahmann took over the project and initiated a large scale extraction of spoiled sweet clover hay, which is the subject of the second JBC Classic. In about 4 months he was able to isolate 1.8 g of recrystallized anticoagulant. This was enough material

This paper is available on line at http://www.jbc.org

for Stahmann and Charles F. Huebner to check their results against Campbell's and to thoroughly characterize the compound. Through degradation experiments they established that the anticoagulant was 3,3′-methylenebis-(4-hydroxycoumarin), which they later named dicumarol. They confirmed their results by synthesizing dicumarol and proving that it was identical to the naturally occurring product.

Several years after the discovery of dicumarol, others showed that a deficiency of vitamin K ("Koagulations-Vitamin") in experimental animals led to a severe tendency to bleed. Subsequently, it was shown that vitamin K-deficient animals were also hyperprothrombinemic. The structure of vitamin K was established in 1939, and Link soon recognized that dicumarol and vitamin K had similar structures. Administration of dicumarol inhibits the formation of normal amounts of prothrombin, and vitamin K counters its action. The exact biochemical basis for these actions has only been established more recently. After testing dicumarol on animals, Link collaborated with clinicians at the Wisconsin General Hospital and the Mayo Clinic to test the compound's ability to control clotting in human patients. Dicumarol was eventually released into clinical medicine in 1941, and it has enjoyed widespread use as an anticoagulant ever since, gaining particular fame after it was used to treat President Eisenhower after his heart attack in 1955.

Link and his colleagues synthesized over 100 analogues of dicumarol and tested many of them for anticoagulant activity. In the final JBC Classic reprinted here Link reports on the anticoagulant activity of 106 synthetic compounds. Although none of the compounds screened in these experiments were more potent than dicumarol, Link would eventually discover that another analogue was many times more potent than dicumarol in animal tests. Link judged the compound to be so toxic that he didn't bother to patent it. Stahmann, on the other hand, believed it had potential and wrote a patent with the aid of an attorney at the Wisconsin Alumni Research Foundation (WARF). The compound, which was later named warfarin (after WARF), became widely used as a rodenticide and a therapeutic agent.

Link was honored for his scientific accomplishments with his election to the National Academy of Sciences in 1946, and was awarded the Kovalenko medal of the Academy in 1967. He also won the Cameron Award in 1952 from the University of Edinburgh, the John Scott medal in 1959 from the city of Philadelphia, the Lasker Award in 1955 from the American Public Health Association, and the Lasker Award in 1960 from the American Heart Association.

Link was valued not only by the scientific community but also by the students at the University of Wisconsin. As well as being a brilliant lecturer he could always be counted on to back the students' position in any issue with staff or administration. He eventually established a legal defense fund for students in trouble with the university or with the law because of their support of unpopular causes. Link was also a great liberal and defender of unpopular causes, serving as faculty sponsor for organizations such as the John Cookson Karl Marx Discussion Group and the Labor Youth League. But perhaps he was best known on campus for his "non-traditional" clothing including large bow ties, flannel shirts, work shoes, shorts, and sometimes even a cape and knickers.[1]

Nicole Kresge, Robert D. Simoni, and Robert L. Hill

REFERENCES

1. Campbell, H. A., Smith, W. K., Roberts, W. L., and Link, K. P. (1941) Studies on the hemorrhagic sweet clover disease. II. The bioassay of hemorrhagic concentrates by following the prothrombin level in the plasma of rabbit blood. *J. Biol. Chem.* **138,** 1–20
2. Burris, R. H. (1994) *Biographical Memoir of Karl Paul Link.* Vol. 65, pp. 176–195, National Academy of Sciences, Washington, D. C.
3. Last, J. A. (2002) The missing link: the story of Karl Paul Link. *Toxicol. Sci.* **66,** 4–6

[1] All biographical information on Karl Paul Link was taken from Refs. 2 and 3.

THE JOURNAL OF BIOLOGICAL CHEMISTRY
© 2005 by The American Society for Biochemistry and Molecular Biology, Inc.

Vol. 280, No. 9, Issue of March 4, p. e6, 2005
Printed in U.S.A.

Classics

A PAPER IN A SERIES REPRINTED TO CELEBRATE THE CENTENARY OF THE JBC IN 2005

JBC Centennial
1905–2005
100 Years of Biochemistry and Molecular Biology

The Fruits of Collaboration: Chromatography, Amino Acid Analyzers, and the Chemical Structure of Ribonuclease by William H. Stein and Stanford Moore

Photometric Ninhydrin Method for Use in the Chromatography of Amino Acids
(Moore, S., and Stein, W. H. (1948) *J. Biol. Chem.* 176, 367–388)

Chromatography of Amino Acids on Starch Columns. Separation of Phenylalanine, Leucine, Isoleucine, Methionine, Tyrosine, and Valine
(Stein, W. H., and Moore, S. (1948) *J. Biol. Chem.* 176, 337–365)

William H. Stein (1911–1980) graduated from Harvard in 1929 with a major in chemistry. He then spent a year as a graduate student in chemistry at Harvard but transferred to the Department of Biological Chemistry at the College of Physicians and Surgeons, Columbia University, to study biochemistry. He completed his thesis research on the amino acid composition of elastin in 1937 and joined Max Bergmann at The Rockefeller Institute for Medical Research in New York. Stein's initial project with Bergmann was to improve gravimetric methods of amino acid determination. In 1939, Stanford Moore (1913–1982), a graduate of Vanderbilt University who had just earned his Ph.D. from the University of Wisconsin, joined the Bergmann laboratory. In what marked the beginning of one of the longest and most fruitful collaborations in science, the two postdoctoral fellows pooled their efforts to develop the gravimetric methods based on the solubility product of salts of the amino acids into a practical analytical procedure.

Stein and Moore's research was soon interrupted by the war. To help the war effort, Moore enlisted to serve as a technical aid on the National Defense Research Council in Washington to coordinate academic and industrial projects on chemical warfare agents. Stein, on the other hand, remained in Bergmann's laboratory to aid in studies on the physiological actions of vesicant war gases at the molecular level. In 1944, Bergmann died of cancer, but the laboratory work continued until 1945 after which most of the lab members moved on to other positions. Moore and Stein, however, were offered an opportunity by the Director of The Rockefeller Institute, Herbert S. Gasser, to continue, on a trial basis, Bergmann's work on amino acid analysis.

The two immediately started working with the premise, developed in the Bergmann laboratory, that establishing the amino acid compositions of proteins was the first step towards the determination of their chemical structures. Earlier studies on chromatographic fractionation techniques by A. J. P. Martin and R. L. M. Synge and the work by Lyman C. Craig on countercurrent distribution mentioned in a previous *Journal of Biological Chemistry* (JBC) Classic (1) inspired Stein and Moore to explore the use of partition chromatography in determining protein composition. They settled on furthering a method developed by S. R. Elsden and Synge that used potato starch as a column matrix and eluants of various two-phase mixtures of alcohols and aqueous organic acids to separate amino acids and peptides.

The two JBC Classics reprinted here describe how Stein and Moore used starch columns to separate and quantitate phenylalanine, leucine, isoleucine, methionine, valine, and tyrosine in synthetic mixtures of amino acids and hydrolysates of β-lactoglobulin and bovine serum albumin. The first Classic discusses the starch column procedure, the photoelectric drop-

This paper is available on line at http://www.jbc.org

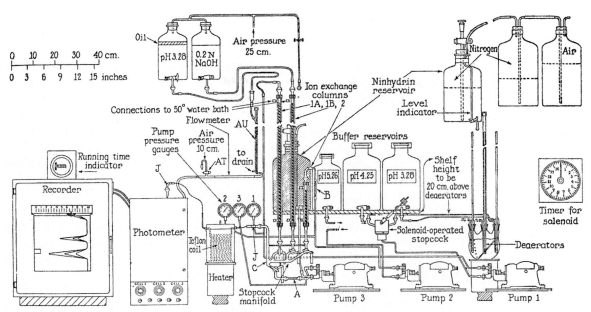

FIG. 1. **Schematic of the automatic recording apparatus used in the chromatographic analysis of mixtures of amino acids.** (Reprinted with permission from Ref. 6.)

counting fraction collector developed by Stein and Moore (the prototype for the fraction collectors in wide use today), and the quantitation of the amino acids.

To make their procedure quantitative, Stein and Moore needed a method to determine the amino acid composition of their fractions, which is the subject of the second JBC Classic. They used a variation on the ninhydrin reaction, discovered by Siegfried Ruhemann in 1911, in which ninhydrin reacts with NH_2 groups to form a blue product. Because the reaction is sensitive to oxidation, they created an oxygen-free environment in solution by including dissolved reducing agents such as stannous chloride or reduced ninhydrin (hydrindantin). They also added a water-miscible organic solvent, methyl Cellosolve (and later dimethyl sulfoxide) to keep the blue-colored reaction product in solution. The eluate was measured spectrophotometrically, and the concentration of product in each fraction was plotted against fraction number to produce an effluent-concentration curve. The area under each peak gave the amount of amino acid in the sample.

Over the next several years, Stein and Moore developed starch columns for quantifying all of the amino acids in protein hydrolysates and eventually applied their analysis to determine the compositions of β-lactoglobulin and bovine serum albumin (2). Because it took an average of 2 weeks to run the three columns necessary to analyze a single protein, Stein and Moore began to look at ways to decrease analysis time. They employed ion-exchange chromatography with sulfonated polystyrene resins and buffers with different salt concentrations and pH at different temperatures to reduce the time to 5 days by the early 1950s. Next, in collaboration with Daryl Spackman, they rendered the process automatic, creating the first amino acid analyzer in 1958. Fig. 1 shows a diagram of the automated system. Early on, they recognized the impact their discoveries would have in biochemistry and made every effort to provide detailed descriptions of their procedures for use in other laboratories. They facilitated this effort by widely circulating preprints to any biochemists who desired them.

In the early 1950s, Stein and Moore started using ion-exchange chromatography to separate peptides and proteins. Encouraged by their success, they decided to embark on the structural analysis of an entire protein. They chose ribonuclease, an enzyme about twice the size of insulin, which was the first protein to be fully sequenced as a result of the pioneering studies of Fred Sanger in Cambridge, England. They performed their work in parallel with Christian B. Anfinsen. To determine the sequence of ribonuclease, Stein and Moore first hydrolyzed the protein with trypsin and then separated the peptide mixture by ion-exchange chromatography. The peptide sequences were then analyzed by Edman degradation. By repeating this experiment with chymotrypsin and pepsin they were able to deduce the sequence of the entire protein, which they published in 1963 (3). Not content to stop at the sequence of ribonuclease, they also studied the inactivation of the enzyme by iodoacetate and were able to identify residues in and around its active site. This work on ribonuclease was recognized in 1972 when Stein and Moore were awarded the Nobel Prize in Chemistry, which they shared with Anfinsen.

Stein and Moore, with many students and postdoctoral fellows, studied the structure/function relationships of a number of other proteins including pancreatic deoxyribonuclease, chymotrypsin, pepsin, streptococcal proteinase, ribonuclease T1, carboxypeptidase Y, and pancreatic ribonuclease.

Independently, Stein also applied chromatographic methods to the analysis of physiological fluids including urine and blood plasma, as well as human tissue. In addition to his research, Stein was extensively involved in service to the scientific community including the publisher of JBC, the American Society of Biological Chemists (ASBC, now the American Society for Biochemistry and Molecular Biology). Stein was elected to the ASBC Editorial Committee in 1955 and was chairman of the Committee from 1958 to 1961. He joined the JBC Editorial Board in 1962 and assumed one of the three associate editorships in 1964. Stein eventually became editor of JBC and played an active role in setting up administrative procedures to handle the increasing number of manuscripts the *Journal* was receiving, including organizing a central office at the Society's headquarters in Bethesda. Herbert Tabor, the current editor of JBC, succeeded Stein several years later. Unfortunately, Stein was found to have Guillain-Barré syndrome in 1969 and was a paraplegic for the rest of his life. However, Stein continued to remain actively involved in research at Rockefeller until his death in 1980.[1]

Like Stein, Moore was very involved in service to the biochemistry community, including serving as President of the ASBC (1966–67), President of the Federation of American Societies for Experimental Biology (1970–71), and chairman of the Organizing Committee for the International Congress of Biochemistry in 1964. During this Congress he started the custom of inviting eight to ten scientists for breakfast or lunch in his suite so that they could meet their colleagues in intimate surroundings. He continued this practice for another 15 years at both international congresses and ASBC meetings. Moore's loyalty to the Rockefeller University and devotion to biochemistry were ultimately reflected in his will, which bequeathed his estate to the university to be used as an endowment to support an investigator in the field of biochemistry.[2]

Nicole Kresge, Robert D. Simoni, and Robert L. Hill

REFERENCES

1. JBC Classics: Craig, L. C. (1943) *J. Biol. Chem.* **150**, 33–45; Craig, L. C. (1944) *J. Biol. Chem.* **155**, 519–534 (http://www.jbc.org/cgi/content/full/280/7/e4)
2. Moore, S. and Stein, W. H. (1949) Amino acid composition of β-lactoglobulin and bovine serum albumin. *J. Biol. Chem.* **178**, 79–91
3. Smyth, D. G., Stein, W. H., and Moore, S. (1963) The sequence of amino acid residues in bovine pancreatic ribonuclease: revisions and confirmations. *J. Biol. Chem.* **238**, 227–234
4. Moore, S. (1987) *Biographical Memoir of William H. Stein*, Vol. 56, pp. 414–441, National Academy of Sciences, Washington, D. C.
5. Smith, E. and Hirs, C. H. W. (1987) *Biographical Memoir of Stanford Moore*, Vol. 56, pp. 354–385, National Academy of Sciences, Washington, D. C.
6. Spackman, D. H., Stein, W. H., and Moore, S. (1958) Automatic recording apparatus for use in the chromatography of amino acids. *Anal. Chem.* **30**, 1190–1206

---

[1] All biographical information on William H. Stein was taken from Ref. 4.
[2] All biographical information on Stanford Moore was taken from Ref. 5.

THE JOURNAL OF BIOLOGICAL CHEMISTRY
© 2005 by The American Society for Biochemistry and Molecular Biology, Inc.

Vol. 280, No. 10, Issue of March 11, p. e7, 2005
Printed in U.S.A.

Classics

A PAPER IN A SERIES REPRINTED TO CELEBRATE THE CENTENARY OF THE JBC IN 2005

JBC Centennial
1905–2005
100 Years of Biochemistry and Molecular Biology

The Biosynthetic Pathway for Cholesterol: Konrad Bloch

On the Utilization of Acetic Acid for Cholesterol Formation
(Bloch, K., and Rittenberg, D. (1942) *J. Biol. Chem.* 145, 625–636)

The Utilization of Acetic Acid for the Synthesis of Fatty Acids
(Rittenberg, D., and Bloch, K. (1945) *J. Biol. Chem.* 160, 417–424)

The Biological Conversion of Cholesterol to Pregnanediol
(Bloch, K. (1945) *J. Biol. Chem.* 157, 661–666)

Konrad Emil Bloch (1912–2000) was born in Neisse, eastern Germany (now Nysa in Poland). Growing up he was more interested in engineering and natural sciences than chemistry, but an organic chemistry course taught by future Nobel laureate Hans Fischer at the Technische Hochschule in Munich provided a turning point. Bloch said of Fischer's class, "As he presented it, the subject matter was fascinating, the organization superb, and the delivery monotonous" (1). Despite Fischer's monotone delivery, Bloch was influenced enough to become a chemistry student in his laboratory.[1]

In early 1934, Bloch was told by Nazi authorities, in line with new racial laws, that he could no longer study at the Technische Hochschule. Fischer managed to arrange for Bloch to work at the Schweizerisches Höhenforschung's Institut in Davos. There, he studied the lipids of human tubercle bacilli and was able to show that a previous report of the presence of cholesterol in this organism was erroneous. This was Bloch's first encounter with cholesterol, a subject in which he would eventually play a great role.

In 1936, with the help of R. J. Anderson at Yale University, Bloch immigrated to the United States and started working with Hans Clarke at the College of Physicians and Surgeons (P & S), Columbia University. He received his Ph.D. a year and one-half later, after completing a relatively straightforward piece of research on amino acid chemistry, and was then invited by Rudolf Schoenheimer to join his group.

Also in Schoenheimer's laboratory at this time was a scientist named David Rittenberg who had done his graduate work on deuterium with Harold Urey. Shortly after receiving his degree, Rittenberg approached Schoenheimer with the prospect of using deuterium as a biological tracer. This resulted in the publication of several seminal papers authored by Rittenberg and Schoenheimer on the use of deuterium to study metabolism, which was the subject of a previous *Journal of Biological Chemistry* (JBC) Classic (2).

Schoenheimer was eager for Bloch to apply the isotope tracer method to study the biosynthesis of cholesterol and had him start by investigating whether the hydroxyl oxygen in cholesterol came from water or oxygen. Unfortunately, Bloch was unable to solve this first problem because no method existed at that time for the mass spectrometric analysis of stably bound oxygen in complex organic compounds. Eventually, in 1956, Bloch's student T. T. Tchen would show that molecular oxygen is the source of the hydroxyl oxygen (3).

Schoenheimer died in 1941, and his laboratory's research projects were divided up among its members. Bloch inherited lipids, and Rittenberg acquired protein synthesis. Although he was still working on the cholesterol oxygen problem at that time, Bloch's attention was quickly diverted with the publication of a paper by R. Sonderhoff and H. Thomas, which reported that "The nonsaponifiable fraction of yeast grown in a medium supplemented with deuterated

---

[1] All biographical information on Konrad Bloch was taken from Refs. 1, 7, 8, and 9.

Konrad Bloch. Photo courtesy of the National Library of Medicine.

acetate had a deuterium content so high that a direct conversion of acetic acid to sterols has to be postulated" (4). Schoenheimer and Rittenberg had also done experiments with D_2O that indicated that animal cholesterol is synthesized from small molecules (5). Combining their areas of expertise, Rittenberg and Bloch did the next obvious experiment: they fed labeled acetates to rats and mice. As reported in the first JBC Classic reprinted here, they found that a substantial amount of deuterium was incorporated into cholesterol. However, their results did not tell them how many of the 27 sterol carbon atoms were supplied by acetic acid. The definitive answer came 10 years later when Bloch used an acetateless mutant of *Neurospora crassa* to show that the mutant's sterol derived all its carbon atoms from exogenous acetate (6).

Over time, Rittenberg added ^{15}N, ^{13}C, and ^{18}O to the isotopes he used to study biological processes. This led to a second labeling experiment with Bloch, this time showing that acetic acid is used in the synthesis of fatty acids. This work is described in the second JBC Classic. Rittenberg and Bloch fed sodium acetate labeled with ^{13}C and deuterium to mice and rats and found that the animals' lipids and cholesterol contained both labeled carbon and hydrogen. From this they concluded that both carbon atoms in acetic acid were used for the synthesis of fatty acids and cholesterol.

Eventually Rittenberg became director of the isotope laboratory at P & S in 1941 and remained there until he retired. His research with isotope tracers encompassed a wide variety of subjects, including the study of hippuric acid metabolism, the dynamics of red blood cell survival in patients with blood abnormalities, the development of a method to assay amino acids in protein hydrolysates, and investigations into the synthesis of porphyrin, which will be the subject of a future JBC Classic. Rittenberg's many contributions to the isotope tracer technique were recognized when he was awarded the Eli Lilly Award in Biological Chemistry from the American Chemical Society and also with his election to the National Academy of Sciences in 1953.[2]

In addition to using isotopes to study the biosynthesis of cholesterol, Bloch also used the tracers to examine the precursor role of cholesterol in bile acids and steroid hormones. In the final JBC Classic reprinted here, Bloch demonstrates that cholesterol is converted into progesterone. However, Bloch encountered several logistical problems when starting this experiment. First, labeled cholesterol was unavailable commercially so he had to spend much of his time introducing deuterium into cholesterol by platinum-catalyzed exchange in heavy water-acetic acid mixtures. Second, the only practical source for isolating the progesterone metabolite pregnanediol in sufficient quantity was from human pregnancy urine, and his request to the P & S department of obstetrics and gynecology for permission to administer labeled cholesterol to one of its patients was denied. Bloch eventually managed to obtain his pregnanediol due to a "willingness to cooperate at home" (1) and proved that progesterone was indeed synthesized from cholesterol.

In 1946 Bloch moved to the Department of Biochemistry at the University of Chicago and then to Harvard University in 1954. He continued to study fatty acids and cholesterol as well as the enzymatic synthesis of the tripeptide glutathione. Eventually, through the combined

---

[2] All biographical information on David Rittenberg was taken from Ref. 10.

efforts of Bloch, John Cornforth, and George Popják, the origin of each of the 27 individual carbon atoms of cholesterol (from the methyl or carboxyl group of acetate) was established. Bloch also aided in the identification of several important landmarks in the series of more than 30 reactions in the biosynthesis of cholesterol, including the cyclization of squalene to lanosterol. His work on fatty acids and cholesterol was eventually rewarded when he shared the 1964 Nobel Prize in Physiology or Medicine with Feodor Lynen "for their discoveries concerning the mechanism and regulation of the cholesterol and fatty acid metabolism."

The elucidation of the pathway from acetic acid to cholesterol was not only a tremendous achievement for biochemistry but also of great importance to medicine. Knowledge of the biosynthetic pathway for cholesterol eventually aided in the discovery of statins, drugs that interfere with cholesterol synthesis, which are now widely used to treat high cholesterol.

Nicole Kresge, Robert D. Simoni, and Robert L. Hill

REFERENCES

1. Bloch, K. (1987) Summing up. *Annu. Rev. Biochem.* **56**, 1–19
2. JBC Classics: Schoenheimer, R., and Rittenberg, D. (1935) *J. Biol. Chem.* 111, 163–168; Rittenberg, D., and Schoenheimer, R. (1937) *J. Biol. Chem.* **121**, 235–253 (http://www.jbc.org/cgi/content/full/277/43/e31)
3. Tchen, T. T., and Bloch, K. (1956) On the mechanism of cyclization of squalene. *J. Am. Chem. Soc.* **78**, 1516–1517
4. Sonderhoff, R., and Thomas, H. (1937) *Ann. Chem.* **530**, 195–213
5. Rittenberg, D., and Schoenheimer, R. (1937) Deuterium as an indicator in the study of intermediary metabolism. XI. Further studies on the biological uptake of deuterium into organic substances, with special reference to fat and cholesterol formation. *J. Biol. Chem.* **121**, 235–253
6. Ottke, R. C., Tatum, E. L., Zabin, I., and Bloch, K. (1951) Isotopic acetate and isovalerate in the synthesis of ergosterol by *Neurospora*. *J. Biol. Chem.* **189** 429–433
7. Kennedy, E. P. (2001) Hitler's gift and the era of biosynthesis. *J. Biol. Chem.* **276**, 42619–42631
8. Goldfine, H., and Vance, D. E. (2001) Obituary: Konrad E. Bloch (1912–2000) *Nature* **409**, 779
9. Kennedy, E. P. (2003) Biographical memoirs: Konrad Bloch. *Proc. Am. Philos. Soc.* **147**, 65–72
10. Shemin, D., and Bentley, R. (2001) *Biographical Memoir of David Rittenberg*, Vol. 80, pp. 256–275, National Academy of Sciences, Washington, D. C.

THE JOURNAL OF BIOLOGICAL CHEMISTRY
© 2005 by The American Society for Biochemistry and Molecular Biology, Inc.

Vol. 280, No. 11, Issue of March 18, p. e8, 2005
Printed in U.S.A.

Classics

A PAPER IN A SERIES REPRINTED TO CELEBRATE THE CENTENARY OF THE JBC IN 2005

JBC Centennial
1905–2005
100 Years of Biochemistry and Molecular Biology

Severo Ochoa's Contributions to the Citric Acid Cycle

Enzymatic Synthesis of Citric Acid. I. Synthesis with Soluble Enzymes
(Stern, J. R., and Ochoa, S. (1951) *J. Biol. Chem.* 191, 161–172)

Enzymatic Synthesis of Citric Acid. IV. Pyruvate as Acetyl Donor
(Korkes, S., del Campillo, A., Gunsalus, I. C., and Ochoa, S. (1951) *J. Biol. Chem.* 193, 721–735)

Severo Ochoa (1905–1993) was born in Luarca, Spain and became interested in biology while in high school. Because there were few graduate programs in the biological sciences in Spain at that time, he had to enroll in the Medical School at the University of Madrid to study biology. Fortunately, during his second year, Ochoa was offered the opportunity to do research. His first experiment, isolating creatinine from urine, stimulated his interest in the function and metabolism of creatine and creatinine in the body. As a result, he and José G. Valdecasas came up with a simple micromethod for the determination of creatine in muscle. They submitted a paper on this method to the *Journal of Biological Chemistry* (JBC), and to their delight, it was published in 1929 (1). Said Ochoa, "Not even in my wildest dreams could I have dreamt that, years later, I would become a member of the editorial board of the JBC and serve as President of the American Society of Biological Chemists (now the American Society for Biochemistry and Molecular Biology)" (2).[1]

After completing his medical degree in 1929, Ochoa spent the next 13 years in a total of 12 different laboratories (9 in Europe and 3 in the United States), partly because he sought out laboratories at the frontier of physiology and medicine but mostly because of social and political turbulence in Europe.

Ochoa's first stop was the Kaiser Wilhelm Institute for Biology in Berlin-Dahlem where he worked with Otto Meyerhof, Nobel laureate and author of a previous JBC Classic (3), on the chemistry of muscle contraction. In 1932, Ochoa moved on to the National Institute for Medical Research in London to work with Harold W. Dudley on glyoxalase and Sir Henry Dale on the influence of the adrenal glands on the chemistry of muscular contraction. He then returned to Madrid where he studied glycolysis in heart muscle.

Unfortunately, in 1936 Ochoa's work came to a standstill with the Spanish Civil War, and it became apparent to him that he would have to leave the country if he wanted to continue doing research. With that in mind, he returned to Heidelberg to work with Meyerhof on some of the enzymatic steps of glycolysis and fermentation. However, with Adolf Hitler's rise to power Meyerhof left for Paris, and Ochoa went to work with Archibald Vivian Hill at the Marine Biological Laboratory in Plymouth, England, and later R. A. Peters at Oxford University.

At Oxford, Ochoa began working on oxidative phosphorylation and showed that oxidation is coupled to phosphorylation of AMP to ATP followed by a transfer of phosphate from ATP to the sugar. Ochoa's research was again cut short by war, this time World War II, and he left for the Washington University School of Medicine in St. Louis to work with Carl and Gerty Cori, future Nobel Laureates and authors of a previous JBC Classic (4). After spending 2 years with the Coris working on the enzymatic mechanism of conversion of fructose to glucose in liver

---

[1] All biographical information on Severo Ochoa was taken from Refs. 2 and 7.

This paper is available on line at http://www.jbc.org

Severo Ochoa. Photo courtesy of the National Library of Medicine.

extracts, Ochoa finally acquired a permanent faculty position at New York University (NYU) and remained there until his retirement.

At NYU Ochoa resumed his studies on oxidative phosphorylation, this time concentrating on the enzymatic reactions that were coupled to phosphorylation. Hans Krebs had shown that the citric acid cycle was the main oxidative pathway for food in the cell, and David Keilin, Otto Warburg, and others had discovered many of the enzymes that were involved in transferring hydrogens and electrons from oxidizable substrates to molecular oxygen. However, very little work had been done on the enzymes involved in the primary oxidation of citric acid cycle substrates. Ochoa decided to focus on these enzymes, including what he termed was "the most elusive enzyme of the citric acid cycle," the enzyme that condensed oxalacetate with "active acetate" to form citrate in the first reaction of the cycle.

$$\text{Acetyl-CoA} + \text{oxalacetate} + H_2O \rightarrow \text{citrate} + \text{CoA} + H^+$$

REACTION 1

Ochoa believed that this "condensing enzyme" was soluble but that the enzyme(s) that made "active acetate" (acetyl-CoA) were insoluble, at least in animal tissues. Thinking the enzymes might, however, be soluble in bacteria, Ochoa and his postdoc Joe Stern combined an *Escherichia coli* extract with an extract of pigeon liver, as described in the first JBC Classic reprinted here. Ochoa and Stern reported that their pigeon liver extract could catalyze the synthesis of citrate from acetate, ATP, and oxalacetate if coenzyme A and magnesium were added. When these extracts, or other types of animal extracts, were complimented with "acetate-activating" *E. coli* extracts (which by themselves may or may not synthesize citrate) in the presence of oxalacetate, citric acid was formed. Ochoa and Stern concluded that the *E. coli* extract provided transacetylase (an enzyme discovered by Earl Stadtman), which catalyzed the transfer of phosphate from acetyl phosphate to CoA to form acetyl-CoA and phosphate. Using this reaction as an assay, Ochoa was eventually able to crystallize the condensing enzyme from pig heart (5) and show that it catalyzed the reversible conversion of acetyl-CoA and oxalacetate to CoA and citrate (6).

Ochoa was also interested in the early steps of pyruvate oxidation and the mechanism by which pyruvate and oxalacetate reacted to form citrate. In the second JBC Classic, I. C. Gunsalus, who was spending a few months in Ochoa's laboratory on a Guggenheim Fellowship, and Seymour Korkes isolated the pyruvate oxidation system from *E. coli* in two fractions (A and B). They found that in the presence of diphosphopyridine nucleotide (DPN, now called nicotinamide adenine dinucleotide or NAD) and CoA, their fractions catalyzed the conversion of pyruvate to acetyl phosphate or to citrate when condensing enzyme and oxalacetate were added. They concluded that their fractions catalyzed the following reaction to produce acetyl-CoA from pyruvate.

$$\text{Pyruvate} + \text{CoA} + \text{NAD}^+ \rightarrow \text{acetyl-CoA} + \text{CO}_2 + \text{NADH} + \text{H}^+$$

REACTION 2

Although Ochoa's contributions to the citric acid cycle were significant, they were eclipsed by a chance finding he made in 1955 that would win him the Nobel Prize 4 years later. He and his postdoc Marianne Grunberg-Manago discovered an enzyme that converted ADP and other nucleoside diphosphates into RNA-like $(\text{NMP})_n$ polymers. Initially they hoped this enzyme, named polynucleotide phosphorylase, might be responsible for the biosynthesis of RNA. However, the realization that polynucleotide phosphorylase did not need a DNA template for RNA synthesis dispelled this idea. This initial disappointment was soon forgotten when Ochoa realized that he could use polynucleotide phosphorylase to synthesize a variety of RNA-like polymers and identify many of the nucleotide triplets that encoded for amino acids. In 1959 he was awarded the Nobel Prize in Physiology or Medicine with Arthur Kornberg, one of his first postdocs at NYU, "for their discovery of the mechanisms in the biological synthesis of ribonucleic acid and deoxyribonucleic acid." It was subsequently determined that the function of polynucleotide phosphorylase was to degrade RNA, not synthesize it, despite the fact that the enzyme runs its natural reaction in reverse *in vitro*.

Nicole Kresge, Robert D. Simoni, and Robert L. Hill

REFERENCES

1. Ochoa, S., and Valdecasas, J. G. (1929) A micromethod for the estimation of total creatinine in muscle. *J. Biol. Chem.* **81**, 351–357
2. Ochoa, S. (1980) The pursuit of a hobby. *Annu. Rev. Biochem.* **49**, 1–30
3. JBC Classics: Meyerhof, O., and Junowicz-Kocholaty, R. (1943) *J. Biol. Chem.* **149**, 71–92; Meyerhof, O. (1945) *J. Biol. Chem.* **157**, 105–120; Meyerhof, O., and Oesper, P. (1947) *J. Biol. Chem.* **170**, 1–22 (http://www.jbc.org/cgi/content/full/280/4/e3)
4. JBC Classics: Cori, C. F., and Cori, G. T. (1928) *J. Biol. Chem.* **79**, 321–341; Cori, G. T., Colowick, S. P., and Cori, C. F. (1938) *J. Biol. Chem.* **124**, 543–555; Cori, G. T., Colowick, S. P., and Cori, C. F. (1939) *J. Biol. Chem.* **127**, 771–782; Green, A. A., and Cori, G. T. (1943) *J. Biol. Chem.* **151**, 21–29; Cori, G. T., and Green, A. A. (1943) *J. Biol. Chem.* **151**, 31–38 (http://www.jbc.org/cgi/content/full/277/29/e18)
5. Ochoa, S., Stern, J. R., and Schneider, M. C. (1951) Enzymatic synthesis of citric acid. II. Crystalline condensing enzyme. *J. Biol. Chem.* **193**, 691–702
6. Stern, J. R., Ochoa, S., and Lynen, F. (1952) Enzymatic synthesis of citric acid. V. Reaction of acetyl coenzyme A. *J. Biol. Chem.* **198**, 313–321
7. Kornberg. A. (2001) Remembering our teachers. *J. Biol. Chem.* **276**, 3–11

THE JOURNAL OF BIOLOGICAL CHEMISTRY
© 2005 by The American Society for Biochemistry and Molecular Biology, Inc.

Vol. 280, No. 12, Issue of March 25, p. e9, 2005
Printed in U.S.A.

Classics

A PAPER IN A SERIES REPRINTED TO CELEBRATE THE CENTENARY OF THE JBC IN 2005

JBC Centennial
1905–2005
100 Years of Biochemistry and Molecular Biology

Launching the Age of Biochemical Genetics, with *Neurospora*: the Work of George Wells Beadle

An Inositolless Mutant Strain of *Neurospora* and Its Use in Bioassays (Beadle, G. W. (1944) *J. Biol. Chem.* **156,** 683–690)

George Wells Beadle (1903–1989) grew up on a 40-acre farm near the small town of Wahoo, Nebraska. Beadle might have become a farmer himself had it not been for the influence of his high school science teacher, Bess MacDonald, who persuaded him to enroll at the University of Nebraska College of Agriculture. After earning a B. S. in 1926, Beadle remained at Nebraska to obtain an M. A. with Franklin D. Keim. Through his work with Keim, Beadle became interested in fundamental genetics and was persuaded to apply to graduate school at Cornell University rather than return to the farm.

Beadle entered Cornell in 1927 and joined Rollins Adams Emerson's laboratory to work on the cytogenetics of maize. Over the next 5 years he published 14 papers dealing with his investigations on maize, all initiated while he was a graduate student at Cornell. With the completion of his graduate work in 1931, Beadle headed off to the California Institute of Technology to work with future Nobel laureate Thomas Hunt Morgan. There he became interested in *Drosophila* and began doing research on genetic recombination. In 1934, Boris Ephrussi, a Rockefeller Foundation Fellow from Paris, came to Morgan's laboratory at Caltech to study *Drosophila* genetics. Beadle and Ephrussi teamed up and began examining eye pigment development in *Drosophila* after devising a method for larval embryonic bud transplantation. These studies were performed in Ephrussi's laboratory in Paris. From these experiments, they proposed that eye color changes in mutant strains of *Drosophila* could be caused by inactivation of specific proteins, acting in a single biosynthetic pathway. This suggested that development could be broken down into a series of gene-controlled biochemical reactions and laid the foundation for the one gene-one enzyme theory that Beadle would eventually propose and make famous.

The idea that specific proteins were produced by specific genes was first alluded to in 1909 by Sir Archibald Garrod, an English physician. Garrod proposed that alkaptonuria, an inherited condition in humans in which the urine is black due to the presence of homogentisic acid, was associated with a recessive gene, Garrod called them Factors, in some way responsible for the further metabolism of homogentisic acid. In 1958 others showed that the liver of a patient with alkaptonuria was without measurable homogentisic acid oxidase activity (1). However, the first explicit articulation of the one gene-one enzyme phrase, and probably the concept, would have to wait until the 1940s when Beadle and biochemist Edward L. Tatum performed several experiments, with a simpler organism, that confirmed the direct relationship between one gene and one enzyme.

In 1937 Beadle accepted an appointment as Professor of Biological Sciences at Stanford University and invited Tatum to join him as a research associate. While auditing a course that Tatum was teaching on comparative biochemistry, Beadle learned that although microbial species share the same basic biochemistry, they differ in their nutritional requirements. He reasoned that if these differences were genetic in origin, it should be possible to induce gene mutations that would produce new nutritional requirements. This would allow identification of the genes governing biochemical reactions that form known products.

For his experimental organism, Beadle chose the red bread mold *Neurospora crassa*, whose life cycle had been characterized, making it an ideal organism for genetic study. He and Tatum

George W. Beadle. Photo courtesy of the National Library of Medicine.

knew from the studies of others that *Neurospora* could grow on a minimal medium composed of a sugar, salts, and the one vitamin, biotin. Then they used x-rays to attempt to produce *Neurospora* mutants that had lost the ability to grow on their minimal medium. Beadle once recalled upon reflecting on these experiments, "We believed so thoroughly that the gene-enzyme reaction relation was a general one that there was no doubt in our minds that we would find the mutants we wanted. The only worry we had was that their frequency might be so low that we would get discouraged and give up before finding one" (2).

The 299th mutagenized culture they tested proved to be the lucky one. It did not grow in their minimal medium, but it did survive and grow when vitamin B_6 was added. To prove that a single gene had been mutated, Beadle and Tatum performed a genetic cross between the mutant strain and a wild type strain and tested cultures derived from the eight single spores that were the progeny of a single meiosis. Their tests showed that cultures from four progeny spores required vitamin B_6 whereas the other four did not, confirming that a single gene had been mutated (3). Before long, mutants requiring amino acids, purines, and pyrimidines were also found, and the science of biochemical genetics was born.

In the *Journal of Biological Chemistry* (*JBC*) Classic reprinted here, Beadle discusses some of the practical applications in the isolation and characterization of one of his *Neurospora* mutants. He and Tatum had produced five *Neurospora* strains that required inositol for normal growth and had established that each of these mutants was altered in the same gene. Because mutant growth rate was a function of inositol concentration, Beadle reasoned that any one of these mutants could be used to assay for inositol. In the Classic, Beadle focuses on one strain and shows that his bioassay is reproducible and fairly precise at quantitatively estimating inositol concentrations in a variety of natural materials.

Beadle and Tatum's *Neurospora* investigations further showed that the biosynthesis of any one substance is dependent upon the function of a set of nonallelic genes. A mutation in any of these genes results in loss of synthesis due to the presumed inactivation of a single enzyme catalyzing a reaction in a multistep biosynthetic pathway. Beadle summarized this concept in an historic article in 1945 in which he claimed that "a given enzyme will usually have its final specificity set by one and only one gene" (4). This statement eventually became known as the "one gene-one enzyme" theory of gene action.

However, when Beadle first presented this theory few scientists accepted the concept that one gene specifies the sequence of one enzyme. This was due in part to the widespread belief in the pleiotropic action (multiple effects) of genes, which was somewhat correct since single gene mutations often had multiple consequences. Several scientists still suspected that genes governed only trivial biological traits whereas important characteristics were determined by cytoplasmic interactions involving as yet unknown mechanisms. The one gene-one enzyme theory was eventually verified and accepted, when subsequent investigations by others established that genetic material was DNA and that DNA had a double helical structure, and determined how genetic material is replicated and how it functions in protein synthesis.

Tatum later applied their methods to produce bacterial mutants. Using these mutants, Tatum's graduate student, Joshua Lederberg, demonstrated genetic recombination in *Escherichia coli*, thereby founding the field of bacterial genetics. In 1958, Beadle, Tatum, and Lederberg shared the Nobel Prize in Physiology or Medicine for their pioneering studies with *Neurospora* and *E. coli*.

In 1946 Beadle returned to Caltech, succeeding Morgan as chairman of the Division of Biology. He continued to work in the laboratory until administrative demands absorbed all of his time. He published his last experimental paper on *Neurospora* in 1946, after which his scientific writings consisted of reviews, lectures, historical essays, and a prize-winning book for young people he wrote with his wife Murial called *The Language of Life: an Introduction to the Science of Genetics* (5). In 1961 Beadle left Caltech to become president of The University of Chicago. After retiring in 1968, he resumed research, returning to a problem he studied during his Cornell days—the origin of maize.[1,2]

Nicole Kresge, Robert D. Simoni, and Robert L. Hill

REFERENCES

1. LaDu, B. N., Zannoni, V. A., Laster, L., and Seegmiller, J. E. (1958) *J. Biol. Chem.* **230**, 251–260
2. Beadle, G. W. (1964) Genes and chemical reactions in *Neurospora*. From *Nobel Lectures, Physiology or Medicine 1942–1962*, Elsevier Publishing Co., Amsterdam
3. Beadle, G. W., and Tatum, E. L. (1941) Genetic control of biochemical reactions in *Neurospora*. *Proc. Natl. Acad. Sci. U. S. A.* **27**, 499–506
4. Beadle, G. W. (1945) Biochemical genetics. *Chem. Rev.* **37**, 15–96
5. Beadle, G. W., and Beadle, M. B. (1966) *The Language of Life: an Introduction to the Science of Genetics*, Doubleday and Co., Inc., New York
6. Horowitz, N. H. (1990) *Biographical Memoir of George Wells Beadle*, Vol. 59, pp. 26–53, National Academy of Sciences, Washington, D. C.
7. Beadle, G. W. (1974) Recollections. *Annu. Rev. Biochem.* **43**, 1–13
8. Berg, P., and Singer, M. (2003) *George Beadle, an Uncommon Farmer*, Cold Spring Harbor Laboratory Press, Cold Spring Harbor, NY

[1] All biographical information on George Wells Beadle was taken from Refs. 6 and 7. Additional information on George Wells Beadle can be found in the biography written by Paul Berg and Maxine Singer (8).

[2] We thank Charles Yanofsky, Emeritus Professor of Biological Sciences at Stanford University, and Paul Berg, Emeritus Professor of Biochemistry at Stanford University Medical School, for their assistance in writing this JBC Classic Introduction.

THE JOURNAL OF BIOLOGICAL CHEMISTRY
© 2005 by The American Society for Biochemistry and Molecular Biology, Inc.

Vol. 280, No. 13, Issue of April 1, p. e10, 2005
Printed in U.S.A.

Classics

A PAPER IN A SERIES REPRINTED TO CELEBRATE THE CENTENARY OF THE JBC IN 2005

JBC Centennial
1905–2005
100 Years of Biochemistry and Molecular Biology

Esmond E. Snell and the B Vitamins

The Vitamin Activities of "Pyridoxal" and "Pyridoxamine"
(Snell, E. E. (1944) *J. Biol. Chem.* **154,** 313–314)

Vitamin B$_6$ and Transamination
(Schlenk, F., and Snell, E. E. (1945) *J. Biol. Chem.* **157,** 425–426)

A previous *Journal of Biological Chemistry* (*JBC*) Classic (1) on Esmond Emerson Snell (1914–2003) offered a look into Snell's early career, including his Ph.D. studies at the University of Wisconsin (Madison), his postdoctoral work with Roger J. Williams at the University of Texas (Austin), and their research on biotin. This Classic focuses on the later part of Snell's life and his numerous contributions to vitamin B research.

After discovering biotin, Snell turned his attention to *Streptococcus faecalis* R. Unlike other lactic acid bacteria, *S. faecalis* is unable to grow when supplemented only with a purine base and uracil but grows well when large amounts of thiamine or small amounts of yeast extract are added. Teaming up with Herschel Mitchell, Snell mounted a major effort to purify this new growth factor from spinach. Using a steam kettle and filter press, they processed roughly 4 tons of spinach and came up with a concentrate 130,000 times more active than a standard liver extract at supporting *S. faecalis* growth (2). They named their new growth factor folic acid, from the Latin word for leaf, folium.

Folic acid marked the last of the unidentified bacterial vitamins required by *S. faecalis* and *Lactobacillus casei*, and the two bacteria could now be used to assay for substances required for growth. However, when Snell used *S. faecalis* to assay tissue extracts for pyridoxine (vitamin B$_6$), he noticed that the values he obtained were hundreds to thousands of times higher than those obtained with yeast or animal assays. He reasoned that the extracts contained a substance, which he called he called "pseudopyridoxine," that the bacteria either responded to in addition to pyridoxine or that enhanced bacterial response to pyridoxine. Snell also found that pseudopyridoxine was elevated in the tissues of animals fed extra pyridoxine as well as in his own urine when he ingested pyridoxine (3).

He eventually concluded that when he autoclaved the bacterial media, oxidation or amination probably converted pyridoxine to an aldehyde or amine, both of which promoted the growth of the bacteria. Snell enlisted the aid of Karl Folkers at Merck & Co. to synthesize the possible structures for the aldehyde and amine compounds (4). He tested the compounds for growth-promoting activity in lactic bacteria and determined that the active aldehyde was 2-methyl-3-hydroxy-4-formyl-5-hydroxymethylpyridine (pyridoxal) and that the amine was 2-methyl-3-hydroxy-4-aminomethyl-5-hydroxymethylpyridine (pyridoxamine). The discovery of these two new forms of vitamin B$_6$ is reported in the first JBC Classic reprinted here.

Because autoclaving the growth medium increased the activity of pyridoxine, Snell tried the same with pyridoxal and pyridoxamine. He found that with autoclaving pyridoxal activity was greatly reduced in *L. casei* but was slightly increased in *S. faecalis*. Because previous experiments had shown that only pyridoxal promoted growth in *L. casei*, but both pyridoxal and pyridoxamine promoted growth in *S. faecalis*, the autoclaving result was consistent with the transformation of pyridoxal to pyridoxamine. Snell confirmed this by heating glutamate with

This paper is available on line at http://www.jbc.org

pyridoxal and isolating the products. The transamination reaction was fully reversible and corresponded to Reaction 1.

Glutamate + pyridoxal $\rightleftharpoons$ pyridoxamine + α-ketoglutarate

REACTION 1

Because pyridoxal could also react with other α-amino acids and α-ketoacids including aspartate and oxalacetate, Snell hypothesized that pyridoxal and pyridoxamine should be able to catalyze the following reaction (Reaction 2).

Glutamate + oxalacetate $\rightleftharpoons$ α-ketoglutarate + aspartate

REACTION 2

In the second JBC Classic, Snell and Fritz Schlenk test tissues from control and vitamin B_6-deficient rats for their ability to catalyze the above reaction. They found that tissues from the B_6-deficient rats had low transaminase activity. However, when they attempted to increase the transamination rate by adding pyridoxine, pyridoxamine, and pyridoxal, they got variable results. Some experiments showed that the vitamins could catalyze the reaction whereas others showed the opposite. Eventually, Snell would discover that pyridoxal phosphate was the active catalyst and that it also participated in a variety of enzyme-catalyzed reactions involving amino acids.

In 1945 Snell returned to Madison as a faculty member at the University of Wisconsin. However, he moved back to Texas in 1951 after being offered a position as Professor of Chemistry with a part-time appointment in the Biochemical Institute. In 1956, he was invited to chair the Department of Biochemistry at University of California Berkeley and served in that role for 6 years. He retired from Berkeley in 1976 and returned to Austin to be chair of the Department of Microbiology. In 1990 Snell retired as an active faculty member but remained a professor emeritus until 2003.

During his long and productive career, Snell received numerous awards, including the Meade-Johnson Vitamin B Complex Award in 1946, the Osborne-Mendel Award from the American Institute of Nutrition in 1951, and the William C. Rose Award from the American Society of Biological Chemists in 1985. He was elected to the National Academy of Sciences in 1955 and was elected a Fellow of the American Institute of Nutrition in 1982. He also served as the editor of the *Annual Review of Biochemistry* from 1968 to 1983.[1]

Nicole Kresge, Robert D. Simoni, and Robert L. Hill

REFERENCES

1. JBC Classics: Eakin, R. E., Snell, E. E., and Williams, R. J. (1940) *J. Biol. Chem.* 136, 801–802; Eakin, R. E., Snell, E. E., and Williams, R. J. (1941) *J. Biol. Chem.* 140, 535–543 (http://www.jbc.org/cgi/content/full/279/41/e5)
2. Mitchell, H. K., Snell, E. E., and Williams, R. J. (1941) The concentration of folic acid. *J. Am. Chem. Soc.* **63**, 2284–2284
3. Snell, E. E., Guirard, B. M., and Williams, R. J. (1942) Occurrence in natural products of a physiologically active metabolite of pyridoxine. *J. Biol. Chem.* **143**, 519–530
4. Harris, S. A., Heyl, D., and Folkers, K. (1944) The structure and synthesis of pyridoxamine and pyridoxal. *J. Biol. Chem.* **154**, 315–316
5. Miles, E. W., and Metzler, D. E. (2004) Esmond Emerson Snell (1914–2003) *J. Nutr.* **134**, 2907–2910
6. Snell, E. E. (1993) From bacterial nutrition to enzyme structure: a personal odyssey. *Annu. Rev. Biochem.* **62**, 1–27

---

[1] All biographical information on Esmond E. Snell was taken from Refs. 5 and 6.

THE JOURNAL OF BIOLOGICAL CHEMISTRY
© 2005 by The American Society for Biochemistry and Molecular Biology, Inc.

Vol. 280, No. 14, Issue of April 8, p. e11, 2005
Printed in U.S.A.

Classics

A PAPER IN A SERIES REPRINTED TO CELEBRATE THE CENTENARY OF THE JBC IN 2005

JBC Centennial
1905–2005
100 Years of Biochemistry and Molecular Biology

The ATP Requirement for Fatty Acid Oxidation: the Early Work of Albert L. Lehninger

The Relationship of the Adenosine Polyphosphates to Fatty Acid Oxidation in Homogenized Liver Preparations
(Lehninger, A. L. (1945) *J. Biol. Chem.* 157, 363–382)

Albert Lester Lehninger (1917–1986) was born in Bridgeport, Connecticut. In 1935 he enrolled at Wesleyan University as an English major. Although his interests soon changed to chemistry, Lehninger would later make use of his writing talents to author three classic textbooks: *Biochemistry*, *The Mitochondrion*, and *Bioenergetics*. Inspired by the work of Otto Warburg and Hans Krebs, Lehninger went on to graduate school at the University of Wisconsin and received his Ph.D. in 1942. His graduate research with Edgar J. Witzemann was on the metabolism of acetoacetate and the oxidation of fatty acids by disrupted liver preparations.

The *Journal of Biological Chemistry* (*JBC*) Classic reprinted here concerns Lehninger's work on fatty acid oxidation. At the time, much of what was known about glycolysis and the citric acid cycle had been elucidated from minced tissue and tissue extracts. However, similar studies on fatty acid oxidation had been hampered by the fact that ruptured liver cells lost their ability to oxidize fatty acids. Luis F. Leloir and Juan M. Muñoz had some success with liver homogenates at low temperatures in the presence of oxygen, inorganic phosphate, fumarate, cytochrome *c*, adenylic acid, and magnesium ions (1), but these experiments were not always reproducible. When the reaction was carried out successfully, Leloir and Muñoz noted that there was a decrease in ATP phosphorus and phosphopyruvic acid phosphate and an increase in inorganic phosphate, indicating the reaction was somehow coupled with phosphorylation.

In examining these early experiments, Lehninger realized that high concentrations of ATP or ADP might be required to activate or facilitate oxidation by the liver extracts. He came to this conclusion for a number of reasons including the fact that ATP is rapidly dephosphorylated when cells are disrupted and that the fumarate needed for the reaction might provide a substrate for oxidations capable of phosphorylating adenylic acid to ATP. In the Classic, Lehninger proves his hypothesis by adding ATP to a homogenized liver preparation and demonstrating that it consistently and reproducibly carried out fatty acid oxidation. Subsequent work would show that fatty acids are activated by the formation of a thioester linkage between the carboxyl group of the fatty acid and the sulfhydryl group of coenzyme A. This reaction is driven by ATP.

With the start of the war, Lehninger abandoned his fatty acid studies and joined the wartime research effort of the Plasma Protein Fractionation Program led by Edwin Joseph Cohn, who was the author of a previous *JBC* Classic (2). During this time, Lehninger discovered several papers on oxidative phosphorylation, and from then on the mechanisms of energy capture and transduction in cells became the central focus of his research.

In 1945 Lehninger accepted a faculty position at the University of Chicago. During his 6 years in Chicago, Lehninger and two of his students would make two significant discoveries that would contribute greatly to the study of metabolism. First, Lehninger and Eugene P. Kennedy would discover that virtually all of the cell's oxidative activity occurred in the mitochondria. Second, Lehninger and Morris E. Friedkin would show that electron transport

This paper is available on line at http://www.jbc.org

Albert L. Lehninger. Photo courtesy of the National Library of Medicine.

from NADH to oxygen is an immediate and direct energy source for oxidative phosphorylation. Lehninger's work with Kennedy and the latter part of his research career will be the subject of a future *JBC* Classic.[1]

Nicole Kresge, Robert D. Simoni, and Robert L. Hill

REFERENCES

1. Muñoz, J. M., and Leloir, L. F. (1943) Fatty acid oxidation by liver enzymes. *J. Biol. Chem.* **147**, 355–362
2. JBC Classics: Cohn, E. J., Hendry, J. L., and Prentiss, A. M. (1925) *J. Biol. Chem.* **63**, 721–766 (http://www.jbc.org/cgi/content/full/277/30/e19)
3. Lane, M. D., and Talalay, P. (1986) Albert Lester Lehninger 1917–1986. *J. Membr. Biol.* **91**, 194–197

[1] All biographical information on Albert Lester Lehninger was taken from Ref. 3.

THE JOURNAL OF BIOLOGICAL CHEMISTRY
© 2005 by The American Society for Biochemistry and Molecular Biology, Inc.

Vol. 280, No. 15, Issue of April 15, p. e12, 2005
Printed in U.S.A.

Classics

A PAPER IN A SERIES REPRINTED TO CELEBRATE THE CENTENARY OF THE JBC IN 2005

JBC Centennial
1905–2005
100 Years of Biochemistry and Molecular Biology

David Rittenberg: Exploring Porphyrin Synthesis with Duck Blood and Isotope Tracers

The Utilization of Glycine for the Synthesis of a Porphyrin
(Shemin, D., and Rittenberg, D. (1945) *J. Biol. Chem.* **159,** 567–568)

The Synthesis of Protoporphyrin *in Vitro* by Red Blood Cells of the Duck
(Shemin, D., London, I. M., and Rittenberg, D. (1950) *J. Biol. Chem.* **183,** 757–765)

The Role of Acetic Acid in the Biosynthesis of Heme
(Radin, N. S., Rittenberg, D., and Shemin, D. (1950) *J. Biol. Chem.* **184,** 755–767)

David Rittenberg (1906–1970) was born, raised, and educated in New York City. Almost all of his life was spent working in New York, and once he enrolled in graduate school at Columbia University he never strayed from that institution. At Columbia, Rittenberg did his graduate work with Harold Urey, who would soon be awarded a Nobel Prize for his identification and isolation of deuterium. In 1934, the same year that Urey was awarded the Prize, Rittenberg obtained a Ph.D. for his 30-page thesis entitled, "Some Equilibria Involving Isotopes of Hydrogen." Enthused by his initial work on deuterium and wanting to promote its biological uses, Rittenberg joined the Department of Biochemistry at Columbia University's College of Physicians and Surgeons (P & S). The chair of the department, Hans T. Clarke, suggested that Rittenberg talk to members of the department about using ^2H in their studies. This suggestion led to the beginning of a fruitful collaboration between Rittenberg and Rudolph Schoenheimer that resulted in the publication of several seminal papers on using deuterium to study metabolism, which was the subject of a previous *Journal of Biological Chemistry* (JBC) Classic (1).

By 1937, thanks to Urey, ^{15}N became available and opened up the investigation of nitrogen metabolism. At that time, the only practical method for ^{15}N assay required a mass spectrometer, which was not yet commercially available. Undaunted by this obstacle, Rittenberg, with the help of several others at P & S, constructed his own mass spectrometer. To do the assay, a sample of dinitrogen gas was bled into the mass spectrometer through a glass capillary leak. The size of the leak was very important, and eventually the international standard was defined as the diameter of a hair from Rittenberg's head. The first ^{15}N work to be carried out by Rittenberg was a study of hippuric acid metabolism in which ammonia was found to be converted to both glycine and hippuric acid in animals (2).

The initial isotope work had led to the realization that the body's constituents were in a dynamic state; macromolecules were constantly involved in rapid chemical reactions with their smaller component units in a continuing process of degradation and resynthesis. This overthrew the previous notion that dietary constituents were used only for repair and energetic purposes. Around this time Rittenberg was appointed director of the isotope laboratory. The laboratory's research group included many scientists who would later become well known, including Konrad Bloch (who was the subject of a previous JBC Classic (3)), Sarah Ratner, and David Shemin.

In 1945, Rittenberg and Shemin started using ^{15}N to follow the path of glycine in the body. They found that glycine is used to synthesize the pyrrole rings of protoporphyrin, as reported in the first JBC Classic reprinted here. Shemin himself ingested 66 g of [^{15}N]glycine over a 3-day period. His blood was drawn at intervals, and its ^{15}N content was assessed. Because the ^{15}N content of the heme component of hemoglobin first increased, then remained constant, and

This paper is available on line at http://www.jbc.org

finally declined, Rittenberg and Shemin concluded that, unlike other many other macromolecules, hemoglobin was not in a dynamic state.

From these initial experiments, Shemin and Rittenberg calculated that the life span of the human red blood cell was 127 days. This led to a study of the life span of red blood cells in patients with blood abnormalities in collaboration with Irving M. London and Randolph West in the Department of Medicine at P & S (4) and resulted in investigations into the origin of bile pigment derived from hemoglobin (5).

The [^{15}N]glycine experiments also led to more heme labeling experiments. Rittenberg, Shemin, and London found that when they incubated sickle cell anemia patient blood or duck blood with [^{15}N]glycine *in vitro*, ^{15}N-labeled heme was formed (6, 7). Using the red blood cells of this duck blood system, they were able to initiate studies on the biosynthesis of heme, as described in the second JBC Classic.

Subsequently, Rittenberg and Shemin, along with Norman S. Radin, used their duck blood system to determine the origins of the carbon atoms in heme. Using ^{15}N-labeled glycine they found that 8 of the heme carbon atoms are derived from the glycine α-carbon (8). Next, as explained in the final JBC Classic, they incubated duck blood with acetic acid, pyruvic acid, acetone, and CO_2 labeled with ^{14}C. They discovered that both carbon atoms of acetate as well as the α-carbon atom of pyruvic acid are used in heme synthesis but that acetone and CO_2 are not utilized in their *in vitro* system.

Rittenberg remained at P & S until he retired. He was appointed chair of the Department of Biochemistry in 1956. His contributions to the isotope tracer technique were recognized when he was awarded the Eli Lilly Award in Biological Chemistry from the American Chemical Society and also when he was elected to the National Academy of Sciences in 1953.[1]

Nicole Kresge, Robert D. Simoni, and Robert L. Hill

REFERENCES

1. JBC Classics: Schoenheimer, R., and Rittenberg, D. (1935) *J. Biol. Chem.* **111,** 163–168; Rittenberg, D., and Schoenheimer, R. (1937) *J. Biol. Chem.* **121,** 235–253 (http://www.jbc.org/cgi/content/full/277/43/e31)
2. Schoenheimer, R., Rittenberg, D., Fox, M., Keston, A. S., and Ratner, S. (1937) The nitrogen isotope (N^{15}) as a tool in the study of the intermediary metabolism of nitrogenous compounds. *J. Am. Chem. Soc.* **59,** 1768
3. JBC Classics: Bloch, K., and Rittenberg, D. (1942) *J. Biol. Chem.* **145,** 625–636; Rittenberg, D., and Bloch, K. (1945) *J. Biol. Chem.* **160,** 417–424; Bloch, K. (1945) *J. Biol. Chem.* **157,** 661–666 (http://www.jbc.org/cgi/content/full/280/10/e7)
4. London, I. M., Shemin, D., West, R., and Rittenberg, D. (1949) Heme synthesis and red blood cell dynamics in normal humans and in subjects with polycythemia vera, sickle-cell anemia, and pernicious anemia. *J. Biol. Chem.* **179,** 463–484
5. London, I. M., West, R., Shemin, D., and Rittenberg, D. (1950) On the origin of bile pigment in normal man. *J. Biol. Chem.* **184,** 351–358
6. London, I. M., Shemin, D., and Rittenberg, D. (1948) The *in vitro* synthesis of heme in the human red blood cell of sickle cell anemia. *J. Biol. Chem.* **173,** 797–798
7. Shemin, D., London, I. M., and Rittenberg, D. (1948) The *in vitro* synthesis of heme from glycine by the nucleated red blood cell. *J. Biol. Chem.* **173,** 799–800
8. Radin, N. S., Rittenberg, D., and Shemin, D. (1950) The role of glycine in the biosynthesis of heme. *J. Biol. Chem.* **184,** 745–754
9. Shemin, D., and Bentley, R. (2001) *Biographical Memoir of David Rittenberg*, Vol. 80, pp. 256–275, National Academy of Sciences, Washington, D. C.

---

[1] All biographical information on David Rittenberg was taken from Ref. 9. We thank Irving M. London, Emeritus Professor of Medicine at Harvard Medical School, for helpful comments in the preparation of this JBC Classic Introduction.

THE JOURNAL OF BIOLOGICAL CHEMISTRY
© 2005 by The American Society for Biochemistry and Molecular Biology, Inc.

Vol. 280, No. 16, Issue of April 22, p. e13, 2005
Printed in U.S.A.

Classics

A PAPER IN A SERIES REPRINTED TO CELEBRATE THE CENTENARY OF THE JBC IN 2005

JBC Centennial
1905–2005
100 Years of Biochemistry and Molecular Biology

Chester H. Werkman and Merton F. Utter: Using Bacteria Juice and ^{13}C to Explore Carbon Dioxide Fixation

Reversibility of the Phosphoroclastic Split of Pyruvate
(Utter, M. F., Lipmann, F., and Werkman, C. H. (1945) *J. Biol. Chem.* **158,** 521–531)

Chester Hamlin Werkman (1893–1962) was born in Fort Wayne, Indiana. His career in science began at Iowa State University in 1920 when he became a graduate student under Robert E. Buchanan, an internationally recognized microbiologist. Werkman's interest in bacteria stemmed from the fact that he thought of them as simple models for studying the basic chemical transformations involved in living processes. He completed his dissertation in 1923 and remained with Buchanan until he was offered a faculty position at the University of Massachusetts in 1924. However, he returned to the Department of Bacteriology at Iowa State a year later and remained there as a faculty member for the rest of his life.

Upon returning to Iowa State, Werkman's research interests underwent a slow evolution. Initially he continued to publish papers related to his thesis work on immunology and vitamins, but soon he developed an interest in food microbiology and the role of vitamins as growth factors for bacteria. During the early 1930s, the Iowa State agricultural experimental station started investigating the use of bacterial fermentation to dispose of farm waste, and Werkman became involved in this effort. This resulted in his publication of a series of papers describing organic techniques to isolate and quantify the products of various fermentation processes. Soon Werkman became interested in investigating the intermediate mechanisms of these fermentations and embarked on what would become a lifelong study of reaction intermediates in bacteria.

One of Werkman's most important contributions to physiological microbiology was done with his graduate student, Harland G. Wood. Werkman and Wood established the existence of heterotrophic carbon dioxide fixation (the concept that all organisms, not just plants or specialized bacteria, can utilize CO_2), which could be summarized by the "Wood Werkman reaction."

$$CO_2 + CH_3COCOOH \rightleftharpoons COOHCH_2COCOOH$$

Werkman and Wood used ^{13}C-labeled compounds to confirm heterotrophic carbon dioxide fixation and also to study the utilization of carbon in metabolism. To do this, they built a mass spectrometer and a 72-foot thermal diffusion column (to produce concentrated ^{13}C) in the elevator shaft of the science building. They published their first detailed papers on the use of ^{13}C-labeled compounds in the *Journal of Biological Chemistry* (*JBC*) (1, 2). These and other papers by Wood will be the subject of a future *JBC* Classic.

In 1938, Merton Franklin Utter (1917–1980) joined Werkman's laboratory as a graduate student. Utter, who was born in Westboro, Missouri, had just graduated from Simpson College in Indianola, Iowa. The first paper he published with Werkman was entitled "The Preparation of an Active Juice from Bacteria" (3). This was a very modest title considering that active enzyme systems had not yet been isolated from bacteria.

Werkman and Utter used these bacterial extracts and ^{13}C-labeled compounds to further investigate carbon dioxide fixation, which is the subject of the *JBC* Classic reprinted here. The Wood Werkman reaction had already established that carbon dioxide could be combined with a C_3 compound, but the existence of a $C_1 + C_2$ reaction had not been demonstrated. Werkman and Utter knew that the phosphoroclastic split, in which pyruvic acid is split to make acetyl phosphate and formic acid, was common in *Escherichia coli*.

$$\underset{\text{Pyruvic acid}}{CH_3COCOOH} + H_3PO_4 \rightleftharpoons \underset{\text{acetyl phosphate}}{CH_3COOPO_3H_2} + \underset{\text{formic acid}}{HCOOH}$$

If they could prove that this reaction was reversible, it would be an example of a $C_1 + C_2$ addition. Although the C_1 compound in the reaction is formic acid rather than carbon dioxide, formic acid is in equilibrium with carbon dioxide and hydrogen in *E. coli*, so carbon dioxide fixation is ultimately involved in the reaction.

Werkman and Utter teamed up with Fritz Lipmann (the author of a future *JBC* Classic), who had just discovered the role of acetyl phosphate in metabolism. To prove the reversibility of the reaction, they added ^{13}C-labeled formic acid to *E. coli* extracts and tested for ^{13}C in the resulting pyruvic acid. In separate experiments they added $CH_3{}^{13}COOH$ and adenyl pyrophosphate (which would react to form labeled acetyl phosphate) to the extracts. In both cases the pyruvic acid formed contained ^{13}C, demonstrating the reversibility of the phosphoroclastic split and the occurrence of $C_1 + C_2$ carbon dioxide fixation. As a final test they added $^{13}CO_2$ to whole cell suspensions of *E. coli* and showed that the bacteria produced ^{13}C-labeled pyruvic acid.

After earning his Ph.D. with Werkman in 1942, Utter was appointed instructor in bacteriology at Ohio State. In 1944 he was offered an assistant professorship at the University of Minnesota and moved to Minneapolis. He moved again in 1946, this time to Cleveland, Ohio, to become an associate professor of biochemistry at Western Reserve University School of Medicine. Utter was promoted to professor in 1956 and became chairman of the biochemistry department in 1965. He remained as chairman until 1976 and then devoted all of his time to research and teaching in the Department of Biochemistry. Utter was also an associate editor for the *JBC* and helped to guide the journal's editorial policies during its rapid expansion.

Utter continued to study metabolism and soon became interested in gluconeogenesis, which is where he made his most significant contribution to biochemistry. For many years it was believed that the synthesis of glucose (gluconeogenesis) occurred by the reversal of the Embden-Meyerhof pathway in glycolysis. Utter demonstrated that this was incorrect by discovering phosphoenolpyruvate carboxykinase and pyruvate carboxylase, two enzymes that are involved in the conversion of pyruvate to phosphoenolpyruvate in a sequence of reactions that differ from those in glycolysis. Utter, along with Bruce Keech, also provided one of the first examples of allosteric control of an enzyme when he demonstrated that acetyl-CoA regulates pyruvate carboxylase activity.[1,2]

Nicole Kresge, Robert D. Simoni, and Robert L. Hill

REFERENCES

1. Wood, H. G., Werkman, C. H., Hemingway, A., and Nier, A. O. (1941) Heavy carbon as a tracer in heterotrophic carbon dioxide assimilation. *J. Biol. Chem.* **139**, 365–376
2. Wood, H. G., Werkman, C. H., Hemingway, A., and Nier, A. O. (1941) The position of carbon dioxide carbon in succinic acid synthesized by heterotrophic bacteria. *J. Biol. Chem.* **139**, 377–381
3. Wiggert, W. P., Silverman, M., Utter, M. F., and Werkman C. H. (1940) Preparation of an active juice from bacteria. *Iowa State Coll. J. Sci.* **14**, 179–186
4. Brown, R. W. (1974) *Biographical Memoir of Chester Hamlin Werkman*, Vol. 44, pp. 328–358, National Academy of Sciences, Washington, D. C.
5. Singleton, R. (2000) From bacteriology to biochemistry: Albert Jan Kluyver and Chester Werkman at Iowa State. *J. Hist. Biol.* **33**, 141–180
6. Wood, H. G., and Hanson, R. W. (1987) *Biographical Memoir of Merton Franklin Utter*, Vol. 56, pp. 474–499, National Academy of Sciences, Washington, D. C.

---

[1] All biographical information on Chester Hamlin Werkman was taken from Refs. 4 and 5.
[2] All biographical information on Merton Franklin Utter was taken from Ref. 6.

THE JOURNAL OF BIOLOGICAL CHEMISTRY
© 2005 by The American Society for Biochemistry and Molecular Biology, Inc.

Vol. 280, No. 17, Issue of April 29, p. e14, 2005
Printed in U.S.A.

Classics

A PAPER IN A SERIES REPRINTED TO CELEBRATE THE CENTENARY OF THE JBC IN 2005

JBC Centennial
1905–2005
100 Years of Biochemistry and Molecular Biology

A Theory for the Molecular Basis of Bioelectricity: the Work of David Nachmansohn

Studies on Cholinesterase. I. On the Specificity of the Enzyme in Nerve Tissue (Nachmansohn, D., and Rothenberg, M. A. (1945) *J. Biol. Chem.* 158, 653–666)

David Nachmansohn (1899–1983) was born in Jekaterinoslav, Russia, but moved to Berlin at an early age.[1] He entered the University of Berlin in 1918 hoping to study the humanities, but with Germany's defeat in World War I and the social, political, and economic problems facing the newly established republic, he decided to pursue medicine instead. As his studies progressed, Nachmansohn became more interested in biology, and he eventually joined Peter Rona at the Charité (the university hospital of Berlin University Medical School) for training in biochemistry when he graduated. Two years later he went to the Kaiser-Wilhelm Institut für Biologie in Berlin-Dahlem to work with Otto Meyerhof, who was featured in a previous *Journal of Biological Chemistry* (*JBC*) Classic (www.jbc.org).

At that time, Meyerhof was beginning studies on a newly discovered compound in muscle called phosphocreatine. The function of this compound was unknown, and Nachmansohn was given the task of looking for the relations between phosphocreatine breakdown, lactic acid formation, and muscle tension during isometric contraction in anaerobiosis. He discovered that rapidly contracting muscles contained more phosphocreatine than slowly contracting ones, which eventually led to the theory that phosphocreatine was involved in the regeneration of ATP that was broken down to provide energy in muscular contraction.

When Hitler came to power Nachmansohn left Germany. He was offered the opportunity to work at the Sorbonne and moved to Paris in 1933. While at the Sorbonne, Nachmansohn often attended the meetings of the British Physiological Society, held in London. One of the main topics of discussion at these meetings was the role of acetylcholine in nerve activity. Sir Henry Dale had proposed that acetylcholine transmits nerve impulses across junctions between neurons or nerve and muscle. It was also known that acetylcholine was rapidly hydrolyzed by acetylcholine esterase. Nachmansohn felt that more studies needed to be done on the nature, distribution, and concentration of acetylcholine esterase in tissues in order to determine its role in nerve activity. He began to work on this problem and soon discovered that acetylcholine esterase was present at high concentrations in many different types of excitable nerve and muscle fibers and in brain tissue but was hardly detectable in organs such as the liver or kidney. The concentration of acetylcholine esterase was also much higher at neuromuscular junctions than in nerve fibers.

An article by J. Linhard describing the electric organs of fish as muscle fibers in which the muscular elements were either missing or present only in rudimentary form caught Nachmansohn's attention. He had seen a *Torpedo* fish at the 1937 Paris World's Fair and managed to procure some tissue for his studies. He discovered that the electric fish tissue contained exceedingly high concentrations of acetylcholine esterase. Later, in 1939, he and Egar Lederer purified acetylcholine esterase from the electric organ of the *Torpedo* fish. Then, in 1940, Nachmansohn, together with W. Feldberg and A. Fessard, provided the first unequivocal evidence for the electrogenic action of acetylcholine.

In 1940, Nachmansohn joined the faculty at Yale University and began studying the electric organ of the electric eel, which he obtained from the New York Aquarium. He found that not

---

[1] All biographical information on David Nachmansohn was taken from Ref. 3.

This paper is available on line at http://www.jbc.org

David Nachmansohn. Photo courtesy of the National Library of Medicine.

only did the organ contain high levels of acetylcholine esterase but that its phosphocreatine and ATP concentrations were comparable to those in striated muscle. He also discovered that the electrical discharge was accompanied by phosphocreatine breakdown. From this he hypothesized that the electric organ obtained the energy it required for the resynthesis of acetylcholine broken down during electric discharge by the same processes used to supply energy for muscular contraction: ATP and phosphocreatine breakdown and lactic acid formation.

Nachmansohn moved to New York in 1942 to become a faculty member at the College of Physicians and Surgeons at Columbia University. Soon after arriving he proved that electric tissue contains enzymes capable of utilizing the energy of ATP for the acetylation of choline by choline acetylase. This was the first time ATP had been shown to drive a synthetic reaction other than phosphorylation. Nachmansohn and A. L. Machado published this discovery in the *Journal of Neurophysiology* (1). Interestingly, three journals (*Science*, the *JBC*, and the *Proceedings of the Society for Experimental Biology and Medicine*) refused to publish this paper because the reviewers could not believe that ATP would participate in reactions other than phosphorylations. It was later found by Fritz Lipmann and others that acetylation requires acetyl-CoA and that ATP was needed for the synthesis of acetyl-CoA, which acetylates choline.

Meanwhile, work in a number of other laboratories confirmed that membranes of axons and conducting fibers, not just synaptic membranes, contained high concentrations of acetylcholine esterase. This led Nachmansohn to propose that acetylcholine acts as a signal that binds to a membrane-bound receptor and produces a conformational change. This increases local membrane permeability to ions and leads to depolarization and generation of an action potential. The acetylcholine is then rendered inactive by the esterase.

However, this hypothesis was based on the assumption that acetylcholine esterase was a specific enzyme that metabolized acetylcholine. In order for his theory to be true, Nachmansohn had to prove the enzyme's specificity and to establish its identity in the tissues he and others had used in their studies. The JBC Classic reprinted here contains these specificity and identity-proving experiments, done by Nachmansohn and Mortimer A. Rothenberg. They compared the abilities of acetylcholine esterases from a number of different tissues (used in previous experiments) to hydrolyze a variety of substrates. No matter what the tissue source, they found that no other substrate was split at a higher rate than acetylcholine, confirming that the enzyme was specific for acetylcholine.

Nachmansohn also proposed a theory for nerve conduction, postulating that a nerve impulse is generated through membrane depolarization by acetylcholine released by stimulus from an inactive complex with protein. The action potential causes the release of acetylcholine in adjacent sites leading to the propagation of the current along the nerve fiber. A rapid hydrolysis of acetylcholine by the esterase and the ion pump mechanism coupled to the breakdown of ATP restores the membrane potential. Nachmansohn presented this theory in 1959 in his book, *Chemical and Molecular Basis of Nerve Activity* (2).

However, his ideas were not readily accepted by neurophysiologists. Today the current belief is that acetylcholine functions only as a synaptic transmitter that is released into the synaptic cleft. Axonal conduction, on the other hand, is believed to involve electric field effects on conformational transitions of protein-ion channels.

Nicole Kresge, Robert D. Simoni, and Robert L. Hill

REFERENCES

1. Nachmansohn, D., and Machado, A. L. (1943) The formation of acetylcholine. A new enzyme choline acetylase. *J. Neurophysiol.* **6**, 397–403
2. Nachmansohn, D. (1959) *Chemical and Molecular Basis of Nerve Activity*, Academic Press, New York
3. Ochoa, S. (1989) *Biographical Memoir of David Nachmansohn*, Vol. 58, pp. 356–405, National Academy of Sciences, Washington, D. C.

THE JOURNAL OF BIOLOGICAL CHEMISTRY
© 2005 by The American Society for Biochemistry and Molecular Biology, Inc.

Vol. 280, No. 18, Issue of May 6, p. e15, 2005
Printed in U.S.A.

Classics

A PAPER IN A SERIES REPRINTED TO CELEBRATE THE CENTENARY OF THE JBC IN 2005

JBC Centennial
1905–2005
100 Years of Biochemistry and Molecular Biology

The Discovery of Heterotrophic Carbon Dioxide Fixation by Harland G. Wood

Heavy Carbon as a Tracer in Heterotrophic Carbon Dioxide Assimilation
(Wood, H. G., Werkman, C. H., Hemingway, A., and Nier, A. O. (1941) *J. Biol. Chem.* 139, 365–376)

The Mechanism of Carbon Dioxide Fixation by Cell-free Extracts of Pigeon Liver: Distribution of Labeled Carbon Dioxide in the Products
(Wood, H. G., Vennesland, B., and Evans, E. A. (1945) *J. Biol. Chem.* 159, 153–158)

The Fixation of Carbon Dioxide in Oxalacetate by Pigeon Liver
(Utter, M. F., and Wood H. G. (1946) *J. Biol. Chem.* 164, 455–476)

Harland Goff Wood (1907–1991) was born in Delavan, a small village in south central Minnesota. He attended Macalester College in Minnesota where he majored in chemistry. Wood graduated during the Depression, and because jobs were scarce, he decided that he would need a higher degree to meet the competition. His biology professor, O. T. Walters, suggested he apply for a fellowship in bacteriology at Iowa State College. Wood's application was reviewed by Chester Werkman, author of a previous *Journal of Biological Chemistry* (JBC) Classic (1), who was starting to investigate the chemistry of bacterial fermentations and was looking for a chemistry student. Werkman accepted Wood's application, and in 1931 Wood moved to Ames, Iowa.

For his thesis research, Wood was assigned an investigation of fermentation by propionic acid bacteria, a group of bacteria that ferment compounds such as glycerol with the formation of propionic acid. He started by looking into glucose fermentation and determined that succinate is formed from glucose. Next, he decided to investigate glycerol fermentation in propionic acid bacteria. He determined the products of glycerol fermentation in a bicarbonate buffer system and calculated the carbon and oxidation-reduction balances to account for the carbon of the fermented substrate. Surprisingly, Wood found that the products from glycerol fermentation contained more carbon than was supplied by the fermented glycerol. He subsequently discovered that the extra carbon was derived from CO_2 in the buffer and eventually proposed that CO_2 and pyruvate combine to form oxalacetate, which is subsequently reduced to succinate (2, 3). This ultimately became known as the Wood-Werkman reaction.

However, as with many new findings, Wood's discovery of heterotrophic CO_2 fixation was extremely controversial. At that time CO_2 fixation was believed to occur only in plants and a few unusual autotrophic bacteria, and the publication of his results was met with much skepticism. For example, C. B. van Niel stated that, "Wood and Werkman claim that carbon dioxide is reduced during the fermentation of glycerol by propionic acid bacteria. The published results cannot, however, be considered conclusive, although the data do seem to favor their claim" (4). Even Wood thought his results might be wrong and didn't include them in his thesis.

In 1935 Wood went to the University of Wisconsin where he worked as a postdoctoral fellow with W. H. Petersen for 4 years. At Wisconsin he studied the growth factor requirements for propionic acid bacteria with Ed Tatum. They showed, for the first time, that vitamin B_1 is required for the growth of a microorganism (5).

Harland G. Wood. Photo courtesy of the National Library of Medicine.

Werkman then offered Wood a position as an Assistant Research Professor at Iowa State, and he returned to Ames in 1936 to continue his work on CO_2 fixation. At that time they only had indirect evidence that CO_2 was fixed in succinate. Wood's brother, who was studying for his Ph.D. and M.D. at the University of Minnesota, mentioned some studies being done with ^{13}C and suggested that he collaborate with a young physicist named Alfred Nier who would be able to supply labeled carbon and measure it with a mass spectrometer. As reported in the JBC Classic reprinted here, Wood was able to prove that $^{13}CO_2$ is fixed in succinate and that the ^{13}C is located exclusively in the carboxyl groups (6). Thus, Wood concluded, "all the carbon dioxide is fixed originally by union of 3-carbon and 1-carbon compounds." Eventually, as shown in a previous JBC Classic (1), Werkman and Merton Utter would also prove that a $C_1 + C_2$ reaction is possible.

Although the labeling experiments lent credibility to heterotrophic CO_2 fixation, Wood was convinced that the full significance of CO_2 utilization would not be fully appreciated until it was demonstrated in animals. Unfortunately, Earl Evans and Louis Slotin beat Wood to it and, using ^{11}C, demonstrated CO_2 fixation by the liver in 1940 (7).

Up until this time, all of Wood's ^{13}C experiments had been done in collaboration with Nier. However, it became increasingly clear that having a ^{13}C facility at Iowa State would facilitate the studies. Wood and several other microbiologists in the department built a mass spectrometer and a thermal diffusion column to concentrate ^{13}C. The thermal diffusion column extended five stories in an elevator shaft from the basement to the attic of the science building. Shortly after helping to build this new research facility, Wood accepted an Associate Professorship in the Department of Physiological Chemistry at the University of Minnesota. In 1943 he moved to Minnesota and started studying the conversion of $[^{13}C]NaHCO_3$ to glycogen in animals. These studies are the subject of the second and third JBC Classics reprinted here.

In the second Classic, Wood demonstrates CO_2 fixation in pigeon liver extracts by showing that $^{13}CO_2$ can combine with pyruvate and fumarate to produce products with ^{13}C-labeled carboxyl groups. However, his attempts to investigate the mechanism of fixation were unsuccessful. Using the liver extracts, he was unable to demonstrate the formation of oxalacetate from pyruvate and CO_2. However, Wood would eventually discover that the reaction does occur in pigeon liver extracts when ATP is added to the reaction mixture. These results are reported in the final JBC Classic, along with the finding that ATP also stimulates CO_2 fixation when fumarate and pyruvate are used as substrates.

In 1946 Wood accepted a position as Chairman of the Department of Biochemistry at the School of Medicine at what was then Western Reserve University in Cleveland (the University merged with Case Institute of Technology in 1968 to become Case Western Reserve University). As Chairman, Wood made many changes. He brought in an entire new faculty to focus on using isotopic tracers to study metabolism, and he reformed the curriculum at the medical school. He also instituted a policy that all faculty honoraria should go onto a student travel fund because he believed that outside activities should have an intrinsic value based on science and not money.

Wood retired as chairman in 1965 so that he could have more time for research, which for him meant spending time at both the bench and his desk. In the 19 years between his 70th birthday and his death in 1991 he published 96 papers. The overall direction of Wood's research continued to follow the trail of CO_2. His later scientific contributions include establishing the reaction mechanism of transcarboxylase from propionic acid bacteria, discovering a novel pathway for CO fixation in a group of anaerobic bacteria, and studying the role of pyrophosphate and polyphosphate as energy sources.

Wood was president of the American Society of Biological Chemistry from 1959 to 1960 and president of the International Union of Biochemistry from 1982 to 1983. He was also a member of the JBC Editorial Board and was instrumental in eliminating self-perpetuating appointments when he resigned after his 5-year appointment was up, saying "Listen, if all you guys died tomorrow, a good board could be picked the next day to replace you" (8). Wood was a member of the National Academy of Sciences and the American Academy of Arts and Sciences and served on the President's Science Advisory Committee under Presidents Johnson and Nixon.[1]

Nicole Kresge, Robert D. Simoni, and Robert L. Hill

REFERENCES

1. JBC Classic: Utter, M. F., Lipmann, F., and Werkman, C. H. (1945) *J. Biol. Chem.* **158**, 521–531 (http://www.jbc.org/cgi/content/full/280/16/e13)
2. Wood, H. G., and Werkman, C. H. (1935) The utilization of CO_2 by the propionic acid bacteria in the dissimilation of glycerol. *Biochem. J.* **30**, 332 (abstr.)
3. Wood, H. G., and Werkman, C. H. (1936) The utilization of CO_2 in the dissimilation of glycerol by the propionic acid bacteria. *Biochem. J.* **30**, 48–53
4. Singleton, R. (1997) Heterotrophic CO_2-fixation, mentors, and students: the Wood-Werkman Reactions. *J. Hist. Biol.* **30**, 91–120
5. Tatum, E. L., Wood, H. G., and Peterson, W. H. (1936) Growth factors for bacteria. V. Vitamin B_{12}: a growth stimulant for propionic acid bacteria. *Biochem. J.* **30**, 1898–1904
6. Wood, H. G., Werkman, C. H., Hemingway, A., and Nier, A. O. (1941) The position of carbon dioxide carbon in succinic acid synthesized by heterotrophic bacteria. *J. Biol. Chem.* **139**, 377–381
7. Evans, E. A., and Slotin, L. (1940) The utilization of carbon dioxide in the synthesis of α-ketoglutaric acid. *J. Biol. Chem.* **13**, 301–302
8. Wood, H. G. (1985) Then and now. *Annu. Rev. Biochem.* **54**, 1–41
9. Goldthwait, D. A., and Hanson, R. W. (1996) *Biographical Memoir of Harland Goff Wood*, Vol. 69, pp. 394–428, National Academy of Sciences, Washington, D. C.

---

[1] All biographical information on Harland Goff Wood was taken from Refs. 4, 8, and 9.

THE JOURNAL OF BIOLOGICAL CHEMISTRY
© 2005 by The American Society for Biochemistry and Molecular Biology, Inc.

Vol. 280, No. 19, Issue of May 13, p. e16, 2005
Printed in U.S.A.

Classics

A PAPER IN A SERIES REPRINTED TO CELEBRATE THE CENTENARY OF THE JBC IN 2005

JBC Centennial
1905–2005
100 Years of Biochemistry and Molecular Biology

Luis F. Leloir and the Biosynthesis of Saccharides

Isolation of the Coenzyme of the Galactose Phosphate-Glucose Phosphate Transformation
(Caputto, R., Leloir, L. F., Cardini, C. E., and Paladini, A. C. (1950) *J. Biol. Chem.* **184,** 333–350)

Uridine Diphosphate Acetylglucosamine
(Cabib, E., Leloir, L. F., and Cardini, C. E. (1953) *J. Biol. Chem.* **203,** 1055–1070)

Guanosine Diphosphate Mannose
(Cabib, E., and Leloir, L. F. (1954) *J. Biol. Chem.* **206,** 779–790)

Luis Federico Leloir (1906–1987) was born in Paris but moved to Buenos Aires with his Argentine parents when he was 2 years old. He attended the University of Buenos Aires and graduated with an M.D. in 1932. Leloir got a job at the University hospital but left the bedside for the bench 2 years later. As he recalled, "When I practiced medicine, except for surgery, digitalis, and a few other active remedies, we could do little for our patients. Antibiotics, psychoactive drugs, and all the new therapeutic agents were unknown. It was therefore not strange in 1932 that a young doctor such as I should try to join efforts with those who were trying to advance medical knowledge" (1).[1]

The most active research laboratory in town was run by Bernardo A. Houssay, who would later be awarded the Nobel Prize with Carl and Gerty Cori for their work on the role of the pituitary gland in carbohydrate metabolism. Leloir joined Houssay's laboratory as a graduate student and studied the role of the adrenals in carbohydrate metabolism.

After Leloir finished his thesis work, Houssay advised him to study abroad. So, in 1936 Leloir moved to England to work at the Biochemical Laboratory of Cambridge University. There, he collaborated with Malcolm Dixon on the effect of cyanide and pyrophosphate on succinic acid dehydrogenase, Norman L. Edson on ketogenesis using liver slices, and David E. Green on the purification and properties of β-hydroxybutyrate dehydrogenase.

Leloir returned to Buenos Aires after his time at Cambridge and started investigating the oxidation of fatty acids in the liver with J. M. Muñoz. They managed to produce an active cell-free system, which was an accomplishment since at that time it was thought that oxidation could only occur in intact cells. Leloir also worked with E. Braun Menéndez, Juan Carlos Fasciolo, and A. C. Taquini on the mechanism of renal hypertension and the formation of angiotensin.

In 1944, Leloir left Buenos Aires again. This time he went to Washington University in St. Louis to work with Carl and Gerty Cori, who were featured in a previous *Journal of Biological Chemistry* (*JBC*) Classic (2). While in the States, Leloir reunited with Green and spent some time at the College of Physicians and Surgeons at Columbia University working on the purification of aminotransferases.

After his stay in the United States, Leloir returned to the Institute of Physiology in Buenos Aires. He worked there for a time and then left for a private institution recently created, the Instituto de Investigaciones Bioquimicas Fundacion Campomar (now Fundacion Instituto Leloir), where he remained until his death. In collaboration with Ranwel Caputto, Carlos E.

---

[1] All biographical information on Luis F. Leloir was taken from Refs. 1 and 8. We thank Armando J. Parodi, Ph.D., of the Fundacion Instituto Leloir, for helpful comments in the preparation of this JBC Classic Introduction.

Luis F. Leloir. Photo courtesy of the National Library of Medicine.

Cardini, Raúl Trucco, and Alejandro C. Paladini, Leloir started to work on the metabolism of galactose. The project was initiated when Caputto presented some preliminary results that indicated that mammary gland homogenates could produce lactose when incubated with glycogen. The group performed many experiments with mammary gland extracts but generally got ambiguous results, mainly due to their lack of a reliable method for lactose detection. Discouraged, they decided to focus on the breakdown of lactose by *Saccharomyces fragilis*, hoping that this would give them information on the mechanism of lactose synthesis.

Leloir and his colleagues isolated lactase from the yeast and determined that galactose was phosphorylated to produce galactose 1-phosphate. They synthesized glucose 1-phosphate and galactose 1-phosphate and observed that the esters were used when incubated with enzymes from galactose-adapted yeast. At first they thought that only one factor was required for this reaction, but soon realized that two factors were involved: one for the conversion of galactose 1-phosphate into glucose 1-phosphate and another for the formation of glucose 6-phosphate, as shown in the following reaction.

$$\text{Galactose 1-phosphate} \rightarrow \text{glucose 1-phosphate} \rightarrow \text{glucose 6-phosphate}$$
$$\text{Factor 1} \qquad\qquad \text{Factor 2}$$

REACTION 1

The group first concentrated on finding Factor 2 and eventually determined that it was glucose 1,6-diphosphate (3). Next, they turned their attention to identifying Factor 1. The purified factor absorbed light at 260 nm and had a spectrum similar to that of adenosine, with some differences. They were stumped on the identity of this factor for quite some time until Caputto came in one morning with an issue of the *JBC* that showed a spectrum identical to theirs. The spectrum was that of uridine. The group published their results in a preliminary communication in *Nature* (4) and then in the *JBC*, which is the first classic reprinted here. In addition to uridine, the co-factor was found to contain glucose and two phosphates and hence was named uridine diphosphate glucose (UDPG). The presence of uridine in a co-factor was rather novel as, until then, all known factors (ATP, NAD, FAD) only contained the nucleotide adenosine. The occurrence of a sugar derivative combined with a nucleoside was also novel. Eventually, Leloir determined that UDPG acts as a glucose donor in the synthesis of trehalose (5), sucrose (6), and glycogen (7).

Another result of the discovery of UDPG was the isolation and characterization of the sugar nucleotides UDP-*N*-acetylglucosamine (UDPAG) and guanosine diphosphate mannose (GDPM), which are the subjects of the remaining two *JBC* Classics reprinted here. UDPAG was originally detected as an impurity in UDPG concentrates and was called UDP-X until Leloir was able to identify the sugar moiety as *N*-acetylglucosamine. Similarly, GDPM was first detected by paper chromatography of UDPG preparations that were purified by anion exchange. UDPAG and GDPM are now known to be involved in the biosynthesis of numerous glycoconjugates.

Leloir's extensive work on sugar nucleotides and his contributions to biochemistry received the recognition they deserved when he was awarded the Nobel Prize in Chemistry in 1970, "for his discovery of sugar nucleotides and their role in the biosynthesis of carbohydrates."

Nicole Kresge, Robert D. Simoni, and Robert L. Hill

REFERENCES

1. Leloir, L. F. (1983) Far away and long ago. *Annu. Rev. Biochem.* **52**, 1–15
2. JBC Classics: Cori, C. F., and Cori, G. T. (1928) *J. Biol. Chem.* **79**, 321–341; Cori, G. T., Colowick, S. P., and Cori, C. F. (1938) *J. Biol. Chem.* **124**, 543–555; Cori, G. T., Colowick, S. P., and Cori, C. F. (1939) *J. Biol. Chem.* **127**, 771–782; Green, A. A., and Cori, G. T. (1943) *J. Biol. Chem.* **151**, 21–29; Cori, G. T., and Green, A. A. (1943) *J. Biol. Chem.* **151**, 31–38 (http://www.jbc.org/cgi/content/full/277/29/e18)
3. Cardini, C. E., Paladini, A. C., Caputto, R., Leloir, L. F., and Trucco, R. E. (1949) *Arch. Biochem.* **22**, 87
4. Cardini, C. E., Paladini, A. C., Caputto, R., and Leloir, L. F. (1950) Uridine diphosphate glucose: the coenzyme of the galactose-glucose phosphate isomerization. *Nature* **165**, 191–193
5. Leloir, L. F., and Cabib, E. (1953) The enzymic synthesis of trehalose phosphate. *J. Am. Chem. Soc.* **75**, 5445–5446
6. Cardini, C. E., Leloir, L. F., and Chiriboga, J. (1955) The biosynthesis of sucrose. *J. Biol. Chem.* **214**, 149–155
7. Leloir, L. F., and Cardini, C. E. (1957) Biosynthesis of glycogen from uridine diphosphate glucose. *J. Am. Chem. Soc.* **79**, 6340
8. Leloir, L. F. (1971) Two decades of research on the biosynthesis of saccharides. *Science* **172**, 1299–1302

The Journal of Biological Chemistry
© 2005 by The American Society for Biochemistry and Molecular Biology, Inc.

Vol. 280, No. 20, Issue of May 20, p. e17, 2005
Printed in U.S.A.

Classics

A PAPER IN A SERIES REPRINTED TO CELEBRATE THE CENTENARY OF THE JBC IN 2005

JBC Centennial
1905–2005
100 Years of Biochemistry and Molecular Biology

Henry Lardy's Contributions to Understanding the Metabolic Pathway

The Enzymatic Synthesis of Phosphopyruvate from Pyruvate
(Lardy, H. A., and Ziegler, J. A. (1945) *J. Biol. Chem.* **159**, 343–351)

The Mechanism by Which Glyceraldehyde Inhibits Glycolysis
(Lardy, H. A., Wiebelhaus, V. D., and Mann, K. M. (1950) *J. Biol. Chem.* **187**, 325–337)

Oxidative Phosphorylations: Role of Inorganic Phosphate and Acceptor Systems in Control of Metabolic Rates
(Lardy, H. A., and Wellman, H. (1952) *J. Biol. Chem.* **195**, 215–224)

Henry Arnold Lardy (1917–) was born in Roslyn, South Dakota. He began his scientific career at South Dakota State University in 1935, when, as a freshman, he needed money to pay his tuition and living costs and got a job in the Dairy Department, caring for cows and rats used for vitamin D experiments. In his junior and senior years, he worked part time at the University's Experiment Station Chemistry Laboratory, studying selenium toxicity.

Lardy earned his bachelor's degree in 1939, double majoring in chemistry and dairy science. He received both his M.S. (1940) and his Ph.D. (1945) in biochemistry from the University of Wisconsin-Madison and has remained there since, serving as chair of a section of the Enzyme Institute from 1950 until his retirement in 1988. Lardy's research at Wisconsin covers a wide variety of metabolic phenomena, in part because he wanted his graduate students to have their own thesis research problems.

The first *Journal of Biological Chemistry* (JBC) Classic reprinted here contains Lardy's research on the regeneration of phosphopyruvate during glycogen synthesis. Otto Meyerhof, author of a previous JBC Classic (1), had previously reported that the following reaction was irreversible (2).

$$\text{Phosphopyruvate} + \text{ADP} \rightarrow \text{pyruvate} + \text{ATP}$$

REACTION 1

However, as Lardy points out, the experiment on which Meyerhof based this conclusion was designed to detect an exchange of high energy phosphate ($\sim$P) between ATP and phosphopyruvate and did not depend on an accumulation of phosphopyruvate produced from pyruvate and ATP. Meyerhof acknowledged this shortcoming by saying, "we must concede that the experimental basis for this negative result is not too large and therefore accept it with some reservation until it is more firmly established" (3).

In the JBC Classic, Lardy and John Ziegler prove that the phosphopyruvate reaction is indeed reversible by using radioactive phosphorus. They found that ^{32}P, initially incorporated into ATP, is in turn incorporated into phosphopyruvate. Lardy and Ziegler also discovered that K^+ is necessary to catalyze the reaction, explaining why Meyerhof and his colleagues were unable to demonstrate its reversibility. They carried out their experiments with an enzyme extract that had been dialyzed for 12 h without the addition of any potassium salt.

The second JBC Classic deals with another facet of metabolism, the inhibition of glycolysis by glyceraldehyde. Several laboratories had noticed that adding glyceraldehyde to tumor slices inhibited the formation of lactic acid from glucose but not from polysaccharides or phosphorylated sugars. Although the conditions for glyceraldehyde inhibition had been worked out, the

Henry Lardy. Photo courtesy of the National Library of Medicine.

mechanism by which the inhibition occurred was unknown. It did, however, appear that glyceraldehyde exerted its effects at the first stage of sugar metabolism, namely by inhibiting the hexokinase responsible for phosphorylating glucose.

As reported in the Classic, Lardy and his co-workers found that brain hexokinase was inhibited by L-glyceraldehyde but not D-glyceraldehyde. They also noticed that different hexokinase preparations varied in their sensitivity to L-glyceraldehyde, suggesting that the compound's inhibitory action was not a direct one. Previously, Meyerhof had reported that a racemic mixture of glyceraldehyde could condense with triose phosphate to form D-fructose 1-phosphate and L-sorbose 1-phosphate (4). Thinking that one of these esters might be the inhibitor, Lardy and his colleagues synthesized the compounds and discovered that L-sorbose 1-phosphate strongly and consistently inhibited brain and tumor hexokinase. Thus, the ester, and not L-glyceraldehyde, was the inhibitor of glycolysis. Because L-sorbose 1-phosphate and the product of the hexokinase reaction, glucose 6-phosphate, shared a strong structural similarity, Lardy proposed that, "the inhibitor combines with that portion of hexokinase which has affinity for glucose and prevents the substrate from combining."

In the final JBC Classic reprinted here Lardy looks at the role of phosphate acceptors in controlling oxidation rates in metabolism. It was believed that the availability of intracellular orthophosphate and phosphate acceptors was the basic factor influencing the rates of oxidation and glycolysis. Although experiments had been done to show that creatine enhanced respiration of muscle extracts by 50 to 100%, Lardy believed these experiments were not ideal because the tissue preparations contained active phosphatases. In this Classic, Lardy showed that adding a phosphate acceptor to rat liver mitochondria enhanced the oxidation of a variety of substrates. This respiration-accelerating effect could be duplicated by adding 2,4-dinitrophenol, an agent that uncouples oxidative phosphorylation, preventing phosphate esterification and ATP synthesis, thus keeping the level of ADP (a phosphate acceptor) high. Lardy concludes, "The rates of oxidation apparently are limited by the rate of transfer or hydrolysis of high energy phosphate compounds whose synthesis is coupled with the oxidative electron transport."

Although officially retired now, Lardy maintains an office at the University of Wisconsin and remains a working scientist, leading a research team at the Enzyme Institute. In addition to the above areas of metabolic research, Lardy pioneered work on the preservation and storage of semen, which has made artificial insemination in livestock practical. Currently, his research focuses on dehydroepiandrosterone (DHEA) and its metabolites.

Lardy has more than 370 publications in major journals and books and has received numerous awards, including the American Chemical Society's Paul Lewis Award in Enzyme Chemistry (1949), the Wolf Foundation Award in Agriculture (1981), the National Award of Agricultural Excellence (1982), and the American Society of Biological Chemists' (now the American Society for Biochemistry and Molecular Biology) William C. Rose Award (1988). Lardy was also President of the American Society of Biological Chemists in 1964 and a member of the JBC Editorial Board from 1958 to 1964 and 1980 to 1985. He has been a member of the National Academy of Sciences since 1958.[1]

Nicole Kresge, Robert D. Simoni, and Robert L. Hill

REFERENCES

1. JBC Classics: Meyerhof, O., and Junowicz-Kocholaty, R. (1943) *J. Biol. Chem.* **149**, 71–92; Meyerhof, O. (1945) *J. Biol. Chem.* **157**, 105–120; Meyerhof, O. and Oesper, P. (1947) *J. Biol. Chem.* **170**, 1–22 (http://www.jbc.org/cgi/content/full/280/4/e3)
2. Meyerhof, O., Ohlmeyer, P., Gentner, W., and Maier-Leibnitz, H. (1938) *Biochem. Z.* **298**, 396
3. Meyerhof, O. (1942) *A Symposium on Respiratory Enzymes*, University of Wisconsin Press, Madison
4. Meyerhof, O., Lohmann, K., and Schuster, P. (1936) *Biochem. Z.* **286**, 319
5. Lardy, H. (2003) Happily at work. *J. Biol. Chem.* **278**, 3499–3509
6. Matthees, D. Distinguished biochemist to lecture at SDSU Oct. 20, 21, 2003. *SDSU News Archives* Oct 2003.

---

[1] All biographical information on Henry Lardy was taken from Refs. 5 and 6.

THE JOURNAL OF BIOLOGICAL CHEMISTRY
© 2005 by The American Society for Biochemistry and Molecular Biology, Inc.

Vol. 280, No. 21, Issue of May 27, p. e18, 2005
Printed in U.S.A.

Classics

A PAPER IN A SERIES REPRINTED TO CELEBRATE THE CENTENARY OF THE JBC IN 2005

JBC Centennial
1905–2005
100 Years of Biochemistry and Molecular Biology

Fritz Lipmann and the Discovery of Coenzyme A

Acetylation of Sulfanilamide by Liver Homogenates and Extracts
(Lipmann, F. (1945) *J. Biol. Chem.* 160, 173–190)

Fritz Albert Lipmann (1899–1986) was born in Koenigsberg, Germany. He earned an M.D. degree from the University of Berlin in 1924 but toward the end of his medical studies he began to doubt whether he really wanted to practice medicine. A course in biochemistry and the opportunity to work in a laboratory at the University of Amsterdam for 6 months convinced him to get a Ph.D. in biochemistry. Thus, he joined Otto Meyerhof, author of a previous *Journal of Biological Chemistry* (JBC) Classic (1), at the Kaiser Wilhelm Institute in Berlin in 1926 to do his thesis research on metabolic fluoride effects.

After completing his Ph.D. in 1929, Lipmann joined Albert Fischer's laboratory where he worked on using metabolism as a method to measure cell growth. Fischer was getting ready to move to a new laboratory at the Biological Institute of the Carlsberg Foundation in Copenhagen and asked Lipmann to accompany him there, which he did in 1932. Between 1931 and 1932, Lipmann spent time as a Rockefeller Fellow in the laboratory of P. A. Levene at the Rockefeller Institute in New York.

When he returned to Fischer's laboratory in Copenhagen, Lipmann became interested in the metabolism of fibroblasts, which prompted him to study the Pasteur Effect (the inhibiting effect of oxygen on the process of fermentation). This led to investigations into the mechanism of pyruvic acid oxidation because the pyruvic acid stage is where respiration branches off from fermentation. For these studies, Lipmann used a pyruvic acid oxidation enzyme from a certain strain of *Lactobacillus delbrueckii*. He noticed that pyruvic acid oxidation was completely dependent on the presence of inorganic phosphate. Suspecting an energy-rich intermediary, Lipmann added radioactive phosphate and adenylic acid and found that pyruvate oxidation yielded ATP. He then deduced that acetyl phosphate was the missing link in the reaction chain and showed that a crude preparation of acetyl phosphate could transfer phosphate to adenylic acid. Several years later, Lipmann definitively identified acetyl phosphate as the initial product of pyruvic acid oxidation (2, 3).

Toward the end of 1938, Hitler's fascism was slowly expanding into Denmark, and Lipmann decided it was time to leave. He got in touch with Dean Burk, an American colleague he had met while working with Meyerhof. Burk had just been invited by Vincent du Vigneaud (who was featured in a previous JBC Classic (4)) to join his department at Cornell Medical School. Burk agreed to take Lipmann on as his assistant, and in 1939 Lipmann moved to New York.

During this time, Lipmann continued to think about the role of acetyl phosphate in metabolism and the fact that it not only contained an energy-rich phosphoryl radical but also an energy-rich acetyl. This prompted him to write a landmark paper about group potential and the transfer of acetyl and phosphoryl groups in which he proposed that acetyl phosphate acted as an acetyl donor in the biosynthesis of essential metabolites and that ATP functioned as a generalized energy carrier (5). In this essay he also introduced the term "energy-rich phosphate bond" and the squiggle to denote this distinction ($\sim$P).

In 1941 Lipmann moved to Boston to join the research staff of the Massachusetts General Hospital. There, he set out to study acetyl transfer in animals and to confirm that acetyl phosphate represented active acetate. This work is the subject of the JBC Classic reprinted here. Lipmann worked out an easy method to prepare acetyl phosphate (6) and was able to isolate a potent acetylation system from pigeon liver extract with which he studied the

This paper is available on line at http://www.jbc.org

Fritz Lipmann. Photo courtesy of the National Library of Medicine.

acetylation of the amino group of the drug sulfonamide. Unexpectedly, Lipmann found that acetyl phosphate was a poor acetyl donor in his enzyme system. Adenyl phosphate, on the other hand, was able to acetylate sulfanilamide. Thus, although Lipmann was able to show that energy transfer between respiration and acetylation occurred by way of phosphate bonds, he was unable to prove the involvement of acetyl phosphate.

Despite Lipmann's initial disappointment with the above experiment, his decision to study acetylation would eventually prove fruitful. From the above studies, he noticed the requirement for a heat-stable factor that disappeared from the enzyme extracts on aging or dialysis. Because the cofactor was present in boiled extracts of all organs and could not be replaced by any other known cofactor, Lipmann suspected that he was dealing with a new coenzyme. Eventually, he was able to purify the coenzyme from pork liver and found it to be active in choline acetylation with dialyzed brain extracts (7). He named the factor coenzyme A (CoA), in which "A" stood for "activation of acetate."

Lipmann subsequently showed that CoA is composed of adenosine 5'-phosphate pantothenic acid and a sulfhydryl moiety and that acetyl-CoA is involved in the acetylation of choline, in the synthesis of citrate and acetoacetate, and in pyruvate and fatty acid metabolism. His work on the coenzyme was eventually recognized in 1953 when he shared the Nobel Prize in Physiology or Medicine with Hans Adolf Krebs "for his discovery of co-enzyme A and its importance for intermediary metabolism." (Krebs was awarded the Prize "for his discovery of the citric acid cycle.")

In 1949 Lipmann became Professor of Biological Chemistry at Harvard Medical School. He remained at Harvard until 1957, when he was appointed a Member and Professor of the Rockefeller Institute, New York. He became a Professor Emeritus at Rockefeller in 1970. Lipmann's initial work on CoA led him to investigate the general use of group activation by way of phosphorylation as a common intermediary reaction in biosynthesis. His later research included demonstrating that carbamyl phosphate is a carbamyl donor, exploring the function of ATP in sulfate activation, and investigating the biological mechanisms of peptide and protein synthesis.

In addition to receiving the Nobel Prize, Lipmann was awarded many other honors. In 1966 President Johnson presented him with the National Medal of Science for his original discoveries of molecular mechanisms and his fundamental contributions to the conceptual structure of modern biochemistry. He also received the American Society of European Chemists' Carl Neuberg Medal and the American Society for Nutritional Sciences' Mead Johnson Award and was elected to the National Academy of Sciences in 1950.[1]

Nicole Kresge, Robert D. Simoni, and Robert L. Hill

REFERENCES

1. JBC Classics: Meyerhof, O., and Junowicz-Kocholaty, R. (1943) *J. Biol. Chem.* **149**, 71–92; Meyerhof, O. (1945) *J. Biol. Chem.* **157**, 105–120; Meyerhof, O. and Oesper, P. (1947) *J. Biol. Chem.* **170**, 1–22 (http://www.jbc.org/cgi/content/full/280/4/e3)
2. Lipmann, F. (1940) A phosphorylated oxidation product of pyruvic acid. *J. Biol. Chem.* **134**, 463–464
3. Lipmann, F. (1944) Enzymatic synthesis of acetyl phosphate. *J. Biol. Chem.* **155**, 55–70
4. JBC Classics: du Vigneaud, V., Cohn, M., Chandler, J. P., Schenck, J. R., and Simmonds, S. (1941) *J. Biol. Chem.* **140**, 625–641; du Vigneaud, V., Melville, D. B., Folkers, K., Wolf, D. E., Mozingo, R., Keresztesy, J. C., and Harris, S. A. (1942) *J. Biol. Chem.* **146**, 475–485; du Vigneaud, V., Ressler, C., and Trippett, S. (1953) *J. Biol. Chem.* **205**, 949–957; Katsoyannis, P. G., and du Vigneaud, V. (1958) *J. Biol. Chem.* **233**, 1352–1354 (http://www.jbc.org/cgi/content/full/279/51/e11)
5. Lipmann, F. (1941) Metabolic generation and utilization of phosphate bond energy. *Adv. Enzymol.* **1**, 99–162
6. Lipmann, F., and Tuttle, L. C. (1944) Acetyl phosphate: chemistry, determination, and synthesis. *J. Biol. Chem.* **153**, 571–582
7. Lipmann F., and Kaplan, N. O. (1946) A common factor in the enzymatic acetylation of sulfanilamide and of choline. *J. Biol. Chem.* **162**, 743–744
8. Lipmann F. (1953) Development of the acetylation problem: a personal account. Nobel Lecture, December 11, 1953
9. Lipmann, F. (1984) A long life in times of great upheaval. *Annu. Rev. Biochem.* **53**, 1–33

---

[1] All biographical information on Fritz Lipmann was taken from Refs. 8 and 9.

THE JOURNAL OF BIOLOGICAL CHEMISTRY
© 2005 by The American Society for Biochemistry and Molecular Biology, Inc.

Vol. 280, No. 22, Issue of June 3, p. e19, 2005
Printed in U.S.A.

Classics

A PAPER IN A SERIES REPRINTED TO CELEBRATE THE CENTENARY OF THE JBC IN 2005

JBC Centennial
1905–2005
100 Years of Biochemistry and Molecular Biology

George Emil Palade: How Sucrose and Electron Microscopy Led to the Birth of Cell Biology

Cytochemical Studies of Mammalian Tissues. I. Isolation of Intact Mitochondria from Rat Liver; Some Biochemical Properties of Mitochondria and Submicroscopic Particulate Material

(Hogeboom, G. H., Schneider, W. C., and Palade, G. E. (1948) *J. Biol. Chem.* **172, 619–635)**

George Emil Palade was born in 1912 in Jassy, Romania. He received his bachelor's degree in 1930, and, as he recalls, "At the end of my high school I had to decide where to go. There were all kinds of suggestions. I had a distant cousin who was in medicine and I spent a summer in his company. After speaking with him I decided this is what I should do" (1). So, Palade entered the School of Medicine at the University of Bucharest in 1930 and received his M.D. in 1940. However, during medical school he developed a strong interest in basic biomedical sciences and started working in an anatomy laboratory. After completing his degree, he became an instructor at the University of Bucharest, where he was assistant professor of anatomy from 1941 to 1945. Later, in 1945, he was named associate professor.

In the 1940s it was common for European researchers to spend a year or two abroad pursuing advanced studies. Palade received a 2-year fellowship as a visiting investigator at the Rockefeller Institute for Medical Research (now Rockefeller University) in New York City. He joined Albert Claude's electron microscopy research group at the Institute. Expecting to stay just a year or two, Palade ended up remaining at Rockefeller for 27 years. In 1953, he was named an associate member of the Rockefeller Institute, and in 1956 he was promoted to full professor of cell biology.

At the Rockefeller Institute, Claude was working in the Department of Pathology, collaborating with George Hogeboom and Walter Schneider. In the beginning, Palade worked mainly on cell fractionation procedures and developed the "sucrose method" for homogenation and fractionation of liver tissue with Hogeboom and Schneider. This is the subject of the *Journal of Biological Chemistry* (JBC) Classic reprinted here. The sucrose method was a great improvement over previous methods, which used either water or saline for homogenation and resulted in agglutination and swelling of the isolated subcellular components. By fractionating their cells in 0.88 M sucrose, Palade, Hogeboom, and Schneider were able to isolate and characterize intact mitochondria for the first time. They also noted the presence of a fraction enriched in submicroscopic particles (microsomes) that contained large amounts of nucleic acid.

In the 1950s, after using electron microscopy to study the structures of mitochondria, the endoplasmic reticulum, and chemical synapses, Palade decided to use electron microscopy to monitor cell fractionation. He explains that "after a period of exploration of the organization of the cell by electron microscopy, I decided to move to a correlated approach which was based on one side on electron microscopy and on the other side by biochemical analysis of isolated sub-cellular components. It turned out that it became possible to isolate mitochondria, endoplasmic reticulum, golgi fragments, nuclei and other components. And therefore there was the possibility of having on the one hand morphological information and on the other hand biochemical information about the same sub-cellular component" (1).

George E. Palade

Using these methods, Palade was able to integrate structural and functional information on a number of cellular components including mitochondria. He and Philip Siekevitz also discovered that the microsomes found earlier in Claude's laboratory were part of the endoplasmic reticulum and that they contained large amounts of RNA. These cellular components were subsequently named ribosomes.

At this time, Palade also started to study the secretory process in the guinea pig pancreas using cell fractionation and radioautography. This led to the characterization of the zymogen granules, the discovery of the segregation of secretory products in the cisternal space of the endoplasmic reticulum, and several findings on the synthesis and intracellular processing of proteins for export. Palade also investigated membrane biogenesis in eukaryotic cells and the structural aspects of capillary permeability. And, his name has become attached to the Weibel-Palade bodies (a storage organelle unique to the endothelium), which he described in collaboration with Ewald R. Weibel (2).

The electron microscopy work coming out of Rockefeller soon became known worldwide. Researchers from numerous disciplines, including anatomy, physiology, and pathology came to Rockefeller to work on this new instrument and to train in Palade's laboratory. The result was the birth of the field of cell biology.

In 1973, Palade left Rockefeller University to become Professor and Chairman of the Section of Cell Biology at Yale University, where he focused his attention on the synthesis of cellular and intracellular membranes. He then assumed the role of Senior Research Scientist in the Department of Cell Biology and Special Advisor to the Dean of the School of Medicine in 1983. Then, in 1990, Palade accepted a position as Professor of Medicine in Residence and Dean for Scientific Affairs at the School of Medicine of the University of California at San Diego. He remains in these roles today, as an Emeritus Professor and Emeritus Dean.

As a major figure in the birth of cell biology, Palade was also a founding member of the American Society for Cell Biology (ASCB). He was active in the society and served as its president from 1974 to 1975. During his administration, Palade introduced poster presentations to cell biology meetings. He also served as editor of the *Journal of Biophysical and Biochemical Cytology* (predecessor of the *Journal of Cell Biology*) for more than a dozen years and as editor of the *Annual Review of Cell Biology* with Bruce Alberts and James Spudich for more than 10 years.

Palade's pioneering research was recognized in 1974 when he shared the Nobel Prize in Medicine or Physiology with Albert Claude and Christian Rene de Duve for work on the structure and function of the internal components of cells. In addition to this honor, Palade was elected into the National Academy of Sciences in 1961 and has received numerous awards including the Lasker Award (1966), the Gairdner Special Award (1967), the Hurwitz Prize (1970), and the U. S. National Medal of Science (1986). He was also honored on a postage stamp issued in 2001 by his native Romania.[1]

Nicole Kresge, Robert D. Simoni, and Robert L. Hill

[1] All biographical information on George Palade was taken from Refs. 1, 3, and 4.

REFERENCES

1. ASCB profile: George Palade (2000) *The ASCB Newsletter* **23**, 8–10
2. Weibel, E. R., and Palade, G. E. (1964) New cytoplasmic components in arterial endothelia. *J. Cell Biol.* **23**, 101–112
3. Dumitrascu, D. L., Shampo, M. A., and Kyle, R. A. (2002) George Palade—Nobel Laureate for discoveries in cell biology. *Mayo Clin. Proc.* **77**, 892
4. Tartakoff, A. M. (2002) George Emil Palade: charismatic virtuoso of cell biology. *Nat. Rev.* **3**, 871–876

THE JOURNAL OF BIOLOGICAL CHEMISTRY
© 2005 by The American Society for Biochemistry and Molecular Biology, Inc.

Vol. 280, No. 23, Issue of June 10, p. e20, 2005
Printed in U.S.A.

Classics

A PAPER IN A SERIES REPRINTED TO CELEBRATE THE CENTENARY OF THE JBC IN 2005

JBC Centennial
1905–2005
100 Years of Biochemistry and Molecular Biology

Sidney Weinhouse and the Mechanism of Ketone Body Synthesis from Fatty Acids

Fatty Acid Metabolism. The Mechanism of Ketone Body Synthesis from Fatty Acids, with Isotopic Carbon as Tracer
(Weinhouse, S., Medes, G., and Floyd, N. F. (1944) *J. Biol. Chem.* 155, 143–151)

Sidney Weinhouse (1909–2001) was born and educated in Chicago. He received both his B.S. (1933) and his Ph.D. (1936) from the University of Chicago and then remained at the University to do his postdoctoral work. He moved to Philadelphia in the early 1940s where he joined the staff of the Lankenau Hospital Research Institute, with a joint faculty appointment at Temple University. He was one of an early group of biochemists who pioneered the use of isotopes in metabolic studies. Isotopes became generally available after World War II, but compounds of biological interest, such as fatty acids, had to be synthesized. Weinhouse developed a cordial relationship with the owner of Sun Oil Corp. in Philadelphia, who strongly supported the future of biochemical research. He gave Weinhouse and his colleagues access to the large scale columns needed to isolate the $^{13}CO_2$ that was used for the chemical synthesis of fatty acids, which are the subject of the *Journal of Biological Chemistry* (JBC) Classic reprinted here.

This story starts with the work of Franz Knoop (1), who in 1904 demonstrated that when phenyl derivatives of even-chain fatty acids were fed to dogs, the product found in their urine was phenylacetate. The scheme proposed by Knoop was termed the β-oxidation theory and was later verified by H. D. Dakin (2), who published a similar finding in the *JBC* in 1909 and was the subject of a previous *JBC* Classic (3). This work led to the proposal by Gustav Embden that ketone bodies arise from the last four carbons that are generated during β-oxidation of an even-chain fatty acid. In contrast, Eaton M. McKay and colleagues (4) proposed that two molecules of acetate, which were produced by the β-oxidation of fatty acids, condensed to form acetoacetic acid. Thus, when Weinhouse began his studies of fatty acid oxidation, there were two possible mechanisms suggested for the formation of ketone bodies by the liver.

In their *JBC* Classic paper, Weinhouse, together with Grace Medes and Norman F. Floyd, incubated liver slices from 24-h fasted rats with [^{13}C]carboxyl-labeled octanoic acid. The acetoacetate generated was isolated and degraded, and the ^{13}C in the carboxyl and carbonyl carbon atoms was determined using a mass spectrometer. They found that the ^{13}C content of the carbonyl and carboxyl carbons of the newly formed acetoacetate were equal, as would be predicted by the β-oxidation-condensation hypothesis. With the subsequent discovery of acetyl-CoA by Lipmann in 1947, which was the subject of a previous JBC Classic (5), the pathway of ketone body synthesis was formally elucidated by 1950.

Sidney Weinhouse served as Chair of the Division of Biochemistry at the Institute for Cancer Research at Fox Chase and as Director of the Fels Research Institute at Temple University Medical School. During these years, he made significant contributions in the area of isoenzyme expression in cancer tissue and glucokinase. Weinhouse received many honors and awards throughout his career, including the American Association for Cancer Research's Clowes Memorial Award (1972). He was elected to the National Academy of Sciences in 1979.

In addition to having a productive research career, Weinhouse was active in several other aspects of science. He served three 4-year terms and two *ex officio* terms on the Board of Directors of the American Association for Cancer Research between 1957 and 1984 and was

170

Sidney Weinhouse. Photo courtesy of the Office of NIH History, National Institutes of Health.

president of the Association from 1981 to 1982. Weinhouse also served as editor of *Cancer Research* from 1969 through 1979. During that time he doubled the size of the Editorial Board in order to ensure thorough and equitable review of submitted papers. He also expanded the journal from 2500 pages to more than 5300 pages per year. When his term as Editor was over, Weinhouse served as Associate Editor from 1980 to 1987 and as Cover Editor from 1986 to 1999. He also served two terms as a member of the Editorial Board of the *JBC*.[1]

Nicole Kresge, Richard W. Hanson, Robert D. Simoni, and Robert L. Hill

REFERENCES

1. Knoop, F. (1904) Der Abbau aromatischer Fettsäuren im Tierkörper. *Beitr. Chem. Physiol. Pathol.* **6,** 150–162
2. Dakin, H. D. (1909) The mode of oxidation in the animal organism of phenyl derivatives of fatty acids. Part V. Studies on the fate of phenylvaleric acid and its derivatives. *J. Biol. Chem.* **6,** 221–233
3. JBC Classic: Dakin, H. D. (1908) *J. Biol. Chem.* **4,** 419–435 (http://www.jbc.org/cgi/content/full/277/15/e4)
4. MacKay, E. M., Barnes, R. H., Carne, H. O., and Wick, A, N. (1940) Ketogenic activity of acetic acid. *J. Biol. Chem.* **135,** 157–163
5. JBC Classic: Lipmann, F. (1945) *J. Biol. Chem.* **160,** 173–190 (http://www.jbc.org/cgi/content/full/280/21/e18)
6. Litwack, G., Baserga, R., and Foti, M. (2001) In memoriam: Sidney Weinhouse. *Cancer Res.* **61,** 8930–8931

[1] All biographical information on Sidney Weinhouse was taken from Ref. 6.

THE JOURNAL OF BIOLOGICAL CHEMISTRY
© 2005 by The American Society for Biochemistry and Molecular Biology, Inc.

Vol. 280, No. 24, Issue of June 17, p. e21, 2005
Printed in U.S.A.

Classics

A PAPER IN A SERIES REPRINTED TO CELEBRATE THE CENTENARY OF THE JBC IN 2005

JBC Centennial
1905–2005
100 Years of Biochemistry and Molecular Biology

Chargaff's Rules: the Work of Erwin Chargaff

The Separation and Quantitative Estimation of Purines and Pyrimidines in Minute Amounts
(Vischer, E. and Chargaff, E. (1948) *J. Biol. Chem.* 176, 703–714)

Erwin Chargaff (1905–2002) was born in Czernowitz, which at that time was a provincial capital of the Austrian monarchy. He graduated from high school at the Maximilian Gymnasium in Vienna and went to the University of Vienna in 1923. "I was eighteen and the world was before me," noted Chargaff. "The future scientist should at this moment be able to tell stories out of his brief past, how he always knew that he wanted to be a chemist or a lepidopterist; how he could be nothing else, having blown himself up at six years of age in his basement laboratory or having captured, in tender years, a butterfly of such splendor and rarity as to make Mr. Nabokov blanch with envy. I can offer nothing of the sort. Being gifted for many things, I was gifted for nothing . . . It was quite clear to everybody that I should have to enter the university and acquire a doctor's degree. This had the advantage of postponing the unpleasant decision about my future by four years or so and also of equipping me with the indispensable prefix without which a middle class Austrian of my generation would have felt naked" (1).

At the university, Chargaff decided to study chemistry. Although he had never taken the subject before, it offered the most hope of employment after graduation, specifically the opportunity to work at his uncle's alcohol refinery. Unfortunately, before he even started on his dissertation, the uncle was dead and Chargaff's alcoholic hopes had evaporated. Nonetheless, he stuck with chemistry and received his doctoral degree in 1928. His dissertation, done under the supervision of Fritz Feigl, dealt with organic silver complexes and with the action of iodine on azides. Because there were very few research positions in Austria, Chargaff left for the United States in 1928 as a Milton Campbell Research Fellow at Yale University. Chargaff recalled, "As the time of my departure grew nearer, so grew my fears. I was afraid of going to a country that was younger than most of Vienna's toilets" (1). However, he found America agreeable enough that he remained there for two years, working with R. J. Anderson on tubercle bacilli and other acid-fast microorganisms.

In the summer of 1930, Chargaff returned to Europe and was appointed *Assistent* at the Bacteriology Department of the University of Berlin. His work in Berlin covered a variety of topics including a study of the lipids of the bacillus Calmette-Guérin and a detailed investigation of the fat and phosphatide fractions of diphtheria bacteria. However, with the rise of Hitler, Chargaff felt the need to leave Germany, and in 1933 he transferred to the Pasteur Institute in Paris. During his brief time in Paris, he worked on bacterial pigments and polysaccharides. Then, in 1935 he returned to the United States to become an assistant professor of biochemistry at Columbia University. Seventeen years later he became a full professor and later was chairman of the department from 1970 to 1974, when he retired to emeritus status.

In 1944, Chargaff read Oswald Avery's report that the hereditary units, the genes, were composed of DNA (2). This had a profound impact on Chargaff, as he recollected, "Avery gave us the first text of a new language, or rather he showed us where to look for it. I resolved to search for this text. Consequently, I decided to relinquish all that we had been working on or to bring it to a quick conclusion" (3). Thus started Chargaff's work on the chemistry of nucleic acids.

Erwin Chargaff. Photo courtesy of the National Library of Medicine.

He began with the belief that if DNA from different species exhibited different biological activities, there should also be chemically demonstrable differences between the DNA. His immediate challenge was to devise a method to analyze the nitrogenous components and sugars of DNA from different species. Because large amounts of DNA would be hard to come by, his methods also had to be applicable to small amounts of material. The formulation of this procedure took two years and was aided by several recent technological developments including the introduction of paper chromatography to separate and identify minute quantities of organic substances and the photoelectric ultraviolet spectrophotometer.

The paper describing Chargaff's analytical method is reprinted here as a *Journal of Biological Chemistry* (JBC) Classic. His procedure consisted of three steps. The first was the separation of the DNA mixture into individual components by paper chromatography. Next, the separated compounds were converted into mercury salts. And finally, the purines and pyrimidines were identified via their ultraviolet absorption spectra. Chargaff tested the method on several mixtures of purines and pyrimidines and reported his encouraging results in the Classic. In a separate paper, printed back-to-back with the Classic, he put his method to use and analyzed the DNA composition of yeast and pancreatic cells (4).

A month later, Chargaff submitted two additional papers to the JBC on the complete qualitative analysis of several DNA preparations. The first paper dealt with the purines and pyrimidines of the DNA of calf thymus and beef spleen (5) and the second with the DNA of tubercle bacilli and yeast (6). Although these papers would eventually prove to be invaluable contributions to our understanding of the structure of DNA and the genetic code, they were almost not published. "One curious circumstance attending the publication of these papers deserves mention because it illustrates the ignorance about nucleic acids that then prevailed among the scientific elite," wrote Chargaff. "I had, at that time, already published something like 75 articles in the *Journal of Biological Chemistry* without ever having one sent back by the editor for clarification or revision. The papers about DNA composition, however, were returned to me with a particularly silly objection. How could I, the editor asked, express the composition of a DNA as moles of adenine or guanine, cytosine or thymine, per gram-atom of phosphorus, since the purines and pyrimidines did not contain any phosphorus? After I had repeated, in my answer to the editor, part of the introductory lecture on the nucleic acids, which at that time I was already giving to the first-year medical students at Columbia, we achieved grudging reconciliation" (7).

Over time, Chargaff improved on his initial quantification methods by introducing formic acid hydrolysis for the simultaneous liberation of all nitrogenous constituents and by using a UV lamp to demonstrate the separated adsorption zones on the filter strip. These improvements permitted him to rapidly analyze DNA from a variety of species. Eventually, Chargaff summarized his findings on the chemistry of nucleic acids in a review in 1950 (8). His two main discoveries, (i) that in any double-stranded DNA the number of guanine units equals the number of cytosine units and the number of adenine units equals the number of thymine units and (ii) that the composition of DNA varies from one species to another, are now known as Chargaff's Rules. These results provided the firm evidence needed to disprove the prevailing tetranucleotide hypothesis. The hypothesis, originally put forth by JBC Classic author Phoebus Levene (9), stated that DNA was composed of a large number of repeats of a GACT tetramer, which was obviously no longer valid. Chargaff's research also helped lay the groundwork for James Watson and Francis Crick's discovery of the double-helix structure of DNA.[1]

Nicole Kresge, Robert D. Simoni, and Robert L. Hill

REFERENCES

1. Chargaff, E. (1975) A fever of reason the early way. *Annu. Rev. Biochem.* **44,** 1–18
2. Avery, O. T., Macleod, C. M., and Mccarty, M. (1944) Studies on the chemical nature of the substance inducing transformation of pneumococcal types. Induction of transformation by a desoxyribonucleic acid fraction isolated from pneumococcus Type 111. *J. Exp. Med.* **79,** 137–158
3. Chargaff, E. (1971) Preface to a grammar of biology. *Science* **172,** 637–642
4. Vischer, E., and Chargaff, E. (1948) The composition of the pentose nucleic acids of yeast and pancreas. *J. Biol. Chem.* **176,** 715–734
5. Chargaff, E., Vischer, E., Doniger, R., Green, C., and Misani, F. (1949) The composition of the desoxypentose nucleic acids of thymus and spleen. *J. Biol. Chem.* **177,** 405–416
6. Vischer, E., Zamenhof, S., and Chargaff, E. (1949) Microbial nucleic acids: the desoxypentose nucleic acids of avian tubercle bacilli and yeast. *J. Biol. Chem.* **177,** 429–438
7. Chargaff, E. (1979) How genetics got a chemical education. *Ann. N. Y. Acad. Sci.* **325,** 345–360
8. Chargaff, E. (1950) Chemical specificity of nucleic acids and mechanism of their enzymatic degradation. *Experientia* **6,** 201–209
9. JBC Classic: Levene, P. A. (1919) *J. Biol. Chem.* **40,** 415–424 (http://www.jbc.org/cgi/content/full/277/22/e11)

[1] All biographical information on Erwin Chargaff was taken from Refs. 1, 3, and 7.

THE JOURNAL OF BIOLOGICAL CHEMISTRY
© 2005 by The American Society for Biochemistry and Molecular Biology, Inc.

Vol. 280, No. 25, Issue of June 24, p. e22, 2005
Printed in U.S.A.

Classics

A PAPER IN A SERIES REPRINTED TO CELEBRATE THE CENTENARY OF THE JBC IN 2005

JBC Centennial
1905–2005
100 Years of Biochemistry and Molecular Biology

The Kennedy Pathway for Phospholipid Synthesis: the Work of Eugene Kennedy

Oxidation of Fatty Acids and Tricarboxylic Acid Cycle Intermediates by Isolated Rat Liver Mitochondria
(Kennedy, E. P., and Lehninger, A. L. (1949) *J. Biol. Chem.* 179, 957–972)

The Function of Cytidine Coenzymes in the Biosynthesis of Phospholipides
(Kennedy, E. P., and Weiss, S. B. (1956) *J. Biol. Chem.* 222, 193–214)

Eugene Patrick Kennedy was born in Chicago in 1919. He enrolled at De Paul University in 1937 as a chemistry major and then went to the University of Chicago in 1941 for graduate training in organic chemistry. To pay his tuition, Kennedy also got a job in the chemical research department of Armour and Company, one of the large meat packers in Chicago. As part of the war effort, his job at Armour was to assist in the large scale fractionation of bovine blood to obtain pure bovine serum albumin. It was believed that the bovine serum albumin might be useful for treating shock in soldiers on the battlefield. However, by the end of 1942, hope had faded that bovine serum albumin would be an effective treatment, and the Red Cross started to collect blood from volunteers instead. Armour opened a new facility in Fort Worth, Texas for the fractionation of human blood from donors, and Kennedy was sent to Fort Worth to assist in this effort. He remained in Texas until 1945, when the war was clearly nearing its end and large amounts of human plasma proteins had been stockpiled.

Returning to the University of Chicago, Kennedy immediately transferred from the Department of Chemistry to the Department of Biochemistry. His experience on the plasma project had led to a new appreciation of biochemistry. When he was ready to begin research for his dissertation, Kennedy approached Albert Lehninger, a young faculty member whose earlier research was the subject of a previous *Journal of Biological Chemistry* (JBC) Classic (1). At that time, Lehninger was studying oxidative phosphorylation and fatty acid oxidation. Kennedy writes, "With staggering naiveté, I suggested to him that the proper approach would be to purify the various enzymes undoubtedly involved in fatty acid oxidation and crystallize them. He agreed that this would be desirable, but went on to point out rather gently that fatty acid oxidation had not yet been demonstrated in a soluble extract from which individual enzymes might be isolated. To reach that stage, it would first be necessary to discover the nature of the energy-requiring activation or "sparking" of fatty acid oxidation and the special dependence of the process on particulate structures" (2).

Despite this initial incident, Lehninger agreed to take Kennedy on as a graduate student, and he began to work on the problem of fatty acid oxidation in 1947. Lehninger had observed that both fatty acid oxidation and oxidative phosphorylation were inhibited in a strikingly parallel fashion when particulate enzyme preparations of homogenized rat livers were exposed to hypotonic buffers. The activity could be preserved by adding either salts or iso-osmotic amounts of sucrose to the buffers.

Kennedy's first project in the laboratory was a detailed study of these effects (3). These studies led Lehninger and Kennedy to surmise that fatty acid oxidation, oxidative phosphorylation, and the Krebs cycle must all be taking place in one organelle, bounded by a membrane impermeable to certain solutes. Although their enzyme preparations were quite crude, they were convinced that the organelle was the mitochondrion, even though functionally and morphologically intact mitochondria had not yet been isolated.

Around this time George Palade and his collaborators were developing methods for the separation and identification of organelles. As reported in a previous JBC Classic (4), Palade worked out a method for the isolation of purified mitochondria by differential centrifugation in 0.88 M sucrose. Kennedy immediately tested mitochondria isolated by this method and obtained convincing evidence that oxidative phosphorylation, fatty acid oxidation, and the reactions of the Krebs cycle did indeed occur in the mitochondria. This is the subject of the first JBC Classic reprinted here.

After finishing graduate school, Kennedy went to the University of California, Berkeley, to work with Horace A. Barker. Barker and his graduate student Earl Stadtman, both of whom will be featured in future JBC Classics, had just discovered that soluble extracts of *Clostridium kluyveri* cells could produce short-chain fatty acids from ethyl alcohol. Although the initial discovery had already been made, there was much to be learned about these extracts and Kennedy aided in this effort.

In 1950, Kennedy joined Fritz Lipmann, author of a previous JBC Classic (5), at Harvard Medical School.[1] He then returned to the University of Chicago in 1951, after being given a joint appointment in the Department of Biochemistry and the newly organized Ben May Laboratory for Cancer Research.

In Chicago, Kennedy started to study the origins of the phosphodiester bond of phosphatidylcholine using labeled choline. He found that free choline, but not phosphocholine, was converted to lipid in a reaction dependent on ATP generated by oxidative phosphorylation (6). At the same time, Kornberg and Pricer (7) reported experiments in which phosphocholine was converted to a lipid (later identified as lecithin) in a reaction that required ATP. Determined to understand why he and Kornberg had obtained contradicting results, Kennedy, along with his graduate student Samuel Weiss, undertook a detailed examination of the differences between the two studies. They discovered that they could reproduce Kornberg's results using commercially available ATP. However, large amounts of ATP were needed, suggesting that an impurity, rather than ATP, might be involved in the reaction.

Kennedy and Weiss' discovery of the cofactor involved in the conversion of phosphocholine to lecithin is the subject of the second JBC Classic reprinted here. After testing several nucleoside triphosphates, they realized that cytidine triphosphate (CTP) was the active cofactor in the phosphocholine reaction. They formulated a number of schemes to account for the involvement of CTP in phospholipid synthesis and eventually decided that intermediary formation of cytidine diphosphate choline (CDP-choline) was occurring in the reaction. Although they had no evidence for its involvement, they synthesized CDP-choline and cytidine diphosphate ethanolamine and tested their abilities to act as cofactors in lipid biosynthesis. Using ^{14}C to label the cytidine coenzymes, Kennedy and Weiss proved that CDP-choline and cytidine diphosphate ethanolamine were activated forms of phosphorylcholine and phosphorylethanolamine and were precursors of lecithin and phosphatidylethanolamine. They also showed that the two cytidine coenzymes were present in high quantities in liver and yeast.

In 1959, Kennedy was invited to become a Hamilton Kuhn Professor and head of the Department of Biological Chemistry at the Harvard Medical School. He continued his research on phospholipid biosynthesis and was able to formulate a detailed picture of the pathways of biosynthesis of the principal glycerophosphatides and of triacylglycerol by 1961. Kennedy's interests also led him to investigate membrane biogenesis and function in bacteria, the translocation of membrane phospholipids, and periplasmic glucans and cell signaling in bacteria. Kennedy is currently at Harvard as the Hamilton Kuhn Professor of Biological Chemistry and Molecular Pharmacology, Emeritus.[2]

Nicole Kresge, Robert D. Simoni, and Robert L. Hill

REFERENCES

1. JBC Classic: Lehninger, A. L. (1945) *J. Biol. Chem.* **157**, 363–382 (http://www.jbc.org/cgi/content/full/280/14/e11)
2. Kennedy, E. (1992) Sailing to Byzantium. *Annu. Rev. Biochem.* **61**, 1–28
3. Lehninger, A. L, and Kennedy, E. P. (1948) The requirements of the fatty acid oxidase complex of rat liver. *J. Biol. Chem.* **173**, 753–771

---

[1] Please see Ref. 8 for Kennedy's JBC Reflection on Fritz Lipmann, Rudolf Schoenheimer, and Konrad Bloch.
[2] All biographical information on Eugene P. Kennedy was taken from Ref. 2.

4. JBC Classic: Hogeboom, G. H., Schneider, W. C., and Palade, G. E. (1948) *J. Biol. Chem.* **172,** 619–635 (http://www.jbc.org/cgi/content/full/280/22/e19)
5. JBC Classic: Lipmann, F. (1945) *J. Biol. Chem.* **160**, 173–190 (http://www.jbc.org/cgi/content/full/280/21/e18)
6. Kennedy, E. P. (1953) The synthesis of lecithin in isolated mitochondria. *J. Am. Chem. Soc.* **75**, 249–250
7. Kornberg, A., and Pricer, W. E. (1952) *Fed. Proc.* **11**, 242
8. Kennedy, E. P. (2001) Hitler's gift and the era of biosynthesis. *J. Biol. Chem.* **276**, 42619–42631

THE JOURNAL OF BIOLOGICAL CHEMISTRY
© 2005 by The American Society for Biochemistry and Molecular Biology, Inc.

Vol. 280, No. 26, Issue of July 1, p. e23, 2005
Printed in U.S.A.

Classics

A PAPER IN A SERIES REPRINTED TO CELEBRATE THE CENTENARY OF THE JBC IN 2005

JBC Centennial
1905–2005
100 Years of Biochemistry and Molecular Biology

Fatty Acid Synthesis and Glutamine Synthetase: the Work of Earl Stadtman

Fatty Acid Synthesis by Enzyme Preparations of *Clostridium kluyveri*. I. Preparation of Cell-free Extracts That Catalyze the Conversion of Ethanol and Acetate to Butyrate and Caproate
(Stadtman, E. R., and Barker, H. A. (1949) *J. Biol. Chem.* 180, 1085–1093)

Allosteric Regulation of the State of Adenylylation of Glutamine Synthetase in Permeabilized Cell Preparations of *Escherichia coli*. Studies of Monocyclic and Bicyclic Interconvertible Enzyme Cascades, *in Situ*
(Mura, U., Chock, P. B., and Stadtman, E. R. (1981) *J. Biol. Chem.* 256, 13022–13029)

Earl Reece Stadtman was born in 1919 in Carrizozo, a small town in New Mexico. When he was 10, his family moved to San Bernardino, California, where he attended high school. After graduating from high school in 1937, Stadtman enrolled in several science courses at San Bernardino Valley College, hoping to eventually set up a soil-testing laboratory. However, he soon realized that he needed a more rigorous education and enrolled at the University of California, Berkeley. He earned a B.S. in soil science in 1942.

After spending a year in Alaska, involved in a wartime project of mapping the Alaskan-Canadian (Al-Can) Highway, Stadtman returned to Berkeley looking for work. He paid a visit to Horace A. Barker, a Berkeley biochemist for whom he had worked as a laboratory technician (and author of a future *Journal of Biological Chemistry* (JBC) Classic). At that time, Barker was directing various war efforts in the Department of Food Technology and offered Stadtman a job as principal investigator on a project studying the "Browning of Dried Apricots," the goal of which was to find a way to slow the deterioration of dried fruits during storage. Around this time, Stadtman also met his future wife, Thressa Campbell, who was working as a laboratory assistant in the food technology department.

After the war, Stadtman started graduate studies in the Department of Biochemistry working in Barker's laboratory. Barker had spent a year as a postdoc in Albert J. Kluyver's laboratory at the Technical School in Delft in the Netherlands before coming to Berkeley and had isolated a species of bacteria called *Clostridium kluyveri* (named after Kluyver) from the Delft canal mud. Since then, Barker had been searching for an explanation for the observation that *C. kluyveri* could produce short-chain fatty acids from ethyl alcohol. He made a breakthrough when he obtained some ^{14}C and used the isotope to label acetate and demonstrate that fatty acid synthesis is accomplished by the multiple condensation of 2-carbon molecules (1). He deduced that ethanol is first oxidized to "active" acetate (a 2-carbon compound), which is condensed with acetate to form a 4-carbon compound that is reduced to form butyrate. Active acetate can then be condensed with butyrate to form caproate. Barker surmised that acetyl phosphate might be the active acetate formed in the above reaction.

It was at this point that Stadtman joined Barker's laboratory and started working on fatty acid synthesis. Initially, like Barker, Stadtman used ^{14}C to trace the metabolic pathways in whole cell preparations of *C. kluyveri*. However, he abandoned this approach after a visit to Irwin C. Gunsalus's laboratory at Cornell University. Gunsalus showed Stadtman how to dry bacterial cells and grind the dried preparations to break open cell walls, producing a cell-free extract. Applying this method to *C. kluyveri*, Stadtman was able to produce extracts that could catalyze all of the reactions involved in the conversion of ethanol and acetate to fatty acids of

This paper is available on line at http://www.jbc.org

Earl R. Stadtman. Photo courtesy of the Office of NIH History, National Institutes of Health.

4- and 6-carbon atoms. His preparations also catalyzed the aerobic oxidation of ethanol and butyrate. These experiments are reported in the first JBC Classic reprinted here. This discovery was especially significant because up until that time most biochemists believed that the capacity to make fatty acids was a unique property of specialized cellular systems or particulate organelles.

In a series of additional papers (2–6), all published in the JBC, Stadtman and Barker used the enzyme extracts to study the individual reactions involved in fatty acid synthesis and confirmed that ethanol is oxidized to acetyl phosphate, which condenses with acetate and forms butyric acid. They also discovered that *C. kluyveri* contained an acetyl-transferring enzyme (phosphotransacetylase) and an enzymatic system for using acetyl phosphate to activate other fatty acids. Stadtman later showed that acetyl-CoA was the source of active acetate in the synthesis of butyric acid from acetyl phosphate (7) while working as postdoctoral fellow with Fritz Lipmann (author of a previous JBC Classic (8)).

In 1950, Stadtman began to look for an academic position. However, because his wife Thressa also had a Ph.D., they were looking for an institution at which they could both work at the same professional level. Unfortunately, at that time, most universities had anti-nepotism rules that did not allow more than one family member to work in the same department. Intended to protect universities from charges of favoritism, the rules often had the effect of discriminating against married women. No one seriously challenged the rules until the 1960s, when the American Association of University Women began to protest their unfairness. Fortunately, these polices were not in effect at the National Institutes of Health (NIH), and in September 1950, the Stadtmans moved to Bethesda, Maryland. Both continue to do research at the NIH today.

At the NIH, Stadtman continued his research on fatty acid metabolism. In 1952, he successfully carried out the first *in vitro* net synthesis of acetyl-CoA using only basic materials (acetyl phosphate, CoA, and phosphotransacetylase). Stadtman and his postdoc P. Roy Vagelos also demonstrated that long-chain fatty acid synthesis is catalyzed by an enzyme complex in which malonyl-CoA is the source of active acetate.

Another topic of long term research in Stadtman's laboratory was glutamine synthetase, the enzyme that catalyzes the conversion of glutamate to glutamine. The activity of glutamine synthetase is subject to feedback inhibition by 7 different end products of glutamine metabolism. Stadtman discovered that this end product inhibition was cumulative (the presence of more end products resulted in more inhibition) and that susceptibility to feedback inhibition only occurred when glutamine synthetase was adenylated by adenylyltransferase (ATase). He later found that adenylation was regulated by uridylyltransferase (UTase), which, depending on the cellular concentration of various metabolites, catalyzed the covalent attachment of a uridylyl group to the regulatory protein, P_{II}. The uridylated form of P_{II} stimulates ATase to catalyze glutamine synthetase deadenylation, whereas the unmodified form of P_{II} stimulates ATase catalysis of the adenylation reaction.

In view of these results, Stadtman surmised that glutamine synthetase activity was controlled by a cascade system in which two systems of reversible covalent modification were tightly linked. Each system was composed of two reversible reactions, or two interconvertible enzyme cycles, the linkage of which resulted in the formation of a bicyclic cascade system. This cascade system allowed enzyme activity to be shifted gradually in response to metabolite availability.

In the late 1970s and early 1980s, Stadtman and P. Boon Chock carried out a theoretical analysis of this bicyclic cascade system to understand its implications in enzyme regulation. However, it was not until 1981 that they were able to study the cascade *in vivo*. These experiments are discussed in the second JBC Classic reprinted here. Stadtman had discovered that after a freeze-thaw cycle, treatment of *Escherichia coli* cells with a nonionic detergent rendered them permeable to small metabolites but allowed the cells to retain the protein components of the cascade system. Furthermore, permeabilized cells from cultures containing 10 mM glutamine retained all their cascade enzymes whereas 5 mM glutamine-grown cells had inactivated UTase. Using these cells, they were able to study the effects of different substrates and allosteric effects on the cascade system and to confirm the previous theoretical and *in vitro* studies. A more complete description of Stadtman's work on glutamine synthetase can be found in his JBC Reflections (9).

Stadtman has received many awards and honors for his numerous research discoveries including the 1979 National Medal of Science, the 1983 ASBC-Merck Award, and the 1991 Robert A. Welch Award in Chemistry. Stadtman was also President of the American Society for Biological Chemists (now American Society for Biochemistry and Molecular Biology) from 1982 to 1983 and has been a member of the National Academy of Sciences since 1969.[1]

Nicole Kresge, Robert D. Simoni, and Robert L. Hill

REFERENCES

1. Barker, H. A., Kamen, M. D., and Bornstein, B. T. (1945) The synthesis of butyric and caproic acids from ethanol and acetic acid by *Clostridium kluyveri. Proc. Natl. Acad. Sci. U. S. A.* **31**, 373–381
2. Stadtman, E. R., and Barker, H. A. (1949) Fatty acid synthesis by enzyme preparations of *Clostridium kluyveri.* II. The aerobic oxidation of ethanol and butyrate with the formation of acetyl phosphate. *J. Biol. Chem.* **180**, 1095–1115
3. Stadtman, E. R., and Barker, H. A. (1949) Fatty acid synthesis by enzyme preparations of *Clostridium kluyveri.* III. The activation of molecular hydrogen and the conversion of acetyl phosphate and acetate to butyrate. *J. Biol. Chem.* **180**, 1117–1124
4. Stadtman, E. R., and Barker, H. A. (1949) Fatty acid synthesis by enzyme preparations of *Clostridium kluyveri.* IV. The phosphoroclastic decomposition of acetoacetate to acetyl phosphate and acetate. *J. Biol. Chem.* **180**, 1169–1186
5. Stadtman, E. R., and Barker, H. A. (1949) Fatty acid synthesis by enzyme preparations of *Clostridium kluyveri.* V. A consideration of postulated 4-carbon intermediates in butyrate synthesis. *J. Biol. Chem.* **181**, 221–235
6. Stadtman, E. R., and Barker, H. A. (1950) Fatty acid synthesis by enzyme preparations of *Clostridium kluyveri.* VI. Reactions of acyl phosphates. *J. Biol. Chem.* **184**, 769–794
7. Stadtman, E. R., Novelli, G. D., and Lipmann, F. (1951) Coenzyme A function in and acetyl transfer by the phosphotransacetylase system. *J. Biol. Chem.* **191**, 365–376
8. JBC Classic: Lipmann, F. (1945) *J. Biol. Chem.* **160**, 173–190 (http://www.jbc.org/cgi/content/full/280/21/e18)
9. Stadtman, E. R. (2001) The story of glutamine synthetase regulation. *J. Biol. Chem.* **276**, 44357–44364
10. Park, B. S. The Stadtman way: A tale of two biochemists at NIH. http://history.nih.gov/exhibits/stadtman/index.htm (An online exhibit produced by the Office of NIH History in collaboration with the National Heart, Lung, and Blood Institute)

---

[1] All biographical information on Earl R. Stadtman was taken from Ref. 10.

THE JOURNAL OF BIOLOGICAL CHEMISTRY
© 2005 by The American Society for Biochemistry and Molecular Biology, Inc.

Vol. 280, No. 27, Issue of July 8, p. e24, 2005
Printed in U.S.A.

Classics

A PAPER IN A SERIES REPRINTED TO CELEBRATE THE CENTENARY OF THE JBC IN 2005

JBC Centennial
1905–2005
100 Years of Biochemistry and Molecular Biology

The Entner-Doudoroff Pathway for Glucose Degradation: the Work of Michael Doudoroff

Glucose and Gluconic Acid Oxidation of *Pseudomonas saccharophila*
(Entner, N., and Doudoroff, M. (1952) *J. Biol. Chem.* 196, 853–862)

Michael Doudoroff (1911–1975) was born in St. Petersburg, Russia but moved to San Francisco when he was 12 years old. He entered Stanford University in 1929, planning to major in biology and specialize in entomology. However, as his exposure to different types of science broadened, he became fascinated with bacteriology and protozoology. As a result, he studied the survival of *Paramecium* at elevated temperatures for his Master's thesis with A. C. Giese and the adaptation of *E. coli* to elevated salt concentrations for his Ph.D. thesis with C. B. van Niel at the Hopkins Marine Station.

While assisting van Niel in a course in general microbiology at the Marine Station, Doudoroff was introduced to the physiological and biochemical diversity of the microbial world. He subsequently started to study luminous bacteria, resulting in his discovery that riboflavin is directly involved in bacterial luminescence. Doudoroff also isolated a new species of H_2-oxidizing bacteria, *Pseudomonas saccharophila*, which could oxidize a number of mono-, di-, and polysaccharides. This was a surprising discovery because most bacteria only oxidize di- and polysaccharides after first hydrolyzing them to monosaccharides. *P. saccharophila*, in fact, oxidized sucrose much more rapidly than its constituent monosaccharides, glucose and fructose. This anomaly was later shown to be caused by the lack of permeases in *P. saccharophila* for monosaccharides.

In 1940, Doudoroff joined the bacteriology department at the University of California, Berkeley. There he discovered that *P. saccharophila* extracts catalyze the reversible formation of glucose 1-phosphate and fructose from sucrose and inorganic phosphate. He used the reverse reaction to synthesize sucrose, a compound that had not yet been made by chemical or enzymatic methods. Doudoroff also used the synthetic reaction to make novel analogues of sucrose by replacing fructose with D-ketoxylose and L-sorbose.

He subsequently purified sucrose phosphorylase from *P. saccharophila* and studied its mode of action using radioactive inorganic phosphate. He learned that the enzyme is a transglucosidase that transfers the glucosyl residue from a suitable donor such as sucrose or glucose 1-phosphate to an appropriate acceptor such as fructose or orthophosphate. This was some of the first evidence for the formation of a substrate-enzyme complex as an intermediate in an enzymatic reaction. Doudoroff also discovered a second type of phosphorolytic enzyme, maltose phosphorylase, in *Neisseria meningitides*.

Doudoroff and his associates soon began to study the oxidative degradation of other sugars by *P. saccharophila*. He and Nathan Entner examined the enzymatic oxidation of glucose labeled with C^{14}, as reported in the *Journal of Biological Chemistry* (JBC) Classic reprinted here. They determined that glucose is phosphorylated to glucose 6-phosphate, which is oxidized to 6-phosphogluconic acid. This compound is then split to give rise to pyruvic acid and glyceraldehyde phosphate. 2-Keto-3-deoxy-6-phosphogluconate was thought to be an intermediate in this reaction, and this was subsequently confirmed by Doudoroff and Joseph MacGee who isolated and characterized the compound in 1954 (1). The enzyme that cleaved the keto acid, ketodeoxyphosphogluconate aldolase, was later purified and crystallized in 1967 (2).

These experiments eventually led to the formulation of the Entner-Doudoroff pathway, a series of reactions that catabolize glucose to pyruvic acid using a different set of enzymes from those used in either glycolysis or the pentose phosphate pathway. The novel feature of this pathway is the cleavage of 6-phosphogluconate to yield pyruvate and glyceraldehyde 3-phosphate. Other sugars were shown to be metabolized by similar, but divergent, pathways.

Later in his career, Doudoroff studied assimilatory processes in aerobic and photosynthetic bacteria and showed that poly-β-hydroxybutyric acid is an important energy reserve that is utilized by both intracellular and extracellular enzymes. He was also involved in an extensive clarification of taxonomic and phylogenetic relationships in *Pseudomonas* and other aerobic bacteria. The first publication resulting from this collaboration was a massive survey of 169 phenotypic characters of 267 strains of *Pseudomonas* (3).

Doudoroff also had a profound influence on how bacteriology was taught at Berkeley. When he joined the faculty in 1940, the bacteriology courses emphasized the medical and paramedical aspects of the subject. Doudoroff reorganized the curriculum to present bacteria and other microorganisms as creatures whose structures, behaviors, and metabolic activities were worthy of study independent of their roles in agriculture, industry, or disease. He eventually, along with Roger Y. Stanier and Edward A. Adelberg, wrote the popular textbook, *The Microbial World*, based on the Berkeley courses.

In recognition of Doudoroff's contributions to microbiology and biochemistry he received the first Sugar Research Award from the National Academy of Sciences in 1945 with Horace A. Barker and William Z. Hassid (both of whom will be featured in future JBC Classics). He also became a J. S. Guggenheim Foundation fellow in 1949 and was elected to membership in the National Academy of Sciences in 1962.[1]

Nicole Kresge, Robert D. Simoni, and Robert L. Hill

REFERENCES

1. MacGee, J., and Doudoroff, M. (1954) A new phosphorylated intermediate in glucose oxidation. *J. Biol. Chem.* **210,** 617–626
2. Shuster C. W., and Doudoroff, M. (1967) Purification of 2-keto-3-deoxy-6-phosphohexonate aldolases of *Pseudomonas saccharophila*. *Arch. Mikrobiol.* **59,** 279–286
3. Stanier, R. Y., Palleroni, N. J., and Doudoroff, M. (1966) The aerobic pseudomonads: a taxonomic study. *J. Gen. Microbiol.* **43,** 159–271
4. Barker, H. A. (1993) *Biographical Memoir of Michael Doudoroff*, Vol. 62, pp. 118–141, National Academy of Sciences, Washington D. C.

---

[1] All biographical information on Michael Doudoroff was taken from Ref. 4.

THE JOURNAL OF BIOLOGICAL CHEMISTRY
© 2005 by The American Society for Biochemistry and Molecular Biology, Inc.

Vol. 280, No. 28, Issue of July 15, p. e25, 2005
Printed in U.S.A.

Classics

A PAPER IN A SERIES REPRINTED TO CELEBRATE THE CENTENARY OF THE JBC IN 2005

JBC Centennial
1905–2005
100 Years of Biochemistry and Molecular Biology

The Most Highly Cited Paper in Publishing History: Protein Determination by Oliver H. Lowry

Protein Measurement with the Folin Phenol Reagent
(Lowry, O. H., Rosebrough, N. J., Farr, A. L., and Randall, R. J. (1951) *J. Biol. Chem.*
193, 265–275)

On Tyrosine and Tryptophane Determinations in Proteins
(Folin, O., and Ciocalteu, V. (1927) *J. Biol. Chem.* 73, 627–650)

Oliver Howe Lowry (1910–1996) was born in Chicago, the youngest of five children. He enrolled at Northwestern University in chemical engineering, hoping to combine chemistry and engineering to emulate his two oldest brothers. However, he switched his major to biochemistry two years later, after spending the summer with an enthusiastic pre-med friend who convinced him that "so little was known about biochemistry that anything (he) found out would be new" (1).[1]

Lowry received a bachelor's degree in chemistry in 1932 from Northwestern University and entered the University of Chicago as a graduate student in physiological chemistry. With Frederick Koch as his thesis advisor, Lowry started what would be a lifelong study of micro methods when he developed a method for measuring ketone bodies in one milliliter of blood. During his second year, the Dean asked Lowry if he would like to enroll in the University's M.D.-Ph.D program. The University of Chicago was one of the few schools that offered an M.D.-Ph.D. program at that time. Because he had already taken many of the preclinical courses, Lowry was able to squeeze four academic years into three calendar years, and in 1937, he graduated with both a doctorate in physiological chemistry and a medical degree. Although he never practiced medicine, he said his medical degree "added to my enjoyment of biomedical research, broadened my perspective about living systems, and (was) good for my ego" (1).

While at the University of Chicago, Lowry met A. Baird Hastings, author of a previous *Journal of Biological Chemistry* (JBC) Classic (2). Hastings agreed to let Lowry work in his laboratory at Harvard University, and after graduating from Chicago, Lowry started working on one of Hastings' basic interests: electrolyte metabolism. Lowry was able to develop micro methods to measure electrolytes in milligram-size tissue samples, and the methods allowed them to study electrolyte changes in the myocardium, heart, skeletal muscle, liver, brain, and kidney. He also developed micro methods for measuring collagen and elastin.

Hastings also arranged for a fellowship from the Commonwealth Fund that allowed Lowry to work with Kai Linderstrøm-Lang at the Carlsberg laboratory in Copenhagen. Lowry was greatly influenced by Linderstrøm-Lang, calling him "the most talented human being I have ever known" (1). Linderstrøm-Lang shared Lowry's interest in microanalytical methods and had invented and developed a whole scheme of quantitative histochemistry together with the appropriate devices. During their time together, Lowry's interest in micro methods increased to the point where he declared, "If I was attracted to micro methods before I went to Copenhagen, I was an incorrigible addict by the time I left" (1).

Between 1942 and 1947, Lowry worked at the Public Health Research Institute in New York City, where he developed micro methods that could screen for vitamin deficiencies in children using very small amounts of blood. It was during this period that he also worked out a simple

---

[1] All biographical information on Oliver H. Lowry was taken from Ref. 1.

Oliver H. Lowry. Photo courtesy of the National Library of Medicine.

yet sensitive method for measuring the amount of protein in solutions. This paper, which is featured here as a JBC Classic, is the most highly cited paper in science. As of January 2004, it was cited 275,669 times.

Lowry's method was based on the "Phenol Reagent" developed by Otto Knut Olof Folin (who was featured in a previous JBC Classic (3)) and Vintila Ciocalteu for use in protein determinations. The Folin-Ciocalteu paper is also reprinted here as a JBC Classic. Lowry determined that the Folin phenol reagent (phosphomolybdic-phosphotungstic acid) would bind readily to copper-treated protein. Over time, the bound reagent was reduced, resulting in a color change from yellow to blue, which could then be used to determine protein concentration.

Despite the great practical applications of Lowry's method, he did not publish the details immediately. Instead, he passed them on to whoever wanted them. One of the recipients of the method was Earl Sutherland, who complained of being tired of referring to "an unpublished method of Lowry." With Sutherland's prompting, Lowry finally performed a thorough study of the procedure: its limitations and virtues and the results it gave with different proteins and tissues in comparison with other methods. Lowry's first submission to the JBC was returned for drastic shortening, but the paper was eventually accepted in an abbreviated form.

In 1947, Lowry was invited to become Head of the Department of Pharmacology at Washington University in St. Louis. He recalled, "This was quite a gamble on the part of the university. I had never had a real course in pharmacology, nor had I done any research that was even marginally pharmacological. Moreover, my two predecessors, Carl Cori and Herbert Gasser, were both Nobel Laureates, and there was no sign that I would get to Sweden except as a tourist" (1). Despite these initial doubts, things worked out for Lowry and he chaired the Department of Pharmacology for the next 29 years and was Dean of the School of Medicine from 1955 to 1958.

At Washington University, Lowry's passion for measuring minute quantities of biological substances led him to quantitative histochemistry. He eventually pioneered methods for freeze-drying tissue sections from which he was able to dissect out small portions for weighing and analysis. Since there was no balance sensitive enough for his experiments, he invented a microbalance that could measure less than one-millionth of a gram. Lowry also designed a very sensitive method to measure a wide variety of metabolites and enzymes based on the fluorescence of NADH and NADPH and an amplification technique called enzymatic cycling in which enzyme systems are used to amplify the pyridine nucleotides generated by specific enzyme reactions.

Lowry received many honors in recognition of his scientific achievements, including the John Scott Award (1963) from the Board of City Trusts of Philadelphia and the Borden Award of the Association of American Medical Colleges (1966). He was elected to the American Academy of Arts and Sciences in 1957, the National Academy of Sciences in 1964, and the Royal Danish Academy of Sciences in 1968.

Nicole Kresge, Robert D. Simoni, and Robert L. Hill

REFERENCES

1. Lowry, O. H. (1990) How to succeed in research without being a genius. *Annu. Rev. Biochem.* **59,** 1–27
2. JBC Classics: Conant, J. B., Cramer, R. D., Hastings, A. B., Klemperer, F. W., Solomon, A. K., and Vennesland, B. (1941) *J. Biol. Chem.* **137,** 557–566; Soloman, A. K., Vennesland, B., Klemperer, F. W., Buchanan, J. M., and Hastings, A. B. (1941) *J. Biol. Chem.* **140,** 171–182 (http://www.jbc.org/cgi/content/full/279/2/e2)
3. JBC Classic: Folin, O., and Wu, H. (1919) *J. Biol. Chem.* **38,** 81–110 (http://www.jbc.org/cgi/content/full/277/20/e9)

THE JOURNAL OF BIOLOGICAL CHEMISTRY
© 2005 by The American Society for Biochemistry and Molecular Biology, Inc.

Vol. 280, No. 29, Issue of July 22, p. e26, 2005
Printed in U.S.A.

Classics

A PAPER IN A SERIES REPRINTED TO CELEBRATE THE CENTENARY OF THE JBC IN 2005

JBC Centennial
1905–2005
100 Years of Biochemistry and Molecular Biology

Bernard L. Horecker's Contributions to Elucidating the Pentose Phosphate Pathway

The Enzymatic Conversion of 6-Phosphogluconate to Ribulose-5-Phosphate and Ribose-5-Phosphate
(Horecker, B. L., Smyrniotis, P. Z., and Seegmiller, J. E. (1951) *J. Biol. Chem.* **193,** 383–396)

Bernard Leonard Horecker (1914) began his training in enzymology in 1936 as a graduate student at the University of Chicago in the laboratory of T. R. Hogness. His initial project involved studying succinic dehydrogenase from beef heart using the Warburg manometric apparatus. However, when Erwin Hass arrived from Otto Warburg's laboratory he asked Horecker to join him in the search for an enzyme that would catalyze the reduction of cytochrome c by reduced NADP. This marked the beginning of Horecker's lifelong involvement with the pentose phosphate pathway.

During World War II, Horecker left Chicago and got a job at the National Institutes of Health (NIH) in Frederick S. Brackett's laboratory in the Division of Industrial Hygiene. As part of the wartime effort, Horecker was assigned the task of developing a method to determine the carbon monoxide hemoglobin content of the blood of Navy pilots returning from combat missions. When the war ended, Horecker returned to research in enzymology and began studying the reduction of cytochrome c by the succinic dehydrogenase system.

Shortly after he began these investigation changes, Horecker was approached by future Nobel laureate Arthur Kornberg, who was convinced that enzymes were the key to understanding intracellular biochemical processes. Kornberg suggested they collaborate, and the two began to study the effect of cyanide on the succinic dehydrogenase system. Cyanide had previously been found to inhibit enzymes containing a heme group, with the exception of cytochrome c. However, Horecker and Kornberg found that cyanide did in fact react with cytochrome c and concluded that previous groups had failed to perceive this interaction because the shift in the absorption maximum was too small to be detected by visual examination.

Two years later, Kornberg invited Horecker and Leon Heppel to join him in setting up a new Section on Enzymes in the Laboratory of Physiology at the NIH. Their Section on Enzymes eventually became part of the new Experimental Biology and Medicine Institute and was later renamed the National Institute of Arthritis and Metabolic Diseases.

Horecker and Kornberg continued to collaborate, this time on the isolation of DPN and TPN. By 1948 they had amassed a huge supply of the coenzymes and were able to present Otto Warburg, the discoverer of TPN, with a gift of 25 mg of the enzyme when he came to visit. Horecker also collaborated with Heppel on the isolation of cytochrome c reductase from yeast and eventually accomplished the first isolation of the flavoprotein from mammalian liver.

Along with his lab technician Pauline Smyrniotis, Horecker began to study the enzymes involved in the oxidation of 6-phosphogluconate and the metabolic intermediates formed in the pentose phosphate pathway. Joined by Horecker's first postdoctoral student, J. E. Seegmiller, they worked out a new method for the preparation of glucose 6-phosphate and 6-phosphogluconate, both of which were not yet commercially available. As reported in the *Journal of Biological Chemistry* (JBC) Classic reprinted here, they purified 6-phosphogluconate dehydrogenase from brewer's yeast (1), and by coupling the reduction of TPN to its reoxidation by

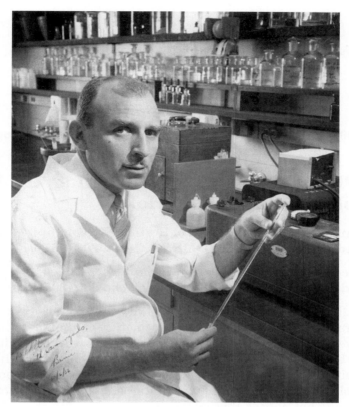

Bernard L. Horecker

pyruvate in the presence of lactic dehydrogenase, they were able to show that the first product of 6-phosphogluconate oxidation, in addition to carbon dioxide, was ribulose 5-phosphte. This pentose ester was then converted to ribose 5-phosphate by a pentose-phosphate isomerase. They were able to separate ribulose 5-phosphate from ribose 5-phosphate and demonstrate their interconversion using a recently developed nucleotide separation technique called ion-exchange chromatography. Horecker and Seegmiller later showed that 6-phosphogluconate metabolism by enzymes from mammalian tissues also produced the same products.

Over the next several years, Horecker played a key role in elucidating the remaining steps of the pentose phosphate pathway. His total contributions included the discovery of three new sugar phosphate esters, ribulose 5-phosphate, sedoheptulose 7-phosphate, and erythrose 4-phosphate, and three new enzymes, transketolase, transaldolase, and pentose-phosphate 3-epimerase. The outline of the complete pentose phosphate cycle was published in 1955 (2). Horecker's personal account of his work on the pentose phosphate pathway can be found in his JBC Reflection (3).[1]

Horecker's contributions to science were recognized with many awards and honors including the Washington Academy of Sciences Award for Scientific Achievement in Biological Sciences (1954) and his election to the National Academy of Sciences in 1961. Horecker also served as president of the American Society of Biological Chemists (now the American Society for Biochemistry and Molecular Biology) in 1968.

Nicole Kresge, Robert D. Simoni, and Robert L. Hill

REFERENCES

1. Horecker, B. L., and Smyrniotis, P. Z. (1951) Phosphogluconic acid dehydrogenase from yeast. *J. Biol. Chem.* **193,** 371–381
2. Gunsalus, I. C., Horecker, B. L., and Wood, W. A. (1955) Pathways of carbohydrate metabolism in microorganisms. *Bacteriol. Rev.* **19,** 79–128
3. Horecker, B. L. (2002) The pentose phosphate pathway. *J. Biol. Chem.* **277,** 47965–47971

---

[1] All biographical information on Bernard L. Horecker was taken from Ref. 3.

THE JOURNAL OF BIOLOGICAL CHEMISTRY
© 2005 by The American Society for Biochemistry and Molecular Biology, Inc.

Vol. 280, No. 30, Issue of July 29, p. e27, 2005
Printed in U.S.A.

Classics

A PAPER IN A SERIES REPRINTED TO CELEBRATE THE CENTENARY OF THE JBC IN 2005

JBC Centennial
1905–2005
100 Years of Biochemistry and Molecular Biology

A Role for Phosphoinositides in Signaling: the Work of Mabel R. Hokin and Lowell E. Hokin

Enzyme Secretion and the Incorporation of P³² into Phospholipides of Pancreas Slices
(Hokin, M. R., and Hokin, L. E. (1953) *J. Biol. Chem.* **203,** 967–977)

Phosphoinositides and Protein Secretion in Pancreas Slices
(Hokin, L. E., and Hokin, M. R. (1958) *J. Biol. Chem.* **233,** 805–810)

Mabel R. Hokin (born Mabel Neaverson) and Lowell E. Hokin met in Hans Kreb's department at the University of Sheffield and married soon after. During their time in Sheffield, the Hokins started investigating what they thought was an increase in the incorporation of ^{32}P into RNA caused by the acetylcholine-induced stimulation of pancreatic slices. However, before they could purify the RNA, they moved to McGill University in Montréal, Québec, and brought their radiolabeled samples with them. Once established in Montréal, they continued with their experiments but noticed that as they purified the RNA the radioactivity was lost. Investigating this phenomenon further, they found that most of the radioactivity was incorporated into the phospholipid fraction. This was a surprising discovery as up until then phospholipids were regarded as inert structural components of membranes.

The Hokins' studies on ^{32}P uptake into phospholipids during enzyme secretion in pancreas slices are published in the first *Journal of Biological Chemistry* (JBC) Classic reprinted here. The Hokins incubated pigeon pancreas slices with various compounds along with ^{32}P to see the effects on phosphate incorporation into phospholipids. They found that when enzyme secretion was stimulated by acetylcholine or carbamylcholine, both of which induce amylase secretion, the incorporation of ^{32}P into phospholipids was on average 7.0 times greater than in control tissue.

Separating individual phospholipids for analysis was difficult at that time, but fortunately Rex Dawson devised a method that permitted the analysis of diacylglycerophospholipids by deacylation and two-dimensional separation of the water-soluble backbone (1). The Hokins used this method to show that hormone stimulation of pancreatic slices mainly increased the rate of ^{32}P incorporation into phosphoinositide but that phosphatidylcholine, phosphatidylserine, and phosphatidic acid also contained radiolabeled phosphate (2). This was the first demonstration of receptor-stimulated lipid turnover, and it later became known as the "PI effect."

The second JBC Classic reprinted here presents the details of the Hokins' study of phosphoinositide metabolism in relation to protein secretion in the pancreas. They incubated pigeon pancreas slices with either $NaH_2P^{32}O_4$, [2-^{3}H]inositol, or [1-^{14}C]glycerol and extracted the lipids from the tissue and separated them by paper chromatography. They were able to identify seven phospholipids containing ^{32}P as well as two radioactive monophosphoinositides. From these data they concluded, "the present work indicates that phosphoinositides are involved in the secretion of protein from the inside of the pancreatic acinar cell into the lumen . . . It is tempting to think that the active transport out of the cell of many other types of molecules may involve phosphoinositides."

In 1957 the Hokins moved to Madison, Wisconsin, where they both joined the faculty of the University of Wisconsin-Madison Medical School. There they showed that other tissues exhibit similar responses when provoked to secrete. In 1964 the Hokins suggested that phospholipase C-catalyzed phosphatidylinositol hydrolysis might initiate the PI effect. Later it was confirmed that the initiating event was the phospholipase C-catalyzed hydrolysis of phosphatidylinositol

This paper is available on line at http://www.jbc.org

4,5-bisphosphate and that 3-kinase-catalyzed formation of phosphatidylinositol 3,4,5-triphosphate was a second widespread signaling reaction.

The Hokins' initial work on stimulated phosphoinositide turnover in secretory tissues motivated a large number of other investigators to focus their research on the PI effect and second messengers. Eventually they would discover that the Hokins' inositol phospholipids play important roles in transmembrane signaling and many other cell regulatory processes.[1]

Nicole Kresge, Robert D. Simoni, and Robert L. Hill

REFERENCES

1. Dawson, R. M. C. (1954) The measurement of ^{32}P labeling of individual kephalins and lecithin in a small sample of tissue. *Biochim. Biophys. Acta* **14,** 374–375
2. Hokin, L. E., and Hokin, M. R. (1955) Effects of acetylcholine on the turnover of phosphoryl units in individual phospholipids of pancreas slices and brain cortex slices. *Biochim. Biophys. Acta* **18,** 102–110
3. Michell, B. (2003) Obituary: Mabel R. Hokin (1924–2003). *The Biochemist.* December
4. Irvine, R. F. (2003) 20 years of Ins(1,4,5)P3, and 40 years before. *Nat. Rev. Mol. Cell. Biol.* **4,** 586–590

---

[1] All biographical information on Mabel R. Hokin and Lowell E. Hokin was taken from Refs. 3 and 4.

THE JOURNAL OF BIOLOGICAL CHEMISTRY
© 2005 by The American Society for Biochemistry and Molecular Biology, Inc.

Vol. 280, No. 31, Issue of August 5, p. e28, 2005
Printed in U.S.A.

Classics

A PAPER IN A SERIES REPRINTED TO CELEBRATE THE CENTENARY OF THE JBC IN 2005

JBC Centennial
1905–2005
100 Years of Biochemistry and Molecular Biology

Albert Dorfman and the Biosynthesis of Hyaluronic Acid

The Biosynthesis of Hyaluronic Acid by Group A Streptococcus. I. Utilization of 1-C^{14}-Glucose
(Roseman, S., Moses, F. E., Ludowieg, J., and Dorfman, A. (1953) *J. Biol. Chem.* **203**, 213–225)

Albert Dorfman (1916–1982) was born and raised in Chicago. While in high school, he became interested in science because of his older brother who was studying chemistry at the University of Illinois. After graduating, Dorfman obtained a scholarship to the University of Chicago where he enrolled as a chemistry major; however, during his senior year he switched to biochemistry and entered the University of Chicago School of Medicine. He eventually found biochemistry so appealing that he dropped out of medical school after 2 years to pursue graduate work. His thesis research was on the identification of nicotinamide as a growth requirement for *Shigella dysenteriae* and the synthesis of various nicotinic acid derivatives to correlate structure with biological activity.

Dorfman received his Ph.D. from the University of Chicago in 1939. He remained at the University as a research associate and started to study the role of bacterial growth factors in metabolism. These studies led to Dorfman's development of the technique of growing deficient cells to determine the role of growth factors in metabolism. He also elucidated the roles of pantothenic acid in pyruvate metabolism and of biotin in aspartic acid biosynthesis.

With the arrival of World War II and lack of an academic position, Dorfman returned to medical school and graduated in 1944. This experience rekindled his interest in medicine, particularly pediatrics. An encounter with a child with rheumatic fever also sparked an interest in the mechanism of action of aspirin and would profoundly affect Dorfman's subsequent career.

When Dorfman finished medical school he got an internship in internal medicine at Beth Israel Hospital and then became a resident in pediatrics at the University of Chicago. After completing his residency, he served 2 years in the U. S. Army where he was assigned to the Army Medical School and was able to resume research in biochemistry. Around this time a study emerged claiming that aspirin exerted its antirheumatic effect by inhibiting hyaluronidase. Dorfman promptly initiated studies on connective tissue polysaccharides, an area of research he would pursue for the next 30 years. He started by studying the biosynthesis of hyaluronic acid in group A streptococci, which led to the development of quantitative methods for assays of hyaluronidase, the discovery that chondroitin sulfate is a substrate for testicular hyaluronidase, and the recognition that hyaluronidase is unusually stable to heat and acid pH.

After his 2 years in the army, Dorfman returned to the University of Chicago as an assistant professor of pediatrics and continued to study the biosynthesis of hyaluronic acid. His goal was to determine the origins of the 14 unique carbon atoms of the polysaccharide using specifically labeled precursors. Dorfman embarked on this project with his postdoc, Saul Roseman, who was an author in a previous *Journal of Biological Chemistry* (JBC) Classic on Karl Paul Link (1) and will be featured in his own Classic in the future. Dorfman and Roseman, along with Julio Ludowieg and Frances Moses, synthesized [1-^{14}C]glucose and incorporated it into medium upon which they could grow streptococcus. They devised a method for isolating the radioactive hyaluronic acid from the streptococcus filtrate and then analyzed its components. It became immediately evident that glucose was the major carbon precursor of hyaluronic acid. The glucose was then converted to the glucosamine and glucuronic acid portions of the

This paper is available on line at http://www.jbc.org

Albert Dorfman. Photo courtesy of the Office of NIH History, National Institutes of Health.

molecule without cleavage of the carbon chain. These results are presented in the JBC Classic reprinted here, which is the first in a series of JBC papers Dorfman published on the biosynthesis of hyaluronic acid by group A streptococcus.

Dorfman and his colleagues subsequently synthesized [6-^{14}C]glucose and [1-^{14}C]acetic acid and used those compounds to establish that acetate is a precursor of the acetyl group of N-acetylglucosamine and that glucosamine but not N-acetylglucosamine serves as a precursor of the N-acetylglucosamine residue in hyaluronic acid. These results were also published in the JBC series (2, 3).

The discovery of uridine nucleotide sugars by Luis Leloir, as reported in a previous JBC Classic (4), suggested to Dorfman that these compounds might be intermediates in polysaccharide synthesis. Together with J. A. Cifonelli, Dorfman established that streptococci contain two uridine nucleotide sugars, UDP-N-acetylglucosamine and UDP-glucuronic acid, which are requisite for the biosynthesis of hyaluronic acid (5). Using labeled nucleotides, they were able to demonstrate the synthesis of hyaluronic acid in a cell-free preparation of streptococci. This was published as the final paper in Dorfman's hyaluronic acid series in the JBC (6).

In addition to his work on hyaluronic acid, Dorfman also contributed significantly to understanding the biosynthesis of other glycosaminoglycans. As well, he discovered the cause of Hurler's syndrome, a genetic disease that affects bones and cartilage and results in mental retardation. He deduced that the condition results from elevated levels of dermatan sulfate and heparin sulfate due to a defect in α-L-iduronidase, an enzyme needed for the normal catabolism of the two glycosaminoglycans.

In 1967 Dorfman became the Richard T. Crane Distinguished Service Professor of Pediatrics and Biochemistry and acted as Chairman of the Department of Pediatrics from 1962 to 1972. He also served as Director of the La Rabida University of Chicago Institute (1957–1972) and Director of the Joseph P. Kennedy, Jr. Mental Retardation Research Center (1967–1982). In addition to his research activities, Dorfman was President of the Society for Glycobiology (1975) and President of the Pediatric Society (1979). His contributions to science were recognized with his election to the National Academy of Sciences in 1973.[1]

Nicole Kresge, Robert D. Simoni, and Robert L. Hill

REFERENCES

1. JBC Classics: Campbell, H. A., and Link, K. P. (1941) *J. Biol. Chem.* **138**, 21–33; Stahmann, M. A., Huebner, C. F., and Link, K. P. (1941) *J. Biol. Chem.* **138**, 513–527; Overman, R. S., Stahmann, M. A., Huebner, C. F., Sullivan,

[1] All biographical information on Albert Dorfman was taken from Ref. 7.

W. R., Spero, L., Doherty, D. G., Ikawa, M., Graf, L., Roseman, S., and Link, K. P. (1944) *J. Biol. Chem.* **153,** 5–24 (http://www.jbc.org/cgi/content/full/280/8/e5)

2. Roseman, S., Ludowieg, J., Moses, F. E., and Dorfman, A. (1954) The biosynthesis of hyaluronic acid by group A Streptococcus. II. Origin of the glucuronic acid. *J. Biol. Chem.* **206,** 665–669

3. Dorfman, A., Roseman, S., Moses, F. E., Ludowieg, J., and Mayeda, M. (1955) The biosynthesis of hyaluronic acid by group A Streptococcus. III. Origin of the *N*-acetylglucosamine moiety. *J. Biol. Chem.* **212,** 583–592

4. JBC Classics: Caputto, R., Leloir, L. F, Cardini, C. E., and Paladini, A. C. (1950) *J. Biol. Chem.* **184,** 333–350; Cabib, E., Leloir, L. F., and Cardini, C. E. (1953) *J. Biol. Chem.* **203,** 1055–1070; Cabib, E., and Leloir, L. F. (1954) *J. Biol. Chem.* **206,** 779–790 (http://www.jbc.org/cgi/content/full/280/19/e16)

5. Cifonelli, J. A., and Dorfman, A. (1957) The biosynthesis of hyaluronic acid by group A Streptococcus. V. The uridine nucleotides of group A Streptococcus. *J. Biol. Chem.* **228,** 547–557

6. Markovitz, A., Cifonelli, J. A., and Dorfman, A. (1959) The biosynthesis of hyaluronic acid by group A Streptococcus. VI. Biosynthesis from uridine nucleotides in cell-free extracts. *J. Biol. Chem.* **234,** 2343–2350

7. Schwartz, N. B., and Rodén, L. (1997) *Biographical Memoir of Albert Dorfman*, Vol. 72, pp. 70–87, National Academy of Sciences, Washington, D. C.

THE JOURNAL OF BIOLOGICAL CHEMISTRY
© 2005 by The American Society for Biochemistry and Molecular Biology, Inc.

Vol. 280, No. 32, Issue of August 12, p. e29, 2005
Printed in U.S.A.

Classics

A PAPER IN A SERIES REPRINTED TO CELEBRATE THE CENTENARY OF THE JBC IN 2005

JBC Centennial
1905–2005
100 Years of Biochemistry and Molecular Biology

Visual Pigment Molecules and Retinol Isomers: the Work of George Wald

The Neo-b Isomer of Vitamin A and Retinene
(Brown, P. K., and Wald, G. (1956) *J. Biol. Chem.* 222, 865–877)

George Wald (1906–1997) was born in New York City. He had an aptitude for mechanics and science from a very young age and was able to successfully construct a crystal detector radio that enabled him and his friends to listen to the 1919 World Series. Wald also had an interest in vaudeville, and he and a friend organized an act that they took to nearby Jewish community centers. His success as a performer suggested a possible future career in law and so he entered Washington Square College of New York University as a pre-law student. However, he soon found that his pre-law studies didn't interest him and felt the need for something "more substantial, more natural, more organic" (1). He became a pre-medical student. But by the time Wald was a senior, he had lost interest in his medical courses. Fortunately at this time he happened upon Sinclair Lewis's *Arrowsmith* and decided to do biological research. After graduating in 1927 he applied to Columbia University for graduate studies in zoology.

As a graduate student, Wald worked on the visual performance of *Drosophila* and human dark adaptation with Selig Hecht. Wanting to know more about the molecules involved in the photoreceptor process, Wald decided to work with Nobel laureate Otto Warburg in Berlin after receiving his Ph.D. in 1932. With Warburg, Wald began to work on rhodopsin. Believing that rhodopsin was a carotenoid-linked protein, he extracted some retinas with chloroform and reacted the extract with antimony trichloride. The solution turned bright blue and had an absorption curve typical of vitamin A (2). Because vitamin A had just been isolated by Paul Karrer in Zürich, Wald went to Karrer's laboratory to verify his results. In just 3 months, Karrer and Wald confirmed the presence of vitamin A in cow, sheep, and pig retinas.

After completing his research in Zürich, Wald went to Heidelberg to work with Nobel laureate Otto Meyerhof, who was featured in a previous *Journal of Biological Chemistry* (JBC) Classic (3). A fortuitous event in the middle of the summer allowed Wald to make a huge leap forward in understanding visual pigment biochemistry. Everyone was away on holiday when a shipment of 300 frogs arrived in the laboratory. The laboratory assistant was about to release the frogs when Wald asked if he could have them. He extracted dark-adapted and bleached retinas from the frogs and was able to detect a novel carotenoid that was similar to but distinct from vitamin A (4). He called this new substance retinene and found that when rhodopsin was stimulated with light it yielded opsin and retinene. The retinene was then gradually converted to vitamin A. Eventually retinene was renamed retinal, and vitamin A became retinol. It had been known for some time that vitamin A deficiency resulted in night blindness, but it was an unexpected discovery that a vitamin would participate directly in a physiological process.

Wald returned to the United States to work in the Department of Physiology at the University of Chicago and started experiments to confirm that the visual cycle was present in vertebrates other than the frog. A year later, in 1934, he assumed his first academic position as tutor in Biochemical Sciences at Harvard. He remained at Harvard for the rest of his academic career, becoming Faculty Instructor in 1939, Associate Professor in 1944, and Professor of Biology in 1948.

In the mid-1930s Wald began spending summers at Woods Hole, studying the dark-adapted retinas of certain fish. He found that, like frogs, the rod visual pigments of marine fish contain

George Wald. Photo courtesy of the National Library of Medicine.

rhodopsin, and when exposed to light, the rhodopsin releases retinal, which is converted to retinol. Freshwater fish, however, had a different rod visual pigment and yielded a different form of retinal and retinol. He called the new pigment porphyropsin and the new carotenoids retinene$_2$ and vitamin A$_2$.

Wald also started studying cone vision in the mid-1930s. Using chicken retinas he extracted a visual pigment that was red-sensitive and called it iodopsin. In the mid-1950s Wald showed that iodopsin bleaches to retinene$_1$ and opsin. His experiments were interrupted by World War II, during which he worked on applied vision research projects for the U. S. Army Board of Engineers. He aided in developing infrared viewing devices as well as studying the spherical and chromatic aberration of the human lens.

With the conclusion of the war, Wald returned his focus to visual pigment molecules. He was joined by Paul Brown who became his research assistant and long time co-worker. Brown showed that rhodopsin could be generated simply by mixing retinal and opsin. However, when Wald and Brown tried to assemble rhodopsin in a test tube using retinol, opsin, and several enzymes, they noticed something odd. When they used retinol from fish oil, a rhodopsin-like pigment was produced, but when synthetic retinol was used nothing happened. They soon discovered that this was due to the *cis-trans* isomerization of retinol and that adding a trace of iodine to synthetic vitamin A in light promotes isomerization allowing the retinol to form a light-sensitive pigment with opsin.

Wald and his co-workers identified the different isomers of retinol in order to determine which one was involved in forming rhodopsin. Of all the possible isomers, the 11-*cis* linkage was thought to be the least probable because the bend caused by the *cis* linkage caused the molecule to be twisted. This departure from planarity was expected to make the molecule so unstable that it should not be present in nature. However, once Wald and his co-workers synthesized the molecule, they realized that it was reasonably stable in the dark, and they eventually determined that the 11-*cis* retinol isomer was a precursor to all visual pigments. The JBC Classic reprinted here describes Wald and Brown's preparation of 11-*cis* retinol, its properties, and its isomerization.

This was the first instance of a role for *cis-trans* isomerization in biology, and the discovery allowed the synthesis of rhodopsin and other visual pigments in the laboratory. Wald eventually showed that light causes 11-*cis* retinal to isomerize to the all-*trans* form, which is eventually converted back to the 11-*cis* form.

In the early 1960s Wald turned his attention to color vision and determined the spectral sensitivity functions of the red-, green-, and blue-sensitive cones in normal and color blind human subjects. He also studied the link between vitamin A deficiency and night blindness. In recognition of his work on chemical visual processes in the eye, Wald was awarded the 1967 Nobel Prize in Physiology or Medicine along with Ragnar Granit and Haldan Keffer Hartline. Wald used his fame as a Nobel laureate to speak out on many political and social issues. He was a vocal opponent of the Vietnam War and the nuclear arms race, and in 1980 he served as part of Ramsey Clark's delegation to Iran during the Iran hostage crisis.

In addition to his research activities, Wald was actively involved in teaching at Harvard and earned the reputation as one of Harvard's best teachers. He taught a popular introductory biology course and published a laboratory manual based on the course called *Twenty-six Afternoons of Biology* (5). Wald gained national attention from the course and was named one of the country's 10 best teachers by *Time* magazine in 1966.

Over the years, Wald received many awards in addition to the Nobel Prize. He won the Eli Lilly Award in 1939, the Lasker Award in 1953, the Proctor Medal in 1959, and the Rumford Prize in 1959. Wald was elected to the National Academy of Sciences in 1950 and to the American Philosophical Society in 1958.[1]

Nicole Kresge, Robert D. Simoni, and Robert L. Hill

REFERENCES

1. Dowling, J. E. (2000) *Biographical Memoir of George Wald*, Vol. 78, pp. 298–317, National Academy of Sciences, Washington, D. C.
2. Wald, G. (1934–1935) Vitamin A in eye tissues. *J. Gen. Physiol.* **18,** 905
3. JBC Classics: Meyerhof, O., and Junowicz-Kocholaty, R. (1943) *J. Biol. Chem.* **149,** 71–92; Meyerhof, O. (1945) *J. Biol. Chem.* **157,** 105–120; Meyerhof, O., and Oesper, P. (1947) *J. Biol. Chem.* **170,** 1–22 (http://www.jbc.org/cgi/content/full/280/4/e3)
4. Wald, G. (1935–1936) Carotenoids and the visual cycle. *J. Gen. Physiol.* **19,** 351
5. Wald, G., Hopkins, J., III, Albersheim, P., Dowling, J. E., and Denhardt, D. (1962) *Twenty-six Afternoons of Biology*, Addison-Wesley, Reading, MA

---

[1] All biographical information on George Wald was taken from Ref. 1.

THE JOURNAL OF BIOLOGICAL CHEMISTRY
© 2005 by The American Society for Biochemistry and Molecular Biology, Inc.

Vol. 280, No. 33, Issue of August 19, p. e30, 2005
Printed in U.S.A.

Classics

A PAPER IN A SERIES REPRINTED TO CELEBRATE THE CENTENARY OF THE JBC IN 2005

JBC Centennial
1905–2005
100 Years of Biochemistry and Molecular Biology

Methanogenesis, Fatty Acid Synthesis, and Cobamide Coenzymes: the Work of Horace A. Barker

The Enzymatic Synthesis of Cobamide Coenzymes
(Brady, R. O., Castanera, E. G., and Barker, H. A. (1962) *J. Biol. Chem.* **237, 2325–2332)**

Horace Albert Barker (1907–2000) was educated at Stanford University and earned a Ph.D. in chemistry in 1933. He then spent the next 2 years with Dutch microbiologist C. B. van Niel at the Hopkins Marine Station isolating marine diatoms and dinoflagellates and studying their physiology and metabolism. Barker also absorbed the concepts of the "Delft school" of microbiology, namely that microorganisms can best be understood and classified by their chemical activities. This time spent at Hopkins Marine Station combined with Van Niel's enthusiasm and gifted teaching and research skills persuaded Barker to choose microbiology for his own career.

In 1935 Barker went to the Netherlands to study with van Niel's mentor, A. J. Kluyver, in the Delft Microbiology Laboratory. There he initiated studies on three topics that he would pursue throughout his career: the biochemistry of methanogenesis, the production of fatty acids by microbial fermentation, and the anaerobic degradation of glutamate.

Barker returned to California in 1936 to take a position as a soil microbiologist in the Agricultural Experiment Station at the University of California, Berkeley. He remained at Berkeley for his entire career, holding appointments first in plant nutrition, then plant and microbial biochemistry, and finally in the new Department of Biochemistry.

Because of the proximity of the Berkeley Radiation Laboratory, radioactive carbon isotopes became available to Berkeley researchers early on. In collaboration with Sam Ruben, Zev Hassid, and Martin Kamen, Barker began investigating methanogenesis in the fermentations of methanol and acetate using $^{11}CO_2$. They were able to show that $^{11}CO_2$ was converted to radioactive methane, even though the half-life of ^{11}C was only 20 min. When the longer lived ^{14}C became available, Barker and his colleagues were able to work out the details of methane biosynthesis and showed that during acetate fermentation methane was derived from the methyl group of acetate and the carboxyl group was converted to carbon dioxide. In 1956 Barker published a generalized pathway for the formation of methane from acetate, methanol, or carbon dioxide (1).

In the early 1940s Barker became involved in a department of food technology wartime project in which he investigated the deterioration of dried fruit during storage. After the War, Barker started studying fatty acid synthesis in *Clostridium kluyveri* with Earl R. Stadtman. The details of these investigations were published in a previous *Journal of Biological Chemistry* (JBC) Classic (2).

Barker's research focus turned to glutamate degradation when Arthur Kornberg, who will be the subject of a future JBC Classic, isolated a histidine-degrading strain of *C. tetanomorphum* while visiting Barker's laboratory. Barker's student, Joseph Wachsman, investigated the early steps of histidine degradation and determined that glutamate is an intermediate in the degradation process. He then studied the degradation of glutamate by tracer and enzymatic methods and established that glutamate was degraded by a novel pathway. A clue to the nature of the pathway was provided when Wachsman identified mesaconic acid and 3-methyl-L-aspartate as intermediates in glutamate degradation. Chemical degradation of [^{14}C]mesaconate formed from [4-^{14}C]glutamate led to the conclusion that a novel isomerization

This paper is available on line at http://www.jbc.org

Horace A. Barker. Photo courtesy of the University of California Berkeley.

of glutamate must occur during its conversion to mesaconate. A. Munch-Peterson determined that the isomerization was inhibited by charcoal treatment of the cell-free extracts and H. Weissbach and R. D. Smyth identified the charcoal-absorbable cofactor as a novel form of pseudovitamin B_{12}.

Barker and his co-workers soon isolated several forms of the new coenzyme. They also prepared an enzyme system from *Propionibacterium shermanii* that catalyzed the conversion of benzimidazolylhydroxocobamide and 5,6-dimethylbenzimidazolylcyanocobamide to their respective cobamide coenzymes. The JBC Classic reprinted here describes Barker's purification of the cobamide coenzyme-synthesizing enzyme from *P. shermanii* and presents the results of his studies on the chemical transformations involved in the biosynthesis of cobamide coenzymes. The experiments also confirmed previous observations that the adenosyl moiety of B_{12} coenzymes arises from the adenosine moiety of ATP.

The impact of Barker's research earned him widespread recognition. In 1953 he was elected to the National Academy of Sciences. He received the 1965 Borden Award in Nutrition and the Hopkins Medal from the Biochemical Society. He was also named California Scientist of the Year in 1966 and was awarded the National Medal of Science in 1968 by President Lyndon Johnson. In 1988, the Biochemistry Building on the Berkeley campus was renamed H. A. Barker Hall.[1]

Nicole Kresge, Robert D. Simoni, and Robert L. Hill

REFERENCES

1. Barker, H. A. (1956) *Ind. Eng. Chem.* **48,** 1438–1442
2. JBC Classics: Stadtman, E. R., and Barker, H. A. (1949) *J. Biol. Chem.* **180,** 1085–1093; Mura, U., Chock, P. B., and Stadtman, E. R. (1981) *J. Biol. Chem.* **256,** 13022–13029 (http://www.jbc.org/cgi/content/full/280/26/e23)
3. Switzer, R. L., Stadtman, E. R., and Stadtman, T. C. (2003) *Biographical Memoir of H. A. Barker*, Vol. 84, pp. 1–21, National Academy of Sciences, Washington, D. C.
4. Barker, H. A. (1978) Explorations of bacterial metabolism. *Annu. Rev. Biochem.* **47,** 1–33

[1] All biographical information on Horace A. Barker was taken from Refs. 3 and 4.

THE JOURNAL OF BIOLOGICAL CHEMISTRY
© 2005 by The American Society for Biochemistry and Molecular Biology, Inc.

Vol. 280, No. 34, Issue of August 26, p. e31, 2005
Printed in U.S.A.

Classics

A PAPER IN A SERIES REPRINTED TO CELEBRATE THE CENTENARY OF THE JBC IN 2005

JBC Centennial
1905–2005
100 Years of Biochemistry and Molecular Biology

Plant Carbohydrates and the Biosynthesis of Lactose: the Work of William Zev Hassid

A Soluble Lactose-synthesizing Enzyme from Bovine Milk
(Babad, H., and Hassid, W. Z. (1964) *J. Biol. Chem.* 239, 946–948)

Soluble Uridine Diphosphate D-Galactose:D-Glucose β-4-D-Galactosyltransferase from Bovine Milk
(Babad, H., and Hassid, W. Z. (1966) *J. Biol. Chem.* 241, 2672–2678)

Zev Hassid (1899–1974) was born in Jaffa, Palestine. He added "William" to his name after he came to the United States in 1920. Hassid was educated in Palestine at a Hebrew language school and then at an Agricultural High School, from which he graduated in 1916. He then worked as a farm laborer until 1918 when he joined the British army to help liberate Palestine from the Turks. While in the army, Hassid was never involved in combat; instead he guarded prisoners and supplies in transit, which allowed him to travel to places like Alexandria in Egypt. It was in Alexandria that Hassid first heard about the University of California from a fellow soldier who had studied there.

After leaving the army, Hassid decided to use his savings to go to California to study agronomy at the University, intending to return to Palestine to assist in the development of scientific agriculture. He arrived in Berkeley in 1920 and registered at the University of California. However, his knowledge of English was so limited that he could not follow the lectures or read the textbooks. After a week of frustration he took a leave of absence from the University and moved to Fresno where he attended Fresno State Teachers College, majoring in Letters and Science with an emphasis on Chemistry, French Language, and Mathematics. In August 1924, he returned to UC Berkeley to major in Chemistry, but he changed his major to general literature and obtained a Bachelor of Arts degree in 1925. He then enrolled in graduate studies at the School of Education and graduated in 1926, at the same time earning a General Secondary School Credential from the State Board of Education. However, instead of teaching, he worked as a chemical analyst for a year.

In 1927, Hassid was offered a position as a research assistant with D. R. Hoagland in the Division of Plant Nutrition at Berkeley's Agricultural Experiment Station. Working with Hoagland, Hassid analyzed plant materials and soils for a variety of inorganic constituents. This renewed his interest in plant research, and he enrolled at UC Berkeley as a graduate student in Plant Nutrition. He earned his Ph.D. in 1934, investigating the structure of polysaccharides in marine algae for his thesis. After graduating Hassid joined the staff of the Division of Plant Nutrition as a junior chemist and rose to the rank of Professor of Plant Biochemistry in 1947. In 1959 he transferred to the Biochemistry Department and in 1965 he became Emeritus.

Hassid's independent scientific research started with his investigation of the structure of a galactan that was a major component of the fleshy marine alga, *Iridea laminarioides*. In elucidating the structure he applied methylation methods that had recently been developed by the English chemist and Nobel laureate, Walter N. Haworth. Later he used the same methods to establish the primary structures of several other types of starch and glycogen, including canna starch, dog liver glycogen, the dextran formed from sucrose by *Betacoccus arabinosaceus*, an insoluble polysaccharide derived from *Saccharomyces cerevisiae,* and glycogen and

William Zev Hassid, professor of biochemistry at the University of California Berkeley. Credit: Bob Lackenbach, University of California Berkeley (1951 or earlier).

starch derived from sweet corn. These initial investigations led to an interest in the biochemistry of carbohydrates that remained with Hassid throughout his career.

Hassid started collaborating with Samuel Ruben and Martin D. Kamen in 1939 on the first application of ^{11}C to the study of photosynthesis. When ^{14}C became available in 1946, Hassid and his students pioneered in the development of biological methods for the preparation of uniformly ^{14}C-labeled carbohydrates from plant tissue, including D-glucose, D-fructose, D-galactose, sucrose, and starch. He generously supplied the radioactive sugars to many other investigators before they became commercially available.

In 1943, Hassid initiated a collaboration with Michael Doudoroff and Horace A. Barker, both authors of previous *Journal of Biological Chemistry* (JBC) Classics (1, 2), as well as Nathan O. Kaplan. They investigated the biosynthesis of sucrose by sucrose phosphorylase, an enzyme from *Pseudomonas saccharophila*. Their demonstration of the first enzymatic synthesis of sucrose caught the attention of officials at the Coca-Cola Company who were having trouble obtaining sucrose because of wartime rationing. The company sent a representative to Berkeley to offer them $500,000 for research on sucrose phosphorylase if a commercial process for sucrose synthesis seemed feasible. Unfortunately, Hassid and his associates were away at the time, and the representative could only discuss the problem with Hoagland who was pessimistic about the method. Due to Hoagland's lack of optimism, Coca-Cola did not end up providing funding for sucrose phosphorylase research.

Subsequent efforts to show the presence of a similar enzyme in plants were unsuccessful until Luis Leloir and his associates discovered uridine diphosphate D-glucose (UDPG) and demonstrated the synthesis of sucrose from UDPG and fructose, as reported in a previous JBC Classic (3). This prompted Hassid and his colleagues to undertake a systematic investigation of the occurrence of nucleoside diphosphate sugars in plants. They isolated nucleoside diphosphate derivatives of D-xylose, L-arabinose, D-galactose, D-galacturonic acid, D-mannuronic acid, and 2-acetamido-2-deoxy-D-glucose and established the roles of several of these compounds in sugar interconversions and polysaccharide formation.

Hassid's reputation attracted scientists from around the world to work in his laboratory. One of these scientists was Winifred N. Watkins, who embarked on a study of the biosynthesis of lactose in mammary tissue with Hassid. Using guinea pig and bovine mammary glands, they established that lactose was synthesized according to the following reaction.

Classics

$$\text{UDP-D-galactose} + \text{D-glucose} \rightarrow \text{lactose} + \text{UDP}$$

REACTION 1

They also discovered that mammary tissue contained an enzyme activity that transfers D-galactose to *N*-acetyl-D-glucosamine.

This led to Hassid's isolation of lactose synthetase with Helene Babad, which is the subject of the two JBC Classics reprinted here. The first Classic is a communication that describes how Hassid and Babad used centrifugation and ammonium sulfate fractionation to obtain a "soluble enzyme preparation from bovine milk capable of catalyzing synthesis of lactose from UDP-D-galactose and D-glucose." They confirmed that their preparation contained lactose synthetase activity using [1-^{14}C]UDP-D-galactose and α-D-[^{14}C]glucose 1-phosphate. The second Classic describes the partial purification and some of the properties of the galactosyl-transferase responsible for the synthesis of lactose. It was later discovered that lactose synthetase is composed of two proteins: galactosyltransferase and α-lactalbumin, which increases the affinity of galactosyltransferase.

Hassid's numerous contributions to understanding plant carbohydrates were recognized by several awards and honors. He was given the first Sugar Research Award (1945) of the National Academy of Sciences (jointly with Doudoroff and Barker), the Charles Reid Barnes Honorary Life Membership Award of the American Society of Plant Physiologists (1964), and the C. S. Hudson Award of the American Chemical Society (1967). In 1972 he was honored at the Sixth International Symposium on Carbohydrate Chemistry as one of three outstanding senior American carbohydrate chemists. He was a member of the National Academy of Sciences and the American Academy of Arts and Sciences, Chairman of the Division of Carbohydrate Chemistry of the American Chemical Society (1949–1950), and a member of numerous editorial boards including that of the JBC.[1]

Nicole Kresge, Robert D. Simoni, and Robert L. Hill

REFERENCES

1. JBC Classic: Entner, N., and Doudoroff, M. (1952) *J. Biol. Chem.* **196,** 853–862 (http://www.jbc.org/cgi/content/full/280/27/e24)
2. JBC Classic: Brady, R. O., Castanera, E. G., and Barker, H. A. (1962) *J. Biol. Chem.* **237,** 2325–2332 (http://www.jbc.org/cgi/content/full/280/33/e30)
3. JBC Classics: Caputto, R., Leloir, L. F, Cardini, C. E., and Paladini, A. C. (1950) *J. Biol. Chem.* **184,** 333–350; Cabib, E., Leloir, L. F., and Cardini, C. E. (1953) *J. Biol. Chem.* **203,** 1055–1070; Cabib, E., and Leloir, L. F. (1954) *J. Biol. Chem.* **206,** 779–790 (http://www.jbc.org/cgi/content/full/280/19/e16)
4. Ballou, C. and Barker, H. A. (1979) *Biographical Memoir of William Zev Hassid*, Vol. 50, pp.196–231, National Academy of Sciences, Washington, D. C.

---

[1] All biographical information on William Zev Hassid was taken from Ref. 4.

THE JOURNAL OF BIOLOGICAL CHEMISTRY
© 2005 by The American Society for Biochemistry and Molecular Biology, Inc.

Vol. 280, No. 35, Issue of September 2, p. e32, 2005
Printed in U.S.A.

Classics

A PAPER IN A SERIES REPRINTED TO CELEBRATE THE CENTENARY OF THE JBC IN 2005

JBC Centennial
1905–2005
100 Years of Biochemistry and Molecular Biology

The Role of the Acyl Carrier Protein in Fatty Acid Synthesis: the Work of P. Roy Vagelos

Acyl Carrier Protein. III. An Enoyl Hydrase Specific for Acyl Carrier Protein Thioesters
(Majerus, P. W., Alberts, A. W., and Vagelos, P. R. (1965) *J. Biol. Chem.* 240, 618–621)

Acyl Carrier Protein. VII. The Primary Structure of the Substrate-binding Site
(Majerus, P. W., Alberts, A. W., and Vagelos, P. R. (1965) *J. Biol. Chem.* 240, 4723–4726)

P. Roy Vagelos was born in Westfield, NJ in 1929. He received an A.B. degree from the University of Pennsylvania in 1950 and an M.D. from Columbia University's College of Physicians and Surgeons in 1954. Following an internship and residency at the Massachusetts General Hospital in Boston, he joined the National Institutes of Health. There he launched a career as a research scientist under the guidance of Earl Stadtman, who authored a previous *Journal of Biological Chemistry* (JBC) Classic (1). With Stadtman, Vagelos demonstrated that long-chain fatty acid synthesis is catalyzed by an enzyme complex in which malonyl-CoA is the source of active acetate.

From 1956 to 1966, Vagelos served as Senior Surgeon and then Section Head of Comparative Biochemistry in the National Heart Institute's Laboratory of Biochemistry. During this time, he continued to study fatty acid synthesis, focusing on the role of acyl carrier protein (ACP). He discovered that the intermediates in fatty acid synthesis in *Escherichia coli* are linked to an acyl carrier protein via a thioester linkage. Vagelos published a series of papers on acyl carrier protein in the JBC, two of which are reprinted here as Classics.

During fatty acid synthesis, the acyl groups of acetyl-CoA and malonyl-CoA are initially transferred by acetyl and malonyl transacylases to the sulfhydryl group of ACP. Acetyl-ACP and malonyl-ACP are then condensed to form acetoacetyl-ACP, which is reduced to D(−)-β-hydroxybutyryl-ACP. The transacylases, condensing enzyme (acyl-malonyl-ACP condensing enzyme), and reductase (β-ketoacyl-ACP reductase) were characterized by Vagelos. This first Classic focuses on the purification and properties of the enol hydrase (3-hydroxyacyl-ACP dehydratase) that catalyzes the dehydration of D(−)-β-hydroxybutyryl-ACP to crotonyl-*S*-ACP.

The second Classic deals with how substrates are linked to ACP. Vagelos had previously reported that, similar to CoA, substrates are bound to ACP via the sulfhydryl group of 4'-phosphopantetheine. However, he noticed that despite this similarity between the two carriers, thioesters of CoA could not substitute effectively for ACP in fatty acid synthesis. Upon further study of the structure of ACP, as reported in the second Classic, Vagelos discovered that 4'-phosphopantetheine is bound to ACP through a phosphodiester linkage to the hydroxyl group of a serine residue.

In 1966, Vagelos assumed the chairmanship of the Department of Biological Chemistry at Washington University's School of Medicine in St Louis, MO. He continued to work on fatty acid biosynthesis and metabolism and expanded his research to the synthesis of complex lipids and the role of cholesterol in the biochemistry of the cell. In 1973 he became Director of the University's Division of Biology and Biomedical Sciences, which he founded. This Division eventually became a model for other universities. It included both the undergraduate Department of Biology and the Medical School in one umbrella unit, which was unheard of at the time.

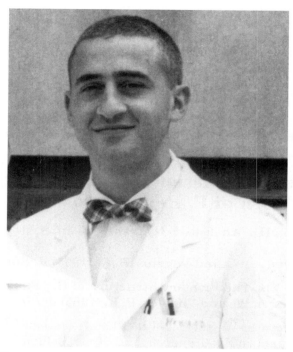

P. Roy Vagelos. Photo courtesy of the Office of NIH History, National Institutes of Health.

Vagelos left academia in 1975 to join Merck Sharp & Dohme Research Laboratories as Senior Vice President for Research. In 1984 he was named an Executive Vice President of Merck and was elected to its Board of Directors, and in 1984 he became Merck's Chief Executive Officer. He served as CEO and Chairman of the Board until 1994. Under his direction, the company expanded its philanthropic efforts as well as its pharmaceutical research. He is perhaps best known for his decision to make Merck's Invermectin (Mectizan) available free to millions of people in Africa and Central America for the treatment of river blindness, a disease spread by black flies that causes chronic rashes, itching, weight loss, and blindness.

In recognition of his contributions to science, Vagelos received the American Chemical Society's Enzyme Chemistry Award in 1967. He was elected to both the National Academy of Sciences and the American Academy of Arts and Sciences in 1972 and to the American Philosophical Society in 1993. In 1989 he received the Thomas Alva Edison Award from then New Jersey Governor Thomas Kean. He is currently Chairman of the Board of Regeneron Pharmaceuticals, Inc. as well as a member of the Board of Directors of the Prudential Insurance Company.[1]

Vagelos' coauthors on several of the JBC acyl carrier protein papers, including the two reprinted here, are Philip W. Majerus and Alfred W. Alberts. Majerus went on to become a Professor at Washington University School of Medicine and has been a leader in phosphoinositide metabolism and signaling, platelet physiology, and blood coagulation. He is a member of the National Academy of Sciences and has won numerous awards for his research, including the 1998 Bristol-Myers Squibb Award for Distinguished Achievement in Cardiovascular/Metabolic Research. Alberts moved from Washington University to Merck with Vagelos and was the lead scientist in Merck's development of the statin drugs Lovastatin and Zocor.

Nicole Kresge, Robert D. Simoni, and Robert L. Hill

REFERENCES

1. JBC Classics: Stadtman, E. R., and Barker, H. A. (1949) *J. Biol. Chem.* **180**, 1085–1093; Mura, U., Chock, P. B., and Stadtman, E. R. (1981) *J. Biol. Chem.* **256**, 13022–13029 (http://www.jbc.org/cgi/content/full/280/26/e23)
2. Hawthorne, F. (2003) *The Merck Druggernaut*, John Wiley & Sons, Inc., Hoboken, NJ
3. Park, B. S. The Stadtman Way: a Tale of Two Biochemists at NIH. http://history.nih.gov/exhibits/stadtman/index.htm (An online exhibit produced by the Office of NIH History in collaboration with the National Heart, Lung, and Blood Institute)

---

[1] All biographical information on P. Roy Vagelos was taken from Refs. 2 and 3.

THE JOURNAL OF BIOLOGICAL CHEMISTRY
© 2005 by The American Society for Biochemistry and Molecular Biology, Inc.

Vol. 280, No. 36, Issue of September 9, p. e33, 2005
Printed in U.S.A.

Classics

A PAPER IN A SERIES REPRINTED TO CELEBRATE THE CENTENARY OF THE JBC IN 2005

JBC Centennial
1905–2005
100 Years of Biochemistry and Molecular Biology

The Sequences of Pea and Calf Thymus Histone H4: James Bonner and Emil Smith

Calf and Pea Histone IV. III. Complete Amino Acid Sequence of Pea Seedling Histone IV; Comparison with the Homologous Calf Thymus Histone
(DeLange, R. J., Fambrough, D. M., Smith, E. L., and Bonner, J. J. (1969) *J. Biol. Chem.* **244, 5669–5679)**

James Frederick Bonner (1910–1996) was born in Ansley, NE to a family of chemists. Bonner's father, Walter Daniel Bonner, became head of the chemistry department at the University of Utah when James was 5 years old, and his mother and paternal grandfather were chemists as well. Bonner also had five brothers and one sister, all of whom received doctoral degrees: four of them became biochemists, two became physical chemists, and one became an applied mathematician and computer specialist. As such, Bonner naturally gravitated toward chemistry, and after graduating from high school in 1927, he entered the University of Utah to major in chemistry. After Bonner's sophomore year, his father took a sabbatical year at the California Institute of Technology (Caltech) and moved the family to California. Because Bonner had a tuition scholarship, he was able to take classes at Caltech and studied physical chemistry and biology. After the year was up, Bonner's family moved back to Utah, but Bonner remained at Caltech for the summer, studying fruit fly genetics with Theodosius Dobzhansky. At the end of the summer Bonner returned to Utah to finish his bachelor's degree.

After graduating in 1931, Bonner returned to Caltech for graduate school and worked on the production of auxin by the fungus *Rhizopus*. He discovered that the addition of Bacto-peptone increased auxin production 100- to 200-fold. Bonner also developed the section growth test for auxin in which sections of oat coleoptiles were floated in auxin solutions and their growth was monitored. He graduated in 1934 with a Ph.D. in biology. Bonner then received a fellowship to support a postdoctoral year in Europe. He chose to study in Utrecht with Hugo R. Kruyt, one of the most famous colloid chemists of the time. In early 1935, Bonner moved to Zürich to work in Albert Frey-Wyssling's laboratory. There he used the polarizing microscope to study cell wall properties and showed that auxin made the cell wall microfibrils slide past each other more easily.

Upon returning home at the end of 1935, Bonner was offered a position as research fellow at Caltech. He advanced to instructor in 1936, assistant professor in 1937, associate professor in 1943, professor in 1946, and finally he became emeritus in 1981. Bonner's research at Caltech began with studies of wound hormones. He then moved on to plant hormones and discovered that vitamin B_1 (thiamine) was important for root growth in tomato plants. He also determined that other roots required thiamine as well as niacin for growth and that the B vitamins were synthesized in the leaves and transported to the roots.

In 1938 Bonner spent a summer at the University of Chicago working with Karl Hamner on photoperiodism. They discovered that the length of the night, rather than the day, was most important in producing flowering in plants. During World War II, Bonner and Frits Went decided to become specialists in rubber production, and they started intensive research on the guayule plant, the one plant in the western world that was a serious rubber producer. Bonner and Went studied the nutrient requirements of guayule plants and how to kill yield-reducing pests. Bonner was appointed a special agent of the U. S. Forest Service assigned to the

James Bonner. Photo courtesy of the Archives, California Institute of Technology.

Emergency Rubber Program. He eventually entered into a long term association with the Rubber Research Institute of Malaysia and developed a technique for adding ethylene to the bark of rubber trees, which increased latex production by the trees and essentially doubled the world's rubber production.

With the end of the War, Bonner turned his focus to cell biology and the isolation of chloroplasts, mitochondria, cytoplasm, and enzymes. This eventually led to his investigation of how chromosomes control cellular metabolism. Along with his postdoctoral fellow Ru-Chih C. Huang, Bonner isolated chromatin from the nuclei of pea epicotyls. They discovered that crude nuclear extract would incorporate ^{14}C-labeled nucleoside triphosphates into something that was soluble in trichloroacetic acid. Further investigation showed that the purified enzyme could incorporate all four riboside triphosphates into RNA and that RNA synthesis depended on the presence of DNA in the reaction mixture. Bonner and Huang also found that RNA transcription worked much better when DNA was stripped of its histones.

With this discovery, the Bonner lab started investigating histones. Bonner sent his graduate student Douglas Fambrough to Kenneth Murray at Stanford University to learn how to isolate histones using amberlite CG-50 chromatography and polyacrylamide gel electrophoresis. Using these techniques they discovered that there were only five different species of histones. When they compared histones III from pea plants and calf thymus they found that the two proteins had similar amino acid compositions except for one cysteine in pea compared to two cysteines in calf histone.

At the 1967 annual meeting of the National Academy of Sciences in Washington, D. C., Bonner approached Emil Smith, who was featured in a previous *Journal of Biological Chemistry* (JBC) Classic (1), and asked him if he would be interested in comparing the sequences of histones from peas and calf thymus. Smith and Bonner's work on histones is reported in the JBC Classic reprinted here. The pair decided to begin their analysis with calf thymus and pea seedling histone H4 because H4 was the smallest of the histones and therefore the easiest to separate from the others. Smith needed 2 g of each protein for the analysis. This was easily done for the calf histone, which was collected from thymuses from slaughter houses, but it took 24 tons of dried pea seeds to obtain the 2 g of pure pea histone. The effort took a full year, but the results were worth it. Smith's analysis showed that cow and pea histones differ in only two residues and that these substitutions are conservative. This discovery was extremely significant because it implied that the amino acid sequence of histone H4 was so essential it had been conserved since the divergence of animals and plants.

In recognition of his contributions to science, Bonner was elected to the National Academies of Sciences in 1950 and was President of the Pacific Division of the American Association for the Advancement of Science (AAAS) in 1965. In addition to being involved in scientific research, Bonner was an active member of the National Ski Patrol, was elected to the American Alpine Club in 1949, traveled over much of the world, and climbed mountains in the Himalayas, Nepal, and many other places.[1]

Nicole Kresge, Robert D. Simoni, and Robert L. Hill

REFERENCES

1. JBC Classic: Smith, E. L., and Bergmann, M. (1944) *J. Biol. Chem.* **153,** 627–651 (http://www.jbc.org/cgi/content/full/279/47/e6)
2. Salisbury, F. B. (1998) *Biographical Memoir of James Frederick Bonner*, Vol. 73, pp. 100–127, National Academy of Sciences, Washington, D. C.

---

[1] All biographical information on James Frederick Bonner was taken from Ref. 2.

THE JOURNAL OF BIOLOGICAL CHEMISTRY
© 2005 by The American Society for Biochemistry and Molecular Biology, Inc.

Vol. 280, No. 37, Issue of September 16, p. e34, 2005
Printed in U.S.A.

Classics

A PAPER IN A SERIES REPRINTED TO CELEBRATE THE CENTENARY OF THE JBC IN 2005

JBC Centennial
1905–2005
100 Years of Biochemistry and Molecular Biology

Four Decades of Research on the Biosynthesis of Urea: the Work of Sarah Ratner

Biosynthesis of Urea. I. Enzymatic Mechanism of Arginine Synthesis from Citrulline
(Ratner, S., and Pappas, A. (1949) *J. Biol. Chem.* **179**, 1183–1198)

Biosynthesis of Urea. VI. Enzymatic Cleavage of Argininosuccinic Acid to Arginine and Fumaric Acid
(Ratner, S., Anslow, W. P., Jr., and Petrack, B. (1953) *J. Biol. Chem.* **204**, 115–125)

Sarah Ratner (1903–1999) was born, raised, and educated in New York City. After graduating from high school, she decided she wanted to attend Cornell University because it was one of the few universities open to women, it had a strong chemistry department, and it offered scholarships. When Ratner entered Cornell in 1920 as a chemistry major she was the only woman in many of her physics and chemistry classes. She graduated in 1924 and decided it would be a good idea to see what it was like to work in a laboratory before making any career decisions. Ratner found a job first at the Long Island College Hospital and then at the Sloane Hospital for Women. From these experiences she became interested in physiological chemistry and began to attend evening graduate courses in chemistry at Columbia University. In the early 1930s she left her job when she was accepted as a graduate student by H. T. Clarke in the Department of Biochemistry at the College of Physicians and Surgeons (P & S) at Columbia University. Ratner's thesis work was on the reaction of cysteine with formaldehyde to form a thiazolidine-4-carboxylic acid.

In late 1936 Ratner started looking for postdoctoral positions but encountered problems because of her gender. Other male students had no problem finding positions, but many labs were reluctant to hire women. Fortunately, Rudolf Schoenheimer, who was featured in a previous *Journal of Biological Chemistry* (JBC) Classic (1), invited Ratner to work with him at P & S. At that time, Schoenheimer was pioneering the use of ^{2}H as a tracer of metabolic processes along with David Rittenberg, who was also featured in a previous JBC Classic (2). When Ratner joined the group, similar work was beginning with ^{15}N. Ratner's involvement in these experiments fostered an interest in biochemistry, especially the biochemistry of nitrogen compounds.

In 1946, Severo Ochoa, author of a previous JBC Classic (3), recruited Ratner as an assistant professor of pharmacology at New York University's School of Medicine. A year later she published a brief but important paper in the JBC on the mechanism of the conversion of citrulline to arginine and urea (4). This marked the beginning of her comprehensive study of the biosynthesis of urea, which would occupy her for the next four decades. A few years later, Ratner published a more comprehensive follow-up paper on the mechanism, which is reprinted here as the first JBC Classic. The Classic is the first in a series of fifteen "Biosynthesis of Urea" papers Ratner published in the JBC between 1949 and 1977 (5–17). In the paper, she uses a partially purified enzyme system isolated from mammalian liver to show that citrulline and aspartic acid are converted to arginine and malic acid in the urea cycle. Ratner also notes that two separate enzymes are involved in the reaction, one to catalyze the formation of an intermediary condensation product and one to catalyze its hydrolysis.

Eventually, Ratner demonstrated that the intermediary condensation product formed in the reaction between citrulline and aspartic acid is argininosuccinic acid, a previously undiscov-

This paper is available on line at http://www.jbc.org

Sarah Ratner. Photo courtesy of Annual Reviews Inc.

ered amino acid. Ratner also purified and characterized the enzyme that catalyzes this reaction, argininosuccinate synthetase. The conversion of argininosuccinic acid to arginine is the subject of the second JBC Classic reprinted here. In it, Ratner reports that fumarate, rather than malate as she originally predicted in her first Classic paper, is formed in a non-hydrolytic cleavage. Ratner also isolates and begins the initial characterization of the enzyme that catalyzes this reaction. She would eventually fully characterize the enzyme, arginosuccinase, and also discover that ATP is necessary for the operation of the urea cycle and that the cycle is closely linked to the citric acid cycle.

In the mid-1950s, Ratner joined the Department of Biochemistry at the Public Health Research Institute of New York where she remained until retirement in 1992. Over the years, she received many awards in recognition of her contributions to biochemistry. In 1959 she received the Carl Neuberg Medal, in 1961 she was awarded the Garvan Medal of the American Chemical Society, and in 1975 she received the New York Academy of Sciences' Freedman Award in Biochemistry. Ratner was also one of the few women to be elected to the National Academy of Sciences (1974). In addition, she was an active member of many boards and committees, including the JBC Editorial Board.[1]

Nicole Kresge, Robert D. Simoni, and Robert L. Hill

REFERENCES

1. JBC Classics: Schoenheimer, R., and Rittenberg, D. (1935) *J. Biol. Chem.* **111,** 163–168; Rittenberg, D., and Schoenheimer, R. (1937) *J. Biol. Chem.* **121,** 235–253 (http://www.jbc.org/cgi/content/full/277/43/e31)
2. JBC Classics: Shemin, D., and Rittenberg, D. (1945) *J. Biol. Chem.* **159,** 567–568; Shemin, D., London, I. M., and Rittenberg, D. (1950) *J. Biol. Chem.* **183,** 757–765; Radin, N. S., Rittenberg, D., and Shemin, D. (1950) *J. Biol. Chem.* **184,** 755–767 (http://www.jbc.org/cgi/content/full/280/15/e12)
3. JBC Classics: Stern, J. R., and Ochoa, S. (1951) *J. Biol. Chem.* **191,** 161–172; Korkes, S., del Campillo, A., Gunsalus, I. C., and Ochoa, S. (1951) *J. Biol. Chem.* **193,** 721–735 (http://www.jbc.org/cgi/content/full/280/11/e8)
4. Ratner, S. (1947) The enzymatic mechanism of arginine formation from citrulline. *J. Biol. Chem.* **170,** 761–762
5. Ratner, S., and Pappas, A. (1949) Biosynthesis of urea. II. Arginine synthesis from citrulline in liver homogenates. *J. Biol. Chem.* **179,** 1199–1212
6. Ratner, S. and Petrack, B. (1951) Biosynthesis of urea. III. Further studies on arginine synthesis from citrulline. *J. Biol. Chem.* **191,** 693–705
7. Ratner, S. and Petrack, B. (1953) Biosynthesis of urea. IV. Further studies on condensation in arginine synthesis from citrulline. *J. Biol. Chem.* **200,** 161–174
8. Ratner, S., Petrack, B., and Rochovansky, O. (1953) Biosynthesis of urea. V. Isolation and properties of argininosuccinic acid. *J. Biol. Chem.* **204,** 95–113
9. Petrack, B., and Ratner, S. (1958) Biosynthesis of urea. VII. Reversible formation of argininosuccinic acid. *J. Biol.*

---

[1] All biographical information on Sarah Ratner was taken from Refs. 18 and 19.

Chem. **233,** 1494–1500

10. Schuegraf, A., Ratner, S., and Warner, R. C. (1960) Biosynthesis of urea. VIII. Free energy changes of the argininosuccinate synthetase reaction and of the hydrolysis of the inner pyrophosphate bond of adenosine triphosphate. *J. Biol. Chem.* **235,** 3597–3602

11. Rochovansky, O., and Ratner, S. (1961) Biosynthesis of urea. IX. Further studies on mechanism of argininosuccinate synthetase reaction. *J. Biol. Chem.* **236,** 2254–2260

12. Hoberman, H. D., Havir, E. A., Rochovansky, O., and Ratner, S. (1964) Biosynthesis of urea. X. Stereospecificity of the argininosuccinase reaction. *J. Biol. Chem.* **239,** 3818–3820

13. Havir, E. A., Tamir, H., Ratner, S., and Warner, R. C. (1965) Biosynthesis of urea. XI. Preparation and properties of crystalline argininosuccinase. *J. Biol. Chem.* **240,** 3079–3088

14. Rochovansky, O., and Ratner, S. (1967) Biosynthesis of urea. XII. Further studies on argininosuccinate synthetase: substrate affinity and mechanism of action. *J. Biol. Chem.* **242,** 3839–3849

15. Schulze, I. T., Lusty, C. J., and Ratner, S. (1970) Biosynthesis of urea. XIII. Dissociation-association kinetics and equilibria of argininosuccinase. *J. Biol. Chem.* **245,** 4534–4543

16. Lusty, C. J., and Ratner, S. (1972) Biosynthesis of urea. XIV. The quaternary structure of argininosuccinase. *J. Biol. Chem.* **247,** 7010–7022

17. Rochovansky, O., Kodowaki, H., and Ratner, S. (1977) Biosynthesis of urea XV. Molecular and regulatory properties of crystalline argininosuccinate synthetase. *J. Biol. Chem.* **252,** 5287–5294

18. Ratner, S. (1977) A long view of nitrogen metabolism. *Annu. Rev. Biochem.* **46,** 1–24

19. Bentley, R. (2003) *Biographical Memoir of Sarah Ratner*, Vol. 82, pp. 220–241, National Academy of Sciences, Washington, D. C.

THE JOURNAL OF BIOLOGICAL CHEMISTRY
© 2005 by The American Society for Biochemistry and Molecular Biology, Inc.

Vol. 280, No. 38, Issue of September 23, p. e35, 2005
Printed in U.S.A.

Classics

A PAPER IN A SERIES REPRINTED TO CELEBRATE THE CENTENARY OF THE JBC IN 2005

JBC Centennial
1905–2005
100 Years of Biochemistry and Molecular Biology

An Escape from Italy, the Discovery of *S*-Adenosylmethionine, and the Biosynthesis of Creatine by Giulio L. Cantoni

S-Adenosylmethionine; a New Intermediate Formed Enzymatically from L-Methionine and Adenosinetriphosphate
(Cantoni, G. L. (1953) *J. Biol. Chem.* **204,** 403–416)

Enzymatic Mechanism of Creatine Synthesis
(Cantoni, G. L., and Vignos, P. J., Jr. (1954) *J. Biol. Chem.* **209,** 647–659)

Giulio Leonard Cantoni (1915–2005) was born in Milano, Italy. After receiving his M.D. from the University of Milan in 1939, Cantoni and his mother and sister decided to leave Italy to escape the anti-Semitic laws that were enacted the previous year. His father had passed away several years earlier. With the help of Nobel laureate Sir Henry Dale, a postdoctoral fellowship with J. H. Gaddum at the National Institute for Medical Research in London was arranged for Cantoni. He went first, leaving his mother and sister to join him later. Unfortunately, shortly after Cantoni arrived, England declared war against Germany, and the lab in London was packed up and moved to a safer place where it was scheduled to carry out war research. Cantoni was not permitted to move with the lab, and his mother and sister were not permitted to join him in England.

Dale arranged for another postdoctoral fellowship for Cantoni, this one at Oxford University. Cantoni remained at Oxford for a year but decided to move to the United States after his mother and sister were able to obtain U. S. immigration visas. Cantoni and his family were about to board the boat that would take them from Liverpool to New York when he was arrested as an enemy alien. It was June 1940, and Italy had just joined Germany and declared war against England and France. Cantoni was shipped across the Atlantic and interned in Canada for 14 months as a prisoner of war. Eventually, his refugee status was recognized by the British Government, and after a detour to Cuba, he finally joined his mother and sister in New York in December of 1941.

The next year, in 1942, Cantoni secured a position as a teaching and research assistant in the Department of Physiology at the University of Michigan. He stayed there until 1943 when he became an instructor in the Department of Pharmacology at New York University, where he remained until 1945. After that, he assumed the position of Assistant Professor of Pharmacology at the Long Island College of Medicine. In 1950, Cantoni moved again, this time to Ohio where he became an Associate Professor of Pharmacology at Case Western Reserve University.

During his time at Case Western, Cantoni discovered that *S*-adenosylmethionine is the active cofactor in the biological methylation reaction. This is the subject of the first *Journal of Biological Chemistry* (JBC) Classic reprinted here. By then, Cantoni had already established that ATP plays an essential role in transmethylation reactions that use methionine as a methyl donor (1) and that ATP is combined with methionine to produce active methionine according to the following reaction (Equation 1) (2).

$$\text{L-Methionine} + \text{ATP} \rightarrow \text{active methionine} + 3\text{IP} \qquad \text{(Eq. 1)}$$

In his JBC Classic paper, Cantoni describes the enzymatic preparation of the active intermediate, its purification, and chemical characterization. The intermediate, which he describes as an addition product of methionine and the adenosine moiety of ATP, is identified as methyl(5-desoxyribosyladenine)(2-aminobutyro)thetin, or *S*-adenosylmethionine. In the paper, Cantoni also deduces that the linkage between methionine and adenosine occurs at the sulfur atom of methionine.

Shortly after submitting the *S*-adenosylmethionine paper to the JBC, Cantoni submitted another paper on the synthesis of creatine, which is reprinted here as the second JBC Classic. The metabolic origin of creatine had been the object of extensive study for decades prior to Cantoni's report. Near the turn of the century arginine was identified as a protein constituent, and it was suspected that it might be degraded to creatine. In 1941 Konrad Bloch and Rudolf Schoenheimer, who were both featured in previous JBC Classics (3, 4), showed that the metabolic synthesis of creatine involves the transfer of an amidine group from arginine to glycine. This results in the formation of guanidinoacetic acid, which is then methylated to produce creatine (5). The methylation reactions were then extensively studied by Vincent du Vigneaud who demonstrated that the methyl group of creatine can be derived from methionine in a transmethylation reaction, as reported in a previous JBC Classic (6). These experiments paved the way not only for Cantoni's elucidation of the enzymatic mechanism of creatine synthesis, but also for his discovery of the active methyl donor, *S*-adenosylmethionine.

On the basis of the reaction proposed in his previous paper, Cantoni deduced that creatine synthesis occurs according to the following reaction by way of an *S*-adenosylmethionine intermediate (Equation 2).

$$\text{L-Methionine} + \text{ATP} + \text{guanidinoaetic acid} \rightarrow \text{creatine} + \text{adenosylhomocysteine} + \text{H}^+ + 3\text{IP} \quad (\text{Eq. 2})$$

In the second JBC Classic, Cantoni confirms this by studying the methylation of guanidinoacetic acid by *S*-adenosylmethionine in partially purified preparations from pork liver and isolating the enzyme, guanidinoacetate methylpherase, that catalyzes the reaction. He verifies that creatine is a product of the reaction by chemical identification and the ability of the product to function as a substrate for creatine kinase. In the years following Cantoni's discovery of *S*-adenosylmethionine it was shown that the molecule is a methyl donor of the utmost importance in many critical biological reactions.

In 1954 Cantoni moved to Bethesda, MD to become chief of the Laboratory of General and Comparative Biochemistry at the National Institute of Mental Health. There, he worked on nucleic acids until he retired as Scientist Emeritus in 1996. In addition to his scientific endeavors, Cantoni served as co-editor of *Procedures in Nucleic Acid Research* with David Davies, a crystallographer at the NIH. Cantoni was a member of the National Academy of Sciences, the American Academy of Arts and Sciences, and the Italian Academy of Science. He published more than 150 papers and was a co-author of several scientific books. In 1968 he founded the Foundation for Advanced Education in the Sciences Chamber Music Concert Series at the National Institutes of Health, which is generally regarded as the best in the Washington, D. C. area.[1]

Nicole Kresge, Herbert Tabor, Robert D. Simoni, and Robert L. Hill

REFERENCES

1. Cantoni, G. L. (1951) Methylation of nicotinamide with a soluble enzyme system from rat liver. *J. Biol. Chem.* **189,** 203–216
2. Cantoni, G. L. (1951) Activation of methionine for transmethylation. *J. Biol. Chem.* **189,** 745–754
3. JBC Classics: Bloch, K., and Rittenberg, D. (1942) *J. Biol. Chem.* **145,** 625–636; Rittenberg, D., and Bloch, K. (1945) *J. Biol. Chem.* **160,** 417–424; Bloch, K. (1945) *J. Biol. Chem.* **157,** 661–666 (http://www.jbc.org/cgi/content/full/280/10/e7)
4. JBC Classics: Schoenheimer, R., and Rittenberg, D. (1935) *J. Biol. Chem.* **111,** 163–168; Rittenberg, D., and Schoenheimer, R. (1937) *J. Biol. Chem.* **121,** 235–253 (http://www.jbc.org/cgi/content/full/277/43/e31)
5. Bloch, K., and Schoenheimer, R. (1941) The biological precursors of creatine. *J. Biol. Chem.* **138,** 167–194
6. JBC Classics: du Vigneaud, V., Cohn, M., Chandler, J. P., Schenck, J. R., and Simmonds, S. (1941) *J. Biol. Chem.* **140,** 625–641; du Vigneaud, V., Melville, D. B., Folkers, K., Wolf, D. E., Mozingo, R., Keresztesy, J. C., and Harris, S. A. (1942) *J. Biol. Chem.* **146,** 475–485; du Vigneaud, V., Ressler, C., and Trippett, S. (1953) *J. Biol. Chem.* **205,** 949–957; Katsoyannis, P. G., and du Vigneaud, V. (1958) *J. Biol. Chem.* **233,** 1352–1354 (http://www.jbc.org/cgi/content/full/279/51/e11)
7. Cantoni, G. L. (2000) *From Milano to New York by Way of Hell: Fascism and the Odyssey of a Young Italian Jew,* Writers Club Press, Lincoln, NE

[1] All biographical information on Giulio Cantoni was taken from Ref. 7.

THE JOURNAL OF BIOLOGICAL CHEMISTRY
© 2005 by The American Society for Biochemistry and Molecular Biology, Inc.

Vol. 280, No. 39, Issue of September 30, p. e36, 2005
Printed in U.S.A.

Classics

A PAPER IN A SERIES REPRINTED TO CELEBRATE THE CENTENARY OF THE JBC IN 2005

JBC Centennial
1905–2005
100 Years of Biochemistry and Molecular Biology

The Structure of NADH: the Work of Sidney P. Colowick

On the Structure of Reduced Diphosphopyridine Nucleotide
(Pullman, M. E., San Pietro, A., and Colowick, S. P. (1954) *J. Biol. Chem.* **206,** 129–141)

Sidney P. Colowick (1916–1985) was born and raised in St. Louis, MO. He attended Washington University and obtained a degree in chemical engineering in 1936 at the age of 20. He was then offered a job working with Carl and Gerty Cori, authors of a previous *Journal of Biological Chemistry* (JBC) Classic (1), at the Washington University School of Medicine. He remained with the Coris for the next 10 years. At the age of 21, he published his first paper on the classical studies of glucose 1-phosphate (2), and a year later he was the sole author on a paper on the synthesis of mannose 1-phosphate and galactose 1-phosphate (3). Both papers were published in the JBC.

Eventually, Colowick became Carl Cori's first graduate student and earned his Ph.D. in 1942. During his time in the Cori lab, Colowick was involved in many projects. Along with Herman Kalckar he discovered myokinase, which is now known as adenyl kinase. This discovery proved to be important in understanding transphosphorylation reactions in yeast and animal cells. Colowick's interest then turned to the conversion of glucose to polysaccharides, and he and Earl Sutherland (who will be featured in an upcoming JBC Classic) published an important paper on the formation of glycogen from glucose using purified enzymes (4). Colowick also carried out studies on hexokinase, which led to his eventual crystallization of the enzyme in 1961 (5).

After 10 years in the Cori laboratory, Colowick joined the staff of the Public Health Research Institute of New York. He remained there from 1946 to 1948. He then became an Associate Professor of Biochemistry at the University of Illinois Medical School in Chicago, and in 1950 became Associate Professor of Biology at Johns Hopkins University. During this period at Johns Hopkins, Colowick made many notable contributions to the field of biochemistry. In collaboration with Maynard Pullman and Anthony San Pietro, Colowick established the correct structure of NADH, which is the subject of the JBC Classic reprinted here. Approximately 20 years earlier, Paul Karrer and his colleagues had concluded that the reduction of NAD occurs *ortho* to the ring nitrogen. Using deuterium as a tracer, Colowick, Pullman, and San Pietro proved that Karrer was incorrect when they showed that reduction occurs at the *para* position. These results also confirmed that Birgit Vennesland was incorrect when she stated that the 6-position of the pyridine ring was the site of oxidation-reduction, as pointed out in a previous JBC Classic on Vennesland (6).

In 1951, Colowick and Nathan Kaplan were approached by Kurt Jacoby of Academic Press to do a series comparable to *Methodem der Ferment Forschung*. Colowick and Kaplan planned and edited the first 6 volumes of *Methods in Enzymology*, launching in 1955 what became a series of well known and useful handbooks. He continued as Editor of the series until his death in 1985.

Colowick moved to the Vanderbilt University School of Medicine in 1959 to become the Charles Hayden-American Cancer Society Professor in the Department of Microbiology. He remained at Vanderbilt for the rest of his research career. At Vanderbilt, Colowick focused on hexokinase and hexose transport in cultured animal cells.

In recognition of his contributions to science, Colowick was awarded many honors. He was the recipient of the Eli Lilly Award in Biological Chemistry (1947) and was elected to both the American Academy of Arts and Sciences (1969) and the National Academy of Sciences (1972).

Sidney P. Colowick. Photo courtesy of the Office of NIH History, National Institutes of Health.

He was also a member of many advisory committees, and served on the editorial boards of a large number of journals including the JBC.[1]

The other two authors on this JBC Classic have also gone on to distinguished careers in biochemistry. San Pietro joined the faculty of Indiana University in 1968 to chair the Department of Plant Sciences and directed its activities and development until it became part of the newly formed Department of Biology in 1977. Now a Professor Emeritus, he continues to maintain an active laboratory for investigating the mechanisms of the light-dependent reactions of photosynthesis and has published over 160 papers. Pullman went on to the Public Health Research Institute in New York and became well known for his discoveries in the field of oxidative phosphorylation.

Nicole Kresge, Robert D. Simoni, and Robert L. Hill

REFERENCES

1. JBC Classics: Cori, C. F., and Cori, G. T. (1928) *J. Biol. Chem.* **79,** 321–341; Cori, G. T., Colowick, S. P., and Cori, C. F. (1938) *J. Biol. Chem.* **124,** 543–555; Cori, G. T., Colowick, S. P., and Cori, C. F. (1939) *J. Biol. Chem.* **127,** 771–782; Green, A. A., and Cori, G. T. (1943) *J. Biol. Chem.* **151,** 21–29; Cori, G. T., and Green, A. A. (1943) *J. Biol. Chem.* **151,** 31–38 (http://www.jbc.org/cgi/content/full/277/29/e18)
2. Cori, C. F., Colowick, S. P., and Cori, G. T. (1937) The isolation and synthesis of glucose-1-phosphoric acid. *J. Biol. Chem.* **121,** 465–477
3. Colowick, S. P. (1938) Synthetic mannose-1-phosphoric acid and galactose-1-phosphoric acid. *J. Biol. Chem.* **124,** 557–558
4. Sutherland, E. W., Colowick, S. P., and Cori, C. F. (1941) The enzymatic conversion of glucose-6-phosphate to glycogen. *J. Biol. Chem.* **140,** 309–310
5. Trayser, K. A., and Colowick S. P. (1961) Properties of crystalline hexokinase from yeast. I. Analyses for possible co-factors. *Arch. Biochem. Biophys.* **94,** 156–160
6. JBC Classics: Fisher, H. F., Conn, E. E., Vennesland, B., and Westheimer, F. H. (1953) *J. Biol. Chem.* **202,** 687–697; Loewus, F. A., Ofner, P., Fisher, H. F., Westheimer, F. H., and Vennesland, B. (1953) *J. Biol. Chem.* **202,** 699–704 (http://www.jbc.org/cgi/content/full/279/3/e3)
7. Kaplan, N. O. (1985) Sidney P. Colowick. *Methods Enzymol.* **113,** xvii–xxii

---

[1] All biographical information on Sidney Colowick was taken from Ref. 7.

THE JOURNAL OF BIOLOGICAL CHEMISTRY
© 2005 by The American Society for Biochemistry and Molecular Biology, Inc.

Vol. 280, No. 40, Issue of October 7, p. e37, 2005
Printed in U.S.A.

Classics

A PAPER IN A SERIES REPRINTED TO CELEBRATE THE CENTENARY OF THE JBC IN 2005

JBC Centennial
1905–2005
100 Years of Biochemistry and Molecular Biology

The Discovery of tRNA by Paul C. Zamecnik

A Soluble Ribonucleic Acid Intermediate in Protein Synthesis
(Hoagland, M. B., Stephenson, M. L., Scott, J. F., Hecht, L. I., and Zamecnik, P. C. (1958) *J. Biol. Chem.* **231, 241–257)**

Paul C. Zamecnik was born in Cleveland, OH in 1912. He attended Dartmouth College, where he majored in chemistry and zoology and graduated with a bachelor's degree in 1933. He then went Harvard Medical School, received his M.D. in 1936, and served his residency at Harvard from 1936 to 1938 and interned at the University Hospitals in Cleveland until 1939.

Although Zamecnik trained to be a medical doctor, science had always appealed to him. He approached Max Bergmann (who was co-author of a previous *Journal of Biological Chemistry* (JBC) Classic (1)) in 1939, hoping to work with him on protein synthesis at the Rockefeller Institute. Bergmann, however, turned him down because Zamecnik had an M.D. and not a Ph.D. Zamecnik did however get a fellowship to work with Kaj Linderstrøm-Lang at the Carlsberg Laboratory in Denmark. Linderstrøm-Lang was a leader in protein chemistry, and Zamecnik obtained enough training and experience that Bergmann offered him a job when he returned to the States in 1940.

Zamecnik didn't stay at the Rockefeller for long. A year later he was offered a job at the Huntington Memorial Hospital of Harvard University at the Massachusetts General Hospital. There he worked with Fritz Lipmann, author of a previous JBC Classic (2), using radioactive isotopes to prove that proteins were built from amino acids in a process requiring ATP. In 1942 Zamecnik became an Associate Professor of Medicine at Harvard Medical School.

Zamecnik's interest soon turned to how protein sequences were specified, and he started to isolate and identify the components necessary for protein synthesis. By 1953 he had succeeded in making the first cell-free system capable of carrying out net peptide bond formation using ^{14}C-amino acids (3). Using this system, he, Elizabeth Keller, and Mahlon Hoagland demonstrated the initial step in protein synthesis: the activation of amino acids by formation of aminoacyl adenylates from amino acids and ATP (4).

A few years later, Zamecnik and Hoagland discovered a molecule that is essential for protein synthesis: tRNA. This discovery is the subject of the JBC Classic reprinted here. Using the cell-free system, Zamecnik and Hoagland noticed that the RNA in a particular cytoplasmic fraction became labeled with ^{14}C-amino acids and that the labeled RNA was subsequently able to transfer the amino acids to microsomal protein. The transfer was dependent upon guanosine triphosphate. From this they concluded that the RNA, later named transfer RNA or tRNA, functions as an intermediate carrier of amino acids in protein synthesis. Zamecnik and Hoagland later contributed to our understanding of how the transfer process works.

In 1978, Zamecnik's research took on a new direction. He demonstrated that short chains of antisense DNA, chemically synthesized to be complementary to selected RNA targets in the cell, could be used to selectively inactivate the expression of specific genes. This led to a new area of research and opened up the possibilities of antisense RNA therapeutics that could halt protein synthesis in viral or cancer cells. Based on this antisense therapeutic technology, Zamecnik co-founded the company Hybridon, Inc. in 1990. He continues to conduct and supervise research at Hybridon and at Massachusetts General Hospital and is a Professor Emeritus at Harvard University.

Zamecnik has earned over a dozen U. S. patents for his therapeutic techniques. He has also won many awards for his work, including the American Cancer Society National Award (1968),

(a)

(b)

a, Mahlon Hoagland, Paul Zamecnik, and Mary Stephenson. *b*, same characters, approximately 35 years later. Reprinted with permission from the *Annual Review of Biochemistry*, Vol. 74. © 2005 by Annual Reviews, www. annualreviews.org.

the National Medal of Science (1991), the Lasker Award for Special Achievement (1996), and the American Society for Biochemistry and Molecular Biology Merck Award (1997). He served as President of the American Association for Cancer Research (1964 to 1965) and was elected to the National Academy of Sciences in 1968.[1]

Hoagland remained at Harvard University Medical School until 1967 when he was appointed professor at Dartmouth Medical School and scientific director of the Worcester Foundation for Experimental Biology in Shrewsbury, MA. In addition to his work on tRNA, Hoagland is known for his investigations on the carcinogenic effects of beryllium and the biosynthesis of coenzyme A. He was elected to the National Academy of Sciences in 1984 and currently writes about science for the public.

Nicole Kresge, Robert D. Simoni, and Robert L. Hill

REFERENCES

1. JBC Classics: Smith, E. L., and Bergmann, M. (1944) *J. Biol. Chem.* **153,** 627–651 (http://www.jbc.org/cgi/content/full/279/47/e6)
2. JBC Classics: Lipmann, F. (1945) *J. Biol. Chem.* **160,** 173–190 (http://www.jbc.org/cgi/content/full/280/21/e18)
3. Zamecnik, P. C., and Keller, E. B. (1954) Relation between phosphate energy donors and incorporation of labeled amino acids into proteins. *J. Biol. Chem.* **209,** 337–354
4. Hoagland, M. B., Keller, E. B., and Zamecnik, P.C. (1956) Enzymatic carboxyl activation of amino acids. *J. Biol.*

[1] All biographical information on Paul C. Zamecnik was taken from Refs. 5 to 7.

    Chem. **218,** 345–358

5. H. Mitchell (2000) Paul C. Zamecnik: Antisense Therapeutics (http://web.mit.edu/invent/iow/zamecnik.html) (An online collection of inventor profiles put together by the Lemelson-MIT Program)

6. Lasker Luminaries: Paul Zamecnik (http://www.laskerfoundation.org/awards/library/lumin_zp.html) (An online biography of Lasker Award recipients)

7. Zamecnik, P. (2005) From protein synthesis to genetic insertion. *Annu. Rev. Biochem.* **74,** 1–28

THE JOURNAL OF BIOLOGICAL CHEMISTRY
© 2005 by The American Society for Biochemistry and Molecular Biology, Inc.

Vol. 280, No. 41, Issue of October 14, p. e38, 2005
Printed in U.S.A.

Classics

A PAPER IN A SERIES REPRINTED TO CELEBRATE THE CENTENARY OF THE JBC IN 2005

JBC Centennial
1905–2005
100 Years of Biochemistry and Molecular Biology

The Discovery of Feedback Inhibition by Arthur B. Pardee

**Control of Pyrimidine Biosynthesis in *Escherichia coli* by a Feed-back Mechanism
(Yates, R. A., and Pardee, A. B. (1956) *J. Biol. Chem.* 221, 757–770)**

**The Enzymology of Control by Feedback Inhibition
(Gerhart, J. C., and Pardee, A. B. (1962) *J. Biol. Chem.* 237, 891–896)**

Arthur B. Pardee began his scientific training as an undergraduate at the University of California, Berkeley where he earned a Bachelor of Science degree in 1942. He then went on to the California Institute of Technology to do his Ph.D. with Linus Pauling, performing some of the first studies with purified antibodies. After earning his Ph.D. in 1947, Pardee took a Merck postdoctoral fellowship with Van Potter at the University of Wisconsin. Because his mother had died of cancer in 1942, Pardee was interested in doing what he could to contribute to cancer research. At Wisconsin, Pardee studied the deregulation of oxidative phosphorylation and the Krebs cycle in cancers using tissue homogenates.

In 1949 Pardee joined the faculty of the biochemistry department and the virus laboratory at the University of California, Berkeley. There he discovered the ribonucleoprotein particles in bacteria that were later named ribosomes as well as the photosynthetic particles that were named chromatophores. Wanting to learn whether virus infection alters host metabolism, he discovered that nine enzyme activities changed after *Escherichia coli* was infected with bacteriophage.

During the 1950s, when biochemists were busy creating a map of metabolism without regard to metabolic regulation, Pardee became interested in how bacteria were able to produce just the right amount of components necessary for growth. Along with Richard Yates, he discovered a general control mechanism for the pyrimidine pathway. This is the subject of the first *Journal of Biological Chemistry* (JBC) Classic reprinted here. Using pyrimidine-requiring mutants of *E. coli*, Pardee and Yates noted that the presence of uracil inhibited the formation of pyrimidine intermediates earlier than orotic acid (1). Following up on this observation, Pardee and Yates undertook additional *in vivo* and *in vitro* studies on *E. coli* pyrimidine-requiring mutants, which confirmed their initial observations. From these experiments, Pardee concluded that the end product of a biosynthetic pathway can be an inhibitor of its initial enzymatic reaction.

However, this molecular mechanism of feedback inhibition created a problem. At that time, it was generally thought that inhibitors compete with substrates for binding to the active site of the enzyme. Yet, end products and substrates often differed greatly in size, shape, and charge, so how could they compete for a site specific for the substrate, which would not be suited for binding the end product? This is the subject of the second JBC Classic reprinted here.

Pardee and John Gerhart approached this problem using aspartate transcarbamylase, an enzyme known to be inhibited by a nucleotide end product, which competes with a structurally unrelated substrate, an amino acid. They discovered that the enzyme was inhibited by cytidine triphosphate and that this inhibition was reversed by high concentrations of its substrate, aspartate. Because cytidine triphosphate had no structural similarity to aspartate, Pardee concluded that there must be a regulatory site distinct from the active site. This was confirmed by the observation that ATP activates aspartate transcarbamylase. ATP, which is not a

This paper is available on line at http://www.jbc.org

Arthur B. Pardee. Photo courtesy of the National Library of Medicine.

substrate, could not bind to the active site because this would be inhibitory, thus it must bind to a different, regulatory site.

Gerhart went on to separate the regulatory and catalytic subunits of aspartate transcarbamylase. Currently, Gerhart is an emeritus professor in the Department of Molecular and Cell Biology at the University of California, Berkeley, studying the early development of the amphibian *Xenopus laevis*. He has received several awards and honors for his research including the American Society for Cell Biology's E. B. Wilson Award (1997) and election to the National Academy of Sciences (1990).

After his studies on feedback inhibition, Pardee turned to the regulation of enzyme expression by repression, and his work became the basis for current concepts of the major mechanism for regulating gene expression in both prokaryotes and eukaryotes. Pardee moved to Princeton to become the first Chairman of the Biochemical Sciences Department in 1961. There, he began to investigate the differences between cancer cells and normal cells, including changes in transport and carbohydrates on the cell surfaces. He also studied the disregulation of the cell cycle in cancer and discovered that regulation for normal cells is exerted in late G_1 phase and that the restriction point requirements are relaxed in cancer cells, providing a basis for the greater proliferative capacity of cancer.

In 1975 Pardee moved to the Dana-Farber Cancer Institute and Harvard University. He served as Chief for the Division of Cell Growth and Regulation at the Dana-Farber Cancer Institute and became an emeritus professor in 1992. His current work focuses on finding methods for detecting cancer earlier and searching for novel agents to treat cancer more effectively. He and Peng Liang are credited with the discovery of the differential display technique, which is widely used in examining the activation of genes in cells. Pardee was elected to the National Academy of Sciences, the Institute of Medicine, and the American Academy of Arts and Sciences. He has served as president of the American Society of

Biochemistry and Molecular Biology and the American Association for Cancer Research. More information on Pardee's research can be found in his JBC Reflections (2).

Nicole Kresge, Robert D. Simoni, and Robert L. Hill

REFERENCES

1. Yates, R. A., and Pardee, A. B. (1956) Pyrimidine biosynthesis in *Escherichia coli. J. Biol. Chem.* **221,** 743–756
2. Pardee, A. B. (2002) Regulation, restriction, and reminiscences. *J. Biol. Chem.* **277,** 26709–26716

THE JOURNAL OF BIOLOGICAL CHEMISTRY
© 2005 by The American Society for Biochemistry and Molecular Biology, Inc.

Vol. 280, No. 42, Issue of October 21, p. e39, 2005
Printed in U.S.A.

Classics

A PAPER IN A SERIES REPRINTED TO CELEBRATE THE CENTENARY OF THE JBC IN 2005

JBC Centennial
1905–2005
100 Years of Biochemistry and Molecular Biology

Earl W. Sutherland's Discovery of Cyclic Adenine Monophosphate and the Second Messenger System

Formation of a Cyclic Adenine Ribonucleotide by Tissue Particles
(Rall, T. W., and Sutherland, E. W. (1958) *J. Biol. Chem.* 232, 1065–1076)

Fractionation and Characterization of a Cyclic Adenine Ribonucleotide Formed by Tissue Particles
(Sutherland, E. W., and Rall, T. W. (1958) *J. Biol. Chem.* 232, 1077–1092)

Earl Wilbur Sutherland, Jr. (1915–1974) was born in Burlingame, KS. After reading a book about Louis Pasteur in high school he decided to go into medical research. He obtained his B. S. from Washburn University in Topeka, KS in 1937 and his M.D. from the Washington University School of Medicine in St. Louis in 1942. He stayed at Washington University for the next 11 years, eventually obtaining the title of Associate Professor of Biochemistry. In 1953, Sutherland moved to Cleveland, OH, where he became professor and director of the pharmacology department at the Western Reserve School of Medicine and remained until 1963 when he became Professor of Physiology at the Vanderbilt University School of Medicine. In 1973 Sutherland moved to the University of Miami. There he was appointed Distinguished Professor of Biochemistry, a position he held until his death.

In 1958, while at Western Reserve, Sutherland made the discovery that would lead to his 1971 Nobel Prize in Physiology or Medicine "for his discoveries concerning the mechanisms of the action of hormones." It was at that time that Sutherland isolated a previously unknown compound, called cyclic adenine monophosphate (cAMP) and proved that it had an intermediary role in many hormonal functions. This is the subject of the two *Journal of Biological Chemistry* (JBC) Classics reprinted here. These two papers by Sutherland are the first in a series of three Nobel pieces of work on epinephrine and cAMP. The next Classic in the series will explain how Edwin Krebs and Edmond Fischer showed that epinephrine and cAMP stimulate glycogen breakdown by activating glycogen phosphorylase via a protein kinase. This will be followed by Classic papers by Alfred Gilman showing how epinephrine stimulates cAMP formation.

Sutherland started his studies on hormones at Washington University in collaboration with Nobel laureates Carl and Gerty Cori, who were the subjects of a previous JBC Classic (1). With the Coris, Sutherland investigated the mechanism by which epinephrine regulates the degradation of glycogen to glucose in the liver. He discovered that epinephrine acts by activating phosphorylase, which leads to the formation of glucose from glycogen.

After moving to Western Reserve, Sutherland, joined by Ted Rall, continued to study the epinephrine-phosphorylase system. They observed that the increased formation of phosphorylase in liver was mediated by a heat-stable factor. Chemical analysis showed that the compound was an adenine ribonucleotide, but its properties were unusual. Sutherland wrote to Leon Heppel hoping that he might be able to help elucidate its structure. Around the same time, David Lipkin wrote Heppel describing a new nucleotide that was produced by treating ATP with barium hydroxide. Heppel deduced that Sutherland and Lipkin were studying the same molecule, which turned out to be adenosine 3′,5′-monophosphate, now commonly referred to as cyclic AMP or cAMP.

In the first JBC Classic reprinted here, Sutherland and Rall discuss the conditions required for the formation of cAMP and its prevalence in various organs. They discovered that the

Earl W. Sutherland. Photo courtesy of the National Library of Medicine.

compound was present not only in liver preparations but also could be found in the heart, skeletal muscle, and brain. Using [8-^{14}C]ATP they also found that the formation of cAMP involves the cyclization of ATP. In the second JBC Classic reprinted here Sutherland and Rall describe the ion exchange purification and crystallization of cAMP as well as some of its properties.

Sutherland's discovery and chemical characterization of the cAMP intermediate or "second messenger" was of crucial importance for understanding the mechanism of action of epinephrine and of many other hormones. His discovery implied that epinephrine induces the formation of cAMP in the liver cells and that the nucleotide then converts the inactive phosphorylase to the active enzyme, which leads to the formation of glucose.

However, this gave rise to the question of how the hormone stimulates the formation of cAMP from AMP. Sutherland found that this took place by way of an enzyme he called adenyl cyclase. Thus, according to Sutherland's scheme, epinephrine binds to a cell surface receptor, which stimulates adenyl cyclase, causing the formation of cAMP, which then exerts its effect in the cell by activating phosphorylase. Sutherland later suggested that the effects of many other hormones could be explained on essentially similar lines and that the various hormones do not enter the cell but instead bind to surface receptors causing the formation of cAMP which then activates or inhibits various metabolic processes.

This general hypothesis was first met with strong criticism by scientists because it seemed to be impossible that a single substance could lead to the numerous effects caused by different hormones. However, eventually it was shown that a large number of polypeptide hormones do exert their effects by way of cAMP, and Sutherland was awarded the 1971 Nobel Prize.

In addition to the Noble Prize, Sutherland has received many honors for his research. He was elected to the National Academy of Sciences in 1966 and was awarded the National Medal of Science in 1973. Sutherland served on the National Institutes of Health Pharmacology Training Committee and the Arthritis and Metabolic Disease Program Committee. He was also active on the editorial boards of many journals, including *Biochemical Preparations* and the *Journal of Pharmacology and Experimental Therapeutics*.[1]

Nicole Kresge, Robert D. Simoni, and Robert L. Hill

REFERENCES

1. JBC Classics: Cori, C. F., and Cori, G. T. (1928) *J. Biol. Chem.* **79,** 321–341; Cori, G. T., Colowick, S. P., and Cori, C. F. (1938) *J. Biol. Chem.* **124,** 543–555; Cori, G. T., Colowick, S. P., and Cori, C. F. (1939) *J. Biol. Chem.* **127,** 771–782; Green, A. A., and Cori, G. T. (1943) *J. Biol. Chem.* **151,** 21–29; Cori, G. T., and Green, A. A. (1943) *J. Biol. Chem.* **151,** 31–38 (http://www.jbc.org/cgi/content/full/277/29/e18)
2. Sutherland, E. W. (1992) Studies on the mechanism of hormone action. *Nobel Lectures, Physiology or Medicine 1971–1980* (Lindsten, J., ed) World Scientific Publishing Co., Singapore

[1] All biographical information on Earl W. Sutherland was taken from Ref. 2.

THE JOURNAL OF BIOLOGICAL CHEMISTRY
© 2005 by The American Society for Biochemistry and Molecular Biology, Inc.

Vol. 280, No. 43, Issue of October 28, p. e40, 2005
Printed in U.S.A.

Classics

A PAPER IN A SERIES REPRINTED TO CELEBRATE THE CENTENARY OF THE JBC IN 2005

JBC Centennial
1905–2005
100 Years of Biochemistry and Molecular Biology

Reversible Phosphorylation and Kinase Cascades: the Work of Edwin G. Krebs

An Adenosine 3′,5′-Monophosphate-dependant Protein Kinase from Rabbit Skeletal Muscle
(Walsh, D. A., Perkins, J. P., and Krebs, E. G. (1968) *J. Biol. Chem.* 243, 3763–3765)

Multiple Components in an Epidermal Growth Factor-stimulated Protein Kinase Cascade. *In Vitro* **Activation of a Myelin Basic Protein/Microtubule-associated Protein 2 Kinase**
(Ahn, N. G., Seger, R., Bratlien, R. L., Diltz, C. D., Tonks, N. K., and Krebs, E. G. (1991) *J. Biol. Chem.* 266, 4220–4227)

Edwin Gerhard Krebs was born in Lansing, IA in 1918. In 1936, he entered the University of Illinois planning to major in a branch of science related to chemistry. By the beginning of his 4th year in college, he had narrowed his choices down to either getting an advanced degree in organic chemistry or going to medical school. After receiving a scholarship to attend the Washington University School of Medicine in St. Louis, he decided to become a physician. However, during his 4th year at the University of Illinois he carried out undergraduate research in organic chemistry and found it to be a fascinating experience. Although he continued on to medical school, this introduction to research influenced his medical training and was a strong factor in his eventual decision to become a research biochemist rather than a clinician.

The Washington University School of Medicine proved to be a place where Krebs could receive classical medical training and also participate in medical research. He undertook several research projects, first with Philip A. Schafer and later with Arda A. Green. It was during this period that Krebs first heard about phosphorylase, which was crystallized by Green and Carl and Gerty Cori, as reported in a previous *Journal of Biological Chemistry* (JBC) Classic (1). Green and the Coris found that phosphorylase exists in two forms, phosphorylase *a*, which was active without the addition of AMP, and phosphorylase *b*, which was inactive without AMP.

After graduating from medical school in 1943, Krebs completed an 18-month residency in internal medicine at Barnes Hospital in St. Louis and then became a medical officer in the navy. He was discharged in 1946 and returned to St. Louis with the idea of continuing his training in internal medicine. However, a 2-year-long waiting list for the residency program caused him instead to begin studying science. Because of his background in chemistry he chose to study biochemistry and was accepted by the Coris as a postdoctoral fellow. Krebs worked with the Coris for 2 years, investigating the interaction of protamine with rabbit muscle phosphorylase. He found the work so rewarding that he decided to continue doing research rather than returning to internal medicine.

In 1948, Krebs was invited to become an assistant professor of biochemistry at the University of Washington School of Medicine. Krebs had been in Seattle for 5 years when Edmond H. Fischer joined the department. Fischer had received his doctorate from the University of Geneva in 1947 studying potato phosphorylase. Because American universities offered more opportunities in the new field of biochemistry, Fischer moved to the United States to do a postdoctoral fellowship at the California Institute of Technology. He was then offered an

Edwin G. Krebs. Photo courtesy of the National Library of Medicine.

assistant professorship at the University of Washington where he began a long association with Krebs.

Together Krebs and Fischer decided to see if they could determine the mechanism by which the inactive phosphorylase *b* was converted to phosphorylase *a*. Based on the work of the Coris, Krebs and Fischer believed that a prosthetic group, which was some form of AMP, was involved in the activation of phosphorylase *b*. However, they soon discovered that the interconversion of phosphorylase was the result of an enzyme-catalyzed phosphorylation-dephosphorylation reaction. Similar work was being carried out on liver phosphorylase at approximately the same by Earl Sutherland. As discussed in a previous JBC Classic (2), Sutherland discovered the second messenger cyclic AMP (cAMP), which he showed promoted the phosphorylation and activation of phosphorylase. The way in which cAMP promoted phosphorylase activation was eventually elucidated when Krebs and Fischer discovered phosphorylase kinase, which was responsible for phosphorylating phosphorylase. Phosphorylase kinase itself existed in a highly activated phosphorylated form and a less active nonphosphorylated form.

Fischer and Krebs continued to work on their own specific areas related to phosphorylase. One of Krebs' projects was concerned with the molecular mechanism of action of cAMP in promoting phosphorylase activation via phosphorylase kinase. This was eventually determined when Krebs' postdoctoral fellow Donal A. Walsh discovered the cAMP-dependent protein kinase (PKA), which is the subject of the first JBC Classic reprinted here. Using rabbit skeletal muscle, Krebs, Walsh, and John P. Perkins isolated a protein kinase that activated phosphorylase kinase and was completely dependent on cAMP for its activity. Because PKA catalyzed the phosphorylation of proteins other than phosphorylase kinase, they proposed a general name rather than calling the new enzyme phosphorylase kinase kinase.

The discovery of PKA established the existence of the first protein kinase cascade in which one kinase activates another kinase. It also stimulated work on the protein phosphorylation process in general. Soon it became evident that reversible protein phosphorylation was a fundamental biological mechanism. By the 1970s biochemical research on protein phosphorylation was so extensive that 5% of papers in biology journals dealt with the subject. As a result of the significance of their discovery, Krebs and Fischer were awarded the 1992 Nobel Prize in Physiology or Medicine "for their discoveries concerning reversible protein phosphorylation as a biological regulatory mechanism."

In 1968 Krebs left the University of Washington to assume the position of founding chairman of the Department of Biological Chemistry at the University of California, Davis. He stayed in California for 8 years and continued to work on PKA. Krebs then returned to the University of Washington as chairman of the Department of Pharmacology. He was also a Howard Hughes Medical Institute Investigator from 1977 to 1990. Currently, he is a Professor Emeritus in the Department of Biochemistry at the University of Washington.

During this second period at the University of Washington, Krebs became interested in protein tyrosine phosphorylation and the mechanism of action of growth factors. In the 1970s it was established that proteins can be phosphorylated on tyrosine as well as on serine and threonine and that protein-tyrosine kinases (PTKs) often acted as receptors for growth factors. Because many cellular responses to growth factors whose receptors were PTKs were mediated by changes in serine/threonine phosphorylation, Krebs wanted to know how protein tyrosine phosphorylation was coupled to protein serine/threonine phosphorylation.

He approached the problem by working upstream from the effect of growth factors on the phosphorylation of the ribosomal protein S6, which is phosphorylated on serine residues in response to PTK receptors. Krebs showed that a growth factor-stimulated mitogen-activated protein (MAP) kinase could phosphorylate and activate an S6 kinase. MAP kinase itself appeared to be activated by serine/threonine phosphorylation, suggesting the existence of a third protein-serine/threonine kinase in this growth factor-stimulated process. In the second JBC Classic reprinted here, Krebs, along with Natalie Ahn, demonstrates the existence of two separable activating factors that catalyze the activation of an inactive form of MAP kinase. Eventually these activating factors were shown to be MAP kinase kinases. Based on this research, Krebs established what is now known as the MAP kinase cascade.

Recognition for Krebs' work on phosphorylation came from various awards and honors in addition to the Nobel Prize. He received the Whitaker Foundation's George W. Thorn Award (1983), the American Heart Association's Research Achievement Award (1987), the FASEB 3M Award (1989), the Albert Lasker Award for Basic Medical Research (1989), and the Robert A. Welch Award in Chemistry (1991). Krebs was also president of the American Society for Biological Chemists in 1985 and was an Associate Editor for the JBC from 1972 to 1993 and a member of the JBC editorial board from 1965 to 1970. He was also elected to the National Academy of Sciences and the American Academy of Arts and Sciences.[1]

Fischer also continues to do research at the University of Washington as an Emeritus Professor. He has received many honors for his scientific research over the course of his long career including election to the American Academy of Arts and Sciences and the National Academy of Sciences. Fischer was awarded the Werner Medal from the Swiss Chemical Society (1952), the Lederle Medical Faculty Award, the Prix Jaubert from the University of Geneva, and jointly with Krebs, the Senior Passano Award and the Steven C. Beering Award from Indiana University.[2]

Nicole Kresge, Robert D. Simoni, and Robert L. Hill

REFERENCES

1. JBC Classics: Cori, C. F., and Cori, G. T. (1928) *J. Biol. Chem.* **79,** 321–341; Cori, G. T., Colowick, S. P., and Cori, C. F. (1938) *J. Biol. Chem.* **124,** 543–555; Cori, G. T., Colowick, S. P., and Cori, C. F. (1939) *J. Biol. Chem.* **127,** 771–782; Green, A. A., and Cori, G. T. (1943) *J. Biol. Chem.* **151,** 21–29; Cori, G. T., and Green, A. A. (1943) *J. Biol. Chem.* **151,** 31–38 (http://www.jbc.org/cgi/content/full/277/29/e18)
2. JBC Classics: Rall, T. W., and Sutherland, E. W. (1958) *J. Biol. Chem.* **232,** 1065–1076; Sutherland, E. W., and Rall, T. W. (1958) *J. Biol. Chem.* **232,** 1077–1092 (http://www.jbc.org/cgi/content/full/280/42/e39)
3. Krebs, E. G. (1993) *Edwin G. Krebs — autobiography. Les Prix Nobel. The Nobel Prizes 1992* (Frängsmyr, T., ed) Stockholm
4. Krebs, E. G. (1998) An accidental biochemist. *Annu. Rev. Biochem.* **67,** xiii–xxxii
5. Fischer, E. H. (1993) *Edmond H. Fischer — autobiography. Les Prix Nobel. The Nobel Prizes 1992* (Frängsmyr, T., ed) Stockholm

---

[1] All biographical information on Edwin G. Krebs was taken from Refs. 3 and 4.
[2] All biographical information on Edmond H. Fischer was taken from Ref. 5.

THE JOURNAL OF BIOLOGICAL CHEMISTRY
© 2005 by The American Society for Biochemistry and Molecular Biology, Inc.

Vol. 280, No. 44, Issue of November 4, p. e41, 2005
Printed in U.S.A.

Classics

A PAPER IN A SERIES REPRINTED TO CELEBRATE THE CENTENARY OF THE JBC IN 2005

JBC Centennial
1905–2005
100 Years of Biochemistry and Molecular Biology

The Regulation of Adenyl Cyclase by G-protein: the Work of Alfred G. Gilman

Resolution of Some Components of Adenylate Cyclase Necessary for Catalytic Activity
(Ross, E. M., and Gilman, A. G. (1977) *J. Biol. Chem.* 252, 6966–6969)

Reconstitution of Hormone-sensitive Adenylate Cyclase Activity with Resolved Components of the Enzyme
(Ross, E. M., Howlett, A. C., Ferguson, K. M., and Gilman, A. G. (1978) *J. Biol. Chem.* 253, 6401–6412)

This is the third and final *Journal of Biological Chemistry* (JBC) Classic in a series of Nobel pieces of work on epinephrine and cAMP. The first Classic described Earl Sutherland's discovery of cyclic AMP and its formation by adenyl cyclase (1). These findings led Sutherland to speculate that epinephrine binds to a cell surface receptor, which stimulates adenyl cyclase, causing the formation of cyclic AMP, which then exerts its effect in the cell by activating phosphorylase. The next two Classics fill in the gaps in Sutherland's scheme. The second Classic told the story of Edwin Krebs' discovery of cyclic AMP-dependent protein kinase, the enzyme that is stimulated by cyclic AMP to activate phosphorylase (2). This third Classic explains how Alfred Gilman discovered that hormone receptors stimulate adenyl cyclase via G-protein. Together, these three Classics provide an excellent overview of how hormone signaling cascades were first elucidated.

Alfred Goodman Gilman was born in 1941 in New Haven, CT. At the time, his father, Alfred A. Gilman, was on the faculty of the Department of Pharmacology at the Yale Medical School. The bulk of Gilman's childhood was spent in White Plains, a suburb of New York City, while his father was first on the faculty of The College of Physicians and Surgeons of Columbia University and then was the founding Chairman of Pharmacology at the new Albert Einstein College of Medicine. Due to his father's influence, Gilman majored in biochemistry at Yale University. He graduated in 1962.

The summer after college Gilman worked in Allan Conney's lab at Burroughs Wellcome in New York and published his first two papers. This experience thoroughly convinced him to do research, and he headed off to Case Western Reserve University in Cleveland in the fall of 1962 enrolled in a novel M D.-Ph. D. program. He initially intended to work with his father's friend, Earl Sutherland, on cyclic AMP. However, shortly after his arrival, Sutherland left for Vanderbilt University. Instead, Gilman worked with Sutherland's collaborator, Theodore Rall, who played a pivotal role in Sutherland's discovery of cyclic AMP and adenyl cyclase, as related in a previous JBC Classic (1). In Rall's lab, Gilman worked on cyclic AMP in the thyroid gland, marking the beginning of his long research career in cyclic nucleotide research.

In 1969 Gilman moved to Bethesda, MD to do a 3-year postdoctoral fellowship with Marshall Nirenberg at the National Institute of General Medical Sciences. There, he developed a simple and sensitive assay for cyclic AMP, which helped make second messengers accessible to everyone. Gilman then became an Assistant Professor of Pharmacology at the University of Virginia in Charlottesville in 1971 and continued to work on cyclic AMP and adenyl cyclase.

According to Sutherland's experiments, the binding of epinephrine and other hormones to cell surface receptors stimulated adenyl cyclase, causing the formation of cyclic AMP, which then exerted its effects in the cell through additional signaling cascades. This gave rise to the

This paper is available on line at http://www.jbc.org

Alfred Gilman at the 1994 Nobel Prize awards.

question of how the cell surface receptors interacted with adenyl cyclase. Martin Rodbell proposed that a transducer acted as an intermediary between receptors and adenyl cyclase, and he also showed that guanosine triphosphate (GTP) needed to be present in order for hormones to activate the enzyme. In Gilman's lab, they were working on solubilizing and purifying the components of hormone-sensitive adenyl cyclase systems. Unfortunately, hormonal responsiveness was quickly lost when detergents were used for solubilization, and adenyl cyclase itself seemed to be very labile.

The turning point for Gilman came when Gordon Tomkins developed S49 cells, which were killed by cyclic AMP, and Henry Bourne subsequently produced a variant (cyc⁻) of these cells that appeared to lack adenyl cyclase. Elliot Ross, a new postdoctoral fellow in Gilman's lab, was able to reconstitute the cyc⁻ mutant *in vitro* by adding adenyl cyclase extracts to the cyc⁻ membranes. However, as reported in the first JBC Classic reprinted here, Gilman and Ross discovered that when they inactivated the adenyl cyclase in the detergent extract, they were still able to use it to restore complete activity in the cyc⁻ membranes. Treatment with proteases revealed that both the detergent extract and the cyc⁻ membranes contained proteins necessary for adenyl cyclase activity. These observations led to their proposal that two proteins were required for adenyl cyclase activity, one contained in the detergent extract and one in the cyc⁻ membranes.

In the second JBC Classic Gilman and Ross, along with Allyn Howlett and Kenneth Ferguson, show that the cyc⁻ membranes contain adenyl cyclase (their adenyl cyclase-deficient phenotype reflects their loss of the other protein components of the system) and that the detergent extract contains a regulatory protein. Gilman and his co-workers also note that the regulatory protein contains two functional components. They proposed that the role of the hormone receptor was to regulate the interaction between adenyl cyclase and the regulatory protein.

This regulatory protein became the central focus of the Gilman laboratory. They soon discovered that the protein was a homogenous guanine nucleotide-binding protein, capable of activating adenyl cyclase in its Gpp(NH)p or fluoride-activated forms. The signal-coupling protein was named G-protein. Eventually, it was determined that a hormone-activated receptor triggers the exchange of GTP for bound GDP in the G-protein, causing a conformational change, which induces the dissociation of its α subunit bearing GTP from its $\beta\gamma$ subunit.

Adenyl cyclase is then activated by Gα-GTP. The GTP bound to the α subunit is eventually hydrolyzed to GDP, and the subunits reassociate.

After Gilman's initial discoveries, it became abundantly clear that the G-protein family plays an essential transducing role in linking hundreds of cell surface receptors to effector proteins at the plasma membrane. The systems are widely used in nature, controlling processes ranging from mating in yeast to cognition in humans. Because of the profound significance of his work, Gilman was awarded the 1994 Nobel Prize in Physiology or Medicine with Rodbell "for their discovery of G-proteins and the role of these proteins in signal transduction in cells."

In 1981, Gilman moved to Dallas to chair the Department of Pharmacology at the University of Texas Southwestern Medical Center. Today, he still chairs this department. He also holds the Raymond and Ellen Willie Distinguished Chair of Molecular Neuropharmacology.

In addition to his research endeavors, Gilman was the primary editor (in 1980, 1985, and 1990) of a well known pharmacology textbook, *The Pharmacological Basis of Therapeutics*, that was started by his father and Louis S. Goodman. Gilman also served on the JBC Editorial Board. He has received a number of honors and awards for his work including the Richard Lounsbery Award (The National Academy of Sciences, 1987), the American Association of Medical Colleges Award for Distinguished Research in the Biomedical Sciences (1988), the Albert Lasker Basic Medical Research Award (1989), the Passano Foundation Award (1990), the American Heart Association Basic Science Research Prize (1990), and the Louis S. Goodman and Alfred Gilman Award in Drug Receptor Pharmacology (American Society of Pharmacology & Experimental Therapeutics, 1990). Additionally, Gilman was elected to the National Academy of Sciences (1986), The American Academy of Arts & Sciences (1988), and the Institute of Medicine of the National Academy of Sciences (1989).[1]

Nicole Kresge, Robert D. Simoni, and Robert L. Hill

REFERENCES

1. JBC Classics: Rall, T. W., and Sutherland, E. W. (1958) *J. Biol. Chem.* **232,** 1065–1076; Sutherland, E. W., and Rall, T. W. (1958) *J. Biol. Chem.* **232,** 1077–1092 (http://www.jbc.org/cgi/content/full/280/42/e39)
2. JBC Classics: Walsh, D. A., Perkins, J. P., and Krebs, E. G. (1968) *J. Biol. Chem.* **243,** 3763–3765; Ahn, N. G., Seger, R., Bratlien, R. L., Diltz, C. D., Tonks, N. K., and Krebs, E. G. (1991) *J. Biol. Chem.* **266,** 4220–4227 (http://www.jbc.org/cgi/content/full/280/43/e40)
3. Gilman, A. G. (1995) Alfred G. Gilman—autobiography. *Les Prix Nobel. The Nobel Prizes 1994* (Frängsmyr, T., ed) Stockholm
4. Gilman, A. G. (1997) G proteins and regulation of adenylyl cyclase. *Nobel Lectures, Physiology or Medicine 1991–1995* (Ringertz, N., ed) World Scientific Publishing Co., Singapore

---

[1] All biographical information on Alfred G. Gilman was taken from Refs. 3 and 4.

THE JOURNAL OF BIOLOGICAL CHEMISTRY
© 2005 by The American Society for Biochemistry and Molecular Biology, Inc.

Vol. 280, No. 45, Issue of November 11, p. e42, 2005
Printed in U.S.A.

Classics

A PAPER IN A SERIES REPRINTED TO CELEBRATE THE CENTENARY OF THE JBC IN 2005

JBC Centennial
1905–2005
100 Years of Biochemistry and Molecular Biology

Amino Acyl Ribonucleic Acid Formation and Recombinant DNA Technology: the Work of Paul Berg

The Enzymic Synthesis of Amino Acyl Derivatives of Ribonucleic Acid. I. The Mechanism of Leucyl-, Valyl-, Isoleucyl-, and Methionyl Ribonucleic Acid Formation
(Berg, P., Bergmann, F. H., Ofengand, E. J., and Dieckmann, M. (1961) *J. Biol. Chem.* **236,** 1726–1734)

The Enzymic Synthesis of Amino Acyl Derivatives of Ribonucleic Acid. II. The Preparation of Leucyl-, Valyl-, Isoleucyl-, and Methionyl Ribonucleic Acid Synthetases from *Escherichia coli*
(Bergmann, F. H., Berg, P., and Dieckmann, M. (1961) *J. Biol. Chem.* **236,** 1735–1740)

The Enzymic Synthesis of Amino Acyl Derivatives of Ribonucleic Acid. III. Isolation of Amino Acid-Acceptor Ribonucleic Acids from *Escherichia coli*
(Ofengand, E. J., Dieckmann, M., and Berg, P. (1961) *J. Biol. Chem.* **236,** 1741–1747)

Paul Berg was born in New York in 1926. By the time he reached junior high school he had already made up his mind to become a scientist, in part because of reading books about medical scientists such as *Arrowsmith* by Sinclair Lewis and *Microbe Hunters* by Paul DeKruif. Berg graduated from high school in 1943 and enrolled at New York's City College to study chemical engineering. However, chemical engineering soon lost its appeal, and Berg became interested in the chemical events that were involved in biological systems. He transferred to Pennsylvania State University, and after a 3-year hitch in the Navy during World War II, he completed his undergraduate degree at Penn State in biochemistry in 1948.

Inspired by several papers on using radioisotopes as tracers to study intermediary metabolism, Berg began graduate work at Western Reserve University in Cleveland, OH, where that work was being done. His doctoral thesis was on C1 metabolism, particularly the conversion of formate and formaldehyde to the methyl groups of methionine. After earning his Ph.D. in 1952, Berg spent a year in Copenhagen studying with Herman Kalckar at the Institute of Cytophysiology where he and Wolfgang Joklik discovered a new enzyme that created the nucleoside triphosphates for nucleic acid assembly. He then went to Washington University in St. Louis to study with Arthur Kornberg, who will be featured in a future *Journal of Biological Chemistry* (JBC) Classic. In St. Louis, Berg was able to establish a new mechanism for converting fatty acids into their activated forms (acyl-CoAs). He then discovered that the same type of reaction was also central to the activation of amino acids as aminoacyl adenylates prior to being linked to tRNAs. This led him to the discovery of aminoacyl-tRNA synthetases, which is the subject of the three Classics reprinted here that appeared back-to-back in one issue of the JBC.

The first Classic deals with Berg's investigations into the mechanism of aminoacyl ribonucleic acid formation. Using preparations of amino acid-acceptor RNA and ^{14}C-labeled amino acids, Berg determined that the *Escherichia coli* enzymes, which form leucyl, valyl, isoleucyl, and methionyl adenylates, also catalyze the formation of the corresponding aminoacyl ribonucleic acid derivatives. He also found that the amino acids are bound via their carboxyl groups to the terminal nucleotide of acceptor RNAs specific for the amino acids and that the synthesis of aminoacyl ribonucleic acid derivatives is reversible. In the second Classic Berg describes the purification and characterization of the leucyl, valyl, isoleucyl, and methionyl

Paul Berg. Photo courtesy of the Office of NIH History, National Institutes of Health.

ribonucleic acid synthetases from *E. coli* that he used in the experiments in the first paper. The final JBC Classic provides details on Berg's procedure for isolating amino acid acceptor-RNA from *E. coli* and describes some of the physical and chemical properties of the purified RNA.

Eventually, Berg was promoted to Associate Professor of Microbiology at Washington University. However, in 1959 he left St. Louis to accept the position of professor of biochemistry at Stanford University School of Medicine. As his interests shifted from studies with microorganisms to mammalian cells, he spent a year experimenting with polyoma and SV40 tumor viruses in mammalian cell culture with Renato Dulbecco at the Salk Institute. Upon his return to Stanford, Berg decided to try to use SV40 to introduce new genes into mammalian cells. He and his colleagues succeeded in developing a method to splice two DNA molecules together *in vitro* and were able to insert a set of three genes responsible for metabolizing galactose in *E. coli* into the SV40 DNA genome. This work led to the emergence of recombinant DNA technology and provided a major tool for analyzing mammalian gene structure and function. As a result of this work and his previous work on nucleic acids, Berg shared the 1980 Nobel Prize in Chemistry with Walter Gilbert and Frederick Sanger "for fundamental studies of the biochemistry of nucleic acids, with particular regard to recombinant-DNA."

Concerned about the potential health and environmental risks of some genetic engineering experiments, Berg and a group of colleagues published in the journal *Science* (1) what became known as the "Berg Letter," which called for the deferral of certain kinds of recombinant DNA experimentation. The ensuing Asilomar Conference, which emphasized that recombinant DNA technology held great promise for genetics and biomedical research, made more specific recommendations for conducting that research safely. Berg then headed a nationwide effort to ensure proper laboratory practices by scientists working in the field. Recently, he has been an articulate and effective spokesman for stem cell research and helped lead the successful campaign for Proposition 71, the California Stem Cell Initiative. This Proposition approves $300 million per year for stem cell research in California and circumvents federal restrictions.

Today, Berg remains at Stanford University as an Emeritus Professor. In addition to the Nobel Prize, he has received many honors for his research. He was awarded the American Chemical Society's Eli Lilly Prize in biochemistry (1959), the V. D. Mattia Award of the Roche Institute of Molecular Biology (1972), the Albert Lasker Basic Medical Research Award (1980), and the National Medal of Science (1983). Berg was also president of the American Society of Biological Chemists in 1975.[1]

Nicole Kresge, Robert D. Simoni, and Robert L. Hill

[1] All biographical information on Paul Berg was taken from Refs. 2 and 3.

REFERENCES

1. Berg, P., Baltimore, D., Boyer, H. W., Cohen, S. N., Davis, R. W., Hogness, D. S., Nathans, D., Roblin, R., Watson, J. D., Weissman, W., and Zinder, N. D. (1974) Potential biohazards of recombinant DNA molecules. *Science* **185**, 303

2. Berg, P. (2004) Paul Berg—autobiography. Nobel Prize website (http://nobelprize.org/chemistry/laureates/1980/berg-autobio.html)

3. Berg, P. (1993) Dissections and reconstructions of genes and chromosomes. *Nobel Lectures, Chemistry 1971–1980* (Frängsmyr, T., ed) World Scientific Publishing Co., Singapore

THE JOURNAL OF BIOLOGICAL CHEMISTRY
© 2005 by The American Society for Biochemistry and Molecular Biology, Inc.

Vol. 280, No. 46, Issue of November 18, p. e43, 2005
Printed in U.S.A.

Classics

A PAPER IN A SERIES REPRINTED TO CELEBRATE THE CENTENARY OF THE JBC IN 2005

JBC Centennial
1905–2005
100 Years of Biochemistry and Molecular Biology

Using Tryptophan Synthase to Prove Gene-Protein Colinearity: the Work of Charles Yanofsky

The Enzymatic Conversion of Anthranilic Acid to Indole
(Yanofsky, C. (1956) *J. Biol. Chem.* 223, 171–184)

A Genetic and Biochemical Analysis of Second Site Reversion
(Helinski, D. R., and Yanofsky, C. (1963) *J. Biol. Chem.* 238, 1043–1048)

Studies on the Position of Six Amino Acid Substitutions in the Tryptophan Synthetase A Protein
(Carlton, B. C., and Yanofsky, C. (1963) *J. Biol. Chem.* 238, 2390–2392)

Amino Acid Substitutions in the A Proteins of Tryptophan Synthetase Mutants and Revertants
(Carlton, B. C., and Yanofsky, C. (1965) *J. Biol. Chem.* 240, 690–693)

The Amino Acid Sequence of the A Protein (α Subunit) of the Tryptophan Synthetase of *Escherichia coli*. V. Order of Tryptic Peptides and the Complete Amino Acid Sequence
(Guest, J. R., Drapeau, G. R., Carlton, B. C., and Yanofsky, C. (1967) *J. Biol. Chem.* 242, 5442–5446)

Charles Yanofsky was born in New York City in 1925 and was one of the early graduates of the Bronx High School of Science. In 1942, he entered the City College of New York to major in biochemistry, but his education was interrupted by his service in the Army during World War II, including active combat in the Battle of the Bulge. He eventually earned a bachelor's degree in 1948 and decided to go to graduate school to explore gene-enzyme relationships using *Neurospora crassa*. He went to Yale University, hoping to work with Edward Tatum. However, Tatum had just left Yale to return to Stanford University. Fortunately, Tatum's research associate, David Bonner, stayed on at Yale and took over the direction of Tatum's remaining group. Yanofsky joined Bonner's lab and earned his master's and doctoral degrees in microbiology in 1950 and 1951, respectively.

Stimulated by the "one gene, one protein" hypothesis put forward by George Beadle and Edward Tatum, which was the subject of a previous *Journal of Biological Chemistry* (JBC) Classic (1), Bonner's lab was focused on establishing the nature of the gene-enzyme relationship by examining *Neurospora* enzymes that appeared to be defective or missing in specific mutants. Yanofsky was involved in a project using niacin-requiring mutants to identify all the intermediates in the niacin pathway. The idea was to eventually exploit this knowledge in investigations on gene-enzyme relationships. Yanofsky was able to identify two intermediates accumulated by the mutants, quinolinic acid and a derivative of kynurenine. However, in his third and last year of graduate school, Yanofsky abandoned his niacin pathway studies and joined the rest of the lab in their attempt to prove the one gene, one protein hypothesis by demonstrating that all mutants altered at a single genetic locus lacked the specific enzyme that catalyzed the corresponding reaction. Having spent several years studying niacin and tryptophan metabolism in *Neurospora*, Yanofsky decided to investigate tryptophan synthase,[1]

---

[1] This enzyme was initially named tryptophan desmolase, then tryptophan synthetase, and finally tryptophan synthase.

This paper is available on line at http://www.jbc.org

Photo of Charles Yanofsky.

the only enzyme of the tryptophan pathway that had been identified experimentally. He was able to show that two tryptophan-requiring mutants lacked tryptophan synthase activity. Other members of the lab joined in, and soon they had isolated 20 additional mutants that were altered at the same locus—each lacked tryptophan synthase activity.

In 1954, Yanofsky moved to Western Reserve University Medical School in Cleveland, Ohio to become an Assistant Professor of Microbiology. He decided to shift his research objectives to a well defined problem for which he could easily determine answers. He chose to focus on determining the missing reactions in the tryptophan biosynthetic pathway, which is the subject of the first JBC Classic reprinted here. At the time the paper was published, only two intermediates in the tryptophan pathway had been identified, anthranilate and indole. In this paper, Yanofsky uses a tryptophan auxotroph of *Escherichia coli* as a source for enzymes that convert anthranilic acid to indole. Using ammonium sulfate he was able to separate two fractions that catalyze successive reactions in the conversion of anthranilic acid to indole. One fraction catalyzed the formation of indole-3-glycerol phosphate from anthranilic acid and 5-phosphoribosyl-1-pyrophosphate, and the other fraction converted indole glycerol phosphate to indole and triose phosphate. With the aid of his graduate student Oliver Smith, Yanofsky was eventually able to identify several more intermediates in tryptophan synthesis including phosphoribosyl anthranilate and carboxyphenylamino-1-deoxyribulose 5-phosphate.

In 1958 Yanofsky was persuaded to join the Biological Sciences Department at Stanford University. There, he decided to mount an all out effort to establish or disprove gene-protein colinearity. Continuing on with tryptophan synthase, Yanofsky and his postdoctoral fellow Irving Crawford established that the enzyme is composed of non-identical polypeptide chains. One subunit, TrpA, hydrolyzes indole glycerol phosphate to indole, and the second subunit, TrpB, covalently joins indole and L-serine to form L-tryptophan. This was the first demonstration that an enzyme could contain two dissimilar subunits. Yanofsky and Crawford also discovered that each subunit activates the other, suggesting that TrpA mutants could be isolated and their altered TrpA proteins assayed by measuring their ability to activate the TrpB subunit. Using this assay to purify TrpA mutant proteins, Yanofsky and his co-workers then identified the single amino acid changes in the mutant proteins and compared the positions of the amino acid changes with the order of the corresponding altered sites on a fine structure genetic map of the *trpA* gene. The second through fourth Classic reprinted here deal with these TrpA experiments.

In the second Classic, Yanofsky determines the position of six amino acid substitutions in TrpA proteins derived from revertants of two *trpA* mutants. All six changes were found at the same amino acid position in the protein. This study was a prelude to establishing colinearity and specific features of the genetic code. The third Classic is a study in which the amino acid change in the TrpA protein of a second site revertant was determined. It was the initial demonstration that a second amino acid change in a protein could reverse the effects of a primary amino acid change. The details of the peptide isolation and sequence analyses with wild type and mutant TrpA proteins are presented in the fourth Classic. This paper once and for all established gene-protein colinearity in the *trpA* gene and TrpA protein of *E. coli*.

Because thoroughness was part of his strategy, the Yanofsky group continued sequencing TrpA until its entire sequence had been determined. This was a huge accomplishment considering the procedures of protein chemistry available at that time. They published the detailed analysis that led to the determination of the complete amino acid sequence of TrpA in a series of five papers in one issue of the JBC (2–5). The final JBC Classic reprinted here is the final paper in the series, and it presents the complete amino acid sequence of the protein. There is one error in the sequence: Ile-36 was subsequently shown to be double Ile (Ile-36–Ile-37); thus the polypeptide has 268 rather than 267 amino acid residues.

Yanofsky was appointed Herzstein Professor of Biology in 1967 and remains at Stanford today as an Emeritus Professor. The focus of his research continues to be the control of gene expression, in particular the molecular regulatory mechanisms of bacterial transcription. He has received numerous awards including the Albert Lasker Award in Basic Medical Research, the Genetics Society of America Medal, and the 2003 National Medal of Science. He was elected to the American Academy of Arts and Sciences in 1964 and the National Academy of Sciences in 1966. Yanofsky is past president of the American Society of Biological Chemists and of the Genetics Society of America and was a Career Investigator of the American Heart Association. In 1980, he and other Stanford scientists founded DNAX, a Palo Alto-based research institute now owned by Schering-Plough Corp. More detailed information on Yanofsky's research can be found in his JBC Reflections (6).[2]

Nicole Kresge, Robert D. Simoni, and Robert L. Hill

REFERENCES

1. JBC Classics: Beadle, G. W. (1944) *J. Biol. Chem.* **156,** 683–690 (http://www.jbc.org/cgi/content/full/280/12/e9)
2. Guest, J. R., Carlton, B. C., and Yanofsky, C. (1967) The amino acid sequence of the A protein (α subunit) of the tryptophan synthetase of *Escherichia coli*. I. Tryptic peptides. *J. Biol. Chem.* **242,** 5397–5412
3. Drapeau, G. R., and Yanofsky, C. (1967) The amino acid sequence of the A protein (α subunit) of the tryptophan synthetase of *Escherichia coli*. II. Amino acid sequences of two large tryptic peptides. *J. Biol. Chem.* **242,** 5413–5421
4. Carlton, B. C., Guest, J. R., and Yanofsky, C. (1967) The amino acid sequence of the A protein (α subunit) of the tryptophan synthetase of *Escherichia coli*. III. The chymotryptic peptides. *J. Biol. Chem.* **242,** 5422–5433
5. Drapeau, G. R., and Yanofsky, C. (1967) The amino acid sequence of the A protein (α subunit) of the tryptophan synthetase of *Escherichia coli*. IV. The cyanogen bromide fragments of the A protein. *J. Biol. Chem.* **242,** 5434–5441
6. Yanofsky, C. (2003) Using studies on tryptophan metabolism to answer basic biological questions. *J. Biol. Chem.* **278,** 10859–10878

---

[2] All biographical information on Charles Yanofsky was taken from Ref. 6.

THE JOURNAL OF BIOLOGICAL CHEMISTRY
© 2005 by The American Society for Biochemistry and Molecular Biology, Inc.

Vol. 280, No. 47, Issue of November 25, p. e44, 2005
Printed in U.S.A.

Classics

A PAPER IN A SERIES REPRINTED TO CELEBRATE THE CENTENARY OF THE JBC IN 2005

JBC Centennial
1905–2005
100 Years of Biochemistry and Molecular Biology

Pioneering the Field of Oxygenases through the Study of Tryptophan Metabolism: the Work of Osamu Hayaishi

Studies on Oxygenases. Enzymatic Formation of Kynurenine from Tryptophan
(Hayaishi, O., Rothberg, S., Mehler, A. H., and Saito, Y. (1957) *J. Biol. Chem.* **229,** 889–896)

Studies on Oxygenases. Pyrocatechase
(Hayaishi, O., Katagiri, M., and Rothberg, S. (1957) *J. Biol. Chem.* **229,** 905–920)

Osamu Hayaishi was born in Stockton, California in 1920. Three years later, he and his family moved to Osaka, Japan. Hayaishi graduated from the Osaka University School of Medicine in 1942 and then served as a medical officer in the Japanese Navy for 3 years. After the war, he returned to Osaka to find a city that was totally demolished. His family home had disappeared, food was scarce, and supplies of most commodities, gas, electricity, and water, were extremely limited. Despite these conditions, Hayaishi decided to remain in Osaka and joined the Department of Bacteriology, in the Institute of Microbial Diseases, at the Osaka University School of Medicine. He earned his Ph.D. in 1949.

At Osaka, Hayaishi was given several grams of tryptophan, kynurenine, and other related compounds by Yashiro Kotake, who had isolated and characterized kynurenine, a key intermediate in tryptophan metabolism in mammals and microorganisms. Because research funds were limited, facilities were poor, chemicals were scarce, and there were no laboratory animals, Hayaishi decided to use microorganisms in his experiments. He dug up some soil samples from the backyard of the Institute and mixed them with tryptophan and water in a test tube. After a few days he observed some cloudiness in the supernatant. Thus, using a simple enrichment culture technique Hayaishi was able to isolate several strains of soil bacteria that could grow on tryptophan as their sole source of carbon and nitrogen.

At that time, it was known that in mammals tryptophan was degraded through kynurenine to kynurenic acid, anthranilic acid, and xanthurenic acid. However, using his soil isolates Hayaishi showed that in microorganisms anthranilic acid was further metabolized into catechol, then to muconic acid, and ultimately oxidized to CO_2, ammonia, and H_2O. Hayaishi isolated and purified the enzyme that catalyzed the oxidative cleavage of the aromatic ring in catechol to produce *cis,cis*-muconic acid. Because two atoms of oxygen were consumed in the reaction, he assumed that the oxygen atoms were incorporated into catechol and named the enzyme pyrocatechase instead of catechol oxidase.

In 1949 Hayaishi received a letter from David E. Green offering him a postdoctoral fellowship at the Enzyme Institute at the University of Wisconsin in Madison. He accepted the position and worked with Green for a year. Next, Hayaishi moved to Bethesda, Maryland to join Arthur Kornberg (who will be featured in a future *Journal of Biological Chemistry* (JBC) Classic) at the National Institute of Arthritis and Metabolic Diseases at the National Institutes of Health (NIH). He worked with Kornberg for 2 years on the bacterial degradation of uracil and characterized the intermediate products, malonyl-CoA and acetyl-CoA. Then Kornberg moved to St. Louis to chair the Department of Microbiology at the Washington University School of Medicine and asked Hayaishi to accompany him as an assistant professor. Hayaishi moved to St. Louis in 1952 but then returned to Bethesda to be Chief of the Section on Toxicology in the Laboratory of Pharmacology and Toxicology at the National Institute of Arthritis and Metabolic Diseases in 1954.

Osamu Hayaishi. Reprinted with permission from the *Annual Review of Biochemistry,* Vol. 63.
©1994 by Annual Reviews, www.annualreviews.org.

During this time at the NIH, Hayaishi decided to revisit tryptophan metabolism. The first step of tryptophan degradation was known to involve the oxidation of L-tryptophan to formylkynurenine followed by its hydrolysis to L-kynurenine and formate. The overall reaction resulted in the incorporation of three oxygen atoms, two into formylkynurenine during oxidation and one into formate during hydrolysis. Enlisting the aid of Simon Rothberg, a mass spectroscopist at the NIH, and enzymologist Masayuki Katagiri, Hayaishi investigated the mechanism of tryptophan oxidation with $^{18}O_2$ and $H_2^{18}O$. This is the subject of the first JBC Classic reprinted here. Using extracts of tryptophan-adapted *Pseudomonas* to oxidize tryptophan, they showed that both atoms of oxygen incorporated in the oxidative step were derived from oxygen gas but not from water.

In the second JBC Classic reprinted here, Hayaishi continues with his investigations into tryptophan metabolism, this time looking at whether or not pyrocatechase can incorporate isotopically labeled molecular oxygen into catechol. Again using $^{18}O_2$ and $H_2^{18}O$, Hayaishi and his colleagues isolated the product, muconic acid, and analyzed its ^{18}O content by mass spectrometry. His results clearly demonstrated that the incorporated oxygen was derived exclusively from molecular oxygen. In the paper Hayaishi also presents a method of purification for the enzyme and a description of its properties. The results of these two papers, along with subsequent findings by other labs, established that "oxygen fixation" occurred in biological systems, and the concept of "biological oxygenation" was introduced. Hayaishi proposed that the new type of oxidative enzyme be called an "oxygenase."

In 1958, Hayaishi moved to Kyoto to be the Chairman of the Department of Medicinal Chemistry at the Kyoto University Faculty of Medicine. Concurrent with his appointment at Kyoto University, he served as Professor at the Department of Biochemistry of Osaka University School of Medicine (1961–1963) and also as Professor at the Department of Physiological Chemistry and Nutrition, Faculty of Medicine of the University of Tokyo (1970–1974). He continued to work on oxygenases and isolated and crystallized a number of the enzymes from animals, plants, and microorganisms. Hayaishi also remained focused on tryptophan metabolism and discovered and studied two new enzymes: indoleamine-2,3-dioxygenase and tryptophan side-chain α,β-oxidase. Later on, he turned his focus to prostaglandins and the molecular mechanisms of sleep regulation. In 1983, Hayaishi retired from Kyoto University and was appointed President of the Osaka Medical College at Takatsuki City. Around the same time, he was also appointed leader of the Hayaishi Bioinformation Transfer Project by the Japanese government. He is currently Chairmen of Trustees at the Osaka Bioscience Institute.

Hayaishi has been the recipient of several awards, including the Asahi Science and Culture Award (1965), the Japan Academy Award (1967), the Order of Culture Award (1972), the Louis and Bert Freedman Foundation Award from the New York Academy of Sciences (1976), the Wolf Medicine Prize (1986), and the Distinguished Scientist Award of the World Federation of Sleep Research Societies (1999). He is also a Foreign Associate of the National Academy of Sciences (1974).[1]

Nicole Kresge, Robert D. Simoni, and Robert L. Hill

REFERENCES

1. Hayaishi, O. (1994) Tryptophan, oxygen, and sleep. *Annu. Rev. Biochem.* **63,** 1–24

---

[1] All biographical information on Osamu Hayaishi was taken from Ref. 1.

THE JOURNAL OF BIOLOGICAL CHEMISTRY
© 2005 by The American Society for Biochemistry and Molecular Biology, Inc.

Vol. 280, No. 48, Issue of December 2, p. e45, 2005
Printed in U.S.A.

Classics

A PAPER IN A SERIES REPRINTED TO CELEBRATE THE CENTENARY OF THE JBC IN 2005

JBC Centennial
1905–2005
100 Years of Biochemistry and Molecular Biology

Lipid Storage Disorders and the Biosynthesis of Inositol Phosphatide: the Work of Roscoe Brady

The Enzymatic Synthesis of Inositol Phosphatide
(Agranoff, B. W., Bradley, R. M., and Brady, R. O. (1958) *J. Biol. Chem.* 233, 1077–1083)

Roscoe Owen Brady was born in 1923 in Philadelphia. He attended Pennsylvania State University from 1941 to 1943 and then received his medical degree from Harvard Medical School in 1947. After interning at the Hospital of the University of Pennsylvania for 1 year, Brady did a postdoctoral fellowship in the Department of Physiological Chemistry at the University of Pennsylvania School of Medicine (1948 to 1950) and then was a fellow in clinical medicine in the Department of Medicine (1950 to 1952). In 1954, following 2½ years on active duty in the U.S. Naval Medical Corps, he joined the National Institutes of Health (NIH) to become section chief of the National Institute of Neurological Diseases and Blindness. He remained in this position until 1967 when he became assistant laboratory chief of neurochemistry at the National Institute of Neurological Diseases and Blindness. Currently, Brady is Chief of the Developmental and Metabolic Neurology Branch of the National Institute of Neurological Disorders and Stroke, a position he has held since 1972.

Early in his career at the NIH, Brady started studying lipids, specifically inositol and the synthesis of inositol phosphatide. This is the subject of the *Journal of Biological Chemistry* (JBC) Classic reprinted here. Although inositol had been isolated more than 100 years before the Classic was published, little was known about its metabolism. In his Classic, Brady uses tritium-labeled inositol and a preparation from guinea pig kidney mitochondria to study inositol metabolism. He found that the enzyme system catalyzed the incorporation of inositol into inositol phosphatide in the presence of Mg^{2+} and cytidine diphosphate-choline (CDP) or cytidine 5′-phosphate. From these results, Brady proposed a mechanism for the synthesis of inositol phosphatide in which CDP is transphosphorylated to form CDP-D-α,β-diglyceride, which then reacts with the hydroxyl group of inositol to form inositol phosphatide.

These early studies stimulated Brady's interest in lipid storage disorders, in particular, Gaucher disease. In 1967, he showed that people with Gaucher disease had low levels of glucocerebrosidase and thus were unable to break down the lipid glucocerebroside and clear it out of their bodies. He also developed a diagnostic test for Gaucher disease, which worked by measuring glucocerebrosidase activity in white blood cells. A year later, Brady suggested a therapy for Gaucher disease based on replacing the enzyme. Using human placentas, his team isolated a tiny sample of purified glucocerebrosidase and gave it to two patients. The patients' health improved, and Brady soon developed large scale purification and targeting methods for glucocerebrosidase to use in further clinical trials. Eventually, in 1991, Brady's macrophage-targeted glucocerebrosidase enzyme replacement therapy was approved as a specific treatment for Gaucher disease by the Food and Drug Administration.

In addition to studying Gaucher disease, Brady has discovered the metabolic basis of Niemann-Pick disease, Fabry disease, and the specific biochemical defect in Tay-Sachs disease. He has applied this knowledge to developing diagnostic tests, carrier identification procedures, and the prenatal detection of such conditions. Currently his research is focused on examining enzyme replacement therapy and gene therapy for patients with these other hereditary metabolic disorders.

This paper is available on line at http://www.jbc.org

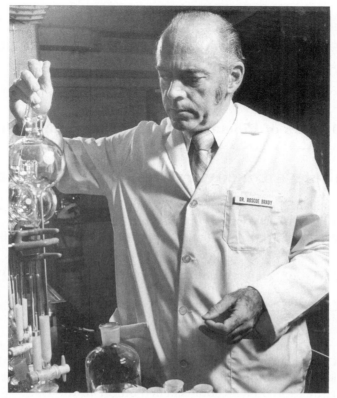

Roscoe Brady. Photo courtesy of the Office of NIH History, National Institutes of Health.

In recognition of his scientific achievements, Brady received the Gairdner International Award (1973), the Cotzias Award from the American Academy of Neurology (1980), the Passano Foundation Award (1982), the Lasker Foundation Clinical Medical Research Award (1982), and the Kovalenko Medal from the National Academy of Sciences (1991). He is a member of the National Academy of Sciences and a member of the Institute of Medicine of the National Academy of Sciences. He has served on the editorial boards and advisory boards of many journals and organizations.

Nicole Kresge, Robert D. Simoni, and Robert L. Hill

THE JOURNAL OF BIOLOGICAL CHEMISTRY
© 2005 by The American Society for Biochemistry and Molecular Biology, Inc.

Vol. 280, No. 49, Issue of December 9, p. e46, 2005
Printed in U.S.A.

Classics

A PAPER IN A SERIES REPRINTED TO CELEBRATE THE CENTENARY OF THE JBC IN 2005

JBC Centennial
1905–2005
100 Years of Biochemistry and Molecular Biology

Arthur Kornberg's Discovery of DNA Polymerase I

Enzymatic Synthesis of Deoxyribonucleic Acid. I. Preparation of Substrates and Partial Purification of an Enzyme from *Escherichia coli*
(Lehman, I. R., Bessman, M. J., Simms, E. S., and Kornberg, A. (1958) *J. Biol. Chem.* **233,** 163–170)

Enzymatic Synthesis of Deoxyribonucleic Acid. II. General Properties of the Reaction
(Bessman, M. J., Lehman, I. R., Simms, E. S., and Kornberg, A. (1958) *J. Biol. Chem.* **233,** 171–177)

Arthur Kornberg was born in Brooklyn, New York in 1918 and was educated in its public schools. He received his undergraduate degree in science from the City College of New York in 1937 and an M.D. degree from the University of Rochester in 1941. After a 1-year internship in internal medicine, he served as a commissioned officer in the U. S. Public Health Service. He was first assigned to the Navy as a ship's doctor and then as a research scientist at the National Institutes of Health (NIH) in Bethesda, Maryland, from 1942 to 1953. He obtained training in enzymology with Severo Ochoa at New York University School of Medicine in 1946 and with Carl Cori at Washington University School of Medicine in 1947. Both Ochoa and Cori were authors of *Journal of Biological Chemistry* (JBC) Classics (1, 2), and additional information on Kornberg's research in these laboratories can be found in his JBC Reflections (3).

Upon returning to Bethesda, Kornberg organized and directed the Enzyme Section at the NIH. He resigned in 1953 with the rank of Medical Director to assume the chairmanship of the Department of Microbiology at the Washington University School of Medicine in St. Louis, Missouri. In 1959, he organized the Department of Biochemistry at the Stanford University School of Medicine, serving as its chairman until 1969 and thereafter as professor. He accepted the title of Professor Emeritus in 1988 and has been on active status to the present.

From his early studies of the mechanisms of the enzymatic synthesis of coenzymes and inorganic pyrophosphate, Kornberg extended his interest to the biosynthesis of the nucleic acids, particularly DNA. After elucidating key steps in the pathways of pyrimidine and purine nucleotide synthesis, including the discovery of 5′-phosphoribosyl-1-pyrophospate (PRPP) as an intermediate, he found the enzyme that assembles the building blocks into DNA, named DNA polymerase. This is the subject of the two JBC Classics reprinted here. Earlier, Kornberg's group had discovered an enzyme system in *Escherichia coli* extracts that catalyzed the incorporation of deoxyribonucleotides into DNA. Joined by two postdoctoral fellows, Maurice J. Bessman and Robert I. Lehman, and his technician, Ernest S. Simms, Kornberg set about purifying the active enzyme from the extracts and elucidating the properties of the DNA synthesis system. In the first Classic, Kornberg and his colleagues describe the purification of DNA polymerase from *E. coli*. In the second Classic, they report that polymerized DNA, Mg^{2+}, and all four deoxynucleoside triphosphates (adenine, guanine, cytosine, and thymine) are needed for DNA synthesis to occur. From these requirements, they hypothesized that the polymerized DNA was serving as a template to guide the formation of new DNA.

These two Classics were declined by the JBC when submitted in the fall of 1957. Among the critical comments were: "It is very doubtful that the authors are entitled to speak of the enzymatic synthesis of DNA"; "Polymerase is a poor name"; "Perhaps as important as the elimination of certain banalities . . . " etc. Through the fortunate intervention of John Edsall,

This paper is available on line at http://www.jbc.org

Arthur Kornberg. Photo courtesy of the National Library of Medicine.

who had just assumed the position of Editor-in-Chief in May 1958, the two papers were eventually accepted and appeared in the July 1958 issue. A more in-depth account of the discovery of DNA polymerase can be found in Lehman's JBC Reflections (4). One year after these Classics were published, Kornberg was awarded the Nobel Prize in Physiology or Medicine with Ochoa "for their discovery of the mechanisms in the biological synthesis of ribonucleic acid and deoxyribonucleic acid."

Continuing his work on DNA synthesis, Kornberg was eventually able to get DNA polymerase to assemble a 5000-nucleotide DNA chain with the identical form, composition, and genetic activity as DNA from a natural virus. This successful synthesis of the biologically active ϕX174 virus in 1967 was the first time a biochemist produced an active virus in the lab. Kornberg's additional work concerning DNA synthesis includes the elucidation of the proofreading and editing functions of DNA polymerase and the discovery of single-strand binding protein, primase, and DNA polymerase III holoenzyme. Later, Kornberg switched his research focus from DNA replication to inorganic polyphosphate (poly(P)), a polymer of phosphates that likely participated in prebiotic evolution and is now found in every bacterial, plant, and animal cell. Kornberg has found a variety of significant functions for poly(P), once neglected and long regarded a molecular fossil, that include responses to stresses and stringencies and factors responsible for motility and virulence in some of the major pathogens.

Although the pursuit of research has been his primary concern, Kornberg's other interests include the formal teaching of graduate, medical, and postdoctoral students, and the authorship of major monographs: *DNA Synthesis* in 1974, *DNA Replication* in 1980, *Supplement to DNA Replication* in 1982, and *DNA Replication*, 2nd Ed., in 1992. A scientific autobiography, *For the Love of Enzymes: the Odyssey of a Biochemist*, Harvard University Press, appeared in 1989. *The Golden Helix: Inside Biotech Ventures*, University Science Books, was released in July of 1995 and provides an insider's view of biotechnology.

In his academic career, Kornberg has served as departmental chairman, on the committees of the Medical School and university, as president of the American Society of Biological Chemistry (1965), and on the advisory boards and councils of numerous university, governmental, and industrial research institutes. He is a founder of the DNAX Research Institute of Molecular and Cellular Biology (a Division of Schering-Plough, Inc.) and a member of its Policy and Scientific Advisory Boards. He serves on the Scientific Advisory Boards of Regeneron

Pharmaceuticals, Inc., Maxygen, and the XOMA Corp. and is also a member of the Board of Directors of XOMA Corp.

Among Kornberg's honors are memberships in the National Academy of Sciences, the Royal Society, American Philosophical Society, a number of honorary degrees, the Nobel Prize in Physiology or Medicine (1959), the National Medal of Science (1979), the Cosmos Club Award (1995), and other medals and awards.[1]

The other authors of the two Classics, Lehman and Bessman, have also had distinguished research careers and remain active in research today. Lehman is currently Hume Professor Emeritus at the Stanford School of Medicine, Department of Biochemistry. He studies the enzymology of eukaryotic DNA replication and is an Associate Editor for the JBC. Some of his work will be featured in an upcoming JBC Classic. Bessman is at Johns Hopkins University where he is currently studying the Nudix hydrolase family of enzymes.

Nicole Kresge, Robert D. Simoni, and Robert L. Hill

REFERENCES

1. JBC Classics: Stern, J. R., and Ochoa, S. (1951) *J. Biol. Chem.* **191,** 161–172; Korkes, S., del Campillo, A., Gunsalus, I. C., and Ochoa, S. (1951) *J. Biol. Chem.* **193,** 721–735 (http://www.jbc.org/cgi/content/full/280/11/e8)
2. JBC Classics: Cori, C. F., and Cori, G. T. (1928) *J. Biol. Chem.* **79,** 321–341; Cori, G. T., Colowick, S. P., and Cori, C. F. (1938) *J. Biol. Chem.* **124,** 543–555; Cori, G. T., Colowick, S. P., and Cori, C. F. (1939) *J. Biol. Chem.* **127,** 771–782; Green, A. A., and Cori, G. T. (1943) *J. Biol. Chem.* **151,** 21–29; Cori, G. T., and Green, A. A. (1943) *J. Biol. Chem.* **151,** 31–38 (http://www.jbc.org/cgi/content/full/277/29/e18)
3. Kornberg, A. (2001) Remembering our teachers. *J. Biol. Chem.* **276,** 3–11
4. Lehman, I. R. (1989) Discovery of DNA polymerase. *J. Biol. Chem.* **278,** 34733–34738
5. Kornberg, A. (1989) Never a dull enzyme. *Annu. Rev. Biochem.* **58,** 1–30

---

[1] Biographical information on Arthur Kornberg was taken from Ref. 5.

THE JOURNAL OF BIOLOGICAL CHEMISTRY
© 2005 by The American Society for Biochemistry and Molecular Biology, Inc.

Vol. 280, No. 50, Issue of December 16, p. e47, 2005
Printed in U.S.A.

Classics

A PAPER IN A SERIES REPRINTED TO CELEBRATE THE CENTENARY OF THE JBC IN 2005

JBC Centennial
1905–2005
100 Years of Biochemistry and Molecular Biology

The Elucidation of the Structure of Ribonuclease by Stanford Moore and William H. Stein

The Sequence of the Amino Acid Residues in Performic Acid-oxidized Ribonuclease
(Hirs, C. H. W., Moore, S., and Stein, W. H. (1960) *J. Biol. Chem.* 235, 633–647)

The Disulfide Bonds of Ribonuclease
(Spackman, D. H., Stein, W. H., and Moore, S., with the assistance of Zamoyska, A. M. (1960) *J. Biol. Chem.* 235, 648–659)

Alkylation and Identification of the Histidine Residues at the Active Site of Ribonuclease
(Crestfield, A. M., Stein, W. H., and Moore, S. (1963) *J. Biol. Chem.* 238, 2413–2420)

A previous *Journal of Biological Chemistry* (*JBC*) Classic (1) on Stanford Moore (1913–1982) and William H. Stein (1911–1980) offered a look into their early careers, including their development of chromatographic methods for determining protein composition, their invention of the photoelectric drop-counting fraction collector, and their creation of the first amino acid analyzer. This Classic focuses on their elucidation of the amino acid sequence of pancreatic ribonuclease, its disulfide bonds and active site residues.

In the early 1950s, Moore and Stein started using their ion-exchange chromatography methods to separate peptides and proteins. Encouraged by their success, they decided to embark on the structural analysis of an entire protein. They chose ribonuclease, an enzyme that is more than twice the size of insulin, which was the first protein to be fully sequenced as a result of the pioneering studies of Fred Sanger in Cambridge, England. At the time that these studies were begun, Christian B. Anfinsen and his associates at the National Institutes of Health also started studying the chemical structure of ribonuclease. Anfinsen's work on ribonuclease will be the subject of a future JBC Classic.

To determine the sequence of ribonuclease, Moore, Stein, and their first postdoctoral associate, Werner Hirs, hydrolyzed the protein with trypsin and then separated the peptide mixture by ion-exchange chromatography. The peptide sequences were then analyzed by Edman degradation. By repeating this experiment with chymotrypsin and pepsin they were able to deduce the sequence of the entire protein, which is published in the first JBC Classic reprinted here. Their sequence, shown in Fig. 1, was almost entirely in agreement with the partial sequence of ribonuclease reported by Redfield and Anfinsen (2, 3), except for a disagreement on the nature of the amino acid residue at position 11. According to Anfinsen, the residue was glutamic acid, whereas Moore and Stein believed it was serine. Eventually, after using improved conditions for Edman degradation, Moore and Stein revised their published sequence (4) and stated that the amino acid was, indeed, glutamic acid.

In the Discussion section of the Classic, Moore and Stein also describe some modifications to their approach that they suggest adopting in future elucidations of the chemical structure of a protein to make the task easier and improve the results. These modifications include performing the peptide separations on larger columns, using highly purified proteolytic enzymes to cleave the protein, and using additional enzymes such as carboxypeptidase B.

While elucidating the sequence of ribonuclease, Moore and Stein also attempted to determine the positions of the four disulfide bonds in the molecule. This is the subject of the second JBC Classic reprinted here. Moore, Stein, and Darrel Spackman hydrolyzed ribonuclease with

Classics

Sequence of Amino Acids in Ribonuclease

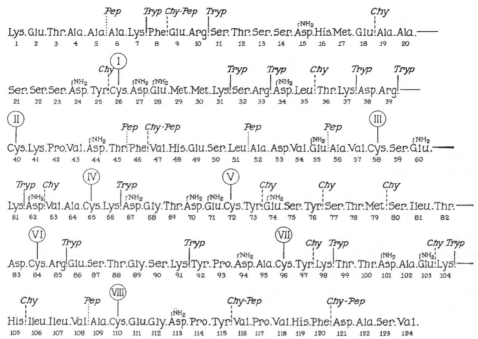

The sequence of amino acid residues in oxidized bovine ribonuclease. This figure was taken from the first JBC Classic reprinted here.

pepsin, trypsin, and chymotrypsin and then used an ion-exchange column to locate the cystine-containing peptides. These peptides were oxidized, separated chromatographically, and then subjected to amino acid analysis. From these experiments, they determined that the following cystine pairings occurred: I-VI, II-VII, III-VIII, and IV-V. Again, their results differed from those obtained by Anfinsen (5). His group had determined that II-VIII and III-VII pairings occurred. It was eventually shown that Moore and Stein were correct in their disulfide bond predictions.

Not content to stop at the sequence of ribonuclease, Moore and Stein also studied the inactivation of the enzyme by iodoacetic acid, which is the subject of the final JBC Classic reprinted here. They, along with Arthur Crestfield, discovered that two monocarboxymethyl derivatives were formed when iodoacetic acid was added. When they subjected these products to amino acid analysis they determined that the alkylation had occurred at the histidine residues occupying positions 119 and 12. From this they concluded that the imidazole rings of histidine 119 and histidine 12 were at the active center of ribonuclease. Using similar methods, they identified additional residues in and around the active site of the enzyme.

Moore and Stein's work on ribonuclease was recognized in 1972 when they were awarded the Nobel Prize in Chemistry, which they shared with Anfinsen "for their contribution to the understanding of the connection between chemical structure and catalytic activity of the active centre of the ribonuclease molecule."

Nicole Kresge, Robert D. Simoni, and Robert L. Hill

REFERENCES

1. JBC Classics: Moore, S., and Stein, W. H. (1948) *J. Biol. Chem.* **176,** 367–388; Stein, W. H., and Moore, S. (1948) *J. Biol. Chem.* **176,** 337–365 (http://www.jbc.org/cgi/content/full/280/9/e6)
2. Redfield, R. R., and Anfinsen, C. B. (1956) The structure of ribonuclease. II. The preparation, separation, and relative alignment of large enzymatically produced fragments. *J. Biol. Chem.* **221,** 385–404
3. Anfinsen, C. B., Sela, M., and Tritch, H. (1956) A method for the specific proteolytic cleavage of protein chains. *Arch. Biochem. Biophys.* **65,** 156–163
4. Smyth, D. G., Stein, W. H., and Moore, S. (1963) The sequence of amino acid residues in bovine pancreatic ribonuclease: revisions and confirmations. *J. Biol. Chem.* **238,** 227–234
5. Ryle, A. P., and Anfinsen, C. B. (1957) Studies on the disulfide bridges in ribonuclease. *Biochim. Biophys. Acta* **24,** 633–635

THE JOURNAL OF BIOLOGICAL CHEMISTRY
© 2005 by The American Society for Biochemistry and Molecular Biology, Inc.

Vol. 280, No. 51, Issue of December 23, p. e48, 2005
Printed in U.S.A.

Classics

A PAPER IN A SERIES REPRINTED TO CELEBRATE THE CENTENARY OF THE JBC IN 2005

JBC Centennial
1905–2005
100 Years of Biochemistry and Molecular Biology

The Discovery of Ferredoxin and Its Role in Photosynthesis: the Work of Anthony San Pietro

Photosynthetic Pyridine Nucleotide Reductase. I. Partial Purification and Properties of the Enzyme from Spinach
(San Pietro, A., and Lang, H. M. (1958) *J. Biol. Chem.* 231, 211–229)

The light reactions of photosynthesis occur in the thylakoids and depend on the interplay of two photosystems. Photosystem I, excited by light of wavelength shorter than 700 nm, generates NADPH via the formation of reduced ferredoxin. Photosystem II, requiring light of wavelength shorter than 680 nm, produces a strong oxidant that leads to the formation of O_2. The resulting accumulation of protons in the thylakoid lumen causes the formation of a transmembrane pH gradient, which is then used to drive the synthesis of ATP.

These light reactions were first recognized in 1939 when Robert Hill demonstrated that isolated chloroplasts could simultaneously produce oxygen and reduce a high potential electron acceptor in the presence of light. Over the next 20 years a variety of substances were found to function as oxidants for the Hill reaction. The ability of chloroplasts to reduce pyridine nucleotides was first demonstrated in 1951, when three laboratories independently reported that illuminated chloroplasts were capable of generating oxygen and reducing NADP (1–3). This was the beginning of enzymatic research on NADP photoreduction in chloroplasts.

Within the next 7 years, three protein factors were isolated: methemoglobin-reducing factor, which is needed for utilizing methemoglobin as a Hill oxidant (4); triphosphopyridine nucleotide-reducing factor, which is a functional catalyst for photosynthetic phosphorylation (5); and photosynthetic pyridine nucleotide reductase (PPNR), which is catalytically active for pyridine nucleotide reduction in illuminated chloroplasts (6). The *Journal of Biological Chemistry* (JBC) Classic reprinted here reports on the isolation of the last protein factor, PPNR.

Anthony San Pietro, a young faculty member at Johns Hopkins University, and his research assistant, Helga M. Lang, had previously shown that when NADP was incubated with chloroplast grana, NADPH accumulated in the reaction mixture, provided that high concentrations of grana and NADP were used (6). Preliminary experiments also showed that reduction of pyridine nucleotides could occur at low grana concentrations if a soluble extract from chloroplasts was added. This Classic describes San Pietro and Lang's isolation of the enzyme from chloroplast extracts that was needed for the photochemical reduction of NADP.

Using chloroplasts from whole spinach leaves, San Pietro and Lang extracted the enzyme and precipitated it. They confirmed that the enzyme did indeed catalyze the transfer of hydrogen to pyridine nucleotides and determined some of its properties. Based on these properties and the role of the enzyme in photosynthesis, San Pietro and Lang suggested it be named "photosynthetic pyridine nucleotide reductase."

Subsequent studies showed that methemoglobin-reducing factor, triphosphopyridine nucleotide-reducing factor, and PPNR were the same chemical compound, and they were collectively referred to as PPNR. In 1962, Tagawa and Arnon compared PPNR and a new electron carrier called "ferredoxin," which was discovered in the hydrogenase system of *Clostridium pasteurianum.* They revealed that while one enzyme was involved in bacterial hydrogen generation and the other in higher plant NADP photoreduction, they were functionally similar and were interchangeable non-heme-iron proteins (7). Thus, PPNR became known as ferredoxin.

San Pietro continued his work on photosynthesis and later isolated transhydrogenase, the enzyme that transfers hydrogen from NADPH, formed by PPNR, to NAD (8). This was the basis of his Transhydrogenase Theory, which states that illuminated grana reduce NADP in the presence of PPNR and transhydrogenase then reduces NAD using reduced NADP.

In 1962, San Pietro joined the Charles F. Kettering Research Laboratory in Yellow Springs, Ohio. While at the Kettering lab, he extended his research to include chromatophores of photosynthetic bacteria. During his 6 years at the Kettering, San Pietro and his group published some 40 papers, and he organized three Symposia that attracted scientists from around the world who were working on photosynthesis and the synthesis of proteins during cellular differentiation. San Pietro moved to the University of Indiana at Bloomington in 1968 to chair the Department of Plant Sciences. While serving as Chairman, he maintained an active laboratory for investigating the mechanisms of the light-dependent reactions of photosynthesis and published over 160 papers. Currently San Pietro is an Emeritus Distinguished Professor of Biochemistry at Indiana University. He edited several of the photosynthetic volumes of *Methods in Enzymology* and also served on the Editorial Board of the JBC. He was honored for his outstanding scientific achievements by election to the National Academy of Sciences in 1983.[1]

Nicole Kresge, Robert D. Simoni, and Robert L. Hill

REFERENCES

1. Vishniac, W., and Ochoa, S. (1951) Photochemical reduction of pyridine nucleotides by spinach grana and coupled carbon dioxide fixation. *Nature* **167,** 768–769
2. Tolmach, L. J. (1951) Effects of triphosphopyridine nucleotide upon oxygen evolution and carbon dioxide fixation by illuminated chloroplasts. *Nature* **167,** 946–948
3. Arnon, D. I. (1951) Extracellular photosynthetic reactions. *Nature* **167,** 1008–1010
4. Davenport, H. E., Hill, R., and Whatley, F. R. (1952) A natural factor catalyzing reduction of methaemoglobin by isolated chloroplasts. *Proc. Roy. Soc. Lond. B Biol. Sci.* **139,** 346–358
5. Arnon, D. I., Whatley, F. R., and Allen, M. B. (1957) Triphosphopyridine nucleotide as a catalyst of photosynthetic phosphorylation. *Nature* **180,** 182–185
6. San Pietro, A., and Lang, H.M. (1956) Accumulation of reduced pyridine nucleotides by illuminated grana. *Science* **124,** 118–119
7. Tagawa, K., and Arnon, D. I. (1962) Ferredoxins as electron carriers in photosynthesis and in the biological production and consumption of hydrogen gas. *Nature* **195,** 537–543
8. Keister, D. L., San Pietro, A., and Stolzenbach, F. E. (1960) Pyridine nucleotide transhydrogenase from spinach. I. Purification and properties. *J. Biol. Chem.* **235,** 2989–2996
9. Vernon, L. P. (2003) Photosynthesis and the Charles F. Kettering research laboratory. *Photosynth. Res.* **76,** 379–388
10. Krogmann, D. W. (2000) The golden age of biochemical research in photosynthesis. *Photosynth. Res.* **63,** 109–121

---

[1] All biographical information on Anthony San Pietro was taken from Refs. 9 and 10.

THE JOURNAL OF BIOLOGICAL CHEMISTRY
© 2005 by The American Society for Biochemistry and Molecular Biology, Inc.

Vol. 280, No. 52, Issue of December 30, p. e49, 2005
Printed in U.S.A.

Classics

A PAPER IN A SERIES REPRINTED TO CELEBRATE THE CENTENARY OF THE JBC IN 2005

JBC Centennial
1905–2005
100 Years of Biochemistry and Molecular Biology

H. Edwin Umbarger's Contributions to the Discovery of Feedback Inhibition

Isoleucine and Valine Metabolism in *Escherichia coli*. V. α-Ketoisovaleric Acid Accumulation
(Adelberg, E. A., and Umbarger, H. E. (1953) *J. Biol. Chem.* 205, 475–482)

Harold Edwin Umbarger (1921–1999) was born in Shelby, Ohio. His undergraduate education was at Ohio University, where he graduated in 1943, and his graduate education was at Harvard University, where he received his Ph.D. degree in bacteriology and immunology in 1950. Umbarger also served as a hospital corpsman in the U. S. Navy on the USS Rescue from 1944 to 1946. After completing his graduate studies, he remained in the Department of Bacteriology and Immunology at Harvard Medical School and eventually became Assistant Professor. In 1960 he was appointed Staff Investigator at the Cold Spring Harbor Biological Laboratory and then joined the faculty of Purdue University in 1964. In 1970, he was named Wright Distinguished Professor of Biological Sciences at Purdue.

Umbarger was a leading researcher in the field of amino acid biosynthesis in bacteria. However, he is probably best known for his contributions to the discovery of feedback inhibition, which is the subject of the *Journal of Biological Chemistry* (JBC) Classic reprinted here. Using isoleucineless mutants of *Escherichia coli*, Umbarger and Edward A. Adelberg showed that the presence of valine in the growth medium inhibited the formation of α-ketoisovalerate, a valine precursor. From this, they concluded that "an end product, in this case valine, can regulate the rate of its own biosynthesis." The phenomenon of end product inhibition had been demonstrated previously (1–3), and Umbarger speculated that this was likely a general control phenomenon, although the mechanism was unclear.

Three years later, in 1956, Umbarger reported that, in *E. coli*, isoleucine specifically inhibited the first enzyme-catalyzed reaction in the sequence of steps leading to its biosynthesis from threonine (4). He stated, "it would seem that the interaction between L-isoleucine and L-threonine dehydrase constitutes a negative-feedback loop that could permit the biosynthesis of isoleucine to proceed only when the level of L-isoleucine in the medium or in the metabolic pool has been reduced to a very low level."

In the same year, Richard Yates and Arthur Pardee reported another example of negative feedback in the inhibition, by cytidine triphosphate, of the first committed step in the pathway leading to its biosynthesis in *E. coli*. This was the subject of a previous JBC Classic (5). The discovery of feedback inhibition offered new insights into ways in which the life processes of cells are regulated and opened new approaches to the design of drugs aimed at inhibiting pathogenic organisms.

Umbarger was honored for his contributions to science by election to the National Academy of Sciences and the American Academy of Arts and Sciences. He received a Medallion of Pioneering Research from the Ben Gurion University of Negev, Israel, the Rosenstiel Award in Basic Medical Sciences from Brandeis University, and the McCoy Award for Contributions to Science from Purdue. In 1999, Purdue established the Umbarger Distinguished Professorship of Biological Sciences in his honor. Umbarger served as Editor of the *Journal of Bacteriology* and was on the editorial board of the JBC. He also served as Chairman of the Division of Microbial Physiology of the American Society for Microbiology.

Umbarger's coauthor on the paper, Adelberg, also went on to a distinguished career in biochemistry. Several years after the paper was published, he became Chairman of the Department of Bacteriology at the University of California, Berkeley (1957–1961) and then joined the faculty at the Yale University Department of Microbiology, becoming chairman of that department for two terms (1961–1964 and 1970–1972). He was also Director of Biological Sciences at Yale (1964–1969), Deputy Provost for the Biomedical Sciences (1983–1992), and Assistant to the Provost (1993 to present). Currently he is Professor Emeritus in the Yale Department of Genetics. He was elected to the National Academy of Sciences in 1971 and the American Academy of Arts and Sciences in 1979.

Nicole Kresge, Robert D. Simoni, and Robert L. Hill

REFERENCES

1. Koch, A. L., Putnam, F. W., and Evans, E. A. (1952) The purine metabolism of *Escherichia coli. J. Biol. Chem.* **197,** 105–112
2. Abelson, P. H., Bolton, E. T., and Aldous, E. (1952) Utilization of carbon dioxide in the synthesis of proteins by *Escherichia coli.* II. *J. Biol. Chem.* **198,** 173–178
3. Gots, J. S., and Chu, E. C. (1952) Studies on purine metabolism in bacteria. I. The role of *p*-aminobenzoic acid. *J. Bacteriol.* **64,** 537–546
4. Umbarger, H. E. (1956) Evidence for a negative-feedback mechanism in the biosynthesis of isoleucine. *Science* **123,** 848
5. JBC Classics: Yates, R. A., and Pardee, A. B. (1956) *J. Biol. Chem.* **221,** 757–770; Gerhart, J. C., and Pardee, A. B. (1962) *J. Biol. Chem.* **237,** 891–896 (http://www.jbc.org/cgi/content/full/280/41/e38)

THE JOURNAL OF BIOLOGICAL CHEMISTRY
© 2006 by The American Society for Biochemistry and Molecular Biology, Inc.

Vol. 281, No. 1, Issue of January 6, p. e1, 2006
Printed in U.S.A.

Classics

A PAPER IN A SERIES REPRINTED TO CELEBRATE THE CENTENARY OF THE JBC IN 2005

JBC Centennial
1905–2005
100 Years of Biochemistry and Molecular Biology

Hexosamine Metabolism, Sialic Acids, and the Phosphotransferase System: Saul Roseman's Contributions to Glycobiology

The Sialic Acids. I. The Structure and Enzymatic Synthesis of *N*-Acetylneuraminic Acid
(Comb, D. G., and Roseman, S. (1960) *J. Biol. Chem.* **235,** 2529–2537)

Sugar Transport. I. Isolation of a Phosphotransferase System from *Escherichia coli*
(Kundig, W., and Roseman, S. (1971) *J. Biol. Chem.* **246,** 1393–1406)

Saul Roseman was born in Brooklyn, New York, in 1921. He received his Bachelor of Science in Chemistry from the City College of New York in 1941 and began his graduate studies in the Biochemistry Department at the University of Wisconsin, earning his masters degree in 1944. He then served for 2 years as an infantryman in Europe in World War II. Upon his return, he completed his Ph.D. in 1947, studying biochemistry with Karl Paul Link and organic chemistry with Homer Atkins. Roseman's graduate work focused on the synthesis and metabolism of coumarin derivatives (*e.g.* Dicumarol), which Link had discovered and which was the subject of a previous *Journal of Biological Chemistry* (JBC) Classic (1). It was during his graduate studies that Roseman's life-long interest in carbohydrates began, when he started working on the metabolism of 4-hydroxycoumarin, which is secreted into the urine of dogs as the glucuronide or glucuronic acid derivative. A growing interest in complex carbohydrates led Roseman to do his postdoctoral studies with Albert Dorfman at the University of Chicago School of Medicine, who was also featured in a previous JBC Classic (2). With Dorfman, Roseman developed new methods of glycan radioisotopic labeling to study hyaluronic acid and chondroitin sulfate biosynthesis and showed that the carbon chain of glucose was converted *in vivo* directly, with no cleavage, to that of glucosamine. He remained at Chicago until 1953 and was promoted to Assistant Professor.

Roseman then became Assistant Professor of Biological Chemistry at the University of Michigan Medical School and Chemist of the Rackham Arthritis Research Unit. In the next few years, he rose in academic rank to Professor. While at Michigan, Roseman started to work with enzymes and cell-free extracts, which took him to glucosamine metabolism, which, in turn, led to the sialic acids. His work on the identification of the structure and metabolism of sialic acids is the subject of the first JBC Classic reprinted here.

In the Classic, Roseman and one of his first postdoctoral fellows, Donald G. Comb (founder and President of New England Biolabs), report on their studies on the structure of one sialic acid in particular, *N*-acetylneuraminic acid, and the properties of the bacterial enzyme, *N*-acetylneuraminic acid aldolase, that cleaves the sialic acid into *N*-acetyl-D-mannosamine (which was not previously known to occur naturally) and pyruvate. Using *N*-acetylneuraminic acid purified from both human blood and *Escherichia coli* and *N*-acetylneuraminic acid aldolase from *Clostridium perfringens*, Roseman and Comb established the products of the cleavage reaction, showed that it was reversible (yielding NAN), and characterized the enzyme. They also used 1-[^{14}C]- and 6-[^{14}C]glucose to follow the biosynthesis of *N*-acetylneuraminic acid and concluded that it is the product of a 3-carbon and 6-carbon condensation.

At that time, and over a period of 3 decades, over 11 possible structures had been suggested for *N*-acetylneuraminic acid. Roseman and Comb's work was critical in establishing the correct

Saul Roseman

structure. Subsequently, Roseman and Comb isolated, characterized, and enzymatically synthesized a unique sugar nucleotide, CMP-sialic acid. This led to a series of novel studies on glycosyltransferases. Roseman and colleagues showed that families of glycosyltransferases existed, in which each family transferred a specific sugar, and that each member of the family had specific requirements for the acceptor and/or the linkage of the newly synthesized glycosidic bond. The sum of these studies was to establish the individual steps in the metabolic pathways between fructose-6-P and complex carbohydrates such as the gangliosides (with Basu), the oligosaccharide chains in the mucins (with Schachter), and the carbohydrate termini in the blood glycoproteins (with Jourdian, Carlson, and others).

In 1965 Roseman was recruited to the McCollum-Pratt Institute and Department of Biology at the Johns Hopkins University, where he later served as Director and Chairman for two terms (1969–1973 and 1988–1990). Just before leaving Michigan for Baltimore, Roseman, while working on N-acetylmannosamine metabolism, discovered what turned out to be a novel sugar transport system in bacteria, the PTS (phosphotransferase system). The system involves a series of sequential phosphotransfer reactions between proteins and simultaneously phosphorylates and translocates its sugar substrates across the membrane. Surprisingly, the source of the phosphoryl group is not ATP or another nucleoside triphosphate but rather phosphoenolpyruvate.

Roseman's isolation of a PTS from *E. coli* is the subject of the second JBC Classic reprinted here. In the paper, Roseman and Werner Kundig purify the two enzymes (Enzyme I and II) and one protein (HPr) that comprise the system and determine that Enzyme I and HPr are soluble while Enzyme II is part of the cell membrane. Using ^{32}P and ^{14}C to assay the activity of the enzymes, they conclude that Enzyme I catalyzes the transfer of phosphate from phosphoenolpyruvate to HPr and Enzyme II catalyzes the transfer of phosphate from phospho-HPr to the carbohydrate. The phosphate is linked to HPr via an imidazole nitrogen atom on a histidine residue. In two subsequent JBC papers (3, 4), Roseman and Kundig further characterized the enzymes that constitute the PTS, and somewhat later, with Simoni, established that it was, in fact, a sugar transport system, not just a novel kinase.

Still at Johns Hopkins, Roseman retains his position of Professor in the Department of Biology. His laboratory continues to make key contributions to the molecular understanding of complex carbohydrate glycosyltransferases, bacterial sugar transport, and intercellular adhesion. Most recently, he has made novel forays into the complex metabolism of chitin, the second most abundant organic compound in nature. More information about the history of glycobiology can be found in Roseman's JBC Reflections (5).

In recognition of his contributions to glycobiology, Roseman has been the recipient of many national and international awards and honors, among which was his election, in 1972, to the National Academy of Sciences, and the degree of Doctor of Medicine *Honoris causa* from the University of Lund. He has also received the Sesquicentennial award from the University of Michigan (1967), the T. Duckett Jones Memorial award from the Helen Hay Whitney Foundation (1973), the Rosenstiehl award from Brandeis University (1974), the International award from the Gairdner Foundation (1981), and the Karl Meyer award from the Society of Glycobiology (1993). Roseman is also a former member of the JBC editorial board and has published 136 papers in the journal over a 60-year period.

Nicole Kresge, Robert D. Simoni, and Robert L. Hill

REFERENCES

1. JBC Classics: Campbell, H. A., and Link, K. P. (1941) *J. Biol. Chem.* **138,** 21–33; Stahmann, M. A., Huebner, C. F., and Link, K. P. (1941) *J. Biol. Chem.* **138,** 513–527; Overman, R. S., Stahmann, M. A., Huebner, C. F., Sullivan, W. R., Spero, L., Doherty, D. G., Ikawa, M., Graf, L., Roseman, S., and Link, K. P. (1944) *J. Biol. Chem.* **153,** 5–24 (http://www.jbc.org/cgi/content/full/280/8/e5)
2. JBC Classics: Roseman, S., Moses, F. E., Ludowieg, J., and Dorfman, A. (1953) *J. Biol. Chem.* **203,** 213–225 (http://www.jbc.org/cgi/content/full/280/31/e28)
3. Kundig, W., and Roseman, S. (1971) Sugar transport. II. Characterization of constitutive membrane-bound Enzymes II of the *Escherichia coli* phosphotransferase system. *J. Biol. Chem.* **246,** 1407–1418
4. Anderson, B., Weigel, N., Kundig, W., and Roseman, S. (1971) Sugar transport. III. Purification and properties of a phosphocarrier protein (HPr) of the phosphoenolpyruvate-dependent phosphotransferase system of *Escherichia coli*. *J. Biol. Chem.* **246,** 7023–7033
5. Roseman, S. (2001) Reflections on glycobiology. *J. Biol. Chem.* **276,** 41527–41542

THE JOURNAL OF BIOLOGICAL CHEMISTRY
© 2006 by The American Society for Biochemistry and Molecular Biology, Inc.

Vol. 281, No. 2, Issue of January 13, p. e2, 2006
Printed in U.S.A.

Classics

A PAPER IN A SERIES REPRINTED TO CELEBRATE THE CENTENARY OF THE JBC IN 2005

JBC Centennial
1905–2005
100 Years of Biochemistry and Molecular Biology

Na,K-ATPase and the Post-Albers Cycle: the Work of Robert L. Post

Membrane Adenosine Triphosphatase as a Participant in the Active Transport of Sodium and Potassium in the Human Erythrocyte
(Post, R. L., Merritt, C. R., Kinsolving, C. R., and Albright, C. D. (1960) *J. Biol. Chem.*
235, 1796–1802)

Robert Lickely Post was born in 1920 in Philadelphia. He was educated at Harvard University, receiving his B.S. in 1942 and his M.D. in 1945. He spent a year as an intern at Hartford Hospital in Connecticut before becoming an instructor at the University of Pennsylvania Medical School. In 1948, Post moved to Nashville, where he joined the faculty at Vanderbilt University. He progressed from instructor to professor at the medical school and remained there until 1991. He is currently a visiting scholar at the University of Pennsylvania Medical School.

Post is best known for his work on the sodium and potassium ion transport adenosine triphosphatase (Na,K-ATPase). The enzyme is embedded in the plasma membrane of animal cells and transports Na^+ and K^+ across the membrane. Transport is stoichiometrically coupled to the hydrolysis of cytoplasmic ATP. Three Na^+ ions are transported outward, and two K^+ ions are transported inward for every one terminal phosphate group of ATP hydrolyzed.

Post started working on the kinetics of active sodium and potassium transport in human erythrocytes in 1954 while at Vanderbilt. Then, in 1957, Jens C. Skou published a paper on ATPase activity in crab nerves (1) in which he reported that the ATPase activity required both sodium and potassium ions simultaneously. Skou concluded, "Characteristics of the system suggest that the ATPase studied here may be involved in the active extrusion of sodium for the nerve fiber." Post decided to search for the same activity in ATPase from human erythrocytes. His studies are the subject of the *Journal of Biological Chemistry* (JBC) Classic reprinted here.

In the Classic, Post, along with his students Cullen Merrit, Richard Kinsolving, and Charlie Albright, report on their identification of an insoluble ATP-cleaving enzyme system involved in the active transport of sodium outward and potassium inward across the membranes of human erythrocyte membranes. They observed that both activities were located in the membranes and that both required sodium and potassium ions together. This paper not only provided a method for identifying a transport system in a preparation of broken membranes but also showed that ions, which were considered simple cofactors, could also be substrates for translocation. The Classic was recognized as a Current Contents Citation Classic in 1981 because it had been cited more than 865 times since 1961.

After publishing this paper, Post continued to study the Na,K-ATPase and eventually worked out the Post-Albers cycle, which describes the sequence of reaction steps of the Na,K-ATPase by which the charge translocations take place (2, 3). Currently, Post continues his research on the reaction sequence. In particular, he is concentrating on the transient kinetics of formation and breakdown of the phosphorylated enzyme, an intermediate in the reaction sequence. In honor of his contributions to science Post was awarded the Biophysical Society's K. S. Cole award in 1984. Post was also a member of the JBC Editorial Board.

Nicole Kresge, Robert D. Simoni, and Robert L. Hill

This paper is available on line at http://www.jbc.org

REFERENCES

1. Skou, J. C. (1957) The influence of some cations on an adenosine triphosphatase from peripheral nerves. *Biochim. Biophys. Acta* **23,** 394–401
2. Albers, R. W. (1967) Biochemical aspects of active transport. *Annu. Rev. Biochem.* **36,** 727–756
3. Post, R. L., Hegyvary, C., and Kume, S. (1972) Activation by adenosine triphosphate in the phosphorylation kinetics of sodium and potassium ion transport adenosine triphosphatase. *J. Biol. Chem.* **247,** 6530–6540

THE JOURNAL OF BIOLOGICAL CHEMISTRY
© 2006 by The American Society for Biochemistry and Molecular Biology, Inc.

Vol. 281, No. 3, Issue of January 20, p. e3, 2006
Printed in U.S.A.

Classics

A PAPER IN A SERIES REPRINTED TO CELEBRATE THE CENTENARY OF THE JBC IN 2005

JBC Centennial
1905–2005
100 Years of Biochemistry and Molecular Biology

Sucrose Gradient Centrifugation for Low Molecular Weight Substances: the Work of Bruce N. Ames

A Method for Determining the Sedimentation Behavior of Enzymes: Application to Protein Mixtures
(Martin, R. G., and Ames, B. N. (1961) *J. Biol. Chem.* 236, 1372–1379)

Bruce Nathan Ames was born in 1928 in New York City. He attended the Bronx High School of Science where he did his first scientific experiments: growing tomato root tips in culture to determine the effects of plant hormones. After graduating from high school, Ames attended Cornell University, receiving his B.A. degree in chemistry/biochemistry in 1950. He then moved to the California Institute of Technology for graduate study with Herschel K. Mitchell in the biology department. There, Ames worked on the biosynthesis of histidine in *Neurospora*. After receiving his Ph.D. in 1953, Ames took a postdoctoral position in the National Institute of Arthritis and Metabolic Diseases at the National Institutes of Health (NIH). He worked with Bernard Horecker, who was featured in a previous *Journal of Biological Chemistry* (JBC) Classic (1).

At the NIH Ames isolated the enzymes involved in the histidine pathway using the intermediates he had isolated and synthesized at Cal Tech. As a result of a collaboration with Philip Hartman, Ames had switched from *Neurospora* to *Salmonella*, and in 1954, as an independent investigator at the NIH, he began work on gene regulation in histidine biosynthesis. He and Hartman showed that the histidine genes, which were in a cluster in *Salmonella*, could be overexpressed if histidine availability limited the growth rate. They also demonstrated that the cluster of genes was controlled by a regulatory sequence.

Ames became convinced that the histidine biosynthetic enzymes were in a complex in the cell. He encouraged Robert G. Martin, a medical student at Harvard who had come to his laboratory for a semester, to see if this was true using sucrose gradient centrifugation. At the time, sucrose gradient centrifugation had mostly been used for analyzing ribosomes and large molecules. Martin worked out a method to adapt the procedure to relatively low molecular weight substances and determined the molecular weights of several enzymes in the histidine biosynthesis pathway. This method is reported in the JBC Classic reprinted here. Although they did not find a complex of histidine biosynthetic enzymes, the Ames and Martin paper became one of the most cited papers in biochemistry.

A year after the Classic was published, Ames became a section head in the newly created Laboratory of Molecular Biology at the National Institute of Arthritis and Metabolic Diseases. Martin enjoyed his time at the NIH so much that he returned to Ames' laboratory as a postdoctoral fellow after finishing medical school. Martin later showed that the histidine biosynthetic genes were turned on and off as a unit and that a single mRNA was produced from the cluster of genes.

Sometime in 1964, Ames read the list of ingredients in a box of potato chips and began to wonder if preservatives and other chemicals caused genetic damage to humans. This led to his development of the "Ames test" for chemical mutagens. Using his mutants of *Salmonella* that required histidine for growth, he added just enough histidine to allow the bacteria to undergo a few cell divisions as well as the synthetic chemical being tested. If the added chemical was a mutagen, it would increase the mutation rate and hence the number of histidine-independent colonies. During the next several years Ames developed a set of sensitive tester strains

Bruce N. Ames. Photo courtesy of the Office of NIH History, National Institutes of Health.

using all of the known mutagens he could get his hands on. The Ames test has been used extensively to help evaluate the mutagenic and carcinogenic risks of a large number of chemicals.

In 1968 Ames moved to the Department of Biochemistry and Molecular Biology at the University of California at Berkeley as a full professor. He served as Chairman of the department from 1983 to 1989. In addition, he formed the National Institute of Environmental Health Science Center at Berkeley in 1979 and served as its director until 2002. At Berkeley, Ames continued to work on the regulation of the histidine operon as well as mutagen testing. He developed a database of chemicals that cause cancer in animals, listing their degree of virulence. Later, Ames' research interest shifted to the question of aging, and he showed that the role of mitochondrial decay was a major contributor to aging and age-related degenerative diseases. Ames was also one of a team of Berkeley scientists who discovered how folic acid deficiency leads to DNA damage. In 1999 Ames moved to the Children's Hospital of Oakland Research Institute (CHORI) where he continues to work today. More can be read about Ames' research in his JBC Reflections (2).

Ames was elected to the National Academy of Sciences in 1972 and has received many awards including the Eli Lilly Award of the American Chemical Society (1964), the Mott Prize of the General Motors Cancer Research Foundation (1983), the Gold Medal of the American Institute of Chemists (1991), the Glenn Foundation Award of the Gerontological Society of America (1992), the Japan Prize (1997), and the National Medal of Science (1998).

Nicole Kresge, Robert D. Simoni, and Robert L. Hill

REFERENCES

1. JBC Classics: Horecker, B. L., Smyrniotis, P. Z., and Seegmiller, J. E. (1951) *J. Biol. Chem.* **193,** 383–396 (http://www.jbc.org/cgi/content/full/280/29/e26)
2. Ames, B. N. (2003) An enthusiasm for metabolism. *J. Biol. Chem.* **278,** 4369–4380

THE JOURNAL OF BIOLOGICAL CHEMISTRY
© 2006 by The American Society for Biochemistry and Molecular Biology, Inc.

Vol. 281, No. 4, Issue of January 27, p. e4, 2006
Printed in U.S.A.

Classics

A PAPER IN A SERIES REPRINTED TO CELEBRATE THE CENTENARY OF THE JBC IN 2005

JBC Centennial
1905–2005
100 Years of Biochemistry and Molecular Biology

Unraveling the Enzymology of Oxidative Phosphorylation: the Work of Efraim Racker

Partial Resolution of the Enzymes Catalyzing Oxidative Phosphorylation. I. Purification and Properties of Soluble, Dinitrophenol-stimulated Adenosine Triphosphatase (Pullman, M. E., Penefsky, H. S., Datta, A., and Racker, E. (1960) *J. Biol. Chem.* 235, 3322–3329)

Partial Resolution of the Enzymes Catalyzing Oxidative Phosphorylation. II. Participation of a Soluble Adenosine Triphosphatase in Oxidative Phosphorylation (Penefsky, H. S., Pullman, M. E., Datta, A., and Racker, E. (1960) *J. Biol. Chem.* 235, 3330–3336)

Efraim Racker (1913–1991) was born in the town of Neu Sandez, Poland. At the age of 2, he and his parents moved to Vienna, where Racker grew up. After finishing high school, he went to the University of Vienna to study medicine. Because his graduation from medical school in 1938 was around the time Hitler marched into Austria, Racker decided to leave while it was still possible and fled to Great Britain where J. Hirsh Quastel offered him a job at Cardiff City Mental Hospital in Wales. There, Racker tried to find biochemical causes for mental diseases. When Great Britain entered the war, Racker lost his job at Cardiff and was interned on the Isle of Man where he practiced medicine for the first time in his life. Although he enjoyed being a doctor, he decided to try his luck as a researcher in the United States.

His first appointment was as a research associate in physiology at the University of Minnesota, Minneapolis, from 1941 to 1942. There, Racker carried on his search for a biochemical basis for brain diseases and showed that polio virus inhibited glycolysis in the mouse brain. Despite spending a year doing research, Racker once again found himself working as a physician when he accepted a position at the Harlem Hospital in New York City. His career in biochemistry began in earnest in 1944 when he was appointed assistant professor of microbiology at the New York University Medical School. During his time in New York, Racker continued his glycolysis studies and found that the inhibition could be overcome by the addition of glutathione. This led to his discovery that glyoxylase converts glyoxal to glycolic acid via a carboxyl-S-glutathione intermediate (1). This was the first "energy-rich" thioester of biological relevance to be identified. Similarly, Racker and his technician Isidore Krimsky showed that glyceraldehyde 3-phosphate oxidation occurred through a thiol ester enzyme intermediate (2).

In 1952, Racker was offered the position of associate professor at Yale Medical School, which he accepted. There, he continued to work on carbohydrate metabolism and discovered and purified *trans*-ketolase, a key enzyme in the pentose phosphate pathway. His stay in New Haven lasted 2 years and then he accepted the position of chief of the Nutrition and Physiology Department at the Public Health Research Institute of the City of New York. At first, Racker continued to work on the mechanism of glycolysis and the pentose phosphate pathway but then turned to the regulation of glycolysis. He showed that glycolysis was dependent on the continuous regeneration of ADP and inorganic phosphate by ATPase.

Soon after Racker moved to the Public Health Research Institute, Maynard E. Pullman joined his department. Pullman had just earned a Ph.D. from Johns Hopkins University (1953) and spent a year as a fellow in pediatrics. Upon his arrival at the Public Health Research Institute he decided he wanted to determine the mechanism of ATP synthesis in mitochondria

This paper is available on line at http://www.jbc.org

and chloroplasts. At that time, it was assumed that ATP synthesis was coupled to respiration through a "high energy" intermediate. Pullman and Racker, joined by Anima Datta and graduate student Harvey S. Penefsky, started by attempting to isolate the enzymes involved in ATP synthesis. They obtained fresh bovine hearts and, using a mechanical blender, isolated several grams of mitochondrial membrane fragments, which catalyzed oxidative phosphorylation. These submitochondrial particles were then vigorously shaken with tiny glass beads in a shaker built by Peter M. Nossal. The shaker was considered so dangerous that Nossal screwed it to the floor of a separate room, operated it by remote control, and allowed nobody else to touch it. When the mitochondrial fragments were sedimented in an ultracentrifuge, they still respired but no longer synthesized ATP. However, Racker and his co-workers discovered that oxidative phosphorylation could be restored if the supernatant was added back to the fragments.

While attempting to isolate the soluble component that made oxidative phosphorylation possible, Racker and co-workers discovered that an ATPase was purified together with the phosphorylation activity. The purification and properties of this ATPase are the subjects of the first *Journal of Biological Chemistry* (JBC) Classic reprinted here. Eventually, the researchers realized that this ATPase was in fact the coupling factor that restored oxidative phosphorylation. They named this first enzyme of oxidative phosphorylation Factor 1 or F_1. The second JBC Classic reprinted here provides the evidence that the coupling and ATPase activity are both catalyzed by F_1.

After the publication of these papers, Pullman remained at the Public Health Research Institute and was eventually promoted to associate director in 1983. He then left the Institute to become a senior research scientist at Columbia University's College of Physicians and Surgeons in 1989 where he remained until 1992.

Racker continued to work on ATP synthesis and together with Vida Vambutas he purified a similar coupling factor from spinach chloroplasts (3). Later, with Yasuo Kagawa, Racker subfractionated submitochondrial particles with cholate and salt and identified a membrane factor that anchored F_1 to the membrane and rendered it cold-stable and sensitive to the toxic antibiotic oligomycin (4). They named this insoluble F_1-binding factor F_o, with the subscript signifying the letter "o" for oligomycin and not zero, as is often thought.

In 1966, Racker left the Public Health Research Institute to help create and lead the biochemistry department of a new biology unit at Cornell University. By this time, Racker was convinced that oxidative phosphorylation was not mediated by a high energy chemical intermediate but by a transmembrane proton gradient as proposed by Peter Mitchell (5). Joined by Walther Stoeckenius, Racker incorporated bacteriorhodopsin, a protein that functioned as a light-driven proton pump, and the F_1F_o-ATPase into liposomes (6). They showed that the protons pumped out by the illuminated bacteriorhodopsin flowed back through the F_1F_o-ATPase and generated ATP from ADP and inorganic phosphate, proving that Mitchell's hypothesis was correct.

In the years that followed, Racker and his colleagues reconstituted a variety of different membrane enzymes into liposomes and established reconstitution as a powerful approach for determining the mechanics of pumps, transporters, and receptors. As a result of his work, numerous prestigious honors and prizes were awarded to Racker, such as the Warren Triennial Prize in 1974, the National Medal of Science in 1976, the Gairdner Award in 1980, and the American Society of Biological Chemistry's Sober Memorial Lectureship. He was elected to the American Academy of Arts and Sciences and the National Academy of Sciences and was an Associate Editor for the JBC as well as a member of the JBC editorial board. Racker also came up with the maxim "Don't waste clean thinking on dirty enzymes," which is one of the Ten Commandments of Enzymology (7).[1]

Nicole Kresge, Robert D. Simoni, and Robert L. Hill

REFERENCES

1. Racker, E. (1951) The mechanism of action of glyoxalase. *J. Biol. Chem.* **190,** 685–696
2. Racker, E., and Krimsky, I. (1952) The mechanism of oxidation of aldehydes by glyceraldehyde-3-phosphate dehydrogenase. *J. Biol. Chem.* **198,** 731–743
3. Vambutas, V. K., and Racker E. (1965) Partial resolution of the enzymes catalyzing photophosphorylation. I. Stimulation of photophosphorylation by a preparation of a latent, Ca^{2+}- dependent adenosine triphosphatase

---

[1] All biographical information on Efraim Racker was taken from Ref. 8.

from chloroplasts. *J. Biol. Chem.* **240,** 2660–2667

4. Kagawa, Y., and Racker, E. (1966) Partial resolution of the enzymes catalyzing oxidative phosphorylation. IX. Reconstruction of oligomycin-sensitive adenosine triphosphatase. *J. Biol. Chem.* **241,** 2467–2474

5. Mitchell, P. (1961) Coupling of phosphorylation to electron and hydrogen transfer by a chemiosmotic type of mechanism. *Nature* **191,** 144–148

6. Racker, E., and Stoeckenius, W. (1974) Reconstitution of purple membrane vesicles catalyzing light-driven proton uptake and adenosine triphosphate formation. *J. Biol. Chem.* **249,** 662–663

7. Kornberg, A. (2000) Ten commandments: lessons from the enzymology of DNA replication. *J. Bacteriol.* **182,** 3613–3618

8. Schatz, G. (1996) *Biographical Memoir of Efraim Racker*, Vol. 70, pp. 320–346, National Academy of Sciences, Washington, D. C.

The Journal of Biological Chemistry
© 2006 by The American Society for Biochemistry and Molecular Biology, Inc.

Vol. 281, No. 5, Issue of February 3, p. e5, 2006
Printed in U.S.A.

Classics

A PAPER IN A SERIES REPRINTED TO CELEBRATE THE CENTENARY OF THE JBC IN 2005

JBC Centennial
1905–2005
100 Years of Biochemistry and Molecular Biology

Salih Wakil's Elucidation of the Animal Fatty Acid Synthetase Complex Architecture

The Architecture of the Animal Fatty Acid Synthetase. I. Proteolytic Dissection and Peptide Mapping
(Mattick, J. S., Tsukamoto, Y., Nickless, J., and Wakil, S. J. (1983) *J. Biol. Chem.* **258**, 15291–15299)

The Architecture of the Animal Fatty Acid Synthetase. II. Separation of the Core and Thioesterase Functions and Determination of the N-C Orientation of the Subunit
(Mattick, J. S., Nickless, J., Mizugaki, M., Yang, C. Y., Uchiyama, S., and Wakil, S. J. (1983) *J. Biol. Chem.* **258**, 15300–15304)

The Architecture of the Animal Fatty Acid Synthetase. III. Isolation and Characterization of Beta-Ketoacyl Reductase
(Wong, H., Mattick, J. S., and Wakil, S. J. (1983) *J. Biol. Chem.* **258**, 15305–15311)

The Architecture of the Animal Fatty Acid Synthetase Complex. IV. Mapping of Active Centers and Model for the Mechanism of Action
(Tsukamoto, Y., Wong, H., Mattick, J. S., and Wakil, S. J. (1983) *J. Biol. Chem.* **258**, 15312–15322)

Salih Jawad Wakil was born in 1927 in Kerballa, Iraq. Because he placed third in the nation on the baccalaureate examination out of high school, he received a scholarship to the American University in Beirut. While at the American University he met Stanley Kerr, who introduced him to biochemistry and gave him the opportunity to work in his laboratory. After graduating in 1948, Wakil was accepted at the University of Washington, which he assumed was located in the U. S. capital. However, he arrived in the United States only to learn that he would have to take a 3-day train journey from New York to his university in Washington State. In Seattle, Wakil worked with Donald Hanahan and finished his graduate studies in biochemistry in 3½ years. Next, he decided to do postdoctoral training at the Enzyme Institute of the University of Wisconsin, where he began to work on fatty acid oxidation. It was there that he helped to elucidate the steps by which fatty acids are oxidized and showed that fatty acids are synthesized and oxidized by different pathways.

Wakil was named assistant professor in 1956, but joined the Department of Biochemistry at the Duke University School of Medicine in 1959 and rose to the rank of professor there (1965). At Duke, Wakil investigated fatty acid synthesis in *Escherichia coli*. He and Roy Vagelos, who was featured in a previous *Journal of Biological Chemistry* (JBC) Classic (1), independently studied the role of acyl carrier protein as well as several of the individual reactions of fatty acid elongation. Wakil left Duke in 1971 to become professor and chairman of the Verna and Marrs McLean Department of Biochemistry and Molecular Biology at Baylor College of Medicine in Houston,Texas. At Baylor, Wakil studied the multifunctional enzyme, fatty acid synthetase. The characterization of this enzyme complex is the subject of the four JBC Classics reprinted here.

In vertebrates, the fatty acid synthetase complex exists as a dimer of what Wakil believed were identical subunits derived from a single large mRNA. The complex contains the seven enzymatic activities needed for the assembly of fatty acids: (i) acetyl transacylase, (ii) malonyl transacylase, (iii) β-ketoacyl synthetase, (iv) β-ketoacyl reductase, (v) β-hydroxyacyl dehy-

Salih J. Wakil

dratase, (vi) enoyl reductase, and (vii) palmitoyl thioesterase, as well as an acyl carrier peptide to which the nascent chain is attached. These Classics, which were printed as a back-to-back series in one issue of the JBC, present Wakil's comprehensive proteolytic analysis of chicken fatty acid synthetase in which he assigned relative locations for the enzymatic activities in the complex.

In the first Classic, Wakil and his colleagues used seven different proteases to digest the synthetase. They found that the sum of the molecular weights of each set of fragments generated by the proteases corresponded to the size of the synthetase subunit rather than the native dimer, indicating that the synthetase was indeed a homodimer. The researchers also reported that the subunit is arranged into three major domains of $M_r = 127,000$, $107,000$, and $33,000$.

Wakil describes the cleavage of chicken fatty acid synthetase by α-chymotrypsin in the second Classic. The complex was cleaved into two fragments. The larger 230-kDa fragment contained all the core activities involved in the assembly of the fatty acyl chain whereas the smaller 33-kDa fragment retained the thioesterase activity which releases the complete product. Using amino acid sequence analysis, Wakil showed that the thioesterase domain is located at the carboxyl terminus of the synthetase monomer.

In the third Classic, Wakil used trypsin and subtilisin to cleave fatty acid synthetase and isolated a polypeptide containing only β-ketoacyl reductase activity. Using a kallikrein/subtilisin double digestion, Wakil and his colleagues also isolated another fragment containing β-ketoacyl reductase activity as well as the phosphopantetheine prosthetic group. From this, Wakil concluded that the acyl carrier protein moiety is located in the 15-kDa segment that separates the β-ketoacyl reductase from the thioesterase domain.

In the fourth and final Classic, Wakil presents an architectural model for the synthetase based on his results from the previous three papers. In Wakil's model, domain I functions as a site for acetyl and malonyl substrate entry and acts as the site of carbon-carbon condensation. Thus, this domain contains the amino terminus of the polypeptide and the β-ketoacyl synthetase and acetyl and malonyl transacylases. Domain II, the reductive domain, contains the β-ketoacyl and enoyl reductases, probably the dehydratase, and the 4'-phosphopantetheine prosthetic group of the acyl carrier protein. Finally, domain III contains the thioesterase activity. Based on his observations, Wakil concluded that even though each subunit contains all the activities needed for fatty acyl synthesis, the actual synthesizing unit consists of one-half of one subunit interacting with the complementary half of the other subunit. This is shown in the model in Fig. 2. Wakil, along with Bornali Chakravarty, Ziwei Gu, Subrah-

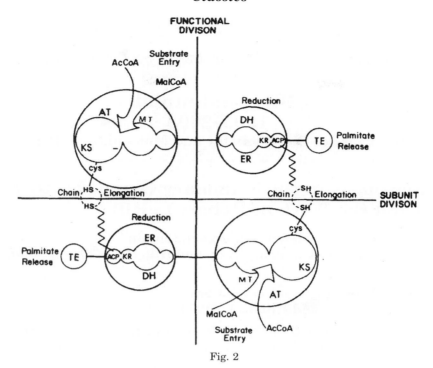

Fig. 2

manyam S. Chirala, and Florante A. Quiocho, subsequently solved the crystal structure of the thioesterase domain of human fatty acid synthetase (2).

Today, Wakil remains at Baylor where he is Distinguished Service Professor and Bolin Professor in the Department of Biochemistry and Molecular Biology. Most recently, his focus has been on acetyl-CoA carboxylase (ACC), which exists in two forms, ACC1 and ACC2. He has developed a transgenic mouse, which does not produce ACC2, and as a result can eat 20–30% more food and weighs 10% less than mice that produce the enzyme.

In honor of Wakil's contributions to the field of fatty acid metabolism, he has received many awards and honors. These include the Paul Lewis Award from the American Chemical Society (1967), the Chilton Award of the University of Texas Southwestern Medical Center (1985), the Kuwait Prize of the Kuwait Foundation for the Advancement of Sciences (1988), the Yamanouchi USA Foundation Award (2001), and the Bristol-Myers Squibb Freedom to Discover Award (2005). In 1990, Wakil was the first Baylor College of Medicine faculty member to be elected to the National Academy of Sciences.

Nicole Kresge, Robert D. Simoni, and Robert L. Hill

REFERENCES

1. JBC Classics: Majerus, P. W., Alberts, A. W., and Vagelos, P. R. (1965) *J. Biol. Chem.* **240,** 618–621; Majerus, P. W., Alberts, A. W., and Vagelos, P. R. (1965) *J. Biol. Chem.* **240,** 4723–4726 (http://www.jbc.org/cgi/content/full/280/35/e32)
2. Chakravarty, B., Gu, Z., Chirala, S. S., Wakil, S. J., and Quiocho, F. A. (2004) Human fatty acid synthase: structure and substrate selectivity of the thioesterase domain. *Proc. Natl. Acad. Sci. U. S. A.* **101,** 15567–15572

THE JOURNAL OF BIOLOGICAL CHEMISTRY
© 2006 by The American Society for Biochemistry and Molecular Biology, Inc.

Vol. 281, No. 6, Issue of February 10, p. e6, 2006
Printed in U.S.A.

Classics

A PAPER IN A SERIES REPRINTED TO CELEBRATE THE CENTENARY OF THE JBC IN 2005

JBC Centennial
1905–2005
100 Years of Biochemistry and Molecular Biology

Lactose Synthesis in the Mammary Gland: Lactose Synthase and the Work of Robert L. Hill

The Complete Amino Acid Sequence of α-Lactalbumin
(Brew, K., Castellino, F. J., Vanaman, T. C., and Hill, R. L. (1970) *J. Biol. Chem.* **245,** 4570–4582)

The Disulfide Bonds of Bovine α-Lactalbumin
(Vanaman, T. C., Brew, K., and Hill, R. L. (1970) *J. Biol. Chem.* **245,** 4583–4590)

The Purification and Properties of the A Protein of Lactose Synthetase
(Trayer, I. P., and Hill, R. L. (1971) *J. Biol. Chem.* **246,** 6666–6675)

Robert L. Hill was born in Kansas City, Missouri in 1928. He earned a B.A. in chemistry in 1949 and a Ph.D. in biochemistry in 1954 from the University of Kansas. After receiving his Ph.D., he went to the University of Utah as a National Institutes of Health (NIH) postdoctoral fellow, where he worked with Emil L. Smith, who was featured in two *Journal of Biological Chemistry* (JBC) Classics (1, 2). Although Hill's Ph.D. thesis research concerned bacterial metabolism, his postdoctoral studies introduced him to protein and enzyme chemistry, research areas he pursued during his subsequent career. At Utah, he published papers on proteolytic enzymes and human hemoglobin and myoglobin. Hill remained at the University of Utah as a faculty member of the Department of Biochemistry until 1961. He then joined the faculty of the Department of Biochemistry at Duke University School of Medicine, where he remains today.

At Duke, Hill continued his work on human hemoglobins, including several abnormal variants, but soon turned his attention to the structure-function relationships of other proteins and enzymes, including human fibrinogen and other blood coagulation factors, immunoglobulins, egg white lysozyme, bacterial acyl carrier protein, and lactose synthase. In subsequent years he studied glycosyltransferases and worked in several areas of glycobiology. Hill's work on lactose synthase is the subject of the three JBC Classics reprinted here.

Lactose synthase consists of a catalytic galactosyltransferase in the endoplasmic reticulum of the mammary gland and a regulatory protein, α-lactalbumin, secreted in milk. Without α-lactalbumin, galactosyltransferase cannot synthesize lactose and instead catalyzes the attachment of galactose to *N*-acetylglucosamine units on glycoproteins. The presence of α-lactalbumin changes the specificity of galactosyltransferase so that it can transfer galactose to glucose.

In the first JBC Classic, Hill, along with Keith Brew, Francis J. Castellino, and Thomas C. Vanaman, reports the complete amino acid sequence of bovine α-lactalbumin. They deduced the sequence by characterizing the tryptic, chymotryptic, and peptic peptides of α-lactalbumin cleaved with cyanogen bromide. Because the amino acid sequence of α-lactalbumin is very similar to that of egg white lysozyme, Hill and his colleagues aligned the two sequences and found that 49 of the residues were identical and 23 were conservative replacements. Thus, they concluded that the three-dimensional structures of the two proteins were probably very similar (3) and that they most likely arose from a common ancestral gene.

Hill, Brew, and Vanaman confirmed this structural similarity in the second Classic in which they describe the locations of the four disulfide bonds in α-lactalbumin. They found that the disulfide bonds are arranged in a manner similar to those in egg white lysozyme and proposed

260

Robert L. Hill

a three-dimensional structure for α-lactalbumin based on the three-dimensional structure of lysozyme, as shown in Fig. 2. Later, Hill, Brew, and Vanaman showed how α-lactalbumin serves as a regulatory protein for lactose synthase and permits the enzyme to synthesize lactose in the mammary gland.

In the final Classic reprinted here, Hill and Ian P. Trayer describe the purification of the galactosyltransferase component of lactose synthase or what they refer to as the "A protein." A key step to their purification was the use of columns of α-lactalbumin attached covalently to Sepharose. In the presence of glucose, galactosyltransferase would bind to the column and could then be removed by omission of glucose from the elution buffer. Using this method, Hill and Trayer were able to purify galactosyltransferase from bovine milk about 12,000-fold.

In 1969 Hill became the chairman of the Department of Biochemistry, and in 1974, the James B. Duke Professor. He served as chairman until 1993. He was President (1976) and Secretary (1972–1975) of the American Society of Biological Chemistry and was also on the Editorial Board (1965–1970, 1972–1977) and an Associate Editor (1988-present) of the JBC. Hill served on the FASEB Board (1972–1978), was General Secretary of the International Union of Biochemistry (1982–1991), and chair of the Organizing Committee of the 17th International Congress of Biochemistry and Molecular Biology in San Francisco in 1997. He was elected to the National Academy of Sciences in 1975, the Institute of Medicine in 1978, and the American Academy of Arts and Sciences in 1974. Hill received the Rose Award from the American Society for Biochemistry and Molecular Biology in 1991, the North Carolina Gold Medal (Science-1985), and the Karl Meyer Award from the Society for Glycobiology (2001).

Each of the coauthors on these Classic papers was a student or postdoctoral fellow in Hill's laboratory, and all have had productive, independent careers in biochemistry. Thomas Vanaman was a Ph.D. student who subsequently became Professor of Biochemistry and Chair at the University of Kentucky. The others were postdoctoral fellows. Keith Brew went to the University of Leeds (UK) before returning to the U. S. where he became Professor of Biochemistry at the University of Miami. He is now at Florida Atlantic University. Francis J. Castellino is currently Professor of Biochemistry at the University of Notre Dame, and Ian P. Trayer was

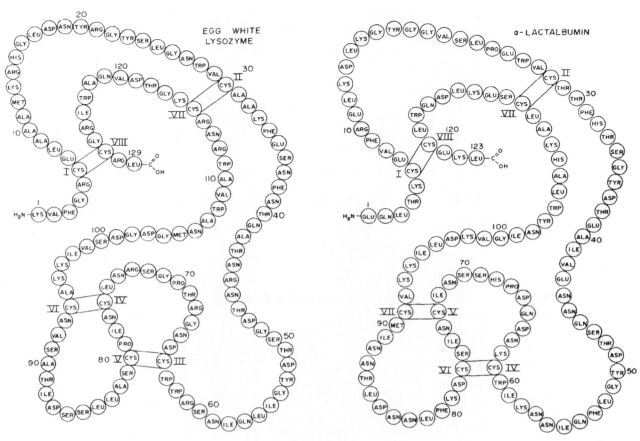

Fig. 2

Professor and Head of the School of Chemistry at the University of Birmingham (UK). Brew and Castellino served on the JBC editorial board. Vanaman also served on the JBC board and currently is an Associate Editor.

Nicole Kresge and Robert D. Simoni

REFERENCES

1. JBC Classics: Smith, E. L., and Bergmann, M. (1944) *J. Biol. Chem.* **153,** 627–651 (http://www.jbc.org/cgi/content/full/279/47/e6)
2. JBC Classics: DeLange, R. J., Fambrough, D. M., Smith, E. L., and Bonner, J. J. (1969) *J. Biol. Chem.* **244,** 5669–5679 (http://www.jbc.org/cgi/content/full/280/36/e33)
3. Browne, W. J., North, A. C., Phillips, D. C., Brew, K., Vanaman, T. C., and Hill, R. L. (1969) A possible three-dimensional structure of bovine α-lactalbumin based on that of hen's egg-white lysozyme. *J. Mol. Biol.* **42,** 65–86

THE JOURNAL OF BIOLOGICAL CHEMISTRY
© 2006 by The American Society for Biochemistry and Molecular Biology, Inc.

Vol. 281, No. 7, Issue of February 17, p. e7, 2006
Printed in U.S.A.

Classics

A PAPER IN A SERIES REPRINTED TO CELEBRATE THE CENTENARY OF THE JBC IN 2005

JBC Centennial
1905–2005
100 Years of Biochemistry and Molecular Biology

The Purification and Sequencing of Alanine Transfer Ribonucleic Acid: the Work of Robert W. Holley

Purification of the Alanine-, Valine-, Histidine-, and Tyrosine-acceptor Ribonucleic Acids from Yeast
(Apgar, J., Holley, R. W., and Merrill, S. H. (1962) *J. Biol. Chem.* 237, 796–802)

Nucleotide Sequences in the Yeast Alanine Transfer Ribonucleic Acid
(Holley, R. W., Everett, G. A., Madison, J. T., and Zamir, A. (1965) *J. Biol. Chem.* 240, 2122–2128)

Robert William Holley (1922–1993) was born in Urbana, Illinois. In 1938, he enrolled at the University of Illinois where he majored in chemistry and received his B.A. in 1942. He then took up graduate studies with Alfred T. Blomquist at Cornell University and was awarded a Ph.D. in organic chemistry in 1947. He would have finished sooner, but his research was interrupted by the war during which he spent 2 years (1944–1946) with Vincent du Vigneaud at Cornell University Medical College, assisting in the first chemical synthesis of penicillin. Some of du Vigneaud's research was featured as a *Journal of Biological Chemistry* (JBC) Classic (1).

After completing his graduate work, Holley did a year of postdoctoral work at Washington State College (now University) with Carl M. Stevens. He then went to Cornell University as Assistant Professor of Organic Chemistry at the Geneva Experiment Station. In 1948, he became assistant professor at the New York State Agricultural Experiment Station, a branch of Cornell, in Geneva. He was promoted to associate professor in 1950, full professor in 1964, and was chairman of the department in 1965 and 1966.

In 1955, Holley went to the California Institute of Technology on a Guggenheim Memorial Fellowship to work with James Bonner, who was the author of a previous JBC Classic (2). There he started to investigate protein synthesis and the chemistry of nucleic acids. Toward the end of his year away from Cornell, Holley began to look specifically at the structure of transfer RNA (tRNA). Back at Cornell he set out to isolate an individual tRNA for chemical study. This is the subject of the two JBC Classics reprinted here.

Holley's first problem was to find a fractionation technique that could be used on tRNA. He settled on Lyman Creighton Craig's countercurrent distribution technique, which was discussed in a previous JBC Classic (3). In collaboration with Jean Apgar and Susan H. Merrill, Holley adapted the countercurrent distribution procedure into an applicable method for the fractionation of tRNA. This method is presented in the first JBC Classic. Using the modified countercurrent distribution technique, Holley, Apgar, and Merrill purified alanine, valine, histidine, and tyrosine tRNA.

Using purified alanine tRNA, Holley and his colleagues set out to determine its sequence. However, the amount of alanine tRNA they could isolate was very limited, even when they used a large countercurrent apparatus and a modified solvent system to increase the solubility of the RNA. During his 3 years of work on the structure of the alanine tRNA, Holley used a total of only 1 g of highly purified material, which he isolated from approximately 200 g of bulk yeast tRNA, which in turn was obtained by phenol extraction of approximately 140 kg of commercial bakers' yeast.

To determine its sequence, Holley cleaved the 77-nucleotide alanine tRNA polynucleotide chain into 16 fragments, identified the small fragments, and then reconstructed the original

Robert W. Holley. Photo courtesy of the National Library of Medicine.

nucleotide sequence by determining the order in which the small fragments occurred in the RNA molecule. This is the subject of the second JBC Classic. Specifically, Holley, George A. Everett, James T. Madison, and Ada Zamir first used pancreatic ribonuclease to cleave the RNA chain next to pyrimidine nucleotides and then used takadiastase ribonuclease T1 to cleave the RNA chain at guanylic acid residues. They isolated the resulting fragments by ion-exchange chromatography. The components of dinucleotide fragments were then identified by chromatographic and electrophoretic properties and spectra. Larger fragments were digested with snake venom phosphodiesterase and sequenced. The determination of the structures of all the fragments took approximately 2½ years.

In the above paper, Holley was also able to determine the identities of the two end fragments of alanine tRNA. What remained then was to establish the arrangement of the remaining 14 fragments. Holley and his colleagues did this by isolating and sequencing a number of large fragments from the RNA (4). This was the first nucleotide sequence for a known nucleic acid. For his work on tRNA, Holley, along with Har Gobind Khorana and Marshall Warren Nirenberg, was awarded the 1968 Nobel Prize in Medicine or Physiology.

In 1968, Holley joined the Salk Institute as a resident fellow where he began to study the molecular factors that regulate growth and multiplication of cells. He discovered that the concentrations of peptide and steroid hormones determine the rate of cell division. Holley also studied the effects of nonhormonal factors, such as certain sugars and amino acids, on cell proliferation and identified growth inhibitors. He remained at the Salk Institute as an American Cancer Society Professor of Molecular Biology until his death in 1993.

Holley was a member of the National Academy of Sciences and the American Academy of Arts and Sciences. He received the Albert Lasker Award in Basic Medical Research in 1965, the Distinguished Service Award of the U. S. Department of Agriculture in 1965, and the U. S. Steel Foundation Award in Molecular Biology of the National Academy of Sciences in 1967.[1]

Nicole Kresge, Robert D. Simoni, and Robert L. Hill

REFERENCES

1. JBC Classics: du Vigneaud, V., Cohn, M., Chandler, J. P., Schenck, J. R., and Simmonds, S. (1941) *J. Biol. Chem.* **140,** 625–641; du Vigneaud, V., Melville, D. B., Folkers, K., Wolf, D. E., Mozingo, R., Keresztesy, J. C., and

[1] All biographical information on Robert W. Holley was taken from Refs. 5 and 6.

Harris, S. A. (1942) *J. Biol. Chem.* **146,** 475–485; du Vigneaud, V., Ressler, C., and Trippett, S. (1953) *J. Biol. Chem.* **205,** 949–957; Katsoyannis, P. G., and du Vigneaud, V. (1958) *J. Biol. Chem.* **233,** 1352–1354 (http://www.jbc.org/cgi/content/full/279/51/e11)

2. JBC Classics: DeLange, R. J., Fambrough, D. M., Smith, E. L., and Bonner, J. J. (1969) *J. Biol. Chem.* **244,** 5669–5679 (http://www.jbc.org/cgi/content/full/280/36/e33)

3. JBC Classics: Craig, L. C. (1943) *J. Biol. Chem.* **150,** 33–45; Craig, L. C. (1944) *J. Biol. Chem.* **155,** 519–534 (http://www.jbc.org/cgi/content/full/280/7/e4)

4. Holley, R. W., Apgar, J., Everett, G. A., Madison, J. T., Marquisee, M., Merrill, S. H., Penswick, J. R., and Zamir, A. (1965) Structure of a ribonucleic acid. *Science* **147,** 1462–1465

5. Holley, R. W. (1969) Robert W. Holley—Biography. *Les Prix Nobel en 1968* (Odelberg, W., ed) Stockholm

6. Holley, R. W. (1972) Alanine transfer RNA. *Nobel Lectures, Physiology or Medicine 1963–1970*, Elsevier Publishing Co., Amsterdam

THE JOURNAL OF BIOLOGICAL CHEMISTRY
© 2006 by The American Society for Biochemistry and Molecular Biology, Inc.

Vol. 281, No. 8, Issue of February 24, p. e8, 2006
Printed in U.S.A.

Classics

A PAPER IN A SERIES REPRINTED TO CELEBRATE THE CENTENARY OF THE JBC IN 2005

JBC Centennial
1905–2005
100 Years of Biochemistry and Molecular Biology

Lester J. Reed and the α-Keto Acid Dehydrogenase Complexes

α-Keto Acid Dehydrogenation Complexes. IV. Resolution and Reconstitution of the *Escherichia coli* Pyruvate Dehydrogenation Complex
(Koike, M., Reed, L. J., and Carroll, W. R. (1963) *J. Biol. Chem.* **238,** 30–39)

Lester James Reed was born in 1925 in New Orleans, Louisiana. He received his B.S. degree from Tulane University in 1943 and completed his Ph.D. in organic chemistry with Reynold C. Fuson at the University of Illinois, Urbana in 1946. He then took a position as a postdoctoral research associate at Cornell University Medical College with Vincent du Vigneaud, who was featured in a previous *Journal of Biological Chemistry* (JBC) Classic (1). In 1948, Reed joined the faculty of the Department of Chemistry at the University of Texas at Austin, where he became Professor in 1958, Director of the Clayton Foundation Biochemical Institute in 1963, and Ashbel Smith Professor in 1984. He retired in 1999 and is currently Ashbel Smith Professor Emeritus.

About 6 months after Reed joined the faculty of the University of Texas he started working on the isolation of a factor that replaced acetate in the growth medium for certain lactic acid bacteria. The project was inherited from Esmond Snell, a JBC Classic author (2, 3) who had initiated the studies while at the University of Wisconsin and continued them after he moved to Texas. Reed eventually purified this acetate-replacing factor and named it α-lipoic acid (4). Intrigued by this compound, he started to investigate its biological function. He determined that protein-bound lipoic acid was involved in the CoA- and NAD^+-linked oxidative decarboxylation of pyruvate and α-ketoglutarate. This discovery led Reed to studies on the α-keto acid dehydrogenase complexes, which is the subject of the JBC Classic reprinted here.

At that time, enzyme complexes that catalyzed the oxidative decarboxylation of pyruvate and α-ketoglutarate had been isolated from both pig heart and *Escherichia coli*, and it was believed that as many as four separate enzymes were involved in the reactions. Reed developed a mild procedure for purification of the pyruvate and α-ketoglutarate oxidation systems from *E. coli*, and by the late 1950s Masahiko Koike in his laboratory succeeded in isolating the enzyme systems as highly purified functional units. Over a period of several years, Reed, Koike, and William Carroll dissected the pyruvate and α-ketoglutarate dehydrogenase complexes into their component enzymes, characterized them, and reassembled the large functional units from the isolated enzymes. Reed's Classic paper describes the separation of the *E. coli* pyruvate dehydrogenase complex into three components: (*a*) pyruvic carboxylase, (*b*) a component containing bound lipoic acid and exhibiting dihydrolipoic transacetylase activity (the lipoic reductase-transacetylase), and (*c*) a flavoprotein, dihydrolipoic dehydrogenase. These later became known as the E_1 (pyruvate dehydrogenase), E_2 (dihydrolipoyl transacetylase), and E_3 (dihydrolipoyl dehydrogenase) enzymes, multiple copies of which make up the pyruvate dehydrogenase complex.

After publishing this Classic, Reed continued to study the structure and function of the pyruvate and α-ketoglutarate dehydrogenase complexes and their individual components from both mammals and bacteria. Details of this subsequent research can be found in Reed's JBC Reflections (5).

Reed has served on the editorial boards of the *Archives of Biochemistry and Biophysics*, the *Journal of Biological Chemistry*, and *Biofactors*. His honors and awards include the American

Chemical Society's Eli Lilly Award in Biological Chemistry (1958), an Honorary Doctor of Science Degree from Tulane University (1977), and the American Society for Biochemistry and Molecular Biology's Merck Award (1994). Reed was elected to the National Academy of Sciences in 1973 and the American Academy of Arts and Sciences in 1981. His family and friends established the Lester B. Reed Professorship in Biochemistry in his honor.

Nicole Kresge, Robert D. Simoni, and Robert L. Hill

REFERENCES

1. JBC Classics: du Vigneaud, V., Cohn, M., Chandler, J. P., Schenck, J. R., and Simmonds, S. (1941) *J. Biol. Chem.* **140,** 625–641; du Vigneaud, V., Melville, D. B., Folkers, K., Wolf, D. E., Mozingo, R., Keresztesy, J. C., and Harris, S. A. (1942) *J. Biol. Chem.* **146,** 475–485; du Vigneaud, V., Ressler, C., and Trippett, S. (1953) *J. Biol. Chem.* **205,** 949–957; Katsoyannis, P. G., and du Vigneaud, V. (1958) *J. Biol. Chem.* **233,** 1352–1354 (http://www.jbc.org/cgi/content/full/279/51/e11)
2. JBC Classics: Eakin, R. E., Snell, E. E., and Williams, R. J. (1940) *J. Biol. Chem.* **136,** 801–802; Eakin, R. E., Snell, E. E., and Williams, R. J. (1941) *J. Biol. Chem.* **140,** 535–543 (http://www.jbc.org/cgi/content/full/279/41/e5)
3. JBC Classics: Snell, E. E. (1944) *J. Biol. Chem.* **154,** 313–314; Schlenk, F., and Snell, E. E. (1945) *J. Biol. Chem.* **157,** 425–426 (http://www.jbc.org/cgi/content/full/280/13/e10)
4. Reed, L. J., DeBusk, B. G., Gunsalus, I. C., and Hornberger, C. S., Jr. (1951) Crystalline α-lipoic acid: a catalytic agent associated with pyruvate dehydrogenase. *Science* **114,** 93–94
5. Reed, L. J. (2001) A trail of research from lipoic acid to α-keto acid dehydrogenase complexes. *J. Biol. Chem.* **276,** 38329–38336

THE JOURNAL OF BIOLOGICAL CHEMISTRY
© 2006 by The American Society for Biochemistry and Molecular Biology, Inc.

Vol. 281, No. 9, Issue of March 3, p. e9, 2006
Printed in U.S.A.

Classics

A PAPER IN A SERIES REPRINTED TO CELEBRATE THE CENTENARY OF THE JBC IN 2005

JBC Centennial
1905–2005
100 Years of Biochemistry and Molecular Biology

The Prostaglandins, Sune Bergström and Bengt Samuelsson

Prostaglandins and Related Factors. 15. The Structures of Prostaglandin E_1, $F_{1\alpha}$, and $F_{1\beta}$
(Bergström, S., Ryhage, R., Samuelsson, B., and Sjövall, J. (1963) *J. Biol. Chem.* **238,** 3555–3564

On the Mechanism of the Biosynthesis of Prostaglandins E_1 and $F_{1\alpha}$
(Hamberg, M., and Samuelsson, B. (1967) *J. Biol. Chem.* **242,** 5336–5343)

Sune Karl Bergström (1916–2004) was born in Stockholm, Sweden. Upon completing high school he went to work at the Karolinska Institute as an assistant to Erik Jorpes where he did research on the biochemistry of fats and steroids. Jorpes was sufficiently impressed with Bergström that in 1938 he sponsored a year-long research fellowship for him at the University of London. Then, in 1940, Bergström received a Swedish-American Fellowship, which allowed him to study for 2 years at Columbia University and to conduct research at the Squibb Institute for Medical Research in New Jersey. He returned to Sweden in 1942 and received doctorates in medicine and biochemistry from the Karolinska Institute 2 years later. He was then appointed assistant in the biochemistry department of Karolinska's Medical Nobel Institute.

Bergström's involvement with prostaglandins started in 1945 at a meeting of the Physiological Society of the Karolinska Institute. There he met Ulf von Euler who had been doing research on prostaglandins. Von Euler asked Bergström if he might be interested in studying some of his lipid extracts of sheep vesicular glands. Using Lyman Craig's countercurrent extraction device, which was the subject of a previous *Journal of Biological Chemistry* (JBC) Classic (1), Bergström was able to purify the crude extract about 500 times. However, his work was interrupted for a few years when he was appointed chair of physiological chemistry at the University of Lund in 1948.

When Bergström resumed his research on prostaglandins, he was aided by his graduate student Bengt Ingemar Samuelsson. Samuelsson, who was born in Halmstad, Sweden, in 1934, had enrolled at the University of Lund to study medicine when he came under the mentorship of Bergström. Using countercurrent fractionations and partition chromatography, Bergström was able to isolate small amounts of prostaglandin E_1 and $F_{1\alpha}$ by 1957 (2). A year later, Bergström was appointed professor of chemistry at Karolinska, and he moved his research group with him to Stockholm. Samuelsson received his doctorate in medical science from the Karolinska Institute in 1960 and his medical degree in 1961.

At Karolinska, Bergström started to collaborate with Ragnar Ryhage who had built a combination gas chromatograph and mass spectrometer. Using this instrument, Bergström, Samuelsson, and Ryhage were able to deduce the structures of prostaglandins E_1, $F_{1\alpha}$, and $F_{1\beta}$ from mass spectrometric identification of the products formed when the prostaglandins were treated with a weak acid or base. These structure determinations are discussed in the first Classic reprinted here. By 1962, Bergström and his colleagues had isolated and determined the structures of six different prostaglandins.

After completing the structural work on the prostaglandins, Samuelsson spent a year as a postdoctoral fellow with E. J. Corey in the Department of Chemistry at Harvard University, where he was able to study theoretical and synthetic organic chemistry. He returned to the

This paper is available on line at http://www.jbc.org

Sune Karl Bergström. Photo courtesy of the
National Library of Medicine.

Bengt Ingemar Samuelsson. Photo courtesy of
the National Library of Medicine.

Karolinska Institute as assistant professor of medical chemistry and resumed work on the
prostaglandins. The second JBC Classic deals with some of Samuelsson's research on the
biosynthesis of prostaglandins, an area in which he contributed considerable knowledge. In
the paper, Samuelsson follows the conversion of 8,11,14-eicosatrienoic acid to prostaglandin E_1
and prostaglandin $F_{1\alpha}$, using ^3H and ^{14}C labeling, focusing especially on the initial step of the
process.

In 1967, Samuelsson joined the faculty of the Royal Veterinary College in Stockholm as
Professor of Medical Chemistry to explore the veterinary and livestock breeding applications
of prostaglandins. However, he returned to the Karolinska Institute in 1972 to become
Professor and Chairman of the Department of Physiological Chemistry. He was Dean of the
Medical Faculty from 1978 to 1983 after which he was appointed Rector of the Karolinska
Institute.

Bergström remained at Karolinska, serving as dean of its medical school from 1963 to 1966
and as Rector of the Institute from 1969 to 1977. He was chairman of the Nobel Foundation's
Board of Directors from 1975 to 1987, and from 1977 to 1982 he served as chairman of the
World Health Organization's Advisory Committee on Medical Research. He retired from
teaching in 1981, choosing to devote his full time to research at Karolinska.

Independently, both Bergström and Samuelsson continued to investigate prostaglandins
and related compounds throughout their scientific careers. In honor of their contributions to
this field, they were awarded the 1982 Nobel Prize in Physiology or Medicine with John R.
Vane "for their discoveries concerning prostaglandins and related biologically active
substances."

Samuelsson's research has been recognized by numerous awards and honors in addition to
the Nobel Prize. These include the A. Jahres Award in Medicine from Oslo University (1970),
the Louisa Gross Horwitz Prize from Columbia University (1975), the Albert Lasker Medical
Research Award (1977), the Ciba-Geigy Drew Award for biomedical research (1980), the
Gairdner Foundation Award (1981), the Bror Holberg Medal of the Swedish Chemical Society
(1982), and the Abraham White Distinguished Scientist Award (1991). Samuelsson was
elected to the National Academy of Sciences in 1984.[1]

Bergström also received many awards, including the Albert Lasker Award in 1977, Oslo
University's Anders Jahre Prize in Medicine in 1970, and Columbia University's Louisa Gross
Horwitz Prize in 1975. He was a member of the Royal Swedish Academy of Science (and served

---

[1] Biographical information on Bengt Samuelsson was taken from Ref. 3.

as its president from 1983 to 1985), the American Philosophical Society, the National Academy of Sciences (1973), and the American Academy of Arts and Sciences.[2]

Nicole Kresge, Robert D. Simoni, and Robert L. Hill

REFERENCES

1. JBC Classics: Craig, L. C. (1943) *J. Biol. Chem.* **150,** 33–45; Craig, L. C. (1944) *J. Biol. Chem.* **155,** 519–534 (http://www.jbc.org/cgi/content/full/280/7/e4)
2. Bergström, S., and Sjövall, J. (1957) The isolation of prostaglandin. *Acta Chem. Scand.* **11,** 1086
3. Samuelsson, B. I. (1993) Studies of biochemical mechanisms to novel biological mediators: prostaglandin endoperoxides, thromboxanes and leukotrienes. In *Nobel Lectures, Physiology or Medicine 1981–1990* (Frängsmyr, T., ed) World Scientific Publishing Co., Singapore
4. Bergström, S. K. (1993) The prostaglandins: from the laboratory to the clinic. In *Nobel Lectures, Physiology or Medicine 1981–1990* (Frängsmyr, T., ed) World Scientific Publishing Co., Singapore

[2] Biographical information on Sune Bergström was taken from Ref. 4.

THE JOURNAL OF BIOLOGICAL CHEMISTRY
© 2006 by The American Society for Biochemistry and Molecular Biology, Inc.

Vol. 281, No. 10, Issue of March 10, p. e10, 2006
Printed in U.S.A.

Classics

A PAPER IN A SERIES REPRINTED TO CELEBRATE THE CENTENARY OF THE JBC IN 2005

JBC Centennial
1905–2005
100 Years of Biochemistry and Molecular Biology

Precocious Newborn Mice and Epidermal Growth Factor: the Work of Stanley Cohen

Isolation of a Mouse Submaxillary Gland Protein Accelerating Incisor Eruption and Eyelid Opening in the New-born Animal
(Cohen, S. (1962) *J. Biol. Chem.* **237,** 1555–1562)

The Primary Structure of Epidermal Growth Factor
(Savage, C. R., Jr., Inagami, T., and Cohen, S. (1972) *J. Biol. Chem.* **247,** 7612–7621)

Stanley Cohen was born in Brooklyn, New York, in 1922. He attended Brooklyn College where he majored in both biology and chemistry and graduated with a B.A. in 1943. After working as a bacteriologist in a milk processing plant to save enough money to go to graduate school, Cohen received a fellowship from Oberlin College, where he earned an M.A. in zoology in 1945. He then acquired another fellowship from the biochemistry department at the University of Michigan and obtained his Ph.D. in 1948. Cohen's graduate thesis concerned the mechanism by which the end product of nitrogen metabolism in the earthworm is switched from ammonia to urea during starvation. To do this research he had to spend his nights collecting over 5000 worms from the University campus green.

After graduating, Cohen joined Harry Gordon in the pediatrics and biochemistry departments of the University of Colorado, where he was involved in metabolic studies on premature infants. Feeling the need to gain experience in the emerging application of radioisotope methodology to biological research, Cohen left Colorado and went to Washington University in 1952 to work with Martin Kamen in the Department of Radiology. There he learned isotope methodology while studying carbon dioxide fixation in frog eggs and embryos. In 1953 Cohen joined the Department of Zoology at Washington University as an Associate Professor. There he collaborated with Rita Levi-Montalcini on the isolation of a nerve growth factor that Levi-Montalcini had discovered in certain mouse tumors. This was Cohen's introduction to the world of growth factors, which would become the focus of his scientific career.

In 1959 Cohen joined the faculty of the biochemistry department at Vanderbilt University as an Assistant Professor. At Vanderbilt, he continued to focus on growth factors. During his study of a nerve growth factor detected in male mouse submaxillary glands he noted that injection of crude submaxillary gland preparations into newborn mice elicited unexpected side effects not related to the activities of the nerve growth factor. These included precocious eyelid opening and precocious tooth eruption (1). Using these precocious characteristics as an assay, Cohen purified the "tooth-lid factor" from murine submaxillary glands. The isolation of this factor is the subject of the first *Journal of Biological Chemistry* (JBC) Classic reprinted here. In the Classic, Cohen reports, "The tooth-lid factor is a heat-stable, nondialyzable, antigenic protein, whose most distinctive chemical characteristic is the absence of phenylalanine and lysine." Subsequent histological examination showed that the precocious eyelid separation was due to the factor's ability to directly stimulate epidermal cell proliferation. Based on these observations, Cohen named the tooth-lid factor epidermal growth factor (EGF).

Cohen's development of a rapid process for isolation of milligram quantities of EGF from murine submaxillary glands in the early 1970s (2) permitted him to purify sufficient quantities for a thorough characterization. Using this material, he, C. Richard Savage, Jr., and Tadashi Inagami, determined the primary sequence of mouse EGF, as reported in the second JBC Classic reprinted here. They used automatic Edman degradation and chemical and enzymatic cleavage to elucidate the sequence and discovered that EGF is a 53-residue polypeptide with six half-cystines that exist in disulfide linkage. Cohen later determined the positions of the three internal disulfide bonds and published the results in the JBC (3).

In 1976 Cohen was appointed an American Cancer Society Research Professor at Vanderbilt, and in 1986 he was named Distinguished Professor. He retired in 2000 and is currently Distinguished Professor Emeritus at Vanderbilt. Cohen continued to study EGF, its interaction with cell surface receptors, and the intracellular signaling pathways activated by the growth factor. In recognition of this work, he shared the 1986 Nobel Prize in Physiology or Medicine 1986 with Rita Levi-Montalcini "for their discoveries of growth factors."

In addition to the Nobel Prize, Cohen has received many awards and honors, including the National Paraplegia Foundation's Second Annual William Thomson Wakeman Award (1974), Vanderbilt University's Earl Sutherland Prize for Achievement in Research (1977), the National Academy of Science's H. P. Robertson Memorial Award (1981), the General Motors Cancer Research Foundation Alfred P. Sloan Award (1982), the American Academy of Dermatology's Lila Gruber Memorial Cancer Research Award (1983), the Gairdner Foundation International Award (1985), the National Medal of Science (1986), the Endocrine Society's Fred Conrad Koch Award (1986), and the Albert Lasker Basic Medical Research Award (1986). He was elected to the National Academy of Science in 1980 and the American Academy of Arts and Sciences in 1984 and has served on the Editorial Boards of the *Abstracts of Human Developmental Biology* and the *Journal of Cellular Physiology*.[1]

Cohen's co-author on the second JBC Classic, Tadashi Inagami (1931), has also made many important contributions to science. At the time he collaborated with Cohen on the growth hormone work, Inagami was an Associate Professor of Biochemistry at Vanderbilt University School of Medicine. He eventually became Stanford Moore Professor of Biochemistry at Vanderbilt in 1991. The majority of Inagami's research has centered on investigating hypertension. He was the first to purify renin and to elucidate its specific protease activity, and he isolated and determined the structures of multiple forms of the angiotensin receptor. Inagami also discovered the biochemical mechanism by which renin works. In recognition of his research, Inagami has received many honors including the Humboldt Foundation Award (1981), the American Heart Association's Ciba Award (1985), Vanderbilt University's Sutherland prize (1990), the Japan Vascular Disease Research Foundation's Okamoto International Award (1995), the Bristol-Myers Squibb Award for Excellence in Cardiovascular Research (1996), the Japan Society for Cardiovascular Endocrinology and Metabolism's Jokichi Takamine Memorial Award (1998), and the American Heart Association's Research Achievement Award (1994).

Nicole Kresge, Robert D. Simoni, and Robert L. Hill

REFERENCES

1. Cohen, S. (1960) Purification of a nerve-growth promoting protein from the mouse salivary gland and its neuro-cytotoxic antiserum. *Proc. Natl. Acad. Sci. U. S. A.* **46,** 302–311
2. Savage, C. R., and Cohen, S. (1972) Epidermal growth factor and a new derivative. Rapid isolation procedures and biological and chemical characterization. *J. Biol. Chem.* **247,** 7609–7611
3. Savage, C. R., Hash, J. H., and Cohen, S. (1973) Epidermal growth factor. Location of disulfide bonds. *J. Biol. Chem.* **248,** 7669–7672
4. Cohen, S. (1987) Stanley Cohen—Autobiography. In *Les Prix Nobel. The Nobel Prizes 1986* (Odelberg, W., ed) Nobel Foundation, Stockholm

[1] All biographical information on Stanley Cohen was taken from Ref. 4.